JEAN PLAIDY JEAN PLAIDY JEAN PLAIDY JEAN PL.
DY JEAN PLAIDY JEAN PLA JEAN
JEAN PLAIDY JEAN PLAIDY N PL.
DY JEAN PLAIDY JEAN PLA JEAN
JEAN PLAIDY JEAN PLAIDY N PL.
DY JEAN PLAIDY JEAN PLAIDY JEAN PLAIDY JEAN
JEAN PLAIDY JEAN PLAIDY JEAN PLAIDY JEAN PL.
DY JEAN PLAIDY JEAN PLAIDY JEAN PLAIDY JEAN
JEAN PLAIDY JEAN PLAIDY JEAN PLAIDY JEAN PL.
DY JEAN PLAIDY JEAN PLAIDY JEAN PLAIDY JEAN
JEAN PLAIDY JEAN PLAIDY JEAN PLAIDY JEAN PL.
DY JEAN PLAIDY JEAN PLAIDY JEAN PLAIDY JEAN
JEAN PLAIDY JEAN PLAIDY JEAN PLAIDY JEAN PL.
DY JEAN PLAIDY JEAN PLAIDY JEAN PLAIDY JEAN
JEAN PLAIDY JEAN PLAIDY JEAN PLAIDY JEAN PL.
DY JEAN PLAIDY JEAN PLAIDY JEAN PLAIDY JEAN
JEAN PLAIDY JEAN PLAIDY JEAN PLAIDY JEAN PL.
DY JEAN PLAIDY JEAN PLAIDY JEAN PLAIDY JEAN
JEAN PLAIDY JEAN PLAIDY JEAN PLAIDY JEAN PL.
DY JEAN PLAIDY JEAN PLAIDY JEAN PLAIDY JEAN
JEAN PLAIDY JEAN PLAIDY JEAN PLAIDY JEAN PL.
DY JEAN PLAIDY JEAN PLAIDY JEAN PLAIDY JEAN
JEAN PLAIDY JEAN PLAIDY JEAN PLAIDY JEAN PL.
DY JEAN PLAIDY JEAN PLAIDY JEAN PLAIDY JEAN
JEAN PLAIDY JEAN PLAIDY JEAN PLAIDY JEAN PL.
DY JEAN PLAIDY JEAN PLAIDY JEAN PLAIDY JEAN
JEAN PLAIDY JEAN PLAIDY JEAN PLAIDY JEAN PL.
DY JEAN PLAIDY JEAN PLAIDY JEAN PLAIDY JEAN
JEAN PLAIDY JEAN PLAIDY JEAN PLAIDY JEAN PL.
DY JEAN PLAIDY JEAN PLAIDY JEAN PLAIDY JEAN
JEAN PLAIDY JEAN PLAIDY JEAN PLAIDY JEAN PL.
DY JEAN PLAIDY JEAN PLAIDY JEAN PLAIDY JEAN
JEAN PLAIDY JEAN PLAIDY JEAN PLAIDY JEAN PL.
DY JEAN PLAIDY JEAN PLAIDY JEAN PLAIDY JEAN
JEAN PLAIDY JEAN PLAIDY JEAN PLAIDY JEAN PL.
DY JEAN PLAIDY JEAN PLAIDY JEAN PLAIDY JEAN
JEAN PLAIDY JEAN PLAIDY JEAN PLAIDY JEAN PL.
DY JEAN PLAIDY JEAN PLAIDY JEAN PLAIDY JEAN
JEAN PLAIDY JEAN PLAIDY JEAN PLAIDY JEAN PL.
DY JEAN PLAIDY JEAN PLAIDY JEAN PLAIDY JEAN

Jean Plaidy

St. Thomas's Eve

Royal Road to Fotheringay

The Goldsmith's Wife

Perdita's Prince

BOOK CLUB ASSOCIATES
LONDON

St Thomas's Eve first published in Great Britain in
1954 by Robert Hale Limited
Royal Road to Fotheringay first published in Great Britain in
1955 by Robert Hale Limited
The Goldsmith's Wife first published in Great Britain in
1950 by Robert Hale Limited
Perdita's Prince first published in Great Britain in
1969 by Robert Hale Limited

This edition published 1980 by
Book Club Associates
By arrangement with

William Heinemann Limited
10 Upper Grosvenor Street
London W1

Martin Secker & Warburg Limited
54 Poland Street
London W1

and

Octopus Books Limited
59 Grosvenor Street
London W1

Printed in the United States of America

Contents

St. Thomas's Eve
11

Royal Road to Fotheringay
183

The Goldsmith's Wife
435

Perdita's Prince
627

Jean Plaidy

St. Thomas's Eve

Jean Plaidy

St Thomas's Eve

With love to Enid and John Leigh-Hunt

ACKNOWLEDGEMENTS
I wish gratefully to acknowledge the guidance I have received from the undermentioned books:

History of England, *William Hickman Smith Aubrey*
Life of Sir Thomas More, *William Roper*
Thomas More, *R. W. Chambers*
Life of Wolsey, *Cavendish*
Utopia, *Sir Thomas More*
A Dialogue of Comfort, *Sir Thomas More*
The Latin Epigrams of Thomas More, *edited with Translations and Notes by Leicester Bradner and Charles Arthur Lynch*
England in Tudor Times, *L. F. Salzman, M.A., F.S.A.*
British History, *John Wade*
Lives of the Queens of England, *Agnes Strickland*
Old and New London, *Walter Thornbury*
The Divorce of Catherine of Aragon, *James Anthony Froude*
Wolsey *(Great Lives)*, *Ashley Sampson*
Early Tudor Drama, *A. W. Reed, M.A., D.Lit.*

J.P.

Chapter One

'And who is this man who dares oppose us?' demanded the King. 'Who is this Thomas More? Eh? Answer me that.'

The King was angry. He sat very straight in the royal chair, one slender hand lying on the purple velvet which covered the table, the other stroking the ermine which covered his mantle. He was battling to subdue his rage, to preserve his habitual calm; for he was a shrewd man and his life had taught him that unheated words were more effective than the sword.

He looked from one to the other of the two men who sat with him at the velvet-covered table where lay the documents which had absorbed their attention until the entrance of the man Tyler.

'You, Empson! You, Dudley! Tell me this: Who is this man More?'

'Methinks I have heard his name, Your Grace,' said Sir Edmund Dudley. 'But I know him not.'

'We should be more careful whom we allow to be elected as our London burgesses.'

'Indeed yes, Your Grace,' agreed Sir Richard Empson.

The King's fury was getting the better of him. He was glaring distastefully at Master Tyler, that gentleman of the Privy Chamber who had brought the news; and it was not this King's habit to blame men for the news they brought. Tyler trembled; he was fervently wishing that he had allowed someone else to acquaint the King with the news that his Parliament–owing to the pithily-worded arguments of one of the youngest burgesses–had refused to grant him the sum of money for which he had asked.

There was one other in this room of the palace of Richmond, and he–a boy of thirteen–was staring idly out of the window watching a barge on the river, wishing he were the gallant who accompanied the fair young lady as they went gaily on to Hampton; he could see them well, for his eyesight was keen. The sun was shining on the water which was almost the same colour as the dress of the young lady. This Prince was already fond of ladies, and they were fond of him. Although young as yet, he was already as tall as many men and showed promise of shooting up to great stature. His skin was fair and his hair had a tinge of red in it so that it shone like the gold ornaments on his clothes.

Now he had forgotten the young lady; he wished to be playing tennis, beating any who challenged him, listening to the compliments they paid, pretending not to hear, while they pretended not to know he listened. For two years he had been aware of such adulation; and how could he, who so loved adulation, feel really sorry that his brother had died? He had loved Arthur; he had admired him as his elder brother; but it was as though he had lost a coarse frieze garment and, because of his loss, found himself the possessor of a doublet of velvet and cloth of gold.

He was conscious that he was a prince who would one day be a king.

And when I am, he told himself, I shall not sit in council with such mumping oafs as Master Dudley and Master Empson. I shall not worry my head with the hoarding of money, but the spending of it. I shall have merry men about me–fat spenders, not lean misers.

'And you, my son,' he heard his father say, 'what of you? Have you heard aught of this fellow More?'

The boy rose and came to the table to stand in homage before the King.

My son! pondered the King. What a king he will make! What resemblance he bears to the hated House of York! I see his grandfather, Edward of York, in that proud carriage.

And the boy's father was faintly worried, for he remembered Edward the Fourth in his latter years when the tertian fever had laid hold of him and, like a mischievous scribe, had added a smudge here, a line there, until an ugly mask had made a palimpsest of his once beautiful face. But not only the fever had done this; it had been aided by the life he led: too much good food, too much good wine; too many women–anyhow, anywhere, from serving-wenches to duchesses. Such debauchery took toll of a man.

I must speak with this son of mine, thought the King. I must set his feet on the rightful path. I must teach him how to save money and keep it. Money is Power, and Power is a King's heritage; and if that king be a Tudor king–a young tree, the prey of sly and subtle pests, in danger of being overcome by older shrubs who claimed that young tree's territory–then that Tudor king must have wealth, for wealth buys soldiers and arms to support him; wealth buys security.

He was not displeased with his own acquisitions; but when he had filled one coffer, he was eager to fill another. Everything he touched did not turn to gold as easily as he would wish. The touch of Midas was in his shrewd brain, not in his fingers. Ah well, he would then thank God for that shrewd brain. War drained the coffers of other kings; it filled those of Henry Tudor. He used war; he did not allow war to use him. He could draw money from the people by telling them that they must do battle with their enemies the French and the Scots; and the people were ready to pay, for they believed that the bread of righteous anger thrown upon the waters of conquest would yield rich booty. But Henry the Seventh knew that war took all the treasure that was offered, demanded more, and in exchange for so much riches gave pestilence, hunger and poverty. So the King, having collected his money, would make a speedy peace; and that which was intended to bring war to the enemies of England, brought wealth to England's King.

He was a king who had suffered from many insurrections; insecure, since he was a bastard branch of the royal tree, grafted on by an indiscreet widowed queen, there had been many to oppose him. Yet each year saw him more firmly seated on the throne. He did not demand the blood of those who planned to destroy him; he only asked for their lands and goods. Thus he grew richer every year.

He now looked at the boy who stood before him, not as a father might look at his son, but as a king regarding his successor.

Last year, the Queen had died in childbed, and the King was eager to get himself a new wife. This was the only son left to him; and the death of Arthur, so recently a bridegroom, had been a bitter blow. The loss of the Queen was not so important; there were many women in the world–royal women–who would not hesitate to become the wife of the King of England;

and it was pleasurable to contemplate that wives brought dowries.

Secretly he was not sorry to see the end of Queen Elizabeth. She had been a good, meek wife; she had given him several children; but she was of the House of York, and reasonable as he was, he had found that hard to forget.

'Well, my son?'

'I have met the man More, Your Grace.'

'Then tell me what you know of him.'

'He is a lawyer, Sire, and it was when I was at Eltham with my sisters that I saw him. He came with Mountjoy and the scholar, Erasmus; for Erasmus was visiting Mountjoy whom he had once tutored.'

'Yes,' said the King; 'and what manner of man was this More?'

'Of medium height, I should say, Sire. Of bright complexion. And he had merry eyes and a way of speech that provoked much laughter.'

'Methinks his way of speech provoked much parsimony in our Parliament. And that we will not have. Is that all you can tell us?'

'That is all, Sire.'

The King waved his hand and the Prince, bowing, went back to his stool.

'He should be heavily fined,' declared the King.

'He is not a rich man, Your Grace,' murmured Empson. 'A scholar, a writer, a lawyer . . . little could be extorted from him.'

The King could trust his henchmen, Empson and Dudley. They were of his own kind. They had their private greed; they enriched themselves while they enriched the King.

'He has a father, Sire,' said Dudley.

'Who,' added Empson, 'might be good for a hundred pounds.'

'Put him in the Tower.'

'On the charge of possessing a disloyal son, Your Grace?'

'Nay. Nay. You know better than that. Look into his affairs, then bring some charge against him. See what goods he hath; then we will decide on the fine. And do so with all speed.'

The King wished to be alone with his son.

The boy, when he had stood before him, had aroused anxieties within him and temporarily they had swamped his anger at the failure to obtain as much money as he wished. This was because of the boy's appearance; the proud set of the head on the shoulders, the dazzlingly fair skin, the vital hair that was almost the colour of gold, the small sensual mouth, the bright blue eyes had reminded the King so vividly of the boy's maternal grandfather; and he remembered the profligacy of that man.

He felt the need, therefore, to talk with his son immediately.

When they were alone he addressed him: 'Henry.'

The boy rose at once, but his father went on: 'Nay; stay where you are. No ceremony whilst we are alone. Now I would speak to you as father to son.'

'Yes, Father.'

'One day, my boy, you will be king of this realm.'

'Yes, Father.'

'Three years ago, we did not know that you were destined for such greatness. Then you were merely the King's second son, who, your father had decided, should become Archbishop of Canterbury. Now your steps are turned from Church to Throne. My son, do you know that the cares of kingship outweigh the glory and the honour?'

The boy answered: 'Yes, Father.'

But he did not believe this. So it might be with lean, pale men such as his father, whose thoughts were all of filling their coffers; but if a king were young and handsome and the eyes of ladies lightened as they rested upon him, and those of the young men were warm with envy and admiration, that was a different matter. The glory and the honour could outweigh the care; and if they did not do so in the case of Henry the Seventh, Henry the Eighth would see to it that they did so for him.

'Many temptations come to kings, my son. You would do well to study the history of those who have gone before.'

'That I do, Father. My Lord Mountjoy insisted that I did so when he tutored me.'

'There are times when a king is beset on all sides, when traitors rise and threaten him. Then he must act with speed and wisdom.'

'I know it, Sire.'

'You know then why I wish you to be present at our councils. I hope you do not spend your time staring idly through the windows, dreaming of sport and pleasure. I would have you learn from what you hear at these our meetings.'

'I do, Father.'

'There are some who would have sent that fellow More to the Tower and would have had his head on London Bridge for what he has done. But such acts are folly. Remember this: Let the people think that the Parliament guides the King; but let the members of the Parliament know that the King has a hundred ways of striking at them if they obey him not.'

'The people are not pleased,' said the boy boldly. 'They like not taxes, and they say that there have been too many taxes. They murmur against Dudley and Empson.' He dared not say they murmured against the King, but he knew the people would never love his father as he believed they would love his father's son. When he went into the streets they called his name. 'God bless the Prince! God bless Prince Hal!' The sound of their cheers was sweeter than the music of his lute, and he loved his lute dearly. His father could not tell *him* how a king should behave.

'There must be those to do a king's work,' said King Henry, 'and if it be ugly work, then it is the duty of those to bear the reproaches of the people. My son, you will one day be not only a king, but a rich king. When I slew the traitor Crookback at Bosworth Field and took the crown, I found I had inherited a bankrupt kingdom.'

'A right noble act it was to slay the traitor!' said the boy.

'Yet coming to the throne as we have done is a dangerous way. Never forget it. Be watchful. Above all, learn from those who have gone before. Use the lessons of the past to overcome the dangers of the future. You remind me of your grandfather, great King Edward, for you have something of his lineaments and his stature. Ah, there was a man!'

Father and son smiled as they thought of the boy's grandfather.

With his beauty and charm, thought the King, he lured taxes from his people's pockets and he called them 'Benevolences.' Oh, for such power!

He roamed the countryside as an ordinary gentleman, thought the Prince; and such was his charm and beauty that no woman could resist him. Oh, for such power!

The sun's rays slanted through the windows of Richmond Palace and as the father began to talk to the son of the delights and dangers of kingship, they had ceased to think of Thomas More.

Meanwhile in the grounds of a pleasant old mansion in the little village of Stepney, the object of the King's wrath was walking arm-in-arm with one of his greatest friends, his confessor, Dr John Colet, a man whose wit and learning delighted him almost as much as the affection they bore each other.

Colet, some ten years older than Thomas More, was listening gravely to his friend's account of what had happened in the Parliament.

He shook his head. '"Twas a brave act, I'll grant you; but there is a point in human nature where bravery may be called folly, and folly, bravery.'

'Is it better to be a brave fool or a wise coward? Tell me that, John. I love the wise; I love the brave; and I love not cowards nor fools. What a perverse thing is life when the wrong partners walk together!'

John Colet was in no mood for laughter. He was alarmed.

'Had it been anything but money, the King would have been the more ready to forgive you.'

'Had it been anything but money, would the King have been begging it from his Parliament? Nay, the King loves money. He loves the colour of gold. He loves the sight of gold in his coffers . . . gold plate – gold coins. He rejoices in the knowledge that he is not only a king, but a rich king.'

'Friend Thomas, there is one thing you should take to heart. Now, I am an older man than you are. . . .'

'I know it, thou greybeard.'

'Then know this also: If you wish to make an enemy of the King, get between him and the money he hopes to win. Thus–and more quickly than in any other way–can you rouse his wrath. And, Thomas, remember this now and for ever: it is a perilous thing to set yourself against a king.'

'It is an even more perilous thing to set oneself against one's conscience, John. Tell me this: Should the King be allowed to impose such taxes on his people? You yourself have often said it should not be so. Come, admit it.'

'What we have said, we have said in the circle of our friends. It is another matter to say such things in Parliament.'

'I call to mind that there are those of my friends who have lectured in such manner as to attract multitudes. And this they have done in public places.' Thomas put his head on one side and lifted his shoulder in a manner which was characteristic of him. 'I think of one friend, not so far from me at this moment, who has placed himself in high danger by too boldly expressing what are called "dangerous thoughts."'

Colet said impatiently: 'I talked of theology. You have talked of money. There was never a more avaricious king than ours. There was never one more vindictive when his darling money is kept from him. However, there is one thing that pleases me. You are a poor man, my friend. To rob you of your worldly goods would hardly be worth the time of the King's henchmen.'

'Now there we see one of the great compensations in life. Poverty is my shield; it protects me from the onslaughts of mine enemies. But have done with this matter. It was of others that I came hither to talk to you.'

They walked through the orchards, where the fruit was beginning to ripen. 'Ah, John,' said Thomas, 'there'll be a good harvest this year if the wasps and the birds allow it. Hast heard aught of our friend Erasmus of late? Now, John, do not scowl. I know it was a grave blow to you when he would not stay in Oxford and lecture there with you. But it was compulsion that moved him to return to Rotterdam and poverty.'

'He disappoints me,' said Colet. 'He could have stayed in this country.

There was work for him to do. Could he not have studied here as much as he wished?'

'Remember what he said to you, John. He said it was you who disappointed yourself. You made a picture of him–far too learned, he says, far too saintly. *He* has not disappointed you, for he has always been himself; it is you who have disappointed yourself by making a false image of him. He is right, John. And I too have disappointed him. I rejoice that he does not love gold as the King does. For you know I told him it was safe for him to bring his money into England, and that he could safely take it out when he wished. My knowledge of the law was at fault–and I call myself a lawyer! Because of it my friend was deceived, and so . . . he was not allowed to take his money home. If he loved his few pieces of gold as the King loves his full coffers, Erasmus would hate me even as does the King. Hath it occurred to you that money bringeth much trouble to me? Now, that is an odd thing, for it is the love of money that is the root of evil; yet I pay so little court to it that I win the King's anger and, I fear, the scorn of my learned friend Erasmus, through my contempt of it.'

'It would seem,' said John Colet, 'that my wise friends are fools. There is Erasmus who must return to poverty in order to perfect his Greek. There is you who must take great pains to provoke the King . . . like a boy with a stick bent on teasing a bull.'

'But such an insignificant boy . . . a boy who is not worth the tossing.'

'Believe it or not, even those whose passion is the accumulation of money can have other passions. Revenge, for one.'

'Enough, John. Let us speak of my affairs. I have made a decision which will alter the course of my life.'

John Colet turned to look at his friend. The blue eyes were twinkling, the usually pink cheeks were flushed a rosy red. May God preserve him, thought Dr Colet, for his nature is the sweetest I ever knew, and there are times when I fear it will lead him to trouble.

'Come, let us sit on the seat here and watch the barges sail up the river to London. Then tell me of this decision.' They sat down and John went on: 'You have not decided to take your vows?'

Thomas was silent; he laid his hands on his knees and looked across the river to where the willows hung low in the water and the rose-tinted umbels of the flowering rush bloomed among the purple stars of loosestrife, the figwort, with its brown helmets standing guard over them.

Thomas was twenty-six years of age–an age, he had decided, when a man must make decisions. He was fair-haired, blue-eyed, of fresh complexion; and it was the sweetness of expression which people remembered.

Looking at him now, John Colet thought of the friends he loved; there was the great and learned Erasmus, the intellectual Grocyn, the reliable William Lily, and the keen-witted, kindly Linacre; all these men were the great scholars of the day; yet none of them could charm and attract as did Thomas More. Thomas was younger than either Colet or Erasmus, yet both these men counted him as their intellectual equal. He had a first-class brain; he could assimilate knowledge with astonishing speed; he could converse learnedly with humour and a sense of fun, and in the sharpness of his wit he never stooped to wound. Yet it was not only for these qualities that he was loved; it was the sweet kindliness of the man, his courteous manner even towards the humblest; it was the frankness mingling with the courtesy; it was the never-absent sympathy, the understanding of the problems of others and the ever-present desire to help any in distress.

'Nay,' said Thomas. ''Tis not to take the vows.'

John turned to him and grasped his hands. 'Then I am glad that you have at last come to this decision.'

'I am a greedy man,' said Thomas. 'Ah yes, I am, John. I have discovered that one life is not enough for me. I want to live two lives . . . side by side. I would take my vows and be with my dear brothers of the Charterhouse. How that beckons me! The solitude of the cloisters, the sweetness of bells at vespers, the sonorous Latin chants . . . the gradual defeat of all fleshly desires. What victory, eh, John? When the hair-shirt ceases to torment; when a wooden pillow has more comfort to offer than a downy feather bed. I can see great joy in such a life. . . . But, then, I would be a family man. To tell the truth, John, I find that beside this monk within me, there is another–a man who looks longingly at the fair faces of young maidens, who thinks of kissing and caressing them; this is a man who yearns for the married state, for the love of a woman and the laughter of children. I have had to make a choice.'

'I'm glad you have chosen, Thomas; and I am sure that you have chosen well.'

'Then I have not disappointed your hopes of me? I see you did not set me such a high standard as you did our friend from Rotterdam.'

'Nay; I think not of standards. I think how pleasant it will be when you are a family man and I visit you, and your good wife will greet me at your table. . . .'

'And you will listen to my children, repeating their lessons, and you will tell them that you have never known children so skilled in the arts of learning. Ah, John, would it not be an excellent thing if we could live two lives and, when we have reached an age of wisdom, lightly step out of that which pleases us no longer into that one that gives us great pleasure.'

'You are a dreamer, my friend. Indeed, it would bring no satisfaction, for you would be as undecided at fifty as you are at thirty. Each road would have joy and sorrow to offer a man; of that I am sure.'

'There you are right, John.'

'But I'll swear the life you have chosen will be a good one.'

'But is it the right one, John? Is it the right one for me, do you think?'

'It is only at the completion of a man's life that such can be decided.'

'Then tomorrow I ride into Essex,' said Thomas, 'to the house of Master Colt at New Hall. And I shall ask Master Colt for the hand of his eldest daughter in marriage.'

'The eldest! But methought it was one of the younger ones who had taken your fancy.'

Thomas frowned a little; then he smiled, and his smile was one of infinite charm.

'I changed my mind.'

'Oh . . . so you liked the looks of one of the younger girls first, and then . . . you fell in love with her sister. Methinks you are a fickle man.'

'It seems so, John, for first I fell in love with the Charterhouse and a life of retirement; and you see I could not be faithful to that love for long.'

'Ah, but that was not a true love. For all those years you lived with the monks; you fasted and did you penances; but did you take your vows? No. Always you postponed that ceremony. And in the meantime, to please your father, you continued with your law studies. The Charterhouse was never your true love. Then you saw young Mistress Colt, and you thought how fair she was; but you did not ask her father for her. It was only when you saw the eldest girl that you were successfully weaned from your desire to retire from the world. A long and fruitful married life to you, Thomas! May you have many sons and a few daughters . . . for daughters are useful in the house.'

'My daughters will be as important in my eyes as my sons. They shall be educated exactly as my sons will be.'

'Women educated as men! Nonsense!'

'John, what is the greatest gift the world has to offer? You will answer that as I would: Learning. Is it not what you plan to give to the world? How many times have you talked of what you will do with your fortune when it is yours? You worship in the temple of Learning with me. Now would you deny it to one child because its sex is not the same as another?'

'I can see that you wax argumentative. Well, that is what I expect of you. It grows a little chilly here by the river. Let us walk back to the house whilst we talk of this thing. There is not much time, since you say you must ride on towards Essex tomorrow.'

'Yes, I must set out at sunrise.'

'On a mission of love! I will pray for you this night. I will remember the younger daughter on whom your fancy dwelt, and I shall pray that the husband will be less fickle than the lover.'

They walked slowly towards the house, and by the time they reached it they were deep in further discussion.

John Colt welcomed his guest. He considered the lawyer of London a worthy suitor for his eldest girl. As he said to his wife, to tell the truth he had almost despaired of the girl's getting a husband.

Jane lacked something which her sisters possessed. It was not only that she was a little plain; she lacked also their vitality. She seemed to want nothing but to stay in the country, tending the gardens or working in the house; and she seemed to find the company of the servants preferable to that of her own family or their neighbours. It would be good to see her a wife before her sisters married.

'Welcome to New Hall, friend Thomas!' cried Master Colt, embracing the man he hoped would soon be his son-in-law. 'There, groom! Take his honour's horse. Now, come you into the house. You'll be tired after your journey. We've put supper forward an hour, for we thought you'd be hungry. 'Twill be five of the clock this day. And Jane's in the kitchen. Ah! Knowing you were coming, she must be there to see that the meat is done to a turn, and the pastry of such lightness as was never known. You know what girls are!'

He nudged Thomas and broke into hearty laughter. Thomas laughed with him.

'But,' said Thomas, 'it was to do homage neither to the beef nor to the pastry that I came, Master Colt.'

Master Colt broke into more laughter. He was a man of bucolic manners. He could never look at Thomas More without a chuckle. All this learning! It amused him. What was it for? 'God's Body,' he often said to his wife, 'I'd rather one of our boys was hanged than become a bookworm. Books! Learning! What does it do for a man? Ah, if our Jane were like her sisters, I'd not have her throw herself away on a lawyer from London, whose nose, I'll swear, likes better the smell of parchment than good roast beef.'

Now he said: 'Come, Master More, we'll put some flesh on those bones before you leave us. We'll show you that a veal pie has more nourishment to offer you than Latin verse. Don't you agree? Don't you agree?'

'Take the roast beef of England to nourish the muscles of the body,' said Thomas. 'And then digest the wisdom of Plato to develop the mind.'

'Your mind won't build you a fine house to live in, Master More; it won't raise a fine family. A man must live by the strength of his body.'

'Or by the agility of his wits as do the King's ministers.'

'Bah! Who'd be one of them? Here today and gone tomorrow. My Lord this and that today, and tomorrow it's "Off with his head!" Nay, fight your own battles, not the King's.'

'I see that you have gleaned much wisdom from your red roast beef.'

Master Colt slipped his arm through that of his visitor. Queer, he thought, he might be a bookworm, but he was a merry man, and in spite of his oddity, Master Colt could not help being fond of him.

He felt proud of his possessions as he took Thomas through the forecourt and into the house. In the hall which occupied the ground floor of the central block, the great table was already set for the meal. Master Colt had little time for new-fangled town manners, and all his household ate at the same table–those servants who were not waiting, below the salt. Thomas looked at the sunlight slanting through the horn windows, at the vaulted roof, at the two staircases and the gallery from which the doors led to the other wings; but he was not thinking of the house. He was wondering what he would say to Jane.

'Come to my winter parlour and drink a mug of wine with me. Can you smell the juniper and rosemary? That's our Jane. She knows much of the herbs that grow in the fields, and she is for ever burning them in pomanders to make the air sweet.'

Master Colt still thought he had to impress on Jane's suitor the wifely qualities of the girl, as though Thomas needed to be impressed, as though he had not already made up his mind.

His host led the way to the winter parlour and called for wine to be brought.

The winter parlour was a cosy place; it contained hangings embroidered in rich colours by the girls, and there was a table about which were placed several stools; Master Colt was very proud of the polished metal mirror and the new clock.

They sat at the table and wine was brought, but Master Colt noticed that his guest merely touched his with his lips for the sake of politeness.

He sighed. Here was a man he did not understand, who did not care what he ate, and loved books better than wine. Yet any husband for Jane was better than no husband at all.

Then through the window he caught sight of Jane with her flower-basket.

'Why,' said Jane's father, 'there is Jane. You have seen her. You're thinking you'd rather have a word with her than drink wine with her father. Well then, slip out into the garden now. You can speak with her before supper is served.'

So Thomas went out of the house to Jane.

Jane knew he was coming. She was afraid. Her sisters laughed at her for her timidity. She should be grateful, they told her. At last she had a suitor. At last a man was thinking of marrying her. She had better be careful how she acted, for he was not caught yet.

I wish, thought Jane, that I could stay at home with my heartsease and snapdragons, my sweet williams and gilly-flowers. I want to stay and help salt the meat after the killing, and make the butter and cheese, and to see that the servants watch well to roasting meat, to make the bread and pies. I could stay at home and do these things.

But Jane knew that was not what was expected of a girl. She must marry. If she did not, she was scorned; her sisters would marry and shut her out of their confidences; they would laugh at her; they would pity her; even now they called her Poor Jane.

She was Poor Jane because, while she was afraid of marriage, she was even more afraid of not being married at all.

He was very old, this man who had selected her; he was twenty-six, and she was just turned sixteen. Still, it was better to have an old husband than no husband at all. He was very clever, so they said; and he knew much of what had been written in books. But her father did not think very highly of that sort of cleverness. As for Jane, it alarmed her greatly, for she could not understand half of what Thomas More said to her; and when he began to speak she would think, since he was fond of jesting, that she must surely smile; but she was never certain when the smile should come. Perhaps she would learn. She was sure there were many things which she would have to learn, and that was doubtless one of them.

Still, she continually repeated to herself, and she was sure of the wisdom of this: it was better to marry any man than not to marry at all.

When, in the kitchen, she had heard his horse, she had taken her flower-basket and run into the gardens to hide herself. Today he had come to ask her to marry him. Her father had told her this would happen and that she must accept him and tell him that she would be very happy to become his wife.

Happy to become his wife. . . .

Would her young sister have been happy to be his wife, and would he have been happy to wed her?

She wondered why he had suddenly turned from her sister to herself; her father had sent her sister away at that time, and again she wondered why.

Life was difficult to understand. If it were only as simple as tending the garden, how contented she would be!

Now she started, and her heart began to beat in real fear, for Thomas was coming towards her.

He saw her bending over the flowers, rosy colour flooding her neck, for her head was bent so that he could not see her face.

I will make her happy, he swore. Poor, fragile little Jane.

'Why, Mistress Colt,' he said. 'Why, Jane, I trust I find you well.'

She curtsied awkwardly, and the flowers fell from her basket.

'You tremble,' he said. 'Jane, you must not be afraid of me.'

'I . . . I am not afraid.' She lifted her eyes to his face. They reminded him of her sister's and he felt a pang of regret. His feelings for the two girls were so different. The younger girl, whom her father had sent away, was a creature of charm and beauty; he had been fascinated by the smooth, clear skin, the childish line of the cheeks, a certain boldness in her eyes that proclaimed her aware of the fact that she was admired. There had been, in her face and form, a certain promise of carnal delight. It was she who had decided him, who had shown him clearly that he must not take his vows, that he must leave the Charterhouse and make a home with a wife.

Was that love? He thought of others who had attracted him. He was no monk; he was no priest. He was a sensual man, it seemed. God had made him thus; and he believed he would have to control such feelings during the course of his life. All his friends had taken orders: Colet, Linacre, Lily. And what were women to Erasmus? He could see that he himself was fashioned of different clay. He wanted to be a saint; but since women moved him, charmed him, he was right not to turn from them: for it was better to be a layman who knew his weakness and tried to make an ideal family life, than a priest who took his vows and afterwards broke them.

He had loved young Mistress Colt until he had caught a look in Jane's eyes which had moved him–in another manner, it was true–as deeply as his desire for her sister.

He remembered the day well. They had been at dinner; and dinner was a merry meal at New Hall. Master Colt paid the deepest respect to his food. Why, he had his servants doff their hats with respect when the meat was brought in; his table was covered with so many dishes that it was almost impossible to make room for the wooden platters the family used. They had been at dinner, and Thomas had looked at his loved one, merrily chatting, delighting him with the quickness of her retorts. She had not been an educated girl. What girls were? Ah, that was a great mistake, as he had argued many times both with Colet and Erasmus. If women had souls, they also had brains, and it was as wrong to neglect the latter as the former. No, she was not educated, but he had appreciated her quick mind, that little display of wit. He had pictured his married life. They would sit after supper and he would teach her Latin; he would read her some of his epigrams and later perhaps those he was translating with Lily from the Greek anthology into Latin–but that was looking ahead. Then, when he had educated her, he would astonish his friends; and she would talk with them and be one of them. Yes, she should not only make a home for him, and give him children, she should join him and his friends in discussing theology, the need for reforming some of the old tenets of the Church; they would analyse the works of Plato, Socrates and Euripides; they themselves would write verses and essays which they would read to one another. He had looked forward to those days. He saw himself not only caressing her beautiful body, but feeding her mind. It had been an enchanting picture.

And then, as his glance strayed from her, he had been aware of Jane. Jane, the quiet one whom they all twitted because she was not so ready with her tongue, because she was the eldest and because no man had sought her in marriage.

Jane had been looking at her sister with admiration and envy. Not malicious envy. Jane was of too gentle a nature to experience unadulterated envy. It was merely that she became more insignificant than usual when her sister chattered; and as he watched her, Thomas More found his love for the younger girl infringed by his pity for the elder one.

He had tried to draw her into the conversation, but she would keep aloof like a frightened doe. He found her alone in the gardens and he said to her: 'You must not be afraid to speak, little Jane. Tell me, why are you afraid to speak?'

She had said: 'I have nothing to say.'

'But,' he had protested, 'there must be something behind those eyes . . .

some thought. Tell me what it is.'

'It would sound silly if I said it. Everyone would laugh.'

'*I* should not laugh.'

Then she told him how she thought the scent of gilly-flowers was the best in the world, and when she smelt it, she would always–no matter where she was–imagine that she was in the walled garden at New Hall. And she told him she feared she was a coward, for when they killed the animals in November, she shut herself in her room, stopped up her ears and wept. And sometimes she wept during the salting.

'Those are kindly thoughts, Jane,' he had said. 'And thoughts that should be told.'

'But they would laugh if I told them. They would say that I am even sillier than they believed me to be.'

'I should not laugh, Jane,' he had told her. 'I should never laugh.'

Then she had answered: 'But you would laugh more than anyone because you are cleverer than any.'

'Nay. Because I know more of what is in books than do your brothers and sisters, the more I understand. For is not understanding knowledge? When people laugh at others it is often because those others differ from themselves. Therefore the ignorant think them strange. But if you study the ways of men, you learn much; and as your knowledge grows there is little to surprise you. The man who travels the world, in time becomes no longer astonished by the looks and customs of men of other lands. Yet the man who lives in his little village all his life, is amazed by the habits of the man dwelling but ten miles away.'

'I do not entirely understand your words.' Jane had told him. 'But I understand your kindness.'

'Then, Jane, you are clever, for if more understood the intentions behind men's words, the world would be a happier place, and it is those who achieve happiness and lead others to it who are the clever ones of this world.'

Then she had told him how astonished she was that he, who was so much cleverer than others, should not frighten her so much; and that he, who had friends among the most learned of men, should know more than others how to be kind to a simple maid.

After that she would give him her quiet smile, and he would see the pleasure in her face when he spoke to her.

Others had noticed his friendship with Jane; and one day, when he had arrived at New Hall, it was to find that young Mistress Colt had gone away, and, with a sudden shock, he realized that he was expected to marry Jane.

To marry Jane! But it was merely a tender pity that he felt for her. It was her gay, tantalizing sister who had shown him that a monk's life was not for him.

His first impulse had been to ride away or explain his feelings to Master Colt.

Her father might have guessed his reluctance. He said: 'Jane is a good girl. The best in the world. The man who married her would get a good wife.'

Master Colt was not a subtle man; but if Thomas More was not moved by the desire of a country gentleman to get his daughter off his hands, he was deeply touched by the mute appeal of Jane.

He saw at once what he had done. With his kindness he had sown seeds of hope. Jane had a new gown; Jane had won the respect of her family, for which she had always longed, because they believed that a man wished to make Jane his wife.

What could he do? Could he ride away and never return to New Hall? Could he still ask for the hand of the girl with whom he had fallen in love?

And what of Jane? Meek and mild she was; but it was those of her temperament who suffered most cruelly. And her sister–what of her? But she was a gay spirit and there would be many to admire her. She was very young, and he doubted whether she had ever thought very seriously about one who would seem elderly to her.

If he hurt Jane, if he wounded her pride, if he was responsible for bringing upon her her family's scorn, how could he forgive himself? He had meant to make her life easier. Could it be that in his blind folly, he had made it harder for her to bear?

Being the man he was, he saw only one course open to him. He must turn tenderness into love; he must marry Jane. He must turn her into a woman such as he wished to have for his wife. Why should it not be so? She had been a docile daughter; she would be a docile wife. So he removed the girl he loved from the picture of domestic bliss and set Jane there in her place. He saw pleasant evenings when they would sit over their books while he talked to her in the Latin tongue. And after Latin . . . Greek.

And so, as Thomas More came into the garden to speak to Jane, he was picturing the future . . . their happy home, their children and his learned friends . . . all merry together.

'Why, Jane,' he said, 'we saw you through the window and your father bade me join you.'

'You are welcome,' she answered with her quiet smile.

And in the garden, with the hot sun upon him and the girl beside him, her eyes downcast, there came to him a reminder that he had not yet spoken those words which would make it impossible for him to turn back. Suddenly he thought of the quiet of the Charterhouse, of those years when he had lived with the Carthusian monks, and he longed to be back with them. He wanted another chance to think, to brood on this matter, to talk it over with his friends.

But because he was silent so long, she had lifted her eyes to his face; she had been looking at him for some seconds in anxious bewilderment before he realized this.

How young she was! How pathetic! How could he leave her to the mercy of her family? Dear Jane! He guessed what her life would be if he rode away now. Her sisters would taunt her; the whole family would let her see that she had failed; she would become Jane-of-no-account, in very truth.

Life was unfair to such women.

Pity coloured all his thoughts. It was ever so. When he saw the poor in the streets he could never resist giving alms. His friends said: 'The word goes round among the beggars: "Thomas More comes this way!" And they uncover their sores, and some feign blindness. Make sure that in enriching the beggars you do not beggar yourself.' And he had answered: 'There may be some who are not so poor as they would seem to be; there may be some who feign distress to win my pity and with it money from my pocket. But, my friends, I would rather be the victim of a rogue than that any man should be the victim of my indifference to his suffering.'

Pity. Sweet Pity. A nobler emotion than passion or desire. Here then, he thought, is what I most desire: A happy home. And cannot Jane give me that?

'Jane,' he said, 'I want you to be my wife.'

She stared down at the flowers in her basket.

'What say you, Jane?' he asked tenderly.

'My father wishes it.'

'He does. And you?'

She smiled slowly. 'I shall try to be a good wife to you.'

He kissed her tenderly; and she thought: There will be less to fear with him than with anyone else, for he is the kindest man in the world.

'Then come. Let us go into the house and tell your father that you have consented to become my wife.'

They went into the hall, where the servants were now carrying in the dishes. Thomas was amused by the ceremony which was paid to the food.

'I was about to ask you to salute a new son,' he said to his host, 'but I see that he must keep his place until His Majesty the Ox hath been received.'

And only when the great side of beef was set on the table was Master Colt ready to embrace Thomas. Then, taking him to the head of the table, he proclaimed to those assembled there that his daughter Jane was betrothed to Thomas More.

Jane was sitting at the window of her new home, which was called The Barge, looking out along Bucklersbury, thinking that she must be the most unhappy woman in the world. But then, Jane's knowledge of the world was slight.

The Barge! She hated it. It was a foolish name to give to a gloomy old house. 'The Barge,' Thomas had explained, 'will be our home. Why "The Barge"? you may ask. It is because in the days before the Walbrook was covered, the barges came right to this spot. Oh, Jane, we will wander through the City and we will picture it as it was in days gone by. Then you will see what a wonderful old City it is, and you will love it as I do–more than any other place in the world.'

But Jane could not love it. She could love no place but New Hall. She longed for her garden, for the quiet fields of buttercups and marguerites; she hated this great City with its shops and crowds of noisy people. All through the day she could hear the shouts of traders in the Poultry and the Chepe; she could smell the meats being roasted in the cook shops, and the scents from the apothecaries' of which there were so many in Bucklersbury; the scent of musk mingled with that of spices from the pepperers' and grocers' shops; and she was homesick . . . homesick for New Hall and the single life.

She wept a good deal. Often Thomas would look in dismay at her reddened eyelids; but when he asked what ailed her, she would shrink from him. She had not imagined that married life was like this, and she could not understand why so many people longed for it. Why did they think a girl had failed if she did not achieve it?

She had married a man whose heart was in books. In London he seemed older than he had in the country. Men came to the house; they were older even than her husband; and she would sit listening to their talk without understanding anything they said.

She was foolish, she knew. Her family had always said so. How tragic it was that she, the simplest of them all, should be married to one of the most learned men in England!

There was so much to learn. She had always believed that a wife had but to watch the servants and see that there was no waste in the kitchen. That had been her stepmother's duty. But here at The Barge, much was expected of her.

'Jane,' he had said, 'I will lay the whole world at your feet.' She had thought that was one of the most beautiful things a husband could say to his wife; but she had discovered that his way of laying the whole world at her feet was to attempt to teach her Latin and to make her repeat, by way of recreation, the sermons they heard in St Stephen's Church in Walbrook.

'Poor little Jane,' he said, 'they have neglected your education, but we will remedy that, my love. I said I would lay the whole world at your feet, did I not? Yes, Jane, I will give you the key to all the treasures in the world. Great literature–that is the world's greatest treasure; and the key is understanding the languages in which it is written.'

She was a most unhappy bride. She felt bewildered and lost and wished she were dead.

Surely everything a normal woman needed was denied her. In a book he had written, entitled *The Life of John Picus*, there was a dedication to a woman. She had felt a faint stirring of jealousy, but she had discovered that the woman to whom the book was dedicated was a nun–a sister who lived with the Order of the Poor Clares just beyond the Minories. How could she be jealous of a nun? Even that was denied her. She knew that she had married no ordinary man, and she fervently wished that she had a husband whom she could understand–someone like her father or her brothers, even if there were occasions when he was angry with her and beat her. This harping on the value of learning, in spite of his kindness and gentleness, was sometimes more than she could bear.

He was trying to mould her, to make her into a companion as well as a wife. It was like asking an infant to converse with sages.

Dr Lily came to the house, as did Dr Linacre and Dr Colet; they conversed with her husband, and they laughed frequently, for Thomas laughed a good deal; but a woman could not continue to smile when she had no idea of the cause of laughter.

Sometimes her husband took her walking through the City, pointed out with pride what he considered places of interest.

They would walk through Walbrook and Candlewick Street, through Tower Street to the Great Tower. Then Thomas would tell her stories of what had happened within those gloomy walls, but she found she could not remember which of the kings and queens had taken part in them; and she would be worried because she knew she could not remember. Then he would take her to Goodman's Fields and pick daisies with her; they would make a chain together to hang about her neck; he would laugh and tease her because she was a country girl; but even then she would be afraid that he was making jokes which she did not recognize as such.

Sometimes they would walk along by the river or row over to Southwark, where the people were so poor. Then he would talk of the sufferings of the poor and how he visualized an ideal state where there was no such suffering. He loved to talk of this state which he built up in his imagination. She was rather glad when he did so, for he would not seem to notice that she was not listening, and she could let her mind enjoy memories of New Hall.

At other times they would walk through the Poultry to the Chepe and to Paul's Cross to listen to the preachers. He would glance at her anxiously, hoping that her delight in the sermons equalled his own. He would often talk of Oxford and Cambridge, where so many of his friends had studied. 'One day, Jane, I shall take you there,' he promised her. She dreaded that; she felt that such places would be even more oppressive than this City with its noisy crowds.

Once she watched a royal procession in the streets. She saw the King himself–a disappointing figure, unkingly, she thought, solemn and austere, looking as though he considered such displays a waste of money and time. But with him had been the young Prince of Wales, who must surely be the most handsome Prince in the world. She had cheered with the crowd when he had ridden by on his grey horse, so noble, so beautiful in his purple velvet cloak, his hair gleaming like gold, his sweet face, as someone in the crowd said, as lovely as a girl's, yet masculine withal. It seemed to Jane that the Prince, who was smiling and bowing to all, let his eyes linger for a moment on her. She felt herself blushing; and surely all the homage and admiration she wished to convey must have been there for him to see. Then it had seemed that the Prince had a special smile for Jane; and as she stood there, she was happy–happy to have left New Hall, because there she could never have had a smile from the boy who would one day be the King.

The Prince passed on, but something had happened to Jane; she no longer felt quite so stupid; and when Thomas told her of the coming of King Henry to the throne, she listened eagerly and she found that what he had to tell was of interest to her. Thomas was delighted with that interest, and when they reached The Barge he read her some notes which he had compiled when, as a boy, he had been sent to the household of Cardinal Morton, there to learn what he could. The notes were written in Latin, but he translated them into English for her, and she enjoyed the story of the coming of the Tudor King; she wept over the two little Princes who, Thomas told her, had been murdered in the Tower by the order of their wicked, crookbacked uncle, Richard. She could not weep for the death of Arthur, for, had Arthur lived, that beautiful Prince who had smiled at her would never be a King. So the death of Arthur, she was sure, could not be a tragedy but a blessing in disguise.

Thomas, delighted with her interest, gave her a lesson in Latin; and although she was slow to understand, she began to feel that she might learn a little.

She thought a good deal about the handsome Prince, but a conversation she overheard one day sent her thoughts fearfully to the Prince's father, the flinty-faced King.

John More came to see his son and daughter-in-law. Like Thomas, he was a lawyer, a kindly-faced man with shrewd eyes.

He patted Jane's head, wished her happiness and asked her if she were with child. She blushed and said she was not.

Marriage, she heard him tell Thomas, was like putting the hand into a blind bag which was full of eels and snakes. There were seven snakes to every eel.

She did not understand whether that meant he was pleased with his son's marriage or not; and what eels and snakes had to do with her and Thomas she could not imagine.

But there was something which she did understand.

John More said to his son: 'So, your piece of folly in the Parliament has cost me a hundred pounds.'

'My piece of folly?'

'Now listen, son Thomas. I have been wrongfully imprisoned on a false charge, and my release was only won in payment of a hundred pounds. All London knows that I paid the fine for you. You were the culprit. You spoke with such fire against the grant the King was asking that it was all but halved by the Parliament. The King wishes his subjects to know that he'll not brook such conduct. You have done a foolish thing. A pair of greedy royal eyes are turned upon us, and methinks they will never lose sight of us.'

'Father, as a burgess of London, I deemed it meet to oppose the King's spending of his subjects' money.'

'As a subject of the King, you have acted like a fool, even though as a burgess you may have acted like an honest man. You are a meddler, my son. You will never rise to the top of our profession unless you give your mind to the study of law, and to nothing else. I kept you short of money at Oxford. . . .'

'Aye, that you did–so that I often went hungry and was unable to pay for the repair of my boots. I had to sing at the doors of rich men for alms, and to run up and down the quadrangles for half an hour before bedtime, or the coldness of my body would have kept me from sleep altogether.'

'And you bear me a grudge for that, eh, my son?'

'Nay, Father. For, having no money to spend on folly, I must give all my energies to learning; and knowledge is a greater prize than meat for supper–even if it is not always of the law!'

'Thomas, I understand you not. You are a good son, and yet you are a fool. Instead of giving yourself entirely to the study of the law, what do you do? When that fellow Erasmus came to England you spent much time . . . discoursing, I hear, prattling the hours away, studying Greek and Latin together . . . when I wished you to work at the law. And now that you are accounted a worthy and utter barrister, and you are made a burgess, what do you do? You . . . a humble subject of the King, must arouse the King's wrath.'

'Father, one day, if I am a rich man, I will repay the hundred pounds.'

'Pah!' said John More. 'If you are a rich man you will hear from the King, and I doubt you would remain a rich man long enough to pay your father that hundred pounds. For, my son . . . and let us speak low, for I would not have this go beyond us . . . the King will not forget you. You have escaped, you think. You have done your noble act and your father has paid his fine. Do not think that is an end of this matter.' He lowered his voice still more. 'This King of ours is a cold-hearted man. Money is the love of his life; but one of his light o' loves is Revenge. You have thwarted his Love; you have wounded her deeply. You . . . a young man, who have, with your writings, already attracted attention to yourself so that your name is known in Europe, and when scholars visit this country you are one of those with whom they seek to converse. You have set yourself up to enlighten the people, and you have done this in Parliament. What you have said is this: "The King's coffers are full to bursting, good people, and you are poor. Therefore, as a burgess of your Parliament, I will work to remedy these matters." The King will not forget that. Depend upon it, he will seek an opportunity of letting you know that no subject of his–be he ever so learned, and whatever admiration scholars lay at his feet–shall insult the King and his beloved spouse, Riches.'

'Then, Father, I am fortunate to be a poor man; and how many men can truly rejoice in their poverty?'

'You take these matters lightly, my son. But have a care. The King watches you. If you prosper he will have your treasure.'

'Then I pray, Father, that my treasures will be those which the King does not envy–my friends, my writing, my honour.'

'Tut!' said the shrewd lawyer. 'This is fools' talk. Learn wisdom with your Greek and Latin. It'll stand you in better stead than either.'

Jane was frightened. That man with the cruel face hated her husband. *She* took her father-in-law's warning to heart if Thomas did not.

Often she dreamed of the hard-faced King, and in her dreams his great coffers burst open while Thomas took out the gold and gave it to the beggars in Candlewick Street.

She knew she had a very strange and alarming husband; and often, when she wept a little during the silence of the night, she wondered whether it would have been much worse to have remained unmarried all her life than to have become the wife of Thomas More.

Her position was not relieved by the coming of the man from Rotterdam.

Jane had heard much of him; and of all the learned friends who struck terror into her heart, this man frightened her more than any.

He settled in at The Barge and changed the way of life there.

Sometimes he looked at Jane with a mildly sarcastic smile, and there would be a faint twinkle in his half-closed blue eyes as though he were wondering how such a man as his friend Thomas More could have married the insignificant little wench.

She learned a good deal about him, but the things which interested her were, Thomas said, unimportant. He was the illegitimate son of a priest, and this seemed to Jane a shameful thing; nor could she understand why he was not ashamed of it. He had become an orphan when he was very young, and when those about him had realized his unusual powers he had been sent into a convent of canons regular, but, like Thomas, he could not bring himself to take the vows. He had studied in Paris, where he had given his life to literature; and although he had suffered greatly from abject poverty and had been forced to earn his bread by becoming tutor to gentlemen, so dazzling was his scholarship that he had drawn the attention of other scholars to himself and was recognized as the greatest of them all.

Jane, in her kitchen, giving orders to her maids, could hardly believe that she had this great man in her house and that it was her husband with whom he went walking through the streets of London.

To some extent she was glad of this man's visit; it turned Thomas's attention from herself. They were translating something–to which they referred as *Lucian*–from Latin into Greek, she believed; they would spend hours together doing this work, disagreeing on many points. It seemed to Jane that learned conversation involved a good deal of disagreement. And so it happened that as Thomas must engage himself in continual conversation with Erasmus, with his work as a lawyer and with his attendances at the Parliament, he had less time to give to the tutoring of his wife.

But she, since the smile she was sure she had received from the Prince of Wales, began to feel that perhaps she was not so foolish as she had believed herself to be. On looking back, it seemed that that smile of the Prince's had held a certain appreciation. She was not so foolish that she did not realize that the Prince would look for other qualities in a woman than did Thomas;

yet the approbation of such a Prince gave her new courage and confidence in herself.

She listened more carefully to the discourses that went on about her; and when they were in English she found that they were not so dreary as she had believed they must be.

Erasmus disliked the monks; Thomas defended them.

Erasmus declared his intention of one day laying bare to the world the iniquitous happenings which occurred in some of the monasteries of Europe.

He had stories to tell of the evil practices which went on in monasteries. Listening, Jane realized that there was much sin in the world.

In some religious houses, declared Erasmus, lewdness rather than religion was the order of the day. Abortion and child-murder prevailed; for how, demanded Erasmus, can these holy nuns account for the children they bring into the world? They cannot. So they strangle them as soon as they are born and bury them in the grounds of the nunneries. There are lusts of an unnatural nature between the sexes. . . .

Here the men became aware of Jane's attention, and they lapsed into Latin.

Jane thought: The Prince thought me worth a glance. Perhaps I could learn a little Latin. Though I should never be a scholar I might learn a little, for if I can understand English, why not Latin?

Erasmus spoke in English of one monastery in which there was a statue of a boy-saint, hollow and so light that it could be lifted by a child of five. Yet it was said that only those without sin could lift it. Many came to see the holy statue, and rich men found that they could only lift it when they had paid heavily for the monks' intercession with the saints on their behalf. Only when they had given to the monastery as much money as they could be induced to part with were they able to lift the statue. A miracle? In a way. Worked by one of the monks who, remaining out of sight, removed at the right moment that peg which held the statue on the floor. Then there was the case of the phial of blood, reputed to be that of Christ. Only those who were holy enough could see the blood; and it was deemed a sign from Heaven that a man would only be received there if the blood appeared to him. And the blood? The blood of a duck, renewed at regular intervals. And the phial? It was opaque one side. It cost much money to have the phial turned so that the blood was visible to the devout dupe.

'These practices are wicked,' said Erasmus. 'They bring much gain to the monasteries now, but they will eventually bring much loss. I am sure of it.'

'Is it fair,' asked Thomas, 'to condemn all monasteries because of the evil-doing of some?'

'It is well,' said Erasmus, 'to put all under suspicion and let them clear themselves.'

'But should one be assumed guilty until he fails to prove his innocence?'

'You are too lenient, friend More. The greed of these monks will prove their undoing. One day I shall show their criminal follies to the world; I shall set it out that all may read. Then, my friend, they will wish that they had led the lives of holy men, which are more comfortable than the lives of the wandering beggars they will become. What say you, Mistress More? What say you?'

The mildly mocking eyes were turned upon her. Thomas came to her rescue. 'Jane will doubtless agree with you.'

'Then I am glad of that,' said Erasmus. 'And I hope one day to convince you also. For it is the duty of us men of letters to show the world's wrongs to the world.'

'But we must be sure we have something good to offer in its place, before we destroy that which mayhap could be set to rights.'

'Ah, you and your ideal state! That is still on your mind, is it? You set too high a standard. You think the world is made up of potential saints and martyrs. Does your husband talk to you, Mistress More, day in, day out, of this wonder-world of his?'

'He talks . . . a little,' stammered Jane. 'But I am not clever. I am far from learned and there is much I do not know.'

Thomas smiled at her, his eyes telling her not to be nervous. He rose and put an arm about her shoulders.

'Jane is learning,' he said. 'One day she will understand Latin even as you or I.'

'I fear not,' said Jane. 'I am far too foolish.'

'Why,' said Erasmus, 'so he would bother you with lessons would he? You see, it is what I expect of him. The world is not to his liking, so he would build an ideal world. A woman is . . . a woman, and he would make a scholar of her!'

'There is no reason, my dear Erasmus, why women, if taught, should not become every bit as learned as men.'

'There is every reason.'

'And what are these?'

'Women are the weaker sex. Do you not know that? They are not meant to cudgel their brains. They are meant to look to the comfort of men.'

'Nay. I do not agree. I believe that we are mistaken in not giving our girls an education equal to that which we give our boys. If we did, we should find our women able to converse with us in Latin while they cooked the dinner.'

'And Mistress More . . . she is proving as apt a pupil as you once were . . . as I was?'

Thomas answered in Latin, because he was aware of Jane's embarrassment. He was always acutely aware of the feelings of others, and suffered their hurt more deeply than he would his own.

And the two men, having found a subject for discussion, would go on happily until the one led to another.

It will not always be thus, thought Jane. One day Erasmus will go away; one day we shall visit New Hall; and one day, who knows, I may learn to converse in Latin!

But that day must be a long way ahead, and meanwhile she must go on trying not to hate her life at The Barge.

Had he been wrong to marry?

Thomas was unsure. Sometimes he walked alone through the streets of London and his steps invariably took him northwards across the City; he would find himself walking up Charter Lane until he came to the great buildings in which he had spent those four years of indecision.

He would enter the quadrangle, then go to the chapel or the chapter house; and he would think, not without longing, of the life of solitude and meditation, life that was given up to study and contemplation, life that was unharassed by bodily needs, by the great events which were going on in the outside world.

He thought of the rigorous way of life of the Carthusians, each with his separate house of two rooms, closet, refectory and garden, living his solitary life, speaking to his fellow monks only on feast days, fasting at least once a week, never eating flesh of any sort and thus subduing the appetites of the body; he thought of wearing the hair-shirt by night so that sleep did not come easily, until eventually it was possible to indulge in sleep only for an hour each night; using the wooden pillow, dressing in the coarsest clothes to detract from any good looks a man might possess and so subdue his vanity; he thought of shutting himself away from the world, and perhaps by his example helping to lead others to a holier way of life.

The life of retirement seemed very dear to him when he thought of his home in The Barge of Bucklersbury.

Was Erasmus right? Was it as difficult to create an ideal woman as an ideal world? Was he a fool to try to educate Jane to his intellectual standard? Was he making an unhappy woman of her as well as a fool of himself?

This was the state of the marriage of Jane and Thomas More when Jane found that she was going to have a child.

A child! thought Jane. This would be wonderful. A boy whom his father would make a scholar? That would delight him; that would turn his attention from his poor, simple wife. If he had a boy to whom he could teach the Latin tongue, why should he bother to teach it to Jane? And must he not be grateful to the simple woman who could give him such a blessing in life?

But, thought Jane, if it is a girl, how happy I shall be, for then he will see that girls should not be made learned. She will teach him what I could not; and she and I will be together; she will love flowers and we will grow them together, and I shall take her to New Hall; and when I show my child to my family, then I shall know that the world was right when it said that the married state is the best state of all.

So the child could make Jane happy as Thomas never could.

Thomas was gay.

A child! That was the meaning of married life. That was what he wanted. What was the life to be lived in Carthusian solitude when compared with the bringing up of a child? The best tutors in England should be procured for young Master More. They would be glad to come. Dr Lily perhaps? There was the greatest teacher in England. Then there would be Thomas More himself to guide his son.

Those were happy days–awaiting the birth of the child. A son, of course. The first-born should be a son. And after that, more sons and some daughters. And the daughters should be treated in the same way as the sons; no matter what Erasmus, Colet, Lily and the rest said, Thomas was convinced that women should not be denied education. His daughters should prove him to have been right.

But for the present he could dream of his son.

There was laughter in The Barge; and if Jane did not understand all the jokes, she laughed as though she did. She was happy and Thomas was happy to see her happy.

Married life was the best state of all.

His friends were often at the house. Jane did not care. She sat, her needle busy, making clothes for the child. Her body widened and her prestige grew.

Who were these scholars? Who was Dr Colet, with his talk of founding schools for children? It was true that he was no longer a mere vicar of Stepney but had been appointed Dean of St Paul's itself. But what did she care for him. Who was Dr William Lily, who had learned Latin in Italy, had travelled widely, had opened a school in London and had, like Thomas, almost become a monk? Who was this Dr Linacre who had taught Thomas Greek? Who was the great Erasmus himself? Clever they might be, but none of them could bear a child!

New dignity and confidence had come to Jane. She sang snatches of songs as she went about the house.

Married life was indeed good and Jane was very happy.

And one summer's day in the year 1505 Margaret came into the world.

Chapter Two

Margaret was four years old when she first knew the meaning of fear. Until then her world had been a merry place, ruled by the person she loved best: her father.

The only times when she was unhappy were when he was not at home. Then the old house with its dark staircases, its odd nooks and alcoves, seemed a different place. Margaret would sit in the window seat watching for his return, looking out on the shops of the apothecaries and grocers, thinking that they were not quite the same shops which she had passed, her hand in her father's, while he explained to her the uses of spices and drugs, the scent of which filled the air. Nothing could be quite right in Margaret's eyes unless her father was with her.

When she heard his laughter–and she almost always heard his laughter before she heard him speak–she would feel as though she had found the right answer to a problem which had bothered her in her lessons. She would run to him and stand before him, waiting for him to lift her up.

He would say: 'And what has my Meg learned today?'

Eagerly she would tell him, and draw back to see the effect of her answer. Pleasing him was the most important thing in the world to her. She longed to be able to speak to him in Latin; that, she believed, would please him more than anything she could do.

'Meg,' he once said to her when an answer she had given him had especially pleased him, 'to think that when you were born we hoped for a boy!'

'And you would rather have me than any boy, would you not, Father?'

'Rather my girls than any boys in the world.'

She believed that he meant: rather his Meg than any boys; but he would think of the others–Elizabeth who was three and Cecily who was two–and he would tell himself that it was not right for a father to love one child more than the others. And he was a man who must always do right; she knew that. She was a child and not good like he was; and she could love one member of her family so much that if all the affection she had for the others were rolled into one heap it would be as the moon to the great sun of her affection for him. But she would not ask him if he loved her best; she knew he did; and he knew of her love for him. That was their secret.

Sometimes she would go into that room in which he sat with his friends, and he would take her on his knee or sit her on the table. Then the old, solemn-faced men would look at her, and her father would say: 'Margaret will prove to you that I am right. She is young yet, but you will see . . . you will see.'

Then he would ask her questions and she would answer him. They would say: 'Can this be a maid so young?'

'A maid who will show you, my friend, that a woman's brain is equal to a man's.' Then he would bring his smiling face close to hers. 'Meg, they do not believe that you can learn your lessons. They say that because you are a girl this headpiece of yours will not be equal to the task. Meg, you must prove them wrong. If you do not, they will say that I am rightly named. For *Moros* . . . that is Greek for fool, Meg; and it will seem that I shall be worthy of the name if I am wrong. Meg, thou wilt not let them laugh at thy father?'

'Nay, Father,' she said scowling at the men. 'They shall not laugh at thee. We will show them who are the fools.'

They laughed and talked to her, and she answered as best she could, with her heart beating fast for fear she should behave like a very little girl instead of a learned young woman of nearly five years old. She was determined to save her father from the mockery of his friends.

So her lessons were more than a task to her; they were a dedication. She *must* master them.

'It is not natural to sit so long with your books,' said her mother. 'Come . . . play with Bessy.'

But if she played with Bessy it was but to teach her; for, she thought, Father will like all his daughters to be clever. It will not do for one of us to be wise and the rest ignorant.

Yet she hoped that Elizabeth and Cecily would not be able to learn as easily as she could, for she wished to remain the cleverest of her father's daughters.

Thus Margaret, even at the age of four, had become an unusually learned little girl.

One day her father brought home a girl of her own age–a shy and sad little girl.

Margaret heard his voice and rushed down to meet him; she flung her arms about his knees; then she stood solemnly regarding the little girl who stood beside him, her hand in his.

Her father crouched down so that the three of them were all of a size. He put an arm about each of them.

'Margaret,' he said, 'I have brought a playmate for you.'

Margaret wanted to say that she had no wish for a playmate. Her lessons absorbed her; and she had two sisters with whom she could play. If she wanted a new addition to their household it would have been a boy, so that she could have proved to those friends of her father's how right he was when he said that girls could learn as much as boys.

But she knew that she must not make the little girl feel unwanted, for that would surely displease her father.

'This,' he went on, 'is another Margaret. Margaret is my favourite name.'

That made Margaret smile and look with new interest at the little girl who had the same name as herself.

'This Margaret is coming to live with us, Meg.'

'We cannot have two Margarets in one house,' Margaret pointed out. 'If you called me she would think you called her.'

'My wise little daughter!' His laughter was merry but she knew that he had sensed her resentment, and she blushed because she knew it must displease him.

'One of us would have to be given a new name,' she said quickly.

'What other names are there for Margaret?' he asked. 'There is Peg. There is Daisy. There is Meg and Marget. Ah, but we already have a Meg and Marget in our own Margaret. There is Mercy. One of you will have to change her name, will she not?'

'Yes,' said Margaret, her lips trembling slightly. She knew what he expected of her, and she knew that she could not bear to hear him call another Margaret. He knew it too; that was why he expected her to give her name to this girl.

'It is more blessed to give than to receive.' Often he had told them that. He often said: 'Ah, my Meg, if only men and women would realize that it is the unselfish acts that bring most pleasure, then the world would become full of unselfish people; and perhaps the very act of unselfishness would become a selfish one.'

She knew, with his eyes upon her, that she must make the sacrifice now.

'I . . . I will be Daisy or Mercy,' she said.

He kissed her then. 'My Meg . . . my dearest Meg,' he said; and she thought that if that was the last time he called her by her name she would always remember his voice at that moment.

'Mercy is a beautiful name,' he said, 'for mercy is one of the most beautiful of all qualities.'

'Do you like Mercy?' asked Margaret of the newcomer.

'Yes,' she answered. 'I will be Mercy, because this is your house first, and you were the first Margaret in it.'

Then her father kissed them both and said: 'So my Meg stays with me; and in addition I have brought Mercy into the house.'

Her name was Mercy Gigs and she had been left an orphan. She had no fortune, he explained to Margaret, but her own sweet nature. 'So Meg, we must take her into our house. I will be Father to her; your mother will be Mother; and you will be Sister to her as you are to Elizabeth and Cecily.'

And so it was that she acquired a new sister, to learn with her and talk with her. She had the advantage of having started her lessons earlier, but she soon realized that Mercy Gigs was a rival, for she had given her devotion to the man who had taken her into his house and become her foster-father, and, like Margaret, her one thought was to win his respect and approval.

She too worked hard at her lessons and tried to startle him with her ability to learn. Now when the friends came and asked how Margaret was progressing with her lessons, there would be two little girls to confront them; and Mercy Gigs, the orphan, could confound them even more than Margaret who was, after all, the daughter of a learned man.

'So Mercy will prove my point completely,' Thomas would say with glee. 'Mercy is going to be as clever as my own children. Mercy shall be given the best tuition with my own children, and she will show you that most feminine minds are as capable of absorbing knowledge as a sponge absorbs water.'

Then Mercy would blush and smile and be very happy.

Later there came the period of anxiety. It began when, one day, her father took Margaret on his knee and told her that he was going away for a little while.

She put her arms about him and bit her lips hard to hold back her tears.

'But it will not be long, Meg,' he said. 'I am going into foreign lands. I am going to the universities of Paris and Louvain to see my friends who come to see me when they are here; and perhaps one day, Meg, I shall take you and your mother and your sisters there. How will you like that?'

'I would rather stay here and that you should stay too.'

'Well, Meg, that which we would rather have does not always come about. You will have to look after everybody in the house, will you not? And you will work hard at your lessons whilst I am gone?'

She nodded. 'But why must you go? Why must you go?'

'I am going because quite soon I may want to take my family to France. But first I wish to go there alone, to make sure that it is the place my family would like to live in.'

'Of course we should like to live there if you were there. There is no need to you to go first without us.'

He kissed her and put her down.

Her fears had started then. Not only was this due to the fact that he left for France shortly afterwards, but she knew from the looks of the servants, from the voices of the people who spoke with her mother, and from her mother's worried looks, that something frightening had happened.

He had not told her what it was; and she knew that could only be because she was too young to understand.

She talked of this matter with Mercy. Mercy was wise and quiet; she too had noticed that something was wrong; she too was afraid.

Once when her mother was baking bread in the kitchen, Margaret said: 'Mother, when will my father come back?'

'Soon, my child. Soon.'

'Soon,' said Margaret, 'can be a long time for something you greatly wish for. It can be quick for something you hate.'

Jane touched the small head and marvelled at this daughter of hers. Margaret was far more like Thomas than like herself; she was more like Thomas than any of the others. Whenever she looked at the child she remembered those days soon after Margaret's birth, when Thomas had walked up and down the room with her to soothe her cries; she remembered that Thomas could soothe her as no one else could. She remembered also how Thomas had talked of what he would do for this child, how she was to be a great and noble woman, how delighted he was with his daughter, how she had charmed him as no son ever could have done.

And it seemed that Thomas must have had pre-knowledge, for Margaret was all that he had wished. Her cleverness astonished her mother; she had already, though not yet five, started on Latin and Greek, and seemed to find the same pleasure in it that most children would in a game of shuttlecock. Jane could feel satisfied when she surveyed her eldest daughter. Surely she had made his marriage a success when she had given him this quaint and solemn daughter.

'Well, my dearest,' said Jane, 'your father will be away for a few weeks, and I'll swear that that will seem long to all of us. But when he returns you will be all the more pleased to see him because you have missed him so much.'

'Nothing could please me more,' said Margaret, 'than to see him every day.'

Then she went away and gravely did her lessons. Her one aspiration now was to astonish him when he came back.

And eventually he did come back. Margaret must be the first to greet him; and when she heard his voice calling to his family, she sped into the great hall; but Mercy was there beside her.

They stood side by side looking up at him.

He smiled at their grave little faces and lifted them in his arms. He kissed Mercy first; but Margaret knew, and Mercy knew, that that was because he was longing to kiss Margaret more than anyone, for Margaret was his own child and he could never love any as he loved her.

They sat at the big table–the whole household–and everyone was happy because he was home. All the servants, who sat at the table with the family, were happy; and so were those poor travellers who had called in, weary and footsore, because they knew that they could always be sure of a meal in the house of Thomas More.

After the meal, Thomas went first to the schoolroom, and there he marvelled and delighted in the progress his daughters had made. Even two-year-old Cecily had started to learn; and he was, he said, mightily pleased. 'Why,' he declared, ''twas worth being away, for the pleasure it gives me to come back to you.'

But a few days later he took Margaret walking in Goodman's Fields, and made her sit beside him on the grass there; and as they sat, he told her that he had made plans to leave The Barge in Bucklersbury, to leave this City, and to take his family away with him to France.

Margaret cried: 'But . . . Father, you say you love London, and that no other city could ever be home to you.'

'I know, my child. And you?'

'Yes, Father. I love it too.'

'And which would you have–a strange land with your father, or England . . . London . . . and no father?'

'I would rather be anywhere with you, Father, than anywhere without you.'

'Then, Margaret, it will be no hardship for you. "Better is a dinner of herbs where love is . . ." eh? And it will be a dinner of herbs, my dearest, for we shall not be rich.'

'We shall be happy,' said Margaret. 'But why must we go?'

'Sometimes I wonder, my Margaret, whether I have made you grow up too quickly. I so long to see you bloom. I want you to be my little companion. I want to discuss all things with you. And I forget what a child you are. Well, I shall tell you this; but it is our secret. You will remember that?'

'Yes, Father.'

'Then listen. A long time ago, before you were born, before I married your mother, our King asked his Parliament for a sum of money. I was a Member–a very junior Member–of that Parliament, and I argued against the King's wishes. Partly because of the words I spoke, Margaret, the King did not get all the money for which he was asking.'

Margaret nodded.

'When the King is given money by the Parliament, it is the people's money raised by taxes. You do not know what these are, and one day I will explain. But, you see, money has to be taken from the people to give to the

King . . . a little here . . . a little there . . . to make a large sum. The cost of food is increased so that some of the money which is paid for it may go to the King. The people had already paid too many of these taxes and the King wanted them to pay more and more. I thought it wrong that he should have the money for which he asked. I thought it wrong that the people should be made even poorer. And I said so.'

'It *was* wrong, Father.'

'Ah, little Meg, do you say that because you see why it was wrong, or because I say so?'

'Because you say so, Father.'

He kissed her. 'Do not trust me too blindly, Meg. I am a mortal man, you know. I will say this: I thought what I did was right. The King thought I was wrong. And kings, like little girls . . . little boys . . . and even babies, do not like people who prevent their doing those things which they wish to do. So . . . the King does not like me.'

'Everybody likes you, Father,' she said in disbelief.

'*You* do,' he said with a laugh. 'But everyone, alas! has not your kind discernment. No, the King does not like me, Meg, and when a king does not like a man, he seeks to harm him in some way.'

She stood up in alarm. She took his hand and tugged at it.

'Whither would you take me, Meg?'

'Let us run away now.'

'Whither shall we run?'

'To some foreign land where we can have a new king.'

'That is just what I propose to do, Meg. But there is no need for you to be frightened, and there is no need for such haste. We have to take the others with us. That is why I went abroad . . . to spy out the land. Very soon you, I, your mother, the girls and some of our servants are going away. I have many kind friends, as you know. One of these is a gentleman whom you have seen because he has visited us. He is a very important gentleman–Bishop Foxe of Winchester. He has warned me of the King's feelings against me, and he has told me that he can make the King my friend if I will admit my fault to the Parliament.'

'Then he will make the King your friend, Father?'

'Nay, Meg, for how can I say that I was wrong when I believe myself to have been right, when, should I be confronted with the same problem, I should do the same again?'

'If Bishop Foxe made the King your friend, you could stay at home.'

'That is true, Meg. I love this City. Look at it now. Let me lift you. There is no city in the world which would seem so beautiful to me as this one. When I am far from it, I shall think of it often. I shall mourn it as I should mourn the best loved of my friends. Look, Meg. Look at the great bastions of our Tower. What a mighty fortress! What miseries . . . what joys . . . have been experienced within those walls? You can see our river. How quietly, how peacefully it flows! But what did Satan say to Jesus when he showed Him the beauties of the world, Meg? That is what a small voice within me says. "All this can be yours," it says. "Just for a few little words." All I need say is that I was wrong and the King was right. All I need say is that it is right for the King to take his subjects' money, to make them poor that he may be rich. Nay, Meg, it would be wrong to say those words. And there would be no peace in saying them. This City of mine would scorn me if I said them; so I cannot, Meg; I cannot.' Then he kissed her and went on: 'I burden this little head with so much talk. Come, Meg, smile for me. You and I know how to be happy wherever we are. We know the secret, do we not? What is it?'

'Being together,' said Margaret.

He smiled and nodded, and hand-in-hand they walked home by the long route. Through Milk Street they went, that he might show her the house in which he was born, for he knew she never tired of looking at it and picturing him as a child no bigger than herself; they went past the poulterers' shops in the Poultry, through Scalding Alley where the poulterers' boys were running with the birds sold by their masters, that there in the Alley they might be plucked and scorched; the air was filled with the smell of burning feathers. And they went on into the Stocks Market with its shops filled with fish and flesh and its stalls of fruit and flowers, herbs and roots; and so home to Bucklersbury with its pleasant aromas of spices and unguents which seemed to Margaret to have as inevitable a place in her life as the house itself.

It was as though he looked at all these places with loving concentration, so that he might remember every detail and be able to recall them when he became an exile from the City which he loved.

As they approached the house he said: 'Meg, not a word to anyone. It would frighten the children. It would frighten your mother.'

She pressed his hand, proud to share their secret.

But she greatly feared that the mighty King would hurt her father before they could escape him.

There was great excitement in the streets; and there was relief mingling with that excitement which was felt in the house in Bucklersbury.

The King was dead. And fear had died with him.

A new King had come to the throne–a boy not yet eighteen. He was quite different from his father; there was nothing parsimonious about him, and the people looked forward to a great and glorious reign. The household of Thomas More need not now consider uprooting itself.

All over the City the church bells were ringing. In the streets the people were dancing and singing. How could they regret the passing of a mean old King, when a young and handsome one was waiting to take the crown?

Men talked of the terrible taxation demanded by the late King through his agents, Empson and Dudley. Rumours ran through the town. The new King loved his people; he loved to jest and be merry. He was not like his father, who rode in a closed carriage whenever he could, because he did not wish the people to see his ugly face. No, this King loved to ride abroad, clad in cloth of gold and velvet, sparkling with jewels; he liked to show his handsome face to his subjects and receive their homage.

'Father,' said Margaret, 'what will happen now that we have a new King?'

'We shall pass into a new age.' he said. 'The old King's meanness curbed everything but the amassing of money by a few people. England will now be thrown open to scholars. Our friend Erasmus will be given a place here, and enough to keep him in comfort while he continues his studies. Avarice will be stamped out. The new King begins a new and glorious reign.'

'Will he give back all the money his father took from the people?' asked Margaret.

Her father laid a hand on her head. 'Ah, that I cannot tell you.'

'But how can he begin to please the people unless he begins by doing that?'

'Margaret, there are times when the working of your mind seems almost too great a strain for your years.'

But he kissed her to show that he was pleased with her; and she said: 'Even if he does not, there is nothing to fear, is there, Father. Satan does not whisper to you any more: "The cities of the world are yours. . . ."'

'You are right, Meg,' he told her joyfully.

Dr Colet came to the house, and even he, for a time, ceased to talk of literature and theology while he discussed the new King.

'There will be a marriage of the King and the Spanish Infanta, his brother's widow,' he said. 'I like that not. Nor, I gather, does my lord of Canterbury.'

Margaret listened to them; she was eager to learn everything, that she might afford her father great pleasure by her understanding when these matters were referred to.

'There will have to be dispensation from the Pope,' said Thomas. 'But I doubt not that will be an easy matter.'

'Should it be granted?' asked Colet. 'His brother's widow! Moreover, did he not some years ago make a solemn protest against the betrothal?'

'He did–under duress. He protested on the grounds that she was five years his senior, and he quoted the Bible, I believe. No good could come of such a marriage, he said. But it was his father who forced the protest from him. Young Henry, it seems, always had a mild fancy for the Spanish lady; and his father was pleased that this should be so, for you'll remember, only half of her magnificent dowry had fallen into his hands and he greatly longed to possess himself of the other half.'

'I know. I know. And when the old King decided he would marry Katharine's sister Juana, he felt that, if father and son married sisters, the relationship would be a complicated and unpleasant one. I doubt not that he thought it better to secure Juana's great riches than the remaining half of Katharine's dowry.'

'That was so. Therefore young Henry, whatever his private desires, must protest against his betrothal to his brother's widow.'

'Still, he made the protest,' said Colet.

'A boy of fifteen!'

'It was after the protest, so I hear, that he began to fall in love in earnest with his brother's widow. The toy had been offered him; he thought little of it; it was only when there was an attempt to snatch it from him that he determined to hold it. And now he declares nothing will turn him from the match, for she is the woman of his fancy.'

'Well, she is a good Princess,' said Thomas, 'and a comely one. She will provide England with a good Queen. That will suffice.'

'It will, my friend. It must. Do not forget it is the King's wish. There is no law in this land but the King's pleasure. And it will be well for us to remember that this King–be he ever so young and handsome–like his father, is a Tudor King.'

And Margaret, listening, wondered whether fear had entirely left her. This King–young and handsome though he was–might not give back to the people the money his father had taken from them; he wished to marry his brother's widow mainly because his father had said he should not. Would he prove to be such a good King after all? Could she be happy? Could she be reassured that her father was safe?

One event took place which seemed to the family as important as the accession of the new King to the throne.

Little Jack was born.

Jane was happy. A boy at last! She had always wanted a boy; and right from the first she saw that the boy was going to resemble the Colts.

He had her father's nose already; he had Jane's eyes; and she loved him dearly. But his birth had taken its toll of her health. She was ill for many weeks after Jack was born; and when she got up from her bed she felt far weaker than she had been after her previous confinements.

Still, she was happy. She would not have believed five years ago that she could have been so happy in this old City. London now meant home to her; she even enjoyed walking through the crowds to the Chepe, her maid following her, ordering from the tradespeople. She was not afraid of crowds now; nor was she afraid of Thomas. She had even learned a little Latin, and she could join in the children's conversations with their father.

Sometimes she regretted the fact that not one of her children was a simple little soul as she herself had been; for even baby Cecily was showing that she would be a little scholar. Yet, thought Jane, I am glad that they are clever. They will not suffer as I suffered; and how sad it would be for one of them to be a dullard in the midst of so many that are brilliant–like a sad piglet in a litter. I should not like that at all. No, let them all be clever; even though they do surpass their mother, even though they must, as they grow up, look upon her as a simpleton.

There was great excitement because the King and the Queen, whom he had married a few days before, were going to be crowned; and London was in Coronation mood. There was no talk but of the accession, the royal marriage, and the Coronation, and all the streets were now being decorated for the last ceremony. Cornhill, the richest street in London, was hung with cloth of gold, and was a sight to gladden any eye, so Jane was told; she had felt too weak to go and see it for herself, but she had promised the children that she would take them to watch the progress of the King and Queen, and nothing would induce her to disappoint them.

Thomas could not accompany them; he had his duties allotted to him as a burgess of the Parliament; and so, on that sunny June day, leaving the newly-born baby in the care of a nurse, with Cecily clinging to one hand, Elizabeth to the other, and Margaret and Mercy hand-in-hand, the little party set out to watch the King with the Queen ride through the streets from the Tower to Westminster for the crowning.

Jane had decided that Cornhill would be the best place in which to see the procession, for accounts of the beauties of Cornhill had been spread through the City. Moreover, they had but to go through Walbrook, cross the Stocks Market to the corner where Lombard Street and Cornhill met.

But Jane had reckoned without the crowds. Everyone, it seemed, had decided that this would be the best place from which to see the procession.

Jane felt weak and tired and the heat was making her dizzy. There was nothing she would have liked better than to take her party home; but when she looked at the excited faces of the children, she found it impossible to disappoint them.

'Keep close to me,' she warned. 'Margaret, you keep your eyes on Cecily. And Mercy . . . take Bess's hand. Now . . . keep very close. How hot it is! And so many people!'

'Mother,' cried Elizabeth, 'look at the beautiful cloth. Is it real gold? They *are* goldsmiths' shops, are they not? So perhaps it *is* real gold.'

'Yes, yes; they are beautiful,' said Jane.

Cecily wanted one of the hot pies which were being sold nearby. Elizabeth said she would prefer gingerbread.

'Now, now,' said Jane. 'You will miss the King if you do not watch.'

That made the children forget their hunger.

But there was a long time to wait for the procession. The sun seemed to grow hotter; Jane felt faint as the crowds pressed about her. She became very frightened asking herself what would happen to the children in this press of people if she were to faint. Her very panic seemed to revive her.

She lost her purse before they had stood there for ten minutes. The thief must have been the young boy who had pressed against her and given her such an angelic smile of apology that she had thought how charming he was.

She should not have come. She should have told Thomas of her intention. Why had she not? Because, she supposed, there were times when she wished to assert her authority over her little family, to say to them: 'I know I am not wise, but I am the mother, and there are times when I wish to make my own decisions. I wish to say that something shall be done and to see that you do it.'

How glad she was when the sound of trumpets and the tramp of horses' hoofs heralded the approach of the procession. The people shouted; the children stood spellbound. And as the excitement grew Jane felt a little better. There had not been much in her purse, and this would be a lesson to her. She would quote Thomas and say: 'Experience is generally worth the price, however dearly bought.'

Now came the knights and squires and the lords of the land–so handsome, some magnificent in their velvet and cloth of gold. But more handsome than any was the King himself. There he rode, so young, so eager for the approbation of his subjects, smiling, inclining his head, a-glitter with jewels. It was worth a little discomfort, even the loss of her purse, to witness such glory.

And there was the Queen–a bride of a few days although she was a widow of some years' standing. She was in her twenties–too old, some said, for such a hearty youth; but she was beautiful–there was no denying that. Her dark hair, which, it was said, hung to her feet when she stood, now hung about her shoulders, a black, gleaming cloak; she was dressed in white satin, beautifully embroidered, and her headdress was glittering with multi-coloured jewels. Two white horses bore her litter which was decorated with cloth of gold. The people shouted their admiration; and cries of 'God Save Queen Katharine' mingled with those of 'God Bless the King.'

Now came the rest of the procession, and so close did the prancing horses come that the mass of people surged back to avoid being trodden on. Jane grasped her children and pulled them towards her, but the pressure increased. The faces of the people seemed to merge into the blue sky and the fanfares and the trumpeting seemed to come from a long way off. Jane fainted.

'Mother . . . Mother!' cried Margaret in alarm.

But Jane was slipping down and was in danger of being trampled underfoot.

'Stop . . . Stop. . . . I beg of you stop!' cried Margaret.

Cecily began to scream, Elizabeth to cry forlornly, while Mercy tried in vain to hold back the people with her little hands.

Then suddenly a strong voice cried: 'Stand back! Stand back! Can you not see? A woman has fainted.'

It was a loud, authoritative feminine voice; and Margaret lifted fearful eyes to a plump woman who was holding a little girl by the hand. Her fat cheeks quivered, her mouth was tight with indignation, and her eyes snapped contempt at the crowd.

Miraculously she had cleared a space about Jane. She put an arm about the fainting woman and forced her head downwards. After a few seconds, to Margaret's delight, the colour began to return to her mother's face.

'The heat, that's what it is,' said the woman. 'I could have fainted myself. And would have done . . . if I had not had the will to stop myself.'

Margaret, grateful as she was, could not help sensing the reproof to her mother in those words. She said: 'My mother is not strong yet. We have just had a baby brother.'

'Then more fool she to come out on such a day!' was the answer to that. 'Where do you live?'

'At The Barge in Bucklersbury.'

'That's not more than a stone's throw from here. I'll take you back. The crowds will be rougher ere long.'

'You are very good,' said Margaret.

'Tilly valley! What could I do? Leave a baby like you to look after a fainting woman in a crowd like this? Ah, mistress, I see you are looking about you. You fainted and I am looking after your children here. Can you stand? Here, lean on me. You two big girls take the little ones and keep a firm hold of their hands. Now, Ailie, you cling to my gown. I am going to force my way through the crowd. Come, mistress. Take my arm. Your children are here, and we'll push them ahead so that they cannot stray from our sight. We'll be in Bucklersbury in next to no time, and that's where you should be before the mob starts roystering.'

'You are very good,' said Jane. 'I . . .'

'Now keep your breath for walking. Come along now. Come along.'

Forcefully she pushed a way for them, calling sharply to any that stood in their path. 'Can you not see? I have a sick woman here. Stand aside, you oafs. Make way there.'

And the odd thing was that none cared to disobey her; and under such strong guidance the family soon reached Bucklersbury.

The woman sniffed and looked with scorn about her. 'What odours! What odours!' she declared. 'I'm glad my late husband was not one of these apothecaries with their smells. There are no smells in a mercer's shop but goodly smells. But this . . . poof! I like it not!'

'My husband,' said Jane, 'is a lawyer.'

'A lawyer, eh! What the good year! Well, here you are, and if you will take my advice you'll not go into crowds again in a hurry.'

'You will come in and take a little refreshment?'

The widow said she would, and followed them into the big hall, where she sat down.

Margaret saw that the little girl named Ailie was very pretty and more or less of an age with herself and Mercy. Her golden hair escaped from her cap, and her gown was of richer material than that worn by the little More girls.

'Tell me the names of your girls,' said the widow. 'Nay . . . let them speak for themselves. I'll warrant they have tongues in their heads.'

'We have,' said Margaret with dignity, for although she was grateful for the widow's help in bringing them home, she did not like her overbearing manner. 'I am Margaret. This is my foster-sister called Mercy because her name is also Margaret, and . . . my sisters Elizabeth and Cecily.'

'And I am Mistress Alice Middleton, widow of Master John Middleton, mercer of the City and merchant of the Staple of Calais. Here is my daughter. Alice like myself, so, like Mercy there, she is called by a name other than her own. Why, you and she are of an age. That should make you friends.'

The children continued to study each other, and Mistress Middleton turned to her hostess, complimented her on the mead she was offered and told her how she could improve it by using more honey in its making. Still, it was a goodly brew.

She went on: 'Now rest yourself. Keep to the house, for there'll be roystering this night . . . and so there should be, for it is a good day for the land, I'll swear, with such a bonny King come to the throne.'

When she had drunk her mead and had a look at the house, commenting – not always favourably–on its furnishings, she left with her daughter.

'A talkative woman,' said Jane, 'but capable, I'll swear . . . and very kind.'

This was a happy day for Thomas More. The tyrant was dead and in his place was a monarch who promised great things for England.

When Thomas was happy, he liked to take up his pen, and it was natural that his writings should now be concerned with the new reign.

'If ever there was a day, England,' he wrote, 'if ever there was a time for you to give thanks to Those above, this is that happy day, one to be marked with a pure white stone and put in your calendar. This day is the limit of our slavery, the beginning of freedom, the end of sadness, the source of joy. . . .'

He went on to enumerate the virtues of the young King: 'Among a thousand noble companions, does he not stand out taller than any? If only Nature could permit that, like his body, the outstanding excellence of his mind could be visible! This Prince has inherited his father's wisdom, his mother's kindly strength, the scrupulous intelligence of his father's mother, the noble heart of his mother's father. What wonder if England rejoices in such a King as she has never had before!'

Thomas went on to sing the praises of the Queen; he wrote of her dignity and her devotion to religion, of her beauty and her loyalty. There was surely no woman more worthy to be the wife of such a King, and none but the King was worthy to be the husband of such a Queen. Heaven bless such a union; and surely when the crowns had long been worn by Katharine and Henry, their grandson and great-grandson would wear the crown of England in the years to come.

When Thomas recited this composition to John Colet, the Dean of St Paul's remarked in his dry way that the qualities of Henry's ancestors might have been construed differently. For instance, the wisdom of Henry the Seventh might have been called avarice; the kindly strength of Elizabeth of York, meekness dictated by expediency; the scrupulous intelligence of Margaret of Richmond, ambition; the noble heart of Edward the Fourth as lechery and determination to rule at all cost.

'Still,' said the Dean, 'this should be shown to the King. It will surely please His Grace. Much flattery has been poured into the royal ears, but I doubt that any has ever been so elegantly phrased.'

'Flattery?' said Thomas. 'That may be. But, John, it sometimes happens that if a man is shown a flattering picture of himself, he will try to be worthy of that picture. For such reasons it is expedient to flatter kings.'

'Yet when men offer flattery with one hand, they are apt to hold out the other to receive the rewards such flattery may earn. What rewards seek you, friend Thomas?'

Thomas considered this. 'Might it not be,' he said at length, 'that this writing of mine is in payment for his coming to the throne at an opportune time for me? I could sing pæans, my friend, if I had the voice for them, because this King now reigns and there is no need for me to leave the country. Rewards? Perhaps I wish for them. It may be that I long to go on as I have . . . here in London . . . with my family about me. Oh, and perhaps if the King is pleased with my offering, I might ask concessions for Erasmus. It would be good to have him with us again, would it not?'

'It would. Take the verses. Crave audience. I doubt not you will obtain it.'

And so Thomas took his writing to the King.

The happiest person in the palace of Westminster should have been its King. None knew this more than the King himself, and he was sullen on finding that it was not so.

It was a glorious thing to be a King. Wherever he went the people hailed him, for he was not only a King; he was a beloved King. Were he not taller than all those about him, he would have been distinguished as their King by the glittering jewels he wore. He was the richest King in Europe; he was only now realizing how rich, for he had only guessed at the amount of wealth and treasure his father had amassed.

The reason for his discontent was his Queen. He liked his Queen. She was older than he was by five years–but as he did not care to be considered a mere boy, he liked this, for it seemed that she helped to add years to his age.

But they were rich; they were young; and they should be gay. There must be lavish entertainment; masques, jousts and pageants could go on for as long as he wished; and at all these ceremonies he should be the very centre of attention as was meet, considering who he was. All festivities should have one purpose: to honour the King, to display the King in all his glory, to show that the King was more skilled, more daring, than any King who had ever lived before him or would come after him.

But his Queen had disappointed him. Alas! she had not his love of gaiety, his passion for enjoyment; they had made her too solemn in that Spanish court of her childhood. She was comely enough to please him; and he was glad to reflect that she was the daughter of two of the greatest monarchs in the world; it pleased him too that he had married her, for marrying her was like snapping his fingers at his father's ghost. He did not care to disparage the dead, but it had rankled to be *forced* to relinquish his betrothed. It was only at that time that he had discovered how fair she was and how much he desired her–her above all women. It had hurt his pride to be forced into that protest. And now, every time he looked at her, he could say: 'There is none now to force me to that which I desire not; nor shall there ever be again.' Such thought stimulated his desire, made him more ardent than he would otherwise have been; which, he reminded himself, not without a touch of primness, was all for the good of England, since an ardent man will get himself children more speedily than a cold one.

Yet she disappointed him.

It had happened on the day after the Coronation, when the ceremonies were at their height. He and Katharine had sat on a platform covered with velvet and cloth of gold set up within the grounds of Westminster Palace.

What a wonderful sight had met their gaze, with the fountains emitting the best of wine, and more wine flowing from the mouths of stone animals! Many pageants had been prepared for the enjoyment of the royal couple. A fair young lady dressed as Minerva had presented six champions to the Queen, and that was a tribute to her solemnity, for these champions, dressed in cloth of gold and green velvet, were meant to represent scholars. That should have pleased her; and it did. Then drums and pipes heralded more knights who bowed before the Queen and asked leave to joust with the champions of Minerva.

Oh, what a spectacle! And the jousting lasted all day and night!

Then the King disappeared from the Queen's side, and shortly afterwards there came to her a lowly knight who craved leave to joust with the champion. The Queen gave that permission while everyone laughed the lowly knight to scorn until he threw off his shabby cloak and there, in glittering armour, towering above them all, was Henry himself. And Henry must be the victor.

That was all well and good.

But Henry had planned more joys for his Queen. An artificial park had been set up in the grounds of the Palace, with imitation trees and ferns shut in by pales; this contained several fallow deer and was designed to make a seemly setting for the servants of Diana. Suddenly the gates of this park were thrown open and greyhounds were sent therein. Through the imitation foliage they ran, leaping and barking; and out came the frightened deer, to the amusement of all except the Queen–rushing over the grounds and entering the Palace itself. And when all the deer were caught, they were laid, stained with blood, some still palpitating, at the feet of the Queen.

And how did she receive such homage? Shuddering, she turned her eyes away. 'Such beautiful creatures,' she said, 'to suffer so!'

He remonstrated: 'It was a goodly chase. Mercy on us, it was fine, good sport!'

Before the courtiers he had laughed at her squeamish ways. But his voice had been a little threatening when he said: 'You must learn to love our English ways, sweetheart.'

Now, alone with her, as he recalled this incident, his sullen eyes rested upon her. She had not been taught to ride in the chase; she liked better to spend her time with priests; and it spoiled his pleasure that she should not appreciate the amusements which, he told himself, he had prepared for her. If he did not love her, he might have been very angry with her.

Well, it was a small matter and he would teach her. But perhaps he was not so displeased after all, for it must be admitted that she was a most virtuous woman; her virtue was a light that shone on him; and in the midst of pleasure he liked to be sensible of his own virtue.

Every moment he was feeling less displeased with her; and to soothe himself he planned more revels.

He said to her: 'I shall ride into the tiltyard. I'll tilt against Brandon. He'll be a match for me.' He laughed. 'There are few skilled enough for the task. And after that, we'll have a ball – a masque – such as was never seen.'

'You are spending much of your father's treasure on these ceremonies,' said the Queen. 'They are costly, and even great wealth will not last for ever.'

'Is it not better to delight the people with pageants and joyful feasts than to store up treasure in great coffers? I would rather be the best-loved King than the richest King.'

'The people murmured against your father's taxes. Would it not be well to alleviate them in some way? Could we not devise some means of letting the people know that you will make amends for your father's extortions? I am sure that my Lord Norfolk and that very clever Master Wolsey would know what should be done.'

The King narrowed his eyes. 'Mayhap. Mayhap,' he said testily. 'But know this: I too know . . . even more than such as Norfolk and Wolsey, what my people want–and that is to see their King, to know that he will make this land a merry one for the people of England.'

Katharine lowered her eyes. This boy whom she had married was a headstrong boy; he must, she was beginning to understand, be continually humoured. She had been wrong to show her disgust when the warm bodies of the deer were laid before her; she must appear to enjoy the extravagant pageants which so delighted him; she must always feign astonishment when he presented himself before her faintly disguised as Robin Hood or some lowly knight. She must remember that he was young; he would grow up quickly, she was sure; as yet he was but a boy who loved a boy's games. And she must never forget that, although he was a boy, he was the most powerful person in the kingdom. There were times when she thought that to put the sceptre in the youthful hands was like giving a wilful, hot-tempered child a sword to play with.

He was smiling now, and his smile could startle her, for there was a malignant cruelty in it which sat oddly on his fair young face. Although she was growing accustomed to it, it made her uneasy.

'I have prepared a treat for the people which will repay them for all they have suffered,' he said.

'Yes, Henry?'

'You remember when I gave orders that those agents of Empson and Dudley should be placed in the pillory?'

'I do.'

'And what happened to them?'

'The mob set upon them, I believe, and stoned them to death.'

The King's smile deepened. 'Now I shall give them a bigger treat. Oh yes. I will repay the people for their sufferings, never fear.'

'Then will you give back what your father took from them?'

'Better than that!' he said. 'Far better. I will give them Empson and Dudley. *They* were the extortioners. They shall be executed on Tower Hill, and I'll warrant you, Kate, the people will come from far and wide to see their blood flow . . . and they will thank their King for avenging their wrongs.'

Words were on her lips, but each day she learned wisdom. So, she thought, you will offer them the blood of your father's unpopular servants, but their money–the money which was wrung from them in cruel taxes so that they were left with little to show for their labour–you will spend on your jewels, your fine clothes and your rejoicing.

'You do not speak,' he said, frowning. 'Like you not my plan?'

There is nothing I can do, she decided.

Ah yes, she was beginning to understand the man whom she had married.

She said quietly: 'The people will rejoice, I doubt not.'

Now he was laughing, embracing her warmly. He loved and needed approval as much as he loved and needed feasting and revelry.

My Lord Mountjoy was one of those who were with the King when Thomas brought the verses he had written on vellum decorated with the white and red roses of York and Lancaster.

Mountjoy was hopeful; the King had confided to him that he looked to the scholars to make his court bright with learning. Mountjoy was considering writing to Erasmus.

There were also present the King and his chaplain, a man for whom Henry had a deep liking and respect. It was true that he was not a handsome man; his face was slightly marked with the pox, and the lid dragged a little over the left eye, which was not becoming; being in his mid-thirties, he seemed elderly to the King; but although he was, as yet, merely the King's chaplain, Henry was so struck with his discourse that he determined to keep Thomas Wolsey at his side and to heap preferment on him at an early date.

And now came Thomas More, scholar and writer, to offer verses of laudation.

The King held out his hand for the man to kiss. He liked that face; and the royal smile was benign as Henry bade Thomas More rise.

'I remember you,' he said, 'in company with the scholar Erasmus. Was it not at Eltham that we met?'

'It was, Your Grace, and Your Grace's memory of that fact covers me with honour.'

'We like our poets. There is too little learning at our court. We feel ourselves but ignorant when compared with such learned men.'

'Your Grace astonishes the world with his learning.'

The King smiled, meaning to charm; and instinct told him that modesty would appeal to this man with the kind mouth and the shrewd eyes. 'If not with my own,' said Henry, 'with that of my subjects. This is a pretty thing you bring me. Read the verses . . . that all may hear what you have to say to your King.'

Thomas read them, and as he listened the King's heart warmed towards this man. Such elegance of phrase, such finely worded sentiments. He liked what this man had to say of him and his Queen.

'We thank you, Thomas More,' he said when the reading was over. 'We shall treasure the verses. And Mountjoy here has been telling us of that friend of yours . . . Erasmus. We must have him here. I want all to know that I wish to see this court adorned by learned men. I would that I had paid more attention to my tutors. I fear the chase and all manner of sports have pleased me overmuch.'

'Your Grace,' said Thomas, 'your humble subjects ask not that you should become a scholar, for you have a realm to govern. We would beg that you extend your gracious encouragement to scholars in this land and others.'

'We give our word to do it. We need these scholars. They are the brightest jewels in our crown.'

And he kept Thomas More beside him, conversing lightly of theology and the science of astronomy. The Queen joined in and the King was pleased that this should be so.

There were some men whom he liked, whether they were old or young, gay or serious. He had two of those men close to him now . . . his two Thomases, he called them. One was Thomas Wolsey and the other was Thomas More.

Two days after the Coronation Alice Middleton called at The Barge with a posset for Jane.

As soon as she entered the house it seemed to Margaret that she dominated it; but both Margaret and Mercy were pleased that she had brought her daughter with her.

The three children went to one of the window-seats and talked together. Little Alice Middleton, to the astonishment of Margaret and Mercy, had learned no Latin.

'But what will you do when you grow up?' asked Margaret in a shocked voice. 'Do you not wish to please. . . .'

Margaret was stopped by a look from Mercy, which reminded her that as this little girl had no father they must not talk of fathers.

Margaret blushed, and her eyes filled with compassion. Both she and Mercy wished to be very kind to the little girl who had no father. But young Alice was not disturbed.

'When I grow up I shall take a husband,' she said. 'A rich husband.' And she twirled a golden curl which had escaped from her cap, and, fatherless as she was, she seemed very pleased with herself.

Meanwhile her mother was talking in a loud voice:

'This place is not healthful. I'll swear it's damp. No wonder you are not feeling well, Mistress More. But you take a little of this posset, and you'll feel the better for it.'

Jane said it was good of her to call; she repeated her thanks, for, as she said again and again, she did not know how she would have reached home without the help of Mistress Middleton.

'You would have reached home, I doubt not. That which we must do, we find means of doing. . . . So I always say.' And Mistress Middleton smiled as though to imply: And what I say–by the very fact that I say it–is bound to be right.

Jane was glad that Thomas should come in so that he could thank the widow personally for her kindness.

'Thomas,' she said, 'this is Mistress Middleton, the kind lady who brought me home.'

'Right glad I am to meet you, Mistress Middleton. My wife has told me many good things of you.'

Mistress Middleton eyed him shrewdly. A lawyer! A scholar! she believed. She had not much respect for scholars; she doubted they did as well as mercers of London and merchants of the staple of Calais.

'A pity, sir, that you had not the time to take your wife and children into the streets to see the sights.'

'A great pity, madam.'

'Thomas,' cried Jane. 'The King . . . he received you?'

Thomas nodded.

'My husband,' Jane explained, 'is a writer.'

A smile curved Alice Middleton's lips. A writer? A writer of words? What was the use of words? Give her good bales of cloth. That was what people wanted to buy. Who wanted to buy words?

Thomas, grateful to the widow, could not help but be amused by her obvious contempt and her refusal to pretend anything else.

'I perceive,' he said, 'that you do not worship at the shrine of Literature.'

'I worship in church like all good people, and in no other place. And Literature? Tilly valley! What is that? Will it build a house? Will it weave a cloth? Will it look after your wife when she falls fainting in the streets?'

'It might inspire a man or a woman to build a house, madam. And before a man builds a house he must have the will to do so. So might it make a man–or should I say a woman?–so long to possess a new gown that she will weave the cloth. As for its looking after a fainting wife: Well, suppose a lady could read of a great pageant, her imagination, enhanced by literature, might be such that she would feel it unnecessary to stand in a press of people in order to see with her eyes that which she could conjure up by a mental effort.'

'Here's clever talk!' said Alice. 'And my eyes are good enough for me. I can weave with the best, and I don't need words to help me. If I can't build a house I can keep one clean. And as for this Latin the scholars talk one with another, I manage quite well, sir, with my native tongue.'

'May I say, madam, that I am convinced you manage . . . you manage admirably.'

'But my husband is a poet,' said Jane in mild reproof.

'Poetry won't bake bread. Nor make a man wealthy, so I've heard.'

'Who speaks of wealth, madam?'

'I do, sir. For in this world it is a useful thing to have. And no matter what you tell me, riches come through work and thrifty living – not through writing poetry.'

'True riches belong to the spirit, madam, which uses its own resources to improve itself. We can only call a man rich if he understands the uses of wealth. Any man who piles up endless wealth, merely to count it, is like the bee who labours in the hive. He toils; others eat up the honey.'

'I speak of money not of honey, Master More. It seems you are a man who cannot keep to the point. You may smile. Methinks I should be the one to smile.'

A faint colour showed in the cheeks of Alice Middleton. She liked the man; that was why she was giving him what she would call the edge of her tongue; she would not bother to waste that on those she considered unworthy of it.

His face was pleasant and kindly, she concluded. A clever man, this; yet in some ways, helpless. She would like to feed him some of her possets, put a layer of fat on his bones with her butter. She'd warrant he gave too much thought to what went into his head and not enough to what went into his stomach.

'His verses were dedicated to the King,' said Jane. 'And did the King accept them, Thomas?'

'He did. He took them in his own hands and complimented me upon them.'

His lips were smiling. Margaret left the little girls to come and stand close to him. She was so happy because this King loved him. They had nothing to fear from this King. She took his hand and pressed it.

'So the King likes verses!' said Mistress Middleton, her voice softening a little.

'Ah, madam,' said Thomas. 'What the King likes today, may we hope Mistress Middleton will like tomorrow?'

'And he accepted them . . . from your hands?' demanded Mistress Middleton.

'He did indeed.' Thomas was remembering it all. It was only about his writing that he was a little vain; he made excuses for his vanity. Artistic talent, he was wont to say, is a gift from God. But he was conscious of his vanity, and he mocked himself while he treasured words of praise. And now at this moment he could not help recalling with pleasure the King's delight in his verses.

As for Alice Middleton, she was looking at him with new respect.

For a lawyer and a scholar she had little to spare; for a man who had spoken with the King she had much.

The next two years were eventful ones for Margaret. For one thing, two people became very important to her. Both of these were visitors to the house; although one of these was a neighbour and a constant caller, the other lived with them as one of the family.

The first was Alice Middleton who made regular calls. Margaret did not love Mistress Middleton, although she recognized that lady's wish to be kind. Mistress Middleton believed that everyone who did not do as she did must surely be wrong. If any household task was not done according to Mistress Middleton's rule, it was not done in the right way. She would teach them how to bake bread in the only way to bake the best bread, and that was the way she always did it; she would show them how to salt meat in order to make the best of it. She would show how children should be brought up. They should be obedient to their elders; they should be whipped when stubborn; they should be seen and not heard, and not talk in heathen tongues which their elders could not understand.

What disturbed Margaret more than anything was the fact that her father did not feel as she did towards Mistress Middleton. She had watched his face as he listened to her tirades, and had seen the amused twitch of his lips; sometimes he would talk with her, as though he were luring her on to taunt him. She was a rude and stupid woman; yet he seemed to like her rudeness and her stupidity. And Margaret, who followed her father in most things, could not do so in this.

The other person was the exalted Erasmus.

Him, Margaret regarded with awe. He was now more famous than he had been in the days when he had first come to England. He was known all over the world as the greatest Greek scholar, and he was preparing to write a critical edition of the Greek text of the New Testament.

Margaret *could* understand her father's affection for this great man, for Erasmus was worthy of his regard and friendship as Madam Alice could never be.

This Erasmus was a sick man. There were days when he could do nothing but lie abed. On such days Margaret would wait upon him, bringing to him the books he asked for. He had a great affection for Margaret and she was pleased that this should be so, largely because of the delight it gave her father. Thomas would openly sue for praise for his daughter as he never would for himself, and Margaret felt very tender towards him as she watched his delight in the compliments Erasmus paid her.

Once Erasmus said: 'I do not believe there is another girl–or boy–of this child's age who can write and speak the Latin tongue as she does.' And afterwards her father said to her: 'Meg, this is one of the happiest days of my life. It is a day I shall remember on the day I die. I shall say to myself when I find death near me: "The great Erasmus said that of my daughter, my Meg."'

She thought a good deal about Erasmus. He might be a greater scholar than her father–though she doubted this–but she did not believe he was such a brave man. There was a certain timidity in his manner; this had been apparent once when Alice Middleton was present and had spoken quite sharply to him–for Alice was no respecter of scholars, and the fame of Erasmus had not reached her ears. She obviously did not believe that a poor wisp of a man who, as she said, looked as though a puff from the west wind could blow him flat, was as important as they seemed to think. 'Scholar! Foreigner!' she snorted. The sort of men she respected were those like the King: more than six feet tall and broad with it; a man who would know what to do with a baron of beef and a fat roast peacock . . . aye, and anything a good cook could put before him. She liked not this sly-looking man with his aches and pains. Greatest scholar in the world! That might be. But the world could keep its scholars, declared Mistress Alice.

Margaret said to Mercy: 'No; he has not Father's bravery. *He* would not have stood before the Parliament and spoken against the King.'

'He has not Father's kindness,' answered Mercy. 'He would mock where Father pitied.'

'But how could we expect him to be like Father!' cried Meg; and they laughed.

Erasmus spent his days writing what he called an airy trifle, a joke to please his host who loved a joke, he knew, better than anything. He was too tired, he told Margaret, to work on his Testament. He must perfect his Greek before he attempted such a great task. He must feel sure of his strength. In the meantime he would write *In Praise of Folly*.

He read aloud to Thomas when he came home; and sometimes Thomas would sit by his friend's bed with Margaret on one side of him, Mercy on the other; he would put an arm about them both, and when he laughed and complimented Erasmus so that Erasmus's pale face was flushed with pleasure, then Margaret believed that there was all the happiness in the world in that room.

Erasmus poked fun at everybody . . . even at the scholar with his sickly face and lantern jaws; he laughed at the sportsman for his love of slaughter, and the pilgrims for going on pilgrimages when they ought to have been at home; he laughed at the superstitious who paid large sums for the sweat of saints; he laughed at schoolmasters who, he said, were kings in the little kingdoms of the young. No one was spared–not even lawyers and writers, although he was, Margaret noted, less severe with the latter than with the rest of the world.

And this was written with the utmost lightness, so that it delighted not only Thomas, but others of their friends, to picture Folly, in cap and bells, on a rostrum addressing mankind.

He stayed over a year in the house, and while he was there Thomas was made Under-Sheriff of the City of London, which was an honour he greatly appreciated. Alice Middleton, still a constant visitor, was delighted with this elevation.

'Ah,' Margaret heard Thomas say to her, 'how pleasant it is to enjoy reflected honours! We have neither to deserve them nor to uphold them. We bask in the soft light, whilst the other toils in the heat. The temperate rather than the torrid zone. So much more comfortable, eh, Mistress Middleton?'

'Tilly valley! I know not what you mean,' she told him sharply. 'So you but waste your breath to say it.'

He explained to Margaret as he always explained everything: 'The Mayor of London and the Sheriffs are not lawyers; therefore they need a barrister to advise them on various matters of law. That, my Margaret, is the task of the Under-Sheriff who is now your father.'

And when he dealt with these cases he refrained, if the litigants were unable to pay them, from accepting the fees which had always previously been paid. This became known throughout the City. It was about this time that the people of London began to love him.

Margaret was very happy during those two years; she had learned the meaning of fear, and that lesson had made her happier, for with it had come the joy of being without fear. But there was another lesson to learn: It was that, nothing in life was static.

First, Erasmus left for Paris, where he hoped to publish *In Praise of Folly*; and that was the end of the pleasant reading and discourse. Then Margaret's mother took to her bed with a return of that weakness which had rarely left her since the birth of little Jack.

What they would have done during this time but for Alice Middleton, no one could say. Alice swept through the house like a fresh east wind, admonishing lazy servants, administering possets and clysters to Jane, boxing the ears of maids and men-servants and the children when it seemed to her that they needed such treatment.

Gone was their gentle mother, and in her place was bustling and efficient, though sharp-tongued and heavy-handed, Dame Alice.

The children looked at each other with solemn eyes.

'Will our mother get well?' asked four-year-old Cecily.

Jack cried at night: 'Where is our Mother? I want our Mother.'

'Hush,' said Margaret, trying to comfort him. 'Mistress Middleton will hear your crying, and box your ears.'

When he fell and cut his knees, or whenever any of the children hurt themselves, it was Mercy who could bind up the wound or stop the bleeding. Mercy had the gentlest of hands, and the very caress of them could soothe a throbbing head.

'I should like to study medicine,' she confided to Margaret. 'I believe it is the one thing I could learn more easily than you could. In everything else I believe you would do better than I. But not in that, Margaret.'

And Mercy began growing herbs at the back of the house; and she became very skilful in these matters. Thomas called her: 'Our young doctor'!

But nothing Mercy grew in her border, and nothing she could do, made Jane well.

One day Jane called her eldest daughter to her.

Jane seemed to have grown smaller during the last few days; she looked tiny in the four-poster bed; and her skin was the same colour as the yellow thread in the tapestry of the tester.

Margaret suddenly knew that her mother would not live long to occupy that bed.

'Margaret,' said Jane, 'come close to me.'

Margaret came to the bed.

'Sit near me,' said Jane, 'where I can see you.'

Margaret climbed on to the bed and sat looking at her mother.

'Margaret, you are only six years old, but you are a wise little girl. You seem all of eleven. I feel I can talk to you.'

'Yes, Mother.'

'I am going to die.'

'No . . . you must not. What can we do without you?'

Jane smiled. 'Dear little Meg, those are sweet words. It is of when I am gone that I wish to speak to you. How I wish I could have waited a while! Another seven years and I could have safely left my household in your hands.'

'Mother . . . Mother . . . do not say these things. They make me so sad.'

'You do not wish for change. None of us does. You will take care of your Father, Margaret. Oh, he is a man and you are but a child . . . but you will know what I mean. Margaret, I can die happy because I have left you to your father.'

The tears began to fall down Margaret's cheeks. She wished that she had given her mother more affection. She had loved her father so much that she had thought little of the quiet woman who, she now saw, had taken such an important place in their happy household.

'Mother . . . please . . .' she began.

Jane seemed to understand.

'Why, bless you, Meg, it has been my greatest delight to see that love between you and your father. When we married I was afraid I was quite unworthy of him. I was so . . . unlearned; and at first I was unhappy. I would sit at the table trying so hard to study the Latin he had set me . . . yet knowing I would never learn it to his satisfaction. And then when you were born all my unhappiness vanished, because I knew that, although I could not make him an ideal wife, I had given him someone whom he could love better than anyone in the world. That was worth while, Margaret. I was happy then. And when I saw you grow up and become everything that he had desired, I was even happier. Then there was Elizabeth . . . then Cecily . . . and now Jack. You see, he has, as he would say, his quiver full. And but for me he could not have had you all. That is what I have told myself, and because of it I can die in peace. So do not reproach yourself, my little one, that you love him more than you do me. Love is not weighed. It flows. And how can we stem the flow or increase it? Margaret, always remember, my child, that if you have given him great happiness, you have given me the same. Come, kiss me.'

Margaret kissed her mother's cheek, and the clammy touch of her skin frightened her.

'Mother,' she said, 'I will call Mercy. Mayhap she will know what would ease you.'

'One moment, dearest Meg. Meg . . . look after them all. My little Jackie . . . he is such a baby. And he is like me. I am afraid he will not be as good with his lessons as you girls are. Take care of him . . . and of little Bess and Cecily. And, Meg, I need not tell you to comfort your father, for I know that your very presence will do that. Oh, how I wish that this could have been delayed . . . a year or two . . . so that my Margaret was not such a child. You are a dear child, a clever child–never was one so clever–but . . . if only you had been a few years older I could be content.'

'Mother . . . please do not fret. I will be as though I have lived twelve years. I will. I swear it. But you will get well. You must. For what shall we do without you?'

Jane smiled and closed her eyes; and, watching, Margaret was filled with terror.

She ran from the room, calling Mercy; but it was Alice Middleton who came into the chamber of death.

A week later Jane was dead; and only a month or so after she was buried, Thomas called his children to him and told them that they should not be long motherless.

He was going to marry a lady capable of looking after them, a lady of great virtue. She was without much education and several years older than himself, but he was convinced that she would be the best possible stepmother for them.

Her name was Alice Middleton.

Chapter Three

When Margaret was twelve years old fear again appeared in her life. It seemed like a great cloud which came nearer and nearer to the house until that day when it enveloped it. The cloud formed itself into the shape of a man, of great height, of great girth, on whose head there was a crown. At the age of four, Margaret had learned to fear kings. And now would the cloud pass over the house? Would it pass on as, once before, had a similar cloud?

Much had happened since the death of her mother. The family still lived in Bucklersbury, but it had become a different household under the domination of Mistress Alice.

It must have been the cleanest house in London; the rushes were changed once a week, and very little odour came from them. When they were removed from the house it was only necessary to go upstairs, not to leave the house for a day until the servants had cleared it of its filth. Alice was the most practical of women. She knew exactly how many pieces could be cut from a side of beef, and she saw that they were so cut; her servants must account for every portion of fish, every loaf of bread. She kept strict count of the visitors who called for a meal. She reckoned–and this matter she took up fiercely with her husband–that visitors were costing the household purse the whole of twopence a day, what with food, beds and firing. The family was allowed only sixty candles a year, and if any burnt out his share before the year was over, then, said Alice grimly, must that one sit in the dark. She herself kept the keys of the buttery; she saw that none had more than his portion of ale or mead. She was the martinet of the household.

All Thomas's attempts to teach her Latin failed.

'What the good year!' she cried in scorn. 'Would you have me one of these pale-faced, lantern-jawed scholars? I'll warrant you, Master More, that I do you more good watching the affairs of your household than I ever should tampering with foreign speech. The English tongue, sir, is good enough for me.'

But nevertheless she kept a strict eye on the children.

Thomas had instituted what he called his 'School' in the house, and here all the children spent many hours at their lessons. Alice had a habit of peeping at them at odd moments, and if she found them not at their desks she would take them, throw them across a chair and administer a good beating with her slipper.

'Your father has set you these tasks,' she would say, 'and your father is head of this house.' (Not that she would admit such a fact to his face.) 'He'd not whip you himself, being too soft a man, so there's some that has to do his duty for him. Now . . . get to that Latin . . . or that Greek . . . or that mathematics . . . or whatever nonsense it is, and if you have not learned it by sundown you'll feel more of my slipper where you won't like it.'

Jack was the chief offender, because he could not love learning as his sisters did. Jack would look longingly out of the window, particularly when horsemen rode by. He would like to be out of London, in the green country, climbing trees and riding horses. Jack sometimes felt it was a sad thing to a boy possessed of such clever sisters.

Ailie was not overfond of lessons, but she did not care to be too far outstripped by her stepsisters. She applied herself and as she had a cleverness of her own, a natural wit, she could usually appear to know more than she actually did. Her mother had a habit of looking the other way when Ailie misbehaved, so, although she might have been in trouble as much as Jack was, somehow she managed to escape it. She was very pretty, and Alice believed that one day she would make a very good match.

Alice insisted that each of the girls should study housekeeping under her guidance; for what, she had demanded, would be the use of all that learning if when they married–and if only Master More would make the most of his chances they might marry very well–they had no knowledge of how to run a house and keep the servants in order? So each of the girls must, in addition to her lessons, give orders to the servants, decide on the composition of meals and superintend the cooking for a whole week before the task fell to her sister or stepsister. And if anything went wrong, if the bread was burnt of the meat had been subjected to too many turns of the spit, or not enough, then it was not only the servant who felt the mistress's slipper.

Alice was not above giving any member of this large household the measure of her tongue. Even the tutors came in for their share, learned men though they might be. Master Nicholas Kratzer, fellow of Corpus Oxford, who had come to live in the house to teach the children astronomy, particularly irritated Alice.

She laughed him to scorn. 'You, a scholar . . . and cannot speak the King's English! Here's a pretty state of affairs. And supposed to be a learned man!'

'Madam,' he told her with the humility all these great men seemed to display before Alice, for it was a fact that every one of them wilted under her scornful gaze, 'I was born in Munich; and although I cannot speak your tongue well, I doubt you can speak mine at all.'

'Tilly valley!' said Alice. 'And who would want to when they could make themselves understood in good plain English?'

The poor scholar, to the amusement of Margaret and Mercy, was quite at a loss to answer Alice; for, somehow, her method of delivering what she thought to be wise was so authoritative that temporarily it seemed to be so. Therefore, Master Kratzer returned to his study of the stars feeling a little cowed, and as for Margaret and Mercy, they had their ears boxed for laughing–as Alice said, when Kratzer had left them–at a great and learned man.

Richard Hyrde, the great Greek scholar, also lived in the house. Mercy was his favourite pupil, for he was also a student of medicine, and this science appealed to Mercy more than any other. Master Drew and Master Gunnel, considerable scholars, also lived in the growing household in order that they might tutor the children.

Dr Colet and Dr Lily came to the house now and then, but not so frequently as they had at one time, for all Dr Colet's thoughts and energies were now concentrated on the school he had built in St Paul's Churchyard, at which he planned to educate children of all ages, of all classes and all races. This school was his delight; it was a dream become reality. He had always said that when he was a rich man–and he knew he would be on the death of his father–he would build such a school. Now he watched over it as a mother watches over her child, brooding over it, worrying over it, talking of it continually. Dr Lily shared all his enthusiasm and fears, for Dr Lily had consented to become Headmaster of the school.

Thomas had said: 'There is no man in England who could carry out this task with greater skill. But I wanted Lily for my children.'

Colet laughed gleefully. 'I got there first, Thomas,' he cried. 'I have secured him for my children.'

Now that Margaret was aware of the cloud's coming nearer to her home she thought often of Dr Colet's escape from the King's wrath. This had happened a few years before, and they had trembled for the fate which might overtake this beloved friend. The same cloud must have darkened Colet's house then as it now did that of the Mores.

Why must these great men always express their views with such careless unconcern for the consequences? Why could they not be content to talk in private with their friends, and enjoy the happy lives which they had built up for themselves out of their goodness? Dr Colet had his school–the great wish of a lifetime fulfilled–yet when the King planned war with France, he must get into his pulpit and preach a sermon on the folly and wickedness of war.

It was inevitable that he should be called before an angry King; it was by a miracle that he had escaped with his life. But was it a miracle? What a plausible tongue had this great man, what a way with words!

He came to the house afterwards to tell them about it; and he and her father had laughed together until Margaret had feared they would make themselves ill with such immoderate laughter which in her wisdom, she understood was partly the laughter of relief.

'But, Your Grace,' Colet had said to the King, 'it is true that I preached against war. Aye, and would do so again. I said: "Few die well who die in battle, for how can they charitably dispose of anything when blood is the argument? Men must follow Christ, the King of Peace . . . not the kings of war." Those were my words, Sire.'

'I know your words, sirrah!' the King had cried angrily. 'And I like them not.'

'But, Your Grace,' was the reply, 'I but preached against dishonourable war . . . unjust war . . . and Your Grace must agree with me that there can be no good in unjust war.'

It was at this point, when telling the story, that Colet was overcome with helpless mirth. 'And Thomas, the King looked at me, his little eyes suspicious. Then, suddenly, that tight mouth slackened. He laughed; he slapped my shoulder. "I see, friend Colet," he said. "You spoke not of this just war I would wage against the enemies of England. You spoke of the unjust wars that my enemies would wage on me!" I bowed my head. I feared he might see the laughter in my eyes. For, this King of ours, Thomas, is a King who believes he is God Himself. He believes in all simplicity, in all sincerity, that he himself could not be unjust, could not be dishonourable. The very fact that he acts in a certain way makes that action honourable. What a man! What a King!'

'How easy life must be for him!' mused Thomas. 'He has but to adjust his conscience to his desires.'

'Exactly. And this is what he did. He told himself that his Dr Colet had not spoken against *his* war; he had spoken against unjust war, as he himself would speak, for is he not a just King? He led me out of his privy chamber, his arm about me. You would have been amused to see the faces of his courtiers. They had expected me to appear between two halberdiers, and here I was–His Grace's arm through mine. He embraced me before them all, and he cried: "Let every man favour his own doctor. This Dr Colet is the doctor for me. . . ."'

They might laugh; but such encounters terrified Margaret. But for a turn of phrase John Colet might not be with them at this time.

Erasmus had stayed in the house during those years, and of all the scholars who came to the house, Alice liked him least.

A 'finicky' man, she declared he was–picking at his food, talking Latin to her husband, laughing with him. Alice was not at all sure that they were not laughing at her. 'And here's a pretty state of affairs when a woman does not know what is being said before her face.'

The climax came when he dropped a ring in the rushes and on recovering it looked at it with such distaste, and wiped it so carefully on a kerchief before restoring it to his finger, that Alice's indignation could not be suppressed.

'So, Master Desiderius Erasmus, you find my house not clean enough for you? You sniff at my rushes, do you, sir? There is one answer to that, and I will give it. If you like not my house, why stay in it? Why not go back to your hovel . . . your native country where houses are so clean that they make you turn up your foreign nose at ours!'

He had tried to placate her, as all tried to placate Alice; but his arguments did not move her. She disliked him, and that was the blunt fact. All the learned tutors–the absent-minded Master Gunnel and the guttural-voiced Master Kratzer, she would endure; but not the sickly, watery-eyed, sarcastically smiling Erasmus. And indeed Erasmus had left England soon after that. He had told Margaret, of whom he was very fond: 'I am a little tired of England, my child; and your stepmother is very tired of me.'

Soon after the great scholar had left them there had occurred the terrible rising of apprentices in the City, and, as Under-Sheriff, her father had played a great part in quelling the rebellion. The rising had come about on account of the citizens' dissatisfaction with the foreigners who lived therein and who, said the citizens, took their livings from Englishmen in their native land. These foreigners brought silks, cloth of gold and merchandise into London and sold them cheaply. Dutchmen brought over timber and leather, baskets and stools, tables and saddles, already wrought; and these they sold in such numbers that there was little work for those who had previously made such goods for their own countrymen.

So it was that during the month of April people gathered in the streets to discuss this matter, and they asked themselves how they could best rid themselves of the foreigners. Thomas Wolsey, now Cardinal, Pope's Legate, Archbishop of York, Chancellor of England and Prime Minister of State, sent for the chief aldermen of the City and told them that it was the King's wish that the foreigners should not be molested, as they brought much trade to the country; but the aldermen, after listening respectfully to Thomas Wolsey, went away and assured each other that their first allegiance was to the City of London, and if the citizens had decided to rid themselves of the foreigners there was nothing they could do about it.

Then came that 'Evil May Day' when the apprentices, with the people behind them, rose and rioted through the streets, sacking and burning the houses of foreigners.

Thomas, as Under-Sheriff, had been able to restore order to some parts of the City. The Cardinal, foreseeing how matters would go, ordered troops to close in on London, and several of the rioters were taken prisoner.

These men and boys were condemned as traitors, but only one of them was executed in the terrible manner–hanging, drawing and quartering–which was the lot of traitors. This one was to prove an example to the people; as for the rest, they provided the King with an opportunity to stage one of those little plays which he so loved, the ending of which was supposed to be a surprise, but which all except the most simple of men knew to be inevitable.

Henry, gloriously clad, a mighty man in sparkling jewels, sat on a lofty dais in Westminster Hall, while before him were brought the condemned men, with ropes about their necks. The Queen must kneel before him–a foreigner herself–and beg the King for leniency since some of the offenders were so young; she asked this as a favour to herself.

The sullen little mouth became less sullen. The King raised the Queen and said that for her sake he would consider pardoning these wretches.

Then it was the turn of the great Cardinal–magnificent in his scarlet robes–to kneel and crave the King's clemency.

All must watch this spectacle, all must know that a beloved Queen, the mother of the King's own daughter, the Princess Mary, must humble herself before the all-powerful monarch, as must the mighty Cardinal who went about the City in such state that men gathered to see him pass as though he were a King himself; this mighty Chancellor, this great Prime Minister of the realm, also must bow the knee to beg a favour from the King.

And eventually the King allowed himself to smile, to temper justice with mercy, to receive the humble thanks of those miserable men and the gratitude of their wives and mothers who called blessings on him–their most clement King, their most handsome King, who in anger was terrible, but who knew how to relent.

It was a touching scene, begun so solemnly, ending so joyously. The memory of it would put the King in a good humour for days.

And it was not forgotten what an excellent part in quelling the rebellion had been played by Thomas More. The King noted it and discussed it with his right-hand man. They would keep their eyes on Master More. They liked the fellow, both of them.

But life was made up of success and failure, of joy and fear; it was like a game of see-saw.

Just as the King's benevolence was shining upon Thomas More during that month of May, something happened to turn the King's smiles to frowns.

One of the Pope's ships had been forced to call at the port of Southampton, and the King had ordered it to be seized.

A week ago a man had called at the house in Bucklersbury to see Thomas and, when he had gone, Thomas told his family that he had agreed to act as interpreter and counsel in a case which the Pope was bringing against the authorities in England.

Alice said: 'This is a good thing. You will win the case for the King, and the King's favour never hurt anyone.'

'Nay,' Thomas answered her. 'You mistake me. It is not for the King I am briefed, but for the Pope.'

Margaret said nothing; she could only look mutely at her father. He saw the way in which she looked at him, and his eyes conveyed reassurance to her.

But Alice cried: ''Tis a marvel to me, Master More, that some men deem you wise. A bigger fool it has not been my misfortune to meet. Here is a lawyer who advises those who would go to law not to waste their money! Here is a lawyer who spends much of his time saving his clients' money that he may keep himself poor. He has won the King's favour, this Master More, on Evil May Day. That will not do. Therefore he must throw away his advantages by working against the King and serving the Pope.'

'I seek no favours of the King,' said Thomas. 'I seek to defend what is right. The ship does not become the property of the King because it calls at an English port.'

'Anything in this land belongs to the King.'

'Madam, you should enter the law. The King would doubtless favour your advancement. I doubt not that you would reap great honours.'

'I beg of you not to mock me, sir,' said Alice. 'And I beg of you not to be such a fool as to take this case.'

'My folly has already run ahead of your wisdom, madam. I have accepted the brief.'

'More fool you!' cried Alice. But she, like Margaret, was afraid. Like the rest of the family, she did not want change to overtake them. If her tongue was sharp, if she must be subject to fools, in her private opinion they were beloved fools.

The weeks seemed like a year; and the cloud about the house grew darker.

Margaret said to her father: 'I remember, a long time ago when I was a little girl, you told me that the King was angry with you. That was another King, but it seems to me that this King can be as angry–perhaps more angry–than his father.'

'That may be so, Meg.'

'Must you do this thing?'

'How could I refuse? The case was brought to me. I know the Pope's cause to be the right one. Would you have me refuse it because I know that, in defending the right, I might offend the King?'

'Let some other do it.'

'Turn away from danger that some other might face it! Or leave it to those who would defy justice for the sake of the King's favour! Nay, Meg! That is not the way to live. You . . . you of all people to ask it!'

'But, Father, I . . .'

'I know, Meg. You love me. But should I be worthy of your love if I turned away from danger? Remember this, Meg. When good fortune is greatest, then is trouble close at hand. When your troubles are at their height, prosperity is at hand. For Fortune delights to strike down those who are too high and to raise those who are low; and if we do not anticipate trouble, should it come, we shall face it with greater fortitude.'

So she trembled, and during that day when he went into the courts she found that she could not keep her mind on her lessons. Nor could Elizabeth and Cecily; and when Alice looked in and found Jack astride a stool, dreaming that he was on horseback, and Ailie pulling at the curls which escaped from her cap, and Cecily and Elizabeth whispering together, and neither Mercy nor Margaret attending to their lessons, she merely shook her head at them and said nothing, which was strange for her. There was about her an alertness, as though she were listening for the sound of horses' hoofs which would herald the return of Thomas.

And at length he came home.

'Wife!' he cried. 'Children! Where are you?'

They rushed to greet him, to look into his face; and there they saw a shining triumph.

'Well, Master More?' demanded Alice.

'The case is won.'

'Won?' cried Margaret.

'There could only be one verdict, and I got it.'

He had won the case, even though it had been tried before the great Wolsey himself. He had won the Pope's case, and in doing so he had defeated the King!

Margaret had felt then that that other occasion had been but a rehearsal for this. Henry the Seventh had gone timely to his grave; but the new King was young and healthy.

What will become of us? wondered Margaret.

Mercy was beside her. 'Come, Margaret. Sit down here.'

Mercy forced her on to a stool and placed a cool hand on her forehead.

'Thank you, Mercy.'

'Do not frighten the little ones,' whispered Mercy.

'You are right,' said Margaret. 'We must not frighten the little ones. But Mercy . . . Mercy . . .'

Mercy pressed her hands. Mercy, even though she loved him as Margaret did, even though she saw his danger, could remain serene.

They were at supper when the messenger came. He was the King's messenger; they knew that by his livery.

The King, declared the messenger, desired the presence of Thomas More at his Palace of Westminster. It would be well for Thomas More to take barge at once.

Margaret felt the piece of cob bread sticking in her throat. Her eyes met those of Mercy. Mercy's eyes, beneath her level brows, were full of fear.

When Thomas was shown into the royal apartments of the Palace of Westminster, the King was alone with his Chancellor.

Thomas went forward, knelt, and a large hand, a-glitter with emeralds, diamonds and sapphires, was extended to him.

Almost immediately it was snatched away and waved impatiently.

'Rise . . . rise . . .' said the King.

Thomas did so and stood before the royal chair. The sparkling hands were laid on the velvet-covered chair-arms; the big face was flushed, the eyes narrowed.

'We have had news, Master More,' said the King, 'of your conduct in this affair of the Pope's ship.' He glared at Thomas. 'That is why we have sent for you.'

Thomas's eyes strayed for a second to those of the Chancellor, who stood by the King's chair. It was impossible to read the thoughts behind those eyes, but Thomas sensed a certain sympathy, a certain encouragement.

During this day in the court he had been aware of Wolsey's approval of his conduct of the case. But what the Chancellor would feel in the absence of the King might be something different from that which he might show in his presence.

'Master More,' went on the King slowly and deliberately, 'you have a fine conceit of yourself.'

Thomas was silent.

'Have you not?' roared the King. 'We hear that this day, when you defended the Pope, you were full of fine phrases. Now, when you should defend yourself, you appear to have lost your voice. What is the meaning of this? What is the meaning of it, eh?'

'Before I begin the case for my defence, Sire, I must know what is the accusation.'

'You dare to stand before us . . . your *King* . . . and to ask what is the accusation! Master More, did you, or did you not, deliberately act against your King this day?'

'Nay, Sire. I acted against injustice.'

The King's hands on the arms of his chair were clenched suddenly; they appeared to tremble.

'Did you hear that, Wolsey, did you hear that?'

'I did, Your Grace.'

'He acted against *me* . . . and he calls that acting against injustice! By God's body, what should I do with such a man, eh? Tell me that. You are the Chancellor of this realm. What should I do with him? Clap him into the Tower? Know this, my friend . . . know this: Those who act against the King are traitors. Master More, do you know the death that awaits the traitor?'

'I do, Your Grace.'

'You should . . . as a lawyer. Well . . . well . . . what have you to say? You stand there. . . . Come, come, repeat to me what you said in the courts this day. You . . . you traitor . . . you . . . you who would work for a foreign power against your own country . . .'

'Your Grace, I was asked by the representative of His Holiness the Pope to argue his case for him. The Chancellor here will tell you that I only did what any lawyer would do.'

'And are you in the habit, Master More, of employing your talents to uphold injustice?'

'Nay, Sire.'

'And if you did not think a case was a just one, you would refuse it, I dare swear?'

'I should, Your Grace.'

The King rose. He put his hands on his hips and rocked on his heels. The little eyes opened very wide and he began to laugh.

'Here, Wolsey!' he cried. 'Here is our man!'

Thomas looked in astonishment from King to Chancellor. Henry walked towards Thomas and laid a hand on his shoulder.

'It grieves us,' he said, 'it grieves us mightily that when we find honest men in our kingdom . . . honest men and brave . . . they are not with us, but against us.' He lifted his hand suddenly and brought it down in an affectionate pat on Thomas's shoulder. 'And when we grieve, Master More, we seek to right the grievance. That is so, is it not, Master Wolsey?'

The Chancellor came forward. ''Tis even so, my gracious lord.'

'Speak to him then, Wolsey. Tell this fellow what I have said of him.'

Then Wolsey spoke: 'Our most gracious King, in his clemency, in his great love of truth and justice, is not displeased, as you might well believe, at the way in which the case went this afternoon. When I told His Grace what had happened, how you, with your learned discourse, with your determination to uphold what you believed right in this matter, had so swayed the court that the verdict went against the holding of the Pope's ship, his most gracious Majesty was thoughtful.'

''Tis so!' interrupted the King. ''Tis so. And I said to Wolsey: "Thomas Wolsey," I said. "Thomas, I like it not when the best men in my kingdom . . . out of their honesty and bravery . . . are not with me, but against me." That is what I said to him. "By God," I said, "we should send for this fellow. He shall work for me in future, for he is a man that I like . . . and he is a man I will have beside me. . . ."'

'I understand not, Your Grace,' said Thomas.

'He understands not my grace!' said the King with a laugh. His eyes were sparkling with benevolence; the little mouth was slack with sentiment. 'Aye, but you shall. You shall see, Thomas More, that I am a King who would surround himself with the best in the kingdom. I like you, Master More. You were against me . . . but I like you. That's the man I am. You dared to speak against your King, but such is your King that he likes you for it.'

Now he stood back like a boy who has all the toys that others envy; and who, because he is wise and kindly, will share those toys with the less fortunate.

'Come here, my friend.' He took Thomas's arm in a gesture of such friendliness that it startled Thomas. 'Don't be afraid of us, Master More. Don't be overcome, my dear fellow. Yesterday you were a poor lawyer. Today the King is your friend. And you, my dear Wolsey, my other Thomas. . . .' He put his arm through that of the Chancellor, and with them walked the length of the apartment. 'We have work for a man like you here at court, Master More. We can lift you up. We can honour you with favours . . . and we will. You shall work with our Chancellor here, for he has taken a fancy to you. He likes you. Do you not, eh, Wolsey?'

'I do, my gracious master.'

'Indeed, you do.' The King stopped and looked with the utmost affection at the Cardinal. 'There's not much missed by those shrewd eyes. Now there shall be two Thomases to serve their master . . . two good and honest men. What have you to say, Master More?'

'Your Grace overwhelms me. I know not what to say.'

The King began to laugh. ''Twas as good as a play, eh, Wolsey? As good as a masque! Master More, present yourself to the King! By God, Master More, when you entered this room you thought you'd march out of it to a dungeon, I doubt not. You did not know that you would find in it the King's warm regard . . . the King's favour.'

'Your Grace,' said Thomas, 'I know you to be a just King. I did not believe that you would condemn a subject because that subject acted in accordance with what he believed to be right.'

'Well spoken,' said the King soberly. 'Your advancement is certain. You will do well in the service of the Chancellor.'

'Your Grace, I . . . I have my duties as a lawyer. . . .'

Both the King and Wolsey had raised their eyebrows, but Thomas went on boldly: 'I have also my duties as Under-Sheriff of the City of London. . . .'

'Enough! Enough!' said the King. 'We shall take care of that. Man, I offer you great rewards. Look at this man here. He was but my chaplain, and I have made him the greatest man in this land . . . under myself. My father raised him up . . . and what was he before that? I'll tell you. . . . No, no. I will not tell you! Suffice it that it was humble . . . *most* humble, eh, Master Wolsey? But I like this man. I like this Wolsey. He is my counsellor and my friend. And so . . . from little I lifted him to greatness. So will I do for you. Now . . . you are overwhelmed. It was a little joke of mine to tease you first, to fill you with fear, then to fill you with joy. You shall be a rich man, Master More. Fortune is favouring you, for the King is giving you his hand in friendship. Go away now . . . and think of the greatness which lies before you. I will let all men see this day how I honour those who are brave and honest men . . . even though they do not always share my views.'

'Your Grace . . .'

'You are dismissed, Master More,' said the King with a smile. 'You shall speak of your gratitude some other time. You need now to be alone . . . to think of this sudden change in your fortunes.'

The King had turned away, calling for a page; and Thomas found himself walking backwards out of the apartment.

Slowly he made his way down to the river, where his barge was waiting for him.

Never had he been at such a loss for words; never in the whole of his life had he received such a surprise. He had gone to the Palace prepared to defend himself and, instead of having to justify his action in the court of law, had found a more difficult task presented to him. He had tried to refuse an appointment at Court which the King himself had offered, when to refuse it would certainly be looked upon as an affront to His Grace.

Yet refuse it he must. He did not want to go to Court. He was no courtier. He did not want his quiet life to be disturbed. He had his work, his writing, his study, his family. They were enough for him; they gave him all that he desired in life. It was ironical; so many yearned for a place at Court; so many were ambitious; and he who did not seek it, who must refuse it, was having it thrust upon him.

As he was about to step into his barge, one of the Cardinal's servants came running to the river's edge.

Wolsey's retinue were as magnificently attired as though they served the King; they wore a livery of crimson velvet trimmed with gold chains; and even his menials wore scarlet trimmed with black velvet.

'His Excellency the Cardinal begs you to wait awhile,' said the man. 'He would have speech with you. He says the matter is of importance. Will you wait for him in his apartments, sir?'

'Assuredly I will,' said Thomas; and he was conducted back to the Palace.

There he was shown into the apartments of the Cardinal, the furnishings of which were as rich as those of the King. Thomas was taken through many rooms to a small chamber, and when he had waited in this chamber for five minutes, the Cardinal came in.

In his scarlet satin dress and tippet of sable, he dominated the room; and he wore his garments as though they delighted him. There were many stories current regarding the magnificence of the Cardinal. He kept several princely households, in which he stored many treasures. York House and Hampton Court were said to vie with the King's own palaces. He lived in great pomp, surrounded by a large retinue of servants; he had his cofferer, three marshals, an almoner, two yeomen ushers and two grooms; he had clerks of the kitchens, a clerk controller, even a clerk of the spicery; his pages, grooms of the scullery and scalding-houses, grooms of the pantry, porters and yeomen were so numerous that even he did not know their number; and his cook was seen to strut in the grounds of his houses like a minor potentate in damask and with a chain of gold about his neck, carrying a nosegay or a pomander in imitation of his master, his own servants of the kitchen about him.

The grandeur of Wolsey exceeded, some said, that of the King himself; and because the Cardinal had risen to great heights from a lowly beginning, he was resented by those of high birth, who felt he should not be among them, and envied by those of low birth who felt he should be on their level. Yet he cared not for these criticisms. He cared not that the mischievous Skelton had written verses concerning the state he kept, and that the people were singing them in the streets, asking each other:

'Why come ye not to Court?
To which Court?
To the King's Court
Or to Hampton Court?

'The King's Court
Should have the excellence.
But Hampton Court
Hath the pre-eminence.'

Perhaps those who sung the verses believed they might rouse the King's resentment; but the King was not resentful towards his favourite, for Henry believed that all the magnificence with which the Cardinal surrounded himself came from his own kingly munificence. Henry had set the fountains playing; if he wished, he had but to give the order and their flow would cease. Hampton Court was in reality the King's Court, and the King's Court was Hampton Court. The Cardinal regarded the King as his puppet; but that was exactly how the King saw the Cardinal; each was unaware of the other's myopia, and while this was so they could feel safe and contented.

The Cardinal, though essentially ambitious, was not an unkindly man. There was no room in his life for malice for its own sake. There was one ruling passion in the Cardinal's life, and that was ambition. To the humble, he was generous; and his servants were fond of him. He had used religion as a ladder to fame and fortune; he used people, and if he found it necessary to destroy them, it was not out of malice or sudden anger; it was merely because they impeded his ambition.

He, like the King, had taken a fancy to Thomas More; he had seen that this man could be useful.

He had also seen what the King had not seen: that Thomas More was not overcome with joy at the prospect of the King's favour. It was not that Thomas More had been at a loss for words to express his gratitude; he had hesitated because he was wondering how to refuse the honours the King was ready to bestow.

It was concerning this matter that the Cardinal wished to see Thomas More.

'I am glad that you returned to the Palace,' said the Cardinal. 'I would converse with you. You may speak frankly with me, as I will with you. And you need have no fear that what you say will go beyond these four walls, for my servant, Cavendish, whom I would trust with my life, will see that none overhears us. So . . . speak your mind freely to me, Master More, as I will speak mine to you.'

'What is it that Your Excellency has to say to me?'

'Merely this: You are considering how to refuse the King's offer, I believe?'

'You are right. I shall refuse it.'

'Such procedure would be misguided.'

'I will try to explain to you.'

The Cardinal lifted his well-cared-for hand. 'Save your breath. I understand. You are not an ambitious man. You are a scholar who wishes to be left alone with the work he has chosen. I understand that point of view, although it is a most unusual one. I have read your literary works–and may I compliment you on their excellence? You prefer the secluded life. But if you rebuff the King's friendly gesture, you will be a foolish man. Nay . . . nay . . . mistake me not. I know that if a man does not seek fame, then he sets no store by it. But I do not talk of fame . . . of the advancement which I know could come to a man of your talents. I speak, Master More, of your life.'

'My life?'

'It could easily be at stake.'

'I do not understand you.'

'That is because you do not understand the man whom we have just left. You see him as a mighty King. Pray do not be alarmed. As I said, I shall speak frankly to you, even of the King. You may think I am incautious. But, my friend, if you carried tales of what I say to you now, I should deny them. Moreover, I should find some means of silencing you. But I speak to you thus because I know you are a man who would respect a confidence. I trust you, as you must trust me. You have just witnessed a little play-acting in the royal apartments. Was it not charming? A humble official believes he has displeased the King; and then he finds that he has pleased him. The King is a boy at heart, Master More. He loves to play, and you have helped him to play a very pretty scene. Now, the King is not always a merry-tempered boy. Sometimes the young cub roars and sometimes he springs; and although I am his very watchful keeper, I cannot always save his victims from those mighty claws; even if I have a will to do so. You marvel? But, listen. I have a fancy for you . . . just as the King has. There are few men in this kingdom with brains and honesty . . . oh, very few. Having found one, I do not intend to let him slip through my fingers. I want you, Master More, to work with me. I can offer you a great career . . . fame . . . advancement . . .'

'Your Excellency . . .'

'You do not want them, I know. But you do want to live. You want to go home to your clever children and your wife, do you not? You want to go on conversing with your learned friends. Oh, life is sweet, Master More, when it brings as much to a man as it has brought to you. But think of this: A child plays his games and he loves his toys; but if a toy displeases him, what does he do? He smashes it. Master More, when you played the honourable lawyer this day, you took a great risk. But the boy liked his playlet; he liked his new role. Perhaps he has heard his praises sung too consistently of late. Who shall say? But you pleased him. You played your part so well that the principal actor was able to outshine us all. Now, the King will not be pleased if you do not continue to make him feel pleased with *himself*, if you do not allow him to show the world what a beneficent monarch he is.'

'You are very bold, Cardinal.'

'You were bold this afternoon, Master More. But you cannot afford to risk offending the King twice in one day. Great good luck has attended you; you could not expect that to be repeated. This King of ours is a mighty lion who does not yet know his strength. He is caged . . . but he does not see the bars. I am his keeper. If he felt his strength, if he knew his power, then we might begin to tremble. I believe he would risk his kingdom to satisfy his appetites. That is why he must be fed carefully. It is the duty of men like yourself . . . like myself . . . who wish to serve our country–some because of honour, some because of ambition; what matters it if we serve our country well?–it is the duty of such men to suppress their personal desires. And if we do not, we may find that the King's frown, instead of his smile, is turned upon us.'

'Are you sure that if I refused to come to Court I should find myself persecuted?'

'I believe this would certainly come to pass. Remember, my friend–and I mean "my friend," for I will be yours if you will be mine–I know him. I served his father as I now serve him; and I have watched him grow up.'

'But I have no wish to come to Court.'

'Master More, you have no choice. I remember, when I served his father, that you were in disfavour. You are a man who cannot fail to attract attention. You would not be here in England at this moment had his father lived, unless you now lay under the earth. The young King is not the old King; but, Master More, he is none the less dangerous for that.'

'I wish to live in peace and quietude with my family.'

'If you wish to live at all, Master More, you will not reject the King's honours.' The Cardinal was smiling quizzically. 'Go now, my friend. There is nothing more to say at this stage. I will tell the King I have talked with you, and that the honour he is about to heap on you has overwhelmed you, robbed you of your native wit. I will tell him that I believe our country is fortunate in the learned honesty of Thomas More . . . and the clemency and astonishing wisdom of its King.'

Margaret flung herself into his arms when he came home.

'Father!'

He kissed her warmly.

'Why these sad looks? This is a time for rejoicing. The King honours me. He sent for me to congratulate me . . . to tell me of his regard.'

Margaret, her arms about his neck, leaned backwards to look searchingly into his face.

'But you are disturbed.'

'Disturbed! My dearest, you will see your father a courtier yet. I met the great Cardinal, and he also honours me with his friendship. Meg, I am weighed down with honours.'

But she continued to look at him uneasily. The others were surrounding him now.

'What is this nonsense?' demanded Alice.

'The King sent for me to tell me he is pleased with me.'

'Pleased with you for losing him his ship?'

'The Pope's ship, madam.'

'Pleased with you. Pleased! Is this another of your jokes?'

''Tis no joke,' said Thomas slowly. 'The King liked what I did this day, and he honours me. I am to go to Court. I am to work with Cardinal Wolsey. When I left this house, Alice, I was a humble lawyer; now I am . . . I know not what.'

Alice cried: ''Tis a marvellous thing and great good luck, though you have done little to deserve it. Come to the table. Tell us more of this. A place at Court! Tilly valley! I was never so excited in my life.'

How strange, thought Margaret, that the same piece of news could be so differently received by members of the same family. Here was her stepmother already looking ahead to a rosy future, to rich marriages for the young members of the family; and here was her father looking ahead–smiling for their sakes, trying to be pleased with advancement, yet unable to hide from his beloved daughter the foreboding which showed in his eyes.

That summer was hot and dry, and the sweating sickness appeared in the City.

Thomas was to begin his service to the King by going on an embassy to Flanders. His life had changed; he must be often at the Palace and he spent much time with the Cardinal. The first trouble which his elevation brought were his absences from home.

'I wish we were a humble family,' said Margaret passionately to Mercy. 'Then we might stay together and attract no attention to ourselves.'

'We should have no education,' Mercy reminded her. 'And can you imagine Father as a man of no education? No, as he says, there is good and bad in life; and there is bad in the good and good in the bad; and the only way to live is to accept the one with the other. Enjoy one; endure the other.'

'How wise you are, Mercy!'

'It is borrowed wisdom . . . borrowed from Father.'

Mercy was happy that year in spite of the pending departure of Thomas, and the reason was that there was a new member of this evergrowing household. This was John Clement, a protégé of the Cardinal's, a young man in his late teens who was to accompany Thomas as his secretary and attendant on the mission to Flanders.

John Clement was a serious and very learned person–a young man after Thomas's own heart–and a warm welcome was given him in the house of his new master. Young Clement quickly became a member of that happy family group, but he found that she who interested him most was not one of the Mores, but Mercy Gigs.

He sought every opportunity of talking with her. He was several years older than she was, but it seemed to him that he had never met a girl of her age so solemnly self-contained; and if she was not quite so learned as Margaret, her scholarship lay in that subject which most interested him.

He never forgot the rapt expression in her eyes when he told her that he had studied medicine at Oxford.

'You are interested in medicine, Mistress Mercy?' he asked.

'In nothing so much.'

Now they had a subject which they could discuss together; Thomas watched them with pleasure. My little Mercy is growing up, he thought. They are all growing up. In two or three years it will be necessary to find husbands for Mercy and Margaret–and Ailie too, though she will doubtless find one for herself.

It was a dream materializing, an ideal becoming palpable. When he had decided on giving up the monk's life for that of a family man, he had visualized a household very like the one which was now his. Had he ever imagined such love as he had for Margaret? Nay, the reality was greater than he had foreseen. And when she marries she must never leave me, he thought, for without Margaret I would not wish to live. And Mercy here is as dear to me as are my own children. Did ever a man possess such a learned and affectionate daughter as Margaret, such charming children as those who made up his household? And Alice herself, she was neither a pearl nor a girl, but he was fond of her; and he knew that her sharp words often hid kindly motives. Where could he find a better housekeeper? And surely she was the best of mothers to his children, for it was well to have a touch of spice in the sweetest dish. There might be times when his beloved children were in need of chastisement, and how could *he* administer a whipping? He was a coward where such matters were concerned. What could he whip his children with but a peacock's feather? Yet Mistress Alice shirked not the task.

He was a lucky man. He must not complain that his life away from his family was not all that he could wish. So many men craved the King's favour; so many would have been honoured to call the Cardinal their friend. He wanted too much of life. He must make the best of his new honours; he must steal away from them as often as he could, to be with his books and his family; and he must be grateful to God for the good life which was his.

Was ever man so loved? Very few, he believed. Only yesterday, when the children were talking together of what they wished for most, he had wandered by and heard their talk. Mercy had said. 'If I could wish for something, I would wish I were Father's true daughter.'

And when he had found her alone, he had said to her: 'Mercy, you have no need to wish for what is already yours. To me you are exactly as though you are my true daughter.'

She had blushed and faltered and said: 'Father, I meant that I wished I were your daughter as Margaret, Elizabeth and Cecily are.'

'That matters not at all, Mercy, my child. I see you as my daughter–my true daughter–as much as any of the others. You are as dear to me.'

'I know it, Father,' she said. 'But . . .'

'But, Mercy, if that love which is between us two is as strong as the love which is between me and the daughters of my own body, what difference can there be? You delight me, Mercy. You are all that I could wish for in a daughter. You must not wish for something which is already yours . . . in all that matters. I remember when you were a little girl and I took you to task for some small fault, your distress hurt me as much as the distress of any of the others would have done.'

She caught his hand and kissed it. 'In those days,' she said, 'I sometimes committed those faults that you might talk to me alone . . . even though it was to reprimand me.'

'Poor little Mercy! You felt you were left out then? You were the foster-child? You wished to have attention . . . even if, to gain it, you must seem at fault?'

'It was that,' she answered. 'But it was also that I might have the pleasure of standing before you and that you should be thinking of me . . . me . . . alone. Me . . . by myself, without Margaret.'

'Oh, Mercy . . . Mercy . . . you must not have such a high opinion of me. We must not set up gods on Earth, you know.'

She said: 'I have set up nothing. I have lifted up my eyes and seen.'

He laughed. 'Now to talk sense. Your wish was that you could be my true

They must write to him for, he said, he missed them sorely, and it was only when he received their letters that he could be happy. He wanted to hear everything, no matter how trivial it seemed to them; if it concerned his home, that was enough to delight him. 'There is no excuse for you girls,' he wrote. 'Cannot girls always find something to chatter about? That is what I want you to do, my darlings. Take up your pens and chatter to your father.'

There was always a special compliment if Jack wrote anything. Poor Jack, now that he was growing up he was beginning to realize how difficult it was for a normal, healthy boy to compete with such brilliant sisters. Alice said it was God's rebuke on his father for having prated so much and so consistently about the equality of men's and women's brains when all the rest of the world opined that men were meant to be the scholars. Here are your brilliant daughters, perhaps God had said. And your son shall be a dullard.

Not that Jack was a dullard by any means; he was merely normal. He could not love lessons as he loved the outdoor life. Therefore his father wrote to his son very tenderly and cherished his efforts with the pen, encouraging him, understanding that all cannot love learning as some do.

He wrote enthusiastically to Margaret. He could not help it if writing to Margaret gave him pleasure which was greater than anything else he could enjoy during his sojourn abroad.

He was writing a book which had long been in his mind, he told her. It consisted of imaginary conversations between himself and a man who had come from a strange land which was called *Utopia*. They discussed the manners and customs of this land. The writing of this book was giving him great pleasure, and when he came home he would enjoy reading it to her.

'I showed one of your Latin essays to a very great man, Margaret. He is a great scholar, and you will be gratified when I tell you who he is. Reginald Pole. My dearest, he was astonished. He said that but for the fact that I assured him this was so, he would not have believed a girl–or anyone of your age, boy or girl–could have done such work unaided. My dearest child, how can I explain to you my pride? . . .'

He was a very proud man. He kept his children's writings with him, that he might read them through when he felt dejected and homesick; nor could he refrain from showing them to his friends and boasting a little. His pride and joy in his family was profound.

> My dearest children, *he wrote to them*, I hope that a letter to you all may find you in good health and that your father's good wishes may keep you so. In the meantime, while I make a long journey, drenched by soaking rain, and while my mount too frequently is bogged down in the mud, I compose this for you to give you pleasure. You will then gather an indication of your father's feelings for you –how much more than his own eyes he loves you; for the mud, the miserable weather and the necessity for driving a small horse through deep waters have not been able to distract my thoughts from you. . . .

Then he went on to tell them how he had always loved them and how he longed to be with them:

> At the moment my love has increased so much that it seems to me that I used not to love you at all. Your characteristics tug at my heart, so bind me to you, that my being your father (the only reason for many a father's love) is hardly a reason at all for my love for you. Therefore, most dearly beloved children, continue to

endear yourselves to your father, and by those same accomplishments, which make me think that I had not loved you before, make me think hereafter (for you can do it) that I do not love you now. . . .

And so they waited, while the sweating sickness passed over Bucklersbury, for the return of the father whom they loved.

One day after his return when the family were gathered at the table, Thomas said to them: 'I have a surprise for you all. There is to be a new addition to our family. I hope you will all make him welcome. I find him an interesting and charming person. I am sure you will too.'

'It is a man?' asked Ailie, her eyes sparkling.

'It is, daughter.'

'Not a grey-bearded scholar this time, Father!'

'Half right and half wrong. A scholar but not a grey-bearded one. He is, I gather, some twenty years of age.'

'It is to be hoped he has not the finical manners of that Erasmus,' said Alice. 'I want no more such foreigners in the house.'

'Nay, Alice, he is not a foreigner. He is an Englishman, and I doubt you will find him over-finical. He is of a very good family, I must tell you, and he comes to study the law with me.'

'Father,' cried Margaret, 'how will you have time to help a young man with his studies, do your law work and serve the King and the Cardinal? You do too much. We shall never have you with us.'

'Do not scold me, Meg. I'll warrant you'll like Friend Roper. He is a serious young man, a little quiet, so he'll not disturb you overmuch. I think he will be ready to join our family circle.'

So William Roper came to the house–a young man of quiet manners and seeming meekness, but, Margaret noticed, with an obstinate line to his mouth. There was one thing about him that Margaret liked, and that was his devotion to her father. It was quite clear that the young man had decided to follow in Thomas's footsteps whenever possible.

John Clement, who had returned to the household of the Cardinal, came to the house whenever he could; and in a few months it became clear that Will Roper and John Clement looked upon The Barge in Bucklersbury as their home.

Margaret was thirteen when Will Roper came; he was twenty; yet in spite of the difference in their ages, Margaret felt as old as he was. As John Clement sought Mercy's company, Will Roper sought Margaret's; and this fact made Ailie pout a little. There was she, by far the prettiest of the three of them, and yet the two eligible young men at the house seemed to seek the friendship of Margaret and Mercy.

'Not,' she said to Cecily who was herself a little frivolous, 'that we could call such as John Clement and Will Roper *men*; one is always sniffing herbs and cures, and the other always has his nose in his law books. Now that Father is at Court, perhaps he will bring home some real men . . . for you, Cecily, and for me. I doubt whether Margaret or Mercy would be interested.'

Alice worried Thomas when they were alone: 'Now that you have such opportunities, you must see to husbands for the girls.'

'Why, Alice, there are some years to go yet.'

'Not so many. Mercy, Margaret and my girl are thirteen. In a year or two

it will be time to settle them.'

'Then we may wait a year or two yet.'

'I know. I know. And by that time who knows what honours will be heaped upon you! It is all very well to be wise and noble and to prattle in Greek, but it seems to me you would be wiser and more noble if you thought a little about your children's future.'

He was thoughtful, and suddenly he laid his hand on her shoulder.

'In good time,' he said, 'I promise you I will do all that a father should.'

Those were the happy days, with few cares to disturb the household. They had grown accustomed to Thomas's working with Wolsey now. He came home at every opportunity, and they would laugh at his tales of how he had managed to slip away from the Court unseen.

At that time the only troubles were petty annoyances. There was an occasion when Thomas went to Exeter to see Vesey, the Bishop, and he came home quite put out; and while they sat at the table he told them why this was so.

'I had some of your work in my pocket . . . a little piece from each of you . . . and the best you have ever done. Well, I could not resist the chance of showing them to the Bishop, and, to tell the truth, it was that which I was longing to do all the time I was with him. So, at the first opportunity I brought out this piece of Margaret's. He read it, and he stared at me. "A girl wrote this!" he said with astonishment. "My daughter Margaret," I answered lightly. "And her age?" "She is just thirteen." And, my dear one, like Reginald Pole, he would not have believed me had I not given him my word. He would not hand the piece back to me. He read it through and through again. He walked about his room in some excitement and then unlocked a box and produced this.'

They crowded round to see what he held up.

'What is it, Father?' asked Jack.

'A gold coin, my son, from Portugal.'

'Is it valuable?'

'It is indeed. The Bishop said: 'Give this to your daughter Margaret with my compliments and good wishes, for I never saw such work from one so young. Let her keep it and look at it now and then and be encouraged to grow into that great scholar which I know she will become.' I begged him to take back the coin. I refused to accept the coin. But the more I refused, the more earnest he became that I should accept it.'

Ailie said: 'But why, Father, did you not wish to take it?'

'Because, my daughter, I wished to show him the work of the others which I had in my pocket. But how could I show it? He would think I was asking for more gold coins. I have rarely been so disappointed. I felt cheated. I wanted to say: "But I have five clever daughters and one clever son, and I wish you to know how clever they all are." But how could I?'

They all laughed, for now he looked like a child–a little boy who has been denied a treat, Margaret told him.

'Well, here is your coin. Meg, do you not like it?'

'No, Father. Every time I look at it I shall remember it brought disappointment to you.' Then she put her arms about his neck and kissed him. 'Father, you must not be so proud of your children. Pride is a sin, you know–one of the deadly sins. I am going to write some verses for you . . . about a father who fell into the sin of pride.'

'Ah, Meg, I shall look forward to hearing them. They will make up for the

disappointment the Bishop gave me.'

In the evenings they would gather together and talk and read; sometimes they would sing. Thomas had taught Alice to sing a little. She had begun under protest. She was too old, she declared, to join his school. And did the man never think of anything but learning and teaching? Latin she would not touch. As for Greek, that was more heathen than anything.

He would put his arms about her and wheedle her gently: 'Come, Alice, try these notes. You've a wonderful voice. You'll be our singing bird yet.'

'I never heard such nonsense!' she declared. But they heard her singing to herself when she sat stitching, trying out her voice; and they knew that one day she would join in; and she did.

Margaret felt that with the passing of that year she had grown to love her father even more–so much more, as he had said, that it seemed that previously she could hardly have loved him at all.

His book *Utopia* taught her more about him. She understood from it his longing for perfection. She enjoyed discussing it with him. 'My pride in you, Father, is as great as yours in your children. Methinks we are a very proud pair. And, Father, there is one thing that pleases me more than any other: That is your tolerance in this matter of religion.' She quoted: '"King Utopus made a decree that it should be lawful for every man to favour and follow what religion he would, and that he might do the best he could to bring others to his opinion, if he did it peaceably, gently, quietly, and soberly, without hasty and contentious rebuking and inveighing against others. . . ." I like the views of King Utopus on religion. I feel them to be right.'

'Ah, Meg, what a wonderful world we could have if men could but be induced to make it so.'

On one occasion he said to her: 'My dearest daughter, there is one matter which I wish to discuss with you. It is something between us two, and I want no other to know of it.'

'Yes, Father?'

'You know that at one time I considered taking my vows. Meg, it is a strange thing but the monastic life still calls to me.'

'What! You would leave us and go into solitude?'

'Nay, never! For you are dearer to me than all the world . . . you . . . you alone–and that is not counting the rest of the family. I once said to Colet, when he was my confessor, that I was a greedy man. I wanted two lives; and it seems I am a determined man, for I want to live those two lives side by side, Meg. While I live here in the midst of you all, while I am happy among you, still I crave to be a monk. While I live with you, while I am happy with you, and I believe we are meant to be happy for a saintly life need not be a gloomy one, I still continue those practices which I followed when I was in the Charterhouse.' He undid the ruff about his neck and opened his doublet.

'Father!' she whispered. 'A hair-shirt!'

'Yes, Meg. A hair-shirt. It subdues the flesh. It teaches a man to suffer and endure. Meg, it is our secret.'

'I will keep it, Father.'

He laughed suddenly. 'Will you do more than that? Will you wash it for me . . . and in secret?'

'Assuredly I will.'

'Bless you, Meg. There is none other to whom I could confide this thing and be certain of understanding.'

'There is nothing you could not confide in me . . . nor I in you.'

'Your mother, God bless her, would not understand. She would ridicule the practice. So . . . I thank you, daughter.'

When she took the shirt and washed it in secret, she wept over it, seeing his blood upon it. Sometimes she marvelled to see him so merry and to know he was wearing that painful thing. But he never gave a sign to the others of the pain he was inflicting on himself. If he was a monk at heart, he was a very merry monk.

There was great excitement when the Greek Testament, which Erasmus had edited and reconstructed, was received into the Mores' home. Thomas read it aloud to the family. Alice sat listening, although she could not understand it, her fingers busy with her needle.

Those were happy days. Looking back, a long time afterwards, Margaret realized that the change came from an unexpected quarter, as such changes usually do. A German monk named Martin Luther had during that eventful year denounced the practices of the monks and the Catholic Church, as Erasmus had denounced them before him; but whereas Erasmus mildly disapproved, this man was bold and passionate in his denunciation; and whereas Erasmus had taken refuge behind his scholarship and attacked with an almost light-hearted cynicism, the German monk did so with passionate indignation; whereas Erasmus had written for the initiated, Luther was fulminating for the multitude.

The climax came when this man Luther nailed to the door of a Wittenberg church his ninety-five theses against Indulgences. And when he did this he had fired the first shot in the battle of the Reformation which was to shake Europe, divide the Church, and plunge the world which called itself Christian into bloodshed and terror.

Men and women began to take sides; they were for the Pope or for Martin Luther. Erasmus crept back to his desk; he was no fighter. It was said that he had laid the egg which Martin Luther hatched; but he wished to be remote from conflict; he wished to live peaceably with his books.

But as Margaret saw it, her father was of a different nature; he was a man with firm opinions. He could agree with much that Erasmus had written, but if it was a matter of taking sides he would be on the side of the old religion.

But that had not yet come to pass.

The happy evenings continued, broken only by the shock produced by the death of Dean Colet, who was struck down by the plague. They wept sincerely for the loss of this old friend.

But, as Thomas said, he had had a good life. He had seen his dearest wish realized–and what more could a man ask? His school was flourishing under the headmastership of William Lily; and his life had not been an idle nor a short one.

Margaret marvelled afterwards that she had not paid more heed to the rumblings of that storm which was breaking over Europe. It was due, of course, to William Roper, who was now seeking her company on every occasion, asking her to walk with him alone, for, he declared, conversation between two people could be so much more interesting in private than in a crowd.

There was a further excitement. One day a very handsome young man came to the house to see Thomas. He was a rich young courtier named Giles Allington, and Ailie, who had received him with her mother, seemed much amused by him, although she did not allow him to know that.

Ailie, when she wished, could be quite charming. She was the prettiest of all the girls, golden-haired, blue-eyed, tall and graceful. She took great pains to preserve her beauty and was for ever looking into her mirror. In vain had Thomas teased her. Often he repeated to her those epigrams which he had translated with William Lily. The one which concerned Lais, who dedicated her mirror to Venus, was a gentle warning. 'For,' said Lais, 'the woman I am, I do not wish to see; the woman I was, I cannot.'

'And that, my dear daughter, is what happens to women who attach great importance to beauty, for beauty is like an unfaithful lover; once gone, it cannot be recalled.'

But Ailie merely laughed and kissed him in her attractive way. 'Ah, dearest Father, but no woman believes her lover is going to be unfaithful while he is faithful; and as you yourself have said, why should we worry about tomorrow's evils? Does not the Bible say, "Sufficient unto the day is the evil thereof"?'

Thomas could not resist her charm, and for all that she set such store by those pleasures which he deemed to hold no real value, for once he found she could score over him with her feminine logic.

So Ailie continued to make lotions for the freshening of her skin, and kept her hands soft and supple, avoiding any household tasks which made them otherwise. As for Alice, she looked the other way when Ailie refused to do such tasks. If Alice wished to see all the girls married well–which she certainly did–she wished Ailie to make the most brilliant marriage of all.

So came Giles Allington, heir to a rich estate and title, with the manners of the Court, and jewels in his doublet; and for all that he was a court gallant, he could not hide his admiration for Ailie as she concealed her interest in him.

'Where she learned such tricks I do not know,' said Cecily wistfully.

''Twas not in this house,' said Elizabeth.

'There are some who are born with such knowledge, I believe,' said Mercy. 'And Ailie is one of them.'

So it seemed, for Ailie grew very gay after the visit of Giles Allington, and although she was interested in Master Allington's lands and titles rather than in himself, she grew prettier every day.

'She blooms,' said Cecily, 'as they say girls bloom when they are in love.'

'She is in love,' said Margaret. 'For a girl can be in love with good fortune as well as with a man.'

Giles Allington came often to the house in Bucklersbury; and Alice and her daughter talked continually of the young man. Alice declared herself pleased that Thomas had won the King's favour and that he was now a man of no small importance. Will Roper was of good family, and he was as a son of the house; John Clement was slowly rising in the service of the Cardinal, and he looked upon this family as his own; and now the handsome and wealthy Giles Allington came to visit them. They were rising in the world.

Life went on pleasantly in this way for many months.

When the King and his lords went to France to entertain and be entertained by the French and their King with such magnificence and such great cost that this venture was afterwards called 'The Field of the Cloth of Gold,' Thomas went with the party on the business of the King and the Cardinal.

And it was at this time that William Roper declared his feelings for Margaret.

Margaret was now fifteen–small and quiet. She knew that–apart from her father–she was the most learned member of the family; but she had always seen herself as the least attractive, except in the eyes of her father.

Ailie was a beauty; Mercy had a quiet charm which was the essence of her gravity, a gentleness, the soothing quality of a doctor–and that was attractive, Margaret knew; Elizabeth, now that she was growing up, showed herself possessed of a merry, sparkling wit which, like her father's, never wounded; Cecily was pretty and gay; Jack was jolly and full of fun. And I, pondered Margaret, I have none of their charms, for although when I have a pen in my hands, words come quickly, they do not always do so in conversation, except perhaps with Father. I most certainly lack Ailie's beauty; I am solemn rather than gay like Cecily; I lack Mercy's gentleness and Elizabeth's wit; and I am not jolly like Jack, who says things which, by their very simplicity, make us laugh.

It had always seemed to Margaret, on those rare occasions when her thoughts unwittingly strayed to the subject, that she would never marry. This did not perturb her for she had no wish to do so.

And now . . . William Roper.

He asked her to talk with him, and they went into Goodman's Fields, where she had so often walked with her father. 'It is not easy,' said Will, as they walked through the grass, 'to talk in the house.'

'We are such a big family.'

'The happiest in London, I trow, Margaret. It was a good day for me when I joined it.'

'Father would be pleased to hear you say that.'

'I should not need to say it. I'll swear he knows it.'

''Tis pleasant for me to hear you say it, Will.'

'Margaret . . . tell me this . . . how do you feel about me?'

'Feel about you? Oh . . . I am glad that you are with us, if that is what you mean.'

'I do, Margaret. Those words make me very happy . . . happier than if anyone else in the world had said them.'

She was astonished, and he went on quickly: 'You are a strange girl, Margaret. I confess you alarm me a little. You must know more Greek and Latin than any other girl in England.'

She was silent, thinking of Ailie, in a new blue gown, exclaiming at her as she sat over her books: 'Latin . . . Greek . . . Astronomy . . . Mathematics. . . . There is more to be learned from life, Mistress Margaret, than you can find in those books!'

Ailie was right. Ailie had been born with that special knowledge.

'Margaret,' went on Will, 'I . . . I am not so alarmed by you as I once was, for there are times when you seem to me like a very young girl.' He turned to her smiling. 'You know what my feelings are for you, Margaret?'

'Why yes, Will. You like me . . . you like Father . . . you like us all.'

'But I like you better than any of them.'

'Not better than Father!'

'Oh, sweet Meg, one of the things I love so much in you is your love for your father. I admire him more than any man I know; but Margaret–do not be shocked–I admire his daughter more.'

She laughed to hide her embarrassment. 'That sounds like one of Father's puns.'

'I must tell it to him.'

'Nay, if you do . . . he will know . . .'

'Oh, Meg, dost think he does not know already?'

'But . . . why should he?'

'I think I must have made my feelings clear to all except you, so it is high time that you began to understand me. Margaret, I want you to marry me.'

'But . . . I am not going to marry.'

'You are young yet. I doubt your father would think it seemly for us to marry for a while. But you are fourteen. . . . Perhaps in a year or so . . .'

'But, Will, I had decided I should never marry. And you have disturbed me. It seems now that I shall not be able to think of you as I do of the others, like John Clement and Giles Allington.'

'But I do not wish you to think of me as you think of them. Oh, Margaret, you have not grown up yet. You have been so busy being a scholar that you have not yet become a woman. You could be both. That is what I wish, Meg: for you to be both. Say no more now. Think of this matter–but not too much so that it oppresses you. Become accustomed to the idea of marriage. Think of it, Meg. It is not that I wish to take you from your father. I do not. I would never take you from him, because I have seen that love which is between you, and it is a rare love. I know that. Nay. I am sure he would wish us to live under this roof . . . here as we do now. You would be my wife. That would be the only difference. I beg of you, think of this matter. Promise me you will think of it, Margaret.'

'I . . . I will. . . . But . . . I do not think I shall want to marry.'

They walked back to the house slowly and thoughtfully.

The year 1521 provided a turning-point in the lives of Margaret and her father.

Thomas was drawn more and more into Court business. To Margaret, from whom he hid nothing, he said: 'I feel like a fly in a web. Mayhap at one time I might have made a mighty effort . . . I might have escaped . . . but now the sticky threads hold me fast.'

'But the King is fond of you. He and the Cardinal find you useful.'

'You are right, Margaret, and I will say to you what I would say to no other: Both the King and the Cardinal are only fond of those who can be useful to them, and only so long as they are useful. A man can grow out of his usefulness.'

There was one matter which shocked Thomas deeply. It concerned both King and Cardinal, and taught him much concerning these men; yet when he looked back he realized that it had taught him little that he had not known before–rather it had confirmed his opinion.

The Cardinal had drawn closer to Thomas in those years during which they worked together. To Thomas he was sometimes frank, and when he was sure they were quite alone he would discuss the King in such a manner that, if it were known, might have cost him his head. Such was the measure of his trust in Thomas.

There was in the Cardinal an overweening pride. He believed himself indispensable to the King; and indeed it seemed that this might be so. The King made few decisions without his chief minister beside him. The King was content to amuse himself, knowing that matters of state rested in the capable hands of Thomas Wolsey.

There was no one–apart from the King and Lady Tailbois–who, in the first place, had been more delighted than the Cardinal when the King's natural son had been born to that lady. This had happened some four years ago, a year after the birth of the Princess Mary.

Now, in the year 1521, when the Queen had failed to give the King a son to follow Mary, the Cardinal was faintly disturbed by the affair and he opened his heart to Thomas.

'Why, Master More, when the boy was born, His Grace was like a child with the finest toy that has ever been given to him. He had a son–and for years he had been longing for a son. The Queen's abortive attempts at child-bearing have worried him considerably, for, as you know, he sets great store upon his manhood; and although it is His Grace's custom to blame his partner in an adventure if blame should be necessary, there has been in him a slight fear that he may not be able to get him a son. Elizabeth Blount–or Lady Tailbois, if you wish–has proved him capable of getting a son; and little Henry Fitzroy is the apple of his eye. I was delighted in His Grace's delight. But the years have passed and there is still no male heir to the throne–nor even another girl. Master More, the King is restive, and the Queen does not grow younger. If she were not such a great Princess, and if I did not fear to offend the Spaniards I would suggest the marriage should be dissolved and another Princess found for him–one who could give him sons as Elizabeth Blount has shown that she can do.'

'But there could be no honourable reason for dissolving the marriage,' argued Thomas. 'The Queen is the most virtuous of ladies and . . . she is not past bearing children.'

'You have a fondness for Her Grace, I know; and she favours you. I, myself, have the utmost respect for the lady. But a Queen's piety is one thing, her usefulness to her King and country another. The main object of a royal marriage is to get heirs, and that she has not done with any marked success.'

'These matters are surely in the hands of God.'

The Cardinal smiled his slow, cynical smile. 'My friend, if God is slow to act, then it is sometimes necessary for a King's ministers to act without Him. Ah, would the lady had not such powerful relatives! Imagine . . . a new Queen. A French princess or a protégée of the Emperor Charles of Spain? Think what I could do . . . keeping them in suspense . . . having them both in fear that I should ally England with the other. A French princess, I think, would at this time hold the balance of power to greater advantage.'

'My lord Cardinal,' said Thomas, 'the gown you wear proclaims you to be a man of God, but the words you speak . . .'

But Wolsey interrupted: 'The words I speak betray me as the Lord Chancellor, the Prime Minister of England. I serve England, which I believe it is my duty to do.'

Nay, thought Thomas, you serve neither God nor England; you serve Thomas Wolsey.

Yet Thomas More understood Thomas Wolsey; he understood that the humble scholar, the tradesman's son, finding himself possessed of a quick brain and great wisdom, together with a quality which could charm a King, could not but rejoice in these possessions. Wolsey was not, by nature, a bad man, but a man made bad by an overwhelming ambition; he was a man who enjoyed his wealth and delighted in it the more because he had earned it.

It was all very well for such as Norfolk, Suffolk or Buckingham lightly to assume the honours which they had inherited by their birth; but the man who had inherited no such glory, who by his quick and clever cunning had created honours for himself, naturally prized them the more highly. And how great Wolsey's pride must have been when he considered those noblemen, and could reasonably believe that had they been born the sons of Ipswich merchants, they would doubtless have remained Ipswich merchants for the whole of their lives.

Nay, Wolsey was not entirely bad, for he was kind to his servants and they loved him. All he asked of them was that they should pay homage to his greatness; then he would be the benevolent father to them, caring for them, feeding them and, in his way, loving them.

He had illegitimate children. Not that he was a sensual man. His union with the woman of his choice would seem to lack nothing but regularity. He did not consort with women promiscuously; there was only one woman. As he had decided to use the Church as his ladder to fame, he was denied marriage; therefore he dispensed with the marriage ceremony; but, being a normal man, he did not intend to dispense with all that marriage would have brought him. So he had settled into a quiet and steady relationship which, but for the facts that there had been no ceremony and he was a priest, would not have seemed different from the marriage of Thomas More himself.

He loved his children, but his love took a different form from that of Thomas; and yet Thomas saw that in some ways it was similar. Thomas wished to give his children that which he most treasured; Wolsey wished to shower on his children what he most treasured in the world–power and riches. His son, who was still a boy, was already Dean of Wells and Archbishop of York and Richmond, and thus the possessor of much wealth and power in his own right.

Not a bad man, but a man who worshipped, according to Thomas, false gods. But as Thomas told himself this he knew that Wolsey would say of him: A clever fellow, but a fool in some ways, for he seems to have no idea how to advance his fortune.

Now Wolsey talked of state affairs and how it would be a simple matter to get the King's approbation of his plans. The King was immersed in a new love affair–a saucy girl had taken his attention and made big demands upon it.

'The daughter of Thomas Boleyn. Doubtless you know him. Well, Master Boleyn will enjoy some favour, I doubt not, when his pretty daughter Mary whispers her requests into the King's ear. He found the girl when we went to France last year. She has pleased him ever since. We shall see the brother's advancement too. George Boleyn is a bright boy. It must be his Norfolk blood–at least, I doubt not Norfolk would tell us so. I believe there is a younger girl . . . in France just now. We must watch this family, for a man like Thomas Boleyn will give himself airs if favoured too highly. If little Mary becomes too demanding we shall have to find another lady for His Grace. Ah, Master More, you like not this talk. You would have the King's household like your own in Bucklersbury. But there are few families like yours in the kingdom. That is why I must take such pains to enlighten you.'

This sign of the Cardinal's favour would have delighted most men; it made Thomas uneasy; it meant that he was in danger of being more closely entangled in that from which he longed to escape.

He was disappointed in the young King. Henry seemed bent on pleasure, and much of that treasure which had been left by his father had already been squandered–not only on war, but on futile displays like this last one of the Field of the Cloth of Gold.

What useful purpose had been served? It was known now that England could squander wealth to glorify the King and his Court; and that France could do the same for its gay young King. But what of that? Both these monarchs were developing into lechers whose minds could be continuously occupied with devising new sensations in amorous adventurings, rather than in studying a wise state policy.

England had Wolsey; and all Englishmen should be glad of that, because with all his pride, with all his ambition and his love of pomp, Wolsey was a great statesman.

Yet how he was hated by some! It was largely due to Wolsey's carelessly expressed hatred of the Duke of Buckingham that Thomas became aware of new and terrible elements about him.

It was Buckingham's duty at this time to hold the gold bowl in which the King washed his hands; and on one occasion–doubtless to avenge a slight which either Buckingham had given Wolsey, or Wolsey imagined he had, and to show his intimacy with the King–when Henry had washed his hands, Wolsey dipped his own into the bowl and proceeded to wash them.

This was more than the noble Duke could endure, for he could never forget that royal blood ran in his veins and that he was related to Edward the Fourth. That he should be expected to hold the bowl while the son of an Ipswich merchant washed his hands was intolerable. He immediately threw the water over Wolsey's feet.

The King might be amused at this incident and Wolsey might appear to take it lightly, but Buckingham had offended that great pride of the Cardinal's, and no man could do that with impunity.

Now Thomas witnessed the beginning of that terrible feud which could only end in tragedy.

Buckingham had forgotten two things when he made an enemy of the Cardinal. He was in a dangerous position, for his royal blood was something Henry had never liked; he also possessed great wealth, which Henry liked very much. He was one of the richest peers in England.

It was therefore a simple matter for the Cardinal to murmur a few well-chosen words into the royal ear. The King could be reminded that were Buckingham executed on a capital charge, his wealth would become the property of the King; moreover, Buckingham had boasted of his royal blood, and it was not difficult to find someone who had heard the haughty Duke's statement that if the King died without heirs he, Buckingham, would be very near the throne.

The Duke was summoned by the King, and came to Court thinking that he was to be asked to take part in some jousting or jollity. He found himself in the Tower, tried by his peers–none of whom dared find him anything but guilty, since this was the will of the King. Old Norfolk, his friend, must find him guilty, though he shed tears as he did so.

The murder of the Duke shocked England and the Continent as well as Thomas More. It showed what manner of King was this fair-faced boy on whom the marks of lechery and good living had not yet appeared. The handsome boy was exposed as a cruel boy; bluff King Hal had set out on his career of royal murder, to which the deaths of Empson and Dudley were but a prelude.

Thomas now longed more than ever for the solitude of his home, for converse with his friends. Erasmus had written to him: 'So you have deserted the scholars for the sake of the Court. Our learned philosopher has become a courtier.'

'Yes,' muttered Thomas; 'but most reluctantly.'

There had been a time when it had been said among scholars that the three most learned men in the world were Erasmus of the Netherlands, More of England, and Budé of France; but now More's name was no longer mentioned in this connection. A young Spaniard, Vives, had taken his place.

Yet those in the King's Court knew nothing of that lost eminence which had meant so much to Thomas. They saw him about the Court, and they knew him as a man destined for greatness.

'Thomas More is rising in the world,' they said.

He could not tell them that he did not wish to rise in their world, but to continue to shine in his own.

Meanwhile Martin Luther had published his book, which he had called *Babylonish Captivity of the Church.* The Pope was up in arms and Europe was divided. The Cardinal had another secret conversation with Thomas More.

'His Grace has been expressing much interest in you of late, Master More.'

'Indeed? And for what reason?'

'There are two people in the world whom he hates, fears and envies, while he most jealously observes them. Doubtless you know to whom I refer?'

'The rulers across the water?'

'You are right. The mighty Emperor Charles, who rules other lands besides his native Spain, is one. And perhaps, more than the King hates Charles, he hates the King of France. They know each other well; they are of an age; they are both seekers after pleasure and sensation. Charles and Francis are servants of the Pope. Charles is the Most Catholic King; and Francis is the Most Christian King. Our King has no title to set beside those two, and that grieves him. He feels that this is a matter on which you, more than any other man, can help him.'

'I?'

The Cardinal laid his hand on Thomas's shoulder. 'You underestimate yourelf. Go now to His Grace. He would have speech with you. Be not too modest. Luck favours you. Go in . . . and win your honours.'

It was with disturbed thoughts that Thomas made his way to the royal apartments.

When Thomas entered the King's audience chamber it was to find him with those three friends and statesmen, the Duke of Norfolk, the Duke's son the Earl of Surrey, and Henry's brother-in-law the Duke of Suffolk.

This, Thomas realized, was honour indeed, to be received in such company. Here was the King, familiarly talking with his friends, and smiling to receive Thomas More among them; but as he knelt before the King, Thomas was aware of the speculating eyes of the three noblemen.

All were well known to him.

Suffolk was not only the King's brother-in-law, but his greatest friend; a dashing handsome fellow, he had accompanied Henry's sister Mary to France when she had married old Louis, and when, after a few months of life with the vital young Mary, the French King had died, Suffolk had, with great daring, married her before their return to England. But Henry had forgiven that rashness long ago.

The old Duke of Norfolk, Lord Treasurer and Knight of the Garter, was a sturdy old warrior, proud head of one of the noblest families in the country, and was still reaping the rewards of his victory at Flodden Field.

His son, Surrey, slightly older than Thomas, was a gallant soldier, shrewd and high in the favour of the King in spite of the fact that his wife was the daughter of the recently murdered Duke of Buckingham. The King was amused by Surrey at this time, and he liked those who amused him. Surrey–the grim, stern soldier–had become enamoured of his wife's laundress, and there was much ribald comment throughout the Court concerning Surrey and Bess Holland.

'Ha,' cried the King. 'Here comes Master More to join us. We were talking of this madman Luther, Master More. You have seen this new outrage of his, I doubt not?'

'I have, Your Grace.'

'By God, I have a mind to answer him with my own pen. Now, you are a master of words, and it is on this matter that I wished to speak to you.'

'Your Grace honours me.'

'We have read some of your writings and found merit in them. We are giving orders that this evil composition of the German monk's shall be publicly burned in St Paul's Churchyard. We are instructing Bishop Fisher to preach a sermon against him. Master More, this man is an agent of the devil. Now . . . my friends, leave us. I would speak alone with our friend here on literary matters.'

The three noblemen retired, and the King smiled at Thomas.

'Now, my friend, we can get down to work. Since I read this . . . this . . . what shall I call it? . . . this evil document . . . I have felt an anger burning within me. I hear the voice of God urging me to act. This cannot go unanswered, Master More; and it needs one to answer it whose writing will astonish the world. Who better than the King of England?'

'Your Grace has written this book?'

'Not yet . . . not yet. I have made my notes . . . notes of what I wish to say. They shall go ringing round Europe. If I had the fellow here in my kingdom he should suffer the traitor's death. But he is not here. I cannot chastise his body, so I will answer him with words. I will show you what I shall call my *Assertion of the Seven Sacraments*, and you will see that what I intend to do is to answer this monstrous piece of writing of this villainous monk. Now, come hither. This is what I have prepared.'

Thomas took the notes which were handed to him. 'And my duty, Your Grace?'

Henry waved a hand. 'Well . . . you will arrange them . . . and set them into a form that . . . you know of. You are a man of letters. You will see what has to be done. I am a King. I have my affairs of state to attend to, but I have written the core of the thing. You will . . .' The King waved his hands in an expansive gesture. 'But you know what is your task, Master More. To make this into a book. I have chosen you out of my regard for you.'

'Your Grace is determined to honour me.'

'As I am always ready to honour those who please me . . . whose learning adds lustre to this realm. Now, Master More, your duties from now on will be undertaken in my small antechamber, to which I shall now conduct you. You shall have everything you require, and I should like the task completed with all expediency. Spare not the evil-doer. We will talk to the world . . . even as he has. And we will speak in literary language, Master More; for they tell me you are a master of such language. You are excused all other duties. My friend, do this task well and you will be rewarded. Ah, it pleases you?'

'Your Grace could not have given me a task which delights me so much. To have a pen in my hand once more and on such a composition! It is something which I have wanted for a long time.'

The King's hand came down on his shoulder; it was a heavy blow, but its very heaviness expressed not only approval, but affection. The eyes were shining with pleasure; the cheeks were flushed.

'Come, Master More. This way.'

The King threw open the door of a small room which was richly carpeted and hung with exquisitely-worked tapestry.

When Thomas saw the young woman, she was on the window-seat in an ungainly attitude, her legs tucked under her skirt. Her bodice was low-cut and her dark hair fell about her bare shoulders. What astonished him in that half-second was that she did not rise when the King entered, but threw him a saucy smile.

The King stopped and stared at her. Then she must have become aware of the fact that he was not alone. She jumped to her feet and fell on her knees.

'What do you here, girl?' demanded the King.

'I crave Your Grace's pardon. I . . . but . . . I thought . . . Your Grace desired my presence here.'

'Get up,' said the King.

She rose, and Thomas recognized her as Mary Boleyn, the King's mistress. Her gaze was almost defiant as she looked at Thomas. There was in that look a certainty that the King's displeasure could not last.

'You have our leave to retire,' said the King.

She curtsied and took two or three steps backward to the door.

Thomas noticed how the King watched her, his mouth slackening, his eyes a brighter blue.

'Come in, come in, man,' he said almost testily. 'Ah, there is where you may sit. Now, look you, these notes are to be made into a great book. You understand me? A great book! You know how to write books. Well, that is what you must do for me.'

The King's attention was straying, Thomas knew; his thoughts had left the room with that dark-haired girl.

Henry said: 'If there is anything you want, ask for it. Start now. See what you can do with these notes . . . and later . . . when you have something ready, you may bring it to me.'

The King was smiling. His mood had changed; he was already away with the girl who had just left.

'Do your work well, Master More. You will not regret it. I like to reward those who please me. . . .'

The King went out, and Thomas sat down to look at the notes.

He found it difficult to concentrate. He thought of the King and the dark-eyed girl; he thought of Surrey and Bess Holland; he thought of the sharp eyes of Suffolk, the wily ones of old Norfolk, and of Thomas Wolsey, who was cleverer than any of them.

And he longed, as he had never longed before, for the peace of his home.

Adjusting the King's notes was a pleasant task, except that it kept him more than ever away from his family. Many times he had been on the point of slipping home to Bucklersbury when a messenger had come to tell him that the King was asking why he was not in his presence.

Henry liked him. He liked the way in which the work was shaping. He read it and re-read it; and he glowed with pride.

'Ah,' he would cry, 'here's the answer to Master Luther. Read it, Kate.'

The Queen would read, and she also was delighted, for she hated the German monk even more than Henry did.

'Would I had him here . . . that German monk!' the King would cry. 'He should die . . . die for the insults he has heaped upon my mother. For my mother is the Church. Ha, Kate, you will see what we shall do with this trumpeter of prides, calumnies and schisms. He is a member of the Devil. He is a low-liver. Mark my words on that. Only the immoral could lose the faith of their fathers in such a way. We are bound to the See of Rome. We could not honour it too much. Anything we could do would not be too great. I swear it.'

'Your Grace will forgive me,' interjected Thomas, 'but those words you have uttered would, in a court of law, be called maintaining papal jurisdiction in England.'

'What's that? What's that?' cried Henry.

'I was thinking, my lord King, of the Statute of Praemunire.'

'Ha!' laughed the King. 'Here's a lawyer for us, Kate. A writ issued against a King in his own realm, eh? Ha, Thomas More, they are right to call you an honest man. You do well to speak thus before your King. He likes you for it. But I say this: So do I love the Papacy that I would hold nothing back to defend it. Remember, Master More, from that See we receive our Crown Imperial.'

'I must put Your Highness in remembrance of one thing,' said Thomas. 'The Pope, as Your Grace knows, is a Prince, as you are yourself, and is in league with other princes. It could fall out that Your Grace and His Holiness may at some time vary in your opinions. I think therefore that his authority might be more lightly touched upon in the book.'

'But I tell you, Master More, so are we bound to the See of Rome that we could not do too much to honour it.'

'Then it is my bounden duty to remind Your Grace again of the Statute of Praemunire.'

'Have no fear, Master More. Have no fear. We know well how to look to these matters. And continue with us as you always have been. We like your honesty.'

And as the book progressed, so did the friendship between Thomas and the King and Queen. He must sup at the King's table; he must walk with the King on the terraces; and he must linger at the Palace until darkness fell, for the Queen had heard that he knew as much of the spheres that moved in the heavens as any man at Court; and the Queen wished him to instruct her.

'The King himself would like to be there at the instruction,' said Henry. 'For while governing this kingdom here on Earth, he would like to learn something of the kingdom of the skies.'

So in the evenings Thomas would be on the balconies of the Palace, the Queen on his left hand, the King on his right, the courtiers ranged about them while he pointed out the constellations to the watching group.

'How the King favours this man!' said the courtiers. 'He is next to the Cardinal himself in the King's favour.'

They would note the Queen's smile as she pointed out how brilliant Orion was that night, and humbly asked if she was right in assuming that the two brilliant points of light in the western sky were the twins, Castor and Pollux, and was that Procyon down in the west-south-west?

They would hear the loud, booming laughter of the King as he declared that the constellation called Cassiopeia did not to him look in the least like a lady in a chair; they would notice how many times the glittering hand would come down upon the sombrely-clad shoulder of Thomas More.

'The King seems more interested in the Pleiades than in Mary Boleyn!' it was whispered among the ladies who watched such matters, for many of them hoped that one day the royal eyes would be turned from Mary Boleyn towards them.

When the book was finished, and such learned men as Fisher, Stephen Gardiner and Wolsey himself had studied it and declared it to be of sound good sense in perfect literary style, the King was so pleased that he said he would have no more of Master More in attendance; in future, it should be *Sir* Thomas More.

Henry the King was deeply gratified. The book was acclaimed throughout Europe by all those who stood against Martin Luther. It was hailed now as a work of genius. The Pope was delighted with his English champion, but he demurred a little at bestowing the title asked for; he had to consider the wrath and jealousy of Francis and Charles, of whom he lived in perpetual fear. But eventually Henry's bribes and offers of friendship prevailed, and the King of England was known throughout the Catholic world as 'Defender of the Faith'.

But Martin Luther was not the man to ignore the publication of the book; he poured scorn on it and the King of England at the same time. Henry nominated Sir Thomas More to answer Luther in the name of the King of England.

Thomas had not only his title; he was now made Under-Treasurer of the Exchequer–Norfolk himself was the Treasurer–and so had become an important member of the King's Council. Thus did the man in the hair-shirt become one of these ministers in constant attendance upon the King.

Luther wrote scurrilous attacks on Henry; Thomas replied with equally scurrilous attacks on the German monk. And Margaret, reading those replies which her father was writing in the name of the King, would often feel depressed and uneasy. It seemed to her that she had lost the father she had once known. The gentle, courteous man had become a master of invective. It made Margaret shudder to read: 'Reverend brother, father, tippler, Luther, runagate of the order of St Augustine, misshapen bacchanal of either faculty, unlearned doctor of theology . . .' How could her gentle father have written such words? How could he have gone on to say that Luther had called his companions together and desired them to go each his own way and pick up all sorts of abuse and scurrility–one to the gambling houses, another to the taverns and barbers' shops, another to the brothels?

What is the Court doing to my father? she asked herself.

When he came home she saw the change in him. There was a fierceness of manner about him. She knew that the hair-shirt, which she still washed for him, was worn more frequently; she knew that he used a piece of wood for his pillow, so that he might not find easy sleep. There was a new emotion in his life which had never been there before; it was hatred for the heretics.

She had to talk to him.

'Father,' she said, 'you have changed.'

'Nay, daughter, I am the same as ever.'

'I do not altogether understand,' she said, 'for you and Erasmus at one time would talk of the wickedness in the monasteries. You planned to set certain matters right in the Church. This Martin Luther . . . does he not think as once you and Erasmus did?'

She thought of Erasmus, essentially a scholar. Now that the work he had started had been taken up by another, he wanted none of it; he would retire to his scholar's desk, to the life of reflection, not of action. Margaret felt that that was the life her father should have chosen. But the King had forced him to the forefront of the fight, and it was the King's battle; he was using words which the King would have used. If he had been any other man she would have believed he did so in order to curry favour.

'A change has been wrought in these affairs, Meg,' he said. 'Erasmus and I once sought to set right what was wrong. This monk seeks to destroy the Church and to set up in its place another which is founded on heresy.'

'But those words you have written of him . . . I . . . I could not believe that you had written them.'

'I have written them, Meg. Doubt not that. As I see it, we have to fight a greater evil, in those who would *destroy* the Church, than we had when he fought those who only abused it. Meg, the Church still stands . . . the Holy Catholic Church. To destroy it would bring horror to the world. Evil would break its bounds. At all costs the Church must be upheld. Oh yes, let us have evil driven from the monasteries, let us have a stricter rule for our priests if we must . . . but those who seek to destroy the Church must be themselves destroyed, for if we allow them to destroy the Church, then evil will prevail.'

'But this monk, Father . . . can you really call him a heathen?'

'I can, Meg, and I do.'

'Yet he claims to be a man of God. It is not God whom he reviles; it is the Church of Rome.'

'But the Church of Rome is the Church of our fathers. You know that, Meg.'

She looked at him and thought: For the first time in my life I doubt his wisdom. I have never known this ferocity in him before. I have never before known him show such anger as he does towards these heretics.

'Father,' she said uneasily, 'the King has said that if this heathen –meaning the monk Luther–does not recant, he should be burnt alive. Burnt alive, Father! *You* cannot believe that that should be done! You used to say that we should be kind to others, treat them as we ourselves would be treated.'

'Meg, if your right hand was evil, if it was touched with a poison that would infect the rest of your body, would you not cut it off?'

She was silent, but he insisted on an answer. 'Yes, Father.'

'Well, then. The suffering of the body is as naught to the eternal damnation of the soul. If, by setting the flames at the feet of this monk Luther, we could restore his soul to God, then would it not be well to burn him alive?'

'I do not know.'

'Meg, it is a glorious thing to subdue the flesh, to become indifferent to pain. What happens to these bodies cannot be of great importance. And if those who deny God are to suffer eternal damnation, what can a few minutes in the fire mean to them?'

Margaret covered her face with her hands. I have lost a part of him, she thought.

He drew her hands from her face and smiled at her; all the gentleness was back in his eyes.

She saw that he was tired, that he longed to escape from the life at Court, to retire to the quietness and peace of family life.

It was a strange revelation to find that she did not entirely agree with him. Yet how she loved him! Even more, now that she believed she had detected a certain weakness in him, than she had when she had loved him for all his strength.

She almost wished that he had not educated her so thoroughly, that he had not trained her mind to be so logical. She wished that she could have gone on seeing him as perfect.

He was begging her to return to the old relationship. He wanted to laugh and be gay.

'Now you have talked to me, Margaret,' he said. 'You have examined me with many questions, and you look at me quizzically, and you are turning over in your mind what I have said, and you doubt the wisdom of my words. Very well, my Meg. We will talk of this later. Now I have something to say to you. Can you guess what it is?'

'No, Father.'

'Well then, it is about Will.'

'Will Roper?'

'Who else? Do you not like him a little, Meg?'

She blushed, and he smiled to see her blush. 'I like him, Father.'

'He loves you dearly. He has told me so.'

'I would rather he did not burden you with his foolish feelings.'

'Is it foolish to love you? Then, Meg, I must be the most foolish man on Earth.'

''Tis different with us. You are my father, and it is natural that you and I should love.'

''Tis natural that Will should also. He is good. I like him. I like him very much. There is no one I would rather see as your husband, Meg. For although he may not be as rich or handsome as our gay young Allington, although he may not make a lady or a duchess of you one day . . . he is none the worse for that.'

'Do you think I should care to be a lady or a duchess, Father? I am not like your wife, who has been so proud since she has become Lady More.'

He laughed. 'Leave her her pleasures, Meg. They are small ones, and we understand her delight in them, do we not? But to return to Will: you are fond of him, I know.'

'As I am of the others. To me he is no more than . . . any of them.'

'But, Meg, he is personable and clever . . . a pleasant boy. What do you look for in a man?'

'He seems to me to be over-young.'

'He is seven years your senior.'

'Still, he seems young. He lacks seriousness. He is no great scholar. If he had written something like *Utopia* . . . something that showed his ideals and . . . Oh, you have set us a high standard, Father. Your daughter measures all men against *you*, which means that she finds them sadly lacking.'

He laughed those words to scorn, but he could not help showing his pleasure.

Now he was himself again, full of laughter, enjoying every moment. This evening they would be together . . . all of them; they would converse in Latin as they were wont to do; and Alice would chide them, but only mildly. Her title, to her, was a bright bauble. They all smiled to see her face when the servants addressed her as 'My Lady.'

It was good to have him back, to forget his fierceness against heretics, to sing and be gay as in the old days.

Perhaps there is always something good in what seems to be evil, thought Margaret. She longed for the days when her father had been a humble lawyer and Under-Sheriff of the City; she remembered with a tender pain the walks through the City; but this was not the case with all the members of the family.

Ailie was bright-eyed with happiness as she came into the schoolroom where Margaret sat with her books.

How lovely she is! thought Margaret. And more beautiful now that she is a member of this distinguished family than she was in the days of our humility.

Ailie pulled off the net which held back her golden hair from her face. That beautiful hair now fell about her shoulders and down to her waist.

'Such news, Meg! I am to be married. My Lady Allington! What do you think of that?'

'So Giles is to be your husband?'

'I shall be the first in the family to find one.'

'That does not really surprise us.'

'To tell the truth, Meg, it does not surprise me. Giles says what a good thing it is that Father has written this book with the King and become such an important person at Court. His father could not withhold his consent to a union with the stepdaughter of Sir Thomas More. Oh Meg, is it not a marvellous thing . . . what great happenings are set in motion by such little things? A mere book is written and *I* become Lady Allington!'

Margaret laughed. There was that in Ailie which amused her as it did her father. Perhaps Ailie was selfish because she saw herself as the centre of the world, but it was a charming little world, and Ailie herself was so pretty and pleasant in her ways that it was impossible not to love her.

'Ailie, you will go away from us, for Giles will not live here.'

'He will certainly have his estates to attend to. But, depend upon it, I shall insist on many visits to my darling family.'

'Then I doubt not that there will *be* many visits, for I believe you will have your way as Lady Allington just as you have as Alice Middleton.'

'So do not fret, dearest Meg. We shall be together often. I shall bring you tales of the great world. I shall tell you what the ladies are wearing and what new dances are being danced . . . and all Court matters which Father never notices. Meg, it will be your turn next . . . yours or Mercy's. I wonder who will first find a husband.'

Margaret turned away, but Ailie was looking at her slyly.

'There is Master Clement who comes here so often. Have you noticed how he looks first for Mercy? It would not greatly surprise me if our solemn Mercy told us she was to be Mistress Clement one day.'

'Mercy is too interested in her studies to think of aught else.'

Ailie laughed. 'John Clement *and* her studies both interest Mercy very much. There they sit, heads close together, talking of drugs and disease. Sometimes when I see them I think I shall die of laughter. I do indeed, Meg. I say to Giles: "You talk of my beauty . . . of my charming ways . . . and that is by far the best way of courtship. But there are other ways, I have discovered, for I live in a strange household. Some lovers exchange recipes and talk of the internal organs of the sick instead of the eyelashes of the loved one."'

'Ailie, have done with such frivolous gossip.'

'I will not. For 'tis a strange thing, Meg that, when a girl has found a husband, she is anxious for all her friends to do the same. However solemn, however learned they may be, I want them to be married as I shall be.' Ailie began to dance a stately measure with an imaginary partner, tossing back her hair, smiling coquettishly into the face she saw in her imagination. 'This is the newest Court dance, Meg. Giles taught it to me. Oh, how I long to be at Court, to dance in the great halls while the King's minstrels play in the gallery. I shall have rich gowns, Meg, and Jewels. . . . I shall be the happiest girl in the whole world . . . and all because Father has won the King's regard; for Meg, had he not done so, I do not think Giles's father would have readily given his consent to our marriage.'

'You think of nothing but yourself, Ailie. Might not father rather be at home as he used to be?'

'How could he prefer that! Giles says that the King is as fond of him as he is of Master Wolsey . . . and mayhap more . . . for while the Cardinal makes great efforts to please the King, Father does it without effort; while the Cardinal has to be a worshipper of the King, Father has but to be himself. Nay, we are going up, Meg. Up and up. Father will win more honours yet, and there are many who will be ready–nay, eager–to wed his daughters. But some of these, I vow, look not farther than their own home.'

Ailie was looking at Margaret slyly, and Margaret said: 'Enough of this. Is it not your turn to be housekeeper this week, and have you not your duties to perform?'

'Lady More will not be hard on the future Lady Allington. So rest in peace, dear Meg. I'll swear Will Roper is a pleasant fellow, but now that our fortunes are rising, do not be rash, Meg.'

'I do not understand you.'

'What? Have you then become a fool? You . . . the cleverest of your father's daughters! Listen to me, Margaret: if you do not look to Will Roper, then he looks to you.'

Margaret packed up her books and set them on a shelf; her cheeks were burning.

'You are making a mistake, Ailie,' she said, 'when you think that everyone shares your desires for the married state.'

That made Ailie laugh, and she went on laughing as Margaret, in most dignified manner, walked out of the room.

Now she must continually think of Will Roper. When, during mealtimes, she lifted her eyes, she would invariably find Will's upon her. While she studied she would find thoughts of Will coming between her and her work.

It was disturbing.

Then she noticed a change in Will. Often when she looked up she would find him staring into space, and if she caught his eye suddenly, he would start and smile at her; and she would know that his thoughts had been occupied with matters which did not concern her.

He would spend a long time alone and seemed to find great pleasure in his own company.

He has changed his mind, thought Margaret. He does not wish to marry me after all. Can it be that his fancy has turned to someone else?

She was astonished by her feelings. Could it be that, not desiring marriage with Will, she desired him to marry no other? She began to think of what the house would be like if he left it. Her father was away so much; how would it be if Will were not there at all?

Her father . . . and Will! She had come to think of them together. She realized how pleased she had always been when her father spoke well of Will.

One day, when she was alone in the schoolroom, Will came in. He carried a book under his arm. She thought it was a law book until she saw that it was the Greek Testament of Erasmus.

'Oh, Margaret, I am glad to find you alone,' he said. 'I want to talk to you. No, don't be alarmed. . . . It is not about marriage. It is another matter which gives me much concern.'

'Please tell me, if it is on your mind, Will. I have seen that something has bothered you of late.'

'I do not know how you will receive this news, Margaret. I have been reading this Testament, and I have pondered on what I have read. I have also read *Babylonish Captivity of the Church*, and I have come to this conclusion, Meg: there is no truth other than this which comes out of Germany.'

'*Will!*'

'I know. You are alarmed. You will hate me now. Your father has expressed his views strongly . . . and your views, of a surety, are his views on this matter. I had to tell you. I do not believe that Martin Luther is a bad man. I believe he is honest and God-fearing. I believe he seeks a better way of life for the world, and, Margaret, I believe that he, and he alone, has fallen upon the truth.'

Margaret stared at him; his eyes were bright and his cheeks flushed; he looked quite unlike the mild law-student whom she had known for the last three years. He looked resolute and noble.

She thought: He knows that this confession of his may mean that he will be banished from the house, and yet he makes it. He knows that it will turn Father from him, and yet he makes it. He knows that Father is one of the brightest stars at the Court, and he knows that heretics are punished in this land. Yet he comes to me and says he will become a Lutheran.

Oh, Will, she thought, you fool . . . you *fool*!

But she was moved by his courage, even though it was inspired by what her loyalty to her father insisted must be his wrong thinking.

She began to repeat her father's arguments, to prevent her thoughts running she knew not whither.

'The man is trying to tear the Church asunder.'

'What of Erasmus? What of your father in the days when they were writing *In Praise of Folly* and *Utopia*?'

She said: 'They exposed certain evils in the Church. They wished these matters to be righted. This man Luther defies the Holy Pope and the whole Church. He would set up a new Church in its place.'

'But, Meg, if that were the true Church . . . is it not a good thing to set it up in place of the false one?'

'You would then deny the faith of your fathers?'

'I want a simpler way of worshipping God. I want to examine the Scriptures more carefully. I do not want to say, "My fathers thought this, therefore must I think it." I have thought much of Martin Luther, Meg.

Can *you* deny that he is a great man? Think of him–the son of poor parents, thrown upon the world at an early age, begging his bread and studying . . . always studying. Meg, he reminds me of your father, for like him he studied the law, and like him he went into a monastery. And while he was there, he found much that was evil, and he determined to fight it with all his might. Margaret, think. These Indulgences against which he rails–are they good? I ask you: Can people buy, with money, forgiveness in Heaven? Picture him on that October day in Wittenberg . . . so boldly marching up to the church door and there nailing upon it his theses. He knew of the danger he was in. He knew that the whole Catholic world was against him. But he cared not, Meg, because he knew that what he did was right. He is a great man; he is a man of genius; he is a *good* man whose teaching I would follow.'

Margaret was deeply moved. There was so much truth in what Will said. She had rarely in her life been so grieved as when across Europe abuse had been flung by this monk of Germany, and by her father in the name of the King. What a terrible thing it was when two good men, because they could not agree on certain points, must forget courtesy and good manners, and fling insults at one another!

She said sternly: 'I do not know what Father will do when he hears of this.'

'Nor I, Meg.'

'He would not wish to harbour a heretic under his roof.'

'That is so. Margaret, I love you. It is for that reason that I could be silent no longer. I could not continue with you under false pretences. Nor can I govern my thoughts. I trust you will understand me. Speak to me, Margaret. Tell me that you will try to understand how I have fought these thoughts.'

'You . . . you should not fight them. All thoughts should be examined.'

'Margaret . . . you . . . you will tell your father now, I know. Then I shall go away from here. That is something I cannot endure. . . .'

He had turned to her, but she ran from him, out of the schoolroom.

How thankful she was that it was daytime and there was no one else in the bedroom. She lay on the bed which she shared with Cecily, and drew the curtains . . . shutting out the house . . . shutting out everything but her thoughts.

Will . . . a heretic! And her father hated heretics! They had inspired him with a fierceness, a hatred of which she had not believed him capable.

This was terrible–nothing more terrible could have happened. Those two were against each other.

She remembered the change in her father, his fierceness against the heretic, his absolute belief in the Church of Rome.

He is wrong to be so certain, she thought. And Will is wrong to be certain that Luther is right. Why must there be this hatred between men? Why cannot they love God simply, without dogmas that must be disputed?

Jesus had told men to love one another. Yet how could they obey that command when they disputed together with such ferocity, and instead of love fostered hatred?

Love must become the ruling passion of the world. If her father was to follow the teaching of Jesus Christ, he must not hate Martin Luther because his views differed from his own; nor must Luther hate her father and the King for similar reasons.

Why could they not say: 'You believe this and I believe that. But let us go our ways in peace. Let us brood on these matters which delight us, and in so doing, if perchance we find the truth, then that is a great and glorious thing which we can show to the world; and let us light it with love, not hatred, so that all may see it.'

She sat up in bed and touched her burning cheeks. She, being Margaret, must see herself as clearly as she saw others. Margaret's brain must examine her heart. She stood between two men–Will Roper and her father–and now she would admit that they were the two whom she loved best in the world. She loved them both so much that she could not bear to be without either of them. A cause for dispute had raised itself between them; it was like an ugly dragon whose nostrils gave out the fire of hatred.

She must turn that hatred into love. She knew suddenly that she was ready to practise deceit if necessary to achieve that end.

Margaret More looked into her mind and discovered that the most important things in the world to her were that her father and Will Roper should continue to be friends, and that she should keep them near her that they might all be happy together. Who was right–the Pope or Martin Luther? She did not know; and she realized with a mighty shock that she believed neither of them was wholly right nor wholly wrong. In any case she wondered whether she would be prepared to take sides if she could believe that one was right and one was wrong.

She wanted to live in harmony with the men she loved.

Now that she knew herself, she was too honest to feign ignorance.

She rose from the bed and went in search of Will.

He was still in the schoolroom where she had left him. He was standing by the window staring out disconsolately. If he was a man who had found the truth, he looked as if he had lost all else he cared for in doing so.

He turned as she entered. 'Margaret!'

She went to him and smiled up at him. Then he put his arms about her.

'Margaret . . . dearest Meg. . . . Then you did love me?'

'I know not whether I did or did not,' she said. 'I only know I do.'

'Margaret . . . now?'

'Yes, now!' she said emphatically. 'For when our thoughts come, as you say, they must be examined. Will, some time ago you asked me to marry you. I answer you now: I will.'

'But, Margaret . . . your father . . . ?'

'He has said he is pleased.'

He kissed her, and she thought: How strange it is! I am no longer Margaret More, the solemn little scholar. I do not care for the arguments in books. I care nothing but that Will loves me and that I can live the rest of my life with him and with Father.

'You are laughing, Meg. Why, you are different.'

'I am happy,' she said. 'I see that it is because I am in love. Do you not like me thus?' Now she seemed coquettish, even as Ailie.

'Meg, I love you now and for ever. But I feel this cannot really be happening, and that I shall wake up in a moment.'

'It is real . . . real as our life shall be.'

He took her to the window-seat and kept his arm about her.

We shall be here together, she was telling herself. Life is good. It must be so. I will make it so.

'Meg . . . how happy I am! I never thought . . . You seemed remote – far too clever for me . . . and now . . . when I had given up hope . . .'

'You should never give up hope, Will. Never . . . never. . . .'

'How you laugh, Meg. I have never heard you laugh like this.'

'It is the laughter of happiness, Will. That is the best sort of laughter. Not to laugh in derision at the misfortunes of others . . . not to laugh with relief because you feel remote from those misfortunes; but to laugh because you are happy . . . happy . . . because you have found that life is good.'

'When did you decide that you would marry me?'

'I think it must have been a long time ago, but I knew it only when you spoke to me just now. I knew then that I loved you.'

'When I told you . . . when I *confessed*?'

'It was seeing you, Will, so sure that you were right. . . .'

'Then you, too, feel as I do.'

'I? I feel nothing but love. Sometimes I think I never have. I loved Father and I wanted to be clever to please him. You see, that was love of Father, not love of learning. Now I know that I love you too. So I have two people to love, and I love you both so much that there seems hardly room for anything else in my life.'

'Margaret! Is this *Margaret*?'

'Yes, it is the same Margaret. She was there all the time, I suppose, but she was hidden by the solemn scholar. She did not know herself. She saw herself as others saw her. Now she has seen herself as she is.'

They talked of marriage and he said: 'What will your father say? Will he consent now?'

She was silent, amazed at herself, amazed that she who had never thought to deceive her father, could think of deceiving him now.

But she had become a woman who thought in terms of love. It only mattered that there should be amity in her house; that she, the woman, should hold her home together; and so make peace and love between those whom she loved more than her own life.

Therefore she was ready to temporize.

She said to herself: There is no need to tell Father. He has much to occupy his mind. He should not be worried with Will's affairs. Moreover, Will may discover that he has not yet found the truth. Who knows, in a short time he may come to the conclusion that there is no truth in the teaching of this man Luther. Then shall we have had our storms for nothing. I can neither lose Will nor Father; therefore the two I love must love each other. Today let us think of love; and let us hope that tomorrow there will be no need to think of anything but love.

So now she said to Will: 'Father is so rarely at home. It is a pity to worry him with your doubts and your leanings. Moreover, men's minds change. Perhaps he will change; or you will change. For the time, let us keep this secret. You and I will discuss these matters when we are alone . . . and only then. . . .'

And she smiled at him, wondering whether she would be able to mould his thoughts to her father's way of thinking, or her father's to his.

She thought tenderly: They are obstinate, both of them. They are brave, and they will never accept other than what they believe to be the truth.

But she would wait.

Meanwhile she had discovered love, and for the time being she had determined that nothing should disturb it.

Chapter Four

Margaret was married in the July of that year. Will continued to live in the house, and none was more happy than Thomas in his daughter's marriage. He saw his new son-in-law as a serious young man–he did not know of his religious opinions–who would rise in his profession; he would be a devoted husband, an affectionate father; he would not want to go to Court; he would be content to stay in the heart of the family. His beloved daughter was married, but not lost to him.

Ailie too was married, and she left the house to live in state in her husband's country mansions or his London house.

The family star was steadily rising.

Ailie visited the house often. When she was in London she was continually in and out. She had discovered that, much as she wished for gaiety and excitement, the family circle in Bucklersbury meant more to her than she had realized. She confessed to the girls: 'I feel sentimental about home . . . and when I say *home*, I mean this house; for nowhere else can be home to me in quite the same way.'

She was not displeased with marriage. Her Giles adored her; he was ready to satisfy every whim, and there was nothing that pleased Ailie more than having her whims satisfied; nevertheless, sometimes she would talk of the old family gatherings round the fire in winter, and out of doors in summer, of the dreams they discussed, the tales they had invented, the songs they had sung; and there would be a wistfulness in her voice.

She delighted in her fine jewels; she was gratified to display them when she came home, and endeavoured to arouse the envy of the girls; but when she went away it seemed that she was often the one who was a little envious.

She had tales to tell of the grandeur of Giles's father's country estates. She had been to Court and had even spoken to the King.

She would gather the girls about her and talk of the King. 'So gay . . . so eager for the balls and the masques.' And the Queen? Ailie would grimace lightly when she talked of the Queen. 'She is old . . . and so serious. Older than His Grace; and methinks he is considering the fact with some displeasure. Of course, there is his boy, Henry Fitzroy, to prove that he has not been faithful to the Queen, and that he can get himself sons. . . . And now he is deeply enamoured of Mary Boleyn.'

Cecily enjoyed listening to the stories.

She would urge Ailie to continue, while she plied her with eager questions. 'And what is the girl like? Is she very beautiful?'

'I would not say that. But she has something . . . something that men like. She is plump and full of fun and laughter . . . and the King has loved her for a long time . . . a long time, that is, for him.' Then Ailie would stifle her laughter. 'We must not let Margaret hear such talk. Dear Margaret. She likes to think everyone is as pure and noble as she is herself. And the King, my dear, has heaped titles on Mary's father. He is the Steward of Tonbridge, Keeper of the Manor of Penshurst . . . and I don't know what else. And George . . . the brother . . . is not forgotten. George is very attractive. Oh, very handsome! And such poetry he writes! And he has such a way of making the revels successful. The King likes him, as he likes all those who amuse him.'

'As much as he likes Father?' asked Cecily.

'Oh, quite different! With Father he is solemn. Father is a statesman-courtier. George Boleyn is a courtier-statesman.'

'Yet they are both poets.'

'I wish you could see him, Cecily. You would fall in love with him. George, I mean. Oh, assuredly you would.'

And the frivolous creature would go on to describe the balls and banquets, the dresses and jewels, so that it was clear that, although at times she missed her home, Ailie was enjoying life.

And Margaret? She also was happy, but her happiness was tinged with uneasiness. Always she was afraid that discord would flare up between Will and her father. She read with Will; she fortified herself with reasoning which, should the need arise, she could put before her father. She would also be ready with her father's reasoning to set before Will.

And who was right? She, who for Will's and her father's sake had studied both points of view, could not say.

There came a day when Will did not return to the house. She knew that he had set out that afternoon to visit some of his friends. These were mostly merchants in the City, some English, some German traders from the Hanseatic ports. It was Will's custom to visit one of the houses of these merchants where they would agree to congregate, and there to read and discuss the Lutheran doctrines.

Supper was eaten; yet Will had not come home.

To the enquiries of the family, Margaret said: 'He has some business in the City which I knew must keep him.'

But she was frightened; she was always frightened on such occasions, for she knew that since the King had become 'Defender of the Faith', heresy in England was looked upon as a crime.

She went to that bedroom which she now shared with Will, and she sat at the window all through the night. But he did not come home.

Thomas entered the small private closet that adjoined the splendid Council Chamber of the Cardinal.

Wolsey was looking grave. 'I am concerned about your son-in-law,' he said.

Thomas was astonished. How could the Cardinal be interested in insignificant Will Roper or Giles Allington?

'Your son-in-law Roper,' explained Wolsey. 'He has been caught with some heretics in the house of a London merchant.'

'What! Will Roper . . . with heretics!'

'So it would seem. And bold withal. He declares that he holds the beliefs of these people and that, had he the chance, he would proclaim his beliefs from a pulpit.'

'But . . . I can scarcely believe this. You . . . you are sure?'

Wolsey nodded grimly. 'It is a sad affair. A heretic–the son-in-law of a member of the King's Council! We cannot have that said, Master More.'

'My lord Cardinal, I do not understand. It seems impossible to believe this. Where is he now?'

'Doubtless he will be in your house, whither I sent him. His friends will be punished . . . severely. But as regards your son-in-law . . . I sent him home and bade him have a care in future.'

'You mean . . . that he is as guilty of heresy as these others?'

Wolsey nodded.

'Then, my lord, should he not be judged with them?'

The Chancellor-Cardinal, that master of nepotism whose illegitimate sons held offices which, at their tender age, they could not possibly administer, smiled tolerantly at his assistant.

'The son-in-law of the Under-Treasurer! Indeed not!'

'So, because he is my son-in-law, he will go unpunished while the others suffer?'

'Oh, come, come, Master More. We will hush up this matter. But, I beg of you, see that nothing of this nature occurs again.'

Thomas was pacing up and down the apartment. Will . . . a heretic! Margaret's husband! And he knew nothing of it. Did Margaret know?

A new emotion had come into his life since his wordy battle with Martin Luther; he had not known that he could feel such fierce hatred as he felt for that monk and the people who followed him. Margaret was as astonished as he was by the depth of his feelings. Why did he feel thus? She was right to remind him that he had said with Erasmus that there were anomalies in the Church which must be stamped out; she had been right to remind him that, in a perfect state, he had visualized freedom of opinion. Why, then, had he changed so suddenly, lost his meekness, that understanding of others who did not share his views? Did he really believe that Martin Luther, the monk who had risked his life, who had given his burning energy to reforming the old religion into a new one, was a rogue?

When he had written *Utopia* he had imagined a state governed by wise men. But when he visualized the future, he was certain that drastic change, such as Luther advocated, could mean nothing but misery and bloodshed, the smashing of an institution which, while it was not ideal, had its roots in righteousness. The man Luther, it seemed, would smash the Catholic Church, and in so doing he would destroy all those who were as equally determined as he was; then would he set in its place another edifice, as yet untried, which would, Thomas did not doubt, grow up with all the frailty which now beset the Catholic Church.

How could such a disaster be prevented? Only by stamping out the heretic, by making sure that the change did not take place. For the sake of the many who would be bound to suffer cruelly in a mighty war of religion, the few upstarts must be made to suffer. They must be punished as a warning to the people. Those who considered following them must be made to fear the consequences.

Death–torture even–of the few, was a small price to pay for the death and torture of many, for the chaos which, as he saw it, must surely come to the world if the movement was tolerated and allowed to grow.

Thomas had believed when he wrote *Utopia* that in an ideal state freedom of religious thought was essential; but before such freedom could be given, there must be the ideal state.

He himself suffered physical torture daily. His body was tormented perpetually by his hair-shirt, and at this time he had taken to whipping it with knotted cords; in the small chamber which he occupied as his sleeping apartment, he lay with a piece of wood for a pillow. The afflictions of the body, he believed, were as nothing to the triumph of the spirit. If he believed that heretics must be punished, he must punish himself. He believed that those who declared they gave their lives to a spiritual cause would care no more than he did for the torments of the body.

These ideas, he felt, came to him as a divine inspiration. He must do all in his power to preserve the Holy Catholic Faith which had its roots in Rome; for this reason he had exercised all his talents in his writings against Luther. He saw himself as one of those who must lead the fight. He was no Erasmus, who, having thrown the stone that shattered the glass of orthodox thought, must run and hide himself lest he should be hurt by the splinters.

And now . . . one of those whom he must fight was his own son-in-law; moreover, he was the husband of her whom he loved more than anyone on Earth.

Wolsey watched the man with some amusement. They were growing farther and farther apart–he and the Under-Treasurer. More disapproved of the Cardinal's policy, and did not hesitate to say so. A brave man, this, thought Wolsey, but a misguided one; he is a man whose talents would take him far, but whose emotions will hold him back and doubtless ruin him, for in the political arena there is no time for a man to serve anything but his ambition. And of Wolsey, Thomas often thought: A clever man, a shrewd and wise and greatly talented man, but a man who puts his own glory before honour, who will serve his ambition rather than his God.

And now, mused the Cardinal, he is turning over in his mind whether or not this man Roper should be spared the consequences of his action merely because he has a father-in-law in a high place. To what depth of folly will this man's idealism carry him?

Wolsey shrugged his shoulders. He had done what he considered his duty towards a friend and fellow councillor by covering up the misdemeanours of a near relative. Now he washed his hands of the matter. His mind was occupied with affairs of greater moment that were pending in Europe. Pope Leo was sick. How long could he last? And when the new Pope was sought among the Cardinals, who would that man be?

What a splendid climb it would be from Ipswich to Rome, from a humble tutor to a mighty Pope. A Pope was a Prince even as was a king, and the Pope stood equal to Charles of Spain, Francis of France and Henry of England.

Why should his new Holiness not be Cardinal Wolsey?

And since his mind was occupied with such great matters, how could he give more than the lightest attention to the consideration of the King's philandering or to this matter of the foolish son-in-law of Sir Thomas More?

Thomas shut himself into that small private room in which he tortured his body. He leaned against the locked door.

What could he do? Love and Duty stood before him. Which was he to obey? His duty, he knew, was to refuse the intervention of the Cardinal, to send Roper from his house, to say: 'This man is a heretic. He is one of those who would undermine the Church and bring bloodshed to the land.'

But Love involved his daughter Margaret, and only now did he know fully what she meant to him. She loved Roper, and he could not think of this matter without imagining Margaret tormented and tortured, turning from him to her husband or from her husband to him. But if he were strong enough to torture himself, he could not bear to hurt Margaret.

Yet it was wrong, was it not, that some guilty ones suffered whilst others went free?

But . . . his own son-in-law . . . and Margaret's husband!

He must speak to Margaret first.

He called one of the servants and asked that Margaret should be told that he wished to speak with her. She would know, of course, what was wrong, because Will had been detained for a day and night, and he would have told her why he had been allowed to come home. Therefore she would know that the news of his arrest must have reached Thomas's ears.

Moreover, when Thomas had arrived at the house, Margaret had not been at hand to greet him; doubtless she was in the bedroom which she shared with Will, talking to him. Was she trying to make him accept her father's views? Or was she . . . but this he shuddered to contemplate . . . was she too a heretic?

At length she came and stood before him; her face was pale and there were dark shadows under her eyes; and as she stood there with the marks of anxiety and suffering on her face, he knew that his love for this daughter was so strong that it would turn him from his duty.

'Well, Margaret,' he said, 'so your husband is a heretic.'

'Yes, Father.'

'You knew of this?'

'I did.'

He ought to ask her that further question: And you, Margaret? But he could not ask it; he was afraid of the answer.

'Why did you not tell me? You and I have always shared everything, have we not?' Almost immediately he was contrite. 'But he is your husband. . . . A husband's place is before a father's. . . . You were right in what you did. Of course you were right.'

He saw the tears in her eyes now. She came to him and put her arms about him. He rested his cheek against her hair.

'Oh, Margaret . . . my dearest daughter.'

'Father,' she said, 'how can anyone mean more to me than you do?'

'Hush, my daughter. You must not say that.' All his resolutions were crumbling. He saw himself as weak as other men. He understood the Cardinal's gross action in bestowing favours on his beloved sons. How could he, who so loved his daughter, blame the Cardinal for loving his sons?

'We must be truthful, Father. We always have been. I knew before I married Will that he was leaning towards the new faith. I must tell you everything that is in my mind. I knew your mind and I knew his . . . and, strangely, because they were different and because I feared a quarrel between you, it was then that I knew I loved him even as I love you, and that what I cared for more than anything in the world was to guard the peace between you. So I married Will, and I have known that he was meeting these merchants . . . and I knew what books he has been reading . . . and I know how his thoughts run.'

'He has made his thoughts . . . your thoughts?'

'Father, you have always said that I was your clever daughter. You have said that my mind equals that of any man you know.'

'I believe that to be true, Meg.'

'Yet in this matter my mind is so clouded that I fear you are mistaken in me. When I listen to Will I see there is reason in what he says; and I think that is perhaps because I love him. Then I know *your* mind, and I see reason in your beliefs; perhaps that is because I love you. Father, I do not believe it is important whether men follow Luther or the Pope . . . as long as they obey Christ's commandments. I have tabled the differences and pondered them. Are they real differences? Neither creed excludes Love; and Love is surely the whole meaning of good in life, is it not? Father, I know your thoughts. You think that these differences of opinion will eventually bring bloodshed, and you are doubtless right. In fact, is it not already happening in some degree? It would be a terrible tragedy. So in all you do and in all you say there is reason, there is love of your fellow men. Will believes that these questions raised by Martin Luther must be examined; and if Luther is right, his way must be followed . . . no matter what the cost. In a way *he* is right. You see, I am swayed . . . this way and that. And I know that the most important thing in the world is that men should live in amity together and love, not hate each other. I know that the two I love best must assuredly do that, and that I will do all in my power–for this seems the most important thing in the world to me–to make them.'

'That is women's reasoning, Meg,' he said.

'I know it. You have said that there should be no differences between the education of men and women. Might it not be that a woman's reasoning on certain matters could be more clear, more precise, more true than that of a man?'

'That could be so, Meg.'

'Oh, Father, you must try to understand Will.'

'Margaret, we must try to turn him from his folly. But for the fact that I have a high place at the Court, he would not be with us now.'

'I know. He would be in some prison awaiting his sentence.'

'He has broken the laws of the country as well–as I see it–as the law of God.'

'Will thinks that if he keeps the law of God as he understands it, it matters not if he breaks the law of the country.'

'We should refuse to accept this concession, Margaret. If he has stated such views, he should be ready to defend them.'

'He is ready, Father. He is not lacking in courage.'

'That is true. It is I who am the coward.'

'You?'

'Because, Meg, I love you so much that I could not bear to refuse to accept this favour. There are some things I have not learned to bear. Once I wished to be a monk, yet I could not resist my dreams of a family life. Now I wish to be an honest statesman, and I cannot be that if it will bring suffering to my beloved daughter.'

She smiled. 'Oh, Father, do not be a saint. Do not torture your body with whips and this hair-shirt. You are yourself. You are our beloved father. We do not want a saint. And if your love makes you weak . . . then that is yourself . . . far more lovable than any saint. Father, if you could only be less determined to do what you think is right! If only you could be more like other men! You have written your replies to Luther for the King. Any statesman might have done it, were he blessed with your gift for writing. Cannot it be left at that? What have heresies and religious opinions to do with our happy home?'

'They are part of the world about us, Meg. They are here with us, like the sun and the light. You may shut your doors, but the light will find some way of penetrating. Will you help me to recall your husband from his heresy?'

'As to that I cannot say,' she answered. 'There is one thing I wish to do, and that is to foster love between you, to bring you back to that state which you once enjoyed. I cannot help it, Father. Perhaps it is because I am a woman. But I want you and Will to love each other. I want us all to be happy. I know that is right for us.'

He embraced her tenderly. He said: 'I shall talk with your husband, and I shall pray for him. I trust ere long I shall call him home.'

'Father, I too shall pray for him and for you. I shall pray that all may be well between you, and that he who is right shall call the other home, so that you may be together–the two whom I love–in friendship, amity and devotion.'

And when Margaret left him, Thomas fell on his knees and prayed for the soul of William Roper, and that his daughter's wishes should be granted.

Following that, there were disputes and arguments between Thomas and Will. In these Will waxed hot, and Thomas was always calm; which meant that Will must come out the worse from the dispute.

With his wide knowledge of the world and men, with his skill with words, Thomas's arguments must seem the more sound. Thomas was a practised lawyer; Will was a very young and inexperienced one. Will became, quite naturally, a little less sure of his ideas.

Margaret was glad of this, for she saw that the obstinacy of her father was slightly greater than that of her husband; and she continued to wish above all things for peace between these two.

Will no longer consorted with the merchants, no longer attended illegal meetings. He felt he owed it to his father-in-law to abstain; for if Thomas suffered because he had accepted a concession which it was against his conscience to accept, Will suffered equally. He would not put his father-in-law in a false position again. For that reason he would no longer run risks; no longer did he speak openly of his beliefs; he studied in the privacy of his apartments, and he talked no more of his ideas except with Margaret and her father.

Margaret had one great matter with which to occupy her mind during that year. She was to have a child.

Now, more than ever, Thomas regretted that he could not spend much time at home. But events were moving fast. Wolsey had been deeply disappointed when, on the death of Leo, Adrian, Cardinal of Tortosa, became Pope instead of Wolsey, Cardinal of York. But Adrian was a sick man, with little hope of occupying for long the Papal chair, and Wolsey's eyes were still on Rome; his ambition had grown to such an extent that it seemed to blind him to all else.

Margaret's emotions were divided between her joy in the unborn baby and her anxieties for her father who was becoming even more important at the Court. She could never forget that day when she had learned that he had aroused the displeasure of Henry the Seventh; she remembered also the law-suit when there had been a dispute over the possession of the Pope's ship. That had been the beginning of advancement; but whither did advancement lead? So many men had found the axe waiting for them when they reached the top of the ladder which led to fame.

Now Thomas had been elected Speaker of the Parliament.

England was at war that year with France and Scotland, and Thomas had succeeded in delaying the collection of those taxes which Wolsey had imposed for the purpose of carrying on the war. Thomas was against war; he had always been against it. If he talked continually thus, what would become of him?

The Cardinal was now openly hostile towards Thomas. He was suffering acute disappointment over the election of the Pope. It seemed incredible to him that a man could be as foolish as Thomas More, so blind to his own chances of advancement.

As he left Parliament Wolsey forgot his usual calm so much as to mutter, so that several heard him: 'Would to God, Master More, that you had been in Rome before I made you Speaker of this Parliament.'

Wolsey went straight to the King, and a few days later Thomas was told that he was to be sent on an embassy to Spain.

How could he leave London when Margaret was soon to have a child? He was beset by fears. How many women died in childbirth? It was the birth of Jack which had led to Jane's death. He *must* be beside Margaret when her child was born.

She had said: 'Father, I hope you will be near me. Do you remember when I was a very little girl and the pain was better when you sat by my bed, holding my hand?'

He had answered: 'Meg, thus shall it be now. I shall be with you.'

But Spain! The strain of working for the King was beginning to undermine his health; he was often painfully fatigued. He did not believe he could keep in good health if he undertook the long journey in a trying climate. He thought of the many weary months away from his family. Was it too late even now to break away from the life of the Court which he did not want?

Greatly daring, and saying nothing to his family, he craved audience with the King. It was immediately granted, for Henry liked him for himself, and there were times when he wished to desert his frivolous companions and be with this serious-minded man. It gave him pleasure to see himself as a serious King who, while often gay could also appreciate the company of a scholar.

Thomas had asked for a private interview, so the King sent all his courtiers from him, and when they were alone he turned to his protégé with a pleasant smile.

'Well, Thomas, what is this matter of which you would speak?'

''Tis the embassy to Spain, Your Grace.'

'Ah, yes. You will be leaving us soon. We shall miss you. But Wolsey thinks you are the best man we could send.'

'I fear the Cardinal is mistaken, Your Grace.'

'Wolsey . . . mistaken! Never! Wolsey knows your talents, my friend, as well as I do.'

'Your Highness, I feel myself unfit for the task. The climate does not agree with my health, and if I am ill I cannot do justice to Your Grace's mission. I feel that if you send me thither you may send me to my grave. If Your Grace decides that I must go, then you may rest assured that I shall follow your instructions to the very best of my ability. But I fear the journey, Sire; I greatly fear the journey.'

The King looked gravely at the man before him. He had grown thin,

Henry saw. That was too much poring over books. Not enough good food. From what the King had heard, the fellow did not pay enough attention to what he ate; he did not drink wine. Poor Thomas More! He did not know how to live. And he was married to a woman older than himself. The King frowned at the thought, for it reminded him that he was in a similar position; and it was a position which he was beginning to find irksome.

Poor Thomas! thought Henry. He has his misfortunes . . . even as I. And he lacks my good health.

'There is another matter, Sire,' went on Thomas. 'My daughter, recently married, is expecting her first child; and I should die of anxiety if I were not at hand.'

The King slapped his knee. 'Ah, so that's it, eh? That's it, friend Thomas.' Henry's eyes filled with tears. 'I like well such fatherly devotion. So should we feel for our daughter, the Princess Mary, were she in similar plight. But you have a big family in Bucklersbury, eh, Thomas? You have a fine son, I hear.'

'Yes, Your Highness. Three daughters, a son, a foster-daughter and a stepdaughter.'

'I like to hear that, Thomas. Would it surprise you if your King told you that–in some respects–he envies you?'

'Your Highness is gracious indeed. And I know that in some ways I have been a lucky man.'

'Lucky indeed! A fine son, eh? Would to God I could say the same. And this child of yours . . . this daughter . . . Let us hope she will be brought to bed of a fine boy.' The King brought his face closer to that of Thomas. 'And we consider it meet that her father should be in London . . . be here when his grandson comes into the world. Rest happy, my friend. We shall find another to send on that embassy to Spain.'

That was the extent of Thomas's favour with the King.

Yet, delighted as she was to hear the news, Margaret was uneasy.

The King's favour was pleasant while it lasted, but now it seemed to her that her father had won it at the cost of the Cardinal's friendship.

Margaret had quickly recovered from her confinement, and it was a very happy family that lived in Bucklersbury during those months.

Thomas was delighted with his grandson.

'But,' he said, 'now that my secretary, John Harris, is living with us and I have a grandson, this house is not big enough; and in the years to come when I have many grandsons and grand-daughters–for the other girls will marry one day and I trust that they, like Margaret, will not leave their father's roof–I must have a bigger house.'

So he bought Crosby Place in the City–a beautiful house, the tallest in London, built of stone and timber and situated close to Bishopsgate.

One day he took Margaret along to see it.

They went through the great rooms of this house which was so much grander than the one they were now occupying. Margaret stood with her father in the great hall, looked up at the vaulted roof, and tried to imagine the family in it.

'You like it not?' said Thomas.

'Well, Father, you have bought it, and doubtless we shall make it ours when we settle in, but . . .'

'But?' he insisted.

'I know not. Perhaps I am foolish. But it is not like our house.'

'*Propria domus omnium optima!*'

'But we should make this our house, Father. Yet . . . I cannot see it as ours. There is an air of gloom about it.'

'You are fanciful, daughter.'

'Indeed I am. Why, when we have the family here and we sit talking and singing together . . . then it will be our home . . . and quite a different place from the one it is now.'

'Richard Crookback lived here for a time,' said Thomas. 'I wonder if that is why you feel this repulsion. I wonder if you think of him and all the miseries that must have been his. Is that it, Meg?'

'It might be.'

She sat on a window-seat and looked thoughtfully at her father.

'Come, Margaret, what is on your mind?'

'That we shall make this place our home.'

'Come, be frank with me.'

'It is just a foolish thought of mine. We have often talked of the house we would have . . . when you have not been with us.'

'And it has not been like this?'

'How could you expect it to be? Where should we find all that we have planned? Moreover, if there could be such a house we should have to pull it down once a week and rebuild it, because we have added to it and altered it so persistently that it could not stay the same for more than a week. There is Mercy with her hospital; and there is the library that I have built for you; there is the chapel which Mother thinks should be attached to all great houses. . . . And Jack, of course, has set all this in the midst of green fields.'

He was silent for a few seconds. Then he turned to her. 'Why, Meg,' he said, 'did I not think of this before? We will build our own house. And all of us shall have a hand in it. We shall build what we would have. There *shall* be Mercy's hospital, your mother's chapel, your library for me and Jack's green fields. . . .'

'But, Father, you have bought this place.'

'We can sell the lease.'

'Father, it sounds wonderful, but could it really be done?'

'Why not? I am high in the King's favour, am I not? I have money which I have not spent. That is the answer, Meg. We will not live in this gloomy house which is full of unhappy ghosts. We will seek our own land and we will build our own house . . . our ideal house.'

'As you would build an ideal state,' she reminded him.

'A house is easier to build that a state, Meg, and I doubt not that, with the help of my family, I can do it.' He was as excited as a boy. 'There I shall pass my days with my children and my grandchildren about me. My father will have to be with us soon. He and his wife are getting too old to be alone. Elizabeth, Cecily and Mercy must marry and fill our new house with children. It must be outside the City . . . but not too far out. We shall have to be within reach of London, for I am still bound to the Court. And Meg . . . Meg, whenever I can, I shall slip away. I shall come home. Let us go. Let us decide where we shall live. I can scarcely wait to discuss this with the others. Meg, we will call a conference this night; and the land shall be bought without delay and the ideal house shall be built . . . and we shall live in it happily for many years.'

They walked home, talking of the house.

Thomas was as good as his word. In a short time he had sold his lease of Crosby Place to a rich Italian merchant friend who was looking for a house in London.

Antonio Bonvisi, the merchant from Lucca, settled in at Crosby Place and Thomas bought land in Chelsea.

Building their ideal house occupied the minds of the family so much that they gave little thought to what was happening about them.

The Cardinal had again been disappointed of his hopes of the Papacy. On the death of Adrian, Giulio de' Medici, called Clement the Seventh, was elected. The Emperor Charles came to London and was made a Knight of the Garter. This meant that Thomas was taken from his family to be in constant attendance at the Court, but it was regarded as an annoyance rather than a fact of political importance.

It seemed more interesting that that great friend of the family, Dr Linacre, who was now the King's physician, brought the damask rose to England. It should be awarded a special place of honour in the Chelsea gardens. There was again war with France; but that seemed remote, for meanwhile the house at Chelsea was being built.

It stood back from the river, with about a hundred yards of garden between it and the water. There were four bay windows and eight casements, allowing a superb view of the river. The centre block was occupied largely by the great hall, and there were numerous rooms in the east and west wings.

'Mercy,' Thomas had said, 'once you said your dearest wish was to own a hospital of your own in which you could tend the sick. Now that we are building at Chelsea, that hospital shall be yours.'

And so it was built, separated from the house by pales; for Mercy had said: 'What if I should have contagious diseases in my hospital? I could not have my patients passing them on to my family.'

They had never seen Mercy quite so happy as she was when she showed Dr Clement over her hospital. It seemed that when she had the young doctor there, Mercy had all she desired in life–John Clement, her family, and her hospital on the other side of the pales.

There was Thomas's library and the chapel in a separate building–just as they had pictured it.

Elizabeth and Cecily planned the gardens; and Jack decided where they would grow their wheat, keep their cows and have their dairy. Alice designed her buttery and her kitchens; Thomas planned his library, gallery and chapel, with Margaret to help him.

It was to be a house in which one family, who had discovered the means of being happy, would live together, cherishing each other.

Will and his father-in-law were now the best of friends, although Will was not altogether weaned from the new ideas. Thomas prayed for him; Will prayed for Thomas; Will was wavering, for it seemed to him that a man such as his father-in-law, who seemed so right in all other matters, could not be entirely wrong on what seemed to Will the greatest matter of all.

By the end of the year they had moved into the house.

They were a bigger family now, for Thomas's father, the judge, Sir John More, and his wife came to live with them.

In spite of his cynical views on marriage, Sir John had taken a fourth wife and lived amicably with her. He had ceased to fret about his son, and he would often laugh when he remembered how he had worried in the old days because Thomas had paid more attention to Greek and Latin than to law. He admitted that he had been wrong. He had seen Thomas as an ordinary man; and, like the rest of the household, he now knew that to be an error.

He was content in his old age to rest in this great house at Chelsea, to wander in the gardens watching the gardeners at work, now and then discussing a point of law with Thomas, who never failed to give him that deference which he had given him as a young and obscure student. Occasionally he worked in the courts at Westminster; he was treated with greater respect as the father of Sir Thomas More than he was as a judge of these courts.

It was a very happy family that lived in the house at Chelsea.

Soon after they were established there, Sir John Heron, the Treasurer of the King's Chamber, approached Sir Thomas concerning his son Giles. Sir John admired Sir Thomas More and, having heard of the large house which had been built in the village of Chelsea, he would esteem it a favour if his son might live there with the Mores, after the fashion of the day.

Alice was a-twitter with glee when she heard this.

'The Herons!' she cried. 'Why, they are a most wealthy family. I shall look after that young man as though he were my own son.'

'And doubtless will endeavour to turn him into that,' said Thomas wryly.

'I have told you, Master More, that I shall cherish the young man. . . . He shall be my son in very truth.'

'Nay, by very law, Alice . . . the law of marriage. I'll warrant that before you have seen him you have decided that he will make a suitable husband for one of the girls.'

'They are becoming marriageable. Have you not noticed that?'

'I have indeed.'

'Well, then, it is time we had more such as Master Giles Heron in our household, for one day he will inherit his father's goodly estates.'

'And that is a good thing, for I doubt young Giles will ever win much for himself.'

'Tilly valley! Is it a clever thing, then, to be turned against a young man merely because one day he will inherit his father's fortune?' demanded Alice.

'It is wise, you would no doubt tell me, to be turned towards him because he will inherit one.'

'Now, Master More, will you endeavour to arrange a marriage between this young man and one of your daughters?'

'I would rather let one of my daughters and the young man arrange it themselves.'

Alice clicked her tongue and talked of some people's folly being past all understanding. But she was pleased with life. She enjoyed living in the big house at Chelsea; she had more maids than she had ever had in her life. Her daughter had married well; she would do her duty by her stepdaughters and see that they followed in Ailie's footsteps; and she would never forget for one moment that she was Lady More.

She went down to the kitchen, her marmoset following her. She went everywhere with her. She scolded the little thing, but it was an affectionate scolding, the sort of scolding she was fond of bestowing on her husband.

Good marriages for them all, she reflected. Either Elizabeth or Cecily

should have Giles Heron, who ere long would inherit his father's title and lands. Elizabeth it must be; she was more suitable for the position. Cecily was inclined to be slothful, to lie about in the sunshine, under the trees or in the orchard, or wander about gathering wild flowers, spending too much time with her pet animals. Yes, Elizabeth, with her sharp wits, would make the better Lady Heron. Moreover, Elizabeth was the elder and should therefore marry first, for it was a bad thing when a younger sister married before an elder. Not, thought Alice complacently, that there should be any difficulty in finding a good husband for Cecily, a girl whose father was in such high favour at Court.

Fortune had taken a very pleasant turn.

'Lady More!' She whispered that to herself as she went about the house.

Giles Heron protested when his father told him that he would live for some time in the household of Sir Thomas More.

As Giles took barge for Chelsea, he was thinking of his father's remarks: 'There are two daughters. A match between our house and theirs would bring great benefits, my son. Sir Thomas More is in as high favour at Court as any man–not excluding the Cardinal himself, some say. You will one day have land and property. I would like to see added to that the favour of the King's favourite minister.'

That was all very well, but Giles was not interested in ambition. This river trip would have been most enjoyable to him if he could have idly drifted downstream, stopping perhaps to lie on the bank, breaking into song, chatting with merry companions; and then, when he was tired, turning the barge homewards. Instead of that, he was on his way to a new home; and he was uneasy.

Who wanted favour at Court? Not he. What did it mean? Constant work, constant fear that you would displease some high official of the Court–mayhap the King himself. Then you began to realize how much happier you had been lying in the sun, idling the hours away.

Then there was this daughter of Sir Thomas More. It was said that his daughters were almost as learned as he was. The girls were prim creatures who spent their days in a schoolroom writing Latin verses. Latin verses! Scholars! Giles wanted to laugh hysterically at the thought. He frantically sought in his mind for one little phrase which his tutors had taught him and which he might manage to quote; but his mind was a blank.

He had seen Alice Allington, a real little beauty, at not seeming very learned except in matters of manners and general fascination. But she was only a stepdaughter–no blood relation to the learned Sir Thomas More. He doubted if he would find another such as Alice Allington in the Chelsea house.

And one of these girls–there was, fortunately, a choice between two–he must try to make his wife. For, his father had said, if you do not, depend upon it others will. These girls have more than fortune. You yourself have wealth, but the More family can give you what you lack: the interest of the King himself. Marry one of these girls and the King, I am sure, could be induced to smile on you. Thomas More is reputed to be an upright man, a man who seeks no gain for himself; but I'll warrant he'll not be averse to taking a litle for his daughters, since by all accounts he has a very deep regar for them.

Giles pictured the girls. They would be small, for sitting at a table, po

over books, did not develop the body; they would be pale; they would doubtless stoop; they would be ugly; they would give no attention to personal adornments; they would have Latin instead of good looks; they would have Greek instead of charm.

'O God in Heaven,' prayed Giles Heron, 'save me from a daughter of Sir Thomas More.'

He had reached the privy stairs, and, leaving his servants to tie up the boat and take his baggage into the house, he mounted the stairs and went through the wicket gate.

He stood looking over the pleasantly sloping lawns, at the gardens of flowers, at the young trees and the house itself.

Slowly he made his way towards that great building. Which of the rooms, he wondered, was the schoolroom? He had heard of that schoolroom in which the wisest men in Europe taught the son and daughters of Sir Thomas More. He pictured the grey-bearded, solemn-faced tutors; they would be scornful of him. And the girls? They too. Perhaps they would despise him so much that they would beg their father not to let him marry one of them. Giles was hopeful by nature.

How beautiful it was on that summer's day! He could smell the scent of newly-cut grass; and in the distance he could hear the sound of voices. He heard laughter too; that was the last thing he had expected to hear in this domain, but doubtless it came from someone on land nearby, for voices carried far in the country. Mayhap it was some of the servants. Or were the servants as solemn as the family? Did they have to learn Latin and Greek along with their household tasks?

He stopped as a boy appeared from a clump of trees to the right. This boy's gown was open at the neck; his face was hot for he had been running. He stopped short when he saw the visitor. Giles judged him to be about fifteen years of age.

'Good day to you,' said Giles. 'Am I right in thinking these are the gardens of Sir Thomas More?'

'Good day to you,' said the boy. 'And you are right. You must be Giles Heron.'

'I am. Would you please tell me who you are?'

'John More. Always known as Jack. We are worried about the rabbits. They are behaving in such an odd way. They are huddled together and making the strangest noises. I came to look for Father. He would know what to do. Would you . . . come and look at them?'

He turned without more ceremony and began to run. Giles followed him through the trees to a stone wall, on which sat a peacock displaying his gorgeous tail.

The stone wall enclosed a small garden, and in this a girl was kneeling by several rabbit hutches.

'What ails you, Diogenes?' she was saying. 'Tell me, my little one. And you, Pythagoras, you are frightened. What do you see?'

'Any sign of what troubles them?' asked Jack.

'No.'

'This is Giles Heron. I found him coming up from the river.'

'Good day to you,' said the girl. 'Do you know anything about rabbits? We have not had them long. Only since we have been at Chelsea. Can you imagine what could make them as frightened as that?'

Giles looked at her; her face was flushed; her fair hair was escaping from

her cap; and her blue eyes showed her anxiety. It was clear that she was thinking more of the rabbits than of the newcomer. He thought her rather quaint, comparing her with the young ladies whom he met at Court.

'It might be a stoat or a weasel,' said Giles. 'It is terror which makes them behave thus.'

'But where? I can't see anything. . . . Can you?'

'A dog, mayhap?' suggested Giles.

'But Socrates and Plato love the rabbits.'

Diogenes, Pythagoras, Socrates and Plato! thought Giles. Was that not what he would have expected? Even their pets must be named in Greek. Yet both the girl and the boy disarmed him.

The girl went on: 'All the pets love each other. Father says that is because they have been brought up together and know they have nothing to fear from one another. He says that there would be no fear in the world if only everybody understood everybody else. So . . . I don't think they are frightened by the dogs.'

Giles looked about the walled garden, and his quick eyes caught a pair of gleaming ones in the foliage a few yards from the hutch.

'There!' he cried. 'Look.'

They followed his gaze.

'A weasel,' said Giles. 'That explains much.'

'We must drive it off,' said the girl.

Giles caught her arm. 'Nay. It may be dangerous. You stay here. . . .'

Just at that moment a great dog came bounding into the garden, followed by a monkey. There was an immediate movement in the bushes; the dog paused for half a second; and then he was bounding over to the bushes, barking wildly and leaping with great excitement.

The monkey followed. Giles was still holding the girl's arm. He had forgotten Court manners and all ceremony in the excitement of the moment. They were all tense, waiting to see what the animals would do.

It was the monkey who went into the attack. Suddenly she leaped into the bushes. The girl caught her breath; Giles tightened his grip on her arm. They heard a squeaking and a scuffle in the bushes; and the monkey emerged, her bright eyes gleaming, a chatter of gibberish escaping from her little mouth.

'It's gone!' cried Giles in great excitement. 'The monkey has driven it off.'

'Marmot!' cried the girl. 'You brave creature!'

The monkey ran to her and climbed on to her shoulder. The dog leaped about her, barking wildly.

'All you did, Master Plato, was make a noise. You were the herald; but Marmot was the heroine. She is the victor. Do you like her, Master Heron? She is my mother's, and she was given to her by one of our friends from foreign parts. She is very happy here in the summer, but we have to take great care of her in the winter.'

'She is certainly a brave creature,' said Giles. 'But . . . I have not heard your name yet.'

'Have you not? I'm Cecily More.'

'Oh!' cried Giles with a lifting of his spirits. 'You er . . . you are . . . in actual truth?'

She looked surprised. 'I do not understand.'

He smiled. 'I thought that mayhap you would be very small and pale and humped through bending over your desk.'

Cecily laughed at that.

'And,' went on Giles, laughing himself with the immensity of his relief, 'firing questions at me in Latin.'

'Margaret is the clever one of the family. Mercy, too. You may have heard of them. Margaret is quite a scholar, but she is merry too. She takes much delight in writing in Latin and Greek; and with Mercy it is all mathematics and medicine. Elizabeth, who is my elder sister, is clever too. Poor Jack and I . . . we are not so clever. Are we, Jack?'

'I am the dunce of the family,' said Jack. 'I can just manage to write a little Latin and follow their speech.'

'You will feel yourself to be a learned scholar when you compare yourself with me,' said Giles.

'Then welcome!' cried Jack. 'I shall enjoy appearing to be learned for once.'

Cecily said: 'It is pleasant, is it not, Jack, to welcome someone to this house who does not think that a knowledge of Greek is the most important thing in the world.'

'And what, Mistress Cecily, do you think is the most important thing in the world?'

'At the moment, to make sure that the rabbits are safe and that the weasel cannot come back and frighten them.'

'He will not,' said Giles. 'The monkey gave him a great fright. He will remember. Animals have long memories sometimes.'

'Is that so?' said Cecily. 'I am glad of it.'

'You love animals, do you not?' asked Giles.

'Yes. And you?'

'My dogs and horses.'

'I love dogs and horses and the little helpless ones besides . . . like rabbits and birds. We have fowls and dear little pigs.'

'You have a farm, then?'

'Well, we have some land and animals. We grow much for ourselves. That is what we always wanted when we lived in Bucklersbury. They are cutting the grass in the home-field now. I should be helping. So should Jack. But I saw what was happening here. . . .'

'I should not have thought you would have had time to keep so many animals.'

'But we are a big family. Each has his own. Father says that we may have what pets we like. The only rule is that we must care for them, see that they are fed and looked after in every way. The peacock there is Elizabeth's. He is beautiful, do you not think so? He is rather haughty too, for he'll not take food from anyone but Bess . . . unless he is very hungry. He is asking for you to admire him.'

'He is as vain as a Court gallant.'

'Are Court gallants as vain as that?' asked Cecily.

'Some are much more vain.'

'*You* are one of them, are you not?'

'Ah, but out of my setting. Here, among the learned, I feel humble. But you should see me at Court. There I display my fine feathers and invite admiration.'

'I should like to see you do that,' said Cecily.

'Who knows, you may one day. Yet if I stay here for a little while, as your father and my father have arranged that I shall, doubtless I shall see myself so clearly that I shall know there is nothing to be vain about.'

'I do not believe you are vain,' said Cecily, 'because the very basis of vanity is that those who possess it are unaware that they do so. They think the puffed-up vision *they* see is the true one.'

'I see you are very wise,' said Giles.

'Nonsense. See how Marmot regards you, Master Heron. She likes you.'

'Does she? Her bright eyes look at me suspiciously, I fancy.'

'She is looking at you with interest. If she did not like you she would be making strange noises of irritation.'

'I am glad one member of the family has taken to me.'

'She is not the only one,' said Cecily with disarming frankness. 'Here is another.'

She made a gay little curtsy–not at all what Giles would have expected from such a learned little scholar.

'And here is another,' said Jack. 'Let us go to the hayfields. We should be helping there.'

It was all very different from what Giles had expected. In the hayfield Sir Thomas More himself was sitting against a hedge, drinking some beverage from a jug, and his daughters were about him.

Was this Sir Thomas More, the Under-Treasurer, the friend of the King and the Cardinal?

'Welcome! Welcome!' he cried. 'I am glad you came when we are all at home. The hay must be cut at the right moment, and right glad I am to be at home at such a time. You are thirsty, doubtless. Come, join us. Have you a tankard for Master Heron, Meg? And give him a piece of that cob loaf.'

Giles was introduced to the family. The Mistress of the house made him very welcome; and even Mistress Roper, the eldest daughter, whose fame as a scholar had reached even him, alarmed him not at all.

Cecily and Jack sat beside him and told how the monkey had driven off the weasel.

It was quite pleasant there, lying in the shade of the hedge and taking refreshment, joining in the conversation and laughter.

Afterwards Jack showed him the grounds and stables, the orchards, barns, outhouses and, finally, the dairy.

Supper proved to be a merry meal taken at the long table on the dais in the great hall. The food was simple; and there was a newcomer, whom no one seemed to know, who had called just as the meal was about to be served and was given a place at the table.

Conversation was perhaps a little clever, and there was Latin–classical allusions, which Giles did not understand, but when this was the case, he found he had no need to join in, and that Lady More was always ready to poke fun at her scholars, and to smile at him as though to say: 'We are the clever ones.'

When the meal was over they sat on the lawn, for the day was still hot; and some of them brought out their lutes and there was singing.

Giles Heron was very happy that night. He felt that, instead of coming to a strange household and perhaps a hostile one, he had come home.

He sat next to Cecily and listened to her sweet singing voice. He had already decided that by falling in love with and marrying Cecily he might please not only his father, but himself.

When Sir John Heron, Treasurer of the King's Chamber, told his friend Sir

John Dauncey, Knight of the Body to the King, that his son Giles was to marry one of the daughters of Sir Thomas More, Sir John Dauncey was reflective.

His thoughts turned to his son William, and he lost no time in seeking him out.

It was possible to talk frankly to William, for William was a most ambitious young man, and would not have to be told twice to seize any advantage which came his way.

'I hear Giles Heron is to marry one of More's daughters,' he said to his son. 'Master Heron has been quick. But there is still one daughter left.'

William nodded. He did not need to have the implication of those words explained. There was no need to point out the advantages of a match between himself and one of the daughters of so favoured a man.

'I must call at the house in Chelsea,' he said.

His father smiled his approval. There was no need to say: 'Do not make the reason for your call too obvious. More is a strange man, and his daughters will doubtless be equally strange. The matter must be tackled with some delicacy.'

William would know. He was ambitious enough to approach every advantageous situation with the utmost tact and delicacy.

The summer was passing. Among the trees in the orchard, Dorothy Colly, Margaret's maid, was playing with Margaret's young son Will. An apple, part of which had been destroyed by the wasps, fell suddenly to the grass, and the baby began to crawl towards it.

'Come away, my little man, come away,' said Dorothy. 'Don't touch it, darling. Ugh! . . . Nasty!'

The baby crowed and Dorothy picked him up and cuddled him. He was very like his mother, and Dorothy loved his mother, who had treated her more like a friend than a servant, teaching her to read and write, giving her respect and affection.

'You're a lucky boy,' she said. 'We're all lucky here in Chelsea.'

She thought of coming to the house–her life before, her life after.

As soon as she entered the house or the grounds a feeling of peace would steal over her. She knew this was due to the influence of the master, for to be in his presence was to be filled with a determination to live up to his high standards.

At this moment she could hear Lady More at the virginals, practising in her laboured way. Yet even such sounds were harmonious coming from this house, for to hear them was to remember that her ladyship, who had no great love of music, practised the lute and the virginals so that when her husband came home she might show him what progress she had made. Even Lady More had been mellowed by the sweetness of her husband's nature.

It was true that when she stopped playing she would declare that she had done with wasting time for that day; and to reassure herself she would doubtless scold some defaulter in the kitchens; but the next day she would be practising on the lute or the virginals.

Dorothy's heart began to beat faster, for, coming towards her, was Sir Thomas's secretary, John Harris.

John was an earnest young man, fully aware of the importance of his work. He sought to emulate his master in all ways, even adopting that habit of walking with his gown not properly set on the shoulders, and the left shoulder lifted a little higher than the right. Dorothy noticed this, and it made her smile become a little tender.

He was deep in thought and did not immediately see Dorothy.

She spoke first: 'Good day to you, Master Harris.'

He smiled, pleasure transforming his face. 'And a very good day to you,' he said, sitting down beside her and smiling at the baby.

'How big he grows!' said John.

'His sister is nearly as big as he is. So you are not at the Court to-day, Master Harris?'

'No. There is work to do at home.'

'Tell me, do they really think so highly of the master at Court?'

'Very highly indeed.'

Dorothy pulled up a handfull of grass and frowned at it.

'You are not pleased that it should be so?' he asked.

'I was thinking that I would like to see all the girls as happily married as is Mistress Roper. She was married before the master became so important. Master Roper was here . . . they grew to know each other . . . and they eventually married. I was thinking that that is the best way in which to make a marriage.'

'You are thinking of William Dauncey?'

She nodded. 'Mistress Elizabeth does not seem to understand. Of course, he is very handsome . . . and very charming to her . . . but there is a light in his eyes which, it would seem to me, is put there by his love of the advancement Sir Thomas More can provide, rather than for Sir Thomas's daughter.'

'Dorothy, you are a discerning woman.'

'I love them so much. I have been with them so long. Mistress Elizabeth is very clever with her lessons, but that is not being clever in the ways of the world. I wish that some quiet young gentleman like Master Roper would come here to study, and Mistress Elizabeth gradually get to know him. And I would like to see her take him instead of Master Dauncey.'

'You have served Mistress Roper for a long time, Dorothy. She has educated you and moulded your thoughts, and you think that everything she does is always right. The baby is the perfect baby. Master Roper is the perfect husband. There are some who would say that Master William Dauncey is not such a bad match. His father has a high post at Court. What more could you want?'

'Love,' she said. 'Disinterested love. Ah, I have said too much.'

'You need have no fear, Dorothy. But let me say this: When Mistress Roper married, her husband was caught fast in heresy. Heresy, Dorothy! Is that then more desirable than ambition?'

She was thoughtful. 'His heresy,' she said, 'grew out of his searching for the right, his determination to do what he considered best. Ambition–such as Dauncey has–is for self-glorification. There lies the difference.'

'Mistress Dorothy, you are wondrous learned.'

'My mistress has taught me to read; she has given me books. She has taught me to form my own opinions–that is all.'

Dorothy picked up the baby and held him against her. 'Sometimes I wish that the master were not so well received at Court,' she said. 'I would rather see him more often at home . . . with good people about him . . . like you, John Harris . . . than with the most handsome gallants of the Court.'

Then Dorothy left him and walked to the house.

How peaceful was this scene! she thought.

Now came the sound of someone playing the lute. It was too well played to be Lady More. Now she heard Cecily's and Elizabeth's voices, singing a ballad.

'Please God keep them happy,' prayed Dorothy. 'Let us go on just like this . . . for ever and ever . . . until we are called to our rest.'

There came the sound of other voices, singing with the girls–Giles Heron's and William Dauncey's.

Dorothy shivered. The voices of the young men reminded her that life was continually changing.

Too many honours were being thrust upon the master, and honours brought envy; they brought the sycophants, the false friends, who were like wasps that fed on the lovely fruit until it was ruined and dropped from the branches.

That year came the winter of the great frost.

There was no keeping the house warm; the bleak winds penetrated into every room, and there was ice on the river. Blizzards swept across the country.

Mercy was hardly ever at home; she had so many sick people in the hospital. Margaret and Elizabeth were often there helping her.

Mercy was very happy. The hospital was her life. Although others might deplore Sir Thomas's rise in the world, Mercy could not. But for his making a fortune in the service of the King, he could not have supplied the money which she needed to keep her hospital in being. But she was careful in the extreme. There was nothing extravagant about Mercy; she worked hard and enjoyed working hard. She remembered Erasmus's criticism of English houses, and she had no rushes in her hospital; there were windows that could be opened wide; and her success with her patients was gratifying.

Mercy enjoyed those days when her foster-father came to inspect her work. He would go among the patients, a joke on his lips. 'Laughter is one of the best of medicines,' he told her; and she was contented to have him with her whether he praised or questioned what she did.

She would not admit to herself that she was not completely happy; she, who was so frank on all other matters, knew herself to be evasive in this.

She would not admit to herself that she loved Dr Clement. It is merely, she told herself, that there is so much talk of weddings and that makes me wonder if I shall ever be a bride. Ailie and Margaret are married; and now Cecily will have Giles Heron, and Elizabeth her William Dauncey; and because of all this I too look for love.

Had it not always been so? The little foster-sister had always feared that she was not quite a member of the family, in spite of everyone's attempts to assure her that she was. Now from Court came two gallants eager to wed the daughters of Sir Thomas More; but none came to woo his foster-daughter.

Not that Mercy expected it. She laughed at the idea of plain Mercy Gigs being wooed by such a dashing gentleman as William Dauncey.

Moreover, Mercy did not want a Court gallant; she wanted Dr Clement.

And he? Why should he think of Mercy Gigs? But he did think of her–oh, as a friend, as a girl who was interested in medicine, as one who spent her time working in her hospital and who liked to ask his advice on certain matters.

She must not be deluded. She was a nobody. She was an orphan on whom the Mores had taken pity; however much they tried to make her forget that, *she* must not. And John Clement? A young man of good family, high in the service of the great Cardinal, looked on with favour by the King's physician, Dr Linacre. As if he would think of Mercy Gigs as anything but a friend.

Ah yes, she reminded herself, all this talk of marriages makes me want what the others have. I want to be loved by a husband even as, when I was a child, I wished to be loved by their father.

Cecily and Elizabeth had come over to the hospital on this day, although it was as much as they could do to plod through the snow even that far.

They seemed quite pretty–both of them–with a certain glow upon them. That was being in love. Cecily was the happier perhaps; she was more sure of her Giles. But Elizabeth–more reserved than her younger sister–was she a little anxious about William Dauncey? Did she know–as others did–that he was an ambitious young man who believed her father could advance him? Poor Elizabeth! Like Mercy, she wished for marriage. Was she loving the ideal of marriage more than the man who would make it possible? Mercy uttered a silent prayer for Elizabeth. Cecily would be happy with her Giles. He was a lazy boy, good-natured, frank, not hiding the fact that his father had wished him to marry a Mistress More, and that he was delighted to find such a marriage to his liking. He had not William Dauncey's tight-lipped ambition. And was she right, Mercy wondered, when she thought that even Dauncey had changed since he had visited the house? Was his laughter, when he joined their family group and played their games and sang with them, was it a little less forced than it had been?

The two girls laughed as they shook the snow out of their clothes.

'Why, Mercy, what a day! If the blizzard starts again, we shall be snowed up and unable to get out at all . . . and no one will be able to get to us.' That was Elizabeth.

Cecily said: 'And you must come over to dinner to-day. Someone is coming, and he'll be disappointed if you're not there.'

Mercy flushed; she knew, by Cecily's quick glance at Elizabeth, who was coming.

'If the weather is so bad, your guest may not arrive.'

'I doubt if he'll come by barge. The ice is quite thick on the river. Oh, Mercy, what a lovely fire!' Cecily held out her hands to the blaze.

'I was lucky, I gathered much furze and bracken during the autumn. I had those of my patients who were recovering go out and get it for me. We believe that exercise is good, and so is fresh air.'

'We?' said Cecily almost archly.

'You and Dr Clement, I suppose,' said Elizabeth.

'He is learned in these matters.'

'Father says,' said Cecily, 'that one day the King might take him into his personal service, and Dr Linacre thinks that he is the best young doctor he has known. That will doubtless mean that the King will soon hear of it.'

Oh, yes, thought Mercy, he is all that. He is rising in the world, and when he has gone far enough some nobleman of high rank will decide that he is a good match for his daughter.

And John himself? He was as ambitious in his way as Dauncey was in his. He wished to discover new ways of defeating sickness. The favour of the King might help him to do that.

Cecily and Elizabeth did not know that when they talked of the cleverness of John Clement and his chances at Court, they were showing Mercy, more clearly than she had ever seen before, how foolish she had been to dream.

'So,' insisted Cecily, 'you must come to dinner and be early. You will then be able to talk to him of the latest remedies for the pox. I am sure that will make entertaining dinner talk.'

'We just came to tell you this,' said Elizabeth. 'Mother is in a fine mood this morning. It is Margaret's turn to keep house this week. Poor Margaret! Mother is puffing about the kitchen, warning them all that if the beef is not thoroughly basted, someone will suffer. There is much running to and fro . . . and all because Dr John Clement has become such an important personage. It is hard to remember that he was scarcely more than a boy when he first came to us to attend Father on his way to Flanders. The humble secretary has become a great doctor.'

Ah, thought Mercy, too great for me.

Just as the girls were about to leave, a young boy arrived. He was white-faced, and the snow nestled in his hair, so that, on account of the gauntness of his features, he looked like a white-headed man.

'What is it, Ned?' asked Mercy, recognizing him as one of the boys from Blandels Bridge.

'It's my father, Mistress Mercy. He's lying on the straw like a dead man. But he's not dead. He just stares with his eyes wide open, and he can say naught. My mother says to come to you and ask you to see him.'

'You cannot go all the way to Blandels Bridge in this weather,' said Cecily.

'He may be very ill. I must go.'

'But the snow is deep. You could never reach there.'

'It is less than half a mile; and Ned came here.' She looked at his feet. He was wearing a pair of shoes which had belonged to Jack, for Margaret's task was to see to the needs of the poor, and this she did with the help of her family's clothes.

'You will not come back with us, then?'

Mercy shook her head. She must stifle weakness. She was a doctor first. This was her hospital; she believed it must be the love of her life, for Dr Clement–her affectionate friend, though he might be–could not marry her.

'Then you will miss dinner.'

'I fear so. I do not know how long I must stay at the cottage.'

'Mercy,' said Cecily, 'come and have dinner and go there afterwards. Perhaps John Clement will escort you.'

There was temptation. She pictured dinner in the beloved home, herself saying grace as she used to in the old days; she imagined the interesting conversation, and then, afterwards, riding pillion with John Clement to the cottage by Blandels Bridge, listening to his diagnosis of the patient's ailment, offering her own.

But sickness did not wait for such pretty, comforting scenes. Speed was everything in fighting sickness. A life could be lost by the delay of five minutes, let alone hours.

'Nay,' she said. 'I must go at once. Ned, wait for me. I must bring a few simples with me.'

So Elizabeth and Cecily went back to the house on the other side of the pales, and Mercy trudged through the snow to Blandels Bridge.

The blizzard beat at her; the familiar landscape had become unfamiliar; a thick white cloth was laid over everything, disguising the shapes of hedges and cottages.

But Ned knew the way. She followed him blindly. Soon her fingers were numb, her feet icily cold. The journey–uusually a walk of ten minutes–took the greater part of an hour.

She thought: I shall miss him then. It is so long since I have seen him. He is so busy that he comes to see us but rarely. And when he does . . . I cannot be there!

They had reached the cottage. The rushes stank. There seemed no air in the place, yet it was bitterly cold. The woman who had been sitting on a stool shivering as she watched the man on the floor, brightened when she heard Mercy's voice without.

'God bless you for coming!' she cried as Mercy entered the cottage.

And when Mercy looked into her eyes, she thought: That must be my reward.

She knelt by the man on the dirty straw, and laid a hand on his burning forehead. He began to cough.

'He has been coughing like that for hours,' said the woman. 'It seems as though the cough will choke him.'

Mercy said: 'When the weather improves, I want to take him to my hospital. It is not good for him to be here.'

The man's piteous eyes held Mercy's. He seemed to be begging her to make him well.

She took one of the phials from her bag which she had brought, and gave him its contents. The close, cold atmosphere of the room made her shiver, and the smell from the rushes sickened her.

She thought: If only I could get him away from here . . . into one of my warm rooms, with blankets and a comfortable pallet on which to lie. If I could give him hot soup, fresh air, who knows . . . I might cure him.

'How is he, Mistress Mercy?' asked the woman.

'He is very sick.'

'Is he going to die?'

Mercy looked into the panic-stricken eyes. How could she say: 'I can do nothing for him here'? How could she say: 'Clean out these foul rushes'? Why, to disturb them now would double the danger. He was not so far gone in disease that she could not save him. If it were not for the weather, she would go to her foster-father's house; she would get strong men, and boards on which to place this man, and carry him away from this foul-smelling place which was his home. But how could she do this in a snow-storm?

Mercy closed her eyes and prayed for guidance and, as if by some miracle, the door opened and there, seeming strong and all-powerful, was Dr John Clement.

'John!' she cried in delight. 'You . . . here?'

'Indeed yes, Mercy. The girls told me where you were, and I came to see if I could help.'

'Thank God!' she said. 'It is the answer to a prayer.'

'And the patient?'

He knelt in the rushes and looked into the sick man's face.

'This place . . .' said Mercy, and John nodded. 'If I could get him to the hospital,' she went on, 'care for him there . . . I believe I could nurse him back to health.'

John was silent for a while. Then he said: 'I rode here. I tied my horse to a stake by the cottage. We could put him on the horse and get him to the hospital.'

'Through the snow?'

John's answer was to look round the room, at the foul rushes and the earthen walls, damp and noisome.

'He cannot live if he stays here.'

'Can he live if he is taken out into the cold?'

'In a case like this, we have to take a chance.'

'You would take this chance, then, John?'

'I would. Would you?'

'Yes,' she said. 'I would do as you would.'

Happiness came in strange places at strange times. The snow was blowing in Mercy's face; she was wet and numb with cold, yet warm with pleasure.

She had rarely been so happy in her life as she was when she was walking through the snow with John Clement, the sick man, whom they held on John's horse, between them, while the pale-faced boy led the horse.

There was a double wedding that summer.

The marriages of Elizabeth with William Dauncey and Cecily with Giles Heron were to be celebrated in the private chapel attached to one of the mansions belonging to the Allington family.

Ailie–now Lady Allington–was delighted to have her family with her for this occasion.

Ailie was a happy person. Her husband adored her; she had a child now, but that fact had changed her little; she was still the gay and fascinating Ailie.

With great pleasure she showed her mother the kitchens of the house. They were older than those of Chelsea and far more grand.

Alice sniffed her disapproval of this and that, trying hard to find fault while she congratulated herself that it was her daughter who had made the best match of all.

'Look, Mother. Have you seen these ceilings? Giles is most proud of them. You see how cleverly they are painted. You'll find nothing like that in modern houses. Look at these painted cloths. They all represent scenes of some battles. Do not ask me which, I beg of you, for I do not know. In the great hall we have Flemish tapestry which is every bit as fine as that which my Lord Cardinal has in Tittenhanger or Hampton Court.'

'Tilly valley!' said Alice, 'What happens in the kitchen is of more importance than painted hangings or Flemish tapestry, I tell you. That has to be tested yet.'

Ailie kissed her mother; she loved to tease . . . to tease them all, her half-sisters, her stepfather, her mother and her husband. And it was very pleasant to have them all with her again.

Margaret spoke to her of William Dauncey. 'Elizabeth loves him, but does he love Elizabeth? Or is he thinking solely of what Father can do for him?'

'Well,' said Ailie, confident in her own charms, 'if he does not love her, then it is for her to make him do so. And if he will not . . .'

Ailie shrugged her shoulders, but, glancing at Margaret, decided not to finish what she had begun to say. Instead, she added: 'Why, they'll be happy enough, I doubt not. Master Dauncey is a young man who will go far and, believe me, my dear Margaret, it is by no means unpleasant to be the wife of a rising star.'

'Is that so, then?' said Margaret. 'I know what it is to be the daughter of one; and I would rather Father were less favourably looked upon at Court, so that his family might look upon him the more often.'

'Father! Oh, Father is no ordinary man. Father is a saint!'

Then Ailie left her sister; she was a busy hostess, and there was much to which she must attend, for her mansion at Willesden was filled with the most distinguished guests.

Her glance had gone to my Lord of Norfolk, recently the Earl of Surrey, who had succeeded to the title on the death of his father a year or so before.

Ailie curtsied before him and told him how honoured she was to see him at her house. Strange man! He was scarcely conscious of Ailie's charm. He looked grim, as though he had never given a thought to anything but matters of state. It was difficult to believe that his wife was giving him a lively time on account of her laundress, Bess Holland, for whom this grim man had a passion which he could not resist.

Norfolk was aloof, believing that he greatly honoured the Allingtons by attending at their house, being conscious that he was a great nobleman, head of one of the highest families in the land, and–although he dared not say this to any–he could not help reminding himself that the Howards of Norfolk were as royal as the Tudors. The recent death of his father-in-law, Buckingham, was a terrible warning to him, a reminder that he must keep such thoughts to himself; but that did not prevent his private enjoyment of them.

No; he would not be here this day but for his friendship with Sir Thomas More. There had occurred in the July of this year an incident which had startled all men who stood near the throne, and had set them pondering.

The King had said to the Cardinal one day when they were in the grounds of that extravagant and most luxurious of country houses, Hampton Court: 'Should a subject be so rich as to possess such a house?' And the Cardinal, that clever, most shrewd of statesmen, whose quick wits had lifted him from obscurity to a place in the sun, had thrown away the riches of Hampton Court in his answer: 'A subject could only be justified in owning such a place, Sire, that he might give it to his King.'

No more could people sing 'Which Court? The King's Court or Hampton Court?' For now Hampton Court was the King's Court in very truth.

Something was happening between the King and the Cardinal; it was something which put a belligerent light in the King's eyes, and a fearful one in those of the Cardinal.

Norfolk, that ambitious man, that cold, hard schemer–soft only to Bessie Holland–believed that the favour so long enjoyed by the Cardinal was less bright than of yore. This delighted Norfolk, for he hated Wolsey. His father had instilled in him that hatred; it was not only brought about by envy of the favour Wolsey enjoyed; it was not only the resentment a nobleman might feel for an upstart from a humble stratum of society; it was because of the part this Duke's father had been forced to play in the trial of his friend, Buckingham. Buckingham, that nobleman and kinsman of the Howards, had been condemned to death because he had not shown enough respect to one whom Norfolk's father had called 'A butcher's cur'. And one of Buckingham's judges had been the old Duke of Norfolk who, with tears in his eyes, had condemned him to death, because he had known that had he done otherwise he would have lost his own head. This would never be forgiven. However long the waiting must be, Wolsey must suffer, not only for the execution of Buckingham, but for the fact that he had forced Norfolk to condemn his friend and kinsman.

But, besides being a vengeful man, the Duke of Norfolk was an ambitious one. He did not lose sight of the fact that when Wolsey fell from grace there would be only one other clever enough to take his place. It would be well to be on terms of friendship with that man. Not that that in itself presented a hardship. If anyone, besides Bess Holland, could soften the heart of this hard man, it was Thomas More. I like him, thought Norfolk, puzzled by his own feelings. I really like him . . . for the man he is, not only for the greatness which may very well be his.

So it was that Norfolk wished to be More's friend. It was a strange matter –as strange as such a proud man's love for a humble laundress.

Thus was the Duke of Norfolk attending the double wedding of the daughters of a mere knight and the sons of two more mere knights.

Thomas was now approaching him. None would think, to look at him, that he was a brilliant scholar of world fame, and on the way to becoming one of the most important statesmen in the kingdom. He was more simply dressed than any man present, and it was clear to see that he thought little about his clothes. He walked with one shoulder higher than the other–an absurd habit, thought Norfolk, for it gave him an appearance of deformity.

But now Thomas stood before him, and Norfolk felt that strange mixture of tenderness and exasperation.

'I have never seen you so gay, Sir Thomas.'

'I am a lucky man, my lord. My two daughters are marrying this day, and instead of losing them I am to gain two sons. They will live with me–these two new sons–when they are not at Court, in my house in Chelsea. All my own daughters are married now, and I have lost not one of them. Do you not think that is a matter for rejoicing, my lord?'

'Much depends on whether you can live in amity with this large family of yours.'

Norfolk's eyes were narrowed; he was remembering his own stormy family life with its recriminations and quarrels.

'We live in amity at Chelsea. You should come to see us one day my lord, when your barge takes you that way.'

'I will . . . I will. I have heard of your household. It is said: "*Vis nunquam tristis esse? Recte vive!*" Is that how you achieve your happiness, Master More?'

'Perhaps we strive to live rightly in Chelsea. That may be why we are such a happy family.'

Norfolk's eyes were brooding. He changed the subject abruptly. 'There is something brewing at the Court.'

'My lord?'

'The King has created his bastard Fitzroy, Duke of Richmond and Somerset.'

'He loves the boy.'

'But such great titles . . . for a bastard! Might it not be that His Grace feels he may never have a legitimate son?'

'The Queen has been many times disappointed; poor lady, she feels this sorely.'

Norfolk came close and whispered: 'And will feel it more sorely still, I doubt not.'

They went together to the great table on which was laid out a feast so magnificent that it was said it might have graced the tables of the King or the Cardinal.

There was beef, mutton, pork; there was roasted boar and many kinds of fish, with venison and pies of all sorts. There was even turkey–that newest of delicacies imported into the country for the first time that year.

There was drink of all sorts–wine, red and white; malmsey, muscatel and romney; there was metheglin and mead.

And while the company feasted, minstrels played merry tunes in the gallery.

It was after the banquet and during the ball that followed it, that Mercy, standing aside to watch the dancers, found Dr Clement beside her.

'Well, Mercy,' he said, 'this is a merry day indeed. And right glad you must be that, although your sisters are marrying, like Margaret, they are not leaving the family roof.'

'That is indeed a blessing. I think it would have broken Father's heart if any of them had wanted to leave home. It was bad enough when Ailie went.'

'How would he feel if you went, Mercy?'

'I?' She blushed. 'Oh . . . as he did when Ailie went, I suppose. She is a stepdaughter; I am a foster-daughter. He is so good that he will have us believe that he loves us all as his own.'

'I think he would be unhappy if you left, Mercy. But . . . why should you leave? You could stay there . . . with your hospital, and I should be at Court. . . . Like your father, I should seize every opportunity to be with you.'

She dared not look at him. She did not believe that she had heard him correctly. There could not be all that happiness in the world. Surely she could not have her beloved father, her family, her hospital *and* John Clement!

He was close to her, slipping his arm through hers.

'What say you, Mercy? What say you?'

'John . . .'

'You seem surprised. Did you not then know that I love you? Have I presumed too much in letting myself believe that you love me too?'

'Oh, John,' she said, 'do you mean . . . do you really mean . . . that *you* love *me*?'

'When you say *you*, you say it as though I were the King; and when you say *me*, you say it as though you were the humblest serving-girl. Why, Mercy, you are clever; you are good, and I love you. I beg of you, cast aside your humility and tell me you will marry me.'

'I am so happy,' she said, 'that I cannot find the words.'

'Then there must soon be another marriage in this family.'

What a happy day that was! Thomas smiled at each member of his family in turn. Would he rather have had the celebrations in his own home? Not when he looked at the proud smiles of Alice and her daughter. And as for Elizabeth and Cecily, they would have been equally happy wherever the ceremony had taken place.

It was not the banquet with its turkeys, the rich apartments with their painted hangings nor the distinguished guests that were important; it was the blissful happiness of each member of his family. And here was Mercy, as happy as any of them, and John Clement beside her; which could mean only one thing.

The merriment continued. There were morris dancers with bells on their legs; there were riders on hobby horses and there was the more stately dancing of the guests. Ailie was anxious to show that her attendance at Court had not been wasted, and the entertainment she could give her friends–if less luxurious than that given at the King's Court–was such to which the

King himself could have come and found pleasure.

And later, Ailie, in her own chamber, surrounded by her sisters, who had gone thither to rest awhile, allowed them to examine her dress, which was of blue velvet and made in the very latest fashion. The velvet overdress was cut away to show a petticoat of pale pink satin; the lacing across the bodice was of gold-coloured ribbons.

Before them all Ailie turned and twisted.

'You like it, then? It is the very latest fashion, I do assure you. It is cut in the French manner. Do you like my shoes?' She extended a dainty foot for them to see. 'Look at the silver star on them. That is most fashionable. And you should all be wearing bands of velvet or gold about your necks. That is the very latest fashion. And see the sleeves! They fall over the hands. They are graceful, are they not?'

'Graceful?' said Elizabeth. 'But are they comfortable? It would seem to me that they might get in the way.'

'Mistress Dauncey,' cried Ailie, looking severely at her half-sister, 'do we wear our clothes to be comfortable? And what matters it if the sleeves, as you say, get in the way? They are graceful, and it is the only way a sleeve should hang.'

'I care not,' said Elizabeth, 'whether it is the latest thing from France or not. I should find it most uncomfortable.'

Ailie was conspiratorial. 'You know who started this fashion, do you not? But of course you do not. How could you? It was one of the maids of honour. It seems that she decides what we shall and what we shall not wear.'

'Then more fool you,' said Cecily, 'to let one woman decide what you should and should not wear.'

'*Let* her decide! We can do no other. She wears this sleeve because of a deformity on one of her fingers. Then it must seem that all other sleeves are ugly. *She* has a wart on her neck . . . a birthmark, some say; so she wears a band about it; and all see that such bands are so becoming that any without are quite unfashionable. She is lately come from France, and she is Anne . . . the daughter of Sir Thomas Boleyn. She is Mary's sister; and all the men admire her, and all the women are envious, for when she is there, though she may have an ugly finger and a wen on her neck, it seems that everyone else appears plain and insignificant.'

Margaret interrupted with a laugh: 'Oh, have done, Ailie! Have done with your frivolous maid-of-honour. Have done with your Frenchified Anne Boleyn, and let us talk of something that really matters.'

Chapter Five

There were several children in the house now. Margaret had a little girl, and Cecily and Elizabeth both had babies. If Elizabeth had not found complete happiness in her marriage, she had great hopes of finding it in her children.

In the streets the people were singing:

> 'Turkeys, carps, hops, pippins and beer
> Came into England all in one year.'

And that year was the one of the great frost and the marriages of Elizabeth and Cecily.

Margaret thought of that year and the year that followed it as the happy years. So much seemed to happen in the family circle that they were all blinded to what was happening outside . . . all except Thomas.

There were times when, with his family about him, Margaret would notice that he stared beyond them with a strangely remote look on his face. It might be that they were in the fields saving the hay; or it might be when they were in the orchards gathering the fruit, or sitting at table, talking, laughing together.

Once she slipped her arm through his and whispered: 'Father, of what do you think?'

His answer was: 'Of all this, Meg, of this family of mine . . . this perfect contentment. On the day I die–no matter how I die–I shall remember this moment and say that my life brought me much joy.'

Then their eyes had met, and for a moment there was understanding between them as there never was between him and any other.

'Father,' she had cried out in panic, 'I like it not when you talk of death. You frighten me.'

'Fear not, Meg,' he had answered, 'for who knows when death will come? Rejoice, Meg, in that uncertainty. You would be weeping if you knew I had a month to live. You were laughing a moment ago, though I might not have a day.'

'Father, I long for the time when you will leave the Court.'

Then he had smiled his sweet smile and had said: 'Let us be happy in this moment, Meg. Is it not as happy a moment as any could ask?'

There was so much to think about, so much to talk about during those two years. One child was having difficulty with her teeth; another cried too much; another had too many colds. These were such important matters. How could they stop for a moment to consider what was happening in the Courts of Europe? The King of France had been taken prisoner at Pavia and carried to Madrid; Cardinal Wolsey's foreign policy was less successful than it had previously been. There was a certain subject about which there was much whispering in Court circles, and it was known as the King's Secret Matter.

But to the family living in the pleasant house on the bank of the Thames, life was good. The babies were a source of amusement and delight; the Latin verses composed by their mothers provided much entertainment when read aloud. It was enjoyable to stroll in the gardens on a summer's night and watch the stars with Master Kratzer; it was so amusing to try to make Alice take an interest in astronomy and to listen to her scathing comments.

There was the fun of feeding the animals, watching them grow and teaching them tricks; there were the flower gardens to be tended; there was the pleasant rivalry between Elizabeth with her gilly-flowers and Cecily with her daffadowndillies; there was the fun of trying out new dishes. Ailie would come with the very latest recipes and show them how peacocks were served at a Court banquet, and how to make sugarbread and marchpane the royal way. There was the great tapestry to work on in hours of leisure; there were the herbs to be gathered in the surrounding fields, so that Mercy could make them into medicines and Alice use them for flavouring or garnishing a dish.

They were very happy during those two years.

Mercy was married to her Dr Clement, but she lived with them still, dividing her time between the house and the hospital. Thomas had given them the old house in Bucklersbury as a wedding present, and the girls were busy making tapestry to hang in Mercy's new home; but she continued to live at Chelsea during those two happy years. When she went to live in Bucklersbury, Margaret would spend more time at the hospital, but that was not to be yet.

Every evening there were prayers in the private chapel with the family assembled; at meal-times it was always Mercy who read from the Scriptures. They would discuss together what she had read, and there would be interesting argument.

There were three new additions to the family during those years.

One was a poor man, Henry Patenson, who had need of succour. He had a certain sharpness of wit, and since it was not known what task could be given him in the household, he himself suggested that, as all great men whose work led them to the society of the wise needed a fool to amuse them in their leisure hours, Henry Patenson should become the fool of Sir Thomas More.

Thus Henry Patenson joined the household.

Then there was little Anne Cresacre, who came to Chelsea as the betrothed of Jack. Poor little girl, she was very frightened. She knew that she was going to live among the learned, and that terrified her; but she had been so delighted to find that her future husband was the dunce of the family that she saw him as a natural protector. As for Jack, he had himself often felt inadequate among the scholars, and understood her feelings and was able to reassure her. Consequently, Anne Cresacre found that, although her future husband's learned family might terrify her, he did not.

Moreover, Lady More took her to her heart–for she was a very rich little girl–but all the same, riches or no riches, she must learn how to manage a household and take over the arrangement of domestic matters in turn with the other girls.

The third visitor was a painter from Basle–a young man full of enthusiasm and ideals, who had come to England to seek his fortune.

Erasmus–whom Thomas had visited on his trips to Europe and between whom there had been continual correspondence–discovered this man, and he wrote to Thomas asking him to receive him in his house. 'His name,' he wrote, 'is Hans Holbein, and I believe him to be a clever man at his craft. He wishes to come to England in order to earn some money. I beg of you, do all you can to help him.' Such a plea to Thomas could not be made in vain.

He welcomed the young man to his house, and so there was yet another to join the happy family group. He would sit sketching whenever the light allowed, listening to their talk, learning to speak their language, delighted because he could capture their expressions and draw them all with loving care.

'This man hath genius,' said Thomas to Alice.

At which Alice laughed. 'Genius! He was sitting out in the east wind yesterday, sketching away. He'll catch his death, I'll warrant. And *I* shall have to nurse him. *I* shall have to spend my time, which I can ill afford, making hot possets for him. And you call that genius!'

Thus during the happy years life went on.

Ailie came one day with news hot from Court.

'Such a pother! It is Mistress Anne Boleyn. What do you think? She hath betrothed herself to Henry, Lord Percy. The eldest son of the Earl of Northumberland, if you please! Trust Mistress Anne to pick one of the noblest peers in the land.'

'Then the girl hath good sense,' said Alice. 'For why should she not reach for the best plum on the tree?'

'And he was ready to fall to her touch,' cried Ailie, 'like a very ripe plum. Humble Anne Boleyn to mate with a Percy! So to Town comes my Lord of Northumberland, and poor little Percy hath been soundly berated. My Lord Cardinal, in whose service he is, himself administered the scolding. And such a scolding! 'Tis said that poor Percy has not stopped weeping yet. And Mistress Anne? That's a different matter. She has been going about the Court flashing her eyes, swearing she will not be told whom she is or is not to marry. But back she is gone to Hever Castle, and there she will stay for a while, so 'tis said.'

'And what will you do for your fashions now?' asked Margaret wryly.

'She has left us a few. Methinks we must wait until she returns to Court, which, some say, will not be long.'

'Come and help me feed the peacocks,' said Elizabeth. 'I never heard such fuss, and all over one stupid girl!'

Early in the following year, the King sent for Sir Thomas More. He was in his new Palace of Hampton Court, and he suggested that Thomas should take a walk with him, for he had heard that Thomas had made some pretty gardens round his house in Chelsea; he would like to discuss his own plans for altering the gardens at Hampton Court.

So they walked side by side, the man in the sombre garments, his left shoulder a little higher than the right, his gown unadorned by jewels of any sort, and the gigantic, sparkling figure in doublet of purple velvet lined with ermine, his person sparkling with rubies and emeralds worth a fortune.

Now the King talked of the pond garden he would make; he talked of the beds of roses–red and white roses growing together side by side–symbols of the rival houses of Lancaster and York; and these should be enclosed by a wall, the pillars of which were to be made of stone and should be engraved with Tudor roses. All those who looked should see how the roses of York and Lancaster bloomed and faded while the Tudor rose altered not, engraved as it was on pillars of stone. The King enjoyed exploiting his fondness for allegory.

'Now, friend Thomas, what do you think of my pond garden? Have you anything to compare with that at Chelsea?'

'Nay, Sire. Our gardens are simple ones, tended mostly by my family.'

'Ah, that happy family of yours!' The King's heavy hand was on his shoulder; the King's flushed face was near his own and the little mouth was close to Thomas's ear. 'I'll tell you a secret, Thomas, that I believe I have told you before: I envy you, man. Your King envies you. A happy family! How many grandchildren are there now? Six! And grandsons. . . . And your son soon to wed and provide you with more, I doubt not. You are a good man, Thomas More; and God has showered his favours upon you. Yet, Thomas, would you say your King was an evil-doer?'

Into Thomas's mind there flashed a procession of murdered men–Dudley, Empson and Buckingham at the head of them; he thought of Elizabeth Blount, flaunting the King's natural son among her friends; he thought of wanton Mary Boleyn, and the quiet, long-suffering Queen

Katharine. Was this King an evil-doer?

What great good fortune that the King did not expect an answer to that which he considered a question so absurd that none could take it seriously!

'Nay, Thomas,' he went on. 'I hear Mass many times a day. I am a devout man. I have dedicated my life to my country. You, my statesman, my Councillor who has lived close to me, know that. Is it not therefore a marvellous thing that God should deny me that which I most crave! Not for myself do I crave it. Nay. It is for this realm. Thomas, I must have a son. I need a son. I need a son for England.'

'Your Grace is young yet.'

'*I* am young. *I* am in the full vigour of my youth and manhood. *I* could have sons. I have proved . . . I have no doubt of that. And when a man and woman fail to produce an heir, when they wish above all things for a son, there is one explanation only of that, Master More. They have displeased Almighty God.'

'Your Grace, have patience for a while. The Queen has given you a healthy daughter.'

'A healthy daughter! Much good is she! I want sons . . . sons . . . I am King of England, Thomas More; and it is necessary for a King to give his country an heir.'

Thomas was silent and the King frowned as he went on: 'There is a matter which lies heavy on my conscience. The Queen, as you know, was my brother's wife ere she became mine. You are a learned man, Master More, a religious one. You read your Bible. God inflicts a penalty on those who commit the sin of incest. That is what I fear I have done in marrying my brother's wife. Every son has died . . . every son the Queen has borne has died. Is that not significant? Is that not a sign from Heaven that I am a victim of Divine judgment? The more I study this matter, the more certain I become that I have offended God's Holy Laws in my marriage.'

Thomas was deeply shocked. He had heard rumours of the King's Secret Matter, and he had dreaded being asked to give an opinion. He thought of the Queen, that grave and gracious lady, who had offended none but the King; and him she had offended merely because she was growing old and unattractive and had been unable to provide him with a male heir.

The King had stopped in his walk and turned to face Thomas. He rocked on his heels; his face was creased with emotions–sentiment, cruelty, cunning and simplicity, and chiefly with his determination to make Thomas see him as he saw himself.

I was against this marriage ere I made it. You remember the protest I made?'

Thomas looked in surprise at the King. 'I remember, Sire.'

'There, you see, I did not wish to enter into the marriage, then. She was, after all, my brother's widow.'

Thomas dared not say: You protested on your father's orders. It was when you made the protest that you determined to marry Queen Katharine.

Thomas was aware of the selfish cruelty, the predominant desire in the King to see himself as a righteous man. It would not be worth risking his displeasure by making such a remark. It would be folly to anger him at this stage. At this moment Henry was so carefully nursing his conscience that any man who dared suggest that his conscience was really his own desire would surely forfeit his head.

'But . . . I married her,' went on the King. 'I married her, for she was a stranger in a strange land and she had been brought to us for marriage with the heir of England. And, because she was my wife, I cherished her and I loved her, as I still do. To part with her . . . that would be a bitter blow to me. You, who have married two wives and lived with them in amity, know that. It is nearly twenty years since I married the Queen. A man cannot cast off, without a pang, a woman to whom he has been married twenty years. Yet, though I am a man–aye, and a loving husband–I remember first that I am a King. And, Master More, if it were demanded of me to cast off this wife of mine and take another . . . though this matter were hateful to me, I would do it.'

'Your Grace should not sacrifice his happiness so lightly,' said Thomas, seizing the opportunity the King had given. 'If a King has his duty to his country, a husband has his duty to his wife. And if the crowning of a King is a holy sacrament in the eyes of God, so is the ceremony of marriage. You have a daughter, Sire, the Princess Mary. . . .'

The King waved his hand impatiently.

'That gives us such anxious thought. This country has never been happily ruled by a woman. You know that, Master More. And you, who call yourself a religious man, should ponder this: Is an incestuous marriage a holy one? Can it find favour in the sight of God? And what of a man and woman who, disturbed by their conscience, *continue* to live in such a marriage? Nay, this state of affairs cannot go on.' The King smiled slyly. 'Nor will my ministers allow it. Warham, the Archbishop, and Wolsey, the Papal Legate, are bringing a secret suit against me.'

'A secret suit against Your Grace!'

The King nodded mournfully. 'A pretty pass when a King's subjects act thus against him. Mark you, I have tried to be an honest man over this matter and, much as I deplore the action of Warham and Wolsey, I yet admit they act with reason and within their rights.'

So it has come to this! thought Thomas. The King is indeed determined to cast off his wife since he had made Warham and Wolsey accuse him of incest.

'You see,' said the King, 'I am a King who is beset on all sides–by his love for his wife, by the demands of his ministers, by the reasoning of his own conscience. You are an important member of the Council, and there are many who set store by your opinions. You have many friends–Bishop Fisher among them. When this matter is discussed between you, I would have you obey *your* conscience as I am obeying mine. I would have you cast your vote not for Henry the man and Katharine the woman, but for the good of this land and its future heirs.'

'My Lord King, you honour me too much. I feel myself inadequate to meddle in such matters.'

'Nay, nay,' said the King. 'You underestimate your powers.' His voice was kind still, but his eyes flashed a warning. This matter was very near his heart, and he would brook no interference. This was a matter of conscience–the King's conscience and no one else's, for the King's conscience was such a mighty monster that it would tolerate no interference from the consciences of others. 'Come. You agree with these men who will bring a suit against me, do you not? You know, as they know, that your King and Queen are living together in sinful incest. Come! Come! Be not afraid. We ask for the truth.'

'Since your Grace asks for the truth, may I ask for time–time that I may consider this matter?'

The King's eyes were narrow, his mouth sullen.

'Very well, then. Very well. Take your time.'

He turned away abruptly, and several courtiers, who had been watching from a safe distance, asked themselves what Sir Thomas More had done to offend the King.

One of the sights to be seen in the City, rivalled only by that of the marching watch on Midsummer's Eve and the Eve of St Peter, was the ceremonious procession which attended the great Cardinal on all his journeyings. Before him, about him and behind him, went his retinue of servants, extravagantly clad in black velvet with golden chains about their necks; the lower servants were conspicuous in their tawny livery. And in the centre of all this pomp, preceded by the bearers of his silver crosses, his two pillars of silver, the Great Seal of England and his Cardinal's hat, rode the Cardinal himself, in his hand an orange, the inside of which had been replaced by pieces of vinegar-soaked sponge and other substances to counteract the pestilential air; the trappings of his mule were crimson velvet and his stirrups of copper and gold.

He went with as much ceremony as if he were the King himself.

He passed over London Bridge, and the people watched him in sullen silence. They blamed Wolsey for all their ills. Who was Wolsey? they asked themselves. A low-born man who, by great good luck, lived in the state of a King. When taxes were too high–and they always were–they blamed Wolsey. And now that the King wanted to replace the Queen, they blamed Wolsey for that. The people wanted an heir to the throne, yes; but the more serious among them remembered that the Queen was the aunt of the Emperor Charles of Spain; they might not be troubled on account of the Emperor's humiliation, which he would undoubtedly feel if his aunt were cast off, but they feared his armies. So . . . they blamed Wolsey.

He was on his way to France now, and in his retinue rode Sir Thomas More.

The great Cardinal was more deeply perturbed at this time than he had ever been before.

Fortune was turning against him. Had he looked too high when he had coveted the Papal Chair? Ah, if only he instead of Clement had been elected Pope, all his anxieties would be at an end. There he would have been content to rest, at the pinnacle of fame. There he would have had no need to fear any man. He had climbed to great heights, and now he was on a narrow ledge, his foothold precarious; he must retain a very careful balance if he were to continue to climb. About him snapped those angry, jealous wolves–Suffolk, Norfolk and their followers. There was only one man who could save him from those ravening beasts, and that was the most dangerous of them all–the King.

The secret court which he and Warham had called, that the King's marriage might be proved incestuous, had failed because of the obstinacy of the Queen, who insisted that her marriage with Arthur had never been consummated; therefore there were no grounds on which legality could be denied. Wolsey's foreign policy had resulted in his winning for England the enmity of both France and Spain; and now the Pope, on whose help he had relied in this matter of the royal divorce, had been captured during the sack of Rome and was a prisoner in the Emperor's hands.

His mission to France was an uneasy one. He must talk with Francis; he must tell him of the King's doubts regarding the legality of his marriage; he must try to arrange a match between the Princess Mary and the son of Francis; he must cautiously hint that he was looking for a future Queen of England in France. Perhaps the Princess Renée, sister of the Queen of France? Perhaps Francis's own sister, the talented Marguerite de Valois?

Everything depended on the successful termination of the King's Secret Matter; and this was a most delicate matter even for a great statesman to handle. To juggle with the politics of Europe was one thing; to secure the gratification of the King's desires another.

Still he who had achieved so much would achieve this also. What perturbed him was the growing truculence of Norfolk, and particularly of Suffolk–for Suffolk, the King's brother-in-law and his greatest friend, had the King's ear; and there were times when Wolsey felt that Suffolk would not have dared to treat him so scurvily, had he not done so with the sanction of the King.

And at the root of this uneasiness was one factor: the King was no longer that careless boy who could be fed with the sugar plums of masques, jousts and fair women while the able hands of his shrewdest statesman steered the ship of state, which was England, along its perilous journey. This King had done with playing the careless boy; he had come to realize that the fascination of power-politics was as great as a new feast or a new woman. He was breaking the bars of his cage; he was testing his strength; he was roaring with pride in his own glory. And he was saying: 'I will have all . . . all. . . . I will be King in very truth. I will have my rich entertainments, and I will stand on the bridge of my ship, and if any attempt to come between me and my desires they shall not live long to do so.'

On went the procession–all the pomp and glory–and in the midst of it rode an apprehensive man.

Thomas, riding along unnoticed in the glittering throng, was also pensive. All his sympathy was for the Queen. Poor lady, what had she done to deserve this humiliation? Had she wished for marriage with the King in the first place? He doubted it. He remembered her, serene and dignified, at the Coronation. Yet she had accepted her fate with meekness; she had tried to love the King, and she had been a faithful wife to him; the second was to be expected, for she was a virtuous woman; but her love for the King must have been sorely tried during these last years.

Now was his chance to leave his post, to tell the King the state of his mind, to say boldly: 'Sire, I resign my post, for you will wish to have about Your Highness those ministers who can help you to obtain the divorce.'

It was a relief to rest at Rochester on the journey to France, and there to stay in the company of his old friend, Bishop Fisher.

It was pleasanter still to have a private talk with Fisher after Wolsey had sounded him.

In the small panelled room, the two friends were serious together. They talked solemnly of the terrible calamity which had befallen the Pope; then their talk turned on the King's Secret Matter.

How could the divorce be concluded without the sanction of the Pope? And how could the Pope give his consent to the King's divorce from a lady who was a close relation of the man who held him prisoner, even if he was satisfied that he should grant a divorce?

'These are grave matters, my friend,' said Bishop Fisher.

'Grave indeed,' said Thomas, 'for where they will end I do not know.'

And the next day, the Cardinal, with Sir Thomas More in his entourage, left for Canterbury, and so to France.

The sweating sickness had again come to England; it roamed through the streets of the City like a hungry beast who was nourished on the filth which filled the malodorous gutters and the fetid air inside the houses. Men, women and children took the sweat; they lay down where they were, in a state of exhaustion, and died unless they could be roused from the coma into which they fell. This horrible pestilence was no respecter of persons; it struck at beggars and the highest in the land.

In the streets, the people were muttering together, telling each other that it was clear why God had sent this affliction. He was displeased. And why should He be displeased? The Secret Matter was no longer secret; they knew that the King wished to put the Queen from him; and there was no denying the rumour that the woman he wished to make his Queen was Nan Bullen–his mistress, so it was said. Who was this woman? The daughter of a knight. She was no royal Queen.

All the hatred the people felt for the upstart Wolsey they now allowed him to share with the upstart Anne Boleyn.

God was angry with England, and this was His way of showing it; there was the reason for a further visitation of this terrible pestilence.

The King was also angry. He had been deprived of the presence of his beloved mistress, whom he desired to make his wife more than he desired anything on Earth. What had she said to him? 'Your mistress I will not be; your wife I cannot be.' But he must be her lover even if, as she implied, the only way in which he could be was by making her his wife.

And now she had left the Court.

Wolsey had done this. What had happened to Wolsey? He had lost a little of his arrogance. He now knew that the King had not given him his confidence, and that when he, Wolsey, had been trying to negotiate a marriage with one of the princesses of France, the King had already firmly made up his mind that he would have none other than Anne Boleyn. Wolsey now knew that it was mainly Anne Boleyn who had set the King searching his conscience; but he had learned that important factor too late.

Now a sad and anxious Cardinal had advised his royal master that, since the people were angered against the Lady Anne, it would be wise at this stage to send her back to Hever.

So Henry was alone and wretched, longing for her, asking himself why it was that, surrounded as he was by the cleverest men in the world, there was not one of them who could settle this matter to his satisfaction.

There was a message from Hever.

The sweat cared nothing for the wrath and anguish of the King himself. Anne Boleyn–more precious to the King than his kingdom–had become a victim of the sweating sickness.

Now the King was in terror. He wept and stormed and he prayed. How could God put the King's beloved in danger! Had he not been a good King . . . a good man . . . always striving to do God's will! And was it not solely for the good of England that he would take Anne to wife?

He called for his physicians, and the only one who was at Court was his second, Dr Butts. The King threatened this man while he beseeched him to save the Lady Anne, before he despatched him in all haste to Hever.

Then he sat down and, weeping, wrote to her: 'The most displeasing news that could occur to me came suddenly at night. . . .' He wept as he wrote of his laments, of what it meant to him to hear that his mistress, whom he esteemed more than all the world, and whose health he desired as he did his own, should be ill. He told of how he longed to see her and that the sight of her would give him greater comfort than all the precious jewels in the world.

And when he had written and despatched this letter, he paced up and down his apartment, weeping and praying; and all the time longing for Anne, cursing the fate which kept them apart, promising himself how he would reward those who helped him to marry Anne, promising revenge on all those who continued to keep them apart.

In the Court the news spread: The Lady hath the sweat. This will doubtless impair her beauty, even though she should recover. Could she do so and be so charming when and if she returned to the Court?

Important events were being decided in a lady's bedchamber at Hever Castle.

Great sorrow had touched the house in Chelsea.

Margaret had been to the village, taking some garments to one of the families, and she had seemed quite well when she had returned to the house. She had sat with them at the supper table and had joined in the talk. Then, as she had risen, she had tottered suddenly and had been obliged to catch at the table to support herself.

'Margaret!' cried Mercy in terrible alarm.

'What is it?' demanded Alice.

'Let us get Margaret to bed at once,' said Mercy. 'She is sick, I am afraid.'

'Margaret sick!' cried Alice. 'Why, she was eating a hearty meal a moment ago!'

'Yes, Mother, I know. But don't hinder me now. Will! Jack! Father . . . help me.'

It was Will who carried her to her room. Now her eyes were tightly shut and the beads of sweat were beginning to form on her face; she was shivering, yet burning hot.

Thomas followed. He caught his daughter's limp hand.

'O Lord God,' he prayed silently. 'Not Margaret. . . . That I could not endure.'

Will was beside himself with anxiety. 'What shall we do, Mercy? Mercy, in God's name, what *can* we do?'

'Cover her up. Keep her warm. No; don't attempt to undress her. I will try the philosopher's egg. I have it ready, God be thanked.'

She lay on the bed, no longer looking like Margaret; her face was yellow and the sweat ran down her cheeks.

'Please,' begged Mercy, 'everybody go. There is nothing you can do. Leave her with me. No, Will; you can do no good. Make sure that the children do not come into this room. Father . . . please . . . there is nothing . . . nothing you can do.'

Mercy's throat constricted as she looked into his face.

How will he bear it? she asked herself. He loves her best in the world. She is his darling, as he is hers. How could either endure life without the other?

'Father . . . dearest Father . . . please go away. There is nothing . . . nothing to be done.'

But he stood numbly outside the door as though he had not heard.

Margaret ill of the sweat! Margaret . . . *dying*!

Elizabeth and Cecily had shut themselves in their rooms. There was nothing to be done; that was the pity of it. They said to each other that if only there was something they could have done it would have been easier to bear. But to sit . . . waiting . . . in such maddening inactivity. . . . It was all but unendurable.

Alice took refuge in scolding anyone who came near her. 'The foolish girl . . . to go to the cottages at such a time. She should have known. And they tell us she is so *clever* . . . ! And what is Mercy doing? Is she not supposed to be a doctor? Why does she not cure our Margaret?'

Will paced up and down. He could find no words. Margaret, his beloved wife, so calm, so serene; what would he do if he lost her? What would his life be without Margaret?

Giles Heron was all for riding to the Court; he would bring Dr Linacre himself, he declared. What did it matter if Dr Linacre was the King's first physician? Margaret was a member of that family which was now his, and she was in danger. He must get the best doctors for her. He could bring Dr Butts . . . and Dr Clement. He would bring all the greatest doctors in the country.

Dauncey said: 'You would find yourself in trouble, brother. You from an afflicted house . . . to ride to Court!'

Dauncey was astonished that he could be so affected. What was Margaret to him? What could Margaret do to advance his fortunes? Nothing. He trembled, it was true, that her father might catch the disease and die, and that Dauncey's biggest hope of achieving favour at Court would be lost. Yet he was moved, and faintly astonished to find himself sharing in the family's anguish. He had grown fond of them; he had enjoyed their merry games; and, strange as it was, he knew that if any calamity came to them it could not fail to touch him. So there was a streak of sentiment in this most ambitious young man after all.

Thomas shut himself up in the private chapel.

What could he do to save Margaret? What could he do but pray? Now he thought of her–Margaret, the baby, the child, the prodigy who had astonished all with her aptitude for learning. He could think of a hundred Margarets whom he loved, but the one who meant most to him was the loving daughter, the Margaret who was his dearest friend and best companion, who was nearer to him than anyone in the world.

'O God,' he prayed, 'do not take my daughter from me. Anything . . . anything but that.'

He did not leave the chapel. He stayed there on his knees. The hair-shirt lacerated his skin, and he wished its pain were doubled.

Will came to him and they prayed together.

'Ah, son Roper,' said Thomas, 'what religious differences are there between us now? We ask one thing, and that we wish for more than anything in the world. She must not die.'

'I cannot contemplate life without her, Father,' said Will.

'Nor I, my son.'

'They say that if she does not recover during the first day there is no hope.'

'The day is not yet over. How was she when you left her?'

'Unconscious. She lies there with her eyes fast shut, oblivious of the world. I spoke her name. "Margaret," I said. "Margaret, come back to me and our children. . . ."'

'Will, I beg of you, say no more. You unnerve me.'

He thought: I have loved her too well; I have loved her more than all the world. When she was born she gave me contentment; she was the meaning of life to me. She *is* the meaning of life. Have I loved her too well? Oh, how easy it is to torture the body, to wear the hair-shirt, to flagellate the flesh, to deprive the body of its cravings. Those pains are easy to suffer; but how bear the loss of a loved one . . . how endure life when the one you love more than your own life, more than the whole world is taken from you?

'If . . . if aught should happen to her . . .' he began.

Now it was Will's turn to implore him not to go on. Will could only shake his head while the tears ran down his cheeks.

But Thomas continued: 'I would retire from the world. Nothing could keep me leading this life. Oh, my son. I could not go on. If Margaret were taken from me, I would never meddle with worldly affairs hereafter.'

'Father, I implore you . . . I beg of you not to speak of it. Do not think of it. She will get well. She must get well. Let us pray. Let us pray together. . . .'

So they knelt and prayed, and if Will saw God as Martin Luther saw him, and if Thomas saw God as the Pope saw Him, they each knew that their prayers were being offered to the same God.

Thomas rose suddenly. His spirits were lifted.

He said: 'Will, when Margaret was a little girl–scarcely two years old–and we were visiting her mother's old home, New Hall in Kent, Margaret, playing in a field, was lost and could not find the gate through which she had come into the field and which opened on to the path which led to the house. She was frightened, for dusk was settling on the land. Frantically she ran about the field, and still she could not find the gate. Then suddenly she remembered that I had told her that when she was in trouble she must ask the help of her Father upon Earth or her Father in Heaven. "And, Father," she said when she told me this some time later, "I had lost you, so I knelt down and asked God the way home. And when I arose from my knees I was no longer frightened. I walked calmly round the field until I came to the gate." I had missed her, as it happened, and had gone to look for her, and as she came through the gate and ran towards me, she said: "Father, God showed me the way home." What a beautiful thought it is, Will. What a comfort. I have been on my knees now . . . frightened . . . panic-stricken, as Margaret was. I was lost and I could not find the gate, which led to the home I knew . . . to the happiness I knew. "God," I have prayed, "show *me* the way."'

'Father, you look changed. You seem . . . serene . . . as though you *know* she will get well.'

'I seem calmer, my son, do I not? I *am* calmer. I feel as she felt when she rose from her knees. My panic has gone. I know this, son Roper, God will show me the way, as she showed Margaret. My mind is calm; thoughts cease to chase themselves in my head. I am going to the house to see how she is. Come with me, Will.'

Mercy met them at the door of the sick-room.

'No change,' she said. 'I have tried to wake her. If we cannot wake her, she will die.'

'Mercy, I want you to give her a clyster.'

'Father, she is too ill.'

'She is so ill, Mercy, that she cannot be much worse . . . short of death. Do this, I beg of you. Administer this clyster. We must wake her, must we not? Then we *will* wake her.'

'Father, I am afraid. It is too violent, and she is very ill indeed.'

'Mercy, you are imprisoned in fear. Yes, my love, you are afraid because you love her even as I do. She is not your patient; she is your sister. You wrap her up; you watch over her; but you will not take a risk because you are frightened. I have prayed. I feel I have been in close communion with God and, Mercy, I am not afraid. I want you to be calm . . . to forget that this is our beloved Margaret. If she does not wake she will die. We must wake her, Mercy. We *must*. You agree that is so. Give her the clyster.'

Mercy said quietly: 'I will do as you wish, Father. Leave me with her.'

Half an hour later Mercy came out of the sick-room.

Her eyes were shining.

'She is roused from her sleep,' she said. 'Father . . . Will . . . she asked for both of you.'

They went to her and one knelt on either side of the bed.

Margaret, weak and only just able to recognize them, let her eyes wander from one to the other.

Three men were very happy after the next few days. Each had feared to lose the one he loved best in the world, and each experienced the great joy of seeing the return of the loved one to health.

These men were Will Roper, Sir Thomas More and the King of England.

Margaret was about the house again, although thin and pale. Her father seemed unable to let her go out of his sight.

They would wander together through the orchards and the flower gardens, and sometimes he would remind her of the pleasures they had shared during her childhood; they would laugh and sometimes weep together, over their memories.

He spoke to her, more frankly than he did to the others, of Court matters; and sometimes they would read together from Erasmus's Testament.

Margaret's convalescence consisted of many happy hours.

He would care for her in a hundred ways; he would get her a shawl from the house, for fear the wind might be too strong; he would not let her walk on the grass after rain lest her feet should be made damp. He rejoiced to see her gradual return to health, and often she would weep, contemplating the sorrow her illness had brought to her family, and in particular she wept for Will and her father.

The bond between Sir Thomas and his daughter was stronger than it had ever been.

One hot day, when they were sitting in the gardens, being overcome by the warmth of the day he opened the neck of his gown, and little Anne Cresacre, who was sitting near him, caught a glimpse of the strange garment he was wearing next to his skin. Anne's big eyes were round with wonder; her lips began to twitch. Could it be a hair-shirt! But only monks wore those . . . monks and hermits. Little Anne, who was often uncertain in this household of clever people, found that when she was at a loss, irrepressible laughter overcame her.

It was Margaret who followed her look and who rose from her seat and said: 'Father, the air grows cold.' She buttoned up his gown and was angry with Anne for her youth and her stupidity, and because she had dared to giggle at a great and saintly man.

He, seeing what had happened and understanding it, smiled at Anne, who, aware of his kindness, was instantly ashamed. She rose and, murmuring that she was wanted in the kitchens, hurried away.

Thomas turned his smile on his daughter, and it grew very tender. He remembered that when Alice wished to know what happened to his shirts and why they were not given in with the ordinary linen to wash, it was Margaret who had answered her, to prevent his telling the truth; for Margaret could not bear to listen to the ridicule which she knew Alice would heap upon him. 'I wash Father's shirts, Mother, with things of my own. I have always done it, and I shall always do it.' 'What nonsense!' Alice had said. 'Why should you do such a thing when there are maids here to do it?' But Margaret had quietly said that it was her affair, and she said it with such determination that even Alice did not pursue the subject.

Thomas now suggested a walk by the river, and as they set forth he said: 'You would protect me then from the scorn of the young and the gay?'

'The stupid child!' said Margaret. 'I wanted to box her ears.'

'You are too hard on her, Meg. She is but a baby. You must not expect all to be as serious as you were at her age. Have patience with little Anne. She is a good child; and I believe she loves our Jack and that he loves her. Let us ask no more of her than that she shall love him and make him happy.'

'Oh, Father, what matters it after all? The important thing is: how go affairs at the Court?'

'Events move fast, Meg.'

'Is the King as determined as ever to cast off the Queen?'

'I fear so.'

'And if he succeeds in arranging the divorce, he will marry Anne Boleyn?'

'I believe that to be his intention. Meg, I think it will not be long before your father loses his honours and becomes a humble man again. You smile, Meg. One would think I had told you that my fortune was made.'

'So it will be if you are home with us all as you once were. If you take up your duties in the City as you once did. . . .'

'I doubt that I could pick up the threads as easily as that, Meg.'

'Never mind. I should be happy to see you leave the Court for ever.'

'We should be very poor.'

'We should be rich in happiness. You would not have to go away from England or be absent at Court. We should have you with us always.'

'What a happy day it will be when I come home and tell you I have given up my honours!'

'The happiest day we have ever known. And will it be soon?'

'As I said, events move fast. The King will let me go. He knows my views. He has not urged me to change them. He hints that he respects them. I think that must mean, Meg, that when I ask leave to retire from Court, he will readily grant it.'

'I long for that day.'

'It is a sad affair, Meg, to watch the rapid descent of those who have climbed to great heights. I think of the Cardinal.'

'How fares it with him, Father?'

'Badly. Meg, it is a sorry sight; it is a sorry thought.'

'The King has no more need of him?'

'The Cardinal has set up false idols, Margaret. He has worshipped pomp instead of honour; he has mistaken riches for the glory which comes with righteous work. Poor Wolsey! He has too many enemies; the King is his only friend . . . a fickle friend. The Cardinal has offended the Lady Anne. He broke the marriage she desired with Percy; he insulted a relative when he attempted to deprive Eleanor Carey of the post of Abbess of Wilton; but worst of all she knows that he has urged the King to marry one of the French Princesses. They are false steps in his slippery career. He felt so sure of his power. Who is this Anne Boleyn? he asked himself. She is another such as her sister Mary! There he finds his mistake, and the King's mistress is his enemy. He could not have a greater, for she it is who commands the King. Moreover, Norfolk and Suffolk wait for the King to turn his back on the man he once loved; then they will rush in to attack him. He is a sad, sick man, Meg. Poor Wolsey!'

'He has been no real friend to you, Father.'

'He is no true friend to anyone or anything but his own ambition; and now, poor soul, he sees the falseness of *that* friend. Fame! What is fame? Men congratulate themselves if they attain to fame, empty though it is; and because they are light-minded they are lifted to the stars by the fickleness of opinion. What does fame do to a man? Though he be praised by all the world, if he has an aching joint, what does fame do for him? And Wolsey has many an aching joint, Meg . . . and an aching heart. His policy abroad, so successful at one time, has turned sour. He has aroused the hatred of the Emperor without gaining the love of the King of France. Our King cares only for one thing, for he is a single-minded man, and he thinks of little else day and night but ridding himself of Queen Katharine and marrying Anne Boleyn. Wolsey has one hope now–the successful outcome of the case which he and Campeggio are about to try here in London. If Wolsey can arrange the divorce, I doubt not that he will ere long win back the King's favour. If he does not . . . then the King will turn his back on him; and if His Grace continues to look the other way, the wolves will descend on my lord Cardinal, and they will have no mercy, Meg. There are too many slights to be avenged, too many resentments festering.'

'And then, Father?'

'Then, Meg, that will be farewell to his glory, farewell to his pomp and his riches. We shall no longer see our Cardinal ride in state through our streets. Pray God we do not see him riding to the Tower.'

'And you?'

'Here is the way out, Meg. Depend upon it, the King has little use for me. He knows my mind. He will accept my resignation. It will save him the unpleasant task of dismissing me as, Meg, all will be dismissed who do not pander to his wishes.'

'Father, I long for the day of your resignation.'

''Twill not be long now, Meg. I assure you of that.'

The Cardinal's glory was dimmed. None knew it more than he himself. His fate was clear when Campeggio, whom all were expecting to give a verdict in favour of the divorce, with characteristic vacillation rose and adjourned the Court, suggesting that it should be recalled and continued in Rome.

Then the Duke of Suffolk, who, all knew, spoke with the authority of the King, rose in hot anger and, glaring not at Campeggio, but at Wolsey, cried: 'It was never merry in England since we had Cardinals among us.' That was the signal, recognized by all; the King had thrown Wolsey to his enemies.

Events followed rapidly.

The Cardinal returned to his house in Westminster surrounded by his servants, who trembled with him, for he had been a kindly, gracious master. And there they waited for the coming of Norfolk and Suffolk.

They did not have to wait long.

They came in the name of the King and demanded that he deliver the Great Seal of England into their hands.

The King sent for Sir Thomas More.

Margaret went down to the barge with him.

'Depend upon it, Meg: this will mean one thing. When your father returns he will be stripped of his honours. I shall receive my marching orders with the stricken Cardinal.'

'And, dearest Father, how different from Wolsey's will be your feelings. You will rejoice. You will come home to your family, a happier man.'

And she stood at the top of the privy stairs, waving to him and smiling.

She had never felt so happy to see him depart.

The King received Thomas gravely.

'We have a matter of great importance to discuss with you,' he said. 'You have worked in close company with Thomas Wolsey, have you not?'

'I have, Your Grace.'

The King grunted. He glared at his minister. He could not, even at this moment, resist a little acting. He wished to alarm Thomas More; and then speak what was in his mind.

There was, it seemed, only one man worthy to succeed to the office just vacated by Wolsey. The office of Chancellor was the highest in the land, and could only be given to a man capable of filling it. His Councillors had discussed this with the King. A knowledge of the intricacies of the law was a necessity, Norfolk had said. The new Chancellor must be an honest, upright man to whom the country could look with confidence and trust. The Councillors agreed that there was only one man in the country who could satisfactorily fill the office. This decision of his Councillors had set the King pondering. The Church had been reasonable over this matter of his unlawful marriage with Katharine–all except one Bishop, that fool Fisher. He had hummed and ha-ed and maddened the King. But why should a King upset himself over the intransigence of a Bishop? That man should be adequately dealt with when the time came.

Henry did not forget that Sir Thomas More was not in favour of the divorce, that he had supported the Queen; yet he knew, as well as did his Councillors, that Thomas More was the man most fitted to step into Wolsey's shoes. It must be so. Henry was sure of this; so were Norfolk, Suffolk and every member of the Council. Wolsey himself had said, when he knew he was to fall, that there was only one man capable of following him, and that that man was Sir Thomas More.

This man More had a strange effect on all men, it seemed. Even when his opinions differed from theirs, they respected him to such an extent that they must continue to love him.

The King ceased to frown. His smile was turned on Thomas.

'We have good news for you. We have always had a fondness for you. Did we not say so when you first came to us? You remember that affair of the Pope's ship?' The King's smile was now benign. 'Now, we have a task for you. We said we would make your fortune, did we not? It is made, Thomas More. We like your goodness, your honesty, that respect the whole world has for you. We look for one on whom to bestow the Great Seal, and we say to ourselves: "Ah, Thomas More! He is the man for us. He shall be our Lord Chancellor."'

'Lord Chancellor, Your Grace!'

'Now, Thomas, you are overwhelmed. I know. I know. 'Tis a mighty honour. Yet we have given this matter much thought, and we are assured that there is no man in the kingdom who deserves the honour more than you do. Your country needs you, Thomas. Your King commands you to serve your country. Your work with Wolsey, your knowledge of affairs, your love of learning, your erudition, your knowledge of the Law . . . You see, do you not? You see that if I did not love you as I do, did I not respect you as a learned and an honourable man, I still must make you my Chancellor.'

Thomas looked with concern at the dazzling figure before him. 'Your Grace,' he said, 'I must speak to you frankly. I am unsuited to the task.'

'Nonsense! There is not a man in this realm whom the task becomes more. We command you to it, Thomas. We will have no other. It is your bounden duty to your King and your country to accept. We will take no refusal.'

'My lord, Your Highness, your most gracious Majesty, I must speak as my conscience commands me. I cannot give my support to the divorce.'

The King's eyes seemed to disappear in his fleshy face. He flushed and drew back. He was silent for a few moments, as though he were considering which of his roles to play. He might roar: 'Send this traitor to the Tower.' On the other hand, he might continue to play the part of benign monarch who respects an honest man.

He needed this man. He was the only man in the realm fitted for the task. All agreed on that. The learning and integrity of Sir Thomas More, the respect he had inspired on the continent of Europe, were necessary to England.

The King decided.

'Thomas,' he said, 'you have your conscience, and I have mine. By God's Body, I have been worried enough in my thoughts by my most sinful and incestuous marriage. I know the pain of a nagging conscience. And on this matter, Thomas More, you and I are not of one mind. I regret it. Thomas, I regret it mightily. But as a man of conscience, I respect a man of conscience . . . mistaken though I know him to be. For, Thomas, you are a learned man. I doubt it not. You are a good man, and we are proud to have you as a subject. You have been favoured by God. I know of that family at Chelsea, and one day, Thomas, I am going to visit Chelsea. I am going to see it for myself. I am going to give the kiss of friendship to those merry daughters of yours, to that jolly wife. Yea, that I will. You have been favoured in your family. . . .' His voice sank almost to a whisper. 'You do not understand how lonely a man can be–even though he be a King–who lacks that which God has given you with lavish hands. Thomas More, there are a few matters which you do not understand as worldly men understand them. And this is one of them. But I am a man of wide views. I understand you . . . even though you understand me not. And, Thomas, I will have you for my Chancellor and no other. And this matter which plagues me day and night shall put no barriers between us two. Dismiss it, Thomas. It is no affair of yours. Come, Chancellor More. Take the Great Seal of England, and your King will put the seal of friendship on your brow.'

Henry leaned forward and kissed Thomas's forehead.

It was not for the Lord Chancellor to meddle in this matter of the divorce, thought the King. That was the task of the clergy. He had two new friends in mind from whom he hoped much: Thomas Cranmer and Thomas Cromwell.

It would seem that I have a fancy for these Thomases, thought Henry; and he smiled pleasantly as he looked into the face of his new Lord Chancellor.

Chapter Six

Margaret would never forget rushing to greet him when he returned in his barge. She would never forget the jaunty smile on his face; but while he might deceive others, he could never deceive her.

'Father?'

'Well, Meg, see you not the change? The Under-Treasurer left you earlier this day. The Chancellor is now arrived.'

'Chancellor, Father . . . *you*?'

'A worthy Chancellor, though a humble one, as says my lord of Norfolk.'

'But . . . the King's divorce?'

'I have told him that I can have no hand in it; and it seems he accepts my refusal to do so, as Norfolk accepts my humble birth. And, Meg, with so many ready to accept so much that is unpalatable to them, I was perforce obliged to accept that which I would fain refuse.'

'It is not a good thing, Father. It is not a matter for jokes.'

'It is not good, Meg, and therefore is it meet that we should joke, for by doing so we can make light of what we cannot refuse to undertake.'

'Could you not have refused?'

'I tried, Meg.'

'But . . . surely you have a free choice?'

'I am the King's subject and as such must obey the King's command. Come, let us to the house. I'll warrant you'll smile to see the family's reception of this news.'

Slowly they walked towards the house, and Margaret's heart was full of misgiving.

Lord Chancellor!

The family received the news with wonder.

Alice was mockingly proud. 'So, Master More, you have made a great man of yourself in spite of all.'

'Rather say, wife, that they have made a great man of me in spite of myself.'

Alice looked at him with beaming pride. 'To think that a husband of mine should be the Lord Chancellor!'

'Why, Alice, you have grown two inches taller, I'll swear.'

Alice was in no mood for raillery. 'This means we shall need more servants. Why, who knows whom we shall have visiting us now. Mayhap the King himself!' Alice grew a shade paler at the thought. 'Now, Thomas, should His Grace honour us, I shall need to know a day or more ahead.'

'Shall my first duties as Chancellor be to warn the King that if he should visit Lady More he must give her good warning?'

'Have done with your nonsense! 'Twould not be unknown, I trow, for the King to visit his Chancellor. Why, he was so much in and out of the houses of the last Chancellor that people did not know whether they were at the King's or the Cardinal's Court.'

'And now the Cardinal's Courts are the King's Courts. Has it occurred to you that all the last Chancellor's possessions are now the property of the King? Do you not tremble for your own, Alice? For, remember, they are the property of the new Lord Chancellor, and why should the new one fare better than the old?'

'Have done with such foolish talk.'

'Well, Alice, here is something you will like better. There is to be a visitor this night for supper.'

'A visitor. Who is this?'

'His Grace of Norfolk.'

'Tilly valley! And it already three of the clock! Tilly valley! What shall I do? I should have been given notice.'

'But, Alice, since you need twenty-four hours' warning of a King's visit, is not three hours enough for a Duke? Commoners call five minutes before a meal, and may have a seat at our table.'

'My Lord Norfolk!' cried Alice, growing red and white at the thought.

'His Grace will honour us, Alice. He made a delightful speech when I took the Seal. He stressed my virtues which, he said, were so great that they made him indifferent to my humble birth.'

Alice bristled, but she was still thinking: His Grace of Norfolk! The first nobleman in the land . . . and here to supper. Next it will be His Grace the King. I know it.

'And, Alice, my dear, do not fret,' said Thomas, 'for such a second-rate compliment is only worthy of a second-rate supper. Let us be natural with this noble Duke. Let us treat him as we would a passer-by who looks in to join us at supper. After all, he will expect no more of us–because we are such humble folk.'

But Alice was not listening. She must to the kitchen at once. She must see that the beef received the necessary basting. Had she known they were to be so honoured she would have got one of the new turkeys. She was going to make her new sauce, adding the chopped roots of the wild succory and water arrow-head. She would set her cook making further pies. And her latest pickle should be set upon the table. She would show my lord of Norfolk!

'Now, Master More, do not hinder me. If you *will* ask great noblemen to supper, then you must give me time to attend to them.'

And she was off, bustling down to the kitchens, sniffing the savoury smells; excited and a little fearful.

'Come, come, you wenches. There's work to be done. My Lord Chancellor has a guest for supper tonight. I'll doubt any of you have ever served a noble Duke before, eh, eh?'

'No, my lady.'

'Well, then, now you will learn to do so, for it would not surprise me if we shall one day have at our table a guest who is far greater than His Grace of Norfolk. Do you know whom I mean? Do you, wench?'

Alice gave one of the girls a slap with a wooden ladle. It was more an affectionate pat than a blow.

Alice allowed herself one minute to dream that at her table sat a great, glittering man who shouted to her that he had never tasted a better meal than that eaten at the table of his Lord Chancellor.

'Tilly valley!' she cried. 'This is not the way to prepare supper for His Grace of Norfolk!'

The old Judge stood before his son; his hands were trembling and there were tears in his eyes.

'Thomas, my son . . . my dearest son. . . . Thomas, Lord Chancellor of England. So you have the Great Seal, my son. *You* . . . my son, Thomas.'

Thomas embraced his father. 'Your son first, Father; Chancellor second.'

'And to think that I scolded you for not working at the law!'

'Ah, Father, there are many routes to fame.'

'And you found a quick one, my son.'

'I took a byway. I confess I am a little startled still to find where it has led me.'

'Oh, Thomas, would that your mother could have lived to see this day. And my father . . . and my grandfather. They would have been proud . . . proud indeed. Why, your grandfather was only a butler of the Inn; he was, it was true, at the head of the servants and kept the accounts. Would that he could have lived to this day to see his grandson Lord Chancellor of England. Oh, Thomas, my son! Oh, proud and happy day!'

Later Thomas said to Margaret: 'You see, daughter, how there is much good in all things. I am glad to have pleased your grandfather, for he is feeble, and I fear he may not be long for this life. I believe his delight in me is almost as great at this moments as mine has always been in you. And, Margaret, it is a happy child who makes a fond father a proud one, think you not?'

'If I were less fond,' she said, 'I think I should find greater enjoyment in my pride.'

He kissed her. 'Do not ask too much of life, my wise daughter; ask for little, and then, if it comes, you will be happy.'

It seemed to Margaret that the one who was least changed by his elevation was her father.

He was delighted with his importance only when he could use it to do good for others. He had shown to the King the drawings Hans Holbein had made of his family, and the King had been impressed with them; so Master Holbein had, regretfully, left the house at Chelsea to take up his quarters at Court as painter to the King at a salary of thirty pounds a year.

'It is a large sum,' said Hans, 'and I am a poor man. I shall mayhap find fame in Hampton Court and Westminster, but will it give me as much joy as the happiness I have enjoyed in Chelsea?'

'With a brush such as yours, my friend,' said Thomas, 'you have no choice. Go. Serve the King, and I doubt not that your future is secure.'

'I would as lief stay. I wish to do more pictures of your family . . . and your servants.'

'Go and make pictures of the King and *his* servants. Go, Hans; make the best of two worlds. Take up your quarters at the Court, and come to Chelsea for a humble meal with us when you feel the need for it.'

Then Hans Holbein embraced his friend and benefactor, and said with tears in his eyes: 'To think that I should wish to refuse an offer such as this. You have put a magic in your house, dear friend; and I am caught in its spell.'

Yes, those were the things which Thomas greatly enjoyed doing. At such times it was worth while holding a great office.

But he was uneasy–far more uneasy than he would have his family realize.

The King was spending more and more time with Cromwell and Cranmer; they were the two to whom he looked for help in this matter of the divorce, and no other matter seemed of any great importance to him. The Cardinal had slipped down to disgrace and death, and the descent had been more rapid than his spectacular climb to grace and favour. He had first been indicted upon the Statute of *Praemunire*; but Thomas Cromwell had cleared him of the charge of high treason, so that Wolsey had been ordered to retire to York; but before he had long rested there he was charged once more with high treason and had died of a broken heart at Leicester on his way to London.

Thomas Wolsey had come to the Chancellorship with everything in his favour; Thomas More had come to it with everything against him. Wolsey had not realized his peril until within a year or so of his decline and death; More was aware of his from the moment he received the Great Seal.

William Dauncey came to his father-in-law on one of those rare occasions when Thomas found time to be with his family.

There was a determined light in Dauncey's eyes.

'Well, son Dauncey, you would have speech with me?'

'I have thought much of late, Father,' said Dauncey, 'that things have changed since you became the Chancellor of this realm in place of the Cardinal.'

'In what way?'

'When my lord Cardinal was Chancellor, those about him grew rich, for he shut himself away and it was a matter of some cost for any to put their desires before him. Yet, since you have become Chancellor, any man may come to you. He may state his case and receive judgment.'

'Well, my son, is that not a good thing? Why, when my lord Cardinal held the Great Seal there were many cases which must go unheard because there was no time to put them before him. 'Tis easier for me. My interests are not so many, and I am a lawyer to boot. Do you know that when I took office there were cases which men were waiting to present for ten or twelve years! And now, my son–I grow boastful, but this matter gives me great pleasure, so forgive my pride–I called yesternoon for the next case, and I was told that there were no more cases to be heard. So proud was I that I invented a little rhyme as I sat there. This is it:

> '*When More some time had Chancellor been,*
> *No more suits did remain.*
> *The like will never more be seen*
> *Till More be there again.*'

'Yes, Father,' said Dauncey impatiently, after he had given his polite laugh. 'That is good for those who would wish their cases to be heard; but it is not so good for the friends of the Chancellor.'

'How so, my son?'

'When Thomas Wolsey was Chancellor, not only the members of his privy chamber but even the keepers of his doors took great gain to themselves.'

'Ah,' said Thomas. 'Now I understand. You feel that a daughter of this

Chancellor should be at least as profitable as a door in the house of the last.'

'Profit?' said Dauncey. 'But there is no profit. How could I take gifts from those whom I brought to your presence when in bringing them to you I could do no more for them than they could do for themselves?'

'You think I am at fault in making myself accessible to all who desire to see me?'

'It may be a commendable thing,' said Dauncey stubbornly, 'but it is not a profitable thing for a son-in-law. How could I take reward from a man for something which he could get without my help?'

'I admire your scrupulous conscience, my son.' He smiled at Dauncey. Dauncey yearned for advancement. He was not a bad boy; he but obeyed his father, Sir John Dauncey, in his determination to rise. Now Dauncey looked downcast; he did not always understand his father-in-law. Thomas laid a hand on his shoulder. 'If, my son, you have some matter which you wish to place before me, if you have a friend whom you wish to help, well then, you could always put this matter before me. I might hear the cause of a friend of yours before that of another if it could be done. But remember this, son Dauncey–and I assure you this on my faith–that if my father himself stood on one side of me and the Devil on the other, and in this instance the Devil's case was the right one, then must I decide in favour of the Devil. Come, walk with me in the gardens. You too, son Roper. I like to have you with me.'

And he put his arm through Dauncey's, for Dauncey was looking ashamed; and he spoke to him with the utmost kindliness.

It was not Dauncey's fault that he had been brought up on ambition. Moreover, he had softened somewhat since he had come to Chelsea.

Alice was in a flurry of excitement, making preparations for the wedding of Jack to Anne Cresacre. This was to be the peak of her achievements so far; there had been other marriages in the family; ah, yes, but those had been the marriages of the children of Thomas More, later *Sir* Thomas; now the son of the Lord Chancellor was to be married.

Alice was a little disappointed that the King would not be among the guests. She listened to the talk when they did not always think she listened; she heard some of the remarks which had passed between Margaret and her father, and also some of the hints which the Duke of Norfolk–who called at the house quite frequently, to Alice's delight–and she gathered that Thomas, as was to be expected, was not making the most of his opportunities. He was deliberately opposing the King, and all because the King wanted a divorce and Thomas did not think he should have it.

'What the good year!' said Alice to herself. 'This man of mine is a most foolhardy person. He is so careless of his position that he treats it with indifference; and yet, as regards this matter of the King's, he is most firm and resolute. 'Tis nothing but stubborn folly, and I am glad that my lord of Norfolk agrees with me.'

Well, the King would not be at the wedding; nevertheless, it was to be a grand affair. She had bought the young couple one of the new portable clocks which were such a novelty, as they were unknown in England this time last year. It was pleasant to be in a position to buy such things.

Such a feast she would prepare! All should marvel at the good table she kept in Chelsea. She had planned this feast again and again, altering an item here and there, until Margaret cried out in dismay that if she were not careful she would find her feast falling short of perfection because she would forget what she had decided for and what against.

She puffed about the kitchen, taking a look at the boar which was being soaked in vinegar and juniper; she went out to the sties to study the fatness of the pigs which would be killed, she went to the cellars to see how the mead and metheglin were maturing. She inspected her pickles, which must be the best she had ever produced.

Hourly she admonished her servants. 'Do not forget. This is no marriage of a mean person. This is the marriage of the son of the Lord Chancellor of England.'

'Yes, my lady. Yes, my lady.'

My lady! she thought blissfully. My *lady*!

Ah, this was the good and pleasant life. Her only fear was that Thomas would do something to spoil it, for indeed Thomas seemed to have no understanding of the great dignity which should be his. It was all very well for him to poke fun at her, to laugh at *her* dignity. She must have her dignity. She did not forget that she was the wife of the Lord Chancellor, if he was so foolish as to forget the dignity he owed to his office.

She would have ceremony in her household. He was wrong to welcome into the house every humble traveller who, hearing there was a chance of a good meal at the table of Sir Thomas More, arrived at mealtimes. He was wrong always to wear the same sombre dress. Not a jewel on his person! And when it was remembered how glorious had been the Cardinal, and how the crowds had gathered in the streets of London to see him pass . . . well, puffed Alice, it is enough to make a woman wonder what manner of man she has married. He had no sense of his power, of his dignity.

Recently Giles Heron had occasion to bring a case to the courts against a certain Nicholas Millisante. But would Master More favour his own son-in-law? Indeed, he would not. Master Giles had gone confidently to court. Naturally, the somewhat easy-going Giles had expected his father-in-law to decide in his favour and . . . Thomas had decided against him!

'A fine thing!' Alice had chided. 'So the affairs of your family mean nothing to you? People will say that the Lord Chancellor has no power, since he is afraid to give a verdict in favour of his own son-in-law.'

'What matters that, Alice, if they know that the laws of England are just?'

'Tut, tut,' said Alice to herself. 'Tut, tut' was my lord of Norfolk's favourite expression, and Alice was ready to ape the manners of the great, even if Thomas was not.

Thomas scorned all pomp and show. A week ago, when Norfolk had called unexpectedly on matters of business, Thomas had actually been singing in the choir of Chelsea Church. There he had been, wearing a surplice like an ordinary man; and Alice was not surprised that the sight of him, so undignified, had shocked the Duke.

'God's Body! God's Body!' Norfolk had cried. 'My Lord Chancellor playing parish clerk! Tut-tut, you dishonour the King and his office, Master More.'

Had Thomas been contrite? Not in the least. He had merely smiled that slow, maddening smile of his and answered: 'Nay, your Grace, I cannot think that the King would deem the service of God a dishonour to his office.'

And there had been His Grace of Norfolk lost for words, while Thomas smiled and was so sure of himself. Yet the Duke had not been angered by that sharp answer; he had seemed most friendly with Thomas, both during the meal and afterwards in the gardens.

But Alice herself would remember the dignity due to his office, if others did not. And she would have her servants remember also. In Chelsea Church each morning after prayers she had insisted that one of his gentlemen should come to her pew and tell her of the departure of her husband, although she knew the moment when he must leave the church. This gentleman of her husband's must bow before Alice and say: 'Madame, my lord is gone.'

Then she would bow her head and solemnly thank him. It was a ritual which made the others smile. But let them smile, said Alice. Someone must remember the dignity of the house.

Now one of her serving-maids came to her to tell her that there was a poor woman at the door who would have speech with her.

'There are always poor women at the door!' she cried. 'They come here begging from this house, because they know the master's order that none should be turned away without a hearing. It seems to me that beggars are given more honours here than are noble dukes.'

But this poor woman had not come to beg, she assured Lady More. She had a pretty dog, and as she had heard of Lady More's fondness for these animals she had brought it along in the hope of selling it to her ladyship.

Alice was immediately attracted by the engaging little creature. She gave the woman a coin and welcomed yet another pet into the house.

It was only a week or so after the wedding when the absurd controversy about the dog arose.

Alice was annoyed. A beggar-woman, roaming near the house saw the dog being carried by one of the servants and immediately declared that it had been stolen from her.

The servant retorted that this was nonsense. My lady had bought the dog. If the old beggar-woman did not go away at once she would be tied to a tree and whipped.

Alice was indignant. To dare to say I stole the dog! *I!* Does she not know who I am? The wife of none other than the Lord Chancellor!

But the beggar-woman would not go away. She loitered on the river bank, and one day when she saw the Lord Chancellor himself alight from his barge she accosted him.

'My Lord! Justice!' she cried. 'Justice for a poor woman who is the victim of a thief.'

Thomas paused.

'Mistress,' he said with that grave courtesy which altered not whether he addressed a duchess or a beggar, 'what theft is this you wish to report?'

'The theft of a little dog, your honour. I wish to regain what I have lost.'

'If you are speaking the truth, and the animal has been stolen from you, then must it be restored to you. Who now has possession of your property?'

'Lady More, your honour.'

'And is that so? Well then, come to my hall tomorrow morning when I try the cases, and we shall hear yours against Lady More.'

He went smiling to the house and there spoke to Alice.

'Alice, you are summoned to the courts tomorrow morning.'

'What foolish joke is this?'

'No joke. 'Tis true. You are accused of theft, wife, and must needs come to answer the charge.'

'*I* . . . accused of theft!'

'Of a dog.'

'So it is that beggar!'

'She says you have her dog.'

'And I say I have *my* dog.'

'In a court of law, Alice, it is not enough to say an article is yours if another claims it. It must be proved.'

'You cannot mean that you would ask me to go to the courts on a matter like this!'

'I do, Alice.'

She laughed in his face; but he meant it, she realized to her astonishment. She thought it was a most unseemly thing that the Lord Chancellor should summon his own wife to appear before him, and on the word of a beggar too! They would be the laughing-stock of all, she doubted not.

She dressed herself with great care and set out with the dog as Thomas had bidden her. She would show dignity if he did not. She would show the world that if Thomas was unfit for the office of Chancellor, she was not unfit for the position of Chancellor's wife.

And in the hall, there was my Lord Chancellor with his officers about him.

'The next case which we must try this day,' he said 'concerns the possession of this small animal. Let us have a fair hearing of this matter. This lady declares the dog was stolen from her and therefore belongs to her; this lady declares she bought him and therefore he belongs to her. Now let us place the little dog on the table here. Lady More, stand you back at that end of the hall; and, mistress, you stand at the other. You will both call the dog, and we will see whom *he* considers to be mistress; for, I verily believe this is a matter which the dog must decide.

Imperiously Alice called the dog to her, and lovingly the beggar-woman called him; and he, the little rogue, did not hesitate; he did what he had been wanting to do ever since he had seen her; he ran, barking excitedly, to the beggar-woman.

'There can be no doubt,' said Thomas, 'that the dog has once been the property of this lady, and her story that he was stolen from her is doubtless a true one.'

The beggar-woman held the dog tightly against her, and Alice, seeing this, knew herself defeated. She knew too that Thomas had been right in this matter, although she deplored his undignified manners.

The beggar-woman said to her: 'Lady, he has fattened since he was in your care. You can offer him a better home than I can. Take him . . . care for him as you have done. I see it would be for the best that he should be yours.'

Alice was touched, as she always was by animals and those who loved them.

She saw that the old woman really loved her dog and that it was no small sacrifice to give him up.

Alice hesitated. She said: 'The judgment of this court went against me. The dog is yours. But if you would like to sell him, I am ready to buy him of you.'

And so the matter was settled amicably and to the satisfaction of all; but Alice could not help pondering on the strange ways of her husband.

The great day came, as Alice had known it would.

The King was to dine at Chelsea.

All that activity which she had set in train for the entertainment of a noble duke was intensified.

Alice could scarcely sleep at night; and when she did she dreamed of serving at her table beef that was almost burned to a cinder. She dreamed of seeing black piecrust on her table. She called out in the agony of her nightmare.

She could not stop talking of the great event. 'Do you wenches realize that it is tomorrow that the King comes! Hurry, hurry, I say. We shall never be done in time.' Then she would smile and think of His Grace sitting at *her* table, smiling at her. 'His Grace the King, so I have heard, likes to see the blood flow rich and red from his beef. We must make sure that there is not one turn too many of the spit. I hear he has a fancy for his pastry to be well baked. . . .'

Never had the servants lived through such days. Preparations were started four days ahead, and Alice could speak of nothing else during that time. All the girls were pressed into service. Ailie must come and stay, and tell all she knew of Court manners and Court etiquette. 'For,' said Alice, 'your father is a dullard in such things. It is beyond my understanding why they have called him a wise man.'

So again and again Ailie told of the King's habits and how food was laid at a Court banquet; and Alice wept because she had not gold platters to set before the King.

And at length the great day came.

She was at her window when the royal barge sailed along the river.

'The King!' she murmured, touching her coif nervously to make sure that it was exactly as it should be. 'The King is coming to dine at my table!'

She saw him alight. Who could mistake him, surrounded though he was by dazzling courtiers?

The jewels on his clothes caught the rays of the sun. What royalty! What magnificence!

Alice marshalled the family together. They stood, as Ailie had said they should, in the hall, waiting to receive him. Thomas watched them all, and he was smiling as though he found this convulsion somewhat amusing. Amusing! Alice was beside herself with anxiety. Would the beef be done to a turn? How were they faring in the kitchen? She should be there . . . yet she must be here.

And now she heard the great, booming voice. 'Why, this is a pleasant place you have here at Chelsea, Master More. We have heard much of it. Norfolk has sung its praises when he has sung yours.'

And now the King was stepping into the hall.

Alice went forward and sank to her knees. All the rich colour had left her face; she was trembling.

'Why, Lady More,' said the King. 'Rise . . . rise . . . good lady. We have heard much of your excellence. We have come to see for ourselves what it is that calls our Chancellor so frequently from our Court.'

Alice had risen uncertainly. 'Your Grace,' she stammered. 'Your . . . most . . . gracious . . . Grace. . . .'

The King laughed; he liked her. He liked such reverence. It was good to see how his subjects stood in awe of him. He placed his great hands on her shoulders and kissed her heartily.

'There . . . there. . . . We are as glad to come as you are to have us. Now we would see this family of yours.'

One by one they came forward. The King's eyes smouldered as they rested on Jack. A fine healthy boy! He felt angry when he saw the fine healthy boys of other men. Now the girls. He softened. He was fond of young girls. Lady Allington was a fair creature, but all women other than Anne were insignificant to him now; when he compared them with the incomparable they could interest him but little. He gave Lady Allington a kiss for her beauty; and he kissed the others too. Thomas's girls were hardly beauties . . . but pleasant creatures.

Afterwards he sat at the table with the family about him; his courtiers who had accompanied him ranged among the family.

It was an appetizing meal. The food was simple, but well cooked; he complimented the lady of the house and it did him good to see the pleasure he gave her in so doing.

The conversation was interesting–he could rely on More to make it so; and naturally that matter which was becoming more and more a cause of disagreement between them was not mentioned in such company.

More was at his best at his own table–gay and witty, anxious to show the cleverness of his children, particularly the eldest girl. The King liked wit and laughter; and, in spite of the man's folly at times, he liked Thomas More.

It pleased Henry to see himself as the mighty King, accustomed to dining in banqueting halls, the guest of kings and princes, yet not above enjoying a simple meal at the humble table of a good subject.

After the meal he asked Thomas to show him the gardens. Taking it that this meant he wished to talk with his Chancellor alone, the courtiers stayed in the house discoursing with the family.

Alice was beside herself with pride.

This was the happiest day of her life. She would talk of it until the end of her days.

Now she must slip away from the company–she could safely leave the entertaining of her guests to her daughters for a short while–and go to the top of the house, whence she could command a view of the gardens; and there, walking together, were the King and his Chancellor. Alice could have wept for joy. About the Chancellor's neck, in a most affectionate manner, was the arm of the King.

The wonderful visit was nearing its end. With what pride did Alice walk down to the royal barge, receive his words of congratulation and make her deep respectful curtsy!

'I shall remember Your Majesty's commendation of my table to my dying day,' she said.

The King was not to be outdone. 'Ah, Lady More, I shall remember my visit to your house to the end of my life.'

Alice was nearly swooning with delight; and, oddly enough, the others were almost as delighted. They stood in respectful attention while the royal barge slipped along the river.

Alice cried: 'To think I should live to see this day! If I were to die now . . . I should die happy.'

'I rejoice in your contentment, Alice,' Thomas told her.

She turned to her family. 'Did you see them . . . in the gardens together? The King had his arm . . . his *arm* . . . about your father's neck.'

'Then he loves Father well,' said Will. 'For I believe that to be a mark of his highest favour. I have never heard of his doing that with any other than my lord Cardinal.'

Thomas smiled at their excitement; but suddenly his face was grave.

He said slowly: 'I thank our Lord, son Roper, that I find the King my very good lord indeed; and you are right when you say that he favours me as much as any subject in this realm. But I must tell you this: I have little cause to be proud of this, for if my head would bring him a castle in France, it should not fail to go. That, my dear ones, is a sobering thought.'

And the family was immediately sobered–except Alice, who would not allow her happiest day to be spoilt by such foolish talk.

Death touched the house in Chelsea during the early months of the year 1532.

The winter had been a hard one, and Judge More had suffered through this. He had caught cold, and all Mercy's ministrations could not save him. He grew weaker; and one day he did not know those about his bedside.

He passed peacefully away in the early morning.

There was much sorrow, for it seemed that no one could be spared from this home.

Thomas declared that he was sorry he had given the house in Bucklersbury to his son and daughter Clement, for it meant that he saw much less of them than if they had continued to live in Chelsea. There had been regrets when Hans Holbein had left the house and Mr Gunnel had taken Holy Orders. It was a large household, as Thomas said, but none could be spared from it.

They mourned the old man for many weeks, and one day, in April of that year, when Margaret and her father were walking together in the gardens, he said to her: 'Meg, we should have done with grieving, for I believe that your grandfather was a happy man when he died; yet had he lived a few months longer he might have been less happy.'

'What do you mean, Father?'

'Like Mother, he took great pride in my position; and it is a position which I may not always hold.'

'You mean that you are shortly to be dismissed?'

'No, Meg. I do not think that. But I think that I might resign. Oh, Meg, I am happier about this matter than I have been since that day, nearly three years ago, when I was given the Great Seal. Then I saw no way in which I could refuse; now I believe I can resign.'

'The King would let you go?'

'Events have been moving, Meg, though sluggishly, it may seem, to those outside the Court. It is now four years since the King made his wishes for a divorce known to us, and still there is no divorce. That is a long time for a King to wait for what he wants. He grows impatient, and so does the Lady Anne. When I was given the Great Seal, you will remember, the Cardinal, who had managed the affairs of this country for so long, was falling out of favour and there seemed no one else capable of taking his place. So was I pressed into taking office. But now matters have changed. The King has at his elbow two clever men, from whom he hopes much. He loves them dearly because they work for him . . . solely. They have no mind but the King's mind, no conscience but the King's conscience, no other will than his. They have two brilliant suggestions which they have put before the King, and the King likes those suggestions so much that I believe he will follow both of them. Cromwell suggests that the King should break from Rome and declare himself Supreme Head of the Church of England; in which case he would have no difficulty in gaining the divorce he wants. That is Master Cromwell's suggestion. Cranmer's is equally ingenious. He declares that, since the marriage of the King and Queen was no true marriage, there is no need for divorce. The marriage could be declared null and void by the courts of England. You see, Margaret, these two men have, as the King says, "the right sow by the ear." I, His Grace would tell you, have the wrong sow's ear in my grasp.'

'Father, as Chancellor, you would have to agree with these two men?'

'Yes: that is why I believe nothing will be put in the way of my resigning from the Chancellorship. There is a very able man, a great friend of the King's, and one who he knows would willingly work for him. That is Lord Audley. I doubt not that the King would be willing enough that I should hand the Great Seal over to him.'

'Father, that means that you would be home with us . . . you would go back to the law . . . and we should be as we were in Bucklersbury.'

'Nay, Meg. I should still be a member of the Council, and a lawyer cannot leave his practice for years and take up the thread where he dropped it. Moreover, I am not as young as I was in those days.'

'Father, I know. I have watched you with great anxiety. We will nurse you, Mercy and I. Oh, I beg of you, give up the Great Seal. Come home to us as soon as you can.'

'You must no longer be anxious for me, dearest Meg, for this poor health of mine gives me the reason I shall need, and which the King will like, for giving up the Chancellorship.'

'I long for that day.'

'And poverty, Meg? Do you long for that? We shall be poor, you know.'

'I would welcome it. But it will surely not be our lot. Will is well placed in his profession.'

'This is a big house and we are a large household. Meg, in spite of our big family and the positions they have secured for themselves, we shall be poor.'

'We shall have you home, Father, and out of harm . . . safe. That is all I ask.'

'So, Meg, I will continue my little homily. Do not grieve because my health is not as good as it was, since because of it I shall come home to you. And do not grieve for your grandfather; he died the father of the Lord Chancellor; and had he lived he might have died the father of a much humbler man.'

She took his hand and kissed it.

'I shall remember life's compensations, Father. Never fear. And how deeply shall I rejoice when you leave the Court, for that has been my dearest wish for many a long day.'

'Dear Meg, I may not be blessed with good health and the King's favour–but I'd throw all that away for the blessing of owning the dearest daughter in the world.'

Margaret was waiting. She knew that it must happen soon. The King had now declared himself to be Supreme Head of the Church. Her father was detained at Court, and she heard that Bishop Fisher had become ill with anxiety.

They were at church one morning–a lovely May morning when the birds sang with excitement and the scent of hawthorn blossom filled the air.

Morning prayers were over, and suddenly Margaret saw her father. He was standing by the door of that pew in which the ladies of his family sat. Margaret took one look at him and knew.

He was smiling at Alice, who had risen to her feet and, in some consternation, was wondering what he was doing there at that hour. He bowed low to her as his gentleman was wont to do, and he said: 'Madam, my lord is gone.'

Alice did not understand.

'What joke is this now?' she demanded.

He did not answer then, and they walked out of the church into the scented air of spring.

Margaret was beside him; she slipped her arm through his.

'What nonsense is this?' demanded Alice as soon as they had stepped out of the porch. 'What do you mean by "My lord is gone"?'

'Just that, Alice. My Lord Chancellor is gone; and all that is left to you is Sir Thomas More.'

'But . . . I do not understand.'

''Tis a simple matter. I have resigned the Great Seal and am no longer Chancellor.'

'You have . . . what?'

'There was naught else I could do. The King needs a Chancellor who will serve him better than I can.'

'You mean that you have resigned? You really mean that you have given up . . . your office . . . ?'

Alice could say no more. She could not bear this sunny May morning. All her glory had vanished.

Her lord had gone in very truth.

Chapter Seven

They gathered about him that night–all those whom he called his dear children. Mercy and John Clement came from Bucklersbury, for the news had reached them. Ailie had heard, and she also came to the house in Chelsea that she might be with him at the time of his resignation.

'My children,' he said when they were all gathered together, 'there is a matter which I must bring to your notice. We have built for ourselves a fine house here in Chelsea; we have many servants to wait upon us; we have never been rich, as are some noble dukes of our acquaintance. . . .' He smiled at Alice. 'But . . . we have lived comfortably. Now I have lost my office and all that went with it; and you know that, even in office, I was never so rich as my predecessor.'

He smiled now at Dauncey–Dauncey who had hinted that he did not take all the advantages that might have been his. But Dauncey was looking downcast; his father-in-law was no longer Chancellor, and Dauncey's hopes of advancement had not carried him very far. He had a seat in Parliament, representing, with Giles Heron, Thetford in Norfolk; Giles Allington sat for the County of Cambridge, and William Roper for Bramber in Sussex. This they had achieved through their relationship with the Chancellor; but all that seemed very little when compared with the favours which had been showered on Wolsey's relations. Moreover, wondered Dauncey, did these people realize that a man could not merely step from high favour to obscurity, that very likely he would pass from favour into disfavour?

Dauncey and Alice were the most disappointed members of the household; yet, like Alice's, Dauncey's disappointment was overshadowed by fear.

Thomas went on: 'My dear ones, we are no longer rich. Indeed, we are very poor.'

Margaret said quickly: 'Well, Father, we shall have the comfort of your presence, which will mean more to us than those other comforts to which you refer.'

Ailie said: 'Father, Giles and I will look after you.'

'Bless you, my dear daughter. But could you ask your husband to take my big household under his wing? Nay, there will be change here.'

'We have always heard that you are such a clever man,' Alice pointed out. 'Are you not a lawyer, and have not lawyers that which is called a practice?'

'Yes, Alice, they have. But a lawyer who has abandoned his practice for eleven years cannot take it up where he left it. And if he is eleven years older and no longer a promising young man, but an old one who has found it necessary to resign his office, he is not so liable to find clients.'

'What nonsense!' said Alice. 'You have a great reputation, so I have always heard. You . . . Sir Thomas More . . . but yesterday Lord Chancellor!'

'Have no fear, Alice. I doubt not that we shall come through these troubles. I have been brought up at Oxford, at an Inn of Chancery, at Lincoln's Inn, also in the King's Court; and so from the lowest degree I came to the highest; yet have I in yearly revenues at this present time little above one hundred pounds. So we must hereafter, if we wish to live together, be contented to become contributaries together. But, by my counsel, it shall not be best for us to fall to the lowest fare first. We will not therefore descend to Oxford fare, nor to the fare of New Inn, but we will begin with Lincoln's Inn diet, which we can maintain during the first year. We will the next year go one step down to New Inn fare, wherewith many an honest man is contented. If that exceed our ability too, then we will the next year after descend to Oxford fare; and if we cannot maintain that, we may yet with bags and wallets go a-begging together, hoping that for pity some good folks will give us their charity.'

'Enough of your jokes!' cried Alice. 'You have thrown away your high post, and we are not as rich as we were. That is what you mean, is it not, Master More?'

'Yes, Alice. That is what I mean.'

'Then more's the pity of it. No; don't go making one of your foolish jokes about More's pity . . . or such kind. I have no pity for you. You're a fool, Master More, and it was by great good luck, and nothing more than that, that you took the King's fancy.'

'Or great mischance, Alice.'

'Great good luck,' she repeated firmly. 'And His Grace is a kindly man. Did I not see him with mine own eyes? It may be that he will not accept your resignation. I am sure he likes you. Did he not walk in the garden with his arm about your neck? Ah . . . he will be here to sup with us again, I doubt not.'

They let her dream. What harm was there in dreaming? But the others knew that the King had no further use for him; and those who knew the

King's methods best prayed that the King might feel nothing but indifference towards his ex-minister.

They brought out their lutes, and Cecily played on the virginals. They were the happy family circle. There was not one of them during that evening–not even Alice nor Dauncey–who did not feel that he or she would be content if they could all remain as they were this night until the end of their days.

But they knew that this was not possible.

Even the servants knew it, for the news had reached them.

How could the household go on in the same comfortable way? Some of them would have to go; and although they knew that Sir Thomas More would never turn them away, that he would find new places for them–perhaps in the rich households of those whom he had known in his affluent days–that brought little comfort. There was no one who, having lived in the Chelsea household, would ever be completely happy outside it.

A year passed.

They were very poor during that year; the house at Chelsea was indeed a large one and there were many living in it to be fed. Yet they were happy. The hospital continued to provide succour for the sick; there was little to spare in the house, but it was always shared with those who were in need. There was always a place at the table for a hungry traveller, and if the fare was simpler than before, it appeased the hunger. Alice took an even greater pride in her cookery; she discovered new ways of using the herbs which grew wild in the fields. They collected fern, bracken, sticks and logs, which they burned in the great fireplaces; and they would gather round one fire to warm themselves before retiring to their cold bedrooms.

Still, it was a happy year. They would not have complained if they could have gone on as they were.

Alice grew angry when the abbots and bishops collected a large sum of money which they wished to present to Thomas. He had written much, they said; the Church was grateful; and they deemed that the best way in which they could show their gratitude was by presenting him with the money. Thomas, however, would not accept it. 'What I have done,' he said, 'was not for gain.'

So Alice scolded him for what she called his misplaced pride, and they continued to live in simplicity.

Patenson the Fool had left them in tears to work with the Lord Mayor of London; and Thomas, knowing that poor Patenson was a very poor Fool indeed, whose idea of wit seemed to be to laugh at the physical appearances of others, arranged that he should be passed from one Lord Mayor to the next Lord Mayor so that he might not suffer through the decline in fortune of one of his masters.

There were some members of the household who were lulled into a feeling of peace, who believed that life would go on humbly and evenly in the years to come. They did not realize that Thomas More had played too big a part in the affairs of the country to be allowed to remain outside them.

So gradually had matters been changing at Court that they were almost unnoticed by those outside it. The King had declared himself to be the Supreme Head of the Church of England. His marriage with Queen Katharine was declared null and void. He had been forced to this procedure by the pregnancy of Anne Boleyn. He was determined that if she gave him a son it should not be born out of wedlock; and he would wait no longer.

Margaret knew that the shadows were moving nearer.

One day a barge pulled up at the stairs, and in it came a messenger.

Margaret saw him as she was playing with her babies, Will and Mary, on the lawns. Her heart leaped, and then she felt the blood thundering in her head. Her children were looking at her wonderingly; she took their hands and forced herself to walk calmly towards the approaching messenger.

To her great relief, she saw that he was not wearing the King's livery.

He bowed low on seeing Margaret.

'Madame, this is the house of Sir Thomas More?'

'It is. What would you of him?'

'I have a letter here. I am instructed to hand it to no other.'

'Whence do you come?'

'From my lords the Bishops of Durham, Bath and Winchester.'

She was relieved.

'Please come this way,' she said, 'and I will take you to Sir Thomas.'

He was in the library, where he now spent the greater part of his time. He could be happy, she thought, then; he could remain in perfect contentment as he is now. Our poverty matters not at all. He can write, pray and laugh with his family. He asks no more than that. 'O God,' she prayed silently, as she led the messenger to her father, 'let him stay as he is. . . . Let him always be as he is now.'

'Meg!' he cried when he saw her.

The little ones ran to him; they loved him; they would sit on his knee and ask him to read to them; he would read them Latin and Greek, and although they could not understand him, they took great pleasure in watching the movement of his lips and listening to the sound of his voice.

Now they caught his skirts and laughed up at him.

'Grandfather . . . here is a man for you.'

'Father,' said Margaret, 'a message from the Bishops.'

'Ah,' said Thomas. 'Welcome, my friend. You have a letter for me. Let little Will take our friend to the kitchens and ask that he may be given something of what they have there, that he may refresh himself. Could you do that, my little man?'

'Yes, Grandfather,' cried Will. 'Indeed I can.'

'Then off with you.'

'Take Mary with you,' said Margaret.

The two children went off with the messenger, and as soon as they were alone Margaret turned to her father. 'Father, what is it?'

'Meg, you tremble.'

'Tell me, Father. Open your letter. Let us know the worst.'

'Or the best. Meg, you are nervous nowadays. What is it, daughter? What should you have to fear?'

'Father, I am not as the others to be lightly teased out of my anxieties. I know . . . as you know . . .'

He put his arm about her. 'We know, Meg, do we not? And because we know, we do not grieve. We are all death's creatures. I . . . you . . . even little Will and Mary. Only this uncertain air, with a bit of breath, keeps us alive. Meg, be not afraid.'

'Father, I beg of you, open the letter.'

He opened it and read it. 'It is a letter from the Bishops, Margaret; they wish me to keep them company from the Tower to the Coronation. They send me twenty pounds with which to buy myself a gown.'

'Father, this is the beginning.'

He sought to comfort her. 'Who knows, Meg? How can any of us know? At this magnificent Coronation, who will notice the absence of one poor and humble man?'

Then she knew that he would refuse to go to the Coronation; and while she longed that he should accept the invitation of the Bishops and bow to the will of the King, she knew that he would never falter in his way along the path which he had chosen.

There had never been such pageantry as that which was to celebrate the crowning of Queen Anne Boleyn.

In the gardens at Chelsea could be heard the sounds of distant triumphant music, for the river had been chosen as the setting for the great ceremony in which the King would honour the woman for whom he had so patiently waited, and for whose sake he had severed his Church from that of his father.

Many of the servants from Chelsea had gone forth to mingle with the crowds and enjoy the festivities of that day, to drink the wine that flowed from the conduits, to see the new Queen in all her beauty and magnificence.

Margaret had not wished to mingle with those crowds.

On that lovely May day she sat in the gardens at home. Her father, she knew, was in his private chapel, praying, she guessed, that when his testing time came he would have the strength to meet it nobly.

May was such a beautiful time of the year; and it seemed to Margaret that never had the gardens at Chelsea seemed to offer such peaceful charm. Those gardens were beginning to mature; the flower borders were full of colour; there was blossom on the trees, and the river sparkled in the sunshine. From far away came the sounds of revelry. She would not listen to them. They were distant; she must not think of them as the rumbling of the coming storm. The buzzing of bees in the garden was near; the scent of the flowers, the smell of fresh earth–they were the home smells. Sitting there in the heat of the sun, she reminded herself that she was in her home, far from the tumult, at peace in her back-water.

Why should the King care what her father did? she soothed herself. He was of no importance now. Who would notice that Sir Thomas More was not present at the Coronation?

She recalled that meeting of his with the Bishops, whom he had seen after he had received their letter.

'My lords,' he had said in his merry way, 'in the letters which you lately sent me you required two things of me.' He was referring to the money they had asked him to accept and the invitation which they had asked him to accept also. 'The one,' he went on, 'since I was so well content to grant you, the other therefore I might be the bolder to deny you.'

They had protested that he was unwise to absent himself from the Coronation. What was done, was done, they pointed out. By staying away from the ceremony, they could not undo the marriage of the King with Anne Boleyn and set Queen Katharine on the throne.

Then he had spoken in a parable. He had told them the story of an Emperor who had ordained that death should be the punishment for a certain offence except in the case of virgins, for greatly did this Emperor reverence virginity. Now, it happened that the first to commit this offence was a virgin; and the Emperor was therefore perplexed as to how he could inflict this punishment, since he had sworn never to put a virgin to death. One of his counsellors rose and said: 'Why make such an ado about such a small matter? Let the girl first be deflowered, and then she may be devoured.'

'And so,' added Thomas, 'though your lordships have in the matter of the matrimony hitherto kept yourselves pure virgins, take good heed that you keep your virginity still. For some there may be that by procuring your lordships first at the Coronation to be present, and next to preach for the setting forth of it and finally to write books to all the world in its defence, therefore are desirous to deflower you; and when they have deflowered you they will not fail soon after to devour you. Now, my lords, it lieth not in my power that they may devour me, but God being my good Lord, I will so provide that they shall never deflower me.'

These words would be noted by many who had heard them. And what would the King say to their utterance? And what would he do?

These were the questions Margaret asked herself as she sat in the sunshine.

We can be so happy here, she thought. And he is no longer Lord Chancellor. He is of no great importance now.

But, of course, he would always be of importance while men listened to his words and he had the power to turn their opinions.

From the river came the sounds of rejoicing. In vain did Margaret try to shut out those sounds.

Was she really surprised when the persecutions began?

The first came at the end of the year after the King's Council had published the nine articles which justified all he had done in ridding himself of one Queen and providing himself with another.

Thomas was accused of having written an answer to the nine articles and sent it abroad to be published. Thomas had written no such answer. He was still a member of the King's Council, and as such would consider that his membership debarred him from discussing the King's affairs except in Council.

Nothing could be proved against him and the matter was dropped; but to his family it was an indication of how the winds were beginning to blow.

The King was angry with Thomas, as he was with all those who did not agree with him or who made him question the rightness of his actions.

A few peaceful months passed, but every time Margaret heard strange voices near the house she would feel beads of sweat on her brow, and she would place her hand over her heart in a vain attempt to quell its wild leaping.

Another charge was brought against him. This time he was accused of accepting bribes.

Here, thought those who had been set to bring about his downfall, was a safe charge to bring against him, for surely any man in his position must at some time have accepted a gift which could be called a bribe. It was possible to produce people who had presented him with gifts during his term of office, but it could not be proved that any of these had been bribes, or that the donors had gained aught from such gifts. Instead, it was shown how his son-in-law Heron had lost a case which he had brought, and that even the rather comic case, in which his wife had been involved, had gone against her. No, there was no way of convicting him on the score of bribery.

The King was irritated beyond measure by the folly of the man. He knew well that there were many in his kingdom who thought highly of Sir Thomas More and who might change their opinions regarding the King's recent actions if only such a highly respected man as Sir Thomas More could be made to come to heel.

Friar Peto, of the Observants of Greenwich, had actually dared preach a sermon against the King, declaring from the pulpit that if he behaved as Ahab, the same fate would overtake him. This was prophecy, and Henry was afraid of prophets unless he could prove them false–and only the King's death could prove Peto false.

The Carthusians, with whom More had a special connection, were preaching against the marriage.

Fisher, Bishop of Rochester, was another who dared to take his stand against the King.

'By God's Body,' said Henry, 'I do verily believe that if this man More would state in his clever way that he is with me in all I do, he could have these others following him.'

But More would do no such thing; he was an obstinate fool.

If he could be proved false . . . ah, if only he could be proved false!

The King himself wanted to have nothing to do with More's downfall. He wished to turn his back, as he had in the case of Wolsey; he wished to leave More to his enemies. This was not so easy as it had been in the case of Wolsey, for More had few enemies. He was no Cardinal Wolsey. Men loved More; they did not wish him harm. Audley, Cranmer–even Cromwell–became uneasy over the matter of More's downfall.

That was why, when More was accused of taking bribes, with his clever lawyer's words and his proof of this and that, with his knowledge of the law, he was able to rebut the charges.

It was even so with regard to the matter of the lewd nun of Canterbury.

Elizabeth Barton, a mere serving-girl, who had been cured of a terrible sickness by, some said, a miracle, became a nun in the town of Canterbury. She had made certain prophecies during trances, and when Thomas was Chancellor, the King had sent him to examine the woman. Thomas had been impressed by her holiness and, with Fisher, inclined to believe that she was not without the gift of prophecy. Elizabeth Barton had declared that if the King married Anne Boleyn he would, within six months, cease to be King of England. Six months had passed since the marriage, and here was Henry still in firm possession of the throne.

Elizabeth Barton was a fraud; she was a traitor and she should suffer the death penalty.

The King was pleased, for those who had believed the nun's evil utterances were guilty of misprision of treason.

What of my lord Bishop of Rochester? the King asked the devoted Cromwell. What of our clever Sir Thomas More?

Here again he was defeated, for Thomas the lawyer was not easily trapped. He could prove that, as a member of the King's Council, he had always refused to listen to any prophecy concerning the King's affairs.

That was an anxious time for Thomas's family. Now they felt fresh relief. Nothing could be proved against him in this affair of the nun of Canterbury and once more, after an examination, Thomas returned to his family.

It was small wonder that they would sometimes catch a look of alarm in one another's eyes, that sometimes one of them would appear to be alert, listening; then that fearful disquiet would settle on the house again.

The King was fretful.

His marriage was not all that he had believed it would be. He had a child–but a daughter. He was fond of young Elizabeth, but she was not a son; and it was sons he wished his Anne to give to him.

Moreover, Anne the wife was less attractive than Anne the mistress had been.

The King was beginning to feel great need to justify his behaviour. He wanted all the world–and certainly all his own countrymen–to see him as the righteous man who had rid himself of an ageing wife and married an attractive one, not for his own carnal desires, but for the good of the country.

He was very angry with Thomas More, who, while he had done nothing against the King which the law could condemn, yet refused to express his approval of the King's actions. When the list of those who had been guiltily involved in the case of the nun of Canterbury was brought before Henry, he refused to allow Thomas's name to be removed.

But he could do no more about that matter at the moment.

He would pace up and down his apartments with some of his intimates about him.

'It grieves me,' he cried. 'It grieves me mightily. I have honoured that man. What was he before I took him up? A miserable lawyer. I made him great. And what is his answer? What does he offer me? Base ingratitude! A word from him, and there could be peace among these monks. Even Fisher himself could doubtless be persuaded by his old friend. Yet . . . Thomas More will not accept me as Head of the Church! By God's Body, this is treason! He holds that the Pope is still Head of the Church! That's treason, is it not? Was there ever a servant to his sovereign more treacherous, more villainous, or subject to his prince so traitorous as he? What have I given him? Riches. Power. Favour. And what does he give me? Disobedience! I ask nothing but that he does what others of my servants have done. He has but to acknowledge my supremacy in the Church. Audley . . . Cromwell . . . Norfolk, my friends . . . was ever King so plagued?'

He was asking them to rid him of this man.

The little eyes were hot and angry, but the mouth was prim. All over the continent of Europe, Sir Thomas More was respected. The King's conscience must not be offended.

'Bring this man to obedience.' That was what the little eyes pleaded with those about him. 'No matter how . . . no matter how you do it.'

Norfolk took barge to Chelsea.

Margaret, on the alert as she ever was, saw the Duke coming, and ran down to meet him.

'My lord . . . fresh news?'

'Nay, nay. 'Tis naught. Where is your father? I would speak with him at once.'

'I'll take you to him.'

Thomas had seen the Duke's arrival and had come down to greet him.

'It is rarely that we have had this honour of late,' he said.

'I would speak with you alone,' said the Duke; and Margaret left them together.

'Well, my lord?' asked Thomas.

'Master More, you are a foolish man.'

'Have you come from the Court to tell me that?'

'I have. I have come straight from the King.'

'And how did you leave him?'

'Angry against you.'

'I regret that. I regret it deeply.'

'Tut, tut, what is the use of such words? You could turn his anger into friendship an you wished it.'

'How so?'

'Tut, I say again; and tut, tut, tut. You know full well. You have but to agree to the succession of the heirs of Anne Boleyn and the Act of Supremacy. And, Master More, when you should be called upon to sign these Acts, you must cast aside your folly and do so.'

'I would accept the former, because it is the law of this land that the King and the Council may fix the succession. Even though that would mean setting aside a lawful heir for the sake of a bastard, the King and Council can, in law, do it. But I would never take the Oath of Supremacy.'

Norfolk tut-tutted impatiently. 'I come as a friend, Master More. I come from the Court to warn you. The King will not brook your disobedience. He seeks to entrap you.'

'Several charges have been brought against me, but I have answered them all.'

'By the Mass, Master More, it is perilous striving with princes. Therefore I would wish you somewhat to incline to the King's pleasure, for, by God's Body, Master More, *Indignatio principis mors est.*'

'Indeed, indeed,' said Thomas with a smile. 'The indignation of this Prince is turned against Thomas More.'

'I intend no pun,' said Norfolk impatiently. 'I ask you to remember it, that is all.'

'Is that all, my lord?' said Thomas. 'Then I thank you for coming here this day, and I must say this: In good faith, the difference between your Grace and me is but this: that I shall die today and you tomorrow.'

The Duke was so exasperated that he took his leave at once and strode angrily down to the barge without coming into the house.

This annoyed Alice, for she had seen his arrival and hastened to change her dress and put on her most becoming coif; and lo and behold, when she went down to receive her noble guest, it was but to see his abrupt departure.

Gloom hung over the house.

Mercy had called, anxious and pale.

'How go matters, Meg?' she asked.

'Mercy, come out to the gardens where we can be alone. I cannot talk to you here, lest Mother overhears.'

In the quiet of the gardens, Margaret said: 'He has gone before another committee.'

'Oh, God in Heaven, what is it this time?'

'I know not.'

'His name is still on the Parliament's list of those guilty with Elizabeth Barton.'

'Oh, Mercy, that's the pity of it. He has confuted them with his arguments, but it matters not. They still accuse him. Why do they do this, Mercy? I know . . . and so do you. They are *determined* to accuse him. He is innocent . . . innocent . . . but they will not have it so.'

'They cannot prove him guilty, Margaret. He will always triumph.'

'You seek to comfort us, Mercy. Often I think of the happy times . . . when we were cutting the hay, or walking in the gardens, sitting together . . . singing, sewing . . . reading what we had written. Oh, Mercy, how far away those days seem now, for we can never sit in ease or comfort. Always we must listen . . . always be on the alert. A barge comes. Will it stop at our stairs? we ask ourselves. There is a sound of a horse on the road. Is it a messenger from the King . . . from the new Councillor, Cromwell?'

'Meg, you distress yourself.'

But Margaret went on: 'He used to say when he was particularly happy: "I shall remember this moment when I die. I shall remember it and say that my life was worth while. . . ."' Margaret broke down and covered her face with her hands.

Mercy said nothing; she clasped her hands together and felt she would die of the deep distress within her.

She thought: We are realists, I and Margaret. We cannot shut our eyes to the facts as the others can. Bess, Cecily, Jack, they love him . . . but differently. They love him as a father, and I believe that to Meg and me he is a saint as well as a beloved father.

'I remember,' said Margaret suddenly, 'how Ailie came to us and showed us the fashions. Do you remember? The long sleeves? It was that woman . . . the Queen. That woman . . . ! And but for her, Mercy, he would be with us now . . . perhaps he would be reading to us . . . perhaps he would be laughing . . . chiding us for some folly in his merry way. And now, Mercy, he is standing before a Commission, and we do not know of what he is accused; and we do not know when he will come home . . . *if* he will come home.'

'Margaret, this is not like you. You . . . so reasonable, so rational. Margaret, you the cleverest of us all . . . to give way to grief, to mourn for what has not yet come to pass!'

'Oh, Mercy, do not stand there and pretend to be so calm! There are tears in your eyes. You have the same fears. Your heart is breaking too.'

Mercy looked at her, and the tears began to flow silently down her cheeks.

'And all for a woman,' cried Margaret in sudden anger, 'a woman with a deformed hand and a mole on her throat that must be covered with a jewel. . . . For beautiful sleeves . . . for Frenchified manners . . . our father must . . .'

'Don't say it, Meg. It has not happened yet.'

They looked at each other and then began to walk silently back to the house.

He did come home from the Commissioners; he came merrily. Will was with him in the barge when Mercy and Margaret ran down to meet him.

He embraced the girls warmly. He saw the tears on their cheeks, but he did not comment on them.

'Father . . . so you have come back!' said Margaret.

'Yes, daughter, your husband and I came back together.'

'And, Father, all is well?'

'All is well, my daughter.'

'You are no longer on the Parliament's list? You are no longer accused with the nun of Canterbury?'

'It was not of that that they wished to talk.'

'Then what?'

'I was accused of urging the King to write his *Assertion of the Seven Sacraments.*'

'But, Father, he had started to write that when he called you in.'

'Ah, my dear daughter, it was as good a charge as the others, so, I beg of you, do not complain of it.'

'Father, they are seeking to entrap you.'

'They cannot entrap an innocent man.'

'How could they have accused you of this matter?'

'His Majesty was determined to honour the Pope in his book, and he did so. And now it appears he would like to accuse me of writing this book, but for the fact that it is so well done, and he likes better the praise he has received for writing it. But it is said that I have caused him, to his dishonour, to put a sword in the Pope's hand to fight the King.'

'Oh, Father!'

'Have no fear, Meg. I have confounded them. For did I not warn the King of the risk of incurring the penalties of *praemunire*? I reminded them of this, and that the book was the King's book; that he himself had said I had but arranged it to his wishes. They could scarcely bring such a matter against me when the King has so clearly said that the book was his own–aye, and has received the title of Defender of the Faith for having written it.'

'If he is repudiating authorship of the book, then he should abandon the title it brought him,' said Mercy.

'You are right, daughter. I said: "My lords, these terrors be arguments for children and not for me."'

Will's brow was furrowed. He said: 'But, Father, what of the Parliament's list? Have they struck your name from it?'

'By my troth, son Roper, I forgot that matter in this new one.'

Will spoke tartly in his anxiety. 'You did not remember it? A case that touches you so near, and us all for your sake!'

Margaret looked anxiously from her husband to her father. Thomas was smiling; Will was angry.

'I understand not, sir,' said Will, 'why you should be so merry.'

'Then, Will, let me tell you. And I will tell my dear daughters also. This day I have gone so far, I have spoken my mind so clearly to these lords who cross-examined me, that, without great shame, I could not now turn back.'

He lifted his eyes and looked beyond them. He was smiling, but those about him were conscious of a deepening of their fear.

It seemed wrong that the weather should be so beautiful. Surely there had never been a more lovely April. Margaret could not bear the brightness of the spring sunshine. They went about their work silently, forcing their smiles. Everyone in the household knew that it could not be long before he was called before the Commissioners to sign the newly-coined Oath of Supremacy. How would he be able to extricate himself from this trouble? Now he would be presented with the necessity to sign or not to sign. The first would mean a return to the King's pleasure; the other . . . ? They did not know; they dared not think.

Easter Day came, and he, determined not to brood as they did, trying to laugh at their fears, being more gay than even was his wont, had arranged to go with Will to St Paul's to hear the sermon.

On that lovely spring day they set out by barge.

He would not be back until late in the day.

'I shall be within a few minutes of Bucklersbury,' he said, 'and I cannot pass so close without calling on my son and daughter Clement.'

Mercy was waiting for him with a heavy heart. Each time she saw him she wondered whether it would be the last.

'John,' she cried to her husband, 'how *can* I greet him merrily? How can I?'

'You must,' John answered. 'Who knows, this storm may pass.'

Dinner was on the table waiting for him, and she went out along the Poultry to meet him.

She saw him coming, his arm through that of Will Roper; they were deep in discussion, doubtless talking of the sermon they had just heard.

He embraced her warmly when they met; but his searching eyes saw what she could not hide, and that which he must be seeing in the faces of every member of his family now.

'Why, daughter, it is good indeed to see you. And how do I find you? Merry and well?'

'Merry and well,' she repeated. 'Merry and well, Father.'

He put his arm through hers and they walked thus to Bucklersbury; he smiling, a son and daughter on either side of him, happy to be with them, for although they had neither of them been born son and daughter of his, he would have them know that he considered them as such.

Friends and acquaintances greeted him as they passed along. There was warmth in the smiles of these people. They remembered him when he had been Under-Sheriff of the City; they remembered him as the incorruptible Lord Chancellor. But Mercy interpreted the looks in their eyes–fear, pity, warning.

The blow could not be far off.

Margaret, who loved him perhaps more poignantly than any of them, would have him sign the Oath; Margaret would have him do anything so that she might keep him with her. Mercy knew that. And if she, Mercy, could have pleaded with him, would she have urged him to sign the Oath?

She differed from Margaret. Margaret's love was all-important to her. He was, after all, Margaret's father, and if Margaret could keep him with her she would not care what it cost. But Mercy would never ask him to do what was against his conscience. Mercy would have him do what was right . . . whatever the consequences to himself and his family.

But that did not mean her suffering was any less acute.

Here was Bucklersbury with its pleasant apothecaries' smells. Here was the old home.

'I never enter it without a thousand memories assailing me,' he said.

And Mercy knew that he was glad to be here again, to recall those happy memories, to treasure them for that time when he would be unable to visit the house in Bucklersbury.

'Come, Father, you will be hungry. Let us eat at once.'

They were at table when the messenger arrived.

Mercy rose. She was not unduly disturbed. She did not expect them to come for him here. This must be a friend calling. No? Then a messenger from the Court. It must be someone for John, for he was now one of the King's physicians.

The man came forward. He carried a scroll in his hands.

'A message for me?' asked John.

'Nay, sir. I was instructed to deliver this to Sir Thomas More at Chelsea, but, hearing that he was at your house, I have saved myself the journey.'

Thomas rose to receive the scroll. 'Thank you. You were wise to save yourself the journey.'

He did not look at the scroll, but chatted awhile with the messenger in his friendly way; and when the man had left, he still held it unopened in his hands.

'Father . . .' began Mercy fearfully.

'Let us eat this excellent meal you have prepared for us, my daughter.'

'But . . .'

'After,' he said. 'There is time for that.'

Then he began to talk of the sermon he and Will had heard at St Paul's; but none of them was attending; their eyes kept going to the scroll which lay on the table.

'Father,' said Will angrily, 'keep us no longer in suspense. What is this?'

'Have you not guessed, my son? I'll warrant it is an instruction for me to appear before the Commissioners to take the Oath of Supremacy.'

'Then, Father, look at it. Make sure.'

'Why, Will, you fret too much. We knew this must come.'

'Father,' said Will in exasperation, 'your calm maddens me. Read it . . . for pity's sake.'

Thomas read. 'Yes, Will,' he said. 'I am to appear before the Commissioners at Lambeth to take the Oath.'

'It is more than I can bear,' said Will. 'It is more than Margaret can bear.'

'Take hope, my son. Let no trouble drive you to misery. If the trouble is lasting, it is easy to bear. If it is hard to bear, it does not last long.'

'Father, when do you go to Lambeth?' asked Mercy.

'Tomorrow. You see, today I need not fret. Today I may do what I will.'

'We must go back to Chelsea,' said Will.

'Why?'

'They will wish to have you with them as long as possible. Margaret . . .'

'Let her be. Let her have this day in peace. The sooner she knows this notice has been served upon me, the sooner will she fret even as you do, Will.'

'Is the knowledge that this has come any worse than the fear that it will, the knowledge that it must?'

'Yes, Will. For in uncertainty there is hope. Leave Margaret for a while. Come, let us eat, or Mercy will be offended. She and her servants have taken great pains to please us with these foods.'

Eat! Take pleasure in food? How could they?

They sat there at the table, and the pain in their hearts was almost unbearable.

And the only merry one at that table was Sir Thomas More.

They went along the river, back to Chelsea, in the early evening.

'Not a word yet, Will,' said Thomas. 'Leave them in peace. . . . Let them have this day.'

'But, Father,' said Will in distress, 'I doubt that I can keep my fears from them.'

'You have been displaying fears for many a day, Will. Smile, my son. They'll not know. They'll not think this could be served on me anywhere but in my own home. Let us have one more merry night at home. Let us sing and tell tales and laugh and be happy together, Will . . . just for one more night.'

Will did manage to curb his misery. He sang as loudly as the rest; and he was aware of his father-in-law's gratitude.

And that night, when he lay beside Margaret, he was sleepless, and so was she.

She whispered: 'Will, it cannot be long now, can it? There cannot be many more such days left to us.'

And Will said: 'It cannot be long.' He remembered his father's plea and he did not say: 'There can be no more such days. Today is the last, for tomorrow he goes to Lambeth.'

The next morning the family rose as usual. Thomas had an air of resignation which Margaret noticed; it was almost as though he found pleasure in this day. Alice noticed it too; she thought, I do believe he is going to do as the King wishes. I do believe he has come to his senses at last.

But after they had breakfasted he said: 'Come . . . let us go to church.'

They walked across the fields to Chelsea Church as they had done on many other mornings. And after the service, when the sun was high in the sky, he laid his hand on Will's arm and said: 'Will, 'tis time we were away.'

He called to two of the servants and said: 'Have the barge ready. This day I have to go to Lambeth.'

So they knew. The day had come.

Margaret took a step towards him, but his eyes held her off. Not here, Meg, they said. Not here . . . before the others.

'I have to go to Lambeth.' Those words might not sound ominous to the others as they did to Margaret and Will.

He is going to Lambeth on some business of the Parliament, they would think. He will be home ere evening.

But Margaret knew why he must go to Lambeth; and she knew what he would do when he was there. In her eyes was a mute appeal: Father, Father, do as they wish. What does it matter who is Head of the Church, if you are head of your family and continue to live with them to their delight and your own?

He was looking at Margaret now. He said: 'Do not come beyond the wicket gate. I must go in haste. Goodbye to you all.'

He kissed them all, and when her turn came, Margaret clung to him.

'Father . . .'

'Goodbye, my daughter, my beloved daughter. I shall be with you . . . ere long. . . .'

And he went over the lawns, opening the wicket gate, shutting it fast when Will had passed through, down the steps to the barge.

He took one look at the house which he had built, the house in which he was to have known perfect happiness with his family. He looked at the casements glittering in the sunshine, the peacocks on the wall, the blossoming fruit trees in the orchards. Who would gather the fruit this year? he wondered.

One last look at all that contained his happiness on Earth. Then he turned to Will, and as the barge slipped slowly away from the stairs he said: 'I thank the Lord, son Roper, that the field is won.'

He was sent to the Tower, and all the brightness had fled from the house in Chelsea.

There was no more pleasure in that house. There was nothing to do but wait in fear for what would happen next.

Margaret had begged to see her father, and because of the influence Dr Clement and Giles Allington were able to exert, she was at last allowed the privilege.

She had not slept at all the night before; indeed, for many nights she had had little sleep. She would lightly doze and wake with thoughts of her father in his comfortless cell. During the days she would walk along the river until she could more clearly see that grim fortress which had become his prison.

And now that she was to see him, now that she might take boat and go down the river to the Tower, she must be ready to offer him words of comfort. She must try not to beg him to do that which was against his conscience.

She reached the stairs; she alighted from the barge. Will helped her out, for he had insisted on coming as far as the Tower with her. Will would wait for her. Dear, good Will, the best of comforters, the dearest of husbands! She would bless the day her father had brought him to the house; for she must think of her blessings, not her miseries.

How she hated the place–the place that impressed her with its might and its horror! She looked up at the round towers, at the narrow slits which served as windows, at the dungeons with the bars across the slits. And here, in this place, was her father, her beloved father.

A jailor took her up a winding staircase and unlocked a heavy door. She was in a cell, a cell with stone walls and a stone floor; and then she saw no more of it, for there he was, smiling at her, hurrying to greet her.

She looked into his face and noticed how pale he was, how hollow were his eyes. He had changed. Yet . . . he could still smile, he could still feign a gaiety which he could not possibly feel.

'Meg . . . my own Meg!'

'My Father!' She was kissing him, clinging to him. 'Oh, Father, how are you? What have they done to you? You have grown thin and your beard is unkempt, and your clothes . . . Oh, Father . . . Father . . . what can I do? What can I say?'

'Come,' he said. 'Sit down, Meg. My jailor is a kind man. I have these stools. . . . Many people have been kind to me, Meg. My good friend, Bonvisi . . . he sends meat and wine . . . and I am allowed to have my good John a Wood here with me to look after me. You see, I am not treated badly. I am well looked after here.'

She tried to smile.

'Why, Meg, how are you? You are looking well. The sun has touched you. How are my dear sons and daughters? Bid them be of good cheer, Meg. You can do it.'

'To be of good cheer!' she cried. 'Father, let there be no pretence between us. Do not let us deceive ourselves and say, "This will pass," when we know there is only one way in which it could pass, and that you have determined against it.'

'Let us talk of other things, dear daughter.'

'How can I? What can I tell the children?'

'It may be, Meg, that you will have to speak to them of death. And if that be so, let them see it as a beautiful thing. Let them see it as release to beauty, to joy, to happiness such as this Earth cannot offer. Tell them that the man is dreaming who thinks in this life he is rich, for when death wakes him he will see how poor he is. Tell them that those who suffer at the hands of unjust men should take hope. Let kindly hopes console your suffering, Meg. He who is carried away by great wealth and empty pride, he who stands so bold among his courtiers, will not always be so bold. One day he will be equal with the beggars. Ah, what gift has life given that compares with death? You will find that he who can in life inspire fear, in death inspires nothing but laughter. Oh, Meg, Meg, lift up thy spirits. So not grieve because I must come to that which awaits us all. My spirit is ready to break its shell. What matters it who cracks that shell? It may be the King. It may be the King's ministers. It may be the King's mistress.'

'Do not speak of her, Father. When you do, my heart is filled with hatred. I think of her as when we first heard of her and she seemed naught but a silly, frivolous girl. I did not know then that she was a wicked wanton . . . a would-be murderess of saintly men.'

'Hush, Meg! Do not speak ill of her. Pity her rather than condemn. For how do we know, poor soul, to what misery she may come?'

'I will not pity her, Father. I will not. But for her, you would be with us at home in Chelsea . . . all together . . . as we used to be. How can I pity her? How can I do aught but curse her?'

'Meg, you must have pity. She dances gaily at the Court, I hear; and these dances of hers will prove such dances that she will spurn our heads off like footballs; but, Meg, it may not be long before her own poor head will dance the like dance.'

'Father, what does it matter . . . what does anything matter if you but come home to us? Could you not . . . ?'

'Nay, Meg. I know what I must do.'

'But what will happen?'

'We shall see.'

'My lord Bishop of Rochester is also in the Tower.'

'My jailor told me. I knew my dear friend Fisher must do this . . . even as I must.'

'The monks of the Charterhouse refuse to acknowledge the King's Supremacy, Father.'

'My good friends? It is what I would expect of them.'

'But, Father, is it right . . . is it lawful that they should imprison you for this? What have you done? You have merely refused to take an Oath. Is it then the law that a man may be imprisoned for this?'

'Ah, Meg, the King's pleasure is the law. It is a great pity that any Christian prince should, by a flexible Council ready to follow his affections, and by a weak clergy lacking grace constantly to stand to their learning, be so shamefully abused with flattery.'

'But, Father, is it worth it, think you? Could you not . . . take the Oath . . . and retire from Court life altogether? Live with us . . . your family . . . as you long to live. You have your library . . . your home . . . all that you love. Father, you are no longer young. You should be at home with your sons and daughters, with your wife. . . .'

'Why, have you come here to play the temptress, then? Nay, Mistress Eve, we have talked of this thing more than once or twice. I have told you that if it were possible to do this thing that would content the King, and God therewith would not be offended, then no man would have taken the

Oath more gladly than I.'

'Oh, God in heaven,' she cried, 'they are coming to tell me I must go. Father . . . when shall I see your face again?'

'Be of good cheer, Meg. Ere long, I doubt not.'

She embraced him, and she saw the tears on his cheeks.

She thought: My coming has not cheered him; it has distressed him.

Alice had permission to visit him.

She was truculent, more full of scolding than usual; that was because she was so unhappy.

She stood in the doorway, her sharp eyes taking in the cell in all its comfortless gloom.

'What the good year, Master More!' she cried. 'It is a marvellous thing to me that you have always been taken for such a wise man. Here you are, playing the fool, as is your wont. You lie here in this close, filthy prison, and you are content to be shut up with mice and rats, when you might be abroad and at your liberty, enjoying the favour of the King and his Council. And all you must do is as the Bishops and learned men of this realm have done. And seeing you have at Chelsea a right fair house, your library, your gallery, your garden, your orchards and all other necessaries so handsome about you, where you might be in the company of your wife and children and with your household be merry, I muse what in God's name you mean, here so fondly to tarry.'

'Alice . . . Alice, it is good to see you. It is good to hear you scold me. Come, wife. Sit down. Sit on this stool which my good jailor has provided for me. We do well, here, John a Wood and I. My good friend Bonvisi sends more meat and drink than we need. Have no fear.'

'So you like this place better than your home. Is that it? Is that what you would tell me?'

'Is this house not as nigh Heaven as my own?' he asked.

'Tilly valley! Tilly valley! What nonsense you talk! All the prisons in the world could not alter that, I see.'

'But answer me, Alice. Is it not so?'

'By the good God, will this gear never be left?'

'Well, Mistress Alice, if it be so, and I believe you know it to be so and that is why you will answer with nothing but "Tilly valley!" that is well. I see no great cause why I should have much joy in my handsome house or in anything belonging to it, when if I should be but seven years buried under the ground and then arise and come thither, I should not fail to find someone therein who would bid me get out of doors and tell me it was none of mine. What cause have I then to like such a house as would so soon forget its master?'

'Tut and tut! Have done with this talk. What of your clothes? Have you anything for me to wash? And what a filthy place is this! And what does Master a Wood think he is doing not to look to your comforts more? It seems to me, Master More, that you are a fool . . . surrounded by fools. . . .'

And he saw the bright tears brimming over on to her cheeks; he pretended not to see them. She scolded on, while in her way she was begging him to come home, even as Margaret had done.

From the windows of her husband's mansion, Ailie looked out over the park. She was tense and waiting. Soon, she believed, Lord Audley would come riding to the house in the company of her husband, and she had told Giles that when they returned he must leave her that she might have a word with the Chancellor.

'Oh, God help me,' prayed Ailie, more fervently than she had ever prayed before. 'Help me to do this.'

Lord Audley could help her, she believed. But had he the power? He was the Lord Chancellor, and when the father had been Chancellor many had brought their petitions to him.

Ailie could not bear to think of the house in Chelsea now. Margaret wrote to her often; so did Mercy. But the feigned cheerfulness of their letters only served to tell her how changed everything was. Would this dreary summer never pass?

She heard the huntsmen's horns and looked in the polished Venetian mirror which her husband had given her and of which she had once been so proud. Her eyes were hard and bright; her cheeks were flushed; she looked at her trembling, twitching mouth.

Then, composing herself, she ran down to greet the returning huntsmen.

Audley was talking excitedly about the deer he had killed in the park. What could it matter? There was only one thing that mattered now.

Giles was smiling at her tenderly, full of understanding. He led the way to the stables, where the grooms rushed forth to take the horses. Ailie was walking with Lord Audley, and Giles saw that they were left alone.

''Twas a good day's sport, I trust, Lord Audley?'

'It was, Lady Allington. Your husband is fortunate to have such happy hunting grounds at his disposal.'

'You must come often to hunt with us.'

'That I will.'

Ailie laid a hand on the arm of the Lord Chancellor and smiled up at him.

'My lord, you are a man of great influence at Court.'

Lord Audley smiled his pleasure.

'You could do something for me an you wished.'

'Lady Allington, I would willingly do anything in my power to please you.'

'You are gracious, my lord. It is of my father, I would speak.'

Lord Audley gave a quick, rather harsh laugh. 'Why, Lady Allington, he has all the means at his disposal to help himself.'

'That is not so.'

'I beg of you, forgive the contradiction, but it is so. He has but to sign the Oath of Supremacy, and he would be a free man tomorrow.'

'But that he cannot do.'

'Cannot! Cannot sign his name!' Lord Audley laughed. (He was proud of saying, 'I am no scholar!' which meant he had a certain contempt for those who were.) 'But we have always heard that he is such a learned man!' he went on.

'My lord, he feels this to be a matter of conscience.'

'Then he should reason with his conscience. My dear lady, I would do as much for your father as I would for my own . . . for your sake; but what can I do? The remedy lies with him. I marvel that he should be so obstinate in his conceit.'

'Could you not persuade the King that, in my father's case, this matter of the Oath could be waived?'

'My dear lady, you know the ways of Parliament.'

Then the Chancellor began to tell Ailie one of Æsop's fables. 'This,' he said, 'you, being the daughter of such a learned man, have doubtless heard before.' It was the fable of the few wise men who tried to rule the multitude of fools. The few were flogged by the many. 'Were they such wise men after all, Lady Allington? Were they, I wonder.'

Ailie looked into the cold, proud face beside her, and her heart felt leaden.

They had reached the house, and she stepped on ahead of him. Giles came forth and, seeing her state, engaged their guest in conversation so that she was free to run upstairs to her bedroom.

This she did, with the tears flowing down her cheeks, and her face set in a mask of utter hopelessness.

There were no more visits to the Tower, and the months were dragging on. Christmas came; and it was last spring when he had been taken from home.

What a different Christmas was this from that which they usually spent! They were all together, but how could they be happy without him?

They lived for the letters they received from him. They were allowed to send a servant to the Tower to take letters to him and receive his. The faithful Dorothy Colly made the journey, for she was almost one of the family, and Thomas was fond of her. She would come back and tell them everything he had said.

'He wishes to know what you are doing, how you spend your days. No little detail is too small. It pleases him much to hear these things. He must have news of the latest sayings of the children.'

To Margaret, when they were alone, she said: 'He kissed me when I left. And I was to tell you, he said, that he loves me as one of the family. He said: "Have you married John Harris yet, Dorothy? You should. Tell Margaret. She will help you to arrange it, for marriage is a good thing; and if two people grow together in love and comradeship, there is no happier state in the world."'

Margaret kissed her maid. She knew that John Harris loved her; and she knew that her father meant: 'Be happy. Do not continue to grieve. Go about your ordinary business. If there is a wedding among you, rejoice and celebrate. Your father is with you in all you do.'

'I must see him soon, Dorothy,' she said. 'We cannot go on like this.'

He had changed very much since his imprisonment; he was thin and ill. He had his books with him, and they brought him much comfort. He was writing what he called *A Dialogue of Comfort*. This was a conversation between two Hungarians, an aged man Antonio and his nephew Vincent. These two discussed the coming invasion of the Turks. The allegory was easily understood by Margaret–for he sent his writings to her.

'I cannot read this to you,' he wrote, 'but I need your opinions as I ever did.'

Margaret guessed who the Great Turk was meant to be, for Thomas wrote: 'There is no born Turk so cruel to Christian folk as is the false Christian that falleth from his faith. Oh, Margaret, my beloved daughter, I am a prisoner in a foul place, yet I am happy when I take up my pen to write to you, and I would rather be Margaret's father than the ruler of an Empire.'

Rich, the Solicitor-General, paid him many visits. Thomas understood the purpose of these visits; they were to entrap him. Now they were trying to make him *deny* the King's supremacy; but Thomas was too learned in the ways of the law to do this. He was fully aware that he could not be condemned merely for refusing to sign the Oath. If he preserved silence on his views, he must be guiltless. There was no law under which it was possible to punish a man because he refused to sign an oath.

In vain did Rich seek to entrap him; Cromwell, Norfolk, Audley, the whole Council did their best to please the King by making a case against him; but Thomas was the greatest lawyer of them all. Not one of them–even Cranmer–could lure him to say that which would condemn him.

He knew that his friend Bishop Fisher was in the Tower. Fisher was a brave man, but he was no lawyer. Thomas wrote notes to him, and Fisher answered him; their servants found means of exchanging these notes, for the jailors were willing to make the incarceration of two such saintly men as Fisher and More as comfortable as was possible.

'Have great care, my friend,' Thomas begged the Bishop. 'Be on your guard against the questions which are put to you. Take great care that you do not fall into the dangers of the Statutes. You will not sign the Oath. That is not a crime in itself. But guard your tongue well. If any ask you, be sure that you say not a word of the King's affairs.'

The Bishop was a very sick man and his imprisonment had greatly affected his health.

One day Richard Rich came to the Bishop and, smiling in a friendly fashion, assured him that this was not an official visit; he came, not as the King's Solicitor-General, but as a friend.

The Bishop, worn out with sickness, suffering acutely from the closeness of his confinement, from heat and from cold, bade the Solicitor-General welcome. The latter talked about the pity of this affair, the sorrow it was causing many people because such men, so admired and respected as were Bishop Fisher and Sir Thomas More, must lie in prison on account of a matter such as this.

'I talked to the King of you but yesterday,' said Rich, 'and he said that it grieved him to think of you here in prison. He said that he respected you greatly, and that his conscience worried him concerning you. He fears that he may not have been right in what he has done. And indeed, where is the son that God would have given him had He approved the new marriage? He has but a daughter–a healthy child, it is true, but a daughter! The King's conscience disturbs him, and you could lighten it, my lord Bishop. The King has promised absolute secrecy, but he wishes to know your mind. He says that what you say–as a holy man of the Church–will be carefully considered by him. Now, my lord Fisher, if I swear to you that what you say is between you, myself and the King, will you open your mind to me?'

Fisher answered: 'By the law of God, the King is not, nor could be Supreme Head on Earth of the Church of England.'

Rich nodded and smiled: he was well pleased with himself.

Fisher had answered exactly as he had hoped he would.

There were others in the Tower for the same reason as were those two brave men.

The Carthusians had been asked to sign the Oath of Supremacy. This they had found they could not do in good conscience, and the Prior of the London Charterhouse, with those of Lincoln and Nottinghamshire, was very soon lodged in the Tower. Others quickly followed them there.

The King was growing more and more angry, and when he was angry he turned his wrath on Cromwell.

'By God's Body,' roared the King. 'It is this man More who stiffens their resistance. We must make him understand what happens to those who disobey the King.'

'Sire, we have done all we can to bring a charge against him, but he is as wily as a fox in this matter of the law.'

'I know, I know,' said the King testily, 'that he is a clever man in some ways and that I am surrounded by fools. I know that you have tried in many ways to bring charges against him, but every time he has foiled you. He is a traitor. Remember that. But I have no wish to see him suffer. My wish is that he shall end his folly, give us his signature and stop working malice among those who so admire him. These monks would relent if he did. But, no . . . no. These fools about me can in no way foil him. It is Master More who turns their arguments against them and snaps his fingers at us all. Let him be reminded of the death a traitor suffers. Ask him whether or not that is the law of the land. Ask him what clever lawyer can save a man from a traitor's death if he is guilty of treason.'

Cromwell visited Thomas in his cell.

'Ah, Sir Thomas,' he said, 'the King grieves for you. He wishes you well in spite of all the trouble you are causing him. He would be merciful. He would take you to a more comfortable place; he would see you abroad in the world again.'

'I have no wish, Master Cromwell, to meddle in the affairs of the world.'

'The King would feel more inclined towards you if you did not help others to resist him. There are these monks, now lodged in this Tower. The King feels that if you would but be his good friend you could persuade these monks to cease their folly.'

'I am the King's true and faithful subject and I do nobody harm. I say none harm; I think none harm; and I wish everybody good. And if this be not enough to keep a man alive and in good faith I long not to live. Therefore is my poor body at the King's pleasure.'

'I repeat that the King wishes you well. He would do a favour unto you. Yet you would not accept this favour.'

'There is one I would accept. If I could see my daughter, Margaret Roper, there is little else I would ask of the King.'

Cromwell smiled. 'I will do what can be done. I doubt not that the request will soon be granted.'

And it was.

She came on that May day, a year after his imprisonment, when the four monks were to pay the terrible penalty which had been deemed their due.

This was as the King and Cromwell would have it; for, said Cromwell, the bravest of men would flinch when they considered the death accorded to these monks. It was the traitor's death; and there was no reason why a Bishop and an ex-Chancellor should not die the same horrible death as did these monks. Only the King in his clemency could change that dread sentence to death by the axe.

Let Master More reflect on that; and let him reflect upon it in the company of his daughter, for she might aid the King's ministers with her pleas.

So she was with him while preparations were being made immediately outside his prison. He and Margaret heard these and knew what they meant. The hurdles were brought into the courtyard below the window; and they knew that those four brave men were being tied to them and that they would be dragged to Tyburn on those hurdles, and there hanged, cut down and disembowelled while still alive.

To face such death required more than an ordinary man's courage, though that man be a brave one.

Margaret stood before him tight-lipped.

'I cannot bear it, Father. Do you not hear? Do you not know what they are doing to those brave monks?'

And he answered: 'Lo, Meg, dost thou not see that these blessed fathers be now as cheerfully going to their deaths as bridegrooms to their marriage?'

But she turned from him weeping, swooning to the floor; and it was he who must comfort her.

Mercy said to her husband: 'I must do something. Inactivity is killing me. I have a tight pain in my throat, so that I feel it will close up altogether. Think, John. For a year we have suffered this agony. Oh, was there ever such exquisite torture as slow torture? Does the King know this? Is that why he raises our hopes and all but kills them before he seems to bid us hope again?'

'Mercy, it is not like you to give way, you . . . who are always so calm.'

'I cannot go on being calm. I dream of him as he was years ago when he first brought me to the house . . . when I would stand before him while he explained some small fault to me. I think of him when he told me that I was truly his daughter. I am his daughter. That is why I must do something. And you must help me, John.'

'I would do anything in the world for you, Mercy. You know that well.'

'Four of the monks have now suffered most barbarously at Tyburn, John. And there are others who are suffering, less violently, but in a horribly slow, lingering way. They are in Newgate and I am going to help them.'

'You, Mercy? But . . . how?'

'I am going to Newgate to take succour to them.'

'They would never let you in.'

'I think the King's physician could help me.'

'Mercy! If you were discovered . . . have you thought what it would mean?'

'He said I was truly his daughter. I would like to prove that to myself.'

'What would you do?'

'You know their sentence. Those learned monks are tied to posts in confined spaces. They cannot move; there are iron collars about their necks and fetters about their ankles. They are to be left thus to die. That is their punishment for disobedience to the King. They are given no food; they cannot move from that spot. They have been there a day and a night. I am going into Newgate with food and the means to cleanse them . . . so that they do not die of their plight.'

'It is not possible, Mercy.'

'It *is* possible, John. I have planned what I shall do. I shall dress as a milkmaid and carry a pail on my head. It shall be full of food and the means of cleaning them of their natural filth. And this milkmaid shall be allowed into the prison on the recommendation of the King's physician. You can do it, John. And you must . . . you must . . . for I shall die if I stay here thinking . . . thinking. . . . Don't you see it is the only way for me to live? I shall feel I am helping *him*. I must, John; and you must help me.'

He kissed her and gave his promise.

The next day Mercy, dressed as a milkmaid, with a pail on her head, walked into Newgate Jail and was taken to the monks by a jailor who had been paid to do this.

She fed the monks with the food that she had brought; and she cleaned them.

She was happier than she had been since her father had been taken to the Tower.

The King was growing angrier. He was also growing accustomed to the shedding of blood. He was being unfaithful to his Queen, and he was in urgent need of reassurance, for that old monster, his conscience, was worrying him again.

The Pope, hoping to save Fisher, had talked of giving him a Cardinal's hat.

The King laughed aloud when he heard this. 'Then he shall wear it on his shoulders,' he said, 'for he'll have no head to put it on.'

And on a day in June Bishop Fisher, after his examination in the Tower, during which the secret confession he had made to Rich was revealed by the treacherous Solicitor-General, was condemned to death.

But the King was generous. In view of the Bishop's age and position, though he was a traitor indeed, it was not the royal wish that he should suffer the traitor's death. He should die by the executioner's axe.

Now it was Thomas's turn, and on the 1st of July he was taken to Westminster Hall for his trial.

There Norfolk, his kindness forgotten–for he had become exasperated by what he called the obstinacy of the man for whom he had once had a liking–told him that if he would repent of his opinions he might still win the King's pardon.

'My lord,' was Thomas's answer, 'I thank you for your goodwill. Howbeit, I make my petition unto God Almighty that it may please Him to maintain me in this my honest mind to the last hour that I shall live.'

Then he defended himself so ably that those who had been set to try him were afraid that yet again he would elude them. That could not be allowed to happen. There was not one of them who would dare face the King unless Thomas More came out of Westminster Hall convicted of treason. Then the resourceful Rich stepped forth and announced that he had had a secret conversation with More, even as he had had with Fisher.

'Ah,' cried Thomas, 'I am sorrier for your perjury, Master Rich, than for my own peril.'

But the jury was glad of a chance to find him guilty, as each member knew he must or earn the King's displeasure.

They brought him out of Westminster Hall, and Margaret, who was waiting with Jack and Mercy, felt numbed by her pain when she saw him between the halberdiers, and the blade of the executioner's axe turned towards him.

Jack ran forward and knelt at his father's feet. Margaret threw herself into his arms; only Mercy stood back, remembering even in that moment that she was only the foster-daughter.

Margaret would not release her father; and Sir William Kingston, the Constable of the Tower, stood by unable to speak because of his emotion.

'Have patience, Margaret. My Meg, have patience. Trouble thyself not . . .' whispered Thomas.

And when he released himself, she stepped back a pace or two and stood looking at him, before she ran forward to fling her arms once more about his neck.

Now Sir William Kingston laid gentle hands upon her, and Jack had his arm about her as she fell fainting to the ground and lay there while the tragic procession moved on.

The King had been gracious. He would save the man who had been his friend from that terrible death which the monks had suffered.

'The King in his mercy,' said Cromwell, 'has commuted the sentence to death by the axe.'

'God forbid,' said Thomas with a touch of grim humour, 'that the King should use any more such mercy to my friends.'

There were certain conditions, Cromwell explained. There must be no long speeches at the execution. And if Thomas obeyed the King's wishes, the King would graciously allow his family to have his body to bury. The King was indeed a merciful king.

Death by the axe!

Now it was dark indeed in the house at Chelsea. They sat in a mournful circle, and none spoke of him, for they had no words to say.

That which they had feared had come to pass. He who had made this house what it was, who had made their lives so good and joyous, was lost to them.

They would never see him again.

Dauncey was weeping silently–not for frustrated ambition; that seemed to matter little now. He did not know that had happened to him when he had come to this house. He had dreamed of greatness; he had made an advantageous marriage that would lead to the King's favour; and whither had it led him? Being Dauncey, he knew more than the others. He knew that the King's hatred of Sir Thomas More would extend to his family; he knew that goods and lands would be taken from them; that it might be that their very lives were in danger. But he cared not. He, Dauncey, cared not. He would have given all the lands and goods he possessed, he would have thrown away his ambitions for the future, if the door could have opened and the laughing voice of Sir Thomas More be heard again.

His wife Elizabeth smiled at him. She understood and was grateful to him, for it seemed to her that in the midst of her black sorrow there was a touch of brightness.

Cecily and Giles Heron were holding hands, staring before them, thinking . . . thinking back over the past.

Alice was remembering all the scoldings she had given him, and wishing, more than she had ever wished for anything before, that she could have him with her to scold now.

Dorothy Colly slipped her hand into that of John Harris; and they were all very still until they heard the sound of horses' hoofs approaching.

It was a messenger who had brought a letter for Margaret.

She trembled as she took it, for he was to die tomorrow, and she knew that this was the last she would ever receive from him.

It was written with a piece of coal–all that was left to him to write with; for they had taken his writing materials when, some time before, they had taken his books.

She forced herself to read aloud.

'Our Lord bless you, good daughter, and your good husband, and your little boy, and all yours . . . and all my children and all my god-children and all our friends. . . .'

He then mentioned them all by name, and as Margaret spoke their names they hung their heads, for the tears streamed from their eyes.

But Margaret went on steadily reading.

He begged them not to mourn for him. He was to die tomorrow, and he would be sorry to live longer.

'For tomorrow is St Thomas's Eve, and therefore tomorrow I long to go to God. St Thomas's Eve! It is a day very meet and convenient for me. Dear Meg, I never liked your manner towards me better than when you kissed me last, for I love when daughterly love and dear charity hath no leisure to look to worldly courtesy. Farewell, my child, and pray for me, and I shall for you and all my friends; and may we all meet merrily in Heaven.'

Margaret had stopped reading and a silence fell upon them.

Early on the morning of St Thomas's Eve, Master Pope, a young official of the Court, came to tell him that he was to die that day.

The young man came with tears in his eyes, and could scarcely speak for weeping, so that it was Thomas More who must comfort Thomas Pope.

'Do not grieve, Master Pope,' he said, 'for I thank you heartily for these good tidings.'

'It is the King's pleasure that you should not use many words at the execution.'

'You do well to give me warning, for I had planned to speak at length. I beg of you, Master Pope, plead with the King that when I am buried, my daughter Margaret may be there to see it done.'

'The King will consent to that if you do not speak overmuch before your death. Your wife and all your children shall then have liberty to be present.'

'I am beholden to His Grace that my poor burial shall have so much consideration.'

Then Pope, taking his leave, could say nothing because his tears were choking him.

'Quiet yourself, good Master Pope,' said Thomas, 'and be not discomfited, for I trust that we shall, once in Heaven, see each other merrily where we shall be sure to live and love together in joyful bliss eternally.'

Shortly before nine o'clock, wearing a garment of frieze that hung loosely on his thin body, and carrying in his hands a red cross, Thomas More left his prison for Tower Hill.

There was only one member of the family there to see him die. Mercy was that one. She stood among the crowds about the scaffold, watching him, taking her last look at him. Later she would be joined by Margaret and Dorothy Colly for the burial of his body in the Church of St Peter ad Vincula.

Mercy did not stand near, for she did not want her father to witness her grief. She told herself that she should be glad, for he was not subjected to that ignoble death which those poor monks had suffered at Tyburn, while others of their brethren were rotting in their chains at Newgate. The jailor there, fearing discovery, would no longer allow her to visit those monks, and although she had made efforts to reach them she had not been able to do so, and they were slowly perishing where they were chained.

Oh, cruel world she thought, that surrounds that island of peace and happiness in Chelsea like a turbulent sea. They had thought themselves safe on their island, but now the malignant waters had washed over it, destroying peace and beauty, leaving only memories for those who had lived there and loved it.

Thomas was mounting the steps which led to the scaffold. They had been hastily constructed and shook a little.

He smiled and said to one of the Sheriff's officers: 'I pray you, Master Lieutenant, that you will see me safe up. As to my coming down, you may leave me to shift for myself.'

The executioner was waiting for him. This hardened man looked into Thomas's face and, seeing there that sweetness of expression which had won the affection of so many, he turned quickly away murmuring: 'My lord, forgive me. . . .'

Thomas laid a hand on his arm. 'Pluck up your spirits, my friend. Be not afraid of your office . . . for such is all it is. Take heed that you strike not awry for the sake of thine own honesty.'

Then he knelt and prayed. 'Have mercy upon me. O God, in Thy great goodness. . . .'

He rose and the executioner came forward to bind his eyes.

'I will do it myself,' said Thomas.

But first he spoke to the people who were waiting on his last words; very briefly he spoke, remembering the King's displeasure that could fall on those who were left after him.

'My friends, pray for me in this world and I will pray for you elsewhere. Pray also for the King that it may please God to give him good counsel. I die the King's servant . . . but God's first.'

Then he bound his eyes and laid his head on the block, pushing his beard to one side, saying: 'That has no treason. Let it therefore be saved from the executioner's axe.'

There was a great silence on Tower Hill as the axe fell.

Thomas's lips moved slightly.

'The King's good servant . . . but God's first.'

News of the death of Sir Thomas More was brought to the King.

'So perish all traitors!' he cried.

But his little eyes were fearful. In the streets the people were murmuring. It was all they dared to do against the King. They had seen the terrible deaths of the Carthusians; and now the head of Sir Thomas More was on a pole on London Bridge beside that of the saintly Fisher, Bishop of Rochester.

'Come, Norfolk, what are you thinking . . . skulking there?'

Norfolk was a bold man. He said: 'That it was a pity, Your Grace. Such a man of talents to be so obstinate . . . so wrong-minded.'

'You seem sad that it should be so.'

'Your Grace, he was a lovable man . . . for all his faults. Sire, many loved him.'

Many loved him!

The King's eyes narrowed. The people would remember that the man had been put to death because he had obeyed his conscience rather than his King. The King's good servant, but God's first.

The King cursed all martyrs.

This man must not live in the memory of the people. He must be seen as a traitor, a man deserving death, a traitor whose head was in its rightful place, looking down from London's bridge on London's river.

But Henry knew that, as the people passed by the bridge, as they looked at the head of the man, they would mutter prayers and ask his blessing. Too many of them remembered his kindness, his piety and virtue.

Living, he had been Thomas More, the kind, good man; dead, he would be Thomas More, the saint.

That should not be; it must not be.

Had not More stated that he believed the sowing of seditious heresies should be prevented at all costs? During his reign as Chancellor one or two people had been burned as heretics. The King would have it bruited abroad that this great good man had not been averse to inflicting suffering on those who did not share his views. Could he then complain at the King's treatment of himself?

There would be some who would say: 'It is not the duty of a Chancellor to pass sentence on heretics. That lies in the hands of the clergy.' But who would examine that too closely? The Tudors and their friends, who had found it necessary to suppress many historical facts, would have no difficulty in suppressing or garnishing wherever it was expedient to do so.

The King remembered the case of a heretic who had been ordered by Sir Thomas More to be flogged. The King had been amused at the time of the offence, for the man concerned had crept behind women kneeling in the church and, lifting their clothes, had cast them over their heads. The just sentence for such an act was flogging; but this man, as well as being a lewd person, was also a heretic. A little adjustment of the reports of such cases, and there was More, a flogger of heretics.

The King doubted not that his good friends would have no difficulty in providing the necessary evidence.

For, thought the King, we cannot have martyrs in our kingdom. Martyrs are uncomfortable men, and I like them not.

The King must always be right; and the King was uneasy, for he also found it hard to forget the man. Norfolk was right: More had been a lovable fellow.

I liked him, mused Henry. It gave me pleasure to honour him.

He remembered their pleasant talks together over the writing of the book; he thought of evenings on the balcony with his first Queen beside him, and Thomas More pointing out the stars in the heavens; he thought of the pleasant family at Chelsea and walking through those fragrant gardens with his arm about his Chancellor's neck.

'I loved the man,' murmured Henry. 'I . . . as well as the others. It was not my wish that he should die. God bear me witness. I loved him.'

His Queen came in.

He was not pleased with her. She had not brought him all that he had desired. She had filled his heart with jealousy and his mind with misgiving.

He had noticed a quiet, pale girl among her maids of honour. Jane Seymour was her name; and although this young woman was modest, she had shown that she was not unconscious of the King's regard.

The King lost control of his temper suddenly as he looked at his Queen; and he was filled with fear because the murder of a great and good man lay heavily upon his conscience.

'You have done this!' he shouted at his Queen. 'You have done this. You have demanded of me the death of a good man and, God forgive you, I have granted your request.'

Chapter Eight

There was no sound on the river but that of the oars as they dipped in the water.

The stars in the July sky scintillated like jewels in the doublet of a king, and the outline of hedges was clear along the banks.

The bridge and its ghastly relics came into view.

The boat stopped and, when Margaret alighted, Will was beside her. He put his arm about her.

'Meg . . . Meg . . . you still insist?'

She nodded.

''Tis a dangerous thing to do, my darling. I know not what the penalty would be if . . .'

'I know not either,' she said: 'and I care not.'

They walked away from the river's edge up and on to the bridge.

'Meg . . . go back to the boat. I will do it.'

'Nay. 'Tis my task and mine alone.'

The air of the hot summer's night caressed her face as she stood on the bridge and firmly grasped the pole in her hand.

'Meg, you torture yourself.'

'Nay,' she answered. 'Let be, Will. Let be.'

And together they pulled down the pole, and they took that which was set upon it.

Margaret wrapped it tenderly in the shawl which she had brought, and, putting his arm about her, Will led her back to the boat.

Tenderly Will Roper watched his wife and swore to cherish her until the end of their days. He and their children between them would give her such love that Thomas himself, looking down from Heaven, would smile upon them and bless them.

Now Margaret stared before her, her arms about the shawl which held that terrible and precious relic.

London Bridge was behind them, and they went swiftly up the river to Chelsea.

Royal Road to Fotheringay

Jean Plaidy

Royal Road to Fotheringay

For Mildred Ligonier Johnston

Author's Note

It is probable that no historical character has ever aroused more ardent supporters or more fierce detractors than has Mary Stuart. Strangely enough these admirers and detractors extol or defame irrespective of their religious faith. This is most unusual and is no doubt due to the fact that, in contrast with the disputes which almost always involved those who lived in the sixteenth century, those which concern Mary are not, in the main, about religion. The questions so fiercely debated in Mary Stuart's case are: Did she write the Casket Letters? Was she a willing partner in her abduction and rape? Was she a murderess?

My research for *Royal Road to Fotheringay* led me to discover a Mary who was sometimes quick-tempered, sometimes gentle, always charming, tolerant and warm-hearted; but because I have been unable to exonerate her from implication in the murder of Darnley I want to stress that when assessing Mary we must not weigh her deeds and behaviour by present day standards. She lived in an age when life was cheap and cruelty part of daily existence. Many men and women of the past who were considered during their day as patterns of virtue would receive a very different verdict if they had lived to-day. For example: Michelet says that Gaspard de Coligny was the most ennobling character of his times; yet the discipline he imposed on the battlefield would be called cruelty to-day, and it is by no means certain that he was guiltless of the murder of François de Guise. It is very necessary to remember this when considering the part Mary played in luring her husband to the house in Kirk-o'-Field. In her generation she was kinder and more tolerant than most of the people around her; but she herself faced death more than once, and in the sixteenth century, the elimination of human obstacles was not deemed a crime of such magnitude as it is to-day.

Other questions asked are: How could a woman, having lived as virtuously as she had (even Brantôme had no scandalous gossip to record of Mary) suddenly indulge in an adulterous passion, and take part in the murder of the husband who stood between her and her lover? How could she, beautiful and cultured, suddenly become the slave of Bothwell, the uncouth ruffian from the Border?

I have sought explanations by posing questions of my own. Mary was not healthy and her pictures do not support all we hear of those outstanding attractions; so what was the secret of that immense physical charm which she undoubtedly possessed? I believe it was largely due to an extremely passionate nature which was but half awakened when she met Darnley and not fully so until it was recognized by that man–so experienced in amatory adventures–the virile Bothwell. I believe that dormant sensuality to have been the secret of her appeal. And why was it so long in coming to fruition? I think I have found the answer in Mary's relationship with the Cardinal of

Lorraine, that past-master in all things sensual, whose closeness to Mary would have given him every chance to understand her; and, being the knowledgeable man he was, he could not fail to do this. The scandal–the origin of which was traced to Bothwell–that Mary was the Cardinal's mistress, cannot have been justified; yet theirs was no ordinary relationship, and I am of the opinion that it was the reason why the passions of such a passionate woman were so long dormant.

The Casket Letters and the poems are perhaps the most discussed documents in British history. If they were actually written by Mary, there can be no doubt of her guilt. But are they forgeries? It is impossible to answer Yes or No, for the mystery of the Casket Letters has never been solved. It seems clear that some of the poems could have been written by no other hand than Mary's, and it is equally clear that some parts of the letters could never have been her composition. (I refer in particular to the crude reference to Darnley in Letter No. 2, the most incriminating of all the Casket documents.) Yet might it not be that the letters were in some part forgeries, in others Mary's actual writings? Because a part is false it does not follow that the whole is. Who else could have written those revealing poems? Who among the Scots was sufficiently skilled in the French language? Maitland of Lethington? He was a cunning statesman, but was he a poet?

Mary was raped by Bothwell. Those who would proclaim her an angel of virtue are ready to concede that. An important question is: When did the rape occur? Was it in the Exchequer House or later at Dunbar after the abduction? Was Mary herself in the plot to abduct her? If so, she and Bothwell must have been in love before the staging of that extraordinary affair, and it is more than likely that the rape took place at the Exchequer House. Buchanan's ribald account is clearly exaggerated. The story of Lady Reres being lowered into the garden in order to bring Bothwell from his wife's bed to that of the Queen might have been written by Boccaccio and is too crude to be believed; but Mary *was* at the Exchequer House, and Bothwell's servant *did* live next door. Why should not Buchanan's story be *founded* on truth?

I have discarded, selected and fitted my material together with the utmost care and I hope I have made a plausible and convincing picture of Mary, the people who surrounded her, and the circumstances which made Fotheringay the inevitable end of her royal road.

I have studied many works and am indebted in particular to the following:

History of France. M. Guizot.
History of England. William Hickman Smith Aubrey.
British History. John Wade.
Henri II. H. Noel Williams.
Feudal Castles of France. Anon.
Lives of the Queens of Scotland and English Princess (Vols. III, IV, V, VI, VII). Agnes Strickland.
Letters of Mary Queen of Scots (Vols. I and II), with Historical Introduction and Notes by Agnes Strickland.
The Scottish Queen. Herbert Gorman.
The Love Affairs of Mary Queen of Scots. Martin Hume.
The Queen of Scots. Stefan Zweig.
John Knox and the Reformation. Andrew Lang.
The Life of John Knox. George R. Preedy.
Lord Bothwell. Robert Gore-Brown.

J.P.

MARY THE QUEEN

Chapter One

Through the great rooms of the Castle of Stirling five little girls were playing hide-and-seek. They were all in their fifth year and all named Mary.

She, whose turn it was to seek, stood against the tapestry, her eyes tightly shut, listening to the echo of running feet, counting softly under her breath: 'Ten . . . eleven . . . twelve . . .'

It was fair now to open her eyes, for they would all be out of sight. She would count up to twenty and then begin to search. Livy would give herself away by her giggling laughter. She always did. Flem would betray herself because she wished to please and thought it wrong that her beloved Mary should not succeed immediately in everything she undertook. Beaton, the practical one, and Seton, the quiet one, would not be so easy.

'Fifteen . . . sixteen . . .'

She looked up at the silken hangings. They were soft and beautiful because they came from France. Her mother spoke often of France–that fairest of lands. Whenever her mother spoke of France a tenderness came into her voice. In France there was no mist, it seemed, and no rain; French flowers were more beautiful than Scottish flowers; and all the men were handsome.

In France Mary had a grandfather, a grandmother and six uncles. There were some aunts too but they were not so important. The uncles were all handsome giants who could do anything they wished. 'One day,' her mother often said, 'you may see them. I want them not to be ashamed of you.'

'Eighteen . . . nineteen . . . twenty . . .' She was forgetting the game.

She gave a whoop of warning and began the search.

How silent the rooms were! They had chosen this part of the castle for hide-and-seek because no one came here at this hour of the day.

'I am coming!' she called. 'I am coming!'

She stood still, listening to the sound of her voice. Which way had they turned–to the left or to the right?

She wandered through the rooms, her eyes alert. Was that a shadow behind the stool? Was that a bulge behind the hangings?

She had now come into one of the bedrooms and stood still, looking about her. She was sure she had heard a movement. Someone was in this room. Yes, there was no doubt.

'Who are you?' she called. 'Where are you? Come out. You are found.'

There was no answer. She ran about the room, lifting the curtains, looking behind the furniture. Someone was somewhere in this room, she felt sure.

She lifted the curtains about the bed and there was little Mary Beaton.

'Come out, Beaton,' commanded the little Queen.

But Beaton did not move. She just lay stretched out on her stomach, resting on her elbows, propped up on her hands.

Mary cried impatiently: 'Come out, I said.'

Still Beaton did not move.

The colour flamed into Mary's face. She remembered that she was Queen of Scotland and the Isles. Great men knelt before her and kissed her hand. Her guardians, those great Earls–Moray, Huntley and Argyle–never spoke to her without first kneeling and kissing her hand. And now fat little Beaton refused to do as she was bid.

'Beaton, you heard me! You're found. Come out at once. The Queen commands you.'

Then Mary understood, for Beaton could no longer contain her emotions; she stretched full out on the floor and began to sob heartbrokenly.

All Mary's anger disappeared. She immediately got on to her knees and crawled under the bed.

'Beaton . . . dear Beaton . . . why are you crying?'

Beaton shook her head and turned away; but Mary had her arms about her little friend.

'Dear Mary,' said the Queen.

'Dear Mary,' sobbed Beaton.

Rarely did the Queen call one of her four friends by their Christian names. It only happened in particularly tender moments and when they were alone with her, for Mary the Queen had said: 'How shall we know which one we mean, since we are all Maries?'

They did not speak for some time; they just lay under the bed, their arms about each other. The little Queen could be haughty; she could be proud; she could be very hot-tempered; but as soon as those she loved were in trouble she wished to share that trouble and she would do all in her power to comfort them. They loved her, not because she was their Queen whom their parents and guardians had commanded them to love and serve, but because she made their troubles her own. It was not long before she was sobbing as broken-heartedly as Beaton, although she had no idea what Beaton's trouble was.

At last Mary Beaton whispered: 'It is . . . my dear uncle. I shall never see him again.'

'Why not?' asked Mary.

'Because men came and thrust knives into him . . . so he died.'

'How do you know? Who told you this?'

'No one told me. I listened.'

'They say it is wicked to listen.'

Beaton nodded sadly. But the Queen did not blame her for listening. How could she? She herself often listened.

'So he is gone,' said Mary Beaton, 'and I shall never see him again.'

She began to cry again and they clung to one another.

It was hot under the bed, but they did not think of coming out. Here they were close, shut in with their grief. Mary wept for Beaton, not for Beaton's uncle, the Cardinal–a stern man, who had often told the Queen how good she ought to be, how much depended on her, and what an important thing it was to be Queen of Scotland. Mary grew tired of such talk.

Now she had another picture of the Cardinal to set beside those she knew–a picture of a man lying on the floor with knives sticking into him. But she could not think of him thus for long. She could only remember the stern Cardinal who wished her to think continually of her duty to the Church.

They were still under the bed when the others found them. They crawled out then, their faces stained with tears. Mary Fleming began to cry at once in sympathy.

'Men have stuck knives in Beaton's uncle,' announced Mary.

All the little girls looked solemn.

'I knew it,' said Flem.

'Then why didn't you tell?' asked the Queen.

'Your Majesty did not ask,' answered Flem.

Seton said quietly: 'Everyone won't cry. The King of England will be pleased. I heard my father say so.'

'I hate the King of England,' said Mary.

Seton took the Queen's hand and gave her one of her solemn, frightened looks. 'You must not hate him,' she said.

'Mary can hate anyone!' said Flem.

'You should not hate your own father,' said Seton.

'He is not my father. My father is dead; he died while I was in my cradle and that is why I am the Queen.'

'If you have a husband,' persisted Seton, 'his father is yours. My nurse told me so. She told me that you are to marry the English Prince Edward, and then the King of England will be your father.'

The Queen's eyes flashed. 'I will not!' she cried. 'The English killed my father. I'll not marry the English Prince.' But she knew that it was easy to be bold and say before her Maries what she would and would not do; she was a Queen and had already been forced to do so many things against her will. She changed an unpleasant subject, for she hated to dwell on the unpleasant. 'Come,' she said, 'we will read and tell stories to make poor Beaton forget.'

They went to a window seat. Mary sat down and the others ranged themselves about her.

But the vast room seemed full of frightening shadows. It was not easy to chase away unpleasant thoughts. They could read and tell stories but they could not entirely forget that Mary Beaton's uncle had been stabbed to death and that one day the Queen would have to leave her childhood behind her and become the wife of some great prince who would be chosen for her.

The Queen-Mother noticed at once the traces of tears on her daughter's face. She frowned. Mary was too emotional. The fault must be corrected.

The little Queen's stern guardians would have noticed the marks of tears.

Since the Cardinal had been murdered there were only three guardians–Moray, Huntley and Argyle.

The Queen-Mother herself could have shed tears if she had been the woman to give way to them. The Cardinal was the one man in this turbulent land whom she had felt she could trust.

She looked about the assembly. There was the Regent, Arran, the head of the house of Hamilton, and of royal blood, longing to wear the crown of Scotland, Arran, who could not be trusted, whom she suspected of being the secret friend of the English, who had hoped to marry his son to the English King's daughter Elizabeth, and who doubtless had hopes of his son's wearing not only the crown of Scotland but that of England. There was false Douglas, so long exiled in England and only daring to return to Scotland after the death of James, Douglas, who had schemed with the King of England. He it was who had agreed, when in the hands of the English to the marriage between the little Queen and Prince Edward. It was he who had come with soft words to the Queen-Mother setting forth the advantages of the match.

There was the giant Earl of Bothwell who had hopes of marrying the Queen-Mother. Was he loyal? How could she know who in this assembly of men was her friend? Scotland was a divided country, a wild country of clans. There was not in Scotland that loyalty to the crown which the English and French Kings commanded.

And I, she thought, am a woman–a French woman–and my child, not yet five, is the Queen of this alien land.

All eyes were on the little girl. What grace! What beauty! It was apparent even at so young an age. Even those hoary old chieftains were moved by the sight of her. How graceful she stood! How nobly she held her head! She had all the Stuart beauty and that slight touch of something foreign which came from her French ancestors and which could enhance even the Stuart charm.

'God protect her in all she does,' prayed her mother.

She raised her eyes and caught the flashing ones of Lord James Stuart–Stuart eyes, heavy lidded, not unlike Mary's, beautiful eyes; and the proud tilt of the head denoted ambition. He was a boy yet in his early teens. But ambition smouldered there. Was he thinking even now: Had my father married my mother, I should be sitting in the chair of state and it would be my hand those men would kiss!

'God preserve my daughter from these Scots!' prayed the Queen-Mother.

Now the little Queen stood while the great chieftains came forward to kiss her hand. She smiled at them–at Arran, at Douglas. They looked so kind. Now came Jamie–dear Jamie knelt before her but when he lifted his eyes to her face he gave her a secret wink, and she felt the laughter bubble up within her. It was rather funny that tall handsome Jamie should kneel before his little sister. She knew why of course, for she had demanded to know. It was because although his mother was not the Queen, the King, her father, had also been Jamie's father. Mary had other brothers and sisters. It was a pity, she had said to her Maries, that their mothers had not been queens, for it would have been fun to have a large family living about her–even though she was so much younger.

Now her mother would not allow her to stay.

'The Queen is very tired,' she said, 'and it is time she was abed.'

Mary wanted to stay. She wanted to talk to Jamie, to ask questions about the dead Cardinal.

But although they all kissed her hand and swore to serve her with their lives, they would not let her stay up when she wanted to. She knew she must show no annoyance. A Queen did not show her feelings. Her mother had impressed that upon her.

They all stood at attention while she walked out of the apartment to where her governess, Lady Fleming, was waiting for her.

'Our little Queen does not look very pleased with her courtiers,' said Janet Fleming, with one of her gay bursts of laughter.

'No, she is not,' retorted Mary. 'I wanted to stay and talk to Jamie. He winked when he kissed my hand.'

'Gentlemen winking at you already–and you the Queen!' cried Janet. Mary laughed. She was very fond of her governess who was also her aunt.

For one thing red-haired Janet was very beautiful, and, although no longer in her first youth, was as full of fun as her young charge. She was a Stuart, being the natural daughter of Mary's grandfather; and little Mary Fleming was her daughter. She could be wheedled into letting the Queen have much of her own way, and Mary loved her dearly.

'He is only my brother,' she said.

'And should be thankful for that,' said Janet. 'Were he not, it would be an insult to the crown.'

She went on chattering while Mary was prepared for bed; it was all about dancing, clothes, sports and games, and when her mother came to the apartment Mary had temporarily forgotten the grief which Beaton had aroused in her.

The Queen-Mother dismissed all those who were in attendance on the Queen, so Mary knew that she was going to be reprimanded. It was a strange thing to be a queen. In public no one must scold; but it happened often enough in private.

'You have been crying,' accused Marie of Lorraine. 'The traces of tears were on your face when you received the lords.'

Fresh tears welled up in Mary's eyes at the memory. Poor Beaton! She remembered those desperate choking sobs.

'Did your women not wash your face before you came to the audience?'

'Yes, *Maman*, but it was such a big grief that it would not come off.'

The Queen-Mother softened suddenly and bent to kiss the little face. Mary laughed and her arms went up immediately about her mother's neck.

The Queen-Mother was somewhat disturbed. Mary was too demonstrative, always too ready to show her feelings. It was a charming trait, but not right, she feared, in a girl of such an exalted position.

'Now,' admonished Marie, 'that is enough. Tell me the reason for these tears.'

'Men have stuck knives into Beaton's uncle.'

So she knew! thought her mother. How could you keep terrible news from children? Mary had good reason to shed tears. Cardinal Beaton, upholder of the Church of Rome in a land full of heretics, had indeed been her friend. Who would protect her now from those ambitious men?

'You loved the Cardinal then, my daughter?'

'No.' Mary was truthful and spoke without thinking of the effect of her words. 'I did not much like him. I cried for poor Beaton.'

Her mother smoothed the chestnut hair, so soft yet so thick, which rippled back from the white forehead. Mary would always weep for the wrong reasons.

'I share little Beaton's grief,' said the Queen-Mother, 'for the Cardinal was not only a good man, he was a good friend.'

'Why did they kill him, *Maman*?'

'Because of Wishart's death . . . so they say.'

'Wishart, *Maman*? Who is he?'

What am I saying? the Queen-Mother asked herself. I forget she is only a baby. I must keep her from these tales of bloodshed and murder as long as I can.

But Mary was all eager curiosity now. She would find out in some way. Behind those deeply set, beautiful eyes there was an alert mind, thirsting for knowledge.

'Wishart was a heretic, my child, and he paid the penalty of heretics.'

'What penalty was that, *Maman*?'

'The death which is accorded heretics fell to him.'

'*Maman* . . . the flames!'

'How did you know these things?'

How did she know? She was not sure. Had one of her Maries whispered it? Had she seen pictures in the religious books? She covered her face with her hands and the tears began to flow from her eyes.

'Mary! Mary, what has come over you? This is no way to behave.'

'I cannot bear it. He was a Scotsman, and they have burned him . . . they have burned him right up.'

Marie de Guise was alarmed. A little knowledge was so dangerous, and her daughter was so impulsive. What would she say next? She was precocious. How soon before some of these men began to corrupt her faith? They would do everything in their power to turn her into a heretic. It must not be. For the honour of the Guises, for the glory of the Faith itself, it must not be.

'Listen to me, child. This man Wishart met his just reward, but because the Cardinal was a man of the true faith, Wishart's friends murdered him.'

'Then they did right! I would murder those who burned my friends.'

'A little while ago you were crying for the Cardinal.'

'No, no,' she interrupted. 'For dear Beaton.'

The Queen-Mother hesitated by the bedside. How could she explain all that was in her mind to a child of this one's age? How could she expect this baby mind to understand? Yet she must protect her from the influence of heretics. How did she know what James Stuart whispered to the child when he pretended to frolic with her? How did she know what Arran and Douglas plotted?

'Listen to me, Mary,' she said. 'There is one true church in this world. It is the Church of Rome. At its head is the Pope, and it is the duty of all monarchs to serve the true religion.'

'And do they?'

'No, they do not. You must be careful what you say. If you do not understand, you must come to me. You must talk to no one about Wishart and the Cardinal . . . to *no one* . . . not even your Maries. You must remember that you are the Queen. You are but little yet, but to be a Queen is not to be an ordinary little girl who thinks of nothing but playing. We do not know who are our friends. The King of England wants you in England.'

'Oh, *Maman*, should I take my Maries with me?'

'Hush! You are not going to England.' The mother took her child in her arms and held her tightly. 'We do not want you to go to England. We want to keep you here with us.'

Mary's eyes were wide. 'Could they make me go?'

'Not unless . . .'

'Unless?'

'It were by force.'

Mary clasped her hands together. 'Oh, *Maman*, could they do that?'

'They could if they were stronger than we were.'

Mary's eyes shone. She could not help it. She loved excitement and, to tell the truth, she was a little tired of the castle where all the rooms were so familiar to her. She was never allowed to go beyond the castle grounds; and when she played there were always men-at-arms watching.

Her mother came to a sudden decision. The child must be made to understand. She must be shocked, if need be, into understanding.

'You are being foolish, child,' she said. 'Try to understand this. The worst thing that could happen to you would be for you to be taken to England.'

'Why?'

'Because if you went your life would be in danger.'

Mary caught her breath. She drew back in amazement.

It was the only way, thought the Queen-Mother. There was too much danger and the child must be made aware of it.

'The King of England has said that he wishes you to go to England to be brought up with his son.'

'You do not wish me to marry Edward?'

'I do not know . . . as yet.'

The Queen-Mother stood up and walked to the window. She looked across the country towards the south and thought of the ageing monarch of England. He had demanded the marriage for his son, and that Mary be brought up in the Court of England as a future Queen of England. A good enough prospect . . . if one were dealing with any but the King of England. But there was a sinister clause in the agreement. If the little Queen of Scots died before reaching the age of maturity, the crown of Scotland was to pass to England. The royal murderer should never have a chance of disposing of Mary Stuart. How easy it would be! The little girl could fall victim to some pox . . . some wasting disease. No! He had murdered his second and fifth wives and, some said, was preparing to murder his sixth. He should not add the little Queen of Scots to his list of victims.

But how tell such things to a child of five years!

Marie de Guise turned back to the bed. 'Suffice it that I shall not allow you to go to England. Now . . . to sleep.'

But Mary did not sleep. She lay sleepless in the elaborate bed–the bed with the beautiful hangings sent to her by her glorious uncles–and thought of that ogre, the King of England, who might come at any moment to carry her off by force.

Now the little Queen was aware of tension. She knew that the reason why she must never go beyond the castle walls without a strong guard was because it was feared she would be abducted.

She called the Maries together. Life was exciting. They must learn about it. Here they were shut up in Stirling Castle playing hide-and-seek, battledore and shuttlecock, reading, miming, playing games; while beyond the castle walls grown-up people played other games which were far more exciting.

One day when they were all at play, Flem, who happened to be near the window, called to them all. A messenger was riding into the courtyard, muddy and stained with the marks of a long ride, his jaded horse distressed and flecked with foam.

The children watched–five little faces pressed against the window. But the messenger stayed within the castle and they grew tired of waiting for him to come out, so they devised a new game of messengers. They took it in turn to be the messenger riding on a hobby horse, come from afar with exciting news concerning the King of England.

Later they were aware of glum faces about them; some of the serving men and women were in tears and the words Pinkie Cleugh were whispered throughout the castle.

Lady Fleming shut herself in her apartment and the five Maries heard her sobbing bitterly. Little Flem beat on the door in panic and called shrilly to be allowed to come in. Then Janet Fleming came out and looked blankly at the five little girls. Her own Mary ran to her, and Janet embraced her crying over and over again: 'My child . . . my little Mary . . . I still have you.' Then she went back into her room and shut the door, taking Flem with her.

Mary, left alone with her three companions, felt the tears splashing on to her velvet gown. She did not understand what had happened. She was wretched because her dear Aunt Janet and little Flem were in some trouble.

'What *is* Pinkie?' she demanded; but even Beaton did not know.

It was impossible to play after that. They sat in the window seat huddled together, waiting for they knew not what.

They heard a voice below the window, which said: 'They say Hertford's men are not more than six miles from the castle.'

Mary knew then that danger was close. Hertford, her tutors had told her, was the Lord Protector of England who ruled until Edward–that boy who might very well be her husband one day–was old enough to do so himself, for King Henry had died that very year. To Mary, Hertford was the monster now; he was the dragon breathing fire who would descend on the castle like the raiders on the Border and carry the Queen of Scotland off to England as his prize.

That was a strange day–a queer brooding tension filled the castle. Everyone was waiting for something to happen. She did not see her mother that evening and her governess was not present when she went to her apartment for the night.

At last she slept and was awakened suddenly by dark figures about her bed. She started up, thinking: He has come. Hertford has come to take me to England.

But it was not Hertford. It was her mother, and with her were the Earl of Arran, Lord Erskine and Livy's father, Lord Livingstone, so that she knew this was a very important occasion.

'Wake up,' said her mother.

'Is it time to get up?'

'It is an hour past midnight, but you are to get up. You are going away on a journey.'

'What! At night!'

'Do not talk so much. Do as you are told.'

This must be very important, for otherwise even her mother would not have talked to her thus in the presence of these noble lords. She had to be a little girl now; she had to obey without question. This was no time for ceremony.

Lady Fleming–her eyes still red with weeping–came forward with her fur-trimmed cloak.

'Quickly,' said Lady Fleming. 'There is no time to be lost. If your lordships will retire I will get my lady dressed.'

While Mary was hustled into her clothes she asked questions. 'Where are we going? Why are we going now? It's the night . . . the dead of night . . .'

'There is no time for questions.'

It should have been an exciting adventure, but she was too tired to be conscious of most of that journey. She was vaguely aware of the smells of the night–a mingling of damp earth and misty air. Through the haze of sleep she heard the continued thudding of horses' hoofs. Voices penetrated her dreams. 'Pinkie . . . Pinkie. . . . Hertford close on our heels. Cattle driven over the Border. Rape . . . murder . . . fire . . . blood.'

Words to make a grown-up person shudder, but to a child of five they were little more than words.

Now she was in a boat and she heard the sound of oars dipping into water. It became suddenly calm and peaceful as though there was no longer the desperate need for haste.

The violent bump of the boat as it touched land awakened her thoroughly. 'Where are we?' she cried.

'Hush . . . hush!' she was told. '*Maman* is here.' That was her mother talking to her as though she were indeed a baby.

She was taken up and placed in the arms of someone clothed in black. Over his head was a cowl. He might have frightened her had his eyes not been gentle and his voice kind.

'Sleep, little one,' he said. 'Sleep on, little Queen. You have come safely to Inchmahome.'

Inchmahome! The melodious word took the place in her dreams of Pinkie Cleugh and blood . . . murder . . . rape. Inchmahome . . . and peace.

It seemed to Mary that she lived for a long time in the island monastery. At first there was much she missed, but it was not long before her four Maries arrived on the island to bear her company. Lady Fleming stayed with her, and because there was need to comfort her aunt, Mary herself was comforted. Lord Fleming had been killed at the terrible battle of Pinkie Cleugh. He was one of fourteen thousand Scots who had died that day.

Mary wept bitterly. First Beaton's uncle and now Flem's father. And both had been killed. There had been no need for either of them to die. 'Why,' she demanded angrily of Lady Fleming, 'could they not all love each other and be friends?'

'It is the accursed English!' cried Lady Fleming. 'They want Scotland for their own. They have killed my Malcolm. I hate the English.'

'But it was not the English who killed Cardinal Beaton,' said Mary.

'They were behind that murder too. They are a heretic people.'

Mary put her arms round her governess and reminded her that she had five sons and there was big James to be Lord Fleming now.

Janet Fleming took the lovely face in her hands and kissed it. 'When you grow up,' she said, 'many will love you. You have that in you which attracts love. There will be men to love you . . .'

Janet's eyes brightened and her sorrow lifted a little, for she could not help knowing that there would still be men to love Janet Fleming too. It was true that she was no longer young but her appeal seemed ageless. She had been born with it and it did not diminish at all. Here in the monastery she would let her grief subside; her wounds would heal and when she again went into the world she would be her jaunty pleasure-loving self, attracting men perhaps because she herself was so easily attracted by them.

So they were able to comfort each other, and the brief rest on the peaceful island was something they were both to remember in the years to come and look back upon with a certain longing.

Mary grew accustomed to the life of the island. She had soon, with her little friends about her, made a miniature court for herself. She was watched with delight–even by the monks–for in her black silk gown, ornamented by the brilliant tartan scarf, held together by the gold agraffe which was engraved with the arms of Scotland and Lorraine, her lovely hair loose about her shoulders, she was a charming sight.

At first the monks in their musty black had not attracted her; she had been startled to come upon them gliding through the cold bare rooms. But when she grew to know them she found a gentleness in them which appealed to her. They answered her only when she spoke to them, but they did not speak even to each other unless it was absolutely necessary.

It was like a world of which she had dreamed–a strange world shut in by granite walls. The bells rang continually, for life on the island in the lake of Menteith was divided into periods, by the bells. Mary went daily with her four friends to the great room with the stained glass windows; there she prayed to the saints and confessed her sins.

Her curiosity had to be satisfied, and she and the four Maries could not be content until they had wheedled the secret from Lady Fleming.

'Why are we here, Aunt Janet?' asked Mary.

'It is a rest for me . . . after what I suffered.'

'Did they take me out of bed at midnight for that?' asked Mary scornfully.

'It is because of the English,' said Beaton.

'Hertford's men came close to the castle,' added Mary. 'We heard of that.'

Poor Janet! She could never be discreet. 'Well, I do know,' she admitted, 'but nothing would prise it from me.' But the five Maries could, and in a short time Janet was saying: 'If I tell you, you must never mention it to anyone . . . anyone at all.'

She admitted that they had been sent to Inchmahome to escape the English. 'Your mother has plans for you,' she added.

'What plans?' demanded Mary.

'Plans made with the French, so they say.'

'With my uncles?'

'They send messengers to her continually. There are some, my little Queen, who would like to see you sent to England, but your mother has other plans.'

Lady Fleming could not be induced to say what these plans were, so the five little girls, who knew her well, decided that she did not know and that it was no use pestering her further.

When Mary was in her room, which was as bare as a cell, she knelt before the little altar there, but instead of praying she was thinking about plans with the French.

She rose from her knees and studied the ornament her mother had given her and which she always wore to fasten her scarf. Her mother had explained the significance of the emblems on the ornament. The silver eagles were of Lorraine, the double cross was of Jerusalem; and the lilies were of Anjou and Sicily. This was the emblem of Guise and Lorraine. Her mother had said: 'Always remember the emblem when you are afraid or when you are about to do something shameful. It is the emblem of Guise and Lorraine.'

And Guise and Lorraine was France! What had Lady Fleming meant by plans made with the French?

Wherever I go, said Mary to herself, I shall take my four Maries with me. I shall never, never be parted from them.

After a while she grew to love the life of the monastery. There was so much to discover and those black-clad men were so ready to teach. Here she learned to speak and read in French, Spanish and Italian as well as Latin.

She could play as she wished in the grounds about the monastery and there was no one to guard her and her little friends. They could go wherever they wished as long as they remained on the island.

Slowly the days passed and it seemed to all the little girls that they lived for a very long time on the island of Inchmahome.

Then one day when they were wandering close to the lake's edge they saw men rowing to the island. They ran back to tell Lady Fleming what they had seen. Mary was in a flutter of excitement because she believed that the English had come to take her away.

The Abbot himself came running in consternation to the water's edge. Mary Fleming had taken the girls into the monastery, but they could not resist watching from a window.

They saw the Abbot was smiling and bowing to the men.

'English!' cried Lady Fleming excitedly. 'They are not English. They are Scottish noblemen. Depend upon it they have come to take us home.'

She was right.

Lady Fleming put the cloak about the dainty little figure and called to Flem to bring the brooch which was emblazoned with the arms of Guise and Lorraine.

'Back to something a little more gay, the saints be praised!' said Lady Fleming.

But oddly enough Mary was not sure whether she really wanted to go. She had now so many friends in this quiet retreat. She thought of the quiet common room in which she and the four Maries had so often sat together taking lessons from the brothers; she thought of the freedom of wandering on the island, of the peace and silence which had frightened them at first but which they had grown to love.

She wept when she said good-bye to some of the brothers who had become her favourites; she threw her arms about them in a most unqueenly fashion and buried her face in the musty robes which had formerly repelled her.

'Farewell to you all,' she cried. 'Farewell, dear brothers. Farewell, dear Abbot. Farewell, dear Inchmahome.'

She stood waving to them as the boat carried her party across the lake.

Her mother was waiting for her at Stirling Castle. With her were the Lords Lindsay, Livingstone, Montrose and Erskine. And there was another–a stranger.

He was tall and his beard was curled as she had never seen a beard curled before; his hands moved expressively; his eyes flashed and sparkled as they rested on the little Queen.

'This is an emissary from the King of France,' said the Queen-Mother, and as she spoke those words she seemed taller and prouder than ever before. 'He comes with greetings from the King and my brothers.'

Mary was enchanted with the newcomer. She decided he was very pretty and unlike any man she had seen before.

He sank to his knees very gracefully, not as the Scottish nobles knelt; he took her hand and raised it to his lips. 'Your Majesty's most humble servant,' he said. He continued to hold her hand.

Then he rose and turned to the Queen-Mother. 'Forgive me, Madame,' he said in French, but Mary's French was good enough to understand him, 'I am struck dumb by such enchanting beauty.'

The Queen-Mother was smiling. She called him Monsieur l'Amiral.

There was much talk and laughter and the little Queen saw that other strangers had come into the chamber, and they too had curled beards and gay tongues and spoke quickly–far too quickly–in the French tongue.

She retired to her apartment after a while, but no sooner was she there than her mother entered. Mary had never seen her look so excited.

She too talked French, and so rapidly that Mary had to beg her to speak more slowly.

'This will not do,' cried Marie De Guise. 'What will your uncles say if you cannot speak French fluently? You must do so before you step for the first time on the soil of France.'

Marie de Guise's eyes had filled with tears and, in spite of the fact that there were others present, she abandoned ceremony and taking her daughter in her arms she held her tightly.

Then Mary knew that she was to leave for France–not in the distant future–and that these strange men had come to escort her there.

There was a bustle of preparation; there was a packing of baggage; and all this was done at the utmost speed.

Now and then the Queen-Mother found time to talk to her daughter, to tell her of the wonderful future which was being planned for her. 'You are going to my people. The Most Christian King himself will be your father. The Queen of France will be as your mother; and your grandfather, the great Duke of Guise, and your grandmother, who was Antoinette de Bourbon before she became Madame de Guise, will be there, with your uncles, to greet you.'

She had to make this child understand the importance of what was about to happen to her. She was the Queen of Scotland, but a greater throne was coming her way. His Most Christian Majesty was offering her the crown of France through marriage with his son. A great and glorious future was to be hers, and the child would be worthy of it. Surely her beauty must startle even the French.

'Listen to me carefully. The English are close at hand; they have captured some of our towns. They know that our kind friend, the King of France, offers you marriage with his son–and that is the very thing they are anxious shall not take place because they want you for their King Edward. Henri Deux, the King of France has sent ships to Scotland. When we go to Dumbarton you will see those mighty ships, and they have braved the storms and the English fleet to come to us. King Henri is our friend. He is anxious that there shall be great friendship between his country and ours. He has sent these ships to take you back to France.'

'And shall you come with me?'

'I cannot come, my darling. I must stay here. But you will have many of your friends with you. All your little Maries shall go. I shall come to visit you. The King–your new father–will not wish you to be lonely. He wants you to be very happy.'

Mary was too excited to be afraid. She was going to the most beautiful country in the world. But when she looked into her mother's face she was immediately sad. Poor *Maman*, she would stay behind. Poor *Maman*, who must also lose her daughter.

Mary threw her arms about her mother's neck.

'I will not go, dearest *Maman*. I will stay with you.'

'That is nonsense, my child.'

'But you will be unhappy if I go. I would rather never seen France than make you unhappy.'

'Why, you foolish child, it makes me the happiest Queen in the world to know you go to France. It is what I wish for you. I shall come to see you soon. The King says I must. He is very kind.'

'I wonder what the Dauphin is like.'

'François? He is the same age as yourself... or almost. Your birthday is in December and his in January. Some Queens have to marry men old enough to be their grandfathers and others have to marry those young enough to be their children.'

Mary began to laugh. 'That must be very funny.'

'Royal marriages are never funny.'

'No, *Maman*,' said Mary seriously.

'The Dauphin is not very strong. You will have to be careful not to tire him in your play.'

'Yes, *Maman*.'

Already Mary had decided that she would make the care of the Dauphin her special task.

Her mother took her on board the ship. With them were the four Maries–now very solemn and demure in their heavy capes. Lady Fleming bustled about them, her lovely face flushed with excitement, forgetful of her widowhood, keenly aware of the admiration directed towards herself even when it came from the humblest sailors.

The Queen-Mother made her daughter walk before her on to the King's galley. Behind them came all those who were to form part of the little Queen's entourage in her new country. There would be so many of them, Mary thought, that it would be almost like being at home.

As they stepped aboard, accompanied by Admiral Villegaignon, a tall man came towards them and knelt before the Queen so that his eyes were on a level with hers. Mary knew him, for he was the Sieur de Brézé, the French King's ambassador at the Scottish Court.

'Your Majesty's servant,' he said. 'My master has commanded me to act as your French governor until I have conducted you safely to his presence.'

She answered in her high piping French which, with its faint Scottish accent, delighted all these Frenchmen: 'Rise, Monsieur de Brézé. It gives me great pleasure to greet you.'

She held out her hand, from the wrist of which the circles of infant fat had now almost, but not quite, disappeared. He kissed it, and again she was aware of that admiration which all the French seemed to show when they looked her way.

He stood up and she said: 'What does this mean? What will you do as my French governor? Will you teach me?'

'There is only one thing I wish to teach Your Majesty, and that is that all France will take one look at you and fall in love with you.'

It was extravagant talk such as she was unaccustomed to hear, and she was a little bewildered, but delighted all the same. It was true, she was sure, that the French were all that she had been led to believe.

Her mother was smiling, so her French must have passed the test.

Now the Queen-Mother spoke. 'Monsieur de Brézé, I shall wish to know all that happens during the journey. I shall wish to know as soon as possible that my daughter has arrived safely in France.'

He bowed gracefully. 'Madame, I will protect your daughter with my life. Messengers shall be despatched to you; they shall reach you if they have to sink every English ship to do so.'

How vehemently they spoke, thought Mary. How they smiled! How their eyes flashed and how their hands moved with their voices! Strange men! Monsieur de Brézé smelt of violets, or was it roses? His golden beard curled enchantingly. She admired him every bit as much as he admired her.

How happy she could have been if she had not had to part from her mother! But Queen Marie was smiling bravely, although at the last she let affection triumph over ceremony. She held her daughter tightly in her arms, and Mary saw the tears glistening in her eyes.

'The saints preserve you,' were her last words. 'Remember all I have taught you. Never forget that you are a Queen, my dearest, and all will be well.'

'Good-bye, dearest *Maman*.'

'I shall see you soon, I feel sure. And now . . . good-bye.'

The Queen-Mother was escorted off the ship. She stood on the shore gazing after the French fleet, at the fluttering standard bearing the arms of Valois. How small the child looked, wrapped in her heavy cloak, her eyes fixed on the mother she was leaving behind her.

Am I right in letting her go? anxiously wondered Marie de Guise in those moments. What will become of my little one? The King has promised that she shall be as his daughter, but how much can Kings be trusted? What of the Court of France? Is it the right place in which to bring up a child? It was scarcely the most virtuous of courts, but she had heard from her relations that there had been a tightening of morals since the death of François. Was there still that perpetual love-making, seeming so decorous and charming–scented notes bearing verses of poetic merit, delicate compliments overlaying orgies and promiscuity like a gossamer veil? Henri was more *sérieux* than his father had been, and Diane de Poitiers was his faithful mistress, but was Henri's Court so very different from that of his father?

And Mary–so warm-hearted, so eager to love all, so French in many ways–how would she fare in such a Court? Was it right to pass her over to voluptuous Paris? Was that better than sending her to murderous London? But of course it was! In France were her own family, and they were close to the throne. The house of Guise and Lorraine would look after its own.

Marie de Guise stood erect, fighting back tears while the ships set sail; she watched them until she could see them no more. Then she returned to her apartments in Dumbarton and spent long hours on her knees praying that the royal ship and its escort might escape both perilous storms and the English.

It was a wonderful journey. The wind rose and buffeted the ship, but the five Maries, finding themselves free from restraint, first walked sedately about the deck, then ran, calling to each other, taking off their satin snoods and laughing as the wind caught their hair and flung it back across their faces.

Mary's half-brothers, Lord James who was Prior of St Andrews, Lord John who was Prior of Coldingham, and Lord Robert who was Prior of Holyrood, stood together watching the children.

'Jamie! Jamie!' called Mary. 'Is it not wonderful to be at sea, eh, Robert, eh John?'

The brothers smiled at their little sister, but there was a brooding look in the eyes of Lord James. He could not forget that he, a young man who was strong and healthy, was set aside because he was a bastard. He was merely a rich beneficiary of the Church instead of a King.

The Lords Livingstone and Erskine paced the deck in quiet conversation.

'It will not do to trust them too far,' Livingstone was saying.

'Indeed not,' agreed Erskine.

'Artus de Brézé–ambassador and now the Queen's governor–what manner of man is he? A jewelled perfumed dummy!'

'The Fleming woman seems to be taken with him and cannot hide it even under the eyes of her son–and she but recently a widow.'

Artus de Brézé was in his turn laughing at the Scotsmen. Such gaunt features, such ruddy skins. Paris would be amused with them. Nor were the women too handsome. The little girls were charming, especially the *Reinette*. She was someone whom the French would appreciate–a beauty and aware of it already. But the women–with the exception of Lady Fleming–were of small interest. There would be little trouble on their account.

He wondered whether he could seduce the red-haired lady during the voyage. It would be rather piquant. At night with the darkness all about them, on the high seas, in danger of an English enemy sighting them at any moment. A Scot and a King's daughter at that! Very amusing! thought the Sieur de Brézé.

Now the little one was standing beside him.

'Monsieur!'

It was a pleasure to hear her speak; it was a delight to look into the upturned face at those long eyes thickly lashed, that soft mouth which was meant for tenderness. He could not help but picture her–say in ten years' time.

'I am at Your Majesty's service. You must not cease to call on me at any hour of the day and night. It will be my pleasure to see that your smallest wish is granted.'

She laughed, showing her pretty teeth. 'Ah, Monsieur de Brézé, you say such nice things.'

'I say only that which the beauty of Your Majesty impels and inspires me to say.'

'Monsieur de Brézé, if you would lift me up I could sit on the rail, and that is what I wish to do.'

She was light, and she laughed as he lifted her.

'Why do you regard me in that way, Monsieur?'

'Your Majesty is an enchantress. I see it already.'

'What is an enchantress?'

'It is what you are and what you will increasingly become.'

'Is it a good thing for a Queen to be?'

'It is a good thing for anyone to be–man or woman, queen or commoner. Tell me, what do you think of us Frenchmen?'

'I love you all. And do you think the King of France will love me?'

'He could not fail to do so.'

'And the Queen?'

'The Queen also. The King has said: "The little Queen shall be as my daughter." He says that before he has seen you; but when his eyes fall on you, my little Queen, he will say much more. Where is your governess?'

'The sea has made her ill and she will not show herself.'

'You must tell her that I am desolate.'

'Desolate, Monsieur? But you look so happy.'

'I am desolate to know that she suffers. Will you tell her that?'

'Yes. Put me down and I will tell her at once.'

When she was on her feet she retreated a pace or two. She said with a smile: 'I shall tell her that you *say* you are desolate, and look so happy when you say it.'

She started to walk away.

'Your Majesty,' he called. 'I will explain.'

She stopped, turned and regarded him gravely. Then she said demurely: 'My mother and my guardians have told me that we must quickly learn the ways of the French . . . all of us.'

He watched her skipping away. So beautiful! So young! And already with some knowledge of the ways of the world.

The French galleys were in sight of land, and the dangerous journey was nearly over. Mary stood with Lady Fleming, her three brothers and the four Maries, watching the land as they approached it. None of them was more relieved than Lady Fleming that the journey was over. She declared she had come near to dying. So ill had she been that she had implored Monsieur de Villegaignon to let her go ashore when they were within a few miles of the coast of England; she had felt then that she would rather die at the hands of the English than become a victim of the sea. Monsieur de Villegaignon had forgotten his French manners and peremptorily told her that she should not land; she should go to France or drown by the way. What a mercy it had been that they had brought Scottish navigators with them. These men, accustomed to stormy weather and rocky coasts, had been invaluable during the voyage.

And now, praise the saints, thought Lady Fleming, the peril was wellnigh over.

Mary was unable to feel anything but excitement. She had almost forgotten the terror of seeing English ships on the horizon. It seemed a long time ago when her brothers had stood about her with Lords Erskine and Livingstone, determined to defend her should the need arise. The saints had answered their prayers, and the wind had turned in their favour, so that they were able to speed across the rough waters until the English dropped below the horizon. Now here they were in sight of France, and their galley was drawing in to the little Brittany port of Roscoff.

As soon as she stepped ashore Mary was made aware of the magnitude of the welcome which was to be given to her.

The little port was festooned with gay banners, and the people had come for miles round to line the shore and shout a welcome to *la Reinette*. In this they were obeying the orders of the King, who had said: 'Welcome the little Queen of Scots as though she were already my daughter.'

And when these people saw the little girl–so small and dainty–with her four attendants the same age as herself, in their fur-lined capes, they were enchanted.

'*Vive la petite Reine!*' they cried; and Mary, sensing their admiration, smiled and bowed so prettily that they cried out that she was delightful, this little girl who had come to them from the savages.

The progress across France began. From Roscoff the procession made its way to Nantes, Mary sometimes riding on a small horse, sometimes carried in a litter; and each town through which they passed had its welcome for her. Accustomed to the more restrained greetings of her own countrymen and women, Mary was enchanted by the gaiety of these French who were so ready to drink to her health and make a fête-day of her short stay in their towns or villages.

At Nantes a gaily decorated barge was awaiting her and she, in what proved to be a glorious river pageant, sailed with her entourage up the river Loire through the villages and vineyards of Anjou and Touraine, where the people lined the river bank to call a welcome to her. When she left the barge and went ashore in her litter, the people crowded round her, their eyes flashing, laughter bubbling from their lips, and she thought them the merriest people she had ever seen. How could she be homesick for those castles which had been nothing more than prisons! Here the people were not only gay but friendly. It was an informal pageant in which the labourers from the vineyard, the tillers of the soil, and plump peasant women, joined merrily.

She had never witnessed anything like it and she was as delighted with the French as the French were with her.

But when they left the barge at Tours, the journey became more of a royal progress, for waiting to greet her was her grandfather Claude Duc de Guise, and her grandmother the Duchesse was with him–she who before her marriage had been Antoinette de Bourbon.

These great personages received her with much ceremony, but when they were alone her grandmother took the child on her knee and embraced her. 'You are indeed a pretty child,' she said; and her eyes gleamed, as did those of the Duke her husband, for the fortunes of the mighty house of Guise and Lorraine rested on this dainty child's shoulders.

'I shall write and tell your uncle François that he will love you,' went on her grandmother.

'Is my uncle François not here then, Grandmother?'

'No, my child, he is much occupied with the affairs of the country. So are his brothers. But they will be delighted, all of them, to hear what a dear little girl you are.'

Her grandfather talked to her too. He reminded her that while she was Queen of Scotland she was also a member of the noble house of Guise and Lorraine.

'We stand together, my little one. One for all and all for each. That is the rule of our family. Soon you will be meeting your uncles. Your Uncle Charles will keep you under his wing.'

Mary listened gravely. She had heard most of it already from her mother.

The Duchesse travelled with the party by river to Orléans where they disembarked and continued by road through Chartres.

'You will be housed,' the Duchesse told Mary, 'with the royal children–the Dauphin and his little sister Elisabeth. The little Princess Claude and Prince Louis are babies still. The King has decided that you shall live at the palace of Saint-Germain as soon as it is sweetened. Meanwhile you will stay nearby at Carrières.'

'When shall I see the King and Queen?' asked Mary.

'Ah, you go too fast. The Court is at Moulins, so to begin with you will make the acquaintance of the royal children. The King wishes the meeting to be informal. You understand, my child? The King loves children and thinks tenderly of them–not only his own but others also. He has decided that you shall come to know the children with a complete absence of ceremony. He is anxious that you should love each other. You are to share a room with Madame Elisabeth. She is only three and a half. He hopes that you will be particularly fond of the Dauphin.'

'I shall, I know I shall. I am going to take great care of him.'

The Duchesse laughed. 'Ah, my little one, you have the proud spirit of a Guise. So the Queen of a savage land will take great care of the heir of France, eh?'

'But he is younger than I,' protested Mary. 'And I hear that he is not strong.'

Madame de Guise patted her shoulder. 'You are right, my child. You must take every care of him, for on him will depend your future . . . and that of others. Let it not be too obvious care. Let it be loving tenderness. I know you will be a credit to us. There is another matter. The King is pleased to allow your four little friends to be with you, but he wanted them to go away after the first few days at Carrières. No! Do not be afraid. The King has heard of your love for them and he would not for the world part you from them. But for a little while he wishes you to be alone in the royal nursery with François and Elisabeth. He wants no other children to come between you for a little while.'

'It will only be for a little while?'

'For a very little while. You need have no fear, dear child. You will be happy in our royal nurseries.'

'The King is a very good king,' said Mary. 'The Queen . . . is she beautiful?'

'All queens are beautiful,' said the Duchesse lightly.

'Does she too say that she wants me to love Françoise and Elisabeth?'

'The Queen agrees with the King in all things.'

Mary was intelligent. She noticed that the manner of her grandmother changed when she mentioned the Queen of France. Why? wondered Mary.

She was longing to see the Dauphin and his little sister; she was longing to see the King; but oddly enough, as she explained to her Maries, she felt more *curious* about the Queen.

The meeting between the children was unceremonious as it had been intended it should be. In the big room at Carrières Mary went forward to greet them. With them were their Governor and Governess, the Maréchal d'Humières and Madame d'Humières. With Mary were her grandmother and the members of her suite.

The Dauphin stared at Mary. She was taller than he was. His legs were thin and spindly and it seemed as though the weight of his body would break them. His head seemed too large for the rest of him and he was very pale.

Mary's tenderness–always ready to be aroused–overwhelmed her. She knelt and kissed his hand. He stared at her wonderingly; and rising she put her arms about him and kissed him. 'I have come to love you and be your playmate,' she said.

The little boy immediately responded to her embrace.

Mary broke away and glanced with some apprehension at her grandmother. They had said no ceremony, but had she been too impulsive in embracing the Dauphin?

The Duchesse was far from displeased. She had noticed the little boy's response. She glanced at Madame d'Humières. What a pity that the King is not here to see this! that glance implied. He would be quite enchanted.

Madame d'Humières nodded in agreement. It was always wise to agree with the Guises, providing such agreement would not be frowned on by the King's mistress.

Mary had turned to the three-and-a-half-year-old Elisabeth, a frail and pretty little girl; and what a pleasure it was for the Duchesse to see a Princess of France kneel to her grand-daughter! Madame Elisabeth knew what was expected of her. Had not the King said: 'Mary Stuart shall be as one of my own children, but because she is a queen she shall take precedence over my daughter.'

Mary looked into the face of the little girl and, because the child was so small and because she had embraced her brother, the little Queen could not resist embracing the Princess also.

Her grandmother advanced towards the group, at which the two royal children seemed to move closer to Mary as though expecting she would protect them from her important relative.

But the Duchesse merely smiled at them and turned to the Maréchal and Madame d'Humières.

'So charming, is it not?' she said. 'The King will be delighted. They love each other on sight. Let us leave them together. Then they will be more natural, and when the King slips in unceremoniously he will be delighted with our way of bringing them together.'

When Mary was alone with the two children, she took a hand of each and led them to the window seat.

'I have just come here,' she said. 'First I came in a big ship. Then I rode in a litter. Then I came in another ship. I have come from far . . . far away.'

The Dauphin held her hand in his and clung to it when she would have released it. Elisabeth regarded her gravely. Neither of the French children had ever seen anyone quite like her. Her flashing eyes, her vivacious manners, her strange dress and her queer way of talking overwhelmed and fascinated them. Elisabeth's gravity broke into a quiet smile and the Dauphin lifted his shoulders until they almost touched his big head; and all the time he insisted that his hand should remain in that of the newcomer.

He was already telling himself that he was never going to let her go. He was going to keep her with him for ever.

Mary had lived at Carrières for two weeks. She was the Queen of the nurseries. Elisabeth accepted her leadership in everything they did; François asked nothing but to be her devoted slave.

She was a little imperious at times, for after all she was older than they were; she was so much cleverer. She read to them; she would sit on the window seat her arm about François while Elisabeth tried to follow the words in the book. She told them stories and of games she had played with her four Maries with whom she hoped soon to be reunited; she told of the island of Inchmahome in the lake of Menteith whither she had gone one dark night, wrapped in a cloak, fleeing from the wicked English. She told of the long journey across the seas, of the high waters and the roaring winds and of how the English ships had sighted hers on the horizon, for of course they were on the prowl looking for her.

These adventures made her an exciting person; her age made her such a wise one; and her vitality, so sadly lacking in the French children, made her an entertaining companion; but perhaps it was her beauty which strengthened her power.

Thus it was when one day there came into the nurseries unannounced a tall man with a beard which was turning to silver; he was dressed in black velvet and there were jewels on his clothes. With him came a lady–the loveliest Mary had ever seen.

The children immediately ran forward and threw themselves at the man. This was one of the occasions to which they looked forward. If there had been others present it would have been necessary to bow and kiss hands, but this was one of those pleasurably anticipated occasions when the two came alone.

'Papa! Papa!' cried François.

The big man picked him up and the lady kissed François' cheek.

Elisabeth was holding fast to his doublet and there was love and confidence in the way her little fingers curled about the black velvet.

'This will not do! This will not do!' cried the man. 'My children, what of our guest?'

Then he lowered François to the floor. François immediately caught the lady's hand and they all advanced to the Queen of Scots who had fallen to her knees, for she knew that the big man with the silvering beard was Henri, King of France.

'Come,' he said in a deep rumbling voice which Mary thought was the kindest she had ever heard, 'let us look at you. So you are Mary Stuart from across the seas?'

'At Your Majesty's service,' said Mary.

He laid his hand on her head and turned to the lady beside him. 'I think we shall be pleased with our new daughter,' he said.

Mary flushed charmingly and turned to kneel to the lady. She took the slim white hand and kissed the great diamond on her finger.

'Yes, indeed,' said the lady, 'our new daughter enchants me.'

'I am happy,' said Mary, in her charming French, 'to know that I have not displeased Your Majesties.'

They laughed and the Dauphin said: 'Mary has come across the sea. She came in a boat and then in another boat and she reads to us.'

The King stooped then and picked up the boy, swinging him above his head. 'You must borrow Mary's rosy looks, my son,' he said.

Elisabeth was quietly waiting to be picked up and kissed, and when it was her turn she put her arms about her father's neck and kissed him; then she buried her face in his beard.

The beautiful lady, whom Mary assumed to be the Queen, said: 'Come and kiss me, Mary.'

Mary did so.

'Why, what a fine girl you are!' The soft white fingers patted Mary's cheeks. 'The King and I are glad you have come to join our children.' She smiled fondly at the King who returned the smile with equal fondness over the smooth head of Elisabeth. In a sudden rush of affection for them both, Mary kissed their hands afresh.

'I am so happy,' she said, 'to be your new daughter.'

The King sat in the big state chair which was kept in the apartment for those occasions when he visited his children. He took Mary and the Dauphin on his knees. The lady sat on a stool, holding Elisabeth.

The King told them that there was to be a grand wedding at the Court. It was Mary's uncle who was to be married.

'Now, my children, Mary's uncle, the Duc d'Aumale, must have a grand wedding, must he not? He would be displeased if the Dauphin did not honour him by dancing at his wedding.'

The Dauphin's eyes opened wide with horror. 'Papa . . . no!' he cried. 'I do not want to dance at the wedding.'

'You do not want to dance at a fine wedding! You do, Mary, do you not?'

'Yes, I do,' said Mary. 'I love to dance.' She put out her hand and took that of the Dauphin. 'I will teach you to dance with me, François. Shall I?'

The grown-ups exchanged glances and the King said in rapid French which Mary could not entirely understand: 'This is the most beautiful, the most charming child I ever saw.'

The children were alone. Mary was explaining to the Dauphin that there was nothing to be frightened of in the dance. It was easy to dance. It was delightful to dance.

'And the King wishes it,' said Mary. 'And as he is the best King in the world, you must please him.'

The Dauphin agreed that this was so.

While they practised the dance, Elisabeth sat on a cushion watching them. The door silently opened, but Mary did not hear it, so intent was she on the dance. She noticed first the change in Elisabeth who had risen to her feet. The smile had left Elisabeth's face. She seemed suddenly to have become afraid. Now the Dauphin had seen what Elisabeth saw. He too stood very still, like a top-heavy statue.

There was a woman standing in the doorway, a woman with a pale flat face and expressionless eyes. Mary took an immediate dislike to her, for she had brought something into the room which Mary did not understand and which was repellent to her. The woman was dressed without magnificence and Mary assumed that she was a noblewoman of minor rank. Hot-tempered as she was, she let her anger rise against the intruder.

As Queen of the nursery, the spoiled charge of easy-going Lady Fleming, the petted darling of almost everyone with whom she had come into contact since her arrival in this country, fresh from her triumph with the King, she said quickly: 'Pray do not interrupt us while we practise.'

The woman did not move. She laughed suddenly and unpleasantly. The little French children had stepped forward and knelt before her. Over their heads she regarded the Queen of Scots.

'What will you do, Mademoiselle?' asked the woman. 'Are you going to turn me out of my nurseries?'

'Madame,' said Mary, drawing herself to her full height, 'it is the Queen of Scotland to whom you speak.'

'Mademoiselle,' was the reply, 'it is the Queen of France to whom you speak.'

'N . . . no!' protested Mary. But the kneeling children had made her aware of the unforgivable mistake she had made. She was terrified. She would be sent back to Scotland for such behaviour. She had been guilty not only of a great breach of good manners; she had insulted the Queen of France.

'Madame,' she began, 'I humbly beg . . .'

Again the harsh laugh rang out; but Mary scarcely heard it as she knelt before the Queen, first pale with horror, then red with shame.

'We all make mistakes,' said Catherine de' Medici, "even Queens of such great countries as Scotland. You may rise. Let me look at you.'

As Mary obeyed she realized that there were two Queens: one lovely and loving who came with the King, who kissed the children and called them hers and behaved in every way as though she were their mother, and another who came alone, who frightened them and yet, it seemed, was after all their mother and the true Queen of France.

Chapter Two

To Mary, life in those first months was full of pleasure. It was true there were times when the Queen of France would come silently into the nursery, laugh her sudden loud laughter, make her disconcerting remarks, and when little François and Elisabeth would, while displaying great decorum, shrink closer to Mary as though asking her to protect them. But Mary was gay by nature and wished to ignore that which was unpleasant.

Often King Henri and Madame Diane came to the nursery to play with them, to caress them and make them feel secure and contented. It had not taken Mary long to discover that if Queen Catherine were Queen in name, Diane was Queen in all else.

Mary noticed that, when Catherine and Diane were together in the nursery, Catherine seemed to agree with all Diane's suggestions. Being young, being fierce in love and hate, young Mary could not resist flashing a look of triumph at the Queen's flat, placid features at such times.

She is a coward! thought Mary. She is not fit to be a Queen.

The four Maries were now added to the little Queen's adoring circle, but the Dauphin had become her first care. All those who saw Mary and the Dauphin together–except Queen Catherine–declared they had never seen such a charming love-affair as that between the Dauphin and his bride-to-be. As for little Madame Elisabeth, she became one of Mary's dearest friends, sharing her bedchamber and following her lead in all things.

It was at the wedding of her uncle François Duc d'Aumale that she met this important man for the first time. He looked very like the knight she had pictured during her childhood in Scotland and she was not disappointed in the eldest of her uncles. François de Guise, Duc d'Aumale, was tall and handsome; his beard was curled; his eyes were flashing; and he was gorgeously apparelled. He was ready to become–as he soon was to be–the head of the illustrious family of Guise. He filled the role of bridegroom well, as he did that of greatest soldier in the land. His bride was a fitting one for such a man. She was Anne d'Este, the daughter of Hercule, Duke of Ferrara, and was herself royal, for her mother was King Henri's aunt.

There was a good deal of whispering in the Court concerning the marriage. 'Watch these Guises,' said suspicious noblemen. 'They look to rule France one way or another. Old Duke Claude had not the ambition of his sons; that doubtless came from their Bourbon mother. But Duke Claude, who was content with the hunt, his table and his women, is not long for this world and then this Duc d'Aumale will become the Duc de Guise, and he looks higher than his father ever did.

Mary heard nothing of these whisperings. To her the marriage was just another reason for merriment, for wearing fine clothes, for showing off her graces, for being petted and admired for her beauty and charm.

So there she was in the *salle de bal*, stepping out to dance with the Dauphin, enchanting all with her grace and her beauty and her tender devotion to the heir of France.

'Holy Mother of God!' swore the Duc d'Aumale. 'There goes the greatest asset of the House of Guise. One day we shall rule France through that lovely girl.'

Later he talked with his brother Charles. Charles, five years younger than his brother François, was equally handsome though in a different way. François would win his way through boldness, Charles by cunning. Charles was the cleverer of the two, and knowing himself to lack that bravery on which the family prided itself, he had to develop other qualities to make up for the lack.

So Charles, the exquisite Cardinal, with his scented linen and his sensuality, was an excellent foil to his dashing brother; they were both aware of this, and they believed that between them they could rule France through their niece who in her turn would rule the Dauphin.

They had brought rich presents for Mary; they were determined to win her affection and to increase that respect which their sister, the Queen-Mother of Scotland, had so rightly planted in her daughter's mind.

The Cardinal, whose tastes were erotic and who, although he was quite a young man, was hard pressed to think of new sensations which could delight him, was quite enchanted with his niece.

'For, brother,' he said, 'she has more than beauty. There is in her . . . shall we call it Promise? What could be more charming than Promise? She is like a houri from a Mohammedan paradise, beckoning the newcomer to undreamed of delight, inviting him to explore with her that which she herself has not yet discovered.'

François looked at his brother uneasily. 'Charles, for God's sake, do not forget that she is your niece.'

Charles smiled. Blood relationships were of no account in his world of licentiousness. His long slim fingers a-glitter with jewels which put those adorning his brother's person in the shade, stroked his cardinal's robes. Did he enjoy being a man of the church so much because, in his relationships with charming people, that fact added an extra relish? François was a blunt soldier for all that he was a Guise and destined, Charles was sure, to be one of the great men of his day. Rough soldier–he took the satisfaction of his carnal appetites as a soldier takes them. Charles was selective, continually striving for the new sensation.

'My dear brother,' he said, 'do you take me for a fool? I shall know how to deal with our niece. She is a little barbarian at the moment, from a land of barbarians. We shall teach her until she is cultured and even more charming than she already is. But the material is excellent, François, excellent.' The Cardinal waved his beautiful hands, describing the shape of a woman. 'Beautiful . . . malleable material, dear François.'

'There must be no scandal touching her, Charles. I beg of you to remember that.'

'François! My dear soldier brother! You are a great man. You are the greatest man in France. Yes, I will say that, for there is none here to repeat my words to his boorish Majesty. But you have lived the life of a soldier, and the life of the soldier, you will admit, is one that lacks refinement. I am in love with Mary Stuart. She is an enchanting creature. Dear brother, do not think that I mean to seduce her. A little girl of six? Piquant . . . yes. But if I want little girls of six, they are mine. It is her mind that I shall possess. We shall possess it between us. We shall caress it . . . we shall impregnate it with our ideas. What pleasure! I have long since known that the pleasure of the body–after the first rough experimenting–cannot be fully enjoyed without the co-operation of the mind.'

François's brow cleared. Charles was no fool. No fool indeed! If he himself was France's greatest soldier, Charles would be the country's cleverest diplomat.

'I feel,' said François, 'that you should watch over her education carefully, and that the Maréchal and Madame d'Humières should not be given too free a hand. The governess, Fleming, is no danger, I suppose?'

'The governess Fleming is just a woman.'

'If you wish to seduce a royal lady of Scotland, why not . . .' began François.

The cynical mouth turned up at the corners. 'Ten years ago your suggestion would have interested me. The Fleming will be a worthy lover. Very eager she will be. She is made for pleasure. Plump and pretty, ripe, but of an age, I fear, for folly, and the folly of the middle-aged is so much more distressing and disconcerting than that of youth. But there are hundreds such as the Fleming. They are to be found in every village in France. Nay, I'll leave the Fleming for some callow boy. She'll bring him much delight.'

'You could, through the woman, keep a firm hand on Mary Stuart.'

'The time is not yet come. Mary, at the moment, is the playmate of the Dauphin, and as such shares the governor and governess of young François. That is enough for the moment. Let her strengthen that attachment. That is the most important thing. The Dauphin must be completely enslaved; he must follow her in all things. He is willing to do so now, but she must forge those chains strongly so that they can never be broken. He is his father all over again. Would Diane have caught our Henri so slavishly if she had not caught him young? 'How charming!' they say. Madame Diane says it. His Majesty says it. 'Was there ever anything more delightful than for two children who are destined for marriage to be already such tender playmates?' These Parisians! They are not like us of Lorraine. They talk love and think love. It is their whole existence; it is an excuse for everything. It is typically Valois. But we must be more clever; we must see farther. We know that this love between our niece and the King's son is more than charming; it is very good for the house of Guise. Let us therefore help to forge those chains, chains so strong that they cannot be broken, for depend upon it, sooner or later the Montmorencys–or mayhap our somnolent Bourbons–will awake from their slumbers. They will see that it is not a pretty little girl who has made the King-to-be her slave; it is the noble house of Guise.'

'You are right, Charles. What do you suggest?'

'That she remains at present as she is. The chattering Fleming will be useful. She–herself the slave of love–will be delighted to see her mistress installed in the heart of our Prince. She will chatter romance; she will foster romance; and she will do no harm. Leave things as they are, and in a few years' time I shall take over Mary's education. I shall teach her to be the most charming, the most accomplished lady in France. None shall be as beautiful as she, none shall excel her at the dance, at the lute; she will write exquisite verses, and all France–but most of all the Dauphin–will be in love with her. Her mind shall be given to the art of pleasing others; and it shall be as wax in the hands of the uncles who will love and cherish her, for their one desire will be to keep her on the throne.'

François smiled at his elegant brother.

'By God!' he cried suddenly. 'You and I will conquer France and share the crown.'

'In the most decorous manner,' murmured Charles. 'Through our little charmer from the land of savages.'

The days flew past for Mary. At lessons she excelled; she played the lute with a skill rare in one so young; she was a good horsewoman. In the royal processions she was always picked out for her charm and beauty. The King often talked to her. Diane was delighted with her. When she rode out with the Dauphin she would watch over him and seize his bridle if he was in any difficulty. He would be uneasy if she was not always at his side.

All the great chateaux which had been but names to her she now saw in reality. She thought less and less of her native land. Her mother wrote frequently and was clearly delighted with her daughter's success. She had had letters from the King, she said, which had made her very happy indeed.

Mary's four namesakes were now with her, but they had to take second place. The Dauphin demanded so much of her time. She explained this carefully to them for she was anxious that they should know that she loved them as dearly as ever.

They listened to gossip, and there was plenty of that at the French Court. Now the talk was all about the Queen's coronation which was about to take place. The King had already celebrated his coronation shortly after the death of his father, and now it was Catherine's turn.

The celebrations were lavish. Mary had never seen anything quite so wonderful. Even the dreamlike pageants which had accompanied her uncle's wedding seemed commonplace when compared with those of the Queen's coronation. Even the Queen looked magnificent on that day. As for the King he was a dazzling sight, resplendent in cloth of silver; his scabbard flashed with enormous jewels, and his silver lace and white satin hat were decorated with pearls. The sheriffs of Paris held over him a blue velvet canopy embroidered with the golden lilies of France as he rode his beautiful white horse.

Mary would never forget the display of so much beauty. She was, she told Janet Fleming, only sorry that it was not her beloved Diane, instead of Queen Catherine, who was being crowned.

'Well, let her enjoy her coronation,' said Lady Fleming. 'That's all she'll get.'

'All! A coronation *all*! Dear old Fleming, what more could she want?'

'She wants much more,' said Lady Fleming. 'Whom do you think the King has presented with the crown jewels?'

'Diane, of course.'

Lady Fleming nodded and began to laugh. 'And she wears them too. She insists. The King is pleased that she should. What a country! The old Maréchal Tavannes complains that at the Court of France more honour is done to the King's mistress than to his generals. Who is the real Queen of this country, tell me that!'

'Diane, of course. And I am glad that it should be so, for I hate Queen Catherine.'

'She is not worth the hating. She is as meek as a sheep. Look at this. It is one of the new coins struck at the coronation and should bear the heads of the King and Queen. But see! It is Diane riding on the crupper of the King's horse. It means that although he has been forced to marry Queen Catherine and make her the mother of his children, there is only one Queen for him–Diane.'

'And more worthy to be!' cried Mary. 'Queen Catherine is not royal. She has no breeding. She is vulgar. I wish she would go back to her Italian merchants so that the King could marry Diane.'

They looked up sharply. The door had opened so quietly that no one had heard a sound. They were relieved to see that it was not Catherine who stood there; it was Madame de Paroy.

'Yes, Madame de Paroy?' said Mary, immediately assuming the dignity of her rank. 'What is it you want?'

'To ask your Majesty if you would wait on Queen Catherine.'

'I will do so,' said Mary. 'And, Madame de Paroy, when you come to my apartments will you be so good as to be announced?'

'I could find none of your pages or women, Your Majesty. I am sorry that, as you and Lady Fleming were enjoying such mirth, you did not hear me.'

Madame de Paroy curtsied and retired. Mary looked at Lady Fleming who was trembling.

'Why are you afraid, and of what?' demanded Mary.

'I am afraid that she will tell Queen Catherine what she heard you say.'

Mary tossed her head. 'Who cares for that! If Queen Catherine were unpleasant to me I should ask Diane to protect me.'

'There is something about her that frightens me,' said Janet.

'You are too easily frightened, Fleming dear.'

'Do not keep her waiting. Go to her now . . . at once. I shall not rest until I know what she has to say to you.'

Mary obeyed. She returned very shortly.

'You see, you silly old Fleming, it was nothing. She just wished to speak to me about our lessons.'

Diane had fallen ill and had retired to her beautiful chateau of Anet which enhanced the beauty of the valley of the Eure and which Philibert Delorme had helped her to make one of the most magnificent examples of architecture in the country. The King, filled with anxiety, would have dropped all state obligations to be with her, but Diane would not hear of it. She insisted on his leaving her in her chateau with her faithful servants, and continuing with his Court duties.

Everyone in the Court was clearly delighted or anxious–except, of course, the Queen. She, who would surely be most affected, remained as expressionless as ever; and whenever Diane's name was mentioned spoke of her concern for her health.

A melancholy settled over Saint-Germain, and Mary hated melancholy. When the King visited his children he was absent-minded. Nothing was as pleasant as it had been when Diane was there.

Then an alarming incident occurred. Mary would not have heard of this but for the cleverness of Beaton who had quickly improved her French and was now a match for anyone.

Beaton took Mary into a corner to whisper to her: 'Someone tried to poison you.'

Mary was aghast. 'Who?' she demanded; and her thoughts immediately flew to the Queen.

'No one is sure. It was the poisoner's intention to put an Italian posset into a pie for you. But it's all right. They have a man whom they have caught, and I expect they'll tie him to four wild horses and let them gallop in different directions.'

For once Mary was too horrified by what might be happening to herself to feel sorry for the victim of such a horrible punishment.

Mary Beaton had gleaned no further information, so Mary tackled Janet Fleming. Janet had heard the story, although, she said, the King wished it not to be bruited abroad, for he was much distressed that danger should have come so near Mary when she was at his Court.

'He says that the vigilance about you must be intensified. You must not let anyone know you have heard of this.'

'Tell me who did this thing.'

'A man is accused who is named Robert Stuart. Oh, do not look shocked. It is not your brother but a poor archer of the guard who happens to bear his name. He was clearly working for someone else. Some say it was the English. Others that he worked for your kinsman the Earl of Lennox . . . a Protestant. And this would seem most likely as Robert Stuart is clearly a fanatic. He has confessed that he did this thing, and will suffer accordingly. Matthew Lennox declares his innocence, but who shall know?'

'So it was not the Queen,' said Mary.

'The Queen! What do you mean?'

'She hates me. Sometimes I am afraid of her.'

'Nonsense! The Queen is but a name.'

The King came into the nurseries to see the children, and with him was the Queen. How different were these visits from those of Henri and Diane! The children did not rush to their father and climb over him; they curtsied and, under their mother's gaze, paid their respectful homage to him as their King.

The Maréchal and Madame d'Humières were not present on this occasion, and Janet Fleming was in charge of the children. Mary noticed how particularly pretty she was looking, and that the glance the Queen threw in her direction seemed to be faintly amused.

Mary wanted to know if there was any news from Anet, but under the eyes of the Queen, she dared not ask.

'Lady Fleming,' said the Queen of France, 'now that the Dauphin and the Queen of Scotland and Madame Elisabeth are growing older, and Madame Claude will soon be joining them in the nursery, it seems to me that you will need some assistance.'

'Your Majesty is gracious,' said Janet Fleming, with that abstracted look which Mary had noticed lately.

'I am sure,' said the King, 'that Lady Fleming manages very well . . . very well indeed. I am struck with the great care she has always shown of our daughter Mary.'

The Queen's lips twitched very slightly. 'Like Your Majesty I too am sure that Lady Fleming is admirable, but I do not wish her strength to be over-taxed.'

'Over-taxed?' reflected the King, frowning at his wife.

'By so many children. And the Maréchal and Madame d'Humières have so much with which to occupy themselves. I do not wish dear Lady Fleming to work all the time she is with us, and I should like her to have some little respite from her duties. I should like her to enjoy a little gaiety.'

The King looked sharply at the Queen, but Catherine had laid her beautiful white hands on her stomacher and lowered her eyes. Her smile was almost smug. Mary wondered whether the rumours were true and that she was going to have another baby.

'I know,' went on the Queen, smiling affectionately at the King, 'how greatly Your Majesty esteems those who look after our children. Therefore I would beg for a few privileges for my Lady Fleming. I will send someone to assist her so that she may have a little more time for pleasure. Madame de Paroy is well skilled and most fitted to help in the nurseries. If Your Majesty would agree to her doing so, it would give her the greatest pleasure and, as for myself, I should feel that I had assisted our good Lady Fleming to obtain a little of the pleasure she deserves.'

Madame de Paroy in the nurseries! That hideous old woman with the crafty eyes–the Queen's spy! Mary felt the hot colour rise to her cheeks. Forgetting ceremony she ran to the King and took his hand. 'Please . . . please, dearest Papa, do not send Madame de Paroy here. *Please!*'

The King looked down at her in some astonishment. He ought to be angry with her for thus addressing him on an occasion when it was clear that ceremony was demanded; but he found it difficult to be angry with children, and such a beautiful child as this one, whatever she did, could not arouse anything but his wish to please her.

'My dear child,' he began helplessly; then he smiled. 'Why, how vehement you are!'

The Dauphin had come to the other side of his father. 'Papa,' he said, 'please do not send Madame de Paroy here.'

'Why do you not want her?' asked the King.

The Dauphin did not answer. He looked to Mary for guidance. 'Come,' said the King, 'speak for yourself. Why do you not want her?'

'Because . . . because Mary does not.'

The Queen gave her sudden laugh. 'Ah! So in the nursery Scotland already rules France!'

'And Elisabeth, what does she wish?' asked the King.

Elisabeth came forward and keeping her eyes on her father's face while she elaborately turned away from her mother said: 'I wish what François and Mary wish.'

'So Madame de Paroy is unanimously rejected!' cried the King.

The Queen laughed. 'You see, Lady Fleming, your charges defeat my good intentions.'

'Your Majesty is very gracious,' said Janet. 'I thank you for your solicitude.'

'And these young people will have none of my Madame de Paroy, eh? Well, well! We will forget I suggested it.'

Mary could not help throwing a triumphant glance at the Queen. She knew that Catherine had particularly wished Madame de Paroy to come. What she wants, thought Mary, is to set a woman to spy on us, and she lacks the courage to insist. I despise her.

While the Queen talked to the children about their lessons, Lady Fleming showed the King some of their essays. They were bending over them and the King looked pleased. Janet, flushed and excited to find herself so popular in such exalted company, ventured to say something which had been in her mind for some time.

'Your Majesty, may I make a request?'

The King's smile was very friendly. 'Lady Fleming, please do.'

'It concerns my very personal affairs, and doubtless I should not bother Your Majesty with it at all.'

'I shall be happy to give my attention to your personal affairs, and if there is anything I can do to help you, I shall be well pleased indeed.'

'It concerns one of my sons, Your Majesty. He is a prisoner of the English. He has long been in their hands and I cannot bring about his liberation. I thought that if Your Majesty would intercede for me with the Queen-Mother of Scotland, perhaps she might arrange to exchange an English prisoner for my son.'

'It would please me greatly,' said the King, 'if I could be sure of granting this request. As it is I shall do my utmost. I will write this day to my cousin of Scotland and suggest to her that there might be an exchange of prisoners.'

His eyes were very warm and friendly. Janet was excited. It was a long time since she had had a lover, and now it occurred to her that the next one might be none other than the King of France. No wonder she was excited. No wonder that, in spite of her age, she looked like a young girl in her teens.

Even the children noticed the change in her. The only one who did not seem to notice was Queen Catherine.

Mary lay in bed; she could not sleep. She was suffering from pains which were not unfamiliar to her. She had eaten more than usual. She had such a healthy appetite, and she looked upon it as a duty to set a good example to François and Elisabeth who pecked at their food. The meal, presided over by Madame d'Humières and the Maréchal, had been much as usual. There were joints of veal and lamb; there were geese, chickens, pigeons, hares, larks and partridges; and Mary had done justice to all, with the result that, although there was to be a grand ball, she had had to retire early on account of her pains.

There had been some amusement about this ball because it had been arranged by the Queen and, oddly enough, the Constable de Montmorency had helped her with the arrangements. Young as she was, Mary was very intelligent and eager to learn all she could concerning Court matters; and with her four little Maries to assist her she could not help being aware of the tension which was inevitable in a Court where the Queen was submitted to perpetual humiliation, and the King's mistress enjoyed all–and more–of those honours which should have been the Queen's.

With the ageing mistress sick at Anet–some said dying–that tension must increase. Would the Queen seek to regain some of her rights? Would some beautiful and ambitious lady seek to fill Diane's place?

François and Elisabeth and little Claude might have watched the ball from one of the galleries. The French children would have enjoyed that more than mingling with the guests, but Mary would have wished to be with the dancers in a dazzling gown, her chestnut hair flowing, and all the gentlemen paying her laughing compliments and speaking of the enchantress she would become when she grew up. But alas, she was too sick to attend and must lie in bed instead.

Janet Fleming had talked continually of the ball, but Mary had felt too sick to listen. She had drunk the posset Queen Catherine had given her, and afterwards had felt some misgivings. She had heard rumours about the Queen's Italian cupbearer who had been torn asunder by wild horses when the King's elder brother had died–of poison, some said, and others added: poison administered by Catherine de' Medici. Mary could not rid herself of the idea that Catherine wished her ill.

'Here,' Catherine had said, 'this is what I call my gourmand's dose. Do you know what Your Scottish Majesty is suffering from? A surfeit of gooseflesh, like as not. You have been over-greedy at the table.'

Mary had grown hot with indignation as Catherine had bent over to look into her face.

'You're flushed,' said Catherine. 'Is it a fever, or have I upset your dignity? The truth can be as indigestible as gooseflesh, my dear *Reinette*.'

And Mary had had to swallow the hideous stuff and lie in bed nursing a sore stomach while others danced.

It was near midnight but she could not sleep. She could hear the sound of music from the great ballroom.

Before going to the ball Janet Fleming had come into the apartment to show Mary her costume. Everyone was to be masked. Those were the Queen's orders. The idea of the Queen and the Constable planning a ball! The whole Court was rocking with amusement. They would not miss Madame Diane tonight . . . not even the King.

'How I wish I could be with you,' sighed the little Queen.

'Has her Majesty's posset done you no good then?'

'I am not sure that she meant it to. She hates me because I would not have Madame de Paroy in the nurseries.'

'You are a bold creature, darling Majesty, to go against the Queen of France.'

'Would *you* want Paroy in the nurseries?'

'Holy Mother of God, indeed I would not! Why, if she knew that the King had shown me . . . a little friendship, Heaven alone knows what she might tell the Queen. But . . . my tongue runs away with me and I shall be late for the ball.'

Mary put her arms round her aunt's neck and kissed her. 'Come and see me when the ball is over. I shall want to hear *all* about it,' said Mary.

So now she lay in bed waiting for the ball to be over.

She slept for a while, and when she awoke it was to silence. So the ball was over and her aunt had not come as she had promised. Faint moonlight shone through the windows, lighting the room. She sat up in bed, listening. Her pains had gone and she felt well and wide awake. but she was angry; she always was when she suspected she had been treated as a child. Lady Fleming had no doubt come in to tell her about the ball and, finding her asleep, had tiptoed away–just as though she were a baby.

Mary got out of bed and, putting a wrap about her shoulders, crept across the room to that small chamber in which Lady Fleming slept. She drew back the curtains of the bed. It was empty. Lady Fleming had not yet come up, although the ball was over.

Mary got into Janet's bed to wait for her. She waited for a long time before she fell asleep; it was beginning to grow light when she was awakened by Janet's returning.

Mary sat up in bed and stared at her aunt. She was wearing the costume she had worn at the ball, but it appeared to be crumpled and was torn in several places.

'What is it?' asked Mary.

'Hush! For the love of the saints do not wake anybody.' Janet began to take off the costume.

'But what has happened?' insisted Mary. 'You look as though you have been set upon by robbers and yet are rather pleased about it.'

'You must tell no one of this, as you love your Fleming. You should not be here. You should be punished for wandering from your bed in the night. The Queen would punish you.'

'Perhaps she would punish you, too, for wandering in the night. I command you to tell me what has happened to you.'

Janet got into bed and put her arms about Mary. 'What if another has commanded silence?' she said with a laugh.

'I am the Queen . . .'

'Of Scotland, my dearest. What if I had received a higher command?'

'The Queen . . . Queen Catherine?'

'Higher than that!' Lady Fleming kissed the Queen of Scots. 'I am so happy, darling. I am the happiest woman in France. One day I shall be able to serve you as I should wish. One day you shall ask me for something you want, and I will perhaps, through the King's grace, be able to give it to you.'

Mary was excited. Here was one of the mysteries which occurred in the lives of grown-up people; here was a glimpse into the exciting world in which one day she would have a part to play.

'There is one thing I will ask you now,' she said. 'It is never to allow that dreary de Paroy to come near the nursery.'

'That I can promise you,' said Janet gleefully. 'She is banished from this day.'

They lay together smiling, each thinking of the glorious future which lay ahead of her.

Mary forgot the excitement of the Court for a while. With her four friends she went to stay with her grandmother at Meudon. Her grandfather, Duke Claude, was very ill and not expected to live. She knew that soon her uncle François would be the Duke of Guise and head of the house. But she did not see him. It was her uncle, Cardinal Charles, with whom she spent much of her time.

They would walk about the estate together and the Cardinal's eyes would gleam as they watched her. He studied her so closely that Mary blushed for fear he would find some fault in her. There were occasions when he would take her into his private chamber; she would sit on his knee and he would fondle her. He frightened her a little, while he fascinated her; her wide eyes would stare, almost involuntarily, at those long slim fingers which ceaselessly caressed her. She did not know whether she liked or hated those caresses. They fascinated yet repelled. Sometimes he would make her look into his face, and it was as though he were making her subject to his will. His long light eyes with the dark lashes were so beautiful that she wanted to look at them, although she was afraid; they were tender and malicious, gentle and cruel; and beneath them were faint shadows. His mouth was straight and long; it was the most beautiful mouth she had ever seen when it smiled–and it smiled often for her.

There was a delicious odour about his person; it clung to his linen. He bathed regularly; he was, it was said, the most fastidious gentleman of

France. Jewels glittered on his hands, and the colours of those jewels were tastefully blended. Her grandparents were in some awe of him and seemed to have almost as much respect for him as they had for Uncle François.

'Always obey your Uncle François and your Uncle Charles,' she was continually told.

That was what they all wished to impress upon her. Even her new brother–whom she discovered in her grandparents' house–the Duc de Longueville, the son of her mother by her first husband, hinted and implied that it was her duty.

Everyone was telling her that the most important thing in the world was the power of the Guises, and as she played with her Maries she could not completely forget it. She felt like a plant in a forcing house on those occasions in the perfumed chamber of the Cardinal when he talked to her of her duty and how she must make young François her completely devoted slave so that he gave way to her in all things.

'When you are older,' said the Cardinal, putting his hands on her shoulders and pressing her small body to his, 'when you begin to bud into womanhood, then, my sweet and beautiful niece, you must learn how to make the Dauphin entirely yours.'

'Yes, Monsieur le Cardinal.'

He laid his cool lips against her forehead, and, when she received his kiss, for some reason she could not understand she began to tremble.

When Mary returned to Court the excitement regarding the King and Diane had reached its zenith, for Diane was recovered and had come back to Court.

Mary overheard strange whispers.

'Now the fun will start.'

'While the cat is away the mice play.'

'And do you know that mice are very fertile?'

'My dear Duchesse!'

'My dear Count, I assure you, I have noticed!'

Lady Fleming, Mary realized, was more excited than ever.

One day when Mary was in her apartment, she heard her governess talking to one of the Queen's ladies. Janet was saying: 'Yes, it is true, and God be thanked for it. I am with child by the King and I feel honoured. I feel so full of health. There is some magical property in the royal blood, I'll swear!'

Mary was astounded. She decided she would seek out Lady Fleming and demand a full explanation; but when she sought her she could not find her. None of the attendants appeared to know what had happened to her. The King was riding with Madame de Valentinois who had returned from Anet. She was somewhat frail but more beautiful than ever, and the King was like a devoted husband who, after a long separation, is able to enjoy the beloved company of his wife. He could not leave the Duchesse's side; he must spend every minute with her. Perhaps he wished to explain a little affair in which he had regrettably indulged during her absence; perhaps he wished to tell her that it should never have happened–and would not, had she been there–that it had begun in a moment of desperate longing for herself.

And she would understand. She would tell him that she understood him now as she had when he was a shy Prince with no thought of mounting the throne. She had shown him how to act like a great Prince; now she would show him how to act like a great King.

Life would be as it had always been at Court. Queen Diane would rule through the King; those entwined initials H and D were as firm as they had ever been, as closely entwined. The foolish Fleming woman would have to be banished from Court and then forgotten. It was no indiscretion to bear the King's bastard. The folly lay in boasting of the honour.

The Queen of France agreed with her husband and his mistress. She was eager to help. Would the King allow her to deal with this little matter? He knew how she abhorred scandal. The little peccadillo she accepted. It was inevitable. It was the flouting of Court etiquette that she could not endure.

The King and Diane were grateful to her. Neither of them wished to hear any more of the disposal of the matter, which they felt sure could be left entirely to the Queen's capable handling.

Catherine came stealthily into Lady Fleming's chamber. Janet rose from the bed on which she was lying and fell to her knees before the Queen of France. She lifted fearful eyes to the flat expressionless face.

'You may rise,' said Catherine. She laughed suddenly. 'We should not have known yet,' she added, 'had you not boasted so freely.'

'Your Majesty, I implore your forgiveness. . . .'

The Queen lifted her shoulders. 'The King chose to honour you. You should not ask my forgiveness for that. How many times?'

'Your Majesty . . .'

'How many times?' insisted the Queen. Again that laugh. 'So many that you cannot remember? It began on the night of the masque which I arranged. Well, now Madame de Valentinois has returned, and your services are no longer required.'

'Your Majesty, I will be content to obey your command.'

'My command is that you leave the Court this night.'

'Leave the Court . . .'

'Have no fear. Arrangements have been made. Remember you carry a royal bastard. You will be cared for and doubtless the child will be brought to Court. The King, as you have doubtless heard, had a child by a girl of Piedmont. It happened when he was away from France. You understand? The blood is hot and there is always some wanton at hand who can amuse for an hour until something better can be found.' The Queen laughed again. 'It is the way of all men, my dear Lady Fleming, and kings are no exceptions.'

Janet covered her face with her hands and began to cry. 'Madame,' she sobbed, 'I beg of you, let me stay. I have been sent here to guard the Queen of Scots.'

'I have another guardian for her. Do not weep so. It is bad for the child. Be prepared to leave in an hour. Where you are going you will have women to talk to. You may tell them how you were got with child by a most exalted person, but you shall not mention his name although you may describe all else in detail.'

The door opened and Mary stood on the threshold.

'I have looked everywhere . . .' she began, and saw the Queen of France. She immediately curtsied.

'Ah,' said Catherine, 'here is her Scottish Majesty.'

'I . . . I had no idea that I should find you here, Madame,' said Mary. 'I came to look for Fleming.'

'You are just in time to say goodbye to her.'

'Goodbye!'

Mary forgot ceremony. She ran to her aunt and threw her arms about her.

'Dearest Aunt Janet, what does this mean?'

'I . . . I . . . I am going away.'

'Oh, no, no!' cried Mary. 'Is it . . . because of the King's child?'

Catherine interrupted. 'So the Queen of Scots shares the knowledge of your lechery?'

Mary said: 'Madame, Lady Fleming is my governess.'

'No longer, my child.'

'No longer!'

'Lady Fleming is no longer considered a person fit to hold that position.'

'But who says so?'

'I say so.'

'Madame, Lady Fleming is my aunt.'

'We all have our disreputable relations. Pray do not apologize for her.'

'I . . . I wish to have her with me.'

'My dear *Reinette*, you are in the charge of the King and myself and we have decided otherwise.'

'I . . . I do not understand.'

'I am glad of that. I had feared that under the influence of your lecherous relative you might have become quite depraved.'

'Please, Madame, do not torment us.'

'I? I have nothing but your welfare at heart. Young girls can quickly fall into trouble, particularly if they are fairly handsome and have a good opinion of themselves. I have a new governess for you. She will come to you this day. You will be pleased to hear that Madame de Paroy is taking over those duties which Lady Fleming has proved unworthy to perform.' The Queen smiled and turned to Lady Fleming. 'In an hour–do not forget.' And to Mary: 'Madame de Paroy will be with you shortly.'

The Queen walked out of the room and Lady Fleming threw herself on to her bed and gave way to wild weeping.

Mary stood still, her face white and angry, staring at the door.

The Queen of France brought the woman into the apartment. Madame de Paroy could not hide her satisfaction, and the Queen was smiling blandly.

'Ah, Madame de Paroy, here are your charges.'

The four little girls had arranged themselves behind Mary.

'The Queen of Scots waits to welcome you,' said Catherine.

Mary's eyes were sullen. She had seen the King. She had entreated him not to send Lady Fleming away and had begged him not to put Madame de Paroy in her place. The King was as kind as he always was; but he was ill at ease. He had said very kindly that such matters were the business of ladies. It was not his province to appoint a governess for his dear daughter of Scotland. He wished to please her, he wished to make her happy; but he was sure the Queen had the same intentions towards her. It had been necessary for her Scots governess to go away–there were matters beyond the understanding of little girls–and she must trust her guardians to do what was best for her.

In despair Mary had sought out Diane. Diane received her with the utmost affection.

'My dearest child,' said the King's mistress, 'there are matters which you are too young to understand. Lady Fleming has to leave Court, and Queen

Catherine would deeply resent any interference in this matter of choosing your governess. She has your well-being at heart. You may trust her to do what is best for you.'

Mary sensed that neither the King nor Diane were really giving her their attention, and she realized suddenly how impotent she was. They had petted her because it had been easy to pet her, and she had acquired an opinion of herself which was too exalted. She was but a child here as she had been in Scotland; she was at the mercy of the grown-up world, and the love which these charming people had given her was only a minute part of their lives.

She was thinking of these things as she advanced to greet the Queen and Madame de Paroy.

'We wish you to smile for Madame de Paroy,' said Catherine.

But Mary would not or could not smile. Her lips froze; she could only glower at the ugly figure of the new governess. Catherine took Mary's ear and pinched it hard. She smiled as she did so.

'The Queen of Scotland has much to learn, Madame de Paroy,' said the Queen.

Mary wanted to scream because of the pain in her ear. She felt all alone. The King and Diane were riding away from her. They were leaving her to the mercy of these women.

'I have found it necessary,' went on Catherine, 'to chastise my own sons, knowing that one day they may be Kings of France. Kings . . . Queens . . . all have to learn their lessons, and when pride grows to abnormal proportions it can best be subdued with a stick. There is nothing like a stick applied to the body to drive away a false sense of superiority. Do you agree with me, Madame de Paroy?'

'I do indeed, Your Majesty.'

'Now,' said Catherine, 'a smile of welcome for your new governess.'

Mary opened her lips showing her pretty teeth. She had to free her ear or cry out with the pain.

'H'm' said Catherine, 'not a very bright smile. But it will suffice for the present.'

Mary was repeating under her breath: 'Vulgar . . . beast . . . tradesman's daughter . . . no true Queen . . . I hate you.'

She would say it aloud when she was alone with her Maries.

She was looking at the Queen and the new governess through a haze of tears. Catherine was well satisfied. The Queen of Scotland had just begun to learn what it meant to pit her puny strength against that of the Queen of France.

Chapter Three

In the vast room at Saint-Germain the children of the royal household were assembled as was their custom at this hour.

In a window seat sat Mary–one of the eldest and certainly the most beautiful. She was holding court as she loved to do. Monsieur du Bellay was reading one of his poems, and those who gathered about her–among them

Ronsard and Maison-Fleur, those great Court poets–knew that it had been written for her.

> *'Contentez vous, mes yeux,*
> *Vous ne verrez jamais une chose pareille.'*

Ronsard and du Bellay had been the leaders of that coterie which called itself the *Pleïade* after a group of seven ancient Greek poets, and had been chosen by Marguerite, the King's sister, to be literary tutors of the royal children and those young people who shared the nursery. Their favourite pupil was Mary, not only on account of her beauty which inspired them to lyrical verse, but because of her response to their own work and of that literary talent which she herself possessed.

All eyes were on her now. François the Dauphin openly admired her, and he was anxious that all should remember she was to be his bride. His brother Charles, though only seven years old, was already one of Mary's admirers. There was also Henri de Montmorency, the second son of Anne, the great Constable, and he could not take his eyes from her face.

Mary was content at such times. She needed such adulation. The last six years of her life had not been easy; Madame de Paroy was still with her and had turned out to be all that Mary feared. Mean-spirited, she lost no time in reporting the least misdemeanour, and she and the Queen never allowed the smallest error to go unpunished. Mary had been made to understand that she was as subject to discipline as any of the other children. She had been chastised as they had; but she had suffered far more from the loss of her dignity than from any physical pain.

In vain had she tried to rid herself of the woman. She had implored her mother to appoint a new governess; her uncle, the Cardinal, realizing the woman to be a spy of the Queen of France, had added his pleas to Mary's, but in this matter Catherine stood firm, and neither the King nor Diane cared to interfere in a situation which had come about through the indiscretion of the King.

Lady Fleming had never returned to France, although her son remained to be brought up as a royal child; he was often in the nurseries, a bright, intelligent boy who quickly won his father's affection. But Janet had had to take up her residence in Scotland.

So, at such times as this one when she could escape from the supervision of Madame de Paroy, Mary was happy, with François her constant companion and Charles showing his affection for her. She wished that Charles were not so wild and would grow out of those unaccountable rages of his. When they were on him he would suddenly kick walls, his dogs or his servants, whichever happened to be at hand. It was disconcerting. But she loved both brothers with a deep protective love. That did not mean that she was not becoming increasingly aware of the ardent looks sent in her direction by young Henri de Montmorency.

There were so many people at the Court to tell her how lovely she was. Monsieur Brantôme, the writer, assured her that her beauty radiated like the sun in the noonday sky. Her uncle, François, Duc de Guise, the great soldier and idol of Paris, exclaimed when he saw her: 'By the saints! You are the fairest creature in France!' Uncle Charles, the Cardinal of Lorraine, held her face in his beautiful scented hands and looked long into her eyes declaring: 'Your beauty will charm all France!' The King himself whispered to her that she was the loveliest of his daughters; and it seemed that all men were ready to sing the praises of Mary Stuart. Lately, devoted as she was to her dear François, she had begun to wish that he looked a little more like Henri de Montmorency.

There were now thirty children in the royal nurseries, for many of the sons and daughters of noble houses were being brought up there. It was a world in itself consisting of ten chamberlains, nine cellarers, thirty-seven pages and twenty-eight *valets de chambres*, besides doctors, surgeons, apothecaries and barbers. The amount of food consumed by this community each day was prodigious. Twenty-three dozen loaves were baked each morning and eaten before nightfall; eight sheep, four calves, twenty capons as well as pigeons, pullets, hares and other delicacies went the same way. The Dauphin and Mary had in addition their separate establishments with a further retinue of servants, but much of their time was spent in these main apartments.

The family of royal children had grown considerably since Mary had first come to France. These children were scattered about the room now.

Twelve-year-old Elisabeth and her sister Claude who was slightly younger were in Mary's group. Poor little Louis had died seven years ago and Charles was now the boy next in age to François. There was young Henri, who had been christened Edouard Alexandre but was always called Henri by his mother. He had just passed his sixth birthday and was extraordinarily handsome, with dark flashing eyes and the features of his mother's Italian ancestors. He was the only one of the children whom Queen Catherine spoilt, and consequently he was very vain. Mary watched him displaying the ear-rings he was wearing.

There was little Marguerite, whom Charles had nicknamed Margot, precocious and vivacious and looking older than her five years; and lastly Hercule, the baby, a pretty, chubby boy of three.

Pierre de Ronsard was sitting beside her; he saw that her attention was wandering as she surveyed the children.

'Since Monsieur du Bellay's verses do not interest Your Majesty, may I read some of mine?' he asked.

Mary held up her hand, laughing. 'No more verses just now please. Let us talk of you. Tell us of your early life and how, with your friends, you formed that group of poets called the *Pleïade*.'

They gathered round while Ronsard told, in his clever and amusing way, of the Court of Scotland whither he had gone long before the birth of Mary, when her father's first wife had arrived from France.

He told how one day he had discovered a gentleman of the Court reading a small volume, how he had taken it, and once he had experienced the magic of those pages he had known that his life would be barren if it were not devoted to literature. He told of Cassandre, the woman he had loved; he quoted the sonnets he had written to her. He went on to speak of his life in the house of Jean Antoine Baïf where there was great poverty but greater love of literature.

'We were worshippers in the temple of literature. It mattered not that we were cold and hungry. It mattered not that we shared one candle between us. We studied Greek and Latin, and literature was food and drink to us–our need and our pleasure. Then we discussed our great desire to make France the centre of learning. We would enrich France; we would make her fertile. Literature was the gentle rain and the hot sun which would ripen the seed and give us a rich harvest. So we formed the *Pleïade*–seven of us–and with myself, du Bellay and Baïf as the leaders, the *Pleïade* was to shine from the heavens and light all France.'

Henri de Montmorency had moved closer to Mary.

His passionate eyes looked into hers.

'Would it were possible to speak with you alone!' he whispered.

She did meet him alone. She had wandered through the gardens of Fontainebleau, through the great courtyard and past the fountains, and had made her way to the walled garden.

Then she saw Henri de Montmorency approaching her. He was the second son of the great Constable of France whom the King loved and who, to his great grief, had been captured by the Imperial troops at the defeat of Saint Quentin and now lay a prisoner of Philip of Spain. How handsome he was, this Henri; he was so elegant in satin and velvet, the colours of which–pink and green–blended so perfectly. The jewels he wore had been carefully chosen. Henri de Montmorency–one of the most favoured young men of the Court because his father had been, and doubtless would be again, one of the most powerful–was a leader of fashion and good taste.

'Your Majesty!' He took Mary's hand and raised it to his lips. The eyes he lifted to hers were ardent.

She had no wish for such love as she believed was customary throughout the palaces of Fontainebleau, Blois, Amboise, Chambord, or anywhere the Court happened to be. The love which François the Dauphin had for her was the love she wished for. She enjoyed the love of the poets–idealistic and remote; she enjoyed the ardent admiration of Charles. There was, also, the strange and somewhat mystic love which her uncle, the Cardinal of Lorraine, bore her. Those caressing hands which seemed to imply so much, those queer searching looks, those lingering kisses, that spiritual love as he had described it, disturbed her; it frightened her too, but she was child enough to enjoy being a little frightened. She was always afraid, when she was with the Cardinal, that his love for her would change and become something wild and horrible; she fancied that he too was conscious that it might, and that he took a delight in holding his passion on a leash which he would, from time to time, slacken so that it came near to her and yet did not quite reach her. She could not imagine what would happen if it did, but something within her told her that it never would because the Cardinal did not wish it; and in all things the Cardinal's will was hers.

All these loves were different from the love of ordinary mortals; pawing, kissing, giggling and scuffling she would not have. She was a Queen and would be treated as such.

Yet here was Henri de Montmorency, beautiful as she herself was beautiful, young as she herself was young, and offering yet another sort of love, a charming and romantic idyll.

'I saw you enter the garden,' he said breathlessly. 'I could not resist following you.'

'We should not be here alone, Monsieur de Montmorency.'

'I must see you alone sometimes. Sometimes we must do that which is forbidden. Does not Your Majesty agree?'

'It is wrong to do that which is forbidden.'

'Can we be sure of that? I am happier now than I have been since I first set eyes on you.'

'But I do not think you should speak thus to me, Monsieur de Montmorency.'

'Forgive me. I speak thus out of desperation. I adore you. I must let you know of my feelings. Many love you, but none could do so with more passion, with more devotion and more hopelessness than your devoted servant Henri de Montmorency.'

He took her hands and kissed them with passion. She tried to withdraw them for she was conscious of emotion never before experienced, and she was afraid. She could not help comparing him with François! she thought in dismay.

'You are not indifferent to me!' cried Henri.

'We should return to the palace,' said Mary uneasily.

'Just a few more moments, I beg of you. I love you and I am wretched because shortly I must see you married to the Dauphin.'

'That must not make you miserable. It is my destiny, and doubtless you have yours.'

'My father, when he returns, will seek to marry me with the granddaughter of Madame de Valentinois. Oh, how wretched is this life! We are counters to be moved this way and that, and our loves and desires go for naught. You will be married to the Dauphin. Your destiny is to be Queen of France and I . . . mine is a lesser one, but I am to ally my house with that of the King's mistress. I wish we could run away from France . . . to some unknown island far away from here . . . Would you were not a Queen! Would I were not the son of my father! If you were a peasant girl and I a poor fisherman, how much happier we might be!'

Mary could not imagine herself stripped of her royalty. She would never forget that she was a Queen, she believed. But she was moved by his words and the eager devotion she saw in his eyes.

He went on bitterly: 'My father has five sons and seven daughters and all must be used to favour the fortunes of our house. My elder brother loved a girl–deeply he loved her. He thought he would die of love, and for a long time he stood out against our father's wishes. But now you see he is married to the King's bastard daughter, Diane of France, and our house is made greater by alliance with the royal one. Now if I marry the granddaughter of Madame de Valentinois, I shall strengthen the link. Not only shall we be allied to the royal house but with that of the King's mistress. What strength will be ours! What greatness! And all brought about because we have been moved as counters into the right squares on the board. They are flesh and blood, those counters; they cry out in anguish; but that is unimportant. All that matters is that our house grows great.'

'What are you saying, Monsieur de Montmorency?'

'That I would run away with you . . . far away . . . where all are merely men and women and there is no policy to be served, no great house that is of more moment than our happiness. Dearest Mary, if only we could run away together, far away from the kingdom of France where they will make you a Queen, far away from that land where you are already a Queen. Mary, did you know that in your country many of the nobles have signed the Solemn League and Covenant to forsake and renounce what they call the Congregation of Satan? That means they follow the new religion; they have cut themselves off from Rome. Yours will soon be a land of heretics. Oh, Mary, I see trouble there for you. You . . . a good Catholic . . . and Queen of a heretic land!'

'I know nothing of this,' she said.

'Then I should not have spoken of it.'

'I made my mother Regent of Scotland. I signed the documents some years ago.'

'Oh Mary, they tell you what to sign and what not to sign. They tell you to marry and you marry. Oh dearest and most beautiful, let us dream just for a moment of the impossible. Do you love me . . . a little?'

She was excited by his charm and the wild words he spoke. She was happy in this scented garden. But she knew she should not listen to him and that she could never be happy if she were disloyal to François. She turned away frowning.

'I see,' he said bitterly, 'that they have moulded you as they wished. You will be their docile Queen. You will sign the documents they put before you; you will sign away your life's happiness when they ask it.'

'When I am the wife of François,' she said angrily, 'I shall be assured of a lifetime's happiness, Monsieur.'

She turned to leave him and as she did so she saw that two people had entered the garden. The rich red robes of the Cardinal of Lorraine were brilliant beside the more sombre garments of Queen Catherine.

Mary heard the sudden burst of laughter which she had grown to hate over the years. Catherine's amusement was, she believed, invariably provoked at someone else's discomfiture.

'Ah, Cardinal, our birds are trapped,' the Queen was saying. 'And what pleasant-looking birds, eh? We might say 'birds of paradise'. They look startled, do they not? As though they were about to be seized by the hawk.'

'Or by the serpent, Madame,' said the Cardinal.

'Poor creatures! What hope of escape would they have between the two!'

'Very little, Madame. Very little.'

Mary and Montmorency had hurried forward to pay their respects, first to the Queen, then to the Cardinal.

The Queen said: 'So you two charming people are taking the air. I marvel, Monsieur de Montmorency, that you do not do so in the company of another young lady . . . not the Queen of Scotland. And I should have expected to see my son with her Scottish Majesty.'

'We met by chance, Madame,' said Mary quickly, but the colour rose to her cheeks.

The Cardinal was looking at her quizzically. Because he had made her aware of those occasions when she caused him displeasure, she knew now that he was far from pleased at discovering her thus.

As for the Queen, she was delighted. Mary sometimes thought that the Queen did not wish her to marry the Dauphin, and that she would be very pleased if Mary had been seriously attracted by Montmorency.

The Cardinal said: 'Her Majesty and I, as you no doubt did, found the afternoon too pleasant to be spent with walls about us.'

Before Mary could answer, Catherine said: 'The Queen of Scots appears to be in a fever.' Her long slender fingers touched Mary's cheek. 'You are over-heated, my dear.'

'I have a headache. I was about to return to the cool of the palace.'

'Ah yes, the cool of the palace. That is the place for you. The bed, eh . . . with the curtains drawn, and no one to disturb you–that is the best remedy for the sort of fever which possesses your Scottish Majesty.'

Hating the insinuation contained in the Queen's words, conscious of the discomfort of Henri de Montmorency and the displeasure of the Cardinal, Mary said impulsively: 'Your Majesty has vast knowledge of such things. It is due to your keen observation of the conditions of others, rather than your experience of such maladies. But I dare submit you are mistaken on this occasion. It is a slight headache from the heat of the sun.'

The white hand, laden with rings, came down heavily on Mary's shoulder. Mary winced under her grip.

'I am rarely mistaken,' said Catherine. 'You are right when you speak of the keenness of my observation. Little can be hid from me. Now, Monsieur de Montmorency will escort you to the palace.' Catherine released Mary's shoulder. 'And do not forget my remedy. Your bed . . . the curtains drawn . . . the door locked to keep out your women. That is what you need. Go along . . . now. The Cardinal and I will continue our walk in the sunshine.'

Mary curtsied, Montmorency bowed, and the two walked back to the palace. As soon as possible Mary took leave of him and went to her apartments.

Flem and Beaton hurried to her anxiously, but she waved them aside. She had a headache; she would rest and she did not wish to be disturbed.

The curtains about Mary's bed were silently withdrawn. Mary opened her eyes and saw, standing by the bed, the scarlet-clad figure of the Cardinal. She smelt the perfume of musk which accompanied him, and saw the glittering emeralds and rubies on his folded hands.

'Monsieur?' she cried starting up.

'Nay, do not rise, my child,' he said; he sat on the bed and laid a hand on her hot forehead.

She lay back on her pillows.

'How lovely you are!' he murmured. 'You are very beautiful, my dearest. But you are distressed now.'

'I . . . I came here to rest.'

'On the advice of Her Majesty!'

'I did not expect anyone would come in.'

'You would not have your guardian uncle kept out?'

'No . . . no . . . but . . .'

'Rest easily, my dear child. There is no need to be afraid. The Queen was right to suggest you should return to the palace. It is not good for one of your purity and budding beauty to be seen in intimate conversation with a young man of Montmorency's reputation.'

'His . . . reputation!'

'Ah! You are startled. I see that you have more regard for this young man than I believed.'

'I did not know he had an evil reputation.'

'All young men have evil reputations.'

'That, Uncle, is surely not true.'

'Or they would,' went on the Cardinal, smiling, 'if all their deeds and all their thoughts were known. They sport their jewels to show their worldly riches. What if they should wear their experiences to show their worldly wisdom, eh? Then our simple maidens might not so easily become their victims . . . their light-o'-loves to be discussed and dissected for their companions' pleasure. Ah, you should hear the bawdy talk of some of these gallants when they are with others of their kind. You would be horrified. It is quite different from the sweet words which they employ as the prelude to seduction.'

'I will not be included among those simple maidens!'

'Indeed you shall not.' He slipped his arm under her and leaning forward, gazed into her face. He let his lips linger on her throat, and she felt her heart leap and pound. She could not move and it was as though she were bound by invisible cords. In his eyes there was a flame, in his arms a subtle pressure. Now he had unleashed this strange emotion which he had created; now it was about to envelop her. She was terrified, yet fascinated.

He was speaking softly. 'Nay, you are no simple maiden, my dearest, my other self. My Mary, I love you as I have never loved anyone. Together we will explore the world of the spirit. You and I shall be as one, Mary, and together we will rule France.'

'I do not understand you. . . .'

'You cannot expect to yet, but one day you will understand all that you are to me, and how I have preserved you and kept you sweet and pure.'

His mood had changed. The emotions were subdued. He sat up. He was smiling and his eyes were extraordinarily brilliant in his pale face.

'Mary,' he said, 'in your bleak and savage country, I have heard, the men of the Border ravish towns and hamlets. They take the cattle; they take the women. And what do you think they do with these women? They rape them, Mary . . . in the village streets . . . on the village greens. They mock them. They insult and humiliate them in a hundred ways you cannot even imagine. That is your wild country; that is Scotland. Here we are supposed to be a civilized people. But are we? Some of those bejewelled gallants with their pretty looks and their flowery speeches, their odes to your beauty–they are very like your Borderers beneath their exquisite garments and their courtly manners. The Borderer rapes; our gallant seduces. The Borderer takes a woman as he would an apple; he discusses the flavour while he tastes. Our gallants pluck their apples in scented orchards; all is apparently decorous. But afterwards, they discuss the flavour one with another. That is the difference between the Borderers of Scotland and our gallants. One, you might say, is at least candidly licentious; the other, under the cloak of gallantry, is full of deceit.'

'Why . . . why do you tell me this?'

'Because, *ma mignonne*, you are on the verge of womanhood. It is time you were honourably married. Holy Mother of God, your uncle François would run the young Montmorency through with his sword if he knew how he had insulted you in the gardens this day.'

'He did not insult me, Uncle. He was most chivalrous.'

'The first steps towards seduction, my dearest . . . the first indication that the scented couch is prepared. Even now we do not know that he will not boast of his success to his friends.'

'He dare not! He has nothing of which to boast.'

'The braggart will do very well on very little. I shall have him warned. As for you, my dearest, you will not be seen in his company alone again. Do not let your manner change. Be friendly with him as you are with others. Only remember that he is another such as your Border raiders; remember that he is doing his utmost to lead you to seduction. Remember that he will note every weakness . . . any attention you may pay to his words. He will boast to his friends of an easy conquest, and we shall have them all trying to emulate him.'

Mary covered her burning cheeks with her hands.

'Please . . . Uncle . . . stop. I cannot bear such thoughts. It was nothing . . . nothing.'

The Cardinal kissed her forehead.

'My darling, I know it was nothing. Of course, it was nothing. My pure, sweet Mary, who shall remain pure and sweet for the heir of France.' He put his arm about her and held her against him. 'If there should be one, other than the heir of France, it shall not be the son of the Constable!'

She caught her breath, for his lips were on hers. It was one of those moments when she sensed danger close. But almost immediately he had stood up and was smiling down on her.

'Rest, my beloved,' he said. 'Rest and think on what I have told you.'

She lay still after he had gone, trying to shut out the thoughts which the Cardinal had aroused in her. She could not. She could no longer picture Henri de Montmorency as he had seemed to her that day in the gardens; he was a different person, laughing and leering, calling to others to come and see how he had humiliated the Queen of Scots.

She buried her face in her pillows trying in vain to shut out those pictures.

The Cardinal, deeply disturbed, sought out his brother.

'We must hurry on the marriage,' he said. 'I am sure it is imperative that we should do so.'

The Duke looked grave. 'With Mary so young and the Dauphin even younger . . .'

'There are two reasons which make it necessary for us to press the King until this marriage is accomplished. I have it from the Dauphin's doctor that his health is failing fast. What if he were to die before Mary has married him?'

'Disaster!' cried the Duke. 'Unless we could secure young Charles for her.'

'He's nearly ten years younger, and it will be long before he is marriageable. No! Mary must be Dauphine of France before the year is out. I have another reason, brother. I saw her walking in the gardens with the son of our enemy.'

'That remark,' said François cynically, 'might indicate the son of almost any man at Court. As our powers grow, so do our enemies. To which one do you refer?'

'Montmorency. The Queen was with me and I have an idea that she was delighted to see those two together. I fancy she tried to make more of the affair than was justified. She was quite coarse, and talked of a bed as the best place to cool Mary's fever.'

'You alarm me, brother.'

'I mean to. There is reason for alarm. You are the hero of Paris, of all France. You have given back Calais to the King; you bear the mark of heroism on your cheek. The people look at the scar you bear there and cry: '*Vive le Balafré!*' At this moment you could demand the marriage, and the King would find it hard to refuse you. Take my advice, brother. This is our moment. We should not let it pass.'

The Duke nodded thoughtfully. 'I am sure you are right,' he said.

The King and Queen received the Duke.

Françoise de Guise, the man of action, did not waste time. He came straight to the point.

'Your Majesties, I have a request to make, and I trust you will give me your gracious attention.'

'It is yours, cousin,' the King assured him.

'It is many years since my niece came to France,' said the Duke, 'and it is touching to see the love she and the Dauphin bear towards each other. I know that both these children long for marriage, and my opinion is that it should take place as soon as possible. I am hoping that Your Majesties are of the same opinion.'

The King said: 'I think of them as children. It seems only yesterday that I went to the nurseries and found the little Stuart there with François. What a beautiful child! I said then that I had never seen one more perfect, and it holds to-day.'

'It is a matter of deep gratification to our House,' said the Duke, 'that one of our daughters should so please Your Majesty. I venture to say that Mary Stuart will make a charming and popular Dauphine.'

Catherine glanced at her husband and murmured: 'All you say is true, Monsieur de Guise. The little Stuart is charming. It seems that she only has to smile in order to turn all Frenchmen's heads. She will indeed be a beautiful Dauphine . . . when the time comes.'

'That time is now,' said the Duke, with that arrogance which was second nature to him.

The King resented his tone, and the Queen lowered her eyes that neither of the men should see that she was pleased by the King's resentment.

She said quickly: 'In my opinion – which I beg Your Majesty and you, Monsieur de Guise to correct, if it seems wrong to you – these are but two children . . . two delightful children whom everyone loves and wishes the greatest happiness in the world. I know that to plunge two young children into marriage can be alarming for them. It might even injure that pretty comradeship which delights us all.' She was looking at the King appealingly; she knew she had turned his thoughts back to their own marriage all those years ago when he was a boy, of much the same age as François was now, with a girl beside him, a quiet, plain Italian girl . . . Catherine herself . . . whom he had never been able to love.

The King's lips came tightly together; then he said: 'I agree with the Queen. As yet they are too young. Let them wait a year or so.'

In exasperation the Duke began: 'Sire, I am of the opinion that these two are ripe for marriage . . .'

The King interrupted coldly: 'Monsieur de Guise, your opinion can be of little moment if, in this matter of our children's marriage, it differs from that of the Queen and myself.'

The Duke was dismissed. He was furious. He had no alternative but to bow and retire, leaving this matter of the marriage as unsettled now as it had been before he had spoken.

But the Cardinal and the Duke were not the men to let important matters slide. The Cardinal was quite sure that at all costs the delay must be ended.

He walked with the King in the gardens. He was more subtle than his brother. He talked first of the Protestant party in Scotland, of those lairds who were in league with John Knox and were turning his little niece's realm from the Catholic faith. The King, as an ardent Catholic, could well see the danger that lay in that.

'Your Majesty knows that my niece's bastard brother, Lord James Stuart, is one of these men, and with him are the most powerful men in Scotland – Glencairn, Morton, Lorn, Erskine, Argyle. It is open war against the true faith in Scotland. A sad state of affairs, Your Majesty.'

The King agreed that it was so.

'We shall have them repudiating Mary Stuart next and setting the bastard over them. That, no doubt, is his plan.'

'They'll never allow a bastard to rule them.'

'Who knows what the fanatic Knox will lead them to! They might well say, better a baseborn Protestant than a true Catholic Queen.'

Henri said: 'It shall never happen. We'll send armies to subdue them.'

'Sire, since Saint Quentin we are not as strong as we were. If you will forgive the boldness, may I suggest that these barbarians could be made to respect my niece more if her status were raised. If she were not merely a Queen of Scotland but also a Dauphine of France they would think twice about flouting her in favour of the bastard.'

'The Queen and I, as I told your brother, consider that as yet Mary and François are too young.'

'The Queen and Your Majesty are as usual right. Ah . . . these little kings-to-be . . . these queens! Sometimes they must be married before their time. How fortunate it is that our Dauphin is affianced to one whom he has loved almost from her cradle. It is a fate, Sire, which befalls few of any royal house.'

'That's true, Cardinal. I would wish to see them married but I am loth to spoil that happy and tender comradeship which warms my heart every time I see them together.'

'Your Majesty is not only their devoted King; he is their beloved father.'

'That is how I would have it, Cardinal.'

'And that is how they would have it, I know. I hope Your Majesty will consider it wise to have the children married before you need the help of Scotland next year against the English . . . as you assuredly will.'

The King was silent. What the Cardinal said was true. He himself was a soldier of some ability and he knew that he might shortly need the help of Scotland. The marriage would make sure of that.

He continued silent and the Cardinal went on: 'Your Majesty, I have drafted an agreement which, if signed, would bring great good to France. It is premature, I know, and could not, of course, be signed by Mary Stuart until the marriage is certain; but thinking of the good of our country, and the depression we felt after Saint Quentin . . .'

'What is this agreement?' asked the King.

'If she could be induced to sign it, it would give her kingdom to the crown of France should she die without heirs; she would also transfer her rights to the crown of England to Your Majesty, or your successors, until a million gold crowns had been paid to France as an indemnity for those monies which France had paid out for the defence of Scotland.'

The King gasped. 'But . . . how can she sign such a document? She has no power to do so without the consent of the Parliament and the Regent.'

'She is the Queen of Scotland. Her signature on the document would make it valid.'

'Would she sign such a document? Poor child, would she understand what she was doing?'

'I will explain it to her.'

The King was uneasy yet desperately tempted. He must be a King first now, and father second. Scotland was an unruly country; it was an unhappy, a tortured country; how much happier it would be, completely depending on France!

'She would sign,' said the Cardinal softly. 'She would be only too happy to give you these rights. She loves you. You are her beloved father. She would be only too happy to repay something of all you have done for her.'

The King nodded. The crown of Scotland was being offered to him and his heirs. He could not turn away from it. The temptation was too great.

'I am sure,' said the smooth-voiced Cardinal, 'that when she knows she is to be in very truth your daughter, gladly will she put her name to the documents which I shall place before her.'

'I think,' said the King, 'that as they love each other and as they have known each other so long, it would please them to know that they are to be married.'

'Soon,' added the Cardinal. 'I will break this wonderful news to my niece. I am impatient to witness her joy.'

'And I will break the news to my son. I know he will be the happiest boy in Fontainebleau this day.'

So the King smothered his conscience; the Cardinal–having none–was spared such pains.

The Cardinal came to conduct his niece to that chamber wherein the King was waiting for them with Cardinal de Sens, who was the Keeper of the Seals of France, in attendance.

The Cardinal had explained to Mary that this was merely a formality. all she need do was sign her name.

'What paper is it, Uncle?' she asked. 'Should I not read it before I sign? You have always said that I should read everything before signing.'

'There is no need to tire yourself. It is such a bore–this language of the lawyers. I can tell you all you want to know. It is a little matter concerning Scotland's debt to the King. You see, His Majesty and the French have given much money for the defence of Scotland, and you, as the Queen of that land, are going to sign this paper promising that you will arrange that, when Scotland is able to do so, the King is repaid.'

'That is what I would wish,' said Mary.

'Well, that is all it is.'

'But it seems such a solemn occasion for such a small thing, does it not?'

'Remember you are a Queen, my child, and now that you are growing up there will be many occasions when some formality, which may seem unnecessary to you, will have to be carried out.'

Mary smiled and allowed the Cardinal to lead her to that chamber in Fontainebleau, and there, with the April sunshine streaming through the windows, put her signature to the documents which gave away that which she had no right to give, and which, although she was a girl not yet sixteen years of age and innocent of wrong-doing, brought great dishonour to her name.

Mary was being dressed for her wedding. About her were her four Maries and several attendants who were helping, their eyes bright with admiration and excitement.

Now she stood in her bridal dress; it was so heavy that she could scarcely stand, for its white damask was covered in jewels. Her royal mantle and train of bluish grey velvet was decorated with pearls; her golden crown was studded with pearls and diamonds, sapphires and rubies, and the centre piece was a hanging carbuncle which alone was worth five hundred thousand crowns.

'You are the most beautiful bride there has ever been!' cried Flem; and the others agreed.

Mary laughed gleefully as she touched the priceless necklace she was wearing. The people in the streets would cheer her as she went from the palace of the Archbishop of Paris–where she, with the royal family, had spent the night–to the Cathedral of Notre Dame. They loved her because she was their charming *Reinette*, and her marriage to the Dauphin gave them such a show as they had never witnessed before.

François was happy too. He was not very nervous, he had told her, although he would have been terrified if he had had to marry anyone else. The thought of Charles worried Mary a little. He was so sullen; he seemed almost murderous and in deadly earnest when he declared he longed to marry her.

It was a pity that the Commissioners from Scotland had come to see her married, for they reminded her that she was Queen of a kingdom very different from this one. Their odd speech was so strange to her, though she supposed she herself had once spoken it. Their clothes were rough and lacking in elegance; they were suspicious of the French, and it had to be admitted that the French did laugh at them and mock them when they were not present. Mary was a little ashamed of her rough countrymen.

She was worried too about her half-brother, Lord James, who had come with them. He had changed since she last saw him; outwardly he was as friendly as ever, but he seemed to be watching her furtively all the time; and she knew that James was among those covenanters who were in league with John Knox.

She was not to trust her brother, the Cardinal had warned her. She was to tell no one of the documents she had signed a short while ago. They were of no great importance, of course, but the Cardinal wished them not to be mentioned.

Mary had for years obeyed the Cardinal without question and she did so now.

But all her uneasiness vanished as she walked along the gallery which had been set up between the palace of the Archbishop of Paris and the Cathedral of Notre Dame.

The King–magnificently jewelled–held Mary's right hand as they walked along the gallery, while the Duke of Lorraine held her left. Mary's train was borne by young ladies who could scarcely lift it, so heavy was it with the jewels which adorned it. Behind them came Catherine the Queen and Jeanne the Queen of Navarre, followed by the ladies of the Court in order of precedence.

The King of Navarre walked with the Dauphin, and behind them came the two Princes–Charles, still glowering and sullen, and Edouard Alexandre full of gaiety because he had never worn such jewels as he wore that day.

At the door of the Cathedral the procession halted and Mary was brought to stand beside the Dauphin.

Henri Deux took a ring from his finger and gave it to the Cardinal of Bourbon who was waiting to receive it, and there, under the blue sky, so that the people of Paris might witness the marriage ceremony, Mary Queen of

Scots was married to François, Dauphin of France.

She smiled at her bridegroom reassuringly, not forgetting even at that moment that he might be in need of comfort. She knew that the crowds and the shouting would make his head ache. She knew that his jewelled garments would weigh him down and make him very tired.

He held her hand tightly and looked at her continually as though to reassure himself that the beautiful vision, arrayed in such glorious apparel, was after all his beloved Mary.

When the ceremony was over they returned to the Archbishop's palace and sat down to the banquet which had been prepared for them in the grand hall. Mary ate ravenously, for she was very hungry; she urged François to eat, and he did so, saying that although there were so many people about them and the glitter of jewels was almost blinding, and two gentlemen stood behind Mary all the time they ate, holding the crown royal over her head, they were together; they loved each other and everything was the same except that they were married.

Afterwards there was dancing. Mary delighted to dance and was enchanted when the King chose her as his partner. Her hand rested in his as they turned slowly in the stately *pavanne*.

'So you are happy?' asked the King.

'Yes dearest Papa.'

'Then I am happy too. No one in Paris who saw you this day will ever forget you.'

'I shall never forget this day.'

'You and François should be happy. You do not yet know how fortunate you are.'

Mary had caught sight of François who was dancing with his mother. He looked very uneasy. She wished that she could have gone to him, to tell him not to be nervous. The King followed her gaze.

'You will always take care of him, will you not, Mary?' he said very seriously.

'Always, Papa.'

'He will need your care, my dear, and I know I can trust you to give it to him. The saints bless you and keep you.'

"I am happy to be the Dauphine, Papa, but I hope I shall never be Queen of France, for I could not be that while you live–so I would wish never to be.'

'My dear child,' he said, 'I love you very much.'

By four o'clock in the afternoon the ball at the episcopal palace was over, but the celebrations were to continue. The whole company crossed the Seine to the Palais de Justice. Mary was carried in a litter of gold and silver, and the people shouted to her as she passed. 'Long live the Queen-Dauphine!' they cried. And to each other: 'But she is beautiful. What a contrast to the Italian woman!' Catherine did not seem to care what they said of her. She accepted humiliations from the Parisians as she did from her husband, with a resigned and almost patient smile.

How the people cheered the King when he rode by on his magnificently caparisoned war-horse! But the loudest cheers of all, some noticed, were for the man dressed in frosted cloth of gold, ablaze with gems, the man of action whom no amount of fine clothes or jewels could disguise. They knew him at once; his tall figure attracted immediate attention as did the scar on his cheek. '*Vive le Balafré!* Long life to the great Duke of Guise!' shouted the crowds. He knew how to win the hearts of the people. They did not forget that, during the celebrations when the mob had struggled to see the youthful pair but were prevented from doing so by the fine folk on the dais, he had ordered those fine folk to stand aside that the people's view might not be obstructed. 'God bless the Duke! God bless the hero of Metz and the saviour of Calais!'

And so the procession of litters, coaches and prancing horses came to the great hall of the Palais de Justice where a grand supper was waiting, to be followed by such a ball, such masques and mummeries, games and pastimes as were rarely seen even at the Court of France. With relish Mary ate of the dishes which were set before her. This was the happiest day of her life, she told François. He smiled and said that he was happy to be her husband but he would be happier still when they could be alone together.

He laughed with Mary at the children who, led by young Henri de Guise, rode in on hobby horses; each horse–and there were twenty-five of them–was pulled across the hall by a lackey, but the horses were so beautifully decorated with trappings of cloth of gold and silver that they looked more beautiful than real horses. The Princes, looking very charming in their suits of cloth of gold, came to a halt before the bridal pair and sang in praise of marriage and this royal marriage in particular.

Only the Scottish guests were ill at ease. It was clear that they thought the laughter, the dancing, the lavish display of jewels, the fulsome compliments and the soft looks exchanged between the men and women a strange mode of behaviour. They were unable to join in the gaiety and stood apart about Lord James, as though to be ready to protect themselves if the need arose, watching the strange antics of the French through sullen and suspicious eyes.

The peak of the evening was reached with the appearance of the galleons which glided over the floor of the ballroom, the silver gauze sails filled by an artificial breeze; and as the floor cloth had been painted to represent waves, the effect had a certain realism. Lackeys led the ships to the table at which the royal ladies sat, and in the first of these ships the King was disclosed seated on the deck in a chair of state beside which was an empty chair. The King reached for Mary's hand and helped her on to the deck that she might sit beside him. In the next ship was the Dauphin who had been warned he must select his mother to sit beside him; the Prince of Condé, in the next, chose the duchess of Guise; the Duke of Lorraine followed and chose the Princess Claude; the King of Navarre chose his own wife; and the ships went gracefully down the ballroom over the painted floor cloth to the delight of all who saw them, and the immense pride of the Duke of Guise who had organized the pageantry.

Later Mary and François sat side by side listening to the poems of Ronsard and du Bellay; and all those poems–some set to music–were in praise of the King of France and the newly married pair and of the joy this union of the two countries would bring to them.

'Mary,' whispered François wearily, 'will it never end?'

She pressed his hand and looked down into his pale face. Poor little bridegroom! He was so tired. He was longing for it to be over, but the bride was wishing it could last for the rest of her life.

They lay together in the marriage bed divested of their glittering wedding garments.

François was holding her hand tightly. 'I should be so afraid, Mary, if it were anyone but you.'

'So should I,' said Mary, 'if it were anyone but you.'

The Dauphine laughed happily. Mary knew just how to set him at ease. If he was nervous, so was she. How lucky he was to have her for his wife!

'I shall grow stronger, Mary,' he said. 'I'll be like the Duke, your uncle. I will have all Paris shouting for me, and a scar on my cheek. I'll be like my father, quiet and strong. Oh, Mary, how lucky *you* are! You don't have to be like anybody but yourself.'

'Nor do you, François,' she said.

'Mary, I love you so.'

'I love you too, François.'

'Whatever we have to do . . . it will be all right, won't it?'

'Yes, François. But don't worry. Go to sleep now.'

She could see that he was almost asleep. His lids were pressing down over his eyes. He nestled closer to her and she held him in her arms protectively.

'I am so glad, Mary,' he murmured, 'so glad to be married to you.'

Then he fell asleep.

Chapter Four

The king had decreed that the honeymoon should be spent in the lovely old chateau, built by his father François Premier, at Villers-Cotterets. So to this chateau went François and Mary, accompanied by only a few of their attendants, that they might enjoy each other's company in quiet seclusion.

These were the happiest weeks of François' life. The days seemed long and full of sunshine. He would lie on the grassy lawns near the fountains and listen to Mary's reading to him; she read so beautifully. Sometimes she composed verses about their happiness; sometimes they rode in the forest together. It was quite different riding almost alone with Mary, from riding with the company which always surrounded him when he was at Court. They would walk their horses under the trees or gallop side by side over the grassy stretches.

At Villers-Cotterets he learned not to be afraid of horses. Mary showed him what loving, gentle creatures they were. They were like herself, she said, eager to serve him.

What enchanting things Mary said! And how happy he was in her company! She made him forget that he was a sickly boy; she made him feel that he was a man.

To his relief their marriage had not been consummated. He was glad of that. He felt unhappy when he remembered that it would have to be one day; he was so uncertain and he sensed that Mary was also, and that she was glad that everything would be as it had been before their marriage, except that she was Dauphine now and they could be together night and day.

How good it was to be away from everybody who alarmed him! His mother was at Les Tournelles with the court, and that seemed far away. There was another whom he was beginning to fear as much as his mother, another who seemed to be constantly watching him in a manner that was sinister and subtle. This was Mary's uncle, the Cardinal of Lorraine.

Those sunny days were marred slightly because Mary was not feeling well. She had pains and a cough. In her childhood she had been a healthy girl but later certain weaknesses had begun to show themselves. She had a good appetite–perhaps too good, for she was sometimes ill after eating; and she was subject to fainting fits.

Then came a visitor to the honeymoon chateau. When the Dauphin saw who it was he froze with a horror for which he could really find no reason; but Mary ran forward eagerly to greet her uncle.

The Cardinal embraced both children.

'It is a secret visit,' he said. 'I could not resist it. I wished to see how my dear children were enjoying their honeymoon. And when I heard that my dearest Mary was unwell, I found the desire to make the journey irresistible.' The Cardinal looked at her anxiously. Her skin was of waxy pallor like the petal of the magnolia blossom; it was attractive, thought the Cardinal, but not a sign of robust health. As he had said to his brother, the Duke, when he had heard of Mary's illness, it was a terrifying thought that the power of their house depended on the lives of two frail children.

He told his brother that he had had a secret conference with the Dauphin's doctors and had forced them to admit that the likelihood of the boy's reaching the age of twenty was very remote.

Mary's illness and the reports from the doctors were the reasons for the Cardinal's intrusion on their honeymoon.

He knew the Dauphin and he knew Mary. The Dauphin was a frightened boy; he was so weak and sickly that he would have no normal impulses. As for Mary, one day she would be a passionate woman. The Cardinal was fully aware of that. He thought it was the secret of that immense attraction which was felt by almost every man who came into contact with her. Her expression was gentle; hers was a tender beauty; yet her dormant sensuality was ready to be roused, and it was this readiness which made all men who set eyes on her, long–subconsciously perhaps–to be that one who should kindle the fire. Her reserve, upheld by her great dignity, was like a fine gauze covering the intensely passionate nature. If the gauze could be removed the true Mary would be exposed–eager, voluptuous, abandoned. Passion would sweep away her dignity. The woman in her would make her forget she was a Queen. This connoisseur of human frailty, this man who had experienced every sensation, understood Mary completely.

It was his task to keep the gauze intact. Only he had lifted the corner to peep beneath, and then dropped it quickly. He was too old and wise to let his emotions stand in the way of his ambition. Mary must be handled with the greatest care. She must never know herself as a woman, if there was any risk that such knowledge might come between her and her duty to the house of Guise. He had fancied that Henri de Montmorency might, in due course, have stripped Mary of her queenly dignity, of her innocence and her ignorance, and found the woman beneath. That was why he had–as he so well knew how to do–made the Montmorency repulsive to her.

That had not been difficult. He had formed Mary's mind; he had watched over her. His relationship with her had been his great delight. It gave him more satisfaction than any of those obviously erotic entertainments which he devised from time to time. Mary must remain his guileless niece. Yet it was necessary for her to taste the fruit of the tree of knowledge, for it was imperative to the house of Guise that the Dauphin and Mary should have an heir. Yet he himself, when he had been determined that she should not fall to the house of Montmorency, that great enemy of the house of Guise, had shown her how bitter that fruit could be. He had made her turn shuddering away; that was why the task which now lay before him was such a delicate one.

He listened in an avuncular manner to Mary's account of the pleasures of the chateau. He heard about François' prowess with his new horse. Then he patted Mary's cheek and said that it grieved him to see her not as well as when they had last been together. He wished her to rest and insisted on her lying down.

'Not now you have come!' she protested.

'*Because* I have come! I will not have this hearty husband of yours tiring you.'

François could not help feeling rather pleased to be referred to as the vigorous one. Mary saw his quick smile which was replaced immediately by his look of concern for Mary.

Mary said: 'We did ride rather far yesterday. It was a little too far . . . for me.'

'Then you shall rest now, and François shall take me to the stables and show me his horses.'

Mary agreed. She was pleased because on other occasions when her uncle had been present, François had sent out distress signals begging not to be left alone with the imposing Cardinal. It was pleasant to feel that François was less afraid since their marriage, and that he was beginning to be fond of Uncle Charles.

When Mary had left them, the Cardinal smiled at the boy. His smile was warm, and affectionately and successfully masked the contempt he felt for the stripling.

'You . . . you wish to see the stables?' said the Dauphin timorously.

'Why, yes . . . yes,' said the Cardinal. 'We will go alone.'

As he admired the horses he made himself so agreeable that François began to think he had been rather foolish to be afraid; but when they had left the stables and were walking in the grounds about the chateau, the Cardinal said: 'I trust you are being a good husband to Mary.'

'I love her,' said the Dauphin. 'I would die for her.'

'She will need you to do more than die for her.'

'I . . . I would do all that she wished.'

'Poor Mary, she is a little sad.'

'Oh no. She is happy. She says so. She says that this is the happiest time she has ever known. She is happy because of our marriage.'

'She was happy *thinking* of marrying you. I am not sure that she is happy now.'

'I . . . I do not understand.'

The Cardinal smiled. 'You have given Mary a fine title; you have made her Dauphine of France. But there is more to a marriage than that. What Mary needs is a lover. She needs a child.'

The Dauphin flushed scarlet and did not know where to look. He was near to tears. He knew that he had been right to fear the Cardinal who had brought discord into this Eden.

The Cardinal's long mouth sneered. 'Tell me,' he said; 'I am right, am I not, when I say that Mary has been disappointed in her lover?'

'Mary does not want . . .'

'Mary does not want! Of course she wants!'

'But she said . . .'

'Holy Virgin, have you been such a laggard in love as to ask her what she wants in the matter?' The Cardinal laughed aloud. 'Your grandfather, great François would rise in his grave and come to you with a horsewhip if he knew. You have betrayed the honour of France and the Valois.'

'But if we wish . . . if we do not want . . .'

'Poor Mary! So I now understand why she is sick. She is pining. Holy Mother of God! Holy saints! Listen to the boy. He is a poor impotent weakling who begs his wife not to make any demands on his manhood. My boy, all France will reject you. Are you a Frenchman then? Are you the heir of France? Now I know why Mary is sad. Now I know why she pines and droops. She was promised marriage, and she has been given . . . what? I know not. I dare not think. My poor niece! My poor, poor niece!'

'How . . . dare you!' stammered François. 'Remember you speak to the Dauphin.'

'Remember it! I would to God I could forget it. I would I did not belong to this land, the heir of which is a lily-livered timorous girl, masquerading as a man.'

'I . . . I will tell the King.'

'I beg of you, do not. Do not bring down sorrow on his silver hairs. Do not bring shame to his royal crown. Do not let him know that he has fathered an unnatural monster with whom the most beautiful girl in all France has been unfortunate enough to marry.'

'You *have* come here to torment me then!'

The Cardinal seized the boy's arm. His face was a mask of piety as he raised his eyes to the sky. 'No, my son. I have come here to see that you do your duty, not only to my niece but to your ancestors.'

The Dauphin's face quivered. 'I . . . I . . .'

The Cardinal released him and laid an arm about his shoulders. 'My dear boy,' he said gently, 'my beloved Dauphin, I have been harsh. Sometimes one must be cruel to be kind. I wish to help you. I know how young you are and that you have not had the good health of some of your companions. You have not roamed the countryside with them and partaken in their manly sports and pastimes. My dearest boy, believe me, I wish to help you. I am your confessor, your priest. It is my place to help you. This marriage must be consummated without delay. It is your duty.' He laughed gently. 'Ah, that from which you shrink will give you great joy. Do you remember when you first mounted a horse? You were afraid then. The ground seemed so far away. You were terrified that you would fall. In your heart you hoped that you would never have to ride again. But now you are glad you learned to ride. so it will be in this matter. If you are frightened, if you run away from your duty, you will be ashamed for the rest of your life. Do you understand me?'

'Yes,' said the Dauphin.

The Cardinal pressed his shoulder warmly. 'I knew that you would. You will grow strong and noble. You will be a man, a worthy successor to your father.'

They returned to the palace.

'Do not mention to Mary what I have said,' warned the Cardinal. 'That would be folly. It would not please her to know that it had been necessary to force her husband to his duty.'

The Dauphin's face was set and determined. He was no longer the happy bridegroom. A duty lay before him, the execution of which frightened him.

The Cardinal saw his niece before he left. He did not intend to stay. He never made the mistake of over-emphasis. If, when the honeymoon was over, the marriage had not been consummated, he would have to consider other methods. What he had done so far would suffice and was, he felt sure, almost certain to succeed.

It had been the wish of the King that the young people should be left entirely to themselves. The King was sentimental where children were concerned, and he remembered the trials of his own early marriage. As for the Queen, she had no wish for the marriage to be consummated, but the Cardinal believed that her wishes were not founded on sentiment.

The consummation of the marriage was vital to the house of Guise; therefore that consummation should take place.

'And it shall!' mused the Cardinal, as he rode away from Villers-Cotterets. 'I have injected some manhood into that ungainly mass of corrupting flesh which calls itself Dauphin of France. I am only sorry that my darling should have been given such an unworthy partner in her first excursions into the delights of the flesh.'

The King came down to Villers-Cotterets. He had heard that Mary had been ill and that the Dauphin was less happy than he had been on his arrival.

The King came without ceremony, riding there on a hunting expedition.

The young couple were delighted to see him. He scanned their faces eagerly. He was moved as he gazed at them; they were such children, and did he not know what it meant to be a young husband? He remembered even now with a shudder his first weeks of marriage.

'And how are you both, my dear children?' he asked as he embraced them.

'We are very happy, Papa,' they assured him.

Mary was pale; that would be explained by her malady, but the Dauphin seemed shamefaced. They did not tell the King that their happiness had lasted until they had been compelled to indulge in a nightly duty which was distasteful to them both. Henri did not ask. He remembered his own agonies when his witty father had made brilliant remarks to his young son.

They will grow out of it, he promised himself. They are so fond of each other. François turns to her for everything, and she is as ready to comfort him and humour him as she ever was.

Yet so concerned was the King that he decided he would separate the newly married pair for a few weeks and see what effect it had.

'François,' he said, 'I wish you to join the camp at Amiens. Honeymoons cannot last for ever, you know.'

'No, Papa.'

The King saw the fear leap into the boy's eyes. He dreaded leaving Mary and Villers-Cotterets for the camp where there would be rough soldiers.

'You will be able to show your skill on horseback,' said his father. 'And, my boy, remember you are the Dauphin. Your people will wish to see you. Do not be afraid of them. There is nothing to fear. Remember, one day you will be their King.'

So to the camp at Amiens went François. Mary stayed at Villers-Cotterets, which the King felt would be healthier for her than Paris. He sent her four Maries to her to compensate her for the loss of her husband. He fancied that, while she was sorry to say a brief farewell to François, she was, in a way, relieved. The King believed he understood.

There was a great deal of excitement in the Court because the Queen of England was dead. Her place had been taken–usurped, said the King, the Guises and almost every Frenchman–by the bastard daughter of the concubine Anne Boleyn; and if the throne of England had not been taken by the bastard Elizabeth, it would surely have fallen to Mary, Queen of Scotland, now Dauphine of France.

'Holy Mother of God!' cried the Duke, his eye watering above his scar. 'We'll take men-at-arms across the sea. By God, we'll turn the red-headed bastard off the throne.'

But the King was against war. The memory of Saint Quentin rankled. It was no easy task to take men and arms across the Channel. He was all for making peace now with his Imperial enemies. He wished to see the return of Anne de Montmorency, the Constable whom he loved and revered. Even now he was seeking peace and would make no fresh wars.

'An undertaking doomed to failure,' said the King.

He had a better idea. Mary Stuart was rightful Queen of England; therefore on all documents she should be described as such. The armorial bearings of England should be displayed whenever the Dauphin and Dauphine appeared in public. Mary should be known as Dauphine of France, Queen of England, Scotland and the Isles.

The Cardinal and the Duke talked to Mary about her new dignity.

'What will my cousin say when she hears of my claim to her throne?' asked Mary.

'*Her* throne! *Her* throne!' cried the Duke testily. 'It is *your* throne. And if I had ten thousand men I'd set you on it without delay.'

But Mary was happy in France. She wished to stay in France. Let her cousin have the throne of England.

The Duke was impatient. Not so the Cardinal. He put his arm about Mary and drew her to him.

'Listen to me, Mary,' he said, 'we cannot forsake our duty and your duty is clear. All Christendom is shocked by this usurpation of the English throne. To accept it because it is an easy thing to do is a sin in the eyes of God . . . You know full well that Margaret Tudor, daughter of Henry the Seventh of England, married James the Fourth of Scotland and that their son was James the Fifth, your father. Henry the Eighth had one legitimate son and daughter. That son was Edward the Sixth; that daughter was Mary who has now died. Neither left issue. Your grandmother, Margaret Tudor, therefore provides the next line of succession and consequently the Queen of Scotland is the true Queen of England.'

'Yes, Uncle.'

'So now, dearest, I know you will not shirk your duty. You will not be guilty of foolish weakness. How do you think God and the saints regard this usurpation of the throne by one who is known to be as immoral as her mother was?'

'Yet . . . she is my cousin.'

'The daughter of a concubine!'

'But the daughter of the King as well.'

The Cardinal laughed. 'My dear Mary, her mother lost her head because she was found guilty of adultery. Now, my darling, purge your mind of foolish thoughts which would be displeasing to God. Your uncle commands you. Nay, how could he command the Queen of Scotland who is also the Queen of England! He begs you instead, my dearest. Will you disappoint him? Will you have him feel that he has wasted all these years when he has tried to show you the path of righteousness?'

'Oh no, Uncle.'

'Then, my Queen, all is well. Proudly bear your titles, and one day we will drive the red-headed bastard out of England.'

Mary said obediently: 'Yes, Uncle. Of course you are right.' But she was thinking of the gown she would wear at the coming pageant, and the last thing she wanted was to be Queen of England, for it might mean leaving the land she loved and of whose Court she was the petted darling.

Since his marriage the Dauphin had grown much taller, but although he himself was delighted with this, it was clear that the sudden shooting up had done little to improve his health. He now became possessed with a mad desire to shine in all sports and pastimes. He would ride for long hours and return exhausted. Mary remonstrated but he replied: 'Others do it. Why should not I?'

Mary had ceased to be a child when she had married. She had discovered that there was more to life than wearing fine clothes, dancing, riding, writing verses and listening to compliments, and that masques and pageants were often cover for plots and murderous intentions. Life was only pleasant on the surface, and the surface was as thin as the sheets of ice which had been declared dangerous to skaters last winter at Rambouillet.

She was sixteen. It was not very old but she had to learn quickly. She had to be able to see behind the masks on people's faces; she had to understand what was behind their words.

It was terrifying when François returned from the forest with his brother Charles. François was white and exhausted. She saw them ride into the courtyard; François slipped from his horse; she ran to him and said: 'You're tired, dearest.'

He had smiled wanly. 'No,' he said. 'I am not tired. It was a good day's sport.' His voice was hoarse. The doctors said there was some affliction of the throat.

'Come and rest now,' said Mary.

'Rest!' cried François, aware of Charles' complacent smile. 'I have no need of rest.'

Charles who had leaped from his horse, threw the reins to a groom and cried out: 'Come, François, let us go and shoot at the butts. Mary, come and watch.'

Mary, impulsive as she was, hot-tempered and quick to anger, was even quicker to feel sympathy, particularly where those she loved were concerned. She had the endearing gift of putting herself in the place of anyone who was uncomfortable or who suffered in any way, and she had seen the look of sheer exhaustion on her husband's face as he said: 'Come on then. I'm ready.'

She would not let him tire himself out. She took his arm and said pleadingly: 'Oh, François, I did want to read my verses to you. I have scarcely seen you all day.'

With what tenderness he smiled into her eyes! Perhaps he knew that her desire was not to read her verses aloud but to see those tired limbs of his enjoy the rest they needed, and that his young brother should not have the pleasure of beating him at the butts.

Charles scowled. Mary saw that familiar clenching and unclenching of the hands.

She slipped her arm through that of François. 'Come along. I insist. You must hear my verses.'

They left Charles to scowl after them as he shouted to his attendants: 'Come . . . to the butts. I am not in the least tired. I can spend ten hours in the saddle and feel as fresh as when I started.'

Mary led François into the palace and made him lie down while she read to him. He was happy to be with her; he had ridden with Charles and shown that he could do these things; now he was free to do as he wished, to rest his exhausted body while Mary sat beside him, her hand in his, his subtle protectress who never showed the rest of the world how she stood between him and everything that hurt him.

After a while he slept and Mary drew the coverlet over him and left him.

She met Charles coming from the butts. He was with several of his attendants, but when he saw Mary he signed to them to go on. His eyes were wild as he looked at Mary; his lips curled unpleasantly. 'Poor old François,' he said. 'He was worn out.'

'You rode too far.'

'Not for me. I have something to say to you, Mary. It is very secret. Come to the window seat here. Then we shall not be overheard. Speak low, Mary. I have heard that François is very sick.'

'François is well,' said Mary quickly. 'He has grown too fast in the last months and that tires him.'

'They are saying that he will never live to reach the throne.'

'*They* talk too much.'

'Mary . . . Mary . . . if he does not . . . when my father dies, I shall be King of France.'

'Your father will not die, and François will live.'

'If my father dies and François dies, you can still be Queen of France. I will marry you.'

He had taken her hands and was covering them with quick kisses.

Mary drew back in alarm. Here was another of those shocks which were coming to her too frequently. Charles had been a young boy not quite nine years old a few moments ago; now he was behaving like a man . . . a lover.

'I will love you as François never can,' said Charles. 'He is too sick. Mary, when he dies, I will marry you . . . and he will die soon. I know he will.'

Mary snatched her hands away.

'You do not know what you are saying,' she cried, rising. Then, seeing the red blood tinge his face and begin to show in the whites of his eyes, she said soothingly: 'I am glad you love me, Charles. But I am François' wife and I hope I shall always be. Stay as you are . . . my little brother. That contents me.'

'It does not content me,' mumbled Charles.

The only way in which she could treat such an outburst was not to look upon it seriously. She smiled and left him, but her heart was beating furiously.

The Cardinal came to see her and asked to speak with her alone.

'My dearest niece,' he said, 'you are looking pale. Perhaps there is a reason?'

'I was not very well yesterday, Uncle.'

The Cardinal could not hide his frown. 'I had hoped there might be another reason.'

'What reason?' asked Mary.

'It is time a child was conceived.'

She blushed and the Cardinal said anxiously: 'My child, I trust you do your duty.'

'Oh . . . yes.'

'It is imperative that you have a child. François knows that, does he not? You know it?'

'We both know it.'

'I wish the Dauphin had the manhood of some others. My poor sweet Mary, would to God . . .'

She waited, but he sighed deeply.

He went on after a pause: 'One day you will understand how much I love you. There must be a child, Mary. There must. If François died and there was no child, what would be your position here in France, do you think?'

'I do not know.'

'Dearest, try to remember your duty as I have taught it. This is a matter which concerns not only yourself but our entire house. The family looks to you. Oh, my Mary, I know that that which should be a pleasure to you is a painful duty. I read your mind and you can hide nothing from me. I see it through your eyes . . . the shameful fumblings . . . the inadequate lover. Oh, that you might enjoy one worthy of you! Oh that you might be now, in this glory of your youth, the women I see behind those gentle eyes. Ah, what pleasure, what transcendant joy for the one who would be fortunate enough to be your lover! Mary, there must be a child. Somehow, there must be a child.'

She trembled. She was frightened by the meaning she read in his words, by the realization that the world was so different from what it had at first seemed to be.

Henri de Montmorency danced with her in the stately *pavanne*.

He complained: 'I have little chance of speaking to you.'

She thought how handsome he was, how elegant. She understood now what his burning glances meant. She feared she had been very ignorant before. Life was not easy and simple and Henri de Montmorency did not cease to desire her because she was the wife of the Dauphin.

'I must tell you this,' he said; 'I love you still.'

He was bold. He came from a bold family.

'Take care, Monsieur de Montmorency,' she said. 'There are many of your enemies who watch you.'

'Dearest lady, it is you who should take care, for you have more enemies than I could ever have.'

'Enemies . . . ? I?'

'At the Court of France many are in love with you. I mean you yourself. But some are deep in hate for the Dauphine of France.'

'I do not know of these.'

'The Queen of England hates you. She will never forgive you. I have had news from England.'

'What have I done to her?'

'What they have made you do. You have questioned her right. You have established your belief in her bastardy and you have called yourself Queen of England. Others did this, I know, but it is you whom she will blame for it.'

Mary tossed her head. 'She is far away and cannot reach me here. Ah, Monsieur de Montmorency, what do I care for the woman who calls herself the Queen of England? Talk of other things, I beg of you.'

'Your wish is a command. I will say that you grow more beautiful every day and that when I see you I am overwhelmed with love for you.'

'I did not mean that you should change the subject to speak to me thus,' said Mary, but she spoke in such a way as to imply that she did not forbid it. What harm was there in listening to such pleasant compliments from such an elegant young man!

During the weeks which followed, Mary refused to think of the unpleasant. It was exciting to be the Dauphine and enjoy greater power than ever before. She had sent Madame de Paroy from her household, and Catherine had made no attempt to send the woman back to her. Catherine paid greater respect to Mary now, for she was conscious of rank; but Mary did not like her any better.

Now Mary had her own little court–her friends among that little circle in which she and François were as Queen and King. She and François rarely left each other, for he depended on her more than ever. The Cardinal and the Duke of Guise were often in their company; her uncles asked Mary to arrange that this was so, for as they said, François was in truth their nephew now. François admired the Duke but he could not overcome his fear of the Cardinal.

The young pair hunted together, and at such times Mary was always watchful that her husband did not tire himself; and when the Dauphin was not with her she was conscious of a relaxation of responsibility, which brought with it some relief. She loved François but she was very happy without him; then she would listen attentively to the compliments which were poured into her ears; and would dance and laugh more gaily than anyone. And, she was more attractive than ever. The Cardinal, watching her, knew that one day some gallant adventurer would seek to discover the true Mary; then he might find the passionate woman who lived within the Queen.

What could that mean for Mary? Lifelong happiness? That was hardly likely, she being a queen. Lifelong tragedy perhaps, for the, as yet, undiscovered Mary was a woman who would count the world well lost for love.

The Cardinal delighted to watch his puppet; he felt he had made of her a fascinating work of art. But the game of politics must be played with care, and the Cardinal's chief interest was the power which would come to him through the advancement of his house.

The Guises were anxiously watching events. They had succeeded in marrying Mary to the Dauphin, but now the King and Diane were showing their displeasure with the Guise arrogance which had by no means diminished since the royal marriage.

The King wished to make peace with Spain. The Duke of Guise was against peace. There were long, angry discussions between the two, during which the King had to remind François de Guise that the marriage of his niece to the Dauphin did not mean that the Duke was ruler of France.

Henri was angry. Diane had been right when she had pointed out that the Guises were becoming intolerable. It was time the Constable de Montmorency, who had helped to keep the balance of power, was back in France. A peace treaty would mean the return of prisoners and among them Montmorency; thus the power of the Guises could be curtailed. The Duke, so great in war, was less useful in peace. Henri was tired of war, tired of the arrogance of the Guises. He therefore consented to make the Treaty of Cateau-Cambrésis with Philip of Spain.

The Duke ranted: 'By this treaty, by a single stroke of the pen, all the Italian conquests of thirty years are surrendered, except the little marquisate of Saluzzo. Sire, shall we throw away Bress, Bugey, Savoy . . . Piedmont . . . all these and others? Shall we restore Valenza to Spain, Corsica to Genoa, Monteferrato to . . .'

'You need not proceed,' said the King coldly. 'We need peace. We must have peace. You would have us go on until we exhaust ourselves in war. It is not the good of France which concerns you, Monsieur, but the glory of Guise and Lorraine.'

'Guise and Lorraine are France, Sire,' declared the bold Duke. 'And France's shame is their shame.'

The King turned abruptly away. It was time that reliable old ally and enemy of the Guises the Constable de Montmorency was back at Court.

There were other good things to come to France through this treaty. When it was signed, Philip of Spain and Henri of France would stand together against the heretic world. They could make plans for the alliance of their two countries; and such plans would contain, as they invariably did, contracts for royal marriages.

There came that never-to-be-forgotten day in June. There was no one, in that vast crowd which had gathered in the Rue St Antoine near Les Tournelles where the arena had been set up for the tournament, who would ever forget it. It was a day which, by a mere chance, changed the lives of many people and the fate of a country.

The pale-faced Princess Elisabeth was there–a sixteen-year-old bride who had not yet seen the husband she was shortly to join, and whom she had married by proxy a few days earlier. The great Philip of Spain, she had been told, did not come for his brides; he sent for them. So the Duke of Alva had stood proxy for Philip, and the ceremony which had made her Philip's wife had taken place. She was grateful for the haughty pride of Spanish kings which allowed her this small grace.

It was a frightened bride who watched the great events of that summer's day.

Princess Marguerite, the King's sister, was present. She was to marry the Duke of Savoy–which marriage had also been arranged with the signing of the treaty of Cateau-Cambrésis. The Duke of Savoy was present on this fateful day with his gentlemen brilliant in their red satin doublets, crimson shoes and cloaks of gold-embroidered black velvet, for this tournament was to be held in his honour.

All the nobility of France had come to pay respect to the future husband of the Princess Marguerite and the Spanish envoys of Elisabeth's husband.

The Dauphin and the Dauphine came to the arena together in a carriage which bore the English coat of arms, and as they rode through the crowds, the heralds cried: 'Make place! Make place for the Queen of England!'

The Constable de Montmorency was back in France, and Henri, his son, had married Mademoiselle de Bouillon, the granddaughter of Diane de Poitiers.

Did Mary care? She was a little piqued. He had sworn he would be bold; he had sworn that he would never marry, since he could not marry Mary.

Mary laughed. It was all a game of make-believe. She had been foolish to take anyone seriously.

Queen Catherine took her place in the royal gallery at the arena. Her face was not quite as expressionless as usual, for during the preceding night she had had uneasy dreams, and although the sun was shining in the Rue St Antoine and the crowd was loyal, she was conscious of a deep depression.

The jousting began and the noble Princes excelled themselves. Mary was proud to watch the skill of her uncle the Duke of Guise and to hear the people's warm acclamation of their hero.

The Duke of Alva, stern representative of his master, sat beside Elisabeth and applauded. The Count of Nassau, William of Orange, who had accompanied Alva, took part in the jousting.

There came that moment when the King himself rode out–a brilliant figure in his armour, his spurs jewelled, his magnificent white horse rearing–to meet his opponent. The people roared their loyal greeting to their King.

How magnificently Henri acquitted himself that day! His horse–a gift from the bridegroom-to-be, the Duke of Savoy–carried him to victory.

The King had acquitted himself with honour. The people had roared their approval. But he would go in once more. He would break one more lance.

The Dukes of Ferrara and Nemours were trying to dissuade him but he felt like a young man again. He had turned to the box in which sat Diane. Diane lifted her hand. The Queen half rose in her seat. But the King had turned away. He had signed to the Seigneur de l'Orges, a young captain of the Scottish Guards. The Captain hesitated, and then the King was calling for a new lance.

There was wild cheering as the King rode out a second time and began to tilt with the young Captain.

It was all over in less than a minute. The Captain had touched the King on the gorget; the Captain's lance was splintered and the King was slipping from his horse, his face covered with blood.

There was a hushed silence that seemed to last a long time; and then people were running to where the King lay swooning on the grass.

The King was dying. He had spoken little since he had fallen in the joust. He had merely insisted that the Captain was not to be blamed in any way because a splinter from his lance had brought about the accident. He had obeyed the King and had tilted when he had no wish to do so; he had carried himself like a brave knight and valiant man-at-arms. The King would have all remember that.

In the nurseries there was unusual quiet, broken only by sudden outbreaks of weeping.

Little Hercule cried: 'When will my Papa be well? I want my Papa.'

The others comforted him, but they could not comfort themselves. Margot, whose grief, like all her emotions, was violent, shut herself into her apartment and made herself ill with weeping.

Mary and Elisabeth, François and Charles sat together, but they dared not speak for fear of breaking down. Mary noticed an odd speculative look in Charles's eyes as he watched his brother. A King was dying, and when one King died another immediately took his place. The pale sickly boy would soon by King of France, but for how long?

Edouard Alexandre–Henri–was with his mother. She needed all the comfort he could give her. As she embraced him she told herself that he would take the place in her heart of the dying man. She was sure that the King was dying, because she knew such things.

And at last came the summons to his bedside. He was past speech and they were all thankful that he was past his agonies; he lay still and could not recognize any of them. They waited there, standing about his bedside until he ceased to breathe.

In a room adjoining the bedchamber all the leading men of France were gàthering. The Cardinal was there with his brother, the Duke, and they both noticed that the glances which came their way were more respectful than they had ever been before, and that they themselves were addressed as though they were kings.

When it was all over, the family left the bedside–François first, apprehensively conscious, through his grief, of his new importance. Catherine and Mary were side by side, but when they reached the door, Catherine paused, laid a hand on Mary's shoulder and pushed her gently forward.

That was a significant gesture. Queen Catherine was now only the Queen-Mother; Mary Stuart took first place as Queen of France.

Chapter Five

The Queen of France! The first lady in the land! She was second only to the King, and the King was her devoted slave. Yet when she remembered that this had come about through the death of the man whom she had come to regard as her beloved father, she felt that she would gladly relinquish all her new honours to have him back.

François was full of sorrow. He had gained nothing but his father's responsibilities, and dearly he had loved that father. So many eyes watched him now. He was under continual and critical survey. Terrifying people surrounded him and, although he was King of France, he felt powerless to escape from them. Those two men who called themselves his affectionate uncles held him in their grip. It seemed to him that they were always present. He dreamed of them, and in particular he dreamed of the Cardinal; he had nightmares in which the Cardinal figured, his voice sneering: 'Lily-livered timorous girl . . . masquerading as a man!' Those scornful words haunted him by day and night.

There was one other whom he feared even more. This was his mother. If he were alone at any time she would come with all speed to his apartments and talk with him quietly and earnestly. 'My dearest son . . . my little King . . . you will need your mother now.' That was the theme of all she said to him.

He felt that he was no better than a bone over which bandogs were fighting.

His mother had been quick to act. Even during her period of mourning she had managed to shut out those two men. She had said: 'The King is my son. He is not a King yet; he is merely a boy who is grieving for his father. I will allow no one to come near him. Who but his mother could comfort him now?'

But her comfort disturbed him more than his grief, and he would agree to anything if only she would go away and leave him alone to weep for his father. Mary could supply all the comfort he needed, and Mary alone.

Mary's uncles came to the Louvre. They did not ask for an audience with the Queen of France; there could be no ceremonies at such a time, said the Cardinal, between those who were so near and dear. He did not kneel to Mary; he took her in his arms. The gesture indicated not only affection, but mastery.

'My dearest,' he murmured, 'so it has come. It has come upon us unexpectedly. So my darling is Queen of France. That is what I and your uncles and your grandmother have always wished for you.'

Mary said with the faintest reproof: 'We are as yet mourning the dead King.'

The Cardinal looked sharply at her. Had the great honour gone to her head? Was she, as Queen of France, less inclined to listen to her uncle than she had been as Dauphine?

He would not allow that.

'You will need your family more than ever, Mary.'

'Yes, Uncle, I know. I have often thought of being Queen, and now I think much of the King and how kind he always was and how dearly we children loved him. But he was not kind to everybody. Terrible things happened to those who were not of the true faith, and at his command.'

'Heretics could not be tolerated in this country,' said the Cardinal.

'But, Uncle, I am a good Catholic, yet I feel that it is wrong to torture people . . . to kill them because they wish to follow a different line of thought. Now that I am Queen I should like to promise everyone religious liberty. I should like to go to the prisons where people are held because of their religious opinions, open the doors and say: "Go in peace. Live in peace and worship God in the way you wish."'

The Cardinal laughed. 'Who has been talking to you, my dearest? This is not a matter of religious thought. . . .' He remembered his robes suddenly and added: 'only. Why, these men who lie in prison care little for opinions. They wish to set the Protestant Bourbons on the throne. Religion and politics, Mary, are married to one another. A man meets his death on the Place de Grève, perhaps because he is a heretic, perhaps because he is a menace to a Catholic monarch. The world is divided into Catholics and Huguenots. But you shall learn more about these things. For the time being you will, I am sure, with your usual good sense take the advice of your Uncle François and your Uncle Charles who think of nothing but your good.'

'It is a comfort to know that you are with me.'

He kissed her hand. 'We will make the throne safe for you, dearest, and the first thing we must do is to remove all those who threaten us. Where is François? Take me to him. He must send for the Constable de Montmorency at once. The old man's day is over. There you will see disappear the greatest of our enemies; and the other . . .' He laughed. 'I think we may trust the Queen-Mother to deal adequately with Madame de Valentinois.'

'The Constable! Diane!' cried Mary. 'But . . .'

'Oh, Diane was charming to you, was she not? You were her dear daughter. Do not be deceived, my dearest. You were her dear daughter because you were to marry the Dauphin, and it was necessary for all the King's children to be *her* dear children. She is an enemy of our house.'

'But she is your sister by marriage.'

'Yes, yes, and we do not forget it. But she has had her day. She is sixty and her power has been stripped away from her. When the splinter entered the King's eye she became of no importance–no more importance than one of your little Maries.'

'But does not love count for something?'

'She did not love you, child. She loved the crown which would one day be yours. You have to grow up, Mary. You have to learn a great deal in a short time. Do not mourn for the fall of Madame de Valentinois. She had her day; she may well be left to that Queen whom she has robbed of dignity and power for so many years.' He smiled briskly. 'Now, tell the King that you wish to see him.'

She went to the apartment where François sat in lonely state.

He was glad to see Mary, but wished she had come alone; and particularly he wished that she had not brought the Cardinal with her.

He tried to look as a king should look; he tried to behave as his father had. But how could he? In the presence of this man he could only feel that he was a lily-livered girl masquerading as a king.

'Your Majesty is gracious to receive me,' said the Cardinal, and as he took the King's hand noticed that it was trembling.

'My uncle the Cardinal has something to say to you, dearest,' Mary announced.

'Mary,' said François, 'stay here. Do not go.'

She smiled at him reassuringly. The Cardinal, signing to them to sit on their chairs of state, stood before them.

'Your Majesty well knows that your enemies abound,' he said. 'Your position has changed suddenly and you will forgive me, Sir, if I remind you that you are as yet very young.'

The King moved uneasily in his chair. His eyes sought Mary's and sent out distress signals.

'There is one,' continued the Cardinal, 'whom it will be necessary for Your Majesty to remove from his sphere of influence without delay. I do not need to tell you that I refer to Anne de Montmorency, at present the Constable of France.'

'The . . . the Constable. . . .' stammered François, thinking of the old man who alarmed him only slightly less than the sardonic Cardinal himself.

'He is too old for his office, and Your Majesty's first duty will be to summon him to your presence. Now this is what you will say to him–it is quite simple and it will make the position clear. 'We are anxious to solace your old age which is no longer fit to endure the toil and hardship of service.' That is all. He will give up the Seals, and Mary is of the opinion that they should be given to the two men whom you know you can trust. Mary has suggested her uncle, the Duke of Guise and myself.'

'But . . .' murmured François, 'the Constable . . . !'

'He is an old man. He is not trustworthy, Sire. He has been in the hands of your enemies, a prisoner after Saint Quentin. What plight would France be in now had not my brother hurried to the scene of that disaster? As all France knows, François de Guise saved Your Majesty's Crown and your country from defeat. Mary, your beloved Queen, agrees with me. She wishes to help you in all things. She wishes to spare you some of the immense load of responsibility. That is so, is it not, Mary?'

The caressing hand was pressed warmly on her shoulder. She felt her will merge in his. He was right, of course. He was her beloved uncle who had been her guide and counsellor, her spiritual lover, ever since she came to France.

'Yes, François,' she agreed, 'I want to help you. It is too big a load for you, because you are not old and experienced. I long to help you, and so does my uncle. He is wise and knows what is best.'

'But, Mary, the Constable . . . ? And there is my mother. . . .'

'Your mother, Sire, is wrapped up in her grief. She is a widow mourning her husband. You can understand what that means. She must not be troubled with these matters of state. As yet she could not give her mind to them.'

'You must do as my uncle says, François,' insisted Mary. 'He knows. He is wise and you must do as he says.'

François nodded. It must be right; Mary said so; and, in any case, he wished to please Mary whatever happened. He hoped he would remember what to say.

'"We are anxious to solace your old age . . ."'

He repeated the words until he was sure he knew them by heart.

Mary knew that the carefree days were over. Sometimes, at night, she and François would lie in each other's arms and talk of their fears.

'I feel as though I am a ball, thrown this way and that,' whispered the King. 'All these people who profess to love me, do not love me at all. Mary, I am afraid of the Cardinal.'

Mary was loyal, but she too, during the last weeks, had been conscious of a fear of the Cardinal. Yet she would not admit this. She had been too long in his care, too constantly assured of his love and devotion.

'It is because he is so clever,' she said quickly. 'His one thought is to serve you and make everything right for us both.'

'Mary, sometimes I think they all hate each other–your uncles, my mother, the King of Navarre. . . . I think they all are waiting to tear me into pieces and that none of them loves me. I am nothing but a symbol.'

'The Cardinal and the Duke love us both. They love me because I am their niece and you because you are their nephew.'

'They love us because we are King and Queen,' asserted the King soberly. 'My mother loves me because I am the King; she loves Charles because, if I die, he will be King; she loves Elisabeth because she is Queen of Spain. Claude she loves scarcely at all, because she is only the wife of the Duke of Lorraine. Margot and Hercule she does not love as yet. They are like wine set aside to mature. Perhaps they may be very good when their time comes, and perhaps no good at all. She will wait until she knows which, before she decides whether or not she loves them.'

'She loves your brother Henri very much,' Mary reminded him. 'Yet he could not be King unless you and Charles both die and leave no sons behind you.'

'Everybody–even my mother–must do something sometimes without a reason. So she loves my brother Henri. Mary, how I wish we could go back to Villers-Cotterets and live quietly there. How I wish my father had never died and that we were not King and Queen. Is that a strange wish? So many would give everything they have in order to wear the crown, and I . . . who have it, would give away all I have–except you–if, by so doing, I could bring my father back.'

'It is your grief, François, that makes you say that. Papa's death was too sudden.'

'It would be the same if I had known for years that he was going to die. Mary, we are but children, and King and Queen of France. Perhaps if my father had lived another ten or twenty years we should have been wiser . . . perhaps then we should not have been so frightened. Then I should have snapped my fingers at the Cardinal. I should have said: 'I wish to greet my uncle, the King of Navarre, as befits his rank. I will take no orders from you, Monsieur le Cardinal. Have a care, sir, or you may find yourself spending the rest of your days in an *oubliette* in the Conciergerie!' Oh, Mary, how easy it is to say it now. But when I think of saying it to him face to face I tremble. I wish he were not your uncle, Mary. I wish you did not love him so.'

'I wish I did not.' The words had escaped her before she realized she was saying them.

There were items of news which seeped through to her. The persecutions of the Huguenots had not ceased with the death of Henri, but rather had increased. The Cardinal had sworn to the Dukes of Alva and Savoy on the death of Henri that he would purge France of Protestants, not because the religious controversy was of such great importance to him but because he wished to be sure of the support of Philip of Spain for the house of Guise against that of Bourbon. He was eager now to show Philip that he would honour his vow.

This persecution could not be kept from the young King and Queen. The Huguenots were in revolt; there was perpetual murmuring throughout the Court. Never had the prisons been so full. The Cardinal was determined to show the King of Spain that never would that monarch find such allies in France as the Guises.

There was something else which Mary had begun to discover. This uncle who had been so dear to her, who had excited her with his strange affection, who had taught her her duty, who had moulded her to his will, was hated–not only by her husband, but by many of the people beyond the Court.

Anagrams were made on the name of Charles de Lorraine throughout the country as well as in the Court. '*Hardi larron se cèle*,' was murmured by daring men as the Cardinal passed. '*Renard lasche le roi!*' cried the people in the streets.

Prophecies were rife. 'He will not live long, this Cardinal of Lorraine,' said the people. 'One day he will tread that path down which he has sent so many.'

Great men, Mary might have told herself, often face great dangers. Yet she could not fail to know that beneath those scarlet robes was a padded suit, a precaution against an assassin's dagger or bullet. Morever the Cardinal had, in a panic, ordered that cloaks should no longer be 'worn wide', and that the big boots in which daggers could be concealed should be considerably reduced so that they could accommodate nothing but the owner's feet. Every time Mary noticed the new fashions she was reminded that they had been dictated by a man who dispensed death generously to others while he greatly feared it for himself. It was said that the Guises went in fear of their lives but, while the Duke snapped his fingers at his enemies, the Cardinal was terrified of his.

He is a coward, decided Mary with a shock.

The fabric of romance which she had built up as a child in Scotland and which had been strengthened by her first years in France was beginning to split.

She was vaguely aware of this as she held the boy-King tightly in her arms. They were together–two children, the two most important children in France, and they were two desolate lonely ones. On either side of them stood those powerful Princes, the Guises and the Bourbons; and the Valois, represented by Catherine the Queen-Mother, Mary feared more than either Guise or Bourbon.

The Court was moving south on its journey towards the borders of France and Spain. With it went the little bride of Philip of Spain making her last journey through her native land. At each stage of the journey she seemed to grow a little more fearful, a little more wan. Mary, to whom she confided her fears, suffered with her in her deep sympathy.

François's health had taken a turn for the worse. Abscesses had begun to form inside his ear, and as soon as one was dispersed another would appear. Ambrose Paré, who was considered the cleverest doctor in the world, was kept in close attendance.

Mary herself suffered periodic fits of illness, but they passed and left her well again. Her radiant health was gone, but if her beauty had become more fragile it was as pronounced as ever. There was still in her that which the Cardinal had called 'Promise'; there was still the hint of a passionate depth yet to be plumbed, and this was more appealing than the most radiant beauty, it seemed, for in spite of her impaired health, Mary continued to be the most attractive lady of the Court.

They had travelled down to Chenonceaux, that most beautiful of all French chateaux, built in a valley and seeming to float on the water, protected by alder trees. The river flowing beneath it–for it was built on a bridge–acted as a defensive moat. It had always been a beautiful castle, but Diane had loved it and had employed all the foremost artists in France to add to its beauty. Henri had given it to her although Catherine had greatly desired it; and the Queen-Mother had never forgiven this slight. One of her first acts, on the death of her husband, was to demand the return of Chenonceaux. In exchange, she had been delighted to offer Diane the Chateau de Chaumont, which Catherine considered to have a spell on it, for she swore that she herself had experienced nothing but bad luck there, and while living in it had been beset by evil visions.

As the royal party–complete with beds and furnishings, fine clothes and all the trappings of state–rode towards Chenonceaux, the Queen-Mother talked to the Queen of the improvements she intended for the chateau. She would have a new wing, and there should be two galleries–one on either side, so that when she gave a ball the flambeaux would illuminate the dancers from both sides of the ballroom. She would send to her native Italy for statues, for there were no artists in the world to compare with the Italians, as old King François had known; the walls should be hung with the finest tapestries in the world and decorated with the most beautiful of carved marble.

'You are fortunate,' said Mary, 'to find something to do which will help you to forget your grief for the late King.'

Catherine sighed deeply. 'Ah yes, indeed. I lost that which was more dear to me than all else. Yet I have much left, for I am a mother, and my children's welfare gives me much to think of.'

'As does this beautiful chateau, so recently in the possession of Madame de Valentinois.'

'Yes . . . yes. We must all have our lighter moments, must we not? I hope that Chenonceaux will offer rich entertainments to my son and Your Majesty.'

'You are so thoughtful, Madame.'

'And,' went on the Queen-Mother, 'to your children.'

'We are very grateful indeed.'

'I am concerned for my son. Since his marriage he has become weaker. I fear he grows too quickly.' The Queen-Mother leaned from her horse and touched Mary's hand. She gave her ribald laugh. 'I trust you do not tire him.'

'I . . . tire him!'

Catherine nodded. 'He is such a young husband,' she said.

Mary flushed. There was in this woman, as in the Cardinal, the power to create unpleasant pictures. The relationship which she and François knew to be expected of them, and which the Cardinal had made quite clear to them was their duty to pursue, gave them both cause for embarrassment. For neither of them was there pleasure. They could never banish thoughts of the Cardinal and Queen-Mother on such occasions. It seemed to them both that those two were present–the Cardinal watching them, shaking his head with dissatisfaction at their efforts, the Queen-Mother overcome with mirth at their clumsy methods. Such thoughts were no inducement to passion.

'He is so weak now,' said Catherine, 'that I am convinced that even if you did find yourself *enceinte*, no one would believe the child was the King's.'

Again that laugh. It was unbearable.

They came to Chenonceaux, and Mary's anger with Catherine had not left her when her women were dressing her for the banquet that night.

She looked at her reflection in the beautiful mirror of Venetian glass–the first which had ever been brought to France–and she saw how brilliant were her long, beautiful eyes. There was always some meaning behind the words of the Queen-Mother. Mary guessed that, for all her laughter, she was very much afraid that Mary was with child. Mary was beginning to understand why. If she had a child and François died, Catherine's son, Charles, would not be King; and Catherine was longing for the moment when Charles should mount the throne. François had once said: 'My mother loves me because I am the King; she loves Charles because, if I die, he will be King.' But although François was King he was ruled by Mary's uncles, and Catherine wished to reign supreme. That was why she had appointed special tutors for her son Charles. It would seem, thought Mary, in sudden horror, that she *wants* François to die.

She looked round the beautiful room which was her bedchamber. Perhaps here King Henri and Diane had spent their nights, making love in the carved oak bedstead with its hangings of scarlet satin damask. She glanced at the carved cabinets, the state chair, the stools; and she was suddenly glad that she had not Catherine's gift for seeing into the future. She was afraid of the future.

'Bring me my gown,' she said to Mary Beaton, who, with Seton, helped her into it. It was of blue velvet and satin decorated with pearls.

'A dress indeed for a Queen,' said Flem, her eyes adoring. 'Dearest Majesty, you look more beautiful than ever.'

'But Your Majesty also looks angry,' countered Beaton. 'Was it the Queen-Mother?'

'She makes me angry,' admitted Mary. 'How like her to come to this chateau! She says that Chaumont is full of ghosts. I wonder the ghost of the dead King does not come and haunt her here.'

'It is very soon after . . .' murmured Livy.

'She's inhuman!' cried Mary.

One of her pages announced that the Cardinal was come to see her. The ladies left her.

As he kissed her hand, the Cardinal's eyes gleamed. 'Most beautiful!' he declared. 'Everyone who sees you must fall in love with you!'

Mary smiled. Her image looked back at her from the Venetian mirror. There was an unusual flush in her cheeks and her eyes still sparkled from the anger Catherine had aroused. She enjoyed being beautiful; she revelled in the flattery and compliments which came her way. Tonight she would dance more gaily than she ever had before, and so banish from her mind the unpleasantness engendered by the Queen-Mother. François had been advised to rest in his bed. It was wrong of her to feel relieved because of this; but nevertheless it was comforting to remember she need not be anxious because he might be getting tired. Tonight she could be young and carefree. She was, after all, only seventeen; and she was born to be gay.

'Those who have always been in love with you,' went on the Cardinal, 'find themselves deeper and deeper under your spell. But tell me, is there any news?'

She frowned slightly. 'News? What news?'

'The news which all those who love you anxiously wait to hear. Is there any sign of a child?'

Now she was reminded of that which she preferred to forget–François, the lover who could not inspire her with any passion, François, who apologized and explained that it was but their duty. She saw the pictures in her mind reflected in the Cardinal's eyes. She saw the faint sneer on his lips, which was for François.

'There is no sign of a child,' she said coolly.

'Mary, there must be; there must be soon.'

She looked at the sparkling rings on her delicate fingers and said: 'How can you speak to me thus? If God does not wish to bless our union, what can I do about it?'

'You were made to be fruitful,' he said passionately. 'François never!'

'Then how could we get a child?'

His eyes had narrowed. He was trying to make her understand thoughts which were too dangerous to be put into words.

'There must be a child,' he repeated fiercely. 'If the King dies, what will your position be?'

'The King is not dead, and if he does die, I shall be his sorrowing widow who was always his faithful wife.'

The Cardinal said no more; he turned away and began to pace the room.

'I am a very happy wife,' said Mary softly. 'I have a devoted husband whom I love with all my heart.'

'You will hold Court alone tonight?' said the Cardinal, stopping in his walk to look at her. 'You will dance. The most handsome men in the Court will compete for the honour of dancing with you. I'll warrant Henri de Montmorency will be victorious. Such a gallant young man! I fear his marriage is not a very happy one. Yet doubtless he will find many to comfort him, if comfort he needs.'

He looked into his niece's eyes and watched the slow flush rise from her neck to her brow. She would not look at the pictures which he was holding before her; she would not let him have possession of her mind. She feared him, almost as much as François feared him, and she was longing now to break away from him.

'Let us go now,' she said. 'I will call my women.'

There was a satisfied smile about his lips as he left her. But she would not think of him. She was determined to enjoy the evening. She went to see François before going down to the banqueting hall. He lay on his bed, his eyes adoring her, telling her that she looked more beautiful than ever. He was glad that he could rest quietly in his bed, yet he wished that she could be with him.

She kissed him tenderly and left him.

Down to the great hall she went with her ladies about her.

'The Queen!'

All the great company parted for her and fell to their knees as she passed them.

The Cardinal watched her speculatively. If she were in love, he thought, she would know no restraint; then she would turn from a husband who, if not impotent, was next door to it. Then there would be a child. It would be almost certain with one as passionate as Mary would become. It would not be the first time that a King believed the child of another man to be his.

His eyes met those of the Queen-Mother. She composed her features. Ah, thought the Cardinal, you were a little too late that time, Madame le Serpent. You are desperately afraid that she is already with child. That would spoil your plans, Madame. We know that you are waiting for your son François to die, so that your little puppet Charles, his Mother's boy, shall take the throne, and you, Madame, shall enjoy that position behind it which is now mine and my brother's. But he must not die yet. Everything must be done to prevent such a calamity. He must not die until he has fathered Mary's child.

Mary sat at the head of the banqueting table and her eyes glistened as she surveyed the delicacies set before her. The Queen-Mother, in her place at the great table, for the moment forgot her anxiety as to the condition of her daughter-in-law. She relished her food even more than did the little Queen. Fish delicacies, meat delicacies, all the arts known to the masters of cookery were there to be enjoyed. They both ate as though ravenous, and the company about them did likewise.

But when the meal was over and Mary rose, she was beset by such pains that she was forced to grip the table for support; the lovely face beneath the headdress of pearls was waxy pale. Mary Beaton ran to her side to catch her before she fell fainting to the floor.

There was consternation, although all were aware of the attacks which now and then overcame the Queen.

The Cardinal was alert. He had never seen Mary swoon before, although he knew that the pains she suffered, particularly after a meal, were often acute. Could it be that she was mistaken when she had said there was not to be a child? He saw the colour deepen in his brother's face and the eye above the scar begin to water excessively. Could Mary be unaware of her state? Was it the quickening of the child which had made her faint?

In such a moment the brothers could not hide their elation. The Queen-Mother intercepted their triumphant glances. She also was too moved to mask her feelings. This could be as much her tragedy as the Guise brothers' triumph.

She quickly pushed her way to the fainting girl.

Mary Beaton said: 'I will get Her Majesty's *aqua composita* at once, Madame. It never fails to revive her.'

The Queen-Mother knelt down by the Queen and looked searchingly into her face. Mary, slowly opening her eyes, gave a little cry of horror at finding the face of Catherine de' Medici so close to her own.

'All is well, all is well,' said Catherine. 'Your Majesty fainted. Have you the *aqua*? It is the best thing.'

The Queen-Mother herself held the cup to the Queen's lips.

'I am better now,' declared Mary. 'The pain was so sharp. I . . . I am afraid it was too much for me.'

They helped her to her feet and she groped for the arm of Mary Beaton.

'I will retire to my apartments,' she said. 'I beg of you all, continue with your dancing and games. I shall feel happier if you do.'

The Cardinal stepped forward, but Mary said firmly: 'No, my dear Cardinal. I command you to remain. You too, Madame. Come, Beaton, give me your arm. My Maries will conduct me to my chamber and help me to bed.'

They who had crowded all about her drew back and dropped to their knees as, with her four faithful women she went from the banqueting chamber.

She lay on the oaken bedstead, the scarlet damask curtains drawn about it. The pain had subsided but it had left her exhausted. She would sleep until morning and then rise refreshed from her bed.

She was awakened by a movement at her bedside. She knew that it was not late for she could hear the music from the ballroom. She opened her eyes and turning saw the Queen-Mother standing by her bed.

Mary felt suddenly cold with apprehension. 'Madame!' she cried, raising herself.

'I did not mean to disturb Your Majesty,' said Catherine. 'I came to see if you were at rest.' She laid a hand on Mary's forehead. 'You have a touch of fever, I fear.'

'It is good of you to disturb yourself, Madame, but I know that it will pass. These attacks always do. They are painful while they last, but when they are gone I feel quite well.'

'You have no sickness? You must tell me. Your health is of the utmost importance to me. You know that I have some knowledge of cures. Monsieur Paré will tell you that I come near to being a rival of his. You must let me care for you.'

'I thank you, Madame, but I do not need your care. Where are my women?'

'You must not blame them for letting me come to you. They understand my concern, and they dared not refuse my entry. Although now I have taken a step backward, they remember that, only a little while ago, I stood in your exalted position.' She laughed her loud laugh. 'I still have some authority in the Court, my dear daughter.'

Catherine's long delicate fingers were feeling Mary's body–the small, not yet fully developed breasts, she was thinking, were not the breasts of an expectant mother.

Mary sprang up indignantly. 'Madame, you concern yourself too much. I am well. I need only rest.'

'I will send Your Majesty a potion. Drink it and I'll warrant you'll feel better in the morning.'

'Madame, I feel better relying on my own remedies. But it is good of you to take such care of me.'

The Queen blew with her lips–a habit of hers. 'And you my own daughter, the wife of my son? Naturally you are my concern. I think continually of your health. I will bring the potion to you at once.'

'Then I pray you leave it with Beaton or one of my women. I will sleep now and do not wish to be disturbed.'

'It will do you so much good that–as your mother–I shall insist on your taking it at once.'

Catherine went out smiling, and Mary lay still, her heart beating wildly.

It was not long before she heard a commotion in the apartment.

Beaton's voice: 'But, Madame, the Queen gave express orders . . .' Catherine's voice: 'Out of the way, my good woman. I myself will see that the Queen takes this dose.'

Mary kept her eyes tightly shut as the curtains were parted and Beaton with Catherine stood at her bedside.

'Her Majesty needs to sleep,' said Beaton in a high-pitched whisper which betrayed her fear.

Mary could picture the scene: Queen Catherine standing there with the goblet in her hand. Poor Beaton terrified, remembering all the rumours she had heard concerning the Italian woman.

What is in the goblet? wondered Mary. She hates me. She wants François to die so that Charles will be the King. Could it be that she wishes to poison me, as some say she poisoned her husband's brother? How would that serve her? No! It is not *I* whom she wishes to kill; it is the child she thinks is within me. That goblet will contain nothing deadly enough to kill *me*. There will be just enough poison to put an end to the life of an unborn child.

Beaton said, with great presence of mind: 'I dare not disturb Her Majesty. That was her command.'

There was a pause before the Queen-Mother spoke. 'I will leave this draught beside her bed. See that she takes it as soon as she wakes. It will ease her of her pains more quickly than anything the doctors can give her.'

'Yes, Madame.'

There was silence. Then Mary heard the sound of footsteps passing across the floor, and the shutting of a door.

When all was quiet she sat up in bed. 'Beaton,' she whispered. 'Beaton, are you there?'

Beaton came hurrying to her bedside.

'I was awake,' said Mary. 'I heard all that was said.'

'Do not drink of it,' said Beaton. 'I beg of Your Majesty not to drink.'

'Assuredly I shall not drink. Take it and throw it away . . . quickly, lest she comes back.'

Beaton was only too glad to do so. She returned in a few seconds with the empty goblet.

Beaton—strong practical Beaton—suddenly stepped forward and threw herself into the Queen's arms. She did not speak, but tremors passed through her body.

They had said good-bye to Elisabeth. The parting saddened Mary. It was a sobering thought that her dear little playmate was lost to her, perhaps for ever. There would be letters, but how could letters make up for that almost constant companionship which they had enjoyed over so many years?

There was bad news from Scotland where John Knox was demanding that Scotland seek freedom from the 'Roman Harlot' as he called the Catholic Faith. Elizabeth of England was supporting him and appeared to have forgiven him for writing his 'First Blast of the Trumpet against the Monstrous Regiment of Women'. Lord James Stuart was fretting for the Regency and Elizabeth was encouraging him. William Maitland of Lethington stood firmly with Lord James. The Duke of Châtelherault, with his unbalanced son Arran, was not far behind. They were fighting to establish Protestantism and drive Catholicism from the land.

The French sent aid, but it was not enough. All through the winter months came urgent appeals from the Queen Dowager of Scotland.

Mary was beginning to understand something of these matters; they could not be kept from her so easily now. Her thoughts were often with her mother whom she had not seen for nine years, although many letters had been exchanged between them. Mary smiled now to remember how hers had been full of trivialities.

One day she became more uneasy than ever. This was when Seton came to her and told her—when they were alone together—that she had seen a meeting between the King of Navarre and the English ambassador; and as the King of Navarre had evidently thought it advisable to go to the rendezvous heavily disguised, it would seem as though some intrigue was afoot between these two.

'But the King of Navarre is our own cousin,' said Mary. 'He could not be involved in plots against us.'

'He is involved in plots against your uncles mayhap,' said Seton. 'So many are . . . since they came to power.'

Mary shivered. 'There is nothing but intrigue all about us. Seton, what will happen if the English take my Scottish crown from me?'

'Your Majesty will still be Queen of France.'

Mary thought of the sickly boy who was her husband. She thought of Catherine, standing by her bedside with the goblet in her hands.

For how long would she be Queen of France? she wondered. And then what would happen to her?

Mary was sitting on the stone balcony which overlooked the courtyard of the Castle of Amboise. François was beside her and around them were ranged all the notable people of the Court, including the royal children.

It was March and the day was bright and cold. Mary sat shivering, though not because of the weather. These were the most terrible moments through which she had ever lived. She did not believe that she could endure much more. François' face had turned a sickly green. The younger children were staring before them at the spectacle presented to them, with something like astonishment; they could not believe that it could really be happening. The Duchesse de Guise, wife of Uncle François was fainting in her chair, her face the colour of the balcony stone. She was in danger of falling but none dared go to her; they were afraid of the fury of the Duke.

Mary thought: I can no longer bear this. I cannot look on such things.

Who could be unmoved by such cruelty? The Queen-Mother could. She seemed to be watching with a calm interest. The Cardinal was also unmoved. There was a slight lifting of his lip which implied that he was gratified by the knowledge that those martyrs, who were being slaughtered and tortured before the eyes of the royal household, were not only learning but showing others what happened to those who opposed th House of Guise.

Mary's eyes went involuntarily to the gibbet from which hung the limp figure of the Sieur de la Renaudie. The body swayed slightly in the March breeze; oddly enough it seemed to mock all the sightseers on the balcony; it seemed to be jeering at them. He was dead, he seemed to imply as he swayed indifferently, and nothing further could be done to hurt him.

François took Mary's hand and pressed it. She turned her sorrowing eyes to his; silently they pleaded with him to stop this cruelty. But who were they to stop it? Each day they realized more and more that they were powerless. They bore proud titles; the people bowed and called them King and Queen; that was the extent of their power. When Mary was told: 'You are Queen of England!' she had no alternative but to allow herself to be called Queen of England. When the followers of the Sieur de la Renaudie were brought up from the dungeons of Amboise and slaughtered before the eyes of the women and children of the royal household in the King's name, the King had no power to forbid such brutality.

It had been explained to them. These rebels had planned to kidnap the King and Queen and members of the royal family, to banish the Guises and, if the King refused to become a Protestant, to set up a new King on the throne. But if the Guises had enemies, they also had friends. The plot had been concocted with the aid of the English, but English Catholics had heard of it and warned the Duke of Guise, with the result that it had been foiled and many prisoners had been taken.

'And not a single conspirator shall be spared.' declared the Duke. 'They shall all be brought up from their dungeons. This will be a lesson to traitors.'

Heads, recently severed from living bodies, made ugly the beautiful battlements of the castle. The stench of blood was everywhere. Some of the rebels had been tied in sacks and thrown into the river. The beautiful Loire was stained with blood. There was blood everywhere . . . the sight, the smell of blood.

And the royal House of France–even young Margot and Hercule among them–must look on at the slaying of tortured men. They must watch slow and cruel death being meted out.

The Duchesse de Guise had struggled to her feet. She turned and ran from the balcony. Her husband, her brother-in-law and her son watched her with contempt.

Mary said: 'François . . . François . . . I too must go. These sights will haunt me for ever.'

'They will not permit it, Mary,' whispered François. 'The Duchesse may go, but not the King and Queen.'

'It must be stopped. François, you must stop it. I cannot bear it.'

The Duke was looking at her coldly, the Cardinal in astonishment.

'Your Majesty should resume your seat,' said the Cardinal. 'Your Majesty sets a bad example to others present.'

The Duke cried: 'My wife and now my niece! By the saints, this is a sad day for Guise and Lorraine.'

The Queen-Mother came forward and laid a hand on Mary's shoulder. She looked at the Guises with understanding. She had been flirting with the Protestant cause and was anxious to show the powerful brothers–since they were at the moment in the ascendant–that she was with them.

'Your Majesty will never know how to reign if you do not learn how to administer justice,' she said.

François looked at his wife eagerly when she resumed her seat.

He took her hand and tried to soothe her. But she was sickened by the stench of blood. She would never think of Amboise after this, she was sure–dear, beloved Amboise from whose eminence she had looked down on the mingling streams of the Loire and the Amasse–without remembering this terrible day.

She knew, in that moment, that she was afraid not only of Catherine but of her uncles; never, until now, had she realized what an empty title she bore. Her dignity was touched; her anger grew. These terrible deeds were done in her name–hers and that of François. These poor men were crying for mercy to her and to François, and by sitting here, meekly looking on, she and François were registering their approval of the deeds which were done in their names.

She could not stop the slaughter; she knew that. But she would not sit quietly and see it done.

'I *will not* stay here, François,' she said firmly. 'I *will* not.'

'Hush!' he soothed. 'Hush, dearest! They will hear. We have to stay. They say so.'

'You are the King,' she murmured.

The colour was glowing in her face now as she went on: 'The King may remain if he wishes. The Queen shall not.'

She made to rise. Her uncle, the Cardinal, was beside her; she felt his hands forcing her into her seat.

'François,' she cried, 'you are the King.'

And in that moment–for the first time in his life–François *was* the King.

He rose, and suddenly a new dignity came to him. He said: 'Monsieur le Cardinal, I command you to take your hands from the Queen.'

There was silence on the balcony. In very astonishment the Cardinal had dropped his hands to his sides.

'You wish to go to your apartments?' said François to Mary.

His mother came forward. 'My son,' she said, and there was the venom of the serpent in her cold eyes and her cold voice, 'it is the duty of the King and Queen to see that justice is done. Remember you are the King.'

'I do remember, Madame,' said François. 'And I would ask you to do so. You also, Cardinal. Come, Mary. You wish to retire. Then let us go.'

He took Mary's hand and led her from the balcony. No one attempted to stop them. François, for one short moment, was indeed King of France.

François' glory was short-lived. He had not the courage to sustain his new role. He realized that he had succeeded merely because he had taken those clever enemies of his by surprise.

The Cardinal's long mouth continued to sneer at him, continued to command. His mother was for ever at his side. He was growing weaker. There was an abscess in his ear which caused him great pain, and Monsieur Paré could do little to ease it. Each day his strength seemed to wane.

He knew that the people did not love him and that they blamed him for the terrible things which were happening under the reign of the Guises.

Rumours concerning the young King spread throughout the country.

'The King suffers from a wasting disease,' was whispered. 'It is terrible in its consequences and a miracle that he lives at all. He only does so by drinking the blood of freshly-killed babies.'

Wherever the King rode, the people called their children to them in terror; they bolted and barred their doors in the villages through which he passed.

'When my father rode abroad,' said François sadly, 'the people hurried out to greet him. It was the same with my grandfather. Yet they shrink from me; they run from me; they hate and fear me. My father–good man though he was–was responsible for the death of many; my grandfather too. Yet they loved these kings and they run from me who have killed no one. Oh, Mary, life is so unfair. Why was I born like this? Why was I not born tall and strong like my father and my grandfather? Why cannot I be a King, since I am born a King . . . as they were? Why do I have to be the tool of the Cardinal? I hate the Cardinal. I hate him . . . hate him. . . .'

The Cardinal had come into the room. He was smiling slyly, but François' grief was too deep for him to care for the Cardinal's contempt. He ran to the man, grasped his padded robes and shook him.

He cried: 'I believe it is you they hate. I do not believe it is their King. They know I would not hurt them. It is you they hate . . . you . . . *you*! Why don't you leave us alone? Why don't you go away–then we shall know whom it is the people hate . . . you or me . . . you or me . . .' François' voice rose to a shriek as he cried: '*Renard lasche le roi!*' Then he turned away and covered his face with his hands.

The Cardinal laughed. 'Is this a raving lunatic?' he asked of Mary. 'I had thought to parley with the King of France, and I am confronted by a madman.'

'He is not mad,' said Mary. 'He has just awakened. He is no longer a boy to be led. He has discovered that he is the King.'

'These are wild words,' said the Cardinal sadly, 'and foolish ones. I would not have expected to hear them from you.'

Mary thought of all the care he had given her, but she thought also of the love François had always had for her. She would never forget as long as she lived how, because she had been in distress on the balcony, he had forgotten his fear and in the face of all those whose displeasure he dreaded he had, for her sake, remembered he was a King.

François had begun to sob hysterically. He cried: 'You are afraid . . . you are more afraid than I. You are afraid of an enemy's dagger. That is why your clothes are padded. That is why the fashion of cloaks and boots must be changed. In the fashions we see signs of a Cardinal's cowardice.'

'It would seem to me,' said the Cardinal, 'that the King is deranged. Perhaps I should call the Queen-Mother. I thank God that there are others who could readily take his place should his mind become too deranged for him to wear the crown.'

Mary cried: 'Should you call him deranged because he seeks to remind you that he is the King of France?'

The Cardinal looked at the sobbing boy. 'There is the most cowardly heart that ever beat inside the body of a King,' he muttered.

'I beg of you, do not try him too far,' said Mary.

The Cardinal snapped his sparkling fingers to imply his contempt for the King.

Mary's eyes flashed. 'Do not be so sure that you are right, my uncle. I am not the foolish girl you seem to think me. I know what is happening here . . . and in Scotland. You . . . and my uncle . . . have set the English against me. You may well have lost me my Scottish crown.'

The Cardinal looked at her in horror. His face was stern as he said: 'This I cannot endure. I have given my devotion to you. I have thought of nothing but your welfare since you came to France. I have cherished you. I have loved you more than any living person. And you talk to me like this! You break my heart.'

Mary looked at him in anguish. What had she said? It was true that he had loved her. No one had cherished her as he had. She, remembering those intimate moments which they had shared, could not bear to see his proud head bent.

'Uncle,' she said, 'my dearest Uncle . . .' she ran to him. His face relaxed. She was held in those arms; her body was crushed against the scarlet padded robes. His lips were on her forehead, on her cheek, on her mouth.

'So you love me then, beloved? You love me yet?'

'Dearest Uncle, I shall never forget what you have done for me.'

He took her face in his hands, 'Plans,' he said, 'the best plans go wrong sometimes, Mary. What has happened in Scotland is a bitter blow, I grant you. But have no fear. Your Uncle François is the most powerful man in France. He loves you. I love you. Together we will face the world for your sake.'

'I know.'

'It is what happened at Amboise, is it not, which has turned you from me? That shocked you, my dearest. But it was necessary. You ask yourself, How could we order such things to be done? How could we look on with apparent satisfaction? For this reason, Mary: Because these scoundrels were attempting to harm our beloved niece. We may be hard men; but we love the deeper for that.'

Now she was weeping. He was dominating her once more. Now he was, as he had said, her spiritual lover. Nothing could come between them–certainly not a diseased boy, even if he called himself the King.

All was well, thought the Cardinal. Let her comfort the crying boy now if she could.

Mary was his, and the King was hers; and that meant, of course, that the Duke and Cardinal, since they need fear no opposition from the King and Queen, could continue to rule France.

In the antechamber at Saint Germain a young Scots nobleman was waiting to see the Queen of France. He came with letters from the Queen-Regent of Scotland, and he had proved himself to be one of the few men about that Queen whom she believed she could trust.

He was twenty-five years of age. Tall and broad-shouldered, he gave an impression of enormous strength and vitality; his expression was one of cool unconcern; he was arrogant in the extreme, and many of the elegant

Frenchmen who had looked askance at this man who had the appearance of a Norse warrior, had turned quickly away lest that indolent stare, which their faint mockery had aroused, might change to something still less pleasing. No man, looking into that granite-like face, sensing the power in those great arms and shoulders, would care to take the consequences of his anger single-handed.

He stood, legs apart, a man who would be noticed in any assembly, dominant, the over-powering vitality showing itself in the coarse springy hair, the bold flashing eyes, the entirely sensual mouth which suggested that he was a man of many adventures, sexual and warlike; and this impression was by no means a false one. He was as hardy as the granite hills of his native land; he was as wild as the Border from which he came. He was James Hepburn, who had been for the last four years–since the death of his father–the Earl of Bothwell.

As he waited he was wondering what good could come to him through this meeting with the Queen. He had heard a few days ago that her mother had died. She had long suffered from a dropsical complaint and her death was not unexpected. Now the girl who had not reached her eighteenth birthday was his Queen; he would offer her his faithful service, but in return he would expect rewards.

He had heard tales of her fascination but he was sceptical. He did not believe that one woman could be as perfect as she was represented to be. His lips curled a little. The beauty of Queens was apt to be overrated. No Hepburn would join the ranks of their idolators. Queens were women and it was folly to forget that all-important fact. No Hepburn should. There was a story in the family that his ancestor, Adam Hepburn, had found the royal widow, Mary of Guelders, most accessible, and that Queen had become, so it had been recorded, 'lecherous of her body' with the Hepburn. His own father, Patrick Hepburn–who had been called the Fair Earl and had had a way with women–had hoped to marry the Queen, Marie de Guise, and had even divorced his wife, James' mother, to make the way clear. It was true that the royal widow had used his desires in that direction to suit her own purposes, but she had been the loser when, in his pique and anger against her, he had become friendly with the English.

To James Hepburn Queens were women, and he had yet to meet the woman who had been able to show an indifference to him.

He would ask for some high office, for he was an ambitious man. He would never be like his father, whatever the provocation, for he hated the English and wished to serve Scotland and the Queen faithfully; but he wished to be rewarded for doing so.

He whistled the tune of a border song as he waited. He was glad to be in France. He had spent some of his youth here, for a certain amount of education at the Court of France was considered by the Scots nobility as a desirable part of a young man's upbringing. Scotland was closely united with France and the French had the reputation of being the most cultured Court in the world. To France came young Scotsmen, and so to France some years ago had come James Hepburn.

He was particularly glad to be here at this time; not only because it was an important time politically, but in order to escape the tearful and too passionate devotion of Anna Throndsen. Anna was expecting their child; he had promised marriage, but he grew tired of women very quickly.

His upbringing had aggravated those characteristics which made him the man he was. He did not remember very much of his life before he was nine years old. That must have been because it was so easy and pleasant; his mother had had charge of him and his sister Janet, and the two of them had been tenderly cared for. They were perhaps wild by nature; they needed restraint, for the family traits were strongly marked in both of them. Their ancestors were lusty men, strong, wild and sensual.

It was unfortunate that, when James was nine years old, his father had secured a divorce from his mother. Ostensibly the grounds were consanguinity; actually they were brought because the Fair Earl wished to pay court to Mary of Guise.

The Countess of Bothwell was forced to leave her home and with it her two children. Gone was the restraining hand and the two–red-headed Janet and tawny James–ran wild.

As a boy of nine James saw terrible things. Henry the Eighth had declared war on Scotland and with typical ferocity had instructed his soldiers to put all to the fire and sword.

'Burn and subvert!' cried the tyrant. 'Put all men and women to fire and sword without exception where any resistance should be shown to you. Spoil and set upside down, as the upper stone may be the nether, and not one stick stand by another, sparing no creature.'

The life of adventure had begun. James in his flight from one town to another, saw the soldiers of the English King carry out his orders. As a result the boy was filled with a passionate hatred towards the English, a hatred which burned within him and made him long to act as he saw their soldiers acting. Rape, torture and death were commonplace sights to him. They did not disgust; they were part of the adventurous way of life; he merely longed to turn the tables, and he swore he would one day.

He became a man at an early age. He was cynically aware of his father's alliance with the enemy; he knew of his father's fondness for women.

He spent a great part of his youth in the establishment of his great-uncle Patrick, Bishop of Aberdeen. The Bishop was a merry man, eager to educate his great-nephew in such a way as to bring credit to the name of Hepburn. He was a great drinker; food and drink, he declared, were the greatest pleasures in life, apart from one other. He would slap the boy on the back when he told him this. The one other? Did he not know? The Bishop put his hands on his knees and rocked with laughter. He would wager the boy–being a Hepburn–would soon know what he meant; if he did not, then, by all the saints, he could not be his father's son.

In the Bishop's Palace the young James would lie awake and listen to the nightly perambulations of his great-uncle's friends. There were whisperings and laughter, little screams of pleasure. James thought he understood. Life at Crichton, his father's home, had not been without these phenomena, but never had he known them conducted on the scale they were in the Bishop's Palace of Spynie.

The Bishop was very fond of several comely serving women. He would chuck them under the chin or pinch various parts of their bodies as he passed them. Sometimes young James would be with him, but he did not abstain from his intimate greeting for the sake of the boy. Why should he? the boy was a Hepburn.

'A real Hepburn!' he would say; and if there was a woman at hand he would push the boy towards her and she, taking her cue, would caress him and say that he was indeed a lovely boy.

In the banqueting hall James would sometimes sit with the Bishop and his cronies, listening to their conversation which invariably concerned their amatory adventures.

The Bishop's numerous children often came to visit him, and he was very fond of them all. There were so many Janets and so many Patricks that James could not remember them all. It was the Bishop's delight to have them legitimized, several at a time.

James willingly took to the life at the Palace of Spynie. It was the life for him. He very soon began to swagger with the Bishop and his friends. He learned how to carry his liquor and boast of his adventures. The Bishop was delighted in his great-nephew. A true Hepburn! was his frequent comment.

In France, whither he had gone to complete his education, he found nothing that he had learned at Spynie a disadvantage. He never did and never would like what he thought of as the effeminate manners of the French. He would not abandon his Scottish accent; he would not ape anybody. He was himself and was determined to continue to be. Moreover he found that his methods were as effective as any. There was not a gallant in the Court of France who could boast of so many easy conquests as could James Hepburn, for all that he did not write pretty poems, nor dance and scent himself, nor wear jewels in his ears. His attractiveness lay in his dynamic personality, in that obvious virility. Not for him the graces; he would not attempt to woo. It was his way to take at a moment's fancy, for that was the way to enjoy. Too long deliberation was fatal to pleasure; his passions came quickly and as quickly passed.

His most satisfying love affair had been with Janet Beaton, aunt to that Mary Beaton who was one of the Queen's Maries. She had had three husbands and was nineteen years older than James, but a wonderful woman, tempering wisdom with passion, friendship with love. It was a very satisfying relationship to both of them. They had become 'handfast', which meant that they were betrothed and that the betrothal was binding. Handfasting involved no actual ceremony. The couple merely lived together and, if after a certain period, they wished to go through the ceremony of marriage, they were free to do so.

The difference in their ages was too great, James realized; Janet realized it also. Janet was the only reasonable woman he had encountered in his amatory life, for he tired so quickly, the women so slowly. Janet had said that though they ceased to be lovers, there was no reason why they should not remain friends. With Janet he had been as nearly in love as he could be.

It was a pity that Anna Throndsen was not so reasonable.

He had set out on an embassy for the Queen-Mother of Scotland. First he was to go to Denmark where he was to use his persuasive powers on King Frederick that he might lend his fleet to Scotland against the English; secondly he must visit the Court of France, taking letters to the Queen from her mother.

He had set off for Denmark with high hopes, and his sojourn there might have been very successful, for he had won Frederick's promise of help; but with the death of the Queen, the political situation had changed. England was ready to discuss peace with France and Scotland, so that Frederick's offer was no longer needed.

Meanwhile James' personal affairs were giving him some anxiety.

Anna was not only attractive, she was clever; she had been outstanding among the women he had met in Denmark, not only because she was dark among so many who were fair-haired, but because she was a shrewd business woman. The eldest of seven daughters and having one younger brother, she was bold and ruled her parents. James was immediately attracted and they very quickly shared the same bed. Anna had ideas about marriage; she understood that James was a lover without much love, but with lust which came quickly and was quickly satisfied. But his virility was overpowering, and even Anna had succumbed and had felt the need to satisfy passion and make arrangements afterwards.

She believed that she could use him in the future. James was less calculating. He had the borderer's instinct: a successful Lieutenant of the Border it had been his custom to take his choice of the women prisoners, and the affair would be over and done with quickly; he gave it not another thought. He wished it could always be thus, but there were occasions, in a more regulated society than that of a town in the process of ravishment, when certain tiresome preliminaries were necessary.

Anna was attractive enough to occupy his attention for more than one night–or even two. She saw the ambitious man in her lover; she saw the Scots noble from impoverished estates, so she allowed the rumour to be put about that she was an heiress to no small fortune. James swallowed the bait and suggested marriage.

He had never met such a clever woman. In no time she was pregnant. They must be married. She was the daughter of an honourable Danish family.

He had discovered Anna's fortune to be mythical; he had also discovered that his desire for her was on the wane; but he could not elude her altogether. When he was ready to leave Denmark (and at that time he had not heard of the death of the Queen-Mother of Scotland and was therefore a petitioner in a hospitable land) he must take her with him, her family said; and in view of the delicate political situation he could see no alternative.

So he and Anna left Copenhagen, but when they reached Flanders he reasoned with her.

'Should I arrive at the French Court with a mistress big with child?' he demanded. 'We shall have those dandified ninnies laughing behind our backs.'

'You could arrive with the Countess of Bothwell whose condition is a delight to you,' said Anna quickly.

'A speedy marriage . . . and in a foreign land? Impossible!'

'With a man such as you are nothing is impossible.'

There was some truth in that, he thought, and, by God, I'll not take you farther. Hard as it is to rid myself of your company, you are right when you say that with me nothing is impossible.

He was cunning; he had merely been caught by the unexpectedness of her tactics, for previously he had never been forced to plead with a woman; he had said: 'Come hither!' and they came; he coolly walked off afterwards leaving them weeping and hoping for his return. He should have known Anna was no ordinary woman.

'The French,' he said contemptuously, 'are sticklers for their etiquette. the Queen has been brought up as one of them. I have my future to consider.'

'I shall see to it.' said Anna demurely, 'that it is *our* future.'

But Anna, as her pregnancy advanced, grew less truculent. She wished only to lie and rest half the day. The prospect of an uncomfortable journey across Flanders alarmed her, and she knew that he would not marry her until they reached Scotland and that it would be necessary to have their child legitimized after its birth. But she would know how to find him; he was too prominent a man to be able to lose himself.

So when he continued to urge that she should stay in Flanders while he went on alone to the French Court, she at length agreed.

Her farewell was tender, but it held a warning in it. James remembered that warning now. It was ominous. 'Do not think I am a woman to be lightly taken up and then cast off. If you think that, James Hepburn, you do not know Anna Throndsen.'

This would be a lesson to him in future. But he had no great qualms. He was not one to brood on the future; he let that take care of itself. He had been in too many scrapes to worry about consequences; he had faced death so often that he was not to be alarmed by a persistent woman.

A page came to him and, bowing before him, asked if Lord Bothwell would be so good as to follow him.

He did so until the page threw open a door and announced: 'My Lord, the Earl of Bothwell.'

He started forward expecting to see the young Queen of whom he had heard so much. Instead it was a red-clad figure, tall, dignified and imposing; and he recognized the Cardinal of Lorraine who, he had heard, with the help of his brother ruled France.

The two men took each other's measure. The sensuality of each was his most outstanding characteristic, yet there could not have been two men more different. The Cardinal was the gourmet, Bothwell the gourmand. The Cardinal was subtle; Bothwell was direct. One was a man of physical inactivity, the other a man of action. The Cardinal pandered to his sensual appetites, using aphrodisiac means–mental and physical–to stimulate them; Bothwell needed no such stimulation. The Cardinal was a coward; Bothwell did not know the meaning of fear. They were two strong men, but their strength lay in different directions.

The Cardinal disliked the boldness of the coarse Borderer; Bothwell disdained the arrogance of the elegant gentleman. But they were each aware of the power possessed by the other. The Cardinal, by far the cleverer of the two, was able to hide his resentment the more easily.

'I had thought to see my Queen,' said Bothwell.

'Monsieur,' smiled the Cardinal, 'you have come from Scotland where Court manners are slightly different. In France we await the pleasure of the Queen. We do not present ourselves unless commanded to do so.'

'I have letters from the Queen's late mother. Doubtless she will be eager to receive them.'

'Doubtless. But as Queen of France she has much with which to occupy herself. I know you have come from Denmark where you did good work. I heard from my dear sister, before her unfortunate demise, that you were a worthy young man whom she delighted to honour with her trust. I therefore welcome you to the Court of France.'

'You are gracious, Monsieur le Cardinal, but it is my Queen I have come to see.'

'You have the letters from her mother?' The Cardinal extended his slim white hand.

'My instructions were to hand them to none but the Queen herself.'

'The Queen has no secrets from me.'

'So I have heard,' answered Bothwell. 'But those were my instructions.'

The Cardinal sighed. 'There is one matter I must discuss with you. The

Queen does not know of her mother's death. I myself wish to break the news and break it gently. She has suffered from bad health lately and I fear the shock might prove too much for her.'

Bothwell's lips were set in an obstinate line. He did not see why he should take orders from the Cardinal. He disliked taking orders. His policy with the late Queen had been a bold one. He was no Court intrigant and flatterer. Now that her mother was dead it was well for the Queen of Scots to know of the acute danger which such a situation threatened. He had come to warn her of just that; and now, this man, doubtless for reasons of his own, was forcing him to silence on a most important issue.

'I have had no instructions,' declared Bothwell, 'to keep silent on this matter.'

'Until now . . . no,' agreed the Cardinal.

'My lord Cardinal, this is a matter which I must discuss with others of my countrymen. Lord Seton is here at Saint-Germain. I . . .'

'That gentleman has already received his instructions in the matter.'

'And the King of France?' said Bothwell with a trace of insolence. 'These are his instructions?'

'The King, Monsieur, knows nothing of the tragedy. If he knew of it, he would be unable to prevent himself from imparting it to the Queen.'

'So then the King and Queen are kept in ignorance of certain facts which concern them!'

The Cardinal decided to smile at such insolence. He said: 'The King and Queen are very young–little more than children. It is the express desire of her uncle, the Duke of Guise, and myself as well as the Queen-Mother of France, not to overtax them. We lighten their burdens as best we can. It is our considered opinion, in view of the Queen's failing health, that she should not at present suffer the shock such news would give her. Therefore, my lord Bothwell, you will say nothing of her mother's death. I myself will break the news to her when I consider she is fit to receive it.'

'You are not afraid that someone's indiscretion may betray the news?'

'We know how to deal with indiscreet people, my lord. And all of us who love the Queen have no wish to do aught which would bring harm to her. Give me your assurance that you will say nothing of her mother's death, and no obstacle shall be put in the way of your meeting the Queen.'

Bothwell hesitated, but only for a moment. He was sharp enough to see that this man could prevent his meeting with the Queen.

'I give my word,' he said.

The Cardinal was satisfied. There was that about the Scottish adventurer which implied that having given his word he would keep it.

James Hepburn, Earl of Bothwell stood before the Queen of France and Scotland.

He had knelt and kissed her hand and had now been bidden to rise. He was acutely aware, among those about her, of the red clad figure of the Cardinal.

So here was the Queen of Scotland! he pondered. This was the young woman of whom he had heard so much. This was the 'skittering lass' the Hamiltons referred to. She was but a pale and delicate girl.

It was characteristic of James Hepburn that in those few seconds he had stripped her of her royalty and had seen her as a woman. He was aware of curling chestnut hair that gleamed red and gold in places, long–but not large–eyes, a gentle and smiling mouth, a skin that was pale and delicate, a carriage which suggested pride of race and great dignity. He thought her fair enough, but he had been expecting one more dazzling. He thought of Anna's dark beauty; Mary Stuart's was of a different kind.

That underlying, but as yet unawakened sensuality which was the secret cause–far more than her beauty–of Mary's attractiveness, was beyond his perception. He was attracted by the obvious. He thought Mary unhealthy and the unhealthy did not please him. She was French, for all she called herself the Queen of Scots. Her dress and manners–everything about her–was French. She was a fragile and pretty creature–that was all as far as he could judge.

That she was his Queen was quite another matter.

'My Lord Bothwell,' she addressed him, 'you have brought letters from my mother.'

He said this was so and that he was honoured and delighted to have the opportunity of offering them to her.

He took them from the pocket of his doublet and gave them to her. Smiling she took them. Then he saw her charm. A pretty wench, he thought, but, alas, not a bonny one.

The Cardinal was murmuring to the Queen: 'I will relieve Your Majesty of these documents.' Mary handed them to him. 'Later,' went on the Cardinal, 'if it is Your Majesty's pleasure, we will go through them together.'

'That is my pleasure,' said the Queen.

Bothwell's lips tightened. He himself might just as well have handed the documents to the Cardinal. Did she never do anything unless this man allowed her to?

The Queen was smiling at Bothwell. 'Pray sit down,' she said. 'Here beside me. There is much I wish to hear of Scotland.'

He sat down. She threw a sidelong look at him. That virility alarmed while it fascinated. She was not sure whether she found it attractive or repulsive. With the Cardinal hovering beside her she believed she found it repulsive. She had heard of this Bothwell; he was the successful Lieutenant of the Border and would have lived a wild life. She pictured him, ravishing the towns across the Border, driving the cattle before him, herding the women . . . like cattle. She had heard of such things. He would be brutal, this man. He made her shiver.

'You have come by way of Denmark,' she said.

'Yes, Your Majesty. It was the wish of the Queen, your mother, that I should visit the Court of King Frederick to make requests of him.'

'She will doubtless have told me of these requests in the letters you bring.'

Bothwell was astounded. Did she know nothing? Was she left entirely in the dark? He had come to warn her of the state of her Scottish realm. He had come to warn her of the claims of Arran, the treachery she might expect from the Bastard, Lord James Stuart; he had come to warn her of the machinations of Elizabeth of England and her minister Cecil. There was an immediate need to appoint a new Regent. Yet she–a silly, simpering girl–seemed to know nothing of these matters. Could it be true that she gave no thought to anything but dancing prettily and writing and reading verses?

God help Scotland with such a Queen! Bothwell thought with deep regret and affection of the valiant woman who had recently died after enduring continued hardship, fighting a desperate battle, not only against the English, but against her own rebel lords, while this girl, the real Queen, mimed and danced in French chateaux, making simpering Frenchmen fall in love with her!

Bothwell was about to speak, but the Cardinal forestalled him.

'Your Majesty, my lord Bothwell will be at Court for some time. You are tired now. Retire to your apartments and we will read these letters from your mother, the contents of which I am sure you will wish, above all things, to know, and most speedily. Then you will feel strong enough to hear his news.'

Mary hesitated. Then she said: 'Lord Bothwell, please present yourself at this hour tomorrow.'

James bowed. 'Your Majesty's servant.'

The Queen rose and laid her hand on the arm of the Cardinal with whom she went from the chamber.

Mary was thinking of Bothwell while the Cardinal broke the seals of her mother's letters and began to read them aloud to her.

He had made her uneasy. There was a certain insolence in his gaze. She could not complain; he had bowed low enough; he had kissed her hand in the appropriate manner; he had said the right words; but the eyes–that bold glance . . . how could she describe it? Insolent! It was not one of those passionate looks which she so often received and which she understood meant that the one who gave them longed to be her lover. This man was arrogant and cold and yet in a way he seemed to hint that he too imagined himself making love to her. It was too much to endure. Yet how could she complain?

She had not really known whether she wanted to remain with him or dismiss him. She had chosen to dismiss him because she felt he should know that it was for her to command. That was not entirely true. The Cardinal had intervened, had suggested she should retire because she was tired; and she had obeyed.

The Cardinal now saw that her attention wandered. He said: 'What did you think of the messenger? Was he not a crude clown. It is a sad thing that your mother could not find one more worthy of the mission. But, by all accounts, he may be trusted, which is more than can be said for most of these Scotsmen. A rough fellow–but he did good work on the Border. Such works suits him better, I'll vow, than playing ambassador. Murder and rape are his profession. We shall have to warn our ladies. We do not want him to offend them. We shall have to protect our serving girls. I hear he has a fondness for such.'

'I am sorry to hear it,' said Mary. 'My mother says he is a faithful servant. I should not like her ambassador to make trouble here . . . even if it were only with serving girls.'

'I had him watched in Denmark and Flanders. He is in some trouble with a woman now. It is unfortunate. She is the daughter of a retired Admiral–Christopher Throndsen, a man of some standing in Copenhagen. He promised the girl marriage, promptly seduced her, and now there is to be a child and he has left her to fend for herself in Flanders.'

'It is clear that he is a brute,' said Mary.

'He considers, I fancy, that he has behaved with decorum. Seduction is new to him; rape is his business.'

Mary shuddered. 'Dearest Uncle, do you mind if we speak of his affairs no more? I find them distasteful.'

The faintest satisfaction showed in the Cardinal's face. All was well. The man disgusted her. Her womanhood still slumbered.

Lord Bothwell stretched his legs on the bed in the apartment which had been assigned to him. His page, whom he had engaged recently because the fellow's cheeky manners appealed to him, and whom he called 'French Paris' though his name was really Nicholas Hubert, knelt to take off his master's boots.

'Have done!' growled Bothwell. 'I shall be up again in a minute, and then you'd be obliged to put them on again.'

Paris grinned. He enjoyed serving his master. Bothwell's love affairs were Paris's constant delight, and his greatest pleasure was to have some hand in arranging them.

'And what thought my lord of the Queen of France?'

Bothwell was silent for a few seconds. Then he said: 'It would seem to me that she'll not be long for this world. But mayhap it's this Court with its dancing and fancy ways. Mayhap our Scottish breezes would put her on the road to health.'

Paris had not wanted an opinion of the Queen's health. She was, he had heard, the most desirable woman in the world. Surely his lord had noticed that?

'She's a well-formed lass,' went on the Earl. 'But she needs to be taken out of soft wrappings and to rough it as her mother did. She seemed to know nothing of the country she is supposed to rule, and cares, I'll swear, as little. 'Tis as well for her that she's Queen of France and not obliged to live in her own country. We should have to teach her one or two things if she did.'

Paris nodded. 'There's much your lordship could teach her, I doubt not.'

Bothwell was silent for a few moments before he said: 'The Cardinal of Lorraine would seem to be King of this realm . . . with his brother thrown in. "Do this!" "Do that!" he says, and the Queen does it. "Don't listen to this and don't read that!" And she smiles and lets him have his way.'

'He's her uncle, my lord, but his reputation is the worst in the world.'

Bothwell leaped off his bed suddenly. 'And how does hers stand?' he demanded. 'I wonder! It would not surprise me if she were the Cardinal's mistress.'

'My lord!'

'Where I come from we don't mince our words. It would seem to me that she does all the Cardinal asks. And when it is a matter of asking anything of a woman, the Cardinal would not be backward in his demands–niece or no niece, Queen or tavern girl. Moreover I have seen that between them which tempts me to believe it. It would not surprise me at all.'

'And does my lord relish the thought?'

'Our Queen the Cardinal's loose woman to do his commands! What think you?'

Paris came closer and whispered: 'And does your lordship find it hard to stomach the thought for another reason?'

'What reason, fellow?'

'That your lordship would not mind being in the Cardinal's shoes for a spell?'

The Earl cuffed the man, and Paris retired, holding his ears but still grinning.

'A skittering lass!' Bothwell murmured to himself.

Of what could he talk to the Queen? He could tell her of the money he had lost in the defence of Leith; he could ask for the recompense he so sorely needed. He had talked to those men who had been engaged in the defence of Scotland with him and who were now at St Germain-en-Laye–Seton, Martigues and the Sieur d'Oysel. The Queen, they had told him, had been disinclined to grant their claims–on the advice of the Cardinal, of course. They were disgruntled, all of them.

This was not the occasion, Bothwell realized, to talk of his just deserts. He would try then to warn the Queen and to make sure that, when she formed her new government, he was selected to play a prominent part in it.

At this time the Cardinal decided that he could no longer keep the Queen in ignorance of her mother's death.

Mary was stunned by the news. Ignorant as she had been of the state of affairs in Scotland, she realized that, now that her mother was unable to guard her throne, it would be in peril.

She shut herself away to grieve alone, and her grief was great. It was nine years since her mother had visited the Court of France and yet they had remained close through their letters. Mary knew that she had lost one of the best friends she could ever have.

What would happen in Scotland now? Her thoughts went to the Borderer who had disturbed her with his bold personality. He would know, and he had been especially recommended to her by her mother.

It was easier for them to talk of Scotland now that she knew of her mother's death. Bothwell could talk freely of the perilous state of affairs which had sprung up. There was peace with England, it was true; but there were many warring elements within the troubled realm.

She received him in private. She was wan from the past days of mourning.

She said: 'My lord, you have come recently from Scotland. You will have knowledge of how matters go there. How fares my brother? I should like to see him again–dear Jamie! We were always so fond of each other.'

A faint smile curved the Earl's lips. Dear Jamie! The lass was not fit to govern a rough kingdom. Did she not realize that her 'dear Jamie' would never forgive her for being born legitimate when he–older, wiser, stronger and a man–might have been King? These French made her soft. He could see in her eyes the affection she bore her big brother. It did not seem to occur to her that the crown came between her and any love Lord James Stuart might have for her.

But how tell a sentimental and emotional woman to beware of her brother! How speak to her of those hardy men of intrigue–James Douglas, Ruthven, Morton?

All he could do was advise her to form, without delay, a governing party; and because of his knowledge of her Scottish subjects, he could at least give her the names of those whom she could trust–farther than most, he might add.

He himself would take a prominent part in the governing body. He believed Huntley and Atholl too could be trusted.

He did not trust the Bastard of Scotland, but it would be impossible to leave Lord James Stuart out of such a governing body.

The Queen was ready to put her faith in Bothwell.

He looked at her with mild contempt. She was Queen of a troublous realm which she did not even wish to see. He understood perfectly. She liked this soft Court where gallants ducked and bobbed and scented themselves and jangled their jewels in their doublets and even in their ears; she liked pretty verses and music and clever conversation.

It was a sad day, decided the Earl of Bothwell, when Mary of Guise had died and left her frivolous young daughter to fend for herself.

The cold winter had set in, and the Court was preparing to leave the Balliage where they had been staying in the City of Orléans. The royal baggage, with the magnificent beds and tapestries, had been loaded, and they were ready to travel to Chenonceaux.

Lord Bothwell had left France, and Mary was glad. When he went he seemed to take with him her uneasy thoughts of her kingdom across the seas.

Lately Mary had been conscious of a growing alertness in the face of Queen Catherine. François' mother rarely left his side. She was solicitous of the throbbing pain in his ear for which she was constantly supplying lotions and potions to subdue his suffering. Paré, the great doctor, was in attendance upon the King.

Mary knew from the grave face of the doctor and the closed expression on the face of the Queen-Mother, that François was very ill indeed, far worse than he had ever been before.

She was very anxious on this day of departure, for she knew the keen wind would set François' ear throbbing afresh. The swelling was angrily inflamed and the pain almost unendurable.

She and François were about to mount their horses when François suddenly putting his hand to his ear, fell fainting to the ground.

There was great consternation, for it was clear that the King was very ill indeed. Mary knelt beside François, and a great fear overcame her for she recognized the signs of approaching death.

Catherine was on the other side of her son. For a moment it was as though a shutter had been drawn aside and Mary glimpsed that in the Italian woman's face which she would rather not have seen.

Catherine knew her son was dying, but Mary realized she felt no grief; instead she had betrayed her great exultation.

Mary sat by the bed which had been hastily set up. François was too weak for speech, but he knew she was there and that knowledge comforted him. Occasionally his pain-crazed eyes would be turned to her, and one word formed on his lips, though no sound came: Mary.

Mary knew that her uncles would be hurrying to Orléans, but she felt desperately alone. She wanted to put her arms about her dying husband and protect him from the quiet woman who glided about the apartment, masking her elation, saying soothing words, bringing soothing drinks. Could it be true that a mother could wish her son dead? Could it be true that her personal power meant more to her than the boy who had once been part of her body? Mary could not believe that. But there were such strange stories about this woman.

'Something must be done!' she cried passionately.

She summoned Monsieur Paré to her. She said she wished to be alone with him; but her mother-in-law was in the apartment, calm and determined.

'I am his mother,' she said. 'You cannot shut *me* out.'

'Monsieur Paré,' said Mary, 'there must be something which can be done. I beg of you to do it.'

'Your Majesty, I would attempt an operation but it might fail. But if there is no operation the King will certainly die.'

'I will not have my son suffer unnecessarily,' said Catherine. 'I must speak with Monsieur Paré. I must know exactly what this attempt will mean. I cannot allow my son to suffer unnecessarily. I am his mother. I would do anything in the world to save him unnecessary pain.'

'We are speaking of his life,' said Mary fiercely.

Catherine turned to the door: 'Monsieur Paré, the Queen is a young wife who loves her husband. She is filled with grief and that grief overwhelms her. Monsieur Paré, I am his mother. I must speak with you alone. I must know exactly what this means.'

The surgeon cried out in desperation: 'Madame, there is a chance to save the King's life . . . a frail one. It is by no means certain. Immediate action would be necessary. There is a slight hope of success, but if nothing is done he cannot last more than a few hours.'

'It is because of that that I will not have him suffer unnecessarily. My son . . . my poor little François! He is still that to me, though he may be the King.'

'We waste time,' cried Mary frantically. 'Precious time . . .'

'You are right,' said the Queen. 'There is no time to lose.' She took the doctor's arm. 'I must talk with you first, Monsieur Paré. Before this operation is performed I must have careful speech with you alone.'

Paré looked from the face of the wife to that of the mother. One was a young girl–almost hysterical with grief–the other was a calm woman.

Catherine took him by the arm and led him from the room.

They were a long time gone, and when they returned Mary's uncles had arrived.

Mary sat by the bed in desolation. There was now a rattle in the King's throat. Mary knew, when Paré returned to the apartment with Catherine, that it was too late to do anything more to save François.

The snowflakes were tapping gently on the window; the wind moaned outside. All those about the bed watched the wan face of the dying King.

The Cardinal had taken the young man's hand; he bent closer over the bed. Even the Cardinal was awed in the presence of death; even to this man came a glimmer of remorse for all he had done to the dying boy.

'Say after me,' he commanded, as all through the boy's reign he had commanded, 'say this: "Lord, pardon my sins and impute not to me, thy servant, the sins committed by my ministers under my name and authority."'

The wan lips moved and tried to frame the words.

'Oh God, listen to him,' prayed Mary. 'It was not at his command that the waters of the Loire were stained blood-red. He had no hand in what was done at Amboise. Remember that and do not blame François.'

Catherine came closer to the bed. She said: 'It is all over. The King is dead.'

She did not say, but she meant: Long live the King . . . the new King.

She was determined to govern Charles as the Guises had governed François and Mary.

Mary watched her fearfully as she stood there, her white hands folded on her black gown, forcing sorrow into the face which was beginning to inspire great fear in Mary's heart.

They walked solemnly out of the chamber of death–the widowed Queens side by side.

Tears were running slowly down Mary's face. Her one thought was to make her way with all speed to her own apartments, to lie on her bed, draw the curtains, and demand that she be left alone with her grief.

They were at the door; she would have passed through but there was a light detaining touch on her arm.

Queen Catherine was beside her, pressing her large body gently forward, reminding her that she, Mary, must stand aside now as once Catherine had stood aside for her.

Queen Catherine wished her to know in this moment of bitter grief that Mary was no longer first lady in the land. Catherine was in the ascendant; Mary was in decline.

Chapter Six

In the shrouded chamber the young widow sat alone. Her face was pale beneath the white coif; the flowing robes of her white dress fell to the floor; even her shoes were white. The chamber was lighted only by tapers and it seemed like a tomb to Mary.

She paced the room. She had no tears left. Since her first coming to the Court of France, François had been her friend and her devoted slave. Had she been at times a little too arrogant, a little too certain of his devotion? If she could only have him back now, how she would assure him of this love which she only knew went so deep since she had lost him.

What tragic changes had overtaken her life! She thought of her uncles as they had been on the day of François' death, standing with her, one on either side of her, while the nobles of the Court, led by Queen Catherine, went to the apartments of the little Charles to do homage to the new King.

They had said nothing to her, those uncles; but she knew they were disappointed in her. There should have been a child, their eyes accused her. A child would have changed everything. Their sinister implication was: If François could not give you a child, there were others who could.

What was honour to those uncles of hers? What was morality? All that mattered was the power of Guise and Lorraine; and, according to them, she had failed in her duty towards her maternal house.

What would become of her?

She smoothed the folds of the *deuil blanc*, apprehensive of the unknown doom which must soon overtake her.

During those first weeks of mourning she must see no one except her attendants and members of the royal family.

They came to visit her–Charles, the nine-year-old King, and Catherine, his mother.

Mary knelt before the boy, who, in his new-found dignity, commanded: 'Rise, dear Mary.'

She should have been comforted by the love she saw in his eyes, but she realized that, young as he was, the love he bore her was not that of a brother.

The young King's eyes grew feverish as they studied the white-clad figure. It was as though he were saying: 'I am the King of France now that François is dead. There is nothing between us now.'

Could this thing come to pass? Was it possible that she might again be Queen of France? This boy–this unbalanced child who was now the King–wished it; her uncles would do all in their power to bring it about, for if she married Charles the Guises' power would be unchanged. The only difference would be that in place of gentle François, Mary would have a new husband, wild Charles.

Catherine was closely watching her son's face. She said: 'It is sad for you, my daughter, to be thus alone. Forty days and forty nights . . . it is a long time to mourn.'

'It seems a short time, Madame,' said Mary. 'I shall mourn the late King all my life.'

Catherine puffed her lips. 'You are young yet. When you return to your own country you will mayhap have another husband to love.'

Mary could not hide the fear which showed in her face. That was what she dreaded more than anything–to leave the land which she had come to look upon as her own, to sail away to the dismal country of which she had bleak memories and was reminded every now and then when crude-mannered Scots came to the Court of France. She could not bear to lose her husband, her position and her country at one blow. That would be too much to endure.

'Madame, I should wish to remain here. I have my estates in France. I would retire from the Court if necessary.'

The King said: 'It is not our wish that you should do so. We wish you to stay here, dear Mary.'

'Your Majesty is good to me. It is a great comfort to me to know of your kindess.'

'Dearest Mary, I have always loved you,' said the King.

His mother had gripped his shoulder so hard that he winced and, turning angrily, he scowled at her. Mary watched them and she saw the fear which suddenly came into the boy's face.

Catherine laughed loudly. 'The King feels tender towards you,' she said. 'He remembers the love his brother bore you. We shall be desolate when you leave us.'

'Mary is not going to leave us,' cried the King wildly. He took Mary's hand and began to kiss it passionately. 'No, Mary, you shall stay. I say so . . . I say so . . . and I am the King.'

The red blood suffused the King's cheeks; his lips began to twitch.

'I cannot have the King agitated,' said Catherine looking coldly at Mary, as though she were the cause of his distress.

'Perhaps if he speaks his mind freely,' said Mary, 'he will be less agitated.'

'At such a time! And my little son with such greatness thrust upon him, and he but a child . . . scarcely out of his nursery! Oh, I thank God that he has a mother to stand beside him at this time, to guide him, to counsel him, to give freely of her love and the wisdom she has gleaned through experience . . . for he has need of it. He has need of it indeed.'

'I am the King, Madame,' persisted Charles.

'You are the King, my son, but you are a child. The ministers about your throne will tell you that. Your mother tells you. Your country expects wisdom of you far beyond your nine years. You must listen to the counsels of those who wish you well for, believe me, my son, there are many in this realm who would be your deadly enemies if they dared.'

A terrible fear showed in the little boy's face and Mary wondered what stories of the fate which would befall an unwanted King had been poured into his ears.

Charles stammered: 'But . . . everybody will be glad if Mary stays here. Everybody loves Mary. They were so pleased when she married François.'

'But Mary has her kingdom to govern. They are waiting for her, those countrymen of hers. Do you think they will allow her to stay here for ever? I doubt it. Oh, I greatly doubt it. I'll swear that at this moment they are preparing a great welcome for her. She has her brothers there, remember. James Stuart . . . Robert and John Stuart and hundreds . . . nay, thousands of loyal subjects. Her neighbour and sister across the border will rejoice, I am sure, to know that her dear cousin of Scotland is not so far away as hitherto.'

Mary cried out: 'I am so recently a widow. I have lost a husband whom I loved dearly. And you come to me . . .'

'To tell you of my sympathy. You were his wife, my dear, but I was his mother.'

'I loved him. He and I were together always.'

'He and I were together even longer. He was with me before the rest of the world ever saw him. Think of that. And ask yourself whether your grief can be greater than mine.'

'Madame, it would seem so,' said Mary impulsively.

Catherine laid a hand on her shoulder. 'My dear Queen of Scotland, I am an old woman; you are a young one. When you have reached my age you will doubtless have learned that grief should be controlled–not only for the good of the sufferer but for those about her.'

'You cannot care as I do.'

'Can grief be weighed?' asked Catherine, turning her eyes to the ceiling. 'You are young. There will be suitors and you will find a new husband . . . one who, I doubt not, will please you better than my dear son did.'

'I beg of you . . . stop!' implored Mary.

Charles cried: 'Mary . . . Mary . . . you shall not go. I'll not allow it. I am the King and I will marry you.'

Catherine laughed yet again. 'You see the King of France is but a child. He knows not the meaning of marriage.'

'I do!' declared Charles hotly. 'I do.'

'You shall marry at the right time, my darling. And then who knows who your bride will be.'

'Madame, it must be Mary. It must.'

'My son . . .'

Charles stamped his foot; his twitching fingers began to pull at his doublet and the golden fringe came away in his hand. He flung it from him and turned his blazing eyes on his mother. 'It shall be Mary! I want Mary. I love Mary.'

He threw himself at the young widow, flung his arms about her waist and buried his hot quivering face in the white brocade of her gown.

'It is so touching,' said Catherine. 'Come, my dear little King. If this is your wish . . . well then, you are a King and a King's wishes are not to be ignored. But to speak of this . . . so soon after your brother has died and is scarce cold in his grave . . . it frightens me. You want your brother's wife. I beg of you keep quiet on such a matter for, with your brother so recently dead it is a sin. Why, you will be afraid tonight when the candles are doused and your apartment is in darkness. You will be afraid of your brother's accusing ghost.'

Charles had released Mary. He was staring at his mother and biting his lips; his hands began to pull once more at his doublet.

Catherine put her arm about him and held him against her.

'Do not tremble, my son. All will be well. Your mother has that which will protect you from evil spirits. But she needs your collaboration in this. Do not put into words thoughts which could bring disaster to you.'

Mary cried out: 'Madame, I am mourning my husband. I would wish to be alone.'

'You poor child. It is true. You are mourning. This is not the time to remind you that, as Dowager Queen of France, you are no longer in a position to order the Queen-Mother of France from your apartment. We understand that it is the extremity of your grief which has made you forget this little detail. We know that when you emerge from your mourning you will fully realize your changed position. There, my child, do not let your grief overwhelm you. You have had many happy years with us here in France. If, by some ill chance, you should have to leave us, remember you will be going to your own country. It is not France, we know, but you will love it the more because it is yours. You will be a neighbour of your cousin of England . . .'

'Who hates me,' put in Mary.

'Hates you! And you her cousin!'

'She will never forgive me for calling myself Queen of England.'

Catherine looked grave. 'Ah! It is a pity that you could not have foreseen this day. I remember well your riding in your litter proudly bearing England's arms. What pride was yours! Not content with two crowns you must have a third!'

'I but obeyed the orders of your husband, the King, and of my own husband.'

'And now they are no longer here to share the blame! Have no fear. You are young and many have told you that you are beautiful. It is a fact which you know full well, so I have no need to remind you of it. I am sure the Queen of England will soon have the same affection for you as you have inspired of me. We will leave you now to your mourning.'

Mary knelt and took the cold hand. What were those expressionless eyes telling her? You have stepped down from your pedestal and I am in control now. Do not expect friendship from one whose friendship you never sought. You have learned one lesson in France, Mary Stuart. You have learned what a fool you have been to flout Catherine de' Medici, that daughter of tradesmen.

Her uncles came to see her. They had changed since François' death. Their power had been stripped from them. Anne de Montmorency had been recalled; the Queen-Mother was now the Regent of France and it was said that she had complete control over the nine-year-old King. Overnight she had stepped into that position which, during the reign of François and Mary, had been filled by the brothers Guise.

How to recover that position! That was the urgent concern of François de Guise and Charles de Lorraine.

'We have come to discuss the future, Mary,' said the Duke.

'I do not wish to go to Scotland,' said Mary quickly.

'Nor do we wish you to,' the Cardinal assured her. 'If all we have in mind shall come to pass, there would be no need of that.'

'Many suitors are presenting themselves,' the Duke told her. 'There are Frederick of Denmark and Eric of Sweden . . .' began the Duke.

'None of whom we feel are worthy of you,' put in the Cardinal.

'There is Arran, whom his father is urging forward,' added the Duke; 'although he himself is most eager to come.'

'Poor Arran!' murmured Mary.

'They say his brain is soft,' said the Cardinal, 'and has been since he set eyes on you when he was at Court. They say he was first sick with love, and then mad with love for the most beautiful girl in the world. We should not wish you to make so poor a match.'

'Tell her of that other youth,' interrupted the Duke.

The Cardinal's smile was a sneer. 'What impudence! There has arrived at the Court one whose mother has sent him to offer condolences for your loss. Condolences, indeed! The youth is delighted by your loss! That is, if he has the sense to understand what his mother must have been at great pains to hammer into his head. He comes full of hopes . . . conscious of his royalty . . . a youth of fifteen, a tall, gangling boy, unsure of anything but that he has royal blood in his veins. He comes to offer condolences from his parents to their kinswoman and to express the hope–oh, most subtly–that if Your Majesty should be looking for another husband, you might be enchanted by a fellow like himself.'

'Who is this?' asked Mary.

'Young Henry Darnley, whose mother, Lennox's wife, will have all the world know that as she was the daughter of Margaret Tudor, sister of Henry the Eighth of England, her son is not without some pretension to the throne of England . . . and of Scotland too. Madame Lennox presents her long lean son for your inspection. I dare swear she thinks that, once having clapped your eyes on him, you'll find it hard to refuse him your bed, your crown, and all that is yours.'

'My dear Uncles, I am pained by all this talk of marriage. It is too soon as yet. I have so recently been a wife, so short a time a widow.'

The Duke showed impatience, but the Cardinal laid his arm about her shoulders. 'My dearest,' he murmured, 'there should be no wedding for a reasonable time. But your affairs are of great moment . . . not only to us but to the whole world. Do you want to be treated continually as you have been treated since the death of François? Do not tell me! I know that Catherine has made you feel your position keenly. You are a Queen and queenly. You would never be happy in a lowly state. You were meant to rule. Your proud carriage says so. Your dignity demands it. That is why we have two matches in mind for you–either would bring you great glory. The first is with the King of France.'

Mary cried in terror: 'But Charles . . . *Charles* . . . he is not entirely sane. He . . . he frightens me.'

'Frightens you?' said the Duke. 'A King of France frightens you!'

'A madman frightens me,' she retorted. 'You talk of the children I might have . . . with a madman as their father!'

'Madness is no deterrent to fertility,' asserted the Duke.

'Mary,' soothed the Cardinal, 'you would never shirk your duty . . . I know. You could be Queen of France again. You could stay in the land you love. There is no other Court–save one–worthy of you.'

'The Court of Spain!' put in the Duke triumphantly. 'Don Carlos, son of great Philip, has need of a wife. We have approached the King of Spain and he is not averse to the match. He wishes to see Scotland firmly settled in the Catholic Faith. Think, Mary. One day the crown of Spain may be yours.'

'It is too soon,' pleaded Mary. 'I beg of you . . . leave me now.'

The Cardinal put his arm about her and said softly: 'The Queen of Spain . . . the mightiest throne in all Europe . . . a young husband who will adore you. You will be reunited with your dear little friend Elisabeth who is now the Queen of Spain herself. Oh, Mary, some people are born for distinction. You are one of them.'

She closed her eyes. She felt so weary. A terrible depression had come over her. She wished to be alone that she might throw herself on to her bed and weep.

Mary could not help liking the youth who brought such kind messages from his mother. Henry Darnley was handsome. His large blue eyes and fair hair were almost feminine in their charm; and his manners were not without grace, though naturally seeming a little rough compared with those of the French courtiers.

Mary was sorry for his shyness and tried to make him feel at ease, to forget she was the Queen by reminding him that they were cousins.

'Your Majesty is gracious,' he told her.

When she asked him to play the lute for her–she had heard that he was a master of that instrument–he was glad to do so, and she listened with delight; he played quite charmingly.

He told her he wrote poetry also and he brought her some verses he had written for her. She was delighted with them. They made a poor showing against the polished artistry of Ronsard and his fellow poets but they had good feeling in them, as she told him.

He could dance well and was an enthusiastic follower of the chase. His conversation was of sport and pleasure.

When he left after his brief stay at Court, she was sorry to see him go, but in a day she had forgotten him.

When the Court left for Fontainebleau Mary went with it. The Queen-Mother was coolly polite to her, but beneath the veneer of politeness there was an insolence. It was as though she knew some exciting secret which concerned Mary, and which she longed to impart. It must be unpleasant, thought Mary, otherwise it would not have pleased Catherine so much.

Whenever the King saw Mary he would gaze longingly at her. There were times when it appeared as though he would throw himself upon her, and yet always he seemed to be conscious of the invisible restraining hand. It was almost uncanny, but then the power of the Queen-Mother was uncanny.

She was thinking more and more about the journey to Spain. It was alarming to consider Don Carlos. Was he really as degenerate as rumour suggested? He was but a boy. There had been evil rumours concerning François, but how happy she had been with him!

There was one thing she dreaded more than all others: return to Scotland.

Her optimism, never long absent, returned to her during those difficult weeks. She would not return to Scotland. Everything could be easily arranged. Her brother, Lord James, longed for the Regency. Let him have it. It was his great desire to govern Scotland; it was her great desire to stay away from Scotland. She would face the truth. She loved to be gay, and the Scots looked on gaiety as a sin. There was no comfort in their castles; there were no merry dances, no versifying, no pleasant pastimes. Scotland was straining towards Puritanism and Mary Stuart could never be a Puritan.

Now that her uncles had retired from Court her new position was brought home to her afresh. At Fontainebleau the Earl of Bedford and the English ambassador, Sir Nicholas Throgmorton, called upon her; and there was no one to advise her how to deal with these gentlemen.

They surveyed her with solemn dignity. They were aloof and cool.

Inexperienced as she was, hurt and humiliated by Catherine, she allowed herself to show a haughtiness which was dictated by her hot temper rather than a considered diplomatic attitude. It had been all very well to flout the English when she was the wife of the King of France; now she stood alone; she was merely the Queen of a small country whose affairs were in disorder.

'The Queen of England,' Bedford began, 'requires the immediate ratification of the Edinburgh treaty.'

She knew that the Edinburgh treaty claimed for Elizabeth the sole right to the throne of England and that Mary Stuart should recognize her as such 'for all time coming'.

She was not pleased by the Englishmen's arrogant attitude towards her. They implied that their Queen's will should be Mary's. She was bewildered, inexperienced in dealing with such situations alone, so she obeyed those inclinations dictated by her pride.

Her uncles and Henri of France had assured her that she was the rightful heir to England. At the moment she was in decline but she would not always be so. One day she might be Queen of Spain and then these Englishmen would think twice before addressing her as they did now.

She said: 'My lords, I shall not sign the treaty of Edinburgh.'

'It has been signed in Edinburgh, Madame.'

'But it would seem that it does not become valid until you have my signature.'

This they could not deny.

Here was another of those moments of folly, the result of hurt pride and ignorance.

'Then, my lords, I will say to you that I cannot give you the signature for which you ask. I must have time to ponder the matter.'

Exasperated, they left her. They wrote to their mistress; and Elizabeth of England vowed that she would never forgive–and never trust–her Scottish kinswoman as long as that beautiful head remained on those elegant shoulders.

She travelled down to Rheims to stay for a while with her aunt, Renée de Guise at the Abbey Saint-Pierre-les-Dames. Renée, the sister of those ambitious uncles, was quite unlike them. Perhaps she, a member of that mighty and ambitious family, had felt the need to escape to a nunnery and in order to eschew that ambition which was at the very heart of the family's tradition.

There was quietness with Renée, but Mary did not want quiet. She was restless.

Renée, knowing that Mary was troubled, tried to help her through prayer. Mary realized that Renée was suggesting that if she too would shun ambition–as Renée had done–she might find peace in a life of dedication to prayer and service to others.

Mary, emotional in the extreme, thought for a short time–a very short time–of the peace to be found within convent walls. But when she looked in her mirror and saw her own beautiful face, and thought of dancing and masking with herself the centre of attention, when she remembered the admiration she had seen in the eyes of those men who surrounded her, she knew that whatever she had to suffer in the future–even if it meant returning to Scotland–it was the only life that would be acceptable to her.

With Renée she did become more deeply religious; she was even fired with a mission. Her country was straining towards Calvinism, and she would bring it back to the Church which she felt to be the only true one.

'But not,' she told Renée, 'with torture and the fire, not with the thumbscrews and the rack. Perhaps I am weak, but I cannot bear to see men suffer, however wrong they are. Even though I knew the fires of hell lay before them, I could not torment myself by listening to their cries, and if I ever countenanced the torture, I believe those cries would reach me, though I were miles away.'

Renée smiled at Mary's fierceness. She said: 'You are Queen of a country that is strongly heretic. It is your duty to return to it and save it from damnation. You are young and weak . . . as yet. But the saints will show you how to act.'

Mary shuddered and, when she thought of that land in the grip of Calvin and his disciple Knox, she prayed that King Philip would agree to her marriage with his son, or perhaps, better still, she need never leave her beloved France. If Charles broke free of his mother's influence, his first act would be to marry Mary Stuart.

To Rheims at this time came her relations on a visit to the Cardinal. The Duke arrived with his mother, and there followed Mary's two younger uncles, the Duc d'Aumale and the Marquis d'Elboeuf.

There were many conferences regarding Mary's marriage into Spain.

The Cardinal took her to his private chamber and there he tried to revive their old relationship. But she had grown up in the last month and some of her innocence had left her. The Cardinal seemed different. She noticed the lines of debauchery on his face, and how could she help knowing that his love for her depended largely on her ability to give him that which he craved: Power. She was no longer the simple girl she had been.

She was aloof and bewildered. It was no use his drawing her gently to him, laying his fine hands on her, soothing and caressing, bringing her to that state of semi-trance when her will became subservient to his. She saw him more clearly now, and she saw a sly man. She already knew that he was a coward; and she believed that his love for her had diminished in proportion to her loss of power and usefulness.

Marriage with France. Marriage with Spain. They were like two bats chasing each other round in his brain; and he was the wily cat not quite quick enough to catch one of them. But perhaps there was another–more agile, more happily placed than he. Catherine continually foiled him. He was wishing he could slip the little 'Italian morsel' into her goblet, as she was no doubt wishing she could slip it into his.

If he could but remove Catherine he would have Mary married to Charles in a very short time.

To Rheims came the news which sent the spirits of the whole family plunging down to deep depression.

Philip of Spain sent word that he would find it inconvenient, for some time to come, to continue with the negotiations for a marriage between his son Don Carlos and Mary Stuart.

Catherine de' Medici stood between Mary and the King of France. She had–by working in secret–insinuated herself between Mary and the heir of Spain.

Catherine was going to bring about that which she had long desired: the banishment from France of the young and beautiful Queen who had been such a fool as to show herself no friend to Catherine de' Medici.

Word came from Lord James Stuart. He was coming to France to persuade his sister that it was time she returned to her realm.

So she was to leave the land she loved. The Court buzzed with the news. This was farewell to the dazzling Mary Stuart.

She tried to be brave, but there was a great fear within her.

She told her Maries: 'It will only be for a short time. Soon I shall marry. Do not imagine we shall stay long in Scotland; I am sure that soon King Philip will continue with the arrangements for my marriage to Don Carlos.'

'It will be fun to go to Scotland for a while,' said Flem.

'They'll soon find a husband for you,' declared Beaton.

While she too could think thus Mary felt almost gay. It would only be a temporary exile, and she would take with her many friends from the Court of France.

Henri de Montmorency, who had now become the Sieur d'Amville since the return of his father to power, whispered to her: 'So France is to lose Your Majesty!'

She was hurt by his happy expression. She said tartly: 'It would seem that you are one of those who rejoice in my departure.'

'I do, Your Majesty.'

'I pray you let me pass. I was foolish enough to think you had some regard for me. But that, of course, was for the Queen of France.'

He bent his head so that his eyes were near her own. 'I rejoice,' he said, 'because I have heard that I am to accompany your suite to Scotland.'

Her smile was radiant. 'Monsieur . . .' she began. 'Monsieur d'Amville . . . I . . .'

He took her hands and kissed them passionately. For a moment she allowed this familiarity but she quickly remembered that she must be doubly cautious now. As Queen she could more easily have afforded to be lax than now when she was stripped of her dignity.

She said coolly: 'I thank you for you expression of loyalty, Monsieur d'Amville.'

'Loyalty . . . and devotion,' he murmured, 'my most passionate devotion.'

He left her then, and when he entered his suite he was smiling to himself. One of his attendants–a poet, Pierre de Chastelard–rose to greet him.

'You are happy today, my lord,' said Chastelard.

D'Amville nodded and continued to smile. 'Shall I tell you why, Chastelard, my dear fellow? I have long loved a lady. Alas, she was far beyond my aspirations. But now I have gone up and she has come down. I think we have come to a point where we may most happily meet.'

'That is worthy of a poem,' suggested Chastelard.

'It is indeed. I have high hopes.'

'The lady's name, sir?'

'A secret.'

'But if I am to sing her praises in verse . . .'

'Well then, I'll whisper it, but tell no one that Henri de Montmorency is deep in love with the beautiful Mary Stuart who is going to be in need of comfort when she reaches her barbaric land. I shall be there to give it. That is why you see me so gay.'

'Now I understand, my lord. It is enough to make any man gay. She is a beautiful creature and was most chaste, it would seem, when married to our King François. Even Brantôme–who can usually find some delicious titbit of scandal concerning the seemingly most virtuous–has had nothing but praise to sing of the Queen of Scots.'

'She is charming,' said D'Amville. 'And it is true that she is chaste. What is it about her . . . tell me that. You are something of a connoisseur, my friend. She is innocent and yet . . . and yet . . .'

'And yet . . . and yet . . .' cried Chastelard. 'My lady fair is innocent and yet . . . and yet . . . and yet . . .'

The two young men laughed together.

'May all good luck attend you,' said Chastelard. 'I envy you from the bottom of my heart.'

'My hopes soar. She will be desolate. She will be ready to love anyone who is French while she is in that dreary land. You shall accompany me, my dear Chastelard; you shall share in my triumph . . . at second-hand, of course!'

When the two young men went out to follow the hunt they were still talking of the charms of Mary Stuart.

Mary had many causes for anxiety as she contemplated the journey ahead of her. The Queen of England declared she would deny her a safe passage until she signed the treaty of Edinburgh. Mary was on her mettle then. She was determined not to let the Tudor see that she feared her ships and sailors. She said so boldly.

'I may pass well enough home into my realm,' she said to Nicholas Throgmorton, 'without your mistress's passport. I remember your late King tried to prevent my arrival in France; but you see, Monsieur, I came safely without his permission. So I shall journey to my kingdom without that of your mistress.'

It was folly, but she felt stronger for committing it. From now on she would act in accordance with her own wishes. She had gathered some notion of the unhappy state of her country when on her way from Rheims to Lorraine she was met by one of the Catholic lords–John Lesley–who had come to tell her that he brought with him the fealty of the Catholics in Scotland. Caithness, Crawford, Huntley and Atholl were firmly behind her, he assured her. Their plan was that she should land secretly in Scotland, enter Edinburgh with a good force behind her and drive the heretic Lord James from his position as the head of the country in her absence.

She was alarmed. James was her brother–her dear Jamie. She had loved James. She knew he was a Protestant and that it would be his wish to make Scotland Protestant as hers was to make the country Catholic; but she was determined not to be a bigot, dearly as she loved her own faith and sure as she was that the Catholic Church was the true one. She could not feel happy, she said, contemplating that, on her arrival in her country, she would have to fight her own brother.

Fortunately she was able to speak with the Sieur d'Oysel, that French officer who had, in Scotland, worked so faithfully for her mother.

He shook his head over the project. 'Your Majesty,' he said, 'if you will deign to hear the advice of one who has campaigned long in your country and knows the temper of the people, he would say this: No doubt you wish to bring the Catholic Faith back to Scotland, but there are many in your land who are faithful to the Protestant cause, and to take arms against it at this time would plunge the whole of Scotland into a civil war. Your brother, Lord James, is a Protestant and you are a Catholic, but you need him. He will be loyal to you for expediency's sake, if for no other reason. If you lost your crown where would he be? As a Stuart he must support a Stuart. His rivals–as yours are–would always be the Hamiltons or the Gordons. Do not be tempted to rash action. Your brother and Lord Maitland of Lethington are the cleverest statesmen in Scotland. They are both Protestants, but Your Majesty needs them. Therefore be discreet. Shelve the problem of religion until you have tested your people, and your brother with them. He could raise an army, so make sure–and this is what he would prefer to do–that he raises it for you and not against you.'

It was advice which she gladly took, for the prospect of civil war horrified her.

It was only a day or so later when Lord James himself arrived. When she saw him she was glad she had not allowed herself to be caught up in any intrigue against him. He was friendly and courteous; he was also very affectionate. He was very much the big brother whom she remembered. He was nearly thirty now and that seemed, to her, a very wise and experienced age.

He told her how happy he was that she was coming home.

'I am glad you will be there, Jamie.'

He smiled at the use of the childhood name.

'Though you hardly seem like Jamie now,' she went on. 'Why, you are looking so wise, so full of knowledge. A deal must have happened to you since we last met.'

'All my experience I place at your service.'

He talked a little of affairs in Scotland, warning her to beware of certain lords. She listened half-heartedly. She was tired of the stories of continual strife.

'Jamie,' she said, 'I wish you had not gone so far along the road to Protestantism.'

'My dear little sister, you have been brought up with Papists. Wait until you return home. Wait till you hear the sermons John Knox delivers in the Kirk at Edinburgh. Mayhap then you'll come along with me on that road to Protestantism.'

'I shall try to make you turn back, Jamie. I shall try to make *you* come with *me*.'

He smiled indulgently. He still looked upon her as the little sister. She was very charming, with such airs and graces that could be so delightful in a ballroom. She had all the necessary gifts to make her a great lady; none, he believed, to make her a great ruler. She was as different from the red-headed Queen below the Border as any woman could be. It was not surprising. Elizabeth had faced a hundred dangers when she was a child; Mary had been petted from babyhood.

'I am sure,' he said, 'that you can discourse most learnedly and charmingly on all subjects. It is one of the accomplishments they have taught you so well in France.'

'Jamie, Rome would be ready to offer you great honours if you would change your mind.'

'My mind is made up, dear sister; and it is firmly turned away from the Church of Rome.'

'Then there is nothing I can say to turn you back to it?'

'Nothing. And there are other and urgent matters to discuss.'

'It will be a comfort to know that you are at my side to help me.'

He took her hand and let his lips rest lightly on it. 'I shall serve you faithfully while you serve Scotland,' he said.

She believed him; there was that about James which made her believe him. She felt a little happier for her interview with him. But when he had left she still made excuses to stay in France.

Often Mary lay sleepless through the night thinking of the perilous journey across the seas. She would dream that the ships of the Queen of England captured hers; she dreamed that she stood before the red-headed virago, who swore she would have vengeance because Mary had denied her right to the crown of England.

Back in Scotland were the quarrelsome nobles. Her brother and Maitland had not been good friends to her mother, she remembered. The Catholic nobles, led by Huntley, the Cock o' the North, were untrustworthy. Yet she must go amongst them; and to reach them she must brave the perils of the English seas.

Suddenly there came to her memory a man–an insolent man, yet a bold one. He was no friend of the Catholic nobles, and no friend of her brother and Maitland; rather had he stood alone, a chieftain of the Border country, ruthless and despotic; yet her mother had said she would rely on his loyalty more readily than on that of any other man in Scotland.

Then Mary made a sudden decision. She would send a messenger to James Hepburn, Earl of Bothwell, instructing him, as Admiral, to arrange for her safe passage to Scotland.

She was surprised how much happier she could feel knowing that the arrangement for the voyage would be in the hands of a strong man.

Bothwell was delighted to receive the summons. He believed his fortunes were now on the rise. He would ingratiate himself with the Queen. Moreover the prospect of a battle with the English delighted him. He began to plan for immediate departure.

Anna Throndsen watched him with passionate eyes. Their life together was a battle. She would win one skirmish and lose the next. She was clever, but so was he, and he had all the advantages.

'I depart tomorrow,' he told her gleefully.

'But you have just arrived.'

So he had. She was living in one of his houses and he visited her now and then. He snapped his fingers at her. He would not marry her. But there were times when he liked to visit her; he enjoyed the battles between them and delighted to arouse her anger, to hear her swear that she hated him, that she wished never to see him again; and then have her sobbing out her passionate need of him, caught in one of those weak moments when quite effortlessly he could sweep away all her resistance and leave her quivering with passion.

That was his special gift. He had no need to stress it; it was simply there, and his very indifference to it enhanced it.

'I come and go as I please,' he told her.

'And where shall you go this time?' she asked. 'Back to that old hag Janet Beaton? Have you then such a fancy for the aged? Do you prefer grandmothers?'

'I shall not go to Janet this time, but to a young woman. She sends for me because none other will suit her purpose.'

Passion flamed in Anna's face. She ran to him and slapped his cheek. To him the blow was no more than a tap. He laughed aloud and caught her hand.

'Why, Anna,' he said, 'you almost tempt me to stay another night. I like you better in anger than in gentle love.'

'I wish I had never seen you.'

'It might have saved much inconvenience if I had never seen *you*.'

'I thought you never allowed women to inconvenience you?'

'I do not . . . for long.'

'You are quite heartless. Have you no thought for the child?'

'I have so many children, they tell me. Were I to concern myself with all of them, I should have time for nothing else.'

'Who is the woman you are going to see, if it is not Janet?'

'She is very beautiful. I can tell you that.'

'Who, I asked.'

'Try to guess.'

She struggled in his grip while her eyes blazed. 'I'll tell you,' he said. 'Her name is Mary and she is the Queen of Scotland.'

'The Queen!'

'She sends for me to bring her safely back to Scotland.'

'For you! So she too . . . !'

He laughed. 'Anna, you are a fool. You see passion everywhere. This is a command from a Queen to a subject.'

'But why you . . . why *you*?'

'Because her mother knew she could trust me. She knew I hated the English. Mayhap this Queen knows that I shall serve her well for the reason that I am a Borderer and a natural enemy of those on the other side. There is hardly a man in Scotland of any standing who is not in the pay of the English. Lord James himself . . . Maitland . . . anyone you can name. But I have never taken a bribe from them. I have taken their cattle and I have taken their women. I am their enemy and they know it. The Queen knows it. So she now asks me to arrange her safe passage, and, my dear Anna, I go with all speed.'

'The Queen will reward you,' said Anna.

'Doubtless.'

'And when she does, you will do the right thing by our child? You will do the right thing by me?'

He sighed deeply. 'Who knows, Anna? Who knows?'

Now her eyes began to blaze again with anger, and he laughed. As he had told her, he liked her thus; and it would be a long time before he saw her again.

It was August. Through the French countryside passed a brilliant cavalcade at the head of which in a magnificent carriage decorated with cloth of gold and silver and bearing the arms of Guise and Lorraine rode the great Duke and his brother, the Cardinal. There followed in a beautiful chariot Mary

Stuart; and behind her came her four Maries with a company of French noblemen, poets and musicians.

Mary knew that at Calais she would say goodbye to those two uncles who had been her guardians since she had set foot in France, but their three brothers, Mary's uncles, Claude the Duc d'Aumale, François the Grand Prior of Lorraine, and René the Marquis d'Elboeuf, were to accompany her to Scotland. She was glad of this; her Uncle René she liked particularly because he had a gay nature and it was a comfort to have him with her.

She was conscious all the time of Henri de Montmorency, the Sieur d'Amville, who made it his delight to be at her side and gratify her smallest wish. He had introduced to her notice a very personable young man who played the lute with charm and wrote verses which fell not far short of those of Ronsard. This was Pierre de Chastelard, and she had made up her mind that she would reward that young man with a good post when they reached Scotland. She liked him; he was so gay and charming; and she was fond of poets. Unfortunately he was a Huguenot, she had heard; but then, so was Henri de Montmorency, and she would not let a person's religious opinions interfere with the friendship she felt.

She was a little happier than she had feared she would be, and that was due to the people who were going with her. She looked round the company. There were many familiar faces.

She was glad to see Lord Bothwell's among them. She was not sure of her feelings regarding him as a person; he was certainly rather crude but he gave such an impression of strength and power that when she contemplated the journey before her and all its perils, she was glad to know that he was with the expedition.

He had come promptly at her summons; he had arranged for her departure with Lord Eglinton. She trusted them both, for their loyalty and their knowledge of the sea.

Flem had said that Bothwell should travel in the galley with Mary and themselves, but Mary would not have it.

'No,' she said, 'suffice it that he is with the party.'

'But,' persisted Flem, 'Your Majesty says that you feel safer because he is of the party.'

'Safer, yes–but it is enough that he is in one of the galleys. He will be at hand to save us from our enemies. And in my galley I wish to have those about me whom I love . . . my dearest friends and those who delight me with their company.'

'And he does not?'

'He is a Scotsman of rough speech, and we shall see enough of such in the months to come. I wish to enjoy cultured society for as long as I can. Only you, my four darlings, and my dear uncles and a few of our chosen friends shall sail in the first galley. The others may follow, and amongst them the Border-Earl.'

Flem sighed causing Mary to smile. 'You seem to have a fondness for him,' she teased. 'Have a care. I have heard that his reputation is quite shocking.'

'It is simply that he has an air of being able to subdue anyone . . . including the Queen of England.'

'He has a blustering manner, it is true,' agreed Mary, 'but he shall not subdue the Queen of Scotland. No! He shall travel in one of the accompanying vessels with others like himself.'

And so it was arranged.

When Mary stepped into the galley a sense of foreboding had come to her. She looked very lovely, dressed in her mourning costume. Her veil was full and held in place on each shoulder; her head-dress was the shape of a scallop shell and set with pearls, and about her neck was a collar of pearls. Her flowing gown was of cloth of silver and most becoming with its sleeves full from the elbow to shoulder and tight from elbow to wrist; the ruff of point lace set off her face to perfection.

Her uneasiness was enhanced by the terrible accident which took place before her eyes. The sails had not been completely unfurled and the royal galley had not left the harbour when a ship, entering the port, capsized suddenly and all aboard were drowned, as no help could reach them in time.

Mary cried out to those aboard to turn back, to do something; but the galley could not turn round and there was nothing to be done but watch the struggling bodies in the water or turn shuddering away.

It was a bad omen, said everyone; this meant bad luck for the Queen of Scots.

Mary walked up and down the deck, her eyes fixed on the land she was leaving. She longed to move out of sight of those shores, yet she dreaded the moment when she would no longer see them.

She could not forget the terrible screams of those drowning men. She explored the galley in the hope of turning her mind to other things, but her sadness was not relieved by the sight of the slaves, with their shaven heads and despairing faces, who worked at the oars. She could not bear to look at their naked backs which were marked by the lash. She thought of them, sweating over the oars when the wind was against them; she thought of them exposed to the cruel weather, with the chains about their legs; they were such sad creatures that they must have longed continually for death.

Impetuously she called the Captain to her and said: 'The galley slaves shall not be whipped while I am aboard. No matter what happens . . . no matter what, I say . . . the lash shall not be used. Do you hear me?'

The Captain was amazed and about to protest; but she had turned away, and those who were near saw the tears streaming down her cheeks.

As it grew dark her Maries begged her to leave the deck and go to her cabin, which had been decorated in a manner fitting a Queen; but she could not bear to turn her eyes from the last glimpse of that land which she loved.

'It is now, my dear France,' she said, 'that I have lost you, for the envious darkness like a black veil conceals you from my eyes which are thus deprived of their chief desire. Adieu then, my beloved France! I lose sight of you and I shall never see you again.'

'Dearest Majesty,' pleaded Seton, 'meat and drink await you. You must sleep. You can do no good waiting here.'

But Mary shook her head. She turned to the Captain and said: 'Set up a bed for me here.'

'Here Madame, on the poop gallery?'

'Yes, here,' she commanded. 'For when it is again light it may still be possible to see the shores of France. I must not be deprived of a last glimpse of them.'

So the bed was set up on the poop gallery, and Mary lay down while her women drew the curtains.

'As soon as the first glimmer of light is in the sky you must awaken me,' she ordered.

The wind died down during the night so that when the dawn came the galley was still close to the French coast.

It was Flem who awakened Mary, and the young Queen started up from her bed, her eyes red from last night's weeping, her sorrow returning as she remembered where she was.

The curtains about her bed were drawn back and, looking out, she saw the receding land of France.

She wept afresh.

'It is over,' she said. 'Farewell beloved land which I shall behold no more. Farewell, France!'

Thus she remained until there was no longer sight of land.

The perilous journey to Scotland had begun.

MARY THE WOMAN

Chapter One

Although it was August when Mary first saw Leith again after all her years in France, a thick sea mist hid the countryside. The French shivered in the cold damp air; they looked at each other and shrugged. It seemed that all the warnings about this dismal land were by no means exaggerated.

The foreboding in Mary's heart deepened as she stepped ashore. Her thoughts involuntarily went to Calais and that glittering cavalcade which had accompanied her. How different was her arrival in her own country!

There was no one to greet her as she stepped ashore. She was aware of a bunch of fisherfolk, their rags scarcely covering their bodies, their faces scored with weather. There was no welcome; there was only curiosity. One ragged boy came up boldly to stare at her. A child who might have been boy or girl touched her gown, laughed, and ran back to the group of fishermen and women.

Was this the way to greet the returning monarch?

Elboeuf cried out: 'Good people, here comes your Queen!'

But the people were silent; they nudged each other, and although they did not laugh, the faint curl of their lips suggested that the Marquis's brilliant garments and mode of speech aroused some kind of mirth in their bleak minds.

Mary said quietly: 'Is it that they do not know me? Is it that they do not want me?'

Her three uncles conferred together.

'Lord James should have been here. Huntley . . . Maitland . . . some of them surely. What savages!'

Mary found her four namesakes beside her. She said: 'It is no use standing here waiting for them to look as though they are pleased to see me. I am tired and would rest. I need food.'

D'Amville was beside her. 'Your Majesty, I will send pages ahead to find out what lodging may be made ready for you.'

'Better send Scotsmen,' said Mary. 'They will more readily procure it.'

'Procure it!' said d'Amville fiercely. 'It shall be given freely by these subjects to their Queen.'

Chastelard caught the Queen's glance. She smiled faintly at his indignant sorrow. She was ashamed of her country then; she was even wishing that there were no French in her retinue. What must they be thinking, who were accustomed to so much splendour, so much honour afforded to their kings and queens!

Men were sent on in advance to warn the townsfolk of the Queen's arrival. Mary glanced over her shoulder to where the galley lay like a ghost-ship in the mist. More people came out of their hovels to look at her, to stare incredulously at the display of glittering jewels. Their low voices mingled with the doleful cries of the sea-birds and Mary could not understand what they said.

And if she, with her beauty and her fine clothes, startled her subjects, what she had seen of them and the hovels in which they lived startled her. Never during her years in France had she been allowed to glimpse such poverty. These people's houses were little more than mud huts; the children, ill-clad and ill-fed, crawled about on the stones while the women sat at the doors mending nets. Mary believed they did not know who she was. Deeply she pitied them and yet she found herself turning from them in revulsion.

But now the pages and heralds were returning, and with them came hurrying some of the chief burghers of the town. These, though rough men, were a little more aware of what was due to their Queen. They knelt before her and kissing her hand swore their loyalty.

They explained to her that their town had been ravaged over and over again by the English hordes. After raids many of the houses were burned to the ground. In these hard days they had scarcely the time or the inclination, even if they had the money, to rebuild. There was no castle in Leith worthy to shelter the Queen. Where she could rest that night, none could say.

One of the burghers, Andrew Lambie, came forward and, kneeling before her, cried: 'Your Majesty, my house is a humble one, but it is at your service. If you will accept a lodging, although I cannot pretend that it is worthy to receive you, the honour will never be forgotten by your humble subject.'

Mary smiled with relief and gratitude. 'Your offer is accepted, good Master Lambie,' she said. 'I thank you. You are the first who has made me feel really welcome in my country.'

So she lay that night on a humble bed in a small room where the rafters seemed to be pressing down upon her, covered by a homespun blanket. It had been a strange experience.

'It is only for a night,' she said to Beaton. 'To-morrow we shall ride to my capital, and then everything will be different. I shall ride on my palfrey. Perhaps the mist will lift and all the people will come out to greet me. They will know me for their Queen.'

The Maries exchanged glances. They had decided they would not tell her yet that one of the galleys of their little fleet had been captured by the English. It was the one in which the palfrey was being carried, and with it all the beautiful horses which were used in the processions, together with the rich hangings and canopies and magnificent house furnishings which Mary had decided she could not leave behind.

But Mary had seen their glances and she demanded to be enlightened.

'Then how shall we ride into my capital to-morrow?' she asked.

'Doubtless we shall be able to find horses as fine,' said Livy.

'Where?' demanded Mary.

Livy waved her hand. 'Oh . . . here. . . . There are bound to be horses . . . magnificent horses.'

Mary laughed. 'In those mud huts! I doubt if the poor creatures would recognize a fine horse . . . let alone possess one.'

'Let to-morrow's troubles take care of themselves,' said Seton earnestly.

Mary began to laugh. 'I cannot help it. It is funny. Such pomp we enjoyed, did we not? My lord Cardinal . . . my lord Duke in all their robes, and their coaches covered with cloth of gold and silver. What a glittering array! And all to say farewell to me. And then . . . my arrival! That should be a joyous thing, should it not? A Queen comes home . . . but there is no one to greet her . . . no one but a few ragged children who come out of their hovels to see what the tide had thrown up. It is funny. Laugh, Seton. Beaton, you too. Livy! Flem! I command you to laugh.'

They tried to soothe her, but Mary could not stop laughing. The tears were rolling down her cheeks and suddenly her four Maries realized that she was not laughing; she was weeping, wildly and bitterly.

She threw herself on to the burgher's bed which creaked and groaned under her shaking body.

Early next morning, having heard of the Queen's arrival, some Scottish noblemen came riding into Leith.

Mary was delighted to see her brother, Lord James, and with him that man who was his staunchest supporter and of whom she had heard so much–Maitland of Lethington. Immediately on their heels came the Duc de Châtelherault and his son, Arran. She was less pleased to see those two; and the sullen-eyed Arran, whose offer of marriage had been rather curtly refused by her uncles on her behalf, made her very uncomfortable. His brooding eyes did not leave her face; he was already far gone in sickness of the mind.

But she felt more at home to have those men she knew, if only by name, surrounding her. Her brother took command; his clothes might seem shabby beside those of the French, and his horse was by no means a credit to him, yet he had dignity; moreover he was her own flesh and blood.

When he saw the room in which she had spent the night he was greatly disturbed; but she could laugh at it now.

'It was most graciously offered,' she said.

'And was the journey good?' he asked, taking her hand and smiling indulgently at her.

'It could have been worse. Suffice it that we have safely arrived, although we have lost one of the galleys to the English. It contains my palfrey.'

'Then we shall have to find a new one for you. Your subjects wish you to be happy here, but none wishes it more than he who is your most loyal subject . . . your own brother.'

'I know it. Jamie, if you were not a Protestant you would be perfect.'

That made him laugh. He was handsome when he laughed; it was then that the Stuart charm broke through his seriousness.

'You will find Holyrood and Edinburgh Castle very different from Fontainebleau and the Louvre,' he told her. 'You know that, do you not?

There are no Gobelins tapestries . . . none of your fountains and flower gardens, no glittering chandeliers nor Venetian mirrors to which you are accustomed.'

'I brought furnishings with me. It is to be hoped the English have not taken all. I can send for more.'

'You must do that,' said James. 'You must make your own Court as you would have it, and you will be its delightful Queen. I doubt not that ere long you will have made a little France of your apartments in Holyrood, and there you will have your songsters and your poets.'

'Jamie, you are my dear brother. You know how I suffer from homesickness . . . for it is hard not to think of the land in which one has lived so many years as home.'

'I understand,' said James. He was pleased with her. She was charming. She was as beautiful as a butterfly, and so should she be, flitting from pleasure to pleasure. Let her have her Little France in Holyroodhouse; let her have her fancy poets and her mincing gentleman dancers. Let her have all she wanted, provided she left the government of Scotland to Lord James Stuart.

They searched every stable in Leith to find a mount worthy of her, but they had set themselves an impossible task. At last they found a weary old nag who had seen happier days; he was mostly skin and bone and had a pathetic expression which made the Queen want to weep for him. On his back was a scratched old saddle.

Alas, it was a poor substitute for her palfrey, but it was the best they could find; and when she saw the mounts provided for the rest of the party she realized that hers was comparatively handsome.

So they left Leith watched by the silent fisherfolk, and a strange sight they were with the Queen of Scotland, richly clad and glittering with jewels, leading the party with her brother Lord James Stuart, and behind them the colourful courtiers dressed in the French manner riding on a collection of horses which, said Mary, might have been rescued from an *abattoir*.

She said to James: 'I cannot ride through the city thus mounted.'

'Remember, dear sister,' was James' reply, 'the people of Edinburgh have never seen your grand French processions. They will think you magnificent enough.'

'I could weep for chagrin. What must my uncles think?'

'They must take us as they find us,' said James grimly. 'Here we are more prone to admire that which is simple in life than lavish spectacles.'

Mary shivered, and not from the damp air.

They were a few miles from Holyrood when, turning a bend in the road, Mary saw before them a crowd of shouting people. At first she thought they were the citizens of Edinburgh come out to welcome her, but as they drew nearer it seemed to her that this was a menacing crowd. They shouted and, although she could not understand what they said, she heard her name mentioned. Their mottled flesh showed through their rags; their feet were bare and bleeding; and to her horror she saw that many of them were brandishing sticks.

'The Queen! The Queen!' shouted the ringleaders, and the crowd rushed forward, surrounding the cavalcade.

Mary was brought to a standstill, but she was not afraid. Rather she welcomed the excitement. She preferred these raucous shouts to the sullen indifference of the fisherfolk of Leith. She discovered in that moment that she was stimulated by danger; instinctively she drew herself up on the worn-out saddle, and nothing at that moment could make her look anything but queenly.

'What do they say?' she demanded of James. 'They are telling me something. Do not spare me, I beg of you. Are they telling me to go back to France?'

James held up his hand. Mary was proud of him as she watched. There was about him that which commanded immediate respect.

'Silence!' he roared. 'Silence in the presence of the Queen!'

There was an immediate hush. Mary looked into the wild faces of the men and women who were pressing so close to her, as James said: 'They do not come to attack you. They come to ask your clemency. They have broken into the prison and rescued one James Kellone who was to have been hanged. They are asking for a free pardon for him and for themselves.'

'What was his offence?' asked Mary.

'He is guilty of masquing on the Sabbath Day, which is against the law, said Lord James in severe tones.

'But surely not worthy of the death penalty! Indeed I am glad that some of my subjects know how to laugh. I will speak to them.'

'Your Majesty, have a care. Remember the Kirk of Scotland.'

But Mary rarely paused to think. She was with these people of hers. They no longer looked fierce. They had longed for gaiety, for masques and laughter. Dear God! she thought. How I do too, and how I understand their longing!

She forced her horse forward a little so that she was no longer beside Lord James. she lifted her hand and cried: 'Good people of Scotland, bear with me, your Queen, for I have lived in a strange land and, having just come among you, my speech will sound strange to you.'

There was silence all around her, broken only by the squawking of sea-birds. In the crowd it seemed that no one stirred. They stood, their sticks held lightly, their mouths open, waiting for what the Queen would say; and if they did not entirely understand her words, her smile was friendly and her face the fairest they had ever seen.

'You ask pardon for one who has been condemned to die. My subjects, most happily I grant a free pardon to that man and you all.'

A free pardon! That much they could understand. They called out one to another: 'Free pardon! May God bless the Queen.' They cried then as one voice: 'God save the Queen!'

And when the cavalcade pressed on, it was surrounded and followed by a mob of poor people waving their sticks and looking barbarous indeed. The stench, so said the more delicate of the French afterwards, all but made them vomit. But Mary felt happier than she had since she set foot in Scotland. It was pleasant to know that she had made some of her subjects understand her; it was pleasant to know that some–however humble–were proclaiming their loyalty.

Lord James was disturbed. It was a charming gesture, charmingly made, and it might be that she did right to make it at that moment. But as his eyes met those of Maitland of Lethington he knew that the great diplomat agreed with him that Mary Stuart would find trouble in Scotland. The Kirk–and its leader, John Knox–would find good cause to quarrel with her, and the Kirk and John Knox wielded great power in Scotland.

Dusk had fallen before Mary reached her capital city and, as it grew dark, she had the pleasure of seeing the bonfires flare up, first on Calton Hill, then on Salisbury Crag; she saw them burning in the city itself and she could hear the shouts of the people. It was comforting; their welcome might be rough according to French standards, but it was at least a genuine welcome.

Now she could see the fortress which had been built by her father. It looked dark, even menacing. She gazed uneasily at its towers and their crenelated battlements.

Here she would rest, just outside the city's walls; for clearly she could not make her triumphal entry into her capital in darkness.

It was a vast and noble palace, but it seemed chill and without comfort. The few tapestries which hung on the walls lacked the brilliance and beauty of those to which she was accustomed; here were no delicate carpets, no carved furniture; everything was plain, heavy and sparse.

Mary had been warmed by the loyal shouts of the mob which had accompanied her to the palace, and soon she would have some of her cherished possessions about her; she would bring warmth and cheer to the place; so that a little discomfort now seemed of small account. She could endure anything, she believed, provided she had the love and loyalty of her people. Even now she could hear the people from the city, crowding about the walls of the palace and calling: 'God Save the Queen!'

Tired as she was, in need of a hearty meal and the comfort she had known at the Court of France, she was not unhappy.

She found Flem beside her. Flem seemed touched with a glowing excitement; she had not noticed before that Flem was growing into a real beauty. Mary noticed also that the stern Lord Maitland had his eyes on Flem, although he was doubtless old enough to be her father.

That served to remind her that now they were home there would necessarily be a few marriages in her suite. She was going to enjoy bringing happiness to those she loved. There would certainly be other marriages to consider besides her own.

Dear Flem! She was not indifferent to the admiring glances of that important statesman. Mary would tease her about it to-morrow.

The meal was served and it seemed more tasty than it was, so hungry were they. And when it was over Mary retired to the apartment which had been prepared for her. While her Maries helped her to disrobe she talked excitedly of the way in which they would refurnish these apartments. It seemed to her then that the nostalgic melancholy of the first day and night had diminished a little. They were not in love with their new life–any of them–but they were becoming reconciled to it.

Then suddenly there broke out beneath her window what seemed to them a caterwauling, a barrage of the harshest sounds they had ever heard. Mary started up in horror, and hastily caused herself to be robed once more. Just as Flem and Livy were fastening her gown, and as the noise had grown louder and wilder and more discordant, there was a knocking on the door of the apartment.

It was Lord James with Lord Maitland, Mary's three Guise uncles and d'Amville.

'What has happened?' cried Mary in alarm. 'Is someone being murdered?'

'The loyal citizens of Edinburgh have come to give you welcome,' said Lord James dryly. 'They are playing the bagpipes in your honour. It would be well for you to appear at your window and say a few words of gracious thanks to them.'

'And,' said Elboeuf in rapid French, 'mayhap that will have the desired effect of putting an end to such ear-splitting sound.'

Mary, listening, began to detect the stirring music in what had at first seemed harsh to her, and she felt angry with those Frenchmen who put their hands over their ears. This was bad manners. To those people below, the old Scottish airs and melodies were sweet music and intended to be a tribute to her.

The bagpipes were subdued as those outside the palace walls began to sing.

'But what sad songs!' cried Mary. 'It would seem as though they were sorry that I have come. They can hardly be songs of rejoicing.'

'They are the hymns of the Kirk,' said Lord James solemnly.

'Hymns!' cried the irrepressible Elboeuf. 'At such a time! I should have thought sweet madrigals or happy songs expressing joy at the Queen's return would have been more suitable.'

'The people of Edinburgh thank God that the Queen has returned, and they do so sincerely and solemnly. They have been taught that it is sinful to sing profane songs. The Kirk does not allow it.'

'But for the Queen's homecoming . . .'

'They wish to greet her in a godfearing way.'

Elboeuf lifted his shoulders. He was already homesick for Paris and Lorraine. D'Amville and his friend Chastelard were looking at the Queen, and their looks said: 'This is a strange and barbarous country, but we rejoice to be here since you are.'

And while most of the French put their hands to their ears, trying to shut out the sounds, Mary went to a window and cried: 'I thank you all, good people. I thank you with all my heart. You have delighted me with your loyal greetings and I rejoice to be among you.'

The people cheered and shouted. The solemn singing of hymns continued far into the night, and the pipes kept up their stirring strains until far into the morning.

From the windows of Holyroodhouse Mary could look on her capital city. She could see the High Street–the neatest and cleanest in the world–with its stone flags and the channels on either side, made to drain off the rain and filth, and the stone houses with their wooden galleries. There stood the Tolbooth Prison, and as she looked at it she swore none should be incarcerated there during her reign merely for wishing to masque and enjoy laughter; she could see the Lawnmarket and the noble houses and gardens of the Canongate which led to Holyrood.

The great Tron stood in the centre of Market Cross, and there were the stocks and pillories. This was the busiest spot in all Edinburgh, and here, during the days which followed the arrival of the Queen, the people gathered to talk of all that her coming would mean. Apprentices from the goldsmiths' shops in Elphinstone Court, tinsmiths from West Bow, and stallholders from the Lawnmarket all congregated there in Market Cross to discuss the Queen; and when they discussed the Queen they remembered that other who had told them–and the world–that he was her enemy: the man whom they flocked to hear in the Kirk, the man who swayed them with his promises of salvation and–more often–his threats of eternal damnation.

John Knox ruled the Kirk, and the Kirk was ruling Scotland. Preaching armed resistance to the Devil–and the Devil was everyone who did not agree with John Knox–he had on more than one occasion stirred the people of Scotland to rebellion. With his 'First Blast against the Monstrous Regiment of Women' he had told the world of his contempt for petticoat government, although now that Elizabeth was on the throne of England and promising to do much good for the cause which was John Knox's own, he wished that he had been a little more cautious before publishing his 'First Blast.' He was a cautious man for all his fire. He believed God spoke through him; he believed he owed it to the world to preserve himself that he might the better do God's work. For this reason he had often found it necessary to leave Scotland when his person might be in danger. 'All in God's service,' he would say from the safety of England or Geneva. 'I take a back seat for the better service of God.'

In his absence his actions might be questioned, but when the people saw again the fanatical figure with the straggling beard streaming over his chest like a Scottish waterfall, and heard his wildly haranguing voice, they were converted once more to their belief not only in the reformed religion but in the sanctity of John Knox.

'Have you heard Knox's latest sermon?' was the often-repeated question.

They had. They would not have missed it for all the wealth of Holyroodhouse.

Knox was setting himself against the Queen as he had set himself against her mother. He had preached against the Devil's brood and the congregation of Satan. This included the Queen. Had he not prayed to God to take her mother, declaring to his congregation, when she was smitten with the dropsical complaint which eventually killed her: 'Her belly and loathsome legs have begun to swell. Soon God in His wisdom will remove her from this world.' Had he not rejoiced openly in the Kirk when she had died? Had he not laughed with fanatical glee when he had heard of the death of Mary's husband. 'His ear rotted!' cried John Knox. 'God wreaked Divine Vengeance on that ear which would not listen to His Truth.'

John Knox was no respecter of queens; he would rail against the new one. He would do his utmost to rouse the people against her; unless she cast aside her religion and took to his, he would work unceasingly for her defeat and death as he had worked for her mother's.

The French in the palace were inclined to laugh at the preacher; but Mary did not laugh. The man alarmed her, although only slightly as yet. She looked to those two statesmen, her brother James and Lord Maitland, to help and guide her in what she had to do, although she reminded them that when he had come home she had made no bargain to change her religion. She was a Catholic and would always be so. She would, she said, try to show this man the way of tolerance.

Lord James nodded. He was determined that his sister should leave the government of the country to him and Maitland. They were Protestants, but of a different kind from Knox. Religion was not the whole meaning of their existences; it was something with which to concern themselves when more important matters were not at issue. Maitland and Lord James, while agreeing that a happier state of affairs might have existed had the Queen adopted the religion of the majority of her subjects, were quite prepared to let her celebrate Mass in her own chapel.

Mary, characteristically, wished now to concentrate on what was pleasant rather than unpleasant. She renewed her acquaintance with two more of her half-brothers–John and Robert–handsome, merry boys, slightly older than herself, and she loved them both.

Some of the furnishings had been sent from Leith, and it was a pleasure to set them up in her apartments. The lutes and musical instruments had arrived, so the Court was now enjoying music in the evenings. Mary herself sang and danced under the admiring gaze of many, including d'Amville and Chastelard.

The people of Edinbrugh had shown themselves delighted with her youth and beauty. She looked as a queen should; she always had a smile of warm friendliness, and the men whose lives she had saved on the way from Leith to Edinburgh talked of her beauty and wisdom and how, in their belief, she would bring great happiness to her country.

Mary had much to learn of the bitterness and venom which always seemed to attach themselves to religious differences. It did not occur to her that there could be any real reason why she should not continue in her mode of worship, while any of her subjects who wished to follow a different doctrine should do so.

Knox, according to her uncles and d'Amville, was something of a joke, and she did not take him very seriously until her first Sunday in Holyrood Palace. That day she announced her desire to hear Mass in the chapel and, dressed in black velvet and accompanied by her Maries, she was making her way there when she heard the sounds of shouts and screams.

Chastelard came running to her and begged her not to proceed.

'Your Majesty, the mob is at the gates of the Palace itself. They have been inflamed by the man Knox. They swear they will not have the Mass celebrated in their country.'

Mary's temper–always quick–flared up at once. She had intended to play a tolerant role with her people; she was infuriated that they should attempt to do otherwise with herself.

'The mob!' she cried. 'What mob?'

'Knox's congregation. Listen I beg of you. They are in an ugly mood.'

'I, too, am in an ugly mood,' retorted Mary; but she listened and heard the cries of 'Satan worship! Death to the idolators.'

Flem had caught one of her arms, Seton the other. Mary threw them off angrily, but Chastelard barred her way.

'At the risk of incurring Your Majesty's displeasure, I cannot allow you to go forward.'

She laid her hand on the young man's arm and her anger melted a little as she caught the ardour in his eyes, but she was not going to be turned from her anger. She pushed him aside, but even as she started forward, she saw two men bringing back her priest and almoner. There was blood on their faces.

She ran to them in consternation. 'What have they done to you?'

The almoner spoke. 'It was little, Your Majesty. They wrenched the candlesticks from us and laid about them. But Your Majesty's brothers were at hand, and Lord James is speaking to the people now.'

She hurried on. Lord James was addressing the crowd which had gathered about the door of the chapel.

The crowd would stand back, he ordered. None should come a step nearer to the chapel on pain of death. He himself, Lord James Stuart, would have any man answer with his life who dared lay hands on the Queen or her servants.

There was a hush as Mary approached.

James said to her: 'Say nothing. Go straight into the chapel as though nothing has happened. There must be no trouble now.'

There was something in James' manner which made her obey him. Trembling with indignation, longing to turn and try to explain to these people why she followed the Church of Rome, yet she obeyed her brother. He seemed so old and wise, standing there, his sword drawn.

He sent Chastelard back to bring the priest and almoner, that they might celebrate Mass in the chapel according to the Queen's wishes; and after a while Mary was joined by the priest and the almoner, their bandaged heads still bleeding from their wounds.

Mass was celebrated; but Mary was aware of the mob outside. She knew that, but for the fact that her brother stood there to protect her, the crowd would have burst into the chapel.

She sat with her brother in her apartments. Lord Maitland was with them.

She was perusing the proclamation, addressed to the citizens of Edinburgh, which was to be read in Market Cross.

'There,' she said, handing the scroll to James, 'now they will understand my meaning. They will see that I do not like this continual strife. I am sure that with care and tolerance I, with my people, shall find a middle way through this fog of heresies and schisms.'

Maitland and Lord James agreed with the wording of the document. It was imperative to Lord James' ambition that his sister should continue as nominal Queen of Scotland, for the downfall of Mary would mean the downfall of the Stuarts. It was necessary to Maitland that Mary should remain on the throne, for his destiny was interwoven with that of Lord James. They wished for peace, and they knew that the father and mother of war were religious controversy and religious fanaticism.

The proclamation was delivered in Market Cross and then placed where all who wished to could read it.

The citizens stood in groups, discussing the Queen and her Satan worship, or John Knox and his mission from God. To most men and women tolerance seemed a good thing, but not so to John Knox and the Lords of the Congregation. Mary was the 'whore of Babylon' declared the preacher and 'one Mass was more to be feared than ten thousand men-at-arms.' 'My friends,' he shouted from his pulpit, 'beware! Satan's spawn is in our midst. Jezebel has come among us. Fight the Devil, friends. Tear him asunder.'

After that sermon Maitland declared to the Lord James and the Queen that nothing but a meeting between her and Knox could satisfactorily bring them to an understanding.

Mary was indignant. 'Must I invite this man . . . this low, insolent creature . . . to wrangle with me?'

'He is John Knox, Madam,' said Lord James. 'Low of birth he may be, but he is a man of power in this country. He has turned many to his way of thinking. Who knows, he may influence Your Majesty.'

Mary laughed shortly.

'Or,' added the suave Maitland, 'Your Majesty may influence *him*.'

It was a strange state of affairs, Mary said, when men of low birth were received by their sovereign simply because they ranted against her.

The two men joined together in persuading her.

'Your Majesty must understand that, to the people of Scotland, John

Knox's birth matters little. He himself has assured them of that. With his fiery words he has won many to his side. Unless you receive the reformer, you will greatly displease your subjects. And you will weaken your own case because they will think you fear to meet him.'

So Mary consented to see the man at Holyrood, and John Knox was delighted to have a chance of talking to the Queen.

'Why should I,' he asked his followers, 'fear to be received in the presence by this young woman? They say she is the most beautiful princess in the world. My friends, if her soul is not beautiful, then she shall be as the veriest hag in my eyes, for thus she will be in the eyes of God. And shall I fear to go to her because, as you think, my friends, she is a lady of noble birth, and I of birth most humble? Nay, my friends, in the eyes of God we are stripped of bodily adornments. We stand naked of earthly adornment and clothed in truth. And who do you think, my friends, would be more beautiful in the eyes of God? His servant clothed in the dazzling robes of the righteous way of life, or this woman smeared with spiritual fornications of the harlot of Rome?'

So Knox came boldly to Holyroodhouse, his flowing beard itself seeming to bristle with righteousness, his face bearing the outward scars of eighteen months' service in the galleys, which into his soul had cut still deeper. He came through the vast rooms of the palace of Holyrood, already Frenchified with tapestry hangings and fine furniture, already perfumed, as he told himself, with the pagan scents of the Devil, and at length he faced her, the dainty creature in jewels and velvet, her lips, hideously–he considered–carmined and an outward token of her sin.

She disturbed him. In public he railed against women, but privately he was not indifferent to them. In truth, he preferred their company to that of his own sex. There was Elizabeth Bowes, to whom he had been spiritual adviser, and with whom he had spent many happy hours talking of her sins; it had been a pleasure to act as father-confessor to such a virtuous matron. There had been Marjorie, Elizabeth's young daughter, who at sixteen years of age had become his wife, and who had borne him three children. There was Mistress Anne Locke, yet another woman whose spiritual life was in his care. He railed against them because they disturbed him. These women and others in his flock were ready to accept the role of weaker vessels; it was pleasant to sit with them and discuss their sins, to speak gently to them, perhaps caress them in the manner of a father-confessor. Such women he could contemplate with pleasure as his dear flock. He and God–and at times he assumed they were one–had no qualms about such women.

But the Queen and her kind were another matter. Every movement she made seemed an invitation to seduction; the perfume which came from her person, her rich garments, her glittering jewels, her carmined lips were outward signs of the blackness of her soul. They proclaimed her 'Satan's spawn, the Jezebel and whore of Babylon'.

There were other women in the room, and he believed these to be almost as sinful as the Queen. They watched him as he approached the dais on which the Queen sat.

Lord James rose as he approached.

'Her Majesty the Queen would have speech with you.'

Mary looked up into the fierce face, the burning eyes, the belligerent beard.

'Madam . . .' he began.

But Mary silenced him with a wave of her hand.

'I have commanded you to come here, Master Knox, to answer my questions. I wish to know why you attempt to raise my subjects against me as you did against my mother. You have attacked, in a book which you have written, not only the authority of the Queen of England, but of mine, your own Queen and ruler.' He was about to speak, but yet again she would not allow him to do so. 'Some say, Master Knox, that your preservation–when others of your friends have perished–and your success with your followers are brought about through witchcraft.'

A sudden fear touched the reformer's heart. He was not a brave man. He believed himself safe in Scotland at this time, but witchcraft was a serious charge. He had thought he had been brought here to reason with a frivolous young woman, not to answer a charge. If such a charge was to be brought against him, it would have been better for him to have taken a trip abroad before the new Queen came home.

'Madam,' he said hastily, 'let it please Your Majesty to listen to my simple words. I am guilty of one thing. If that be a fault you must punish me for it. If to teach God's Holy word in all sincerity, to rebuke idolatry and to will the people to worship God according to his Holy Word is to raise subjects against the princes, then I am guilty. For God has called me to this work, and he has given me the task of showing the people of Scotland the folly of papistry, and the pride, tyranny and deceit of the Roman Anti-Christ.'

Mary was astounded. She had expected the man either to defend himself or to be so overcome by her charm that he would wish to please rather then defy her.

He went on to talk of his book. If any learned person found aught wrong with it, he was ready to defend his opinions, and should he be at fault he was ready to admit it.

'Learned men of all ages have spoken their judgments freely,' he said; 'and it has been found that they were often in disagreement with the judgment of the world. If Scotland finds no inconvenience under the regiment of a woman, then I shall be content to live under your rule as was St Paul under Nero.'

His comparisons were decidedly discomfiting. Not for a moment would he allow any doubt to be cast on his role of saint and God's right-hand man, and hers as tyrant and sinner.

'It is my hope, Madam, that if you do not defile your hands with the blood of saints, neither I nor what I have written may do harm to you.'

'The blood of saints!' she cried. 'You mean Protestants, Master Knox. Your followers stained their hands with the blood of my priest only last Sunday. He did not die, but blood was shed.'

'I thank God he did not die in the act of sin. There may yet be time to snatch his soul for God.'

Thereupon the preacher, seeming to forget that he was in the Queen's Council Chamber, began to deliver a sermon as though he were in a pulpit at the Kirk. The fiercely spoken words rolled easily from his tongue. He pointed out how often in history princes had been ignorant of the true religion. What if the seed of Abraham had followed the religion of the Pharaohs–and was not Pharaoh a great king? What if the Apostles had followed the religion of the Roman emperors? And were not the Roman emperors great kings? Think of Nebuchadnezzar and Darius. . . .'

'None of these men raised forces against his Prince,' said Mary.

'God, Madam, had not given them the power to do so.'

'So,' cried Mary aghast, 'you believe that if subjects have the power, it is right and proper for them to resist the crown?'

'If princes exceed their bounds and do that which God demands should be resisted, then I do, Madam.'

She was furious with him for daring to speak to her as he had; she felt the tears of anger rising to her eyes; she covered her face with her hands to hide those tears.

Knox went on to talk of the communion with God which he enjoyed, of his certainty that he was right and all who differed from him were wrong.

James was at the Queen's side. 'Has aught offended you, Madam?' he asked.

She tried to blink away her tears, and with a wry smile said: 'I see that my subjects must obey this man and not me. It seems that I am a subject to them, not they to me.'

The reformer turned pale; he read into that speech an accusation which could carry him to the Tolbooth. He was off again, explaining that God asked kings and queens to be as foster parents to the Church. He himself did not ask that men should obey him . . . but God.

'You forget,' said Mary, 'that I do not accept your Church. I find the Church of Rome to be the true Church of God.'

'Your thoughts, Madam, do not make the harlot of Rome the immaculate spouse of Jesus Christ.'

'Do yours set the Reformed Church in that position?'

'The Church of Rome, Madam, is polluted.'

'I do not find it so. My conscience tells me it is the true Church.'

'Conscience must be supported by knowledge, Madam. You are without the right knowledge.'

'You forget that, though I am as yet young in years, I have read much and studied.'

'So had the Jews who crucified Christ.'

'Is it not a matter of interpretation? Who shall be judge who is right or wrong?'

Knox's answer was: 'God!' And by God he meant himself.

Mary's eyes appealed to her brother: Oh, take this man away. He wearies me.

John Knox would not be silenced. There he stood in the centre of the chamber, his voice ringing to the rafters; and everything he said was a condemnation, not only of the Church of Rome, but of Mary herself.

For he had seen her weakness. She was tolerant. Had she been as vehement as he was, he would have spoken more mildly, and he would have seized an early opportunity to leave Scotland. But she was a lass, a frivolous lass, who liked better to laugh and play than to force her opinions on others.

Knox would have nothing to fear from the Queen. He would rant against her; he would set spies to watch her; he would put his own interpretation on her every action, and he would do his utmost to drive her from the throne unless she adopted the Protestant faith.

Mary had risen abruptly. She had glanced towards Flem and Livy, who had been sitting in the window seat listening earnestly and anxiously to all that had been said. The two girls recognized the signal. They came to the Queen.

'Come,' said Mary, 'it is time that we left.'

She inclined her head slightly towards Knox and, with Flem and Livy, passed out of the room.

By the light of flickering candles the Queen's apartment might well have been set in Chenonceaux or Fontainebleau. She was surrounded by her ladies and gentlemen, and all were dressed in the French manner. Only French was spoken. From Paris had come her Gobelins tapestry, and it now adorned the walls. On the floor were rich carpets, on the walls gilt-framed mirrors. D'Amville and Montmorency were beside her; they had been singing madrigals, and Flem and Beaton were in an excited group who were discussing a new masque they intended to produce.

About the Court the Scottish noblemen quarrelled and jostled for honours. The Catholic lords sparred continually with the Protestant lords. On the border the towns were being ravished both by the English and rival Scottish clans.

In the palace were the spies of John Knox, of Catherine de' Medici and of Elizabeth of England. These three powerful people had one object: to bring disaster to the Queen of Scots.

Yet, shut in by velvet hangings and Gobelins tapestry, by French laughter, French conversation, French flattery and charm, Mary determined to ignore what was unpleasant. She believed her stay there would be short; soon she would make a grand marriage–perhaps with Spain. But in the meantime she would make it pass as merrily and in as lively a fashion as was possible; and so during those weeks life was lived gaily within those precincts of Holyrood which had become known as 'Little France'.

Chapter Two

In the small room adorned with the finest of her French tapestries, Mary was playing chess with Beaton. Flem was at her embroidery and Livy and Seton sat reading quietly.

Mary's thoughts were not really on the game. She was troubled, as she was so often since she had come to Scotland. There were times when she could shut herself away in Little France, but she could not long succeed in shutting out her responsibilities. These Scots subjects of hers–rough and lusty–did not seem to wish to live in peace with one another. There were continual feuds and she found herself spending much time in trying to reconcile one with another.

Beaton said that Thomas Randolph, the English ambassador, told her that affairs were managed very differently in the English Court, and that the Tudor Queen's frown was enough to strike terror into her most powerful lords. Mary was too kindly, too tolerant.

'But what can I do?' Mary demanded. 'I am powerless. Would to God I were treated like Elizabeth of England!' She was sure, she said, that Thomas Randolph exaggerated his mistress's power.

'He spoke with great sincerity,' Beaton had ventured.

But Beaton was inclined to blush when the Englishman's name was mentioned. Beaton was ready to believe all that man said.

Mary began to worry about Beaton and the Englishman. Did the man–who was a spy as all ambassadors were–seek out Beaton, flatter her, perhaps make love to her, in order to discover the Queen's secrets?

Dearest Beaton! She must be mad to think of Beaton as a spy! But Beaton could unwittingly betray, and it might well be that Randolph was clever enough to make her do so.

In France, the Cardinal of Lorraine had been ever beside Mary, keeping from her that which he did not wish her to know. Now she was becoming aware of so much of which she would prefer to remain in ignorance. Her brother James and Maitland stood together, but they hated Bothwell. The Earl of Atholl and the Earl of Errol, though Catholics, hated the Catholic leader Huntley, the Cock o' the North. There was Morton whose reputation for immorality almost equalled that of Bothwell; and there was Erskine who seemed to care for little but the pleasures of the table. There was the quarrel between the Hamilton Arran and Bothwell which flared up now and then and had resulted in her banishing Bothwell from the Court, on Lord James' advice, within a few weeks of her arrival in spite of all his good service during the voyage.

She was disturbed and uncertain; she was sure she would never understand these warlike nobles whose shadows so darkened her throne.

She recalled now that warm September day when she had made her progress through the capital. She had been happy then, riding on the white palfrey which had with difficulty been procured for her, listening to the shouts of the people and their enthusiastic comments on her beauty. She had thought all would be well and that her subjects would come to love her.

But riding on one side of her had been the Protestant Lord James, and on the other the Catholic Cock o' the North; and the first allegorical tableau she had witnessed on that progress through the streets had ended with a child, dressed as an angel, handing her, with the keys of the city, the Protestant Bible and Psalter–and she had known even then that this was a warning. She, who was known to be a Catholic, was being firmly told that only a Protestant sovereign could hold the key to Scotland.

Moreover it had been a great shock, on arriving at Market Cross, to find a carved wooden effigy of a priest in the robes of the Mass fixed on a stake. She had blanched at the sight, seeing at once that preparations had been made to burn the figure before her eyes. She had been glad then of the prompt action of the Cock o' the North–an old man, but a fierce one–who had ridden ahead of her and ordered the figure to be immediately removed. To her relief this had been done. But it had spoilt her day. It had given her a glimpse of the difficulties which lay ahead of her.

She had returned from the entry weary, not stimulated as she used to be when she and François rode through the villages and towns of France. But she had determined to make a bid for peace and, to show her desire for tolerance, had appointed several of the Reformers to her government. Huntley, the Catholic leader, was among them with Argyle, Atholl and Morton as well as Châtelherault. Her brother, Lord James Stuart, and Lord Maitland were the leaders; and in view of the service he had rendered her, she could not exclude Bothwell, though that wild young man had succeeded in getting himself dismissed from Court–temporarily, of course. She had no wish to be severe with anyone.

Beaton looked up from the board and cried: 'Check-mate, I think, Your Majesty. I think Your Majesty's thoughts were elsewhere, or I should never have had so easy a victory.'

'Put away the pieces,' said the Queen. 'I wish to talk. Now that we have our rooms pleasantly furnished, let us have a grand ball. Let us show these people that we wish to make life at Court brighter than it has hitherto been. Perhaps, if we can interest them in the pleasant things of life, they will cease to quarrel so much about rights and wrongs and each other's opinions.'

'Let us have a masque!' cried Flem, her eyes sparkling. She was seeing herself dressed in some delightful costume, mumming before the Court, which would include the fascinating Maitland–surely, thought Flem, the most attractive man on Earth–no longer young, but no less exciting for that.

Livy was thinking of tall Lord Sempill who had made a point of being at her side lately, surely more than was necessary for general courtesy, while Beaton's thoughts were with the Englishman who had such wonderful stories to tell of his mistress, the Queen of England. Only Seton was uneasy, wondering whether she could tell the Queen that one of the priests had been set upon in the streets and had returned wounded by the stones which had been thrown at him; and that she had heard there was a new game to be played in the streets of Edinburgh, instigated by John Knox and called 'priest-baiting'.

The Queen said: 'Now, Seton! *You* are not attending. What sort of masque shall it be?'

'Let there be singing,' said Seton. 'Oh, but I forgot . . . Your Majesty's choir is short of a bass.'

'There is a fine bass in the suite of the Sieur de Moretta,' said Livy.

'And who is he?' asked Mary. 'But he will be of little use, for Moretta will soon be returning to his master of Savoy, I doubt not; and he will take your singer with him.'

'Then Your Majesty is not contemplating the marriage which Moretta came to further?' asked Beaton diffidently.

Mary looked at her sharply. Could it be that she was gathering information for Randolph? No! One look at dear Beaton's open face reassured her.

She took Beaton's hand and pressed it warmly. It was a mute plea for forgiveness because she had secretly doubted her. 'No, I shall not marry the Duke of Ferrara, though it was for that purpose Savoy sent Moretta among us–for all that this is reputed to be a courtesy visit. But we stray from the point. What of this singer? Even temporarily he might be of some service to us.'

'He has the voice of an angel!' declared Flem.

'If he is as good as you say, we might ask him to stay with us after his master goes back.

'Does Your Majesty think he would?'

'It would entirely depend on what position he holds under his master. If it is a humble one, he may be glad of the opportunity to serve me; and I doubt his master would refuse to spare him.'

'Madam,' said Seton, 'I heard him sing yesterday, and I have never heard the like.'

'We will have him brought here to my apartments. He shall sing for us. What is his name?'

'That I do not know,' said Flem.

Mary turned to the others, but none knew his name.

Seton suddenly remembered. 'I fancy I have heard him called Signor

David by his fellows.'

'Then we will send for Signor David. Flem dear, send a page.'

The Queen had her lute brought to her, and the five ladies were discussing the music they would sing and play, when Signor David appeared.

He was a Piedmontese, short of stature and by no means handsome, but his graceful manners were pleasing; he bowed with charm, displaying a lively awareness of the honour done to him, while accepting it without awkwardness.

'Signor David,' said the Queen, 'we have heard that you possess a good voice. Is that true?'

'If Your Majesty would wish to judge of it, your humble servant will feel himself greatly honoured.'

'I will hear it. But first tell me–what is your position in the suite of my lord de Moretta?'

'A humble secretary, Your Majesty.'

'Now, Signor David, sing for us here and now.'

She played the lute and rarely had she looked more charming than she did at that moment, sitting there in her chair without ceremony, her delicate fingers plucking at the strings, her eyes shining, not only with her love of music, but because she was about to do this poor secretary a kindness.

And as he sang to her playing, his glorious voice filled the apartment and brought tears to their eyes; it was a voice of charm and feeling as well as power, and they could not hear it and remain unmoved.

When the song ended, the Queen said with emotion: 'Signor David, that was perfect.'

'I am delighted that my poor voice has given Your Majesty pleasure.'

'I would have you join my choir.'

'I have no words to express my delight.'

'But,' went on the Queen, 'when you leave with your master, we shall find my choir will be so much the poorer that I may wish you had never joined it!'

He looked distressed.

'Unless,' said Mary impulsively, 'you wished to remain in my service when your master goes.'

His answer was to fall on his knees. He took her hand and lifted it to his lips. 'Service,' he stammered, 'to the most beautiful lady in the world!'

She laughed. 'Do not forget you will be choosing this land of harsh winters in exchange for your sunny Italy.'*

'Madame,' he replied, 'if I may serve you, that would be sun enough for me.'

How different were the manners of these foreigners, she mused, from those of blunt Scotsmen! She liked the little man with the large and glowing eyes.

'Then if your master is willing, when he leaves Scotland you may exchange his service for mine. What is your name–your full name? We know you only as Signor David.'

'It is David Rizzio, Madame. Your Majesty's most humble and devoted servant henceforth.'

It was Christmas time and the wind howled up the Canongate; it buffeted the walls of Holyrood, and the Queen had great logs burning in the fireplaces throughout the palace. To her great regret, most of the French retinue which had accompanied her to Scotland had now returned to France, and of her immediate circle only Elboeuf remained.

There was trouble in the streets, and at the root of that trouble was the lusty Bothwell and the deranged Arran.

Bothwell did not forget that it was due to Arran that he had been dismissed from the Court. Such a slight to a border warrior could not be allowed to pass. Arran, and the whole Hamilton clan, never missed an opportunity of maligning Bothwell and had spread far and wide the scandal concerning him and Anna Throndsen–the poor Danish girl, they called her–whom he had seduced, made a mother and lured from her home merely to become one of those women with whom he chose to amuse himself as the fancy took him.

Arran–a declared Puritan and ardent follower of Knox–was not, Bothwell had discovered, in a position to throw stones. Accordingly Bothwell devised a plot for exposing the Hamilton heir in the sort of scandal with which he had conspired to smear Bothwell.

Bothwell had two congenial companions. One of these was the Marquis d'Elboeuf, always ready for a carousal to enliven the Scottish atmosphere, and Lord John Stuart, Mary's base-born brother, who admired the Hepburn more than any man he knew and was ready to follow him in any rashness. Bothwell cultivated Mary's brother for two reasons–one because the young man could do him so much good at Court, and the other because he hoped he would marry his sister, Janet Hepburn, a red-headed girl as lusty–or almost–as her brother, and had been involved in more than one scandal and had already been lavishly generous with her favours to Lord John.

The followers of Bothwell and Lord John swaggered about the streets of Edinburgh, picking quarrels with the followers of the Hamiltons. But that was not enough for Bothwell's purpose.

'What a merry thing it would be,' he cried, 'if we could catch Arran *flagrante delicto*. Then we should hear what his friend John Knox had to say to that!'

Elboeuf was overcome with mirth at the prospect. Lord John wanted to know how they could do it without delay.

''Tis simple,' explained Bothwell. 'Often of a night he visits a certain woman. What if we broke into the house where they stay, catch him in the act, and drive him naked into the night? Imagine the puritan heir of the Hamiltons, running through the streets without his clothes on a cold night because he has been forced to leave them in the bedchamber of his mistress!'

'Who is his mistress?' asked Lord John.

'There we are fortunate,' explained Bothwell. 'She is the daughter-in-law of old Cuthbert Ramsay who was my grandmother's fourth husband, and lives in his house.'

'Old Cuthbert is no friend to you.'

'No, but in the guise of mummers we should find easy entry into his house.'

''Tis a capital plan!' cried Elboeuf. 'And what of the poor deserted lady? I could weep for her–her lover snatched from her! Will she not be desolate?'

'We'll not leave her desolate!' laughed Bothwell. 'She will find us three adequate compensation for the loss of that poor half-wit. It would seem our game with Arran would be but half finished if we did not console the lady after dismissing her lover.'

So it was agreed.

The night was bitterly cold as the three conspirators swaggered down to St Mary's Wynd, wherein stood the house of Cuthbert Ramsay. They were dressed as Christmas revellers and masks covered the faces of all three, who were well known as the most profligate men in Scotland.

They found the door of the house locked against them; Bothwell was infuriated because, knowing the customs of Ramsay's house, he realized that there must have been warning of their coming.

'Open the door!' he shouted. He could see the dim lights through some of the windows, but no sound came from behind the door. Bothwell's great shoulders had soon crashed it open and, with the help of his two friends, he forced an entry into the house.

Seeing a shivering girl trying to hide herself, Bothwell seized her and demanded to be shown the apartments of Mistress Alison Craig with all speed. The girl, too terrified to do aught else, ran up the staircase with the three men in pursuit. She pointed to a door and fled.

Bothwell banged on the door. 'Open!' he cried.

'Who is there?' came the instant request. Bothwell turned to his friend and grinned, for the voice was that of Alison Craig.

'It is one who loves you,' said Bothwell, 'come to tell you of his love.'

'My lord Bothwell . . .'

'You remember me? I thought you would.'

'What . . . what do you want of me?'

Still grinning at his companions, Bothwell answered: 'That which I always want of you.'

It was easier to force an entry into Alison's room than it had been into the house. Soon all three of them were in the room, where Alison, half clothed, cowered against the wall. The open window told its own story.

Lord John ran to the window.

'What . . . do you want here?' demanded Alison.

'Where is Arran?' asked Bothwell.

'I . . . do not understand you. I do not understand why you come here . . . force your way into my room . . .'

'He has made good his escape,' said Lord John turning from the window.

Elboeuf had placed his arm about Alison. She screamed and struck out at him.

'How dare you . . . you . . . you French devil!' she cried.

Lord John said: 'Madam, you would prefer me, would you not? See, I am young and handsome, and a Scot . . . a bold brave Scotsman whom you will find very different from the dastard who has just left you. Do not trust Frenchmen, for as the good people of Edinburgh will tell you, the French have tails.'

'Go away . . . you brutes . . . You loathesome . . .'

Elboeuf interrupted: 'Dear Madam, can you tolerate these savage Scots? He who has deserted you at the first sign of trouble is a disgrace to his nation. I will show you what you may expect from one who comes from a race that is well skilled in the arts of love.'

Alison tried to shut out the sight of those three brutal faces. She had had lovers, but this was a different affair. In vain she tried to appeal to some streak of honour in those three. Perhaps in Lord John, she thought. He was so young. Perhaps the Frenchman whose superficial manners were graceful. Never . . . never, she feared, in Bothwell.

He had pushed the others aside. He said: 'Arran is my enemy and it is meet and fitting that I should be the first.'

Feeling his hands upon her Alison gave out a piercing scream. She slipped from his grip and ran to the window.

'Help!' she cried. 'Good people. . . . Help! Save me from brutes and ruffians . . .'

Bothwell picked her up effortlessly. He had played a similar role in many a scene in his border raids. He threw the terrified woman on to the bed.

'Harken!' cried Lord John.

Elboeuf's hand went to his sword.

The servants had not been idle. They had lost no time in making it known that Bothwell and his friends had broken into the house of Arran's mistress. The Hamilton men were rushing up the stairs.

It was a very different matter, attacking a defenceless woman, from facing many armed men, and all three realized that they would be in danger of losing their lives if they hesitated. Already it was necessary to fight their way through those men who were on the staircase. Bothwell led the way, his sword flashing. As for Lord John and Elboeuf–no one cared to wound the Queen's uncle or her brother–and in a short time the three men were clear of the house.

They separated and ran to safety before the streets were filled with the gathering Hamilton clan.

The matter did not end there. The Hamiltons continued to throng the streets, swearing they would do to death their enemy Bothwell. The followers of Elboeuf and Lord John were gathering about them; and it seemed as though a great battle might shortly take place in the streets of Edinburgh.

The Queen, hearing of this, was terrified and uncertain how to deal with the trouble. Once more she was thankful for her resourceful brother, for James acted promptly, and with the Cock o' the North and himself riding at its head led an armed force to disperse the quarrelling clans.

'Every man shall clear the streets on pain of death!' was Lord James' proclamation.

It had the desired effect.

But Bothwell felt the little adventure had not entirely failed. All Edinburgh now knew that, for all his piety, Arran had a mistress, and that was just what he had wished to proclaim.

The Lord James and Maitland were closeted together discussing the affair of Bothwell and Arran.

'Arran,' said Maitland, 'being little more than half-witted, may be the more easily dismissed. It is the other who gives me anxious thoughts.'

Lord James stroked his sparse beard and nodded. 'You're right. Bothwell is a trouble-maker. I would like to see him back in his place on the Border. It may well be a matter for rejoicing, that our Queen has been brought up in the French Court. I fancy she finds us all a little lacking in grace. What she must think of that ruffian Bothwell I can well imagine.'

'Yet he received part of his education in France, remember.'

'It touched him not. He is all Borderer. I think the Queen would be pleased to have him removed from Court.'

'None could be more pleased at that than I. If we can marry the Queen into Spain . . .'

There was no need to say more. Both men understood. Marry the Queen into Spain . . . or somewhere abroad. Leave Scotland for Lord James and Maitland. It was a twin ambition.

'Bothwell would try to prevent such a marriage,' said Maitland. 'He would wish to see the Queen married to a Scot.'

'We will advise the Queen to banish him from Court.'

'What of the others who were equally guilty?'

'Her brother! Her uncle! Let us satisfy ourselves with ridding the Court of Bothwell. He is our man.'

They sought audience with the Queen. She was angry about this brutal outrage which had taken place in the midst of the Christmas celebrations. She was preparing for her brother Robert's marriage to Jane Kennedy, the daughter of the Earl of Cassillis; she had grown fond of Jane and was delighted to do special honour to her. And after that marriage there was to be another: Lord John's to Janet Hepburn. There could be so much gaiety and pleasure, yet these barbarians could not be content to enjoy it–nor would they let others enjoy it in peace.

'Madam,' said Lord James, 'this is a monstrous affair. Such outrageous conduct is a disgrace to our country.'

'Yet it would seem that I am powerless to prevent it.'

'No, no, Your Majesty,' said Maitland. 'The miscreants can be punished–and should be, as a warning to others.'

'How can I punish my uncle Elboeuf?'

'You can only warn him. It will be said that, as a Frenchman from an immoral land, his sins are not to be taken as seriously as those of honourable Scotsmen. Soon he will be leaving our country. A warning will suffice for Elboeuf. As for our brother, he is but a boy–not yet twenty–and I think led astray by more practised ruffians. He can be forgiven on account of his youth. But there is one, the ringleader, who is not so young and should not be forgiven. Bothwell is the instigator of all the trouble, Madam, and as such should be severely dealt with.'

'I have no doubt that you are right,' said Mary. 'But it seems to me wrong to punish one and let the others go free.'

'While Bothwell remains at Court there will be trouble,' said Lord James.

Mary replied: 'I had thought to give them a severe warning, to threaten them with stern punishment if they offend again, and then forget the matter. It is Christmastide . . .'

'Madam,' said Maitland 'these matters cannot be put right by being thrust aside. The Hamiltons were gravely insulted, and for the sake of peace, Bothwell should at least be exiled.'

'Summon him to your presence, dearest sister,' said James. 'Tell him he must leave the Court. I assure you, it is safer so.'

Mary was resigned. 'I suppose you are right,' she said. 'Have him brought here.'

He came into her presence, arrogant as ever; and she was conscious of his veiled insolence.

'My lord Bothwell, you have been guilty of an outrage. You have broken into the house of peaceful citizens and caused much distress. I know that you were not alone. You had two companions. One is a guest in this kingdom–my own guest; the other is a young and impressionable boy. Therefore I hold you responsible for this disturbance.'

'Would you not cast a little blame on the Hamiltons, Madam?'

'From what I hear the trouble started when you forced an entry into a house in St Mary's Wynd.'

'The trouble started long before that, Madam. If you wish for an account of the scores I have to settle with Arran, I shall be pleased to give it.'

Mary waved her hand impatiently. 'Please . . . I beg of you . . . tell me no more. I am tired of your perpetual bickering. You are dismissed the Court. Go back to the Border. Go anywhere, and if you are not soon gone I shall be forced to make your punishment more drastic.'

'Madam,' began Bothwell, 'I appeal to your sense of justice. If you feel I have done aught to deserve blame, then must you cast some blame on Arran. Let me meet him in single combat and settle our affairs thus.'

'No, my lord,' she said sternly, 'there shall be no more bloodshed if I can prevent it.'

She looked up into his face helplessly. Her glance clearly said: What can I do? How can I punish Arran with his father, Châtelherault, and the whole Hamilton clan behind him–to say nothing of his supporter John Knox? Go away. If you must fight, fight the English on the Border. I want Scotland left in peace.

'Leave the Court,' she said. 'Go at once.' She smiled suddenly. 'You will have many preparations to make for your sister's wedding.'

His smile answered hers.

He would retire from Court; he would proceed with his preparations for his sister's wedding; and when the Queen's brother became his brother-in-law, he would be better fitted to pit himself against Lord James and the whole Hamilton clan.

'My sister,' he said, 'will be a sad woman if Your Majesty does not honour us at Crichton with your presence.'

The Queen was still smiling. So he was going. He was not going to plunge into one of those Knox-like arguments which distressed her. 'Of a certainty I shall wish to be present at my brother's wedding,' she told him.

Less than two weeks later Mary set out for Crichton Castle, the chief seat of the Hepburn family.

John Knox thundered against the marriage of these wicked people who disgusted virtuous Scotsmen with their fornications and lecherous lives. This base-born brother of the whore of Babylon, he declared, was known to be a whoremonger; and what of the woman he was marrying? 'A sufficient woman for such a man!'

Knox was left in Edinburgh, reviving old scandals.

'Janet Hepburn, the bride-to-be!' he cried. 'To how many has she been handfast, I should like to know–or rather I should shudder to know–before she prepares herself to enter into this unholy matrimony with the sanction of the Queen?'

Mary was glad to put many miles between herself and the ranting preacher. She was glad to enter the old castle whose unscalable walls had been built to resist the ruffian raiders from across the Border. Sternly it faced the Cheviots and the Tyne–the Hepburn's challenge to marauding Englishmen.

Here she dwelt as the guest of Lord Bothwell. She liked the wild outspoken girl who was as bold as her brother, and was not surprised that John wished to marry her.

Lord James, who accompanied her, was more dour than ever. He did not approve of this alliance with the Hepburns. The girl was wild, he complained to Mary. John was too young to be saddled with such a wife. There were nobles of higher standing who would have been delighted with the honour of marrying a Stuart.

She refused to listen to his gloomy prophecies. Here was an occasion for merriment–a wedding, and the wedding of her own brother at that. Lord Bothwell was making a great entertainment for her and she was determined to enjoy it.

'James,' she coaxed, 'now that Robert and John are married, you must be the next.'

James listened soberly. He had been thinking for a long time of marriage with the Lady Agnes Keith, who was the daughter of the Earl Marischal. Marry he would, but his marriage would in no way resemble this one between Janet Hepburn and his brother John. For all he knew, John had been caught by the woman at one of the handfast ceremonies where young men and women met round a bonfire and went off to copulate in the woods. Lord James had no desire for such questionable pleasures. When he married Lady Agnes it would be because he had made up his mind that such a match would be advantageous. As yet he was hesitant.

Mary was laughing at him. 'Yes, James,' she said, 'I shall insist. Your marriage shall be the next. You cannot allow your young brothers to leave you behind.'

Lord James pressed her hand in a brotherly, affectionate way. It was impossible not to be fond of her. She was so charming and so ready to take his advice.

Mary gave herself up to the pleasure of being entertained. And what an entertainment Lord Bothwell had prepared for her! She knew that he had sent raiders beyond the Border to procure that which made their feast, but what of that! He was a Borderer with many a score to settle. The eighteen hundred does and roes, the rabbits, geese, fowls, plovers and partridges in hundreds, may have come from the land of the old enemy, but it mattered not at all. They made good feasting. And after the feast there were sports on the green haugh below the castle as had rarely been seen in Scotland, and the leaping and dancing of the bridegroom won the acclamation of all.

Mary now felt better and happier than she had for many weeks.

Could it be true–as her Maries suggested–that her native land was more beneficial to her health than France had been? It was absurd. These draughty castles, so comfortless compared with the luxury of the French chateaux, and food which although plentiful was less invitingly prepared . . . could it be possible that these discomforts could make her better? Perhaps it was the rigorous climate, though often when the mist hung about the rooms she felt twinges in her limbs. No. She was growing out of her ailments–that must be it. Of course her Maries declared it was due to Scotland because they were fast becoming reconciled to Scotland: Flem through Maitland; Livy through John Sempill; Beaton through the Englishman, Randolph; and Seton . . . well, Seton was just happy to see the others happy.

When would Mary's time come; and who would be her husband? It seemed to Mary that every day the name of some suitor was presented to her.

The Queen of England was anxious to have a say in plans for Mary's marriage. If the bridegroom did not please her, she had hinted, she would certainly not name Mary and her heirs as successors to the English throne.

That spy Randolph–why was poor Beaton so taken with the man–always seemed to be at her elbow. She pictured him in his apartment, scribbling hard, determined that his mistress should miss little of what went on in Mary's Court.

And now there was to be another marriage. Lord James was at last going to marry Lady Agnes.

Mary wanted to show her gratitude to her brother, and what better time could there be than the occasion of his marriage? She longed to give him what he craved–the Earldom of Moray; but how could she grant him that Earldom when old Huntley, the Cock o' the North–and not without reason–laid claim to it? Instead she would make him Earl of Mar and beg him to be satisfied with that.

Now for the pleasant occupation of arranging the masques and mummeries. She called her Maries to her, and they fell to discussing the music for the wedding. That led to sending for Signor David whose company never failed to delight Mary. It was always such a pleasure to hear his voice, and now and then she would command him to sing for her.

When he came, all five Maries greeted him warmly.

'Come and sit here,' commanded the Queen. 'Now, Signor David, please sing the new song you brought to me last Monday.'

They listened entranced to his beautiful voice.

'You shall lead the choir for my brother's wedding,' declared the Queen.

He was overwhelmed with delight, as he always was by the slightest favour; that was why it was such a pleasure to do little things for him. If she could give him some small task, the doing of it seemed to please him more than praise. His attitude towards her was one of adoring devotion.

David,' she said, 'I am going to make you my *valet de chambre*. Then we shall not have to send for you when we want you. You will be here among us. Where do you lodge now, Signor David?'

'In the porter's lodge, Madame.'

'Well, henceforth you shall lodge in the palace, and your chamber shall be near mine, as I shall need your services often. Can you write in the French language, David?'

'Madame, it is as my native language.'

'Then why did you not tell us before!' cried Mary in French. 'Now we shall all speak French. We like to do so when we are alone.'

'Tell us about yourself, David,' said Flem. 'That is if Her Majesty would permit it.'

'Her Majesty permits,' said Mary, 'and is as eager to hear as you are, my dear Flem.'

'There is little to tell,' began David. 'My life was of no great interest . . . until I came to the Court of Scotland. I was born at Pancalieri. We were very poor, but my father was a musician. From my childhood it was singing . . . singing songs . . . and, of course, playing the lute.'

'Then I am glad of that, David,' said the Queen; 'not the poverty, of course, but the singing and the lute-playing. Doubtless it has made you the musician you are.'

'I am glad of it now, Madame, since it brought me to your notice.'

'What else, David?' asked Beaton.

'When I was of an age to leave home, I was sent to serve the Archbishop of Turin. There I played music, sang in his choir, and acted as his secretary.'

'Were you as competent a secretary as a musician?' asked Beaton.

'I think I gave satisfaction, my lady, since from the Archbishop I was able to go to Nice and the Court of the Duke of Savoy.'

'And there became secretary to Moretta,' added Mary. 'Who knows, I might make use of those secretarial qualities also. I will do this, David: I will pay you a salary of sixty-five pounds a year, and, if you please me, I shall increase it.'

'Madame, your goodness overwhelms me. It is sufficient reward to serve Your Majesty.'

'But it is not sufficient for us, is it?' she demanded of her Maries.

'We would have you dressed in velvets, you see,' explained Flem.

Mary said: 'Beaton, my dear, give David money so that next time he comes to us he may be dressed in velvet. And he must have a jewel too.' She looked down at her hands and drew off a ruby ring. 'The colour suits you, David. And I think it will fit your little finger.'

His dark eyes gleamed, and they saw the tears shining there. He fell to his knees, and taking the ring he put it on his little finger; then he pressed it against his lips.

'There it shall remain,' he said, 'until the day I die. A constant reminder of the day Your Majesty gave it to me.'

John Knox preached the wedding sermon in the Kirk of St Giles.

Lord James was a favourite of his; he looked to the young man, with high hopes. Naturally there were times when it was necessary to admonish his pupil, but John Knox had declared Lord James to be a friend of God and the true religion, which meant a friend to John Knox; and John Knox, the practical man, while keeping his eyes fixed on his place in Heaven, saw no reason for ignoring advantages which might accrue here on Earth.

He was not sure of Agnes Keith. He did not trust women. So now he spoke out. 'Unto this day the Kirk has received comfort from you. Let God and the Kirk not find you fainter in purpose than you were before, or it will be said that your wife has changed your nature.'

Mary was restless, waiting impatiently for the sermon to be over. When would the odious man finish? Was this the way to preach a wedding sermon? But Jamie was listening intently; and others seemed spellbound by the fire-breathing preacher.

Through the streets, when the church ceremony was over, went the wedding procession. It was magnificent, but Mary remembered another in comparison with which this seemed like a village wedding. Yet it was more grand than any seen before in Edinburgh, and it would show the people how she loved this brother of hers. He was a Protestant and she was a Catholic; but that made no difference to their love, she believed, and she wished her people to take this to heart.

James, now Earl of Mar, still hankered after the Earldom of Moray; but Huntley, who lived in the Northern Highlands like a king, could not be persuaded to give it up. James had said: 'It is a sad thing, my dearest sister, that there should be those in this country who endow themselves with a status above that of the Queen.'

'It is,' Mary agreed. James was referring to Huntley; Mary was thinking of John Knox.

The feasting went on for several days, and the citizens gathered outside Holyrood listening to the music and seeing what they could of the dancers. There were banquets and masques; and Mary had arranged that everything should take place in the elegant French manner.

Through the streets of Edinburgh John Knox stalked, shaking his fist at the palace.

'Within those walls,' he roared, 'the Devil dances. Painted harlots mingle with seducers. There'll be fornication in the Palace of Holyrood this night.' That subject dominated his mind; it was one on which he seemed compelled to dwell. 'Jezebel calls the tune, and her four handmaidens–Sin, Lechery, Lust and Evil-living–beckon the weak.'

During the revelry, Mary found time to talk to her brother. 'Jamie, on occasions like this I feel at peace with the whole world. I would like to call my enemies to me and speak peaceably with them. I fear John Knox is too far set against me, but what of the Queen of England? If I could have a meeting with her . . . if we could discuss, in person, our differences, would that not be a good thing?'

James smiled at his sister. 'It would indeed.'

James was indulgent. She was so pretty, and so impetuously foolish at times. She would never be a great ruler; she would be no match for the Queen beyond the Border. Elizabeth of England would never have tolerated in her country such a powerful nobleman as James intended to be in Scotland.

But such thoughts made him fonder of her than ever. He liked to see her dancing and enjoying her French games, laughing at the witticisms of her fool, La Jardinière, frittering away the days whilst the grown-ups got on with the work.

'I am glad,' she said, 'that you are in agreement with me, Jamie. I will sound Randolph on the subject at the earliest possible moment. Oh, Jamie, I do so long to see her. One hears so many tales of her. Her courtiers say she is dazzlingly beautiful, but we hear different reports sometimes. I should enjoy meeting her face to face.'

James looked into his sister's animated face. 'She would never forgive you if she saw you.'

'Forgive me! For what, James?'

'For being a hundred times more beautiful than herself.'

Mary was delighted. Compliments came rarely from James. Poor frivolous lass! James was thinking. Thinking to set herself against the shrewdest woman in the world!

But it was for her frivolity–and all that it might lead to–that he loved her.

At the evening's banquet, Mary, who had previously had a word with the Englishman Randolph, lifted her golden goblet of wine and, rising to her feet, cried: 'I drink to the health of my sister of England, Queen Elizabeth.' Whereupon all at the table rose and drank with her, to the especial delight of Thomas Randolph who adored his Queen, and Mary Beaton who adored Randolph and so was delighted to see friendly relations between him and her beloved Mary.

And as the bridegroom, James, the new Earl, joined in the toast, he was not thinking of a possible meeting between the two Queens, because he did not believe it would come to pass; he was not thinking of his bride and his marriage, because that was something accomplished and he never wasted time in profitless thought; what occupied his mind was how he could openly call himself the Earl of Moray and take possession of the rich lands which went with the title, and he concluded that this could only come about through the downfall of the Cock o' the North.

Bothwell was not pleased by the state of affairs. His prospects had promised to be so fair at that time when the Queen had sent for him to arrange her voyage back to Scotland. Since then he had twice been banished from Court. He was growing ambitious. He knew that James Stuart was against him; he knew too that James Stuart was a friend of the English. The Queen–a foolish woman–did not realize that. In her sentimental way she thought of her dear Jamie merely as her brother, not as the man whose chief aim was to strip her of power that he might add to his own.

He, Bothwell, wanted to see Scotland free from the French and the English. He was ready to serve the Queen; but he wanted a high place for the Earl of Bothwell.

He realized now that he had been foolish to allow his feud with the Hamiltons to put him out of favour. What he had done by his impulsive prank was to play right into the hands of James Stuart and Maitland; but he would beat them at their own game, and to do this he must contrive reconciliation with the Earl of Arran.

How to do this? Bothwell had an idea. He would seek the mediation of John Knox. Knox, of course, would condemn Bothwell for his profligate ways, but even so the Earl would not be so damned in the eyes of the preacher as some were, since he was a professed Protestant; moreover Knox himself came from the Border country and had lived with his parents in a district over which the Hepburns held sway. It was not difficult, therefore, to obtain, through a third party, the desired interview.

Knox received Bothwell in the sparsely furnished room at the manse not far from Market Cross.

'At last,' cried Knox, rising and standing as though he were addressing a meeting, 'you have seen the errors of your ways. You have lived a riotous life and now you have come home . . . like the prodigal son. You wish to leave your sins behind you . . . to lead a better life. . . . You wish to love your neighbour as yourself. . . .'

Patience was not one of Bothwell's virtues. He cut the preacher short. 'If I could have Arran's friendship instead of his enmity,' he said, 'I could stay at Court with a mere handful of servants. As it is, I have about me hundreds of men-at-arms. I must be prepared to meet an attack at any time and it is very expensive.'

Knox was inclined to be lenient. When he was a boy he had been humble before the lords of the estate. This man with the arrogant manner had reawakened that youthful respect. Hard-livers the Hepburns had always been, but they had not been harsh with their own. Moreover, Knox saw in this lusty man one whose friendship could be useful to him.

'My lord,' he said, 'I shall pray for you. I shall pray that I may be given the means of comforting you.'

Bothwell frowned. He had not come for a sermon and he was not going to promise to mend his ways. He interrupted: 'You have influence with Arran. I would have you make him understand that this quarrel between us is fruitless. Arrange a meeting and reconciliation between us. That is what I ask, Master Knox.'

'My lord, the angels are smiling at this moment. Brotherly love, they sing. Rejoice, for he whom we thought to be lost to the Devil has turned to God. You will not lose, my lord, for this night's work.'

Bothwell thanked the preacher and left. He was pleased with what he had done.

He was even more delighted when, at the meeting arranged by Knox, he took Arran's hand in his and, looking into the half crazy eyes, swore eternal friendship.

After that they surprised all Edinburgh. During the next few days wherever Arran was, there was Bothwell. They drank together; they were seen walking arm-in-arm along the Canongate.

Mary, with a small train of followers, had travelled up to Falkland Palace to enjoy a little hawking. To the delight of all who saw her, she rode out, a dainty sight, her falcon on her wrist. Beside her rode her brother, the Earl of Mar, and among those who accompanied them were her brother's new wife, Agnes Keith, and the four Maries.

It was when they had returned after an afternoon's sport that a special messenger came riding to the palace. He must see the Queen at once, he declared; he had a despatch for her which was a warning, and of the utmost importance.

'Whence comes he?' asked Mar.

'From the Earl of Arran, my lord, who declares that the Queen must, without delay, be made aware of the plots against her.'

James Stuart took the despatch at once to Mary and remained with her while she read it.

'But this is . . . incredible!' she cried. 'It cannot be true. Arran is mad. He says that there is a plot concocted by himself, his father Châtelherault, and Bothwell. They plan to abduct me, carry me off to Dumbarton Castle, murder any who resist, and keep me a prisoner until I marry Arran. They will force me to the marriage, if need be. And Bothwell is to see that all is carried out according to plan.'

'Why does Arran let you into the secret?'

'At the last moment he cannot go on with it. He wishes to warn me against Bothwell who is ruthless enough to attempt anything. James, it is ridiculous. Arran is no longer half-mad; he has completely lost his wits.'

James took the despatch and read it. 'It is coherent enough. It does not read like the words of a madman.'

'Jamie . . . you cannot believe . . .'

'My dearest sister, we cannot be too careful. Arran is mad enough for anything. Châtelherault is ambitious enough and Bothwell is wild enough to attempt to carry out this plan.'

'Seize my person! Keep me prisoner!'

'Aye! And inflict God knows what humiliations upon you.'

'It is a mad notion of Arran's, I am sure. The plan has no meaning outside that poor brain. You will remember he once before talked of kidnapping me . . . and it came to nothing.'

'Mary, you are the Queen. You are also a very desirable woman. Do not lose sight of these facts.'

'What am I to do,' Jamie?'

'Have them all placed under arrest. That is the only way to ensure safety.'

'First we should ascertain how deep in madness Arran is.'

'An order should be issued at once for the arrest of Arran, Châtelherault and Bothwell.'

'Let us take Arran first and hear what he has to say.'

'What! And leave his father and Bothwell free to carry out their diabolical plans! Bothwell is at the bottom of this, you may depend upon it. Bothwell and Châtelherault! They are a pair of knaves, using this poor madman to serve their ends.'

'But of what use could my marriage with Arran be to Bothwell?'

'How can we know what plans the Borderer makes?'

Mary was uneasy. She had hoped that the friendship between Arran and Bothwell would put an end to the strife; could it be possible that the insolent Borderer had arranged it in order to sway poor Arran to his will?

Only a few hours after the messenger from Arran had arrived, a member of the Hamilton family came riding with all speed to the castle of Falkland. He was Gavin Hamilton, the Abbot of Kilwinning, and he declared that his kinsman, the Duke of Châtelherault, had begged him to set out with all speed to Falkland as the Duke feared his son had completely lost his reason. He had come to his father's house of Kinneil with a wild story, and the Duke thought the Queen should know that he had put his son under lock and key.

'Madam,' cried Gavin Hamilton, 'the story of this wild plot to kidnap you is untrue. There never was such a plot. The young Earl imagined it. He threw himself at the Duke's feet, crying that he was possessed by devils and that Bothwell had persuaded him to treason. The Duke threatened to kill his son, and now Arran has escaped through a window by means of knotted sheets. It is not known where he is, but the Duke of Châtelherault considered it expedient to put the whole story before Your Majesty.'

Mary commanded Gavin Hamilton to go to a private chamber where he would be given refreshment. When she was alone with her brother she turned her anxious face to him. Though the plan seemed wild, she feared that it might contain some substance, and she could not help picturing herself the prisoner of Arran and Bothwell.

James said: 'We will at least keep Master Gavin Hamilton under restraint until we have thoroughly probed this matter.'

Before Gavin had finished the meal which was brought to him, Bothwell himself appeared at Falkland Castle.

'Send him to me at once,' said Mary when she heard of his arrival.

He came swaggering in, insolent and arrogant as ever. He showed no sign that he was aware that his plan had miscarried.

James and Maitland were both with the Queen.

'My lord Bothwell,' she began, 'we have had strange visitors this day.'

'Madam?' he questioned. His cool eyes appraised her, stripping her of her jewels, her velvets. She believed that in his mind's eye he set her side by side with the peasant women with whom, she had heard, he amused himself from time to time. His gaze made her uncomfortable.

'I beg of you, do not feign ignorance,' she said with heightened colour.

'I feign nothing, Madam. I am entirely ignorant of the comings of your strange visitors.'

'The Abbot of Kilwinning has been here. Does that suggest anything to you?'

'I do not know the fellow, Madam.'

'You know that he is a Hamilton. He brings me news of the Duke of Châtelherault.'

'Bad news, I assume, from Your Majesty's agitation.'

The cold eyes of James Stuart watched him; the shrewd ones of Maitland never left his face.

'He has exposed your plot, my lord.'

'Plot? What plot? To what plot does Your Majesty refer?'

'The plot which was conceived by you, Arran and Châtelherault, to kidnap me.'

'What is this? I know of no such plot, Madam.'

Mary turned helplessly to James and Maitland.

'You will need to convince Her Majesty of that more successfully than you are doing at the moment,' James said.

'I do not understand your lordship.'

'There is a grave accusation against you.'

'Who makes this accusation? Mad Arran?'

'The plot,' said Maitland flippantly, 'does not seem so mad as the man who made it.'

'So Arran has accused me?'

'Arran has laid bare the facts.'

'Bring the fellow here!' cried Bothwell. 'Let him accuse me to my face. By God! I'll challenge him . . . or any who accuse me . . . to single combat.'

'No such combat could serve to elucidate this matter,' said Maitland.

'By God!' cried Bothwell. 'Combat can decide whether a man shall live or die. I give you my word it can be both judge and jury.'

'It shall not be in this case,' said Maitland. 'The Queen is determined to uncover the truth.'

James had given a signal, and six men-at-arms appeared. They knew what they had to do.

Bothwell's hand went to his sword; but deciding this was not the time for violence, he hesitated.

He looked straight at the Queen, and his gaze, which seemed to hold something of contempt in it, made her shiver.

'I demand justice,' he said.

She answered quickly: 'It shall be yours, my lord.'

He allowed himself to be led away.

Mary tried to forget the unpleasant affair. She turned from the subject whenever it was raised.

'I am tired . . . tired of these perpetual quarrels!' she cried.

And then perhaps there would be a wedding at Court to amuse her; then she could briefly forget. She was planning for her meeting with the Queen of England. It should be the most splendid meeting in history. There should be tents set up on the Border and each country should display its chivalry. Her pageants should rival those of the Field of the Cloth of Gold.

But the Queen of England continually found excuses for postponing the meeting.

Meanwhile poor Arran had wandered the countryside, a raving lunatic, and had eventually arrived at the house of an old friend, Sir William Kirkcaldy, in a sorry state, his clothes torn, his body weak from hunger and his mind so distorted that he believed he was the Queen's husband and that, instead of lying in a state of collapse at the door of Hallyards, Sir William's mansion, he was lying in an oak bed at Holyrood with the Queen.

He had wept at the feet of Kirkcaldy and told him he was possessed by devils, that he was the thrall of witches. He was brought to Falkland and later imprisoned in Edinburgh Castle. Bothwell was also imprisoned there. The Duke of Châtelherault had thrown himself at Mary's feet and wept so bitterly that she had embraced him and told him he should not suffer. James, however, had insisted that Dumbarton Castle should be confiscated on the grounds that the son and his confederate could not be imprisoned while the father was held to be guiltless.

'Then,' said Mary, 'let us free Bothwell and Arran.'

'All in good time,' said James.

'Yet should not these men have a speedy trial? Should they be kept imprisoned before they have been proved guilty?'

James smiled tenderly. 'Dearest sister, Arran would have to be restrained in any case, so he suffers no hardship. As for Bothwell, it is as well to keep that rogue out of mischief for a while. Even if he is guiltless in this matter, his sins are many. Let this imprisonment serve to wipe off some of the punishment which is most surely due to him.'

Mary had to be content with that. She was not really sorry. Arran's madness and his preoccupation with marriage to herself perturbed her. Bothwell had a like effect.

Then fresh trouble broke out.

It started when Sir John Gordon, son of Huntley, the Cock o' the North, strolling through the streets of Edinburgh, had come face to face with Lord Ogilvie of Airlie and drawn his sword; in the fight Ogilvie was wounded, and Gordon taken and imprisoned in the Tolbooth.

The story of their feud was then brought to light. Lord Ogilvie had brought an action against John Gordon. One of the Ogilvies–a dissolute youth–had tried to persuade his stepmother to become his mistress, at which his father had been so enraged as to disinherit him and give a portion of his land to Sir John Gordon. Young Ogilvie had called a family conference, and Lord Ogilvie, maintaining that whatever the circumstances, his kinsman had no right to give away to outsiders that which belonged to his family, had brought a lawsuit in the hope of retrieving the property for the Ogilvies.

Sir John Gordon was infuriated at the bringing of the action. In the Highlands Lord Huntley and all the family of Gordon were regarded as rulers; they did not suffer insults, and if any were offered them it was–as was customary with the Borderer Bothwell–a matter for sword-play. Hence, swaggering through the streets of Edinburgh and meeting Ogilvie, it had seemed right and natural to draw the sword. That he–a Gordon–should be thrust into prison for such an action was an insult.

He had immediately found means of escaping and had fled to the stronghold of the North.

When James Stuart heard of this his eyes glistened and he licked his lips. He remembered the rich lands of Strathearn and Cardel which went with the Earldom of Moray and which were at that time held by the Gordons; he immediately began to see ways in which he could turn this affair to his advantage.

'It is time,' he said to the Queen, 'for Your Majesty to journey North. We must settle this affair with Huntley and his Gordons. You cannot allow young Gordon to flout your authority. We shall have every knave and vagabond breaking prison, believing it is a noble thing to do.'

'Jamie,' she said 'cannot we ask him to come back and face a trial?'

'Ask him to come back! He never would. He would flout you again as the Gordons have always flouted you.'

'I have not noticed that *they* have done this. There is *one* who has–in the Kirk and the streets of Edinburgh.'

'You may be sure,' said James quickly, 'that that fellow Randolph has given his account of this to his Queen. What, think you, will she say when she hears of it, if you do nothing in the matter? She will say Arran and Bothwell languish in prison, and those are Protestant nobles; Sir John Gordon goes free–but then he is a Catholic! You cannot afford to show the Queen of England that you so favour the Catholics. It is small wonder that she continually postpones your meeting.'

'Then set Arran and Bothwell free so that she cannot make this charge.'

'My dearest sister, you dare not. These two men are dangerous. You know, do you not, that I would protect you with my life?'

'Yes, Jamie.'

'Then Your Majesty must allow me to do so . . . in my own way.'

'Please, Jamie, show me what I ought to do.'

So James showed her. He insisted that they set out for the North.

The people came to cheer, but instead of poets, musicians and courtiers in her train, there rode men-at-arms.

On James' instructions she demanded that the Earl of Huntley should deliver up his houses, Findlater and Auchendown, as a penalty for his son's breach of the law.

Old Huntley, furious to have been disturbed in his domain, and knowing that James Stuart's desire was to wrest not only the title but the lands which went with it from the Earldom of Moray, gathered a strong force of Highlanders together and prepared to repulse the Queen's men. It was civil war in the Highlands, and the result was the capture of John Gordon–the cause of the trouble–and old Huntley himself; but as the latter was taken he was seized with an apoplectic fit, so great was his chagrin, and he died on the spot.

So ended the Queen's first journey to the North. She was depressed, although she had enjoyed riding through the magnificent country at the head of her troops; yet when she contemplated the huge body of the Cock o' the North, she was hard put to it to hide her tears from her brother James, who had now publicly assumed the grand title of Earl of Moray.

Riding south a pleasant surprise awaited Mary.

A young Frenchman joined the party, one whom she had known and liked both in France and on her first coming to Scotland. He had been forced, most regretfully, to return to France with the rest of those who had accompanied her, but now he was back again bringing letters and messages from her friends–and a devotion which had been enhanced by absence.

This was Pierre de Chastelard, the young poet who had been in the train of Henri de Montmorency, the Sieur d'Amville.

Pierre was young and handsome, related to the Chevalier de Bayard whose good looks he had inherited. He came fresh from romantic Dauphiné, and he cherished romantic dreams concerning the Queen of Scots.

He was a little arrogant; so he had been unable to resist talking of his joy at the prospect of seeing Mary again. He thought of her as his lady; and even as his lady-love.

He could not have said when he had begun to feel so sure of Mary's response. Perhaps his attitude had begun to change when Catherine, the Queen-Mother of France, had selected him for this mission. Perhaps it was something which she had said to him, something such as: 'I know of your admiration for the Queen of Scots. I remember noting it. And I have heard of the sport you have in those gloomy castles across the sea. Ah, my daughter the Queen of Scots is a most comely woman and she will be glad to see an old friend, I doubt not. I remember how devoted she was to my dear son. – And think! It is three years since she had a husband. Poor child! Well, Monsieur de Chastelard, you will comfort her.'

'I . . . Madame . . .?'

'Yes, you. You are a handsome man, are you not?' The laugh which accompanied the words held a hundred suggestions and was more expressive than words. It could be cruel and mocking but it could arouse such hopes. That coarse face had suddenly been near his own, expression suddenly lighting the eyes which were usuallywithout any. 'Well, Monsieur de Chastelard, remember the honour of France.'

He had thought he understood. She was aware of everything that went on in the chateaux, it was said. In France they were beginning to understand her. She had a new name now–Madame le Serpent. She was telling him something. Was it: 'You love the Queen of Scots. Do not be too backward. Hesitancy never leads to victory.' She knew something. She was telling him that Mary was not inaccessible.

So he had set off full of hope, and now he found himself before the Queen, who was a little older but seemed more healthy and was many times more beautiful than he remembered.

How warmly she received him!

'Monsieur de Chastelard, I knew you at once. This is a great pleasure indeed. What news . . . what news of my uncles and my dear aunt the Duchesse de Guise? What news of the King and . . . my mother-in-law? What news of Monsieur d'Amville?'

She seized hungrily on the letters which he had brought. She read them at once. Monsieur de Chastelard must stay beside her. He must tell her all . . . all that was happening to her dear friends and relations in her beloved France.

Her eyes filled with tears. She was homesick afresh.

'Yet,' she said, 'I am so happy that you are here.'

There were many to note her pleasure in the young man and the passionate glances he gave her.

As for Pierre, as soon as he was alone, he put his feelings into verse.

> '*O Déesse immortelle*,' he wrote,
> '*Escoute donc ma voix*
> *Toi qui tiens en tutelle . . .*'

It was pleasant to see Signor David again. His large eyes shone with delight. He did not say how desolate the place had been without her; poor *David le Chante*, as she sometimes called him, was far too modest for that. And with the gallant Chastelard in her train–and what enchanting poems he wrote to her and what a pleasure it was to answer them in verse–and David showing such decorous devotion, she could almost believe that she was back in France.

She liked to discuss her troubles with David; in some inexplicable way he could so sympathetically suggest the solution she was seeking.

She gave him some of her French correspondence to deal with; she was not sure that she liked Raulet, her French secretary. David was delighted to carry out little tasks, and if she gave him a small present, a jewel or some velvet for new clothes, he would seem almost sorry, preferring, as he said, to do it for love of the Queen and not for payment.

So David had become one of those whom it was a pleasure to find waiting for her.

When she returned from that northern journey. David was sad and reticent, she noticed. She waited until they were alone together, for she had some small matter of correspondence with which she wished him to deal, when she said: 'Are you ill, David?'

'Thank you, Madam. My health is excellent.'

'Then you are in some trouble . . . some little thing has gone wrong for you?'

'Not for me, Madam.'

'For someone you love?'

He turned those brilliant eyes upon her. David's eyes she thought, were his one beauty.

'Madam,' he said, 'I would speak if I dared.'

'If you dared! You cannot mean that you are afraid of me? Do you think me such a termagant then?'

'No, Madam, the sweetest and most bountiful lady in the world.'

'Then, David, will you give me a chance to be sweet and bountiful over this affair of yours?'

He had risen to his feet. His face was pale. Then he flung himself on to his knees and, taking the hem of her long robe, he raised it to his lips. 'Madam, have I your permission to speak and, if what I say offends you, will you forgive it and wipe it out as though it had never been said?'

'I give you my word, David. Come. Sit down. Sit here beside me. My poor David, it grieves me to see you thus depressed.'

Even so it was some seconds before he spoke. Then he said: 'Your Majesty is in danger. Oh . . . not in immediate danger. How can I—a humble *valet de chambre*—say this? But—I have been in the Courts of Europe, and I am constantly on the alert for Your Majesty's welfare. Oh, it is nothing to fear at this moment. It is not a wild plot to kidnap you. It is not an assassin's plan which I have discovered. But, Madam, it is equally dangerous. Your Grace is surrounded by foes. Those who seem to be your friends seek to make you powerless. They take to themselves great power, and with every step they weaken Your Majesty. They will remove from your side all those who would work for your good. They will force you to marry whom they wish. Madam, I beg of you take care.'

'Tell me what you have discovered.'

'Nothing that is not already known to many. It is the interpretation of these things which is significant. My lord Bothwell is in prison. He was loyal to your mother, and it may be that some fear he will be equally loyal to you. And now . . . that very clan is removed which would have set itself at the head of your supporters against the Protestant Knox, the ranting preacher who Your Majesty knows has never pretended to be your friend. I mean the Gordons. They are humbled. They are no longer a power. They are imprisoned or exiled . . . or dead.'

'But David, it was necessary to punish John Gordon.'

David smiled apologetically. 'But not to remove power from the clan. You might have need of their help; they would have rallied to your aid, should you have found it necessary to stand against a rebellion which Knox might raise. Now . . . they are powerless to do so.'

'But the Earl of Moray . . . my own brother . . .' She was staring at David;

his brilliant eyes met hers boldly.

'Yes, Madam.'

So David was warning her against Jamie.

He was on his knees now; he was fervently kissing her hands. David was excitable by nature.

'Madam, you promised to forgive and forget. It was merely my desire to serve you. . . .'

She put her hand on his thick hair while the tears sprang to her eyes. 'David,' she said, 'I have no doubt of your devotion. There is nothing to forgive, and I shall never forget. I begin to see that Jamie is ambitious. He has made me his tool. I have suspected it. Oh, David . . . my own brother! What can I do?'

'Madam, have a care. Allow me to serve you. Allow me to keep my eyes ever on the alert. I will serve you with my life if need be. Say nothing. Give no indication that you suspect your brother's motives.'

She nodded. 'You are right, David. I thank you.'

'Madam,' he said, 'I am now the happiest man in Scotland.'

In the light of many candles the apartments at Holyrood were gay. The music was sweet and merry. Mary was dressed in black silk breeches for the part she played in the masque which had just been performed; she made a slender and beautiful boy.

'You are enchanting,' whispered Pierre de Chastelard.

'Monsieur, you repeat yourself.'

'The words escaped me . . . involuntarily . . . sweet Mary.'

He drew back, wondering how she would receive such familiarity. Her answer was a tap on the cheek. His heart leaped with anticipation.

'How liked you that book of my making, the one written in metre . . . the one I wrote for you?'

'It was fair enóugh,' said Mary.

'Madame, will you dance with me?'

'Come,' cried Mary, 'I long to dance.' she clapped her hands and declared they would dance the new dance which Chastelard had introduced from the French Court. It was considered very daring, for during it the partners kissed.

'It is not a dance which Master Knox would much like, I'll swear,' cried Mary, laughing as she tilted her head to receive the kiss of Chastelard.

He was wildly excited that night. The Queen-Mother of France had been right in what she had hinted. If he could but see Mary alone! But she was rarely alone. Even in her most informal moments there would be one or more of her women with her.

The new French dance was a stimulant to the emotions. Again and again they danced it; and there was merry laughter in the apartments. The Queen could be gay on such occasions; it was as though she wished to snap her fingers at the criticism of herself and her Court.

Why not? mused Chastelard. Why not to-night? Her mood is such that I believe her to be ready.

While Mary was saying her farewells for the night, he slipped away. Mary and her four faithful attendants retired to the sleeping apartments, where the girls began to undress their mistress, chattering of the evening as they did so.

'Would we could have brought Master Knox to the apartment,' cried

Flem. 'What fun to watch his fury when he saw Your Majesty dance in these silk breeches!'

'He would have said we were all utterly damned,' said Seton.

'We are already damned . . . according to him!' laughed the Queen. 'As well be damned for a pair of silk breeches as a jewel or two. Seton darling, get my furred robe from the cabinet; I am cold.'

Seton went to the cabinet and, when she opened it, gave a sharp cry. They all turned to stare in amazement at what she had disclosed. There, standing in the cabinet, was Pierre de Chastelard.

'What . . . what are you doing here?' stammered Mary.

'Madame, I . . .'

'Oh!' cried Flem. 'You wicked man!'

Chastelard threw himself on to his knees before the Queen.

'Madame, I crave your forgiveness. I was distraught. A madness seized me. I became intoxicated by your beauty. I do not know what possessed me to do such a thing. I cannot imagine . . .'

'I can,' said the practical Beaton.

'Be quiet, Beaton,' said Mary. 'Let him speak for himself. What was your purpose, Monsieur de Chastelard?'

'Madame, I wished to read a poem to you. I had written it . . . and it was for your ears alone.'

All the girls began to laugh.

'A dangerous procedure, Monsieur,' said Flem, 'for the reading of a poem.'

'Where is the poem?' asked Mary. 'Give it to me.'

'Madame . . . in my excitement, I left it in my own apartment.'

Flem could not contain her laughter. Livy had started to shake with hers.

'You are insolent!' said the Queen; but her voice was broken with laughter.

This was the sort of adventure which occurred again and again at the Court of France. It was like being home again.

Beaton said: 'Shall we call my lord Moray and have this man put in chains, Your Majesty?'

Chastelard said: 'Put me in chains . . . it matters not. I am bound by stronger chains . . . the chains of a hopeless passion.'

'Drive him away,' commanded Mary. The four girls began to push him from the room. 'And Monsieur de Chastelard, I shall devise some punishment for you. You have been guilty of a grave indiscretion.'

'Madame, punish me as you will. Set me on the rack. Tear my limbs with red hot pincers . . . but do not deny me your presence.'

'If you were on the rack,' said Beaton grimly, 'you would have little thought of poetry. Get you gone. You embarrass the Queen. Why, if you were seen. . . .'

'Madame, your forgiveness. Without your smile I would as lief be dead.'

He was pushed outside and the door slammed; Beaton leaned against it, and the others were all overcome with helpless laughter.

'Still,' said Seton, 'it was a grave offence. What if Your Majesty had been alone?'

'Do you think that I would not have given a good account of myself?'

'I doubt it not; but it would have made pleasing news for the ears of Master Knox.'

'How shall you punish him?' asked Livy.

'How can you punish people because in love they are bold? He has brought a little of France to our grim old Court. Let us set that beside his sins. To-morrow I will speak sharply to him. That will suffice.'

A scandal touched the Court about this time. It was unfortunate that the story became known beyond the Court. John Knox learned of it with the utmost pleasure and re-told it from his pulpit, roaring at the people of Edinburgh to note the result of Jezebel's rule.

One of the Queen's minor serving women had been seduced by the Queen's French apothecary.

'Both servants of the Queen!' cried Knox triumphantly. 'Does it not speak for itself? Oh, what wickedness goes on within the walls of Holyroodhouse! What revellings to the call of Satan! Fornication is the order of the day in Holyroodhouse, my friends. Women dress as men . . . men as women . . . the better to stimulate their wretched appetites. Satan stands by, calling them to damnation. The servants follow their masters and their mistresses along the road to hell.'

The serving woman had borne a child and, with the help of her paramour, had kept the matter secret. The child had been born in an outhouse and done to death. Its body had been discovered, and the maid, when accused, had broken down and confessed the whole story. She and her lover had paid the penalty of murder; they were publicly hanged.

John Knox was there to see justice done and to lose no opportunity of calling the people's attention to the life of the Court. He blamed the Queen for her maid's seduction; he blamed the Queen for the murder of the new-born child. The apothecary was a Frenchman–a member of that hated race which had captured John Knox and made a galley slave of him; the Queen was half French by birth and all French in her manners. Let the people see what harlotry, what wickedness had been brought into the country by their queen. Let the people reflect how much happier they would be without her.

'Must I accept the ranting of this man!' demanded Mary; but not to Jamie as she would have done earlier. Now she turned to David. 'Must I, David?'

David's words were comforting. 'For the moment, Madam, yes. But have no fear of that. Between us we will devise some means of clipping the power of that man. We will make the people of Scotland free and happy, and Your Majesty Queen not only in name but in all else.'

'How?' asked Mary.

'We will watch events, Madam. It may be we shall do it through your marriage to a powerful prince–a Catholic like yourself. But patience, Madam, and for the time being–caution!'

'You are right. David, I want you to have this ring.'

'But, Madam, it is too valuable.'

'How could it be, for all you have done for me? Take it. I promise you that one day, when I am able, you shall no longer be called my *valet de chambre*, no longer merely David *le Chante*. You shall be my chief adviser, in all things, David . . . in all things.'

He bowed; his great glowing eyes went from her face to the sapphire she was putting on his finger.

A few days later Mary left Holyrood for St Andrews. The Court, among whom was Pierre de Chastelard, stayed a night at Burntisland.

Chastelard had been in a fever of excitement since that night when he had been discovered in the cabinet. He cursed his bad luck. He was sure that if Mary had not required that particular furred robe, and he had succeeded in being alone with her, they would have been lovers by now. Of course she had feigned anger before her women; but it was not real anger; that had been obvious. They had all looked on the matter as a joke. Joke! He would show them that it was no joke.

Mary had scarcely reprimanded him at all, which surely meant that she expected him to make the attempt again in some way. This time he would do so with more skill; and before the morning he would be her lover.

He had a greater opportunity of concealing himself on this occasion. Mary was closeted with her brother and Secretary of State Maitland, when he went silently to that chamber in which she would spend the night. He examined the bed and gleefully discovered that there was plenty of room for him to hide himself beneath it. It was a pity he was wearing his sword and dagger, for they were rather difficult to manage, but he had not wished to appear before her in anything but his finest array.

He waited in discomfort for a long time, but eventually he heard Mary and two of her women enter the apartment.

'I am tired,' said Mary. 'Come, Flem, hurry. Let me to bed. My feet are so cold. Did you bring my foot polkis?'

'Here they are.' Flem held up the linen foot-bags without which Mary could not sleep on cold nights for her feet would not get warm unless she wore them.

'Such a headache!' said Mary as Livy took off her head-dress.

'Dearest,' said Livy, 'I hope you are not going to start your headaches again.'

'It's the cold weather. How I long for summer!'

It was Livy who noticed a faint movement of the bed valance. She stared at it in silence, but then looked closer. With a swoop she lifted it and disclosed a man's boot. The Queen and Flem hurried to her side. Groaning, Chastelard came from under the bed.

'This is too much!' cried Mary.

'The second time!' muttered Flem.

Chastelard, furious at his own folly in allowing himself to be discovered, furious with Livy for discovering him, overcome by pent-up emotions, did not attempt to apologize. Clumsily and without warning, he sprang at the Queen, seized her and, to her horror and that of the two women, began to kiss her passionately.

Mary cried out: 'How dare you!'

Livy and Flem fell upon Chastelard and tried to free their mistress, but his mad desire and determination seemed to lend him the strength of two men. He succeeded in forcing the Queen on to the bed where all four of them wrestled together.

'Help!' cried Mary, really alarmed. 'Quickly!'

Flem broke away and ran to the door calling: 'Help! Save the Queen!'

There was a great bustle in the apartment as guards came rushing in.

'Take this man!' commanded the Queen.

Chastelard was seized, as Moray, the Queen's brother, came into the apartment.

'What means this?' he demanded.

'He was under the bed!' gasped Flem. 'Hiding!'

'Take this man's sword and dagger,' said Moray to the guards. 'Put him under close arrest.'

Chastelard appealed to the Queen. 'Madame, you know my intentions . . .'

'They were clear,' said Mary.

'The love I bear you . . .'

'Take him away!' roared Moray.

Chastelard was dragged, struggling, from the apartment.

Moray turned sternly to his sister. 'Madam,' he said, 'he shall lose his life for this outrage.'

Mary had grown pale but Moray went on quickly: 'I doubt not that he is the tool of your enemies.' He waved his hand to all those who had come into the apartment. 'Your presence is no longer needed,' he added. 'Fortunately the Queen's life has been saved.'

Moray was not slow to note that among those who had come into the Queen's apartment was Thomas Randolph, and his delight in what he was planning to write to his mistress was betrayed by his expression. A nice titbit to send to his mistress in England–the heroine of many a similar story–and one which would naturally be told and retold against the Queen of Scots. There were several firm supporters of Knox who had witnessed the scene; they had good noses for smelling out the scandals. The fact that Chastelard had been found in the Queen's bed-chamber would be all over Edinburgh by the morning. They would have it in the Highlands and on the Border within a few hours; and as soon as Master Thomas Randolph could arrange it, Madam Elizabeth would be chuckling over it with her paramour Robert Dudley.

As soon as Moray was alone with the three women he said: 'I must have the truth.'

'Livy found him under the bed,' declared Mary. 'He came out and sprang at me.'

'I have fear Your Majesty has given him some encouragement to behave thus.'

'By my appreciation of his poems?' said Mary angrily.

'There has been talk of dances,' growled her brother.

'In France we always danced the latest dances, and none thought the worse of us for that.'

'But Your Majesty is now in Scotland.'

'Jamie . . . what do you propose to do to Chastelard? You spoke of his losing his life. I could not consent to that . . . merely because of a momentary madness, a prank, you might say.'

'He was wearing his sword and dagger. That seems to me significant.'

'What do you mean, Jamie?'

'You must surely know that as Queen of Scotland you have many enemies.'

'Chastelard is no enemy!'

'It would be better for your honour if it could be proved that he is. Get your mistress to bed,' he ordered the Maries. 'Madam,' he went on, turning to Mary, 'we must speak of this matter in the morning.'

When he had gone, Mary said: 'I am sorry we called James in.'

'Madam,' said Flem, 'we had to call for help.'

'Yet . . .' She looked round the room at the shadows cast by the flickering candle light. 'Well . . . nothing can be done till morning. One of you stay with me. You, Flem . . . sleep in my bed this night.'

'Yes, dearest Majesty.'

'I do not know why I am afraid, my darlings, but I am. See! I am shivering.'

'He upset you, dear Madam,' said Livy. 'Come, let us get you warm, and Flem shall stay the night.'

So Flem and Mary lay in the big bed while Livy drew the curtains and tiptoed away.

Flem noticed that the Queen continued to shiver, and it was dawn before they fell asleep.

Mary faced her brother and wished that David were with her at Burntisland. She needed counsel now, because David had opened her eyes and she was beginning to distrust James.

'Does Your Majesty realize,' said James sternly, 'that this day they will be talking in Edinburgh of how your lover was discovered hiding beneath your bed?'

'My lover! A young poet of the Court!'

'All know Your Majesty's fondness for poets.'

'But surely we can simply say that he was *not* my lover. He is a poet and a good dancer.'

'With whom Your Majesty danced in black silk breeches!'

'I'll not be spied on!' said Mary angrily.

'Shall you not, sister? Alas! It is not for you to say whether you will be or not. You *are* spied on, and the whole of Knox's congregation knows that, in black silk breeches, you danced with this man.'

'It was for the purpose of the masque.'

'The Lords of the Congregation have their own ideas as to the purpose.'

'Am I responsible for their evil minds?'

'No, but you must consider them.'

'Chastelard was discovered; he was sent out; there the matter ends. It is no concern of anyone but myself.'

'There again I must most humbly contradict you. It is the concern of Scotland, England, France, Spain, Rome. . . . You are a Queen and your actions are watched. Your chances of making an advantageous marriage will not be enhanced by a scandal such as this might well become.'

'Oh, one day I may take it into my head to marry where I please, and it may not be one of these hesitant gentlemen who, with their governments, are calculating whether I shall bring them a big enough dowry.'

'If Your Majesty will pardon my brotherly comment, I must say that you are not speaking with your usual good sense. This man Chastelard has upset you, and understandably so. He must be made an example. We must show the people what happens to those who dare insult the Queen. There is only one thing to be done. He must go to the block!'

'The block! For hiding in a room!'

'In the Queen's bedchamber . . . under the Queen's bed . . . his sword and dagger handy.'

'I would never agree to that. Poor Chastelard! Why . . . I was fond of him.'

'Too fond for his safety, Madam.'

'I shall never consent.' She thought: I shall talk to David. Together we shall find a way to save poor Chastelard.

Moray looked at her quickly. She had changed. He could almost believe there was some influence working against him. He must get her married to some powerful prince; then he would be free to take up the Regency. If she did not marry abroad she would be here for ever; he would be pushed into the background; she must never be allowed to take another adviser. The matter of immediate moment was that there should be no scandal to disturb wedding plans. Nothing must stand in the way of a match with one of the European princes.

'There is something I must tell Your Majesty,' he said. 'You have been deceived in this man. When he played the lover he acted a part. He is a servant of the Montmorencys, and the Montmorencys with the Bourbons are, as you know, the leading Huguenot faction in France. This, my dearest sister, was a plot on your life which your faithful Maries have foiled. There is only one way to deal with such an offence. I beg you listen to reason.'

'It can't be true!' gasped Mary.

'It is hard for your pride to accept this. It was easy for him to play the role of lover, because so many love you. But I know that he came here to murder you. This I shall tell his judges . . . and I have no doubt of the verdict.'

Mary covered her face with her hands. She remembered the uncontrollable passion of Chastelard when he came from under the bed.

'But . . . it's horrible,' she said. 'Horrible!'

'Mary, have one of your women sleep with you in your bed until we return to Holyrood. The others will be close by, but keep one . . . in your bed. My dear sister, only thus can I feel happy concerning your safety.'

'Flem slept with me last night.'

'Then let her sleep with you until we are in Holyrood once more. Will you do this?'

'Yes, James.'

'I am relieved. Now think no more of this unfortunate business.'

James kissed her hand, and she sat thinking of Chastelard who she had thought had wished only to make love to her, and had come–or may have come–to murder her.

A week later in the market place of St Andrews, Pierre de Chastelard laid his head on the block. He looked very handsome, and many who watched his last moments shed tears. There were few in that crowd of spectators who really believed that he had conspired against the Queen.

'It is clear,' they said to each other, 'why he was in her bedchamber. She had not meant her women to discover him. He was to wait there until they had gone.'

Before he died, Pierre de Chastelard quoted Ronsard's famous Hymn to Death. He stood on the scaffold, his curling hair ruffled by the February wind; the people listened to his beautiful voice and wept afresh, although few understood what he said.

> '*Je te salue, heureuse et profitable Mort*
> *Des extrêmes douleurs medicin et confort . . .*'

Then smiling he laid his head upon the block and, as the axe descended, he was heard to say: '*O cruelle dame . . .*'

But that was not the end of the scandal concerning Pierre de Chastelard. John Knox had decided that it should not be the end. The drama made too useful a scourge with which to attack the Queen.

'"*O cruelle dame!*"' screamed Knox from his pulpit. 'You know what that means, my friends. Cruel mistress–that is what is meant by those words. What that complaint importeth, lovers may divine. Ah, my good friends, now is seen the harvest of sin. A woman of the Court murdered her ill-gotten child, and by God's mercy she and her paramour paid the penalty; now in divine justice another of Satan's imps goes to eternal torment.'

And in her candle-lit apartment, although she tried to dance and sing as gaily as before, Mary was haunted by the memory of Chastelard.

Chapter Three

Two years after the death of Chastelard, Mary was still unmarried. During that time there had been no lack of suitors; but it seemed that a royal marriage was indeed difficult to arrange. There were so many watching Mary. So the suitors were proposed and dismissed, over those two years.

Mary had suffered one great loss in the death of her uncle François de Guise who had been assassinated at Orléans by a young fanatic, Poltrot de Meroy. The Cardinal wrote often and as affectionately as ever, but he was continually pointing out the advantages of a match with Charles, the Archduke of Austria. This she could not understand. She was hoping for the grandest of marriages with Don Carlos of Spain; and yet she had come to understand–with the help of David Rizzio–that the Cardinal was not working for that match but against it, and it seemed incredible that her uncle should be opposed to that which could bring her so much honour.

'There must be some reason for it, David,' she said.

David knew the reason, and it shocked her deeply.

'Madam, the Cardinal is your uncle and you feel great affection towards him, but he works not for your good and your happiness. He works for the power of the Guises in France. A marriage with Don Carlos, while bringing great honour to yourself and to Scotland, would serve to strengthen Spain. France would be less powerful than of yore and, with France, the Guises. No, your uncle as we now know has exerted his strength against the Spanish match for that reason. Now, Madam, a Catholic Scotland with yourself and the Archduke as its rulers would be deemed a firm ally of France, but would in fact be a dependant of that country; there would be a strong France to stand against a weakened Spain. That is the Guisian policy. True, it would do you no good; but your uncle's first concern is not with yourself, Madam, but with the Guises in France.'

'But my uncle has done everything for my good . . . always.'

'When your good was his also, Madam.'

This was a tragic discovery, and yet she knew it to be true. She remembered now with humiliation those tender scenes between herself and the Cardinal. Always he had been subduing her will to his, not because he wished to help her, but because he wished to use her in order to increase the power of himself and his family.

David had shown her this as he had shown her the falseness of her brother James; and she knew that David was right.

She stood alone now with no one but David to help her; strangely enough the thought strengthened her. She would cease to listen to the advice of the

Cardinal, as she had already to that of James. With David to help her she would arrange her own affairs.

Maitland of Lethington had been back and forth during the past years with messages to and from the Queen of England. Maitland was that politician most likely to find favour with the English Queen. He was possessed of suave manners, good looks and a clever tongue; and all those qualities appealed to Elizabeth. Now James Melville was also at the English Court and was sending her regular despatches giving accounts of the state of affairs there.

There was one young man who was in the minds of several people as a possible suitor for the Queen of Scots. This was Henry Darnley, a tall, slim youth of nineteen. He was handsome and graceful, with large, blue, rather prominent eyes, a fair complexion and beardless face which made him seem younger than he actually was. He had the additional advantage of royal blood, being a direct descendant of the Tudors. Elizabeth liked him since he was handsome, a good musician and dancer, but she never–or rarely–allowed her personal dislikes to override her political judgment.

She made an open declaration that she would be much against the marriage of Mary and Darnley, but alone with Cecil who shared some of her secrets, she was less emphatic. Although she declared her desire to see Mary's country living in peace and prosperity, that was far from her wish. An internally peaceful Scotland was a threat to England, and Elizabeth would never forget that Mary had dared to display the arms of England, suggesting thereby that Elizabeth was a bastard and had no right to the throne. In their secret sessions, Elizabeth and Cecil were not at all sure that a marriage between Mary and Darnley would be a bad thing for England after all, for they knew Henry Darnley to be a weak, vain and dissolute young man who would not help–but rather hinder–Mary in the governing of her country. But Elizabeth's policy was to make a display of benevolent friendliness towards her cousin over the border.

Darnley remained at the English Court and, though his ambitious mother, who resided in England where Elizabeth could seize her if she wished, and his equally ambitious father, who had recently been allowed to return to Scotland where he had regained his estates, had high hopes of their son's future, Elizabeth outwardly frowned on these hopes.

There was another young man whom Elizabeth was prepared to offer to Mary. She would not at first disclose his name. Indeed, she declared, she could not bring herself to do so. She offered this man because she loved the Scottish Queen so devotedly and wished to do her so much good, for the man she had in mind was the most perfect man she, Elizabeth, had ever set eyes on, and she could not bear to contemplate his leaving her Court.

But at last she was constrained to whisper the name of this man to Melville, and Thomas Randolph was given instructions to tell it to the Queen of Scots.

When Randolph sought an audience, David Rizzio was with Mary. She had given him more and more work to do, and he was constantly at her side. The Englishman looked askance at the small stunted figure of the Piedmontese, but Mary said: 'You may speak, Master Randolph, before my secretary.'

Randolph then showed her a list of possible suitors suggested by the Queen of England and, on reading the last name on the list, Mary raised her eyebrows and looked full into the Englishman's face.

'Lord Robert Dudley!' she exclaimed.

'The same, Madam.'

'But this man is . . .'

Randolph's look silenced her. He greatly feared she was about to make some indiscreet observation concerning his mistress.

'But this is a man with whom the Queen of England would not wish to part,' said Mary firmly.

'My Queen bids me tell you that she is so desirous for Your Majesty's happiness that she has set herself the task of finding for you the most perfect man she knows. This is Lord Robert.'

Mary was aware of David's eyes upon her; he was pleading: Do not show anger. Do not show that you regard this as an insult. The Queen of England is offering you one who, many would say, is her discarded lover but, Madam, I beg of you, show no anger.

How well she was beginning to co-operate with David. How she delighted in following his lead! He was right, of course. David was always right.

'There are times, Master Randolph,' she said, 'when I think of my dear husband. Although several years have elapsed since he died, the memory of him is still too strong for me to consider remarriage.'

'But, Madam, a handsome living husband would help you to forget one who is dead.'

'I do not know. There has been too much talk of marriage. Sometimes I think I will follow your Queen's example and remain unmarried.'

'That would entail a grievous loss to Scotland, if you will forgive my saying so, Madam. My Queen assures you that if you marry Lord Robert she will then fix the succession. On her death you or your heirs would be rulers of England if my Queen should die without heirs of her body.'

'It may be that I shall not outlive your Queen, Master Randolph. It is true that I am some years younger, but she is possessed of the better health.'

'My Queen enjoys good health and I thank God for it; but it is to Your Majesty's interest to consider this important matter of the succession.'

'Indeed, yes. It is a matter near my heart. I must consider my marriage since it involves so much. But there are other suitors mentioned here by your Queen. I should be loth to rob her of one in whom, I have heard, she takes great pleasure. Moreover, I am a Queen, the daughter of Kings, and I should have to consider whether I demean myself by marriage with a commoner; and, for all the excellencies which your Queen knows Lord Robert to possess, he is, alas, of no royal blood. Your Queen, I see, mentions also Ambrose Dudley, the Earl of Warwick, Lord Robert's elder brother.'

'Yes, Madam. She says what an excellent thing it would be if you might have Warwick, and she Lord Robert; although she admits Warwick lacks the beauty and perfection of his brother. She says there could be only one Lord Robert, and if she were not determined to remain a virgin she would marry him herself; but as she is fixed in her determination, she offers him to you.'

'And my lord Robert–what says he?'

'My lord Robert, realizing the honour this match would bring him, is eager for it.'

'You must give me time to ponder it, Master Randolph. I should have to give the matter much thought.'

Randolph acknowledged his dismissal and, begging her to let him have her answer as soon as she found it conveniently possible, retired.

When he had gone, Mary let loose her anger.

'How dare she! The insolent woman! Her horse-master! Her paramour! Her confederate in murder! They murdered his wife . . . why did she not then take him as her husband? But she did do so . . . of course . . . without the ceremony! And now . . . tired of him . . . she dares to pass him on. It's an insult. David, I should have told Randolph. I have demeaned myself by even pretending to consider this match.'

'Madam, I beg of you to be calm. This is but a trick of the English Queen's. She will not part with him. It is a scheme to cover up some other plot. She has someone else for you, I vow. She wants to make you furious over Dudley, so that you will the more readily turn to the one she wishes you to have.'

'How can you know this?'

'Because, Madam, that woman never follows a straight course. She is full of lies and deceits; she makes a pretence of running in one direction, when all the time she intends to go in another. Be calm, I beg of you. Pretend to consider this match as she herself has pretended to consider so many. We will wait and shall soon see whom the Queen of England really wishes you to marry.'

'I believe she wishes to mock me. He was her lover, is now no longer, and she wishes to rid herself of him, so she offers him to me . . . to *me*!'

'Nay, Your Majesty. She dotes on him as she ever did. Shortly you will be hearing from England that she has greatly honoured him. He is now Earl of Leicester and, during the ceremony of bestowing the earldom upon him, she could not resist putting her fingers between his ruff and his neck and tickling him there before them all. Does that indicate that she has tired of him?'

'Surely she would not be so indiscreet.'

'She is the most indiscreet woman in the world, and the most wily. That is why she succeeds. She hesitates at times; she is reckless at others; therefore she is unaccountable. She covers great schemes with frivolous chatter. Beware of her, Madam. Do not again offend her vanity; you have already done that by assuming the arms of England. That must be lived down. Therefore, thank her for her consideration, pretend to consider Dudley, play her game of coquetry and indecision. It will work as well for Your Majesty as for her.'

'David, you are my wise man. I know it. How did you know that Lord Robert is now Earl of Leicester? How did you know that she tickled his neck?'

David smiled. 'Madam, I took the precaution of sending a servant of mine to the English Court. He went in the role of servant to Melville, and none knew that he worked for . . . us.'

'I cannot imagine what I should do without you.'

'I pray to the saints, Madam, that you will never have to, for if I were dismissed your service there would be no reason for me to live.'

'One does not dismiss those one trusts,' said Mary emotionally. 'One does not dismiss those one loves.'

A few days later she dismissed her French secretary, Raulet, from her service. David had discovered that he was writing to her uncle, the Cardinal, of matters outside French concerns. The man was a Guisian spy, working against the match with Spain on instructions from the Cardinal of Lorraine.

Mary decided that now she would trust only one man–David.

So Rizzio became closer to the Queen; and there were some at the Court who declared that he was fast becoming the Queen's most influential adviser.

It was one of those rare quiet moments when the Queen was sitting alone with Flem while they stitched at their embroidery.

Flem took the opportunity to speak of a matter which had occupied her mind for some time. It concerned the Earl of Bothwell.

Flem had been slightly fascinated by the man. It was something in his courage and manliness which had appealed to her. She knew that he was a rogue, a man of whom to beware, yet she could not help admiring him.

Flem liked to believe that her mistress tempered justice with mercy. Bothwell, she insisted diffidently, had had something less.

Mary raised her eyes from her needle and said: 'How so?'

'Well, first, poor man, he spent four months in Edinburgh Castle, put there on the charge of a man who, we all know, was suspected then of being mad and is now proved to be.'

'Do you not think that there was a real plot to kidnap me?'

'It existed only in mad Arran's brain. And Bothwell, being accused by him, has been made to suffer as though guilty.'

'Has he suffered so? He has escaped from his prison.'

'And why should he not, dear Madam, being wrongfully imprisoned?' Flem laughed. 'Imagine his breaking the bars with his bare hands and swinging down the Castle rock on a rope!'

'It was a bold thing to do, I grant you. I wonder if he has changed. It is a long time since we saw him. Perhaps we shall never see him again.'

'He would give much to return to Court, Madam.'

'We would give much to keep him away.'

'Yet he was not guilty.'

'Flem! Why do you plead for him? Are you in love with the man and unfaithful to Maitland? You speak so favourably of this Border rogue.'

'I do not like it to be said that injustice has been done in your name.'

'You concern yourself too much with those who are unworthy, Flem. Think of his good fortune. How did he manage to make his way to France, do you think? With the help of women! Janet Beaton is one, that Danish woman another; and there are countless others to whom he is a passionate lover for a night, before he passes on. He escaped in a boat, and was shipwrecked on the English coast before he reached France. And how, I wonder, did he fare at the hands of the Queen of England? We know he was her prisoner in the Tower of London. Did he seduce his jailor's daughter? Flem! You put your reputation in jeopardy by pleading leniency for such a man!'

'Well, Madam, he is now far away in France, and he asks a favour of you.'

'Ah! I thought there was a plea in this. How does it come to you?'

'Through his great-uncle, the Bishop of Moray.'

'That old libertine of Spynie?'

'He is a libertine, it is true, Madam; but he is at least fond of his great-nephew. I think we should remember that Bothwell spent a great part of his life in the Bishop's palace, and it was there mayhap he learned to indulge his passions freely. Madam, we have had the advantage of a happy childhood. Should we judge those who have been less fortunate?'

'My dear Flem, if he was allowed to indulge his passions freely, I have no doubt that is what Bothwell would call a happy childhood.'

'Yes, but it has made him the man he is.'

'So the Bishop has been sounding you, has he?'

'He has spoken to me. He tells me that Bothwell is in dire poverty. He has mortgaged his lands to raise money; he reminds me that he has ever been faithful to Your Majesty.'

'Faithful to me . . . when he planned to kidnap me and force me to marry Arran?'

'A madman's fancy, Madam.'

'How can we be sure of that, dear Flem?'

'At least we know that Arran is mad now. He is put away from the world on account of his madness.'

'And because of this you think Bothwell's sins should be forgiven and he should be invited to return to Court?'

'No, Madam, I do not think that, but . . . the Scottish Captain of the Guard in France has recently died. That post is vacant.'

'And you suggest Bothwell would comfortably fill it?'

'At least it would help him to live, Madam. His finances are in a poor state. He is an exile from his own country.'

'Flem dear, ask someone to bring David here.'

Flem rose. She thought: Nothing is done now without the sanction of this David. The Piedmontese is becoming more powerful than Moray, or my dear lord Maitland.

Rizzio came at once to the apartment. How grand he looked these days! His clothes were as magnificent as anyone's at Court. How polished were his manners, and how subtly he flattered the Queen!

'Davie,' said Mary, and all her affection for the young man was in the Queen's voice as she said his name, 'I have received a request.' She smiled at Flem. 'It is that Bothwell should be given command of the Scottish Guard in France. In your opinion would that be a worthy appointment?'

Rizzio considered this gravely. Bothwell was regarded as a dangerous man by Moray, and Moray was David's enemy. Moray did not know as yet how deep David Rizzio was in the Queen's counsels, but he was beginning to learn. The very fact that Bothwell was an enemy of Moray seemed to Rizzio a good enough reason for his receiving this sign of the Queen's favour.

'Madam,' he said, 'this is a brave man, whatever else may be said of him. His bravery makes him stand ahead of his fellows, even in this warlike country where courage would seem to come to men as naturally as breathing. He will do you no discredit as Captain of the Scottish Guard.'

So James Hepburn, Lord Bothwell, found his fortunes taking a turn for the better. He was no longer obliged to borrow money, and, although still an exile from his country, he enjoyed some standing in France as Captain of the Scottish Guard.

Moray was displeased by the appointment. He discussed it with Maitland. They both agreed that it had probably been made at the instigation of David Rizzio, and they were becoming more and more disturbed by the presumption of the Italian and the favour shown to him by the Queen.

But at the moment their main concern was with Bothwell.

'You can depend upon it,' said Moray, 'that man has friends in Scotland still. 'Tis witchcraft, I'll swear. He has to look at a woman, and she's a willing victim. He seduces her and rides away, and if he should return she is ready to be his slave. How could he have got out of the country in the first place, if there had not been a chain of women ready to feed him, offer him a bed for the night–and a bedfellow too–as well as food, money and horses, to speed him on his way!'

'He has friends in the Queen's circle,' admitted Maitland. 'That much is evident.'

'What manner of men are his servants?' asked Moray.

'A parcel of rogues,' replied Maitland.

They smiled at each other. There was no need to say more.

The Captain of the Scottish Guard was not in his house that night. He was, his servants believed, sleeping in the lodging of his latest light-o'-love.

They sat round the table whispering together, listening all the time for his footsteps, though they did not think it likely that he would be home before dawn.

A pity! they all agreed. They had planned the deed for this night.

But was it a pity? In the guttering candle-light, relief showed plainly on every face.

They pictured him, their master. Taller than most men, loud of voice, stronger than two men, his lightest cuff would send any one of them sprawling across the room, and would leave a bruise that would last for days. They feared him and admired him, for he was every inch a man; he was more than a man, they believed. There was magic in him–or some witchcraft. And because he towered above them in all manner of ways, they were conscious of envy; and because of envy they had agreed to carry out instructions which had been given them. Greed too played a part in their willingness, for they would be well paid for their work.

French Paris regarded the Scotsmen about the table. There was Gabriel Semple, Walter Murray and Dandie Pringle. Paris had no great liking for the task, but he had been drawn into it by the others.

Dandie was in charge of operations. He had arranged with his lordship's barber–who was also in the plot because he understood something of poisons–that the powder should be mixed with his lordship's wine. There was the wine, already poured in the goblet, and mixed with it was the poison; but his lordship, as though Fate had intervened, had not come home that evening.

That was what made superstitious Paris tremble.

'Mayhap he knows!' he muttered, his teeth chattering.

'How could he know, man?' demanded Dandie. 'Unless you've told him.'

'I have told him nothing, but he is no ordinary man.'

'We shall see,' said Dandie Pringle with a sneer, 'where he is so much mightier than ordinary men as that the barber's poison will not affect him. Now, Gabriel, when you take up his lordship's goblet to offer it, you must behave as you always do. You must show no sign that the wine you offer is any different from that which he drinks every day of his life.'

'No . . . no . . .' stuttered Gabriel.

'Would this night's work were done with!' said Murray.

''Twill soon be over,' promised Dandie, 'and then we shall all go back to bonny Scotland where we belong; and there we'll live our lives in luxury for this night's work.'

'I tell you,' said Paris, 'our master is no ordinary man.'

'Is he not then?' sneered Dandie.

'He is not,' persisted Paris. 'You have seen what a way he has with the women. There's none can resist him.'

'There is one I know of,' said Dandie. 'The Queen herself! Did he not ask her if he might go home, and was he not refused?'

'The Queen, so says the master, is but half a woman,' declared Paris. 'She and the Queen of England between them would not make one woman, so he says.'

'He says that,' put in Murray, 'because they are two who did not immediately invite him to their bedchambers.'

'And he, feeling himself to tower above all men, is therefore piqued,' laughed Dandie.

'He says,' went on Paris, 'that, when she was in France, the Queen was the mistress of her uncle the Cardinal.'

'Nor would it surprise me,' said Dandie, 'for Cardinals are but human behind locked doors. Hark! He returns.'

It was true. The outer door had been flung open and a well-known voice shouted: 'Is no one at home? Where are you? Paris! Semple! I am returned . . . and hungry.'

There was a second's silence, and all eyes were fixed on the goblet in which was the poisoned wine.

'Take it to him, Gabriel,' said Dandie.

Paris had hurried to his master.

'Not abed then!' said Bothwell. 'How comes it that you are abroad at this hour? Have you quarrelled with your kitchen slut?'

'Nay, master,' stammered Paris. 'But I thought you might return, and so waited.'

Paris was trembling under his master's gaze. Bothwell was looking at him as though he knew something unusual was afoot.

'Then bring me food. Bring me wine. I've a thirst that needs quenching.'

'Yes, master . . . yes, master. . . .'

Paris hurried into the room where the others waited. Dandie thrust the goblet into his hands, but Paris was trembling so violently that some of the wine was spilled.

'For the love of God, you'll betray us all!' hissed Dandie. 'Here, Gabriel. You take it.'

Gabriel cried: 'No . . . n . . . no. I dare not. I tell you he will know. He knows such things. He had special powers. That is why he has returned this night.'

The door was flung open and Bothwell himself stood on the threshold looking at his servants.

'What is this?' he demanded. 'A late night session! Some conspiracy, eh? Or just a friendly feast? And not one woman to enliven the company. Is that wine you have there, Semple? Give it here, man. Did I not tell you I had a thirst?'

Gabriel trembled so much that the wine spilled on his hand, as it had on those of Paris. All the servants watched Gabriel.

'What ails you, Gabriel?' demanded the Earl. 'You're trembling like a virgin nun when the soldiers are about her. What is it, man? I say . . . what is it?' His great hand gripped Gabriel by the wrist and the wine spilled on the man's doublet.

''Tis . . . 'tis nothing, my lord.'

''Tis nothing . . . and you shake like a leaf! You're plotting something, man. Out with it. What is it? Out with it, I say.'

''Twas nothing, my lord. 'Twas just that I spilled the wine . . .'

'Give me the goblet.' He took it, and as he did so he looked from it to the faces of his servants. Then slowly, he put his lips to the goblet, still watching them. Paris gave an audible gasp.

Bothwell sniffed the wine. 'It has an odd smell,' he said. 'I like it not. How dare you serve me such filthy stuff! How dare you, you varlets!' He threw the remaining liquid into the face of Gabriel, and the goblet at Dandie Pringle's head. Dandie cried out with the pain as the goblet struck his head, and the Earl laughed.

'Now, you rogues,' he cried, 'bring me good food and good drink. And do not dare serve such stuff to me again. If you do, you'll wish you had never been born, every man of you. I'll see that you're boiled in cauldrons over slow fires. I'll have you cut into collops. I'll make you wish you had never been born to serve another instead of me. Remember it. And Semple . . . go and wake that kitchen girl and bid her bring me food. You know the one–plump, ripe Jeannie–and keep your lecherous hands off her; you understand? Go and wake her and bring her to me.'

Gabriel was glad to escape and, during his absence, Bothwell remained eying the others who stood wretchedly before him.

He was no ordinary man, and they knew it. He had uncovered their treachery. That in itself was bad enough; but they understood they had betrayed themselves by their clumsy behaviour. It was not that they lacked the courage to carry out this murderous plan, nor that their master had discovered their treachery, which was so alarming; it was his complete indifference to their power to harm him. They were in no doubt that he had witchcraft to aid him, and they knew that they would never dare make an attempt on his life again.

Gabriel returned with the girl from the kitchens. She was young and comely, and Bothwell's eyes lighted up as they rested on her.

'I am returned hungry, girl,' he said. 'Bring me food and drink . . . at once. Let no hands touch it but yours. You understand, my girl?'

'Yes, my lord.'

'Well, hurry and bring plenty, for my hunger is great. Bring it yourself. And hurry . . . I am waiting for you.'

Then he turned and left them–four guilty men and an excited and expectant girl.

It was February, and that winter was bleak. Even in the far south the weather had been rigorous. The Thames had been so frozen that people could walk across it in safety. The bitter wind buffeted the staunch walls of Wemyss Castle on the Firth of Forth whither the Queen had come to stay with her brother, the Earl of Moray.

The Queen was growing more and more uneasy in her brother's company. She knew that he was against her marriage, either with Don Carlos or one of the French Princes, because neither marriage would serve his plans. He was all for her marrying an Englishman; he was working for Elizabeth and the Protestant Faith.

He had told her that a marriage with Robert Dudley, Earl of Leicester, would be desirable. If Mary married Leicester, he pointed out, the Queen of England would declare Mary and her heirs successors to the English crown.

Did he not see that the idea was ridiculous? Elizabeth's cast-off lover! It was meant to be an insult. Whom else did Elizabeth favour? Mad Arran? Robert Dudley's brother, the Earl of Warwick? Mary smiled to remember the English Queen's comments on Warwick. He was not, of course, as handsome as his incomparable brother, declared Elizabeth, but he was by no means ugly. Nor was he ungraceful. It was only when compared with Robert that he might seem so. If one did not set him side by side with Robert, one would find him a husband worthy of a great princess. Clearly Elizabeth meant to be insulting.

There was one other who was a possible husband. That was Henry Stuart, Lord Darnley; but Elizabeth, being against the match, would not let him come to Scotland. Yet Lord Lennox, Darnley's father, who was in Scotland, continually hoped for a meeting between his handsome son and the Queen; so did Darnley's mother, Lady Lennox, who was in England and at the mercy of Elizabeth.

Mary herself was beginning to wish for the meeting, and she was excited when Lord Lennox sent a message to her.

'My son, Lord Darnley,' ran the message, 'has arrived in Scotland. He had the greatest difficulty in leaving England. The Queen however at last gave her consent, though grudgingly, and my son left at once, fearing to be detained once more before he could make his escape. It seems that no sooner had the Queen given her consent than she regretted it and sought means of detaining him, but my son, greatly desiring to see Your Majesty, had already slipped across the Border. He greatly desires to pay his loyal homage to his gracious Queen, and we shall follow this messenger with all speed to wait upon Your Majesty.'

Mary smiled. So at last she would see this young man of whom there had been so much talk. She vaguely remembered seeing him at the Court of France, but he had been a boy of fifteen then. Now he was nineteen–a man.

She called to her women.

'Come! What shall I wear? What is most becoming? It is a long time since my Lord Darnley and I met. I would wish not him to think that time had wrought havoc with my looks.'

'Madam,' all four Maries assured her, 'time has but enhanced your beauty.'

And, looking into the Venetian mirror brought from Fontainebleau, she believed they were right.

Meanwhile Henry Stuart, Lord Darnley, was riding with his father at the head of his retinue on the way to Wemyss Castle.

He was very tall and slim. His face was smooth, for he wore no beard, and because his complexion was so fair this made him seem younger than he really was. His prominent eyes were deep blue in colour, his hair golden, but his chin was weak and his mouth loose. He was so young that the excesses in which he delighted to indulge had scarcely made any mark on his face.

His father was talking to him with great seriousness as they rode along.

'My son, you must act with care. This is the most important moment of your life. It is imperative that you find favour with the Queen. You must curb your drinking habits; and, whilst you are at Court, do not indulge in too much lechery–covertly or otherwise. Make sure that you win the friendship of David Rizzio.'

'That low-born scribe!' said Darnley distastefully.

'Low-born scribe he may be. But what he wills, the Queen *does*.'

'So he is her lover then?' suggested the young man nonchalantly.

'I did not say so. He is her adviser, and she sets store by his counsels. He is an arrogant upstart who must be treated with care.'

'Father,' said Darnley, 'do you think the Queen will take me for her husband?'

'It rests with you, my son. Your looks are fine enough.'

Darnley smirked. He was very vain of his looks.

'But,' went on his father, 'if she should discover your drinking habits and how violent you become when you indulge them; if she learns of your adventures with village girls and tavern sluts . . .'

'She shall not. Father, I will be good. I will be angelic. And then Her Majesty will give me the crown–a present for a good boy.'

She received him in her audience chamber. He knelt before her, a tall, slender youth, and she thought: How charming he is! How young!

'Madam,' he said, 'at last I kneel before you. It has been my dearest wish since parting from you in France.'

'My dear Lord Darnley,' she answered, 'you cannot be happier to be here than I am to see you.'

'Madam, your beauty dazzles me. I fear I shall stammer or be speechless.'

'Why, you have made an excellent beginning. Come, sit beside me. I would hear news of the English Court.'

He sat beside her and many watched them. The Earl of Lennox did so with high hopes. Moray did so with annoyance; the last thing he wished for was Mary's marriage with Darnley. The fellow was arrogant and a Catholic. If such a marriage took place the Catholic lords would be rising and driving the Protestants–and with them John Knox and Moray–out of Scotland.

Mary meanwhile was recalling their meeting at the Court of France. 'You played the lute for me.'

'I blush for shame. I trust Your Majesty will give me a chance of showing that I have improved since then.'

'Certainly you must play for me again. You danced well, I remember. You must lead me in the galliard.'

'Madam, nothing could give me greater pleasure.' He was looking at her ardently. 'Forgive me, Madam,' he murmured. 'I had not known that anyone could be so beautiful.'

'We will ask the musicians to play for us, and we will dance. But first there is the banquet.'

She allowed him, as guest of honour, to lead her to the banqueting hall; he sat beside her and she drank from the same goblet to remind him that he was her blood-relation, and to assure him that he was heartily welcome at her table.

She noticed how his eyes kindled as he drank.

'Madam,' he said, 'I fear I disgrace myself. I am intoxicated.'

'On so little wine?'

'On so much beauty, Madam.'

'And you recently from the Court of England! They say Elizabeth's beauty is like the sun.'

'Madam, the Queen of England has no beauty. She is shrewish–an old woman, and the vainest in the world.'

'You are young, my lord. It may be that I, who am twenty-two seem an old woman to you.'

'I know not what Your Majesty's age may be, but you are the most beautiful and perfect being in the world. That is all I know.'

She had heard similiar flattery before, but this seemed different. It was his youth perhaps which appealed so strongly.

The Cardinal of Lorraine, had he been present, would have realized that the sensual side of Mary was tired of waiting for the gratification so long denied her. Mary was eager to fall in love, and if the ideal lover whom she was beginning to desire so ardently did not come to her, she was ready to invest the nearest and most likely man with the necessary perfection. Mary's sensuality was clamouring for expression, and here was a handsome youth paying extravagant compliments, a youth of the blood royal, a Catholic like herself, and therefore suitable to be her husband.

Mary did not ponder on the qualities of this young man. Outwardly he filled her ideal; she was tremulously eager for passion to overtake her.

They danced. Darnley–by no means inexperienced–realized that he was making a good impression on the Queen. He could, he believed, become King of Scotland if he wished. His ambitions grew as he pictured the future. His father was right. He would step with the utmost care during the coming weeks. He would be modest rather than bold, for he must not forget that she was a Queen. There was more to be gained than a brief pleasure before riding on to the next conquest. If he could continue in the success he had had this night, in a few weeks she would be madly in love with him. And then . . .

These were delightful pictures. Darnley, King of Scotland, the crown matrimonial glittering on his head, and an eager, passionate woman–and a very beautiful one–desperately in love with him!

He was a graceful dancer and the Queen chose again and again to dance with him. The *pavanne* and the galliard were danced; and Mary had torches brought that they might dance–as she had in the *salle de bal* at Fontainebleau–the *branle des torches* in which the dancers passed torches from one to the other. Then they danced the *branle des lavandières*, and that other dance, the Purpose, in which the partners kissed. In this last dance Mary was again Darnley's partner, and the kiss they exchanged was full of meaning to them both.

From that moment the Queen was in love. She had made up her mind who her husband would be. She thought it was because he was the most handsome and charming young man she had ever met. She did not stop to count other reasons. She did not remind herself that she must marry, that she was tired of waiting, that too many and strong forces were against a grand marriage into the royal houses of Spain and France. She did not think: Elizabeth of England is against my marriage with Lord Darnley; therefore I wish to marry Darnley. She did not think: I am young; I long for a lover, and I have waited too long.

The Maries discussed the newcomer while they undressed their mistress.

'Very handsome!' was the verdict.

'He dances so gracefully,' said Mary.

'I noticed how he kissed Your majesty in the dance,' ventured Beaton.

'Well, what of that? It is as necessary to kiss in the Purpose as it is to clap hands in the *branle des lavandières*.'

'Necessary, Madam,' agreed Beaton. 'But not *always* pleasant.'

Mary tapped her cheek with feigned annoyance. 'Livy dear,' she said, to change the subject, 'you are very quiet.'

Livy came forward and, kneeling before the Queen, laid her head in her lap.

'Madam,' she said, 'do you remember that when we were little we all swore we would not marry until you did?'

'I do, darling.'

'You married once . . . and were a widow, but none of us has married. I have often wondered who would be the first. And now this handsome Lord Darnley has come along . . .'

'What are you mumbling into my skirts, Livy? Get up at once and show yourself.'

But Livy continued to kneel.

''Tis clear,' said Flem, 'what has happened. Lord Sempill has been asking her to marry him for these many weeks, and she has put him off by declaring that she has vowed a vow to the Queen.'

'No, Livy! That is ridiculous!' cried Mary. 'You are in love with this tall and handsome Sempill?'

'Yes, Madam, but . . .'

'Rise, Livy. Get up at once. You are to marry Lord Sempill . . . immediately. I insist.'

'Oh, Madam,' said Flem, 'let it not be immediately . . . otherwise Master Knox will have all sorts of suggestions to make against poor Livy and her Sempill.'

Mary stood up and her eyes flashed. 'Who cares for Master Knox! Let him rave. Livy, my dearest, you shall have the grandest wedding ever seen, and all the world shall know how I love you. We shall have masques and mummeries . . . feasting . . . dancing . . .'

'And you, dearest,' said Flem, 'will dance the Purpose with Lord Darnley.'

'Have done with you!' cried Mary. 'You insolent Fleming! And if I dance with Darnley, you shall partner Maitland. Come! You know how I love a wedding, and what wedding would I rather attend than that of my dear Livy?'

'Your own perhaps?' suggested Beaton.

They were all gay that night. The Queen had never seemed so beautiful, but they had never before seen Mary radiantly in love.

They were happy days which followed. Each morning Mary awoke with a feeling of excitement. Each day Lord Darnley waited on her; and each day she was a little more in love with him.

What a delightful young man he was! He was so eager to be liked by everyone. It was a charming quality. Moray looked at him with suspicion, but the young Lord Darnley did not seem to be aware of his dislike. He was open and frank with him; he went with him to hear one of John Knox's sermons, and listened so intently to the preacher that even Knox–knowing Darnley to be a Catholic–was flattered. He was deferential to Maitland and to all the lords of the Court. He seemed to imply: I know that I lack your wisdom, but please remember I am young yet and I long to learn.

Mary was glad that he liked David Rizzio and that David liked him. Darnley did not appear even to consider Rizzio's humble birth. He would be seen in the courtyards walking arm-in-arm with the Piedmontese, or begging him to sing or play the lute for him. He had even taken to sleeping in David's bed, which was a symbol of friendship.

'I wish to be as near to Your Majesty as possible,' he told Mary. 'I sleep with my sword beside me. Then, if need be, I could rush to Your Majesty's defence.'

Mary smiled at that. 'No one will harm me.'

'But if they should try . . . I would wish to be the one there to protect you.'

So charming he seemed, so simple and unspoilt. When they were close together she wanted to kiss his smooth cheek. Her senses bounded at the thought of kissing him.

How delightful he was during that game of the bilies he played with her, Thomas Randolph and Mary Beaton.

Randolph was disturbed by Mary's liking for Darnley, for he was working hard to bring about a marriage between her and Leicester. What, wondered Mary, did he think of the favour she showed Darnley whom Elizabeth considered her subject and whom she now, Mary believed, so deeply regretted allowing to leave England?

Randolph and Mary Beaton had won at the bilies against Darnley and the Queen, and Darnley was obliged to present Mary Beaton with fifty crown's worth of jewellery–a brooch, a ring and two watches–as the stake.

'Madam,' he said to Mary afterwards, 'I humbly ask pardon. I played so badly.'

'You did indeed, my lord,' she agreed. 'You seemed to pay scarcely any attention to the game.'

He lifted those big blue eyes to her face. 'Madam, it was because you were near me. . . .'

She laid a hand, which had begun to tremble, on his shoulder. She moved closer to him. Her body was crying out for him. She wished in that moment that she were not the Queen surrounded by courtiers. She longed to be alone with him, to say: 'I love you. We will marry one day, but for the moment we may be lovers. . . .'

She turned away, dizzy with desire. She heard his voice, hushed and gentle: 'Madam . . . Madam . . . if I dared . . . if I but dared . . .'

Livy was married to Lord Sempill with great pomp–the first of the Queen's Maries to marry.

'It will not be quite the same henceforth,' said Mary sadly. 'Dearest Livy will often be with us, but we must not be selfish. She will wish sometimes to be in her new house with Sempill. How we shall miss her!'

Livy married! thought Mary. So should I be! It is time I married; and here is the one I love; here is the one I will marry.

She could not resist talking of Darnley. 'What think you of my lord?' she asked David.

'Lord Darnley is worthy of Your Majesty's regard.'

'I am so glad you like each other, Davie. He is charming, is he not? I could not have borne it if you two had not been friends.'

She held out her hand. David took it and held it to his lips.

David, who was clever, understood the turmoil within her. He understood the meaning of this new feverish beauty which was hers. She was ripe for marriage; she was longing for the handsome youth; she was all desire, as wise David had always known she could be. David himself had dreamed of arousing that desire; as had others, he had sensed the promise within her. But David was a man of ambition. To be the Queen's lover would indeed have been a dangerous position for a humble musician; as her most trusted secretary and adviser he was much safer.

Everything that David wished for was falling into his hands. The Pope himself congratulated him on the good work he was doing in Scotland. The

Pope sent advice. It seemed incredible that the mighty Pope was sending kind messages to David Rizzio who, when he had first come to Scotland, had slept on a table in the porter's lodge because there was no bed for him. What David wanted, and what the Pope wanted, was to bring Scotland back to the Catholic Faith, while setting her apart from Europe. The Pope did not wish Scotland to be the fief of Spain, nor of France. What the Pope wanted was a Catholic Scotland to stand against Protestant England–yet aloof from the great Continental powers–a Catholic husband for the Queen, yet not a great prince from Europe. Darnley was the suitor favoured by Rome, and therefore by David Rizzio. When the Queen married Lord Darnley more friendly messages would come from the Pope, more rewards would fall to David Rizzio.

David said: 'Madam, there are some in this realm who deplore your interest in that young man.'

'And you are not one of them?'

'Madam, I see that you are happy; and I could never do aught but rejoice in that happiness.'

'And what if I were to marry Lord Darnley, Davie? What would you say then, my faithful secretary?'

'I should say that it was a happy match. I should say: 'May the saints guard you. May all happiness and prosperity be yours!'''

'Davie!' she cried. 'You have made me so happy. You always do.'

'I beg of Your Majesty to keep your feelings as secret as possible. There are many who will do their utmost to prevent this match.'

'I will remember.'

And she did remember as she sat with Thomas Randolph watching the dancers at Livy's wedding.

'My Queen is anxious for your happiness, Madam,' said Randolph. 'She hopes soon to see you married.'

'I wish to please your Queen whenever possible,' Mary answered.

'I pray God that when Your Majesty chooses a husband your choice will be a good one.'

'He must be such a one as God would give me.'

'God has made one fair offer to you, Madam.'

'And that is?'

'My lord of Leicester–a perfect man, says my Queen.'

Mary interrupted gaily: 'And one she would have taken herself had she been of a mind to marry.'

'It is true, Madam.'

'Ah, Master Randolph, if your mistress will be a good sister to me, then shall I be a good sister to her. If this were not so–then we must each do as we may.'

Darnley was claiming her for the dance, and she rose and gave him her hand. Thomas Randolph looked after them uneasily.

As they danced, Darnley said: 'How happy those two are–Sempill and Mary Livingstone.'

'They are in love, and it is rather wonderful, is it not, to be in love?'

'It is the most wonderful thing in the world. Madam . . . but I dare not say it.'

'You must say it. Tell me. What is it? I insist.'

'If I could but forget you were the Queen . . . if I might see you alone . . .'

'It is difficult for a queen to receive a young man alone.'

'If you were not the Queen, we could slip away from the ball.'

'And then?'

'Then I might try to explain.'

Mary's eyes were burning as she said: 'I wish to hear these explanations.'

'But alone, Madam? If it were possible. . . . But I could not trust myself . . .'

'Why should you not? We are both free.'

'Free, Madam?'

'Free to say what we will.'

'Madam, then you mean . . . Forgive me . . . but I cannot believe I have heard aright.'

He knew that the Queen was in love with him–fiercely and passionately in love with him. He believed that if they were alone she would offer no resistance. And once she had surrendered herself to him the way would be clear; she would not wish to draw back. Once he became the Queen's lover, he would be certain of the crown of Scotland.

What a glorious prospect this was! She was young and beautiful; she was passionate; she would be the prime mover in their love affair. He would allow this to be so, for it was what she wanted; and just now everything must be as she wanted it. She had fallen in love with a young and–as she believed–inexperienced boy. He must play the part of callow youth, of lovesick boy, inexperienced yet eager to be led.

She whispered: 'If you would see me alone, come to my apartments this night. Beaton will let you in. When the palace is quiet . . . and all have retired . . .'

She pressed his hand, but she did not dance with him again. She was afraid that she was betraying this great passion which was possessing her.

She did not now want marriage with Spain; she did not care for dignity or pride, nor her rank as Queen. She cared for nothing but the immediate fulfilment of her love for Henry Darnley.

Beaton said: 'Madam, is it wise?'

She turned on Beaton angrily. 'Wise! What do you mean? He has something to say to me. Why should I not hear it?'

'But alone, Madam, in your bedchamber?'

'Beaton . . . you are insolent!'

Seton, the calm quiet one, the one perhaps who was most steadfast in her devotion, said nothing, but watched her mistress with a great anxiety in her eyes. Mary would not look at Seton.

Flem could not hide her excitement. The marriage of Livy was responsible for this. It had made the Queen realize that she too was in love, that she too must have a lover.

'Her Majesty will marry him,' soothed Flem; 'then all will be well.'

'You chatter too much,' said Mary. 'Bring me my robe. The white velvet.'

'White velvet becomes Your Majesty more than anything else,' said Flem.

Mary scarcely heard; a feverish excitement possessed her. If he did not come . . . But he would come. He was knocking at the door now.

'Quick, Beaton, quick!'

Beaton was at the door.

'Come in quickly, my lord. Let no one see you.'

Mary stood up, the white velvet draped about her, her long chestnut hair hanging loose about her shoulders.

'Leave us,' she said in a whisper; and silently and swiftly the three Maries left the apartment.

'Madam,' began Darnley, and would have knelt and taken her hands; but she had thrown herself into his arms, her restless fingers caressing his face and neck.

Darnley shyly put his arms about her.

This was success beyond his dreams. He need not plead with her; he need do nothing but obey, for the passionate Queen was commanding him to be her lover.

Mary was deep in love and determined to marry Darnley. She thought of little else. David advised caution. All the Protestant lords, headed by Moray, were against the match. Mary could wait for marriage, since she had now found a way to enjoy her lover's society in private.

She was continually thinking of fresh gifts to bestow on him. She sent for her tailor William Hoppringle, and commanded him to make the finest suit which had ever been made; he was to work immediately on black velvet and silver lace. Then he was to make garments of taffeta and silk–and all these were for Lord Darnley. Johnnie Dabrow, the finest hatter in Edinburgh, was to make Darnley's hats, and he was to put as much care into the making as he would if the Queen would be wearing them. Fleming Allyard must get busy making shoes. Shirts and ruffs were ordered; all were to be made of the finest materials available.

The jewellers were called in. The Queen wished rubies, emeralds and diamonds to be set into the most perfect patterns to enhance the fair beauty of the young man she loved.

As yet she believed that her determination to marry him was her secret.

Darnley grew a little impatient. For the crown he did not care, he assured her; he but wished to let the whole world know that he was her lover.

She believed him. He was so young, so naïve and, as she was, a stranger to passion.

There was one unfortunate incident which occurred to mar the joy of those days.

It was brought about through the Borderer, Lord Bothwell. He had given up the post for which he had so earnestly begged, that of Captain of the Scottish Guard in France, and had come back to Scotland. He now sent a messenger to the Queen, begging her to grant permission for him to return to the Court.

'And why should he not come back to Court?' asked Mary. 'He was imprisoned for implication with Arran, but now we all know that Arran was mad. We have been unfair to Bothwell.'

Her brother Moray, who was now becoming very uneasy indeed about her relationship with Darnley, assured her that it would be the utmost folly to bring Bothwell back to Court.

'The man is a born trouble-maker,' he said. 'He sows discord. Scotland has been a more peaceful place without him.'

But the Queen was no longer to be dominated thus. She made her own decisions–with the help of Rizzio; and although she deplored the conduct of the Borderer, there was something in his character which appealed to her.

'I think I shall grant him the permission he seeks,' she said.

Moray was furious. He had loved his sister when she followed his advice and allowed him to rule Scotland; he could come near to hating her now, for it seemed to him that she was fast becoming his enemy. His resentment flared up against her. Why should she–a foolish lass–wear the crown when he, their father's son, was far more suitable to do so? The incredibly bad luck which had attended his birth was a chafing sore that ate into his character, corroding it, destroying his finer qualities, breeding within him a treacherous determination to take the power from his sister's hands.

He would not have Bothwell back at Court. Bothwell was his enemy. Bothwell might have discovered that he had tried to have him poisoned; clearly there was scarcely room in Scotland for Bothwell and Moray.

But to keep Bothwell out of Scotland was not so difficult to accomplish after all, for the rogue, Dandie Pringle–now dismissed from Bothwell's service and living in Scotland–was the very man to help in this.

Moray commanded him to come to Edinburgh and had him brought before the Queen.

'Before Your Majesty recalls Lord Bothwell,' said Moray, 'I thought you might care to hear the testimony of this man.'

'Who is this man?' asked Mary.

'One who served Bothwell when he was in France and knows something of his private life. He will tell you that the Hepburn is one of the greatest libertines in Scotland.'

'There are many libertines in Scotland, great and small. Should one more make so much difference?'

'No, Madam,' said James, 'it should not. But this man is more than a libertine. He has spoken cruel slander against persons of high degree.'

'You, brother?'

'Perhaps, my dear sister, but I have not heard of it. I meant against you.'

'What has he said?'

'I have brought Pringle here to tell you how he spoke of you before his servants.'

'Am I to listen to the tittle-tattle of servants?'

'If it concerns yourself, you undoubtedly should.'

'Bring him in then, and let me hear him.'

Dandie Pringle knelt before the Queen.

'So you served with my Lord Bothwell in France?'

'Yes, Your Majesty.'

'And he spoke often of me in your hearing?'

'Not often, Your Majesty, but now and then.'

'And he spoke ill of me?'

'He did, Your Majesty.'

'What said he?'

'Among other things that you and the Queen of England would not make one honest woman between you. He said that the Queen of England had for paramour Lord Robert Dudley, but that if Your Majesty had taken any other than the Cardinal, your uncle, the matter could have been better endured.'

Mary flushed scarlet with anger. 'Take this man away!' she cried. 'How dare he utter such wicked slander? How dare he even think such things!'

Moray signed to Pringle to hurry away.

'The man but repeats the words of that rogue,' he said as soon as they were alone.

'It is so . . . monstrous!'

Mary, overcome with fury and shame that such a thing could be said of her, threw herself into her brother's arms and wept bitterly.

Moray soothed her. He had won this round. Bothwell would not be allowed to remain in Scotland.

The sounds of revelry burst forth at intervals from the palace of Holyrood. The Queen had never seemed so healthy, nor so happy. She must have her lover continually beside her; she could not bear to lose sight of him. The pain in her side had not troubled her for weeks; there was a delicate colour in her usually pale cheeks, and the sound of her laughter frequently rang through the apartment of Little France.

It was true that clouds were gathering about her, but she refused to notice them. She could not spare time to look at them; she had at last let loose her slumbering passion, and it had overwhelmed her, so powerful was it.

She did not realize that she was betraying herself. She would not listen to David's warning that Moray knew the state of affairs between herself and Darnley, and would do his utmost to prevent their marriage. Maitland was back from his English embassy; he was anxious that she should marry to please the Queen of England, but Maitland had one other matter on his mind now for there was one marriage which seemed to him of more importance than the Queen's. His wife had died and he was courting Flem.

Flem and the Queen were closer than the others now. They were both deeply in love; they shared little jokes together; their mingling laughter filled the apartments. Neither would concern herself with what was unpleasant; they were determined to be happy.

David begged the Queen to heed his warning. Moray was gathering together an army for the purpose, he said, of driving Bothwell from the country. A whole army to drive one man from Scotland when that man had already fled back to France? Why did Moray not disband his army? David knew. He wanted Mary to know too.

But if Mary was reckless, if she was almost submerged in the deep seas of her passion, she had attained an even greater dignity than before. In her love-affair with Darnley, she was the leader. She was the Queen; she would protect him from such as Moray who, David said, sought to destroy him. Mary was determined to show all Scotland that she was Queen.

At this time Darnley was confined to his bed with an attack of measles. The Queen was distraught–although he was not seriously ill–and insisted on his staying at Stirling Castle so that she could nurse him herself.

She did not leave the sickroom, and if any had doubted her intentions, they could no longer do so.

John Knox, who had called the godly to witness the black mummeries and wickedness that went on in Holyroodhouse, now commanded his flock to observe that the Queen attended her lover in a most immodest manner in his sick room.

God, he declared, was recording Mary Stuart's sins. They should be paid for . . . every one.

The Queen of England heard the news and publicly declared herself shocked by it. She, being a virgin, she said, could scarcely bear to speak of it. A Queen . . . in a sick room . . . nursing a young man! It was wanton behaviour.

'The Queen of England,' said Mary, 'protests her virtue continually. It is understandable that she should protect what is left to her, for that virtue has been much besmirched by rumour.'

Mary did not know that in private the Queen of England exulted at the success of her plan to bring disorder into Scotland. She laughed with Cecil and Dudley at the accounts of Darnley's good behaviour. 'Let her wait,' said Elizabeth. 'Soon that long lad will begin to show himself in his true colours, once let him be sure that he has secured the Queen in his net.'

It was true that Darnley did become a little peevish during his convalescence. Mary noticed that some of his servants bore bruises; she heard rumours that the spoiled boy beat his servants unmercifully. But she paid little attention to such gossip; she was far too happy to let that happiness be spoiled.

And when he was finally recovered, the Queen was so elated that, with some of her women including her three Maries, she dressed up in the humble garments of citizens' wives and roamed the streets, stopping all the men they met and asking them to give coins towards a ball they intended to give that night.

Laughing through the streets they went and, when it was known that the party of supposedly loose women was headed by the Queen, the gossips increased their scandalous talk, John Knox ranted more than ever, and the Queen of England collected more titbits to gloat over in private and condemn in public.

Now that Darnley had recovered, Mary was determined to wait no longer for her marriage.

It was May now–three months since Darnley had come to Scotland. Mary passionately desired to regularize their union now, for she felt it very wrong that Scotland's strict moral laws, laid down by the Kirk and to which she had given her authority, should be broken by Scotland's Queen.

She called her brother to her and told him that she had determined to marry Lord Darnley. She had prepared a document which she asked him to sign.

'A document?' cried Moray.

'It states that you will give your consent to my marriage with Lord Darnley and do all in your power to bring it about.'

'Madam, this is impossible. It will split Scotland in two.'

'Why so?'

'There are many nobles in Scotland who will not stomach this marriage.'

'You mean yourself.'

'I am one, Madam.'

'Because you fear that we shall bring the Catholic Faith back to Scotland and the Reformed Party and yourself will no longer be in power?'

'You are young, Madam.'

'I am of age now, brother. When you were my age you were planning to rule Scotland. That is what I am planning to do now.'

'You cannot do it through marriage with Darnley.'

'I will be Queen and choose the man I marry.'

'You cannot ignore the nation and your ministers when you make that choice.'

'As Queen, the nation will follow me in my choice.'

'Never!' cried Moray in a fury.

'You forget yourself, brother.'

'It is you who forget yourself, sister. You behave like a slut with this pretty boy of yours. He shares your bed. The whole Court knows it. I beg of you, if you prize your crown, give up this evil life while there is yet time.'

'You quote Master Knox. There is another who will find his claws clipped.'

'You do not know what you say.'

'I know very well that I say what I mean. Sign this paper and I shall think of you as my good subject.'

Moray's answer was to fling out of the room.

David came to her later to tell her that Moray had an army gathered about him. Argyle, Châtelherault and Kirkcaldy of Grange were with him. These were the most important noblemen in Scotland; and there was not a general to match Kirkcaldy. Moray had been astute; this was not the sudden move he had intended it should appear to be; he had looked ahead and this was his answer to the suggested Darnley marriage.

She paced up and down the apartment. Civil war threatened, but she was not afraid. She was not a frivolous girl now; she was a woman of deep emotions which brought her great courage.

'The English are with him,' said David. 'Elizabeth has promised him arms and men.'

'I care not if the whole world comes against me!' said Mary. 'I will be Queen of Scotland at last.'

'The Highlanders might well stand by Your Majesty,' said David. 'Bring George Gordon out of prison. Create him Earl of Huntley. Then you will have a new Cock o' the North to stand at your side. And there is one other whom you could trust. Recall Bothwell. He is only waiting for the summons and he will relish the opportunity to take vengeance on your brother. He will willingly serve you–if only for the opportunity of being back in Scotland.'

'That man! Do you not remember what he has said of me?'

'Forget old grudges, Madam. The need is desperate. He is a foul-mouthed ruffian but a good fighter–the most courageous in Scotland.'

So Mary sent for Bothwell and created George Gordon Earl of Huntley. The new earl came down from the Highlands with thousands of followers–all brave men and bold, longing for a chance to settle scores with Moray and rally to the standard of the Queen.

They camped about Edinburgh, and the sound of their pipes could be heard in the palace. Along the streets the kilts and steel bonnets could be seen. From all over Scotland warriors were coming to fight for the Queen against Moray.

John Knox watched the growth in numbers of the encroaching Highlanders with apprehension. In vain did he threaten them with eternal damnation; they played jaunty airs on the pipes in answer to him. Most of them were Protestants, but they believed in a wee bit of fun and laughter, and John Knox's talk of his God's delight in vengeance was losing its appeal.

Mary was in some doubt as to the loyalty of these men. There was the lecherous Morton who, she knew, had weighed her chances of success against those of her brother, and it was, therefore, a good augury that he had chosen to support her. There was Lord Ruthven, who was supporting her because his children by his first wife were Darnley's cousins.

It might be that these lords had their own private reasons for being with her in Edinburgh instead of with Moray's armies; but for the present it was enough that they were with her and she could rely on the new Earl of Huntley and–when he came–on Bothwell.

There was one thing she intended to do before all else and that was legalize her union with her lover. Scandal was rife concerning her; it was more malignant than it had ever been, for Moray, who had previously endeavoured to quash it, now sought to foster it. He had set going a rumour that the Queen was a lewd woman and that David Rizzio and Darnley were both her lovers. He revived the Chastelard scandal. Knox was his ardent supporter in all this.

On her wedding day Mary walked from her apartments to the chapel at Holyrood dressed in the mourning gown of black with a large mourning hood, the costume of a sorrowing widow. She made a sombre bride. It was necessary however for her to observe the strict royal etiquette which demanded that until she was another man's wife she must, on all state occasions, appear as the widow of her first husband.

The Earls of Lennox and Atholl led her to the chapel and then went to fetch Darnley.

What a contrast he made in his glittering costume! Mary's heart leaped with pride as she contemplated him. This was to be the happiest marriage that had ever been.

The Dean of Restalrig performed the ceremony with his priests to help him. Mary's hand lay in that of Henry Stuart, Lord Darnley, and they were indeed husband and wife.

The bridegroom left the chapel in advance, in order that he might retire to her chamber, where she would join him when her women led her there.

'Come!' he cried when he saw her. 'I like not this black *deuil*. You must be a dazzling bride. Cast aside these sorrowful garments and dispose yourself to a pleasanter life.'

Mary feigned reluctance to do this, remembering what would be expected of her, but it was difficult to hide her elation and her desire to be done with reminders of her widowhood.

At last she was persuaded to wear the brilliant wedding garments which had been prepared for her, and her women lost no time in dressing her.

'The most beautiful bride in the world!' whispered Flem; and Mary had a sudden memory of hearing those words before. Then François had been her husband. She fleetingly remembered his adoration. How different was little François from the handsome Darnley!

There followed feasting and revelry. The bridegroom drank more freely than previously, and was inclined to be peevish, but he smiled with pleasure when he heard the proclamation which made it known to the people that he, Henry Stuart, Lord Darnley, was also Lord Ardmarnock, Earl of Ross, Duke of Albany, and should be called, by the express wish of Her Majesty the Queen of Scotland and the Isles, King of this kingdom.

At last they were alone. This was bliss for which Mary had long yearned. Now she was free to indulge her passion with a good conscience. There need be no hurried partings before the dawn, no furtive whisperings.

But to her surprise and chagrin it was not the same Henry Darnley who now made love to her. It was true that he was a little drunk; it was understandable that the great honours which had come to him this day had turned his head a little. He was fiercely demanding; he was arrogant; it was as though he said: 'I am the master now.'

She submitted to this new lover, willingly and happily. But in the morning she began to see that the character he had worn as a mask when he first came to Court had been cast aside. With apprehension Mary began to understand anew the man to marry whom she had risked civil war.

The turn of events forced Mary to concern herself with matters other than this partial disappointment in her husband. There came a chance to subdue Knox, and Mary took it boldly.

Darnley, at her request and on the advice of Rizzio, went to the Kirk of St Giles to hear Knox preach. Mary knew that many of the warriors, who had rallied to her and were now encamped about the capital, were firm upholders of the Protestant Faith. She wished to show them that–Catholic though she was–she still intended to follow the policy of toleration which she had promised when she first came to Scotland.

Darnley had gone rather sullenly, and the sight of him, sprawling in the pew, sumptuously dressed and glittering with jewels, put Knox into a frenzy of rage against the Queen and her husband. He could not resist preaching at the young man.

'"O Lord, our God,"' he cried, quoting from the book of Isaiah, '"other lords besides Thee have had dominion over us; but by Thee only will we make mention of Thy name."'

He went on to declare that for the sins of the people tyrants were sent to scourge them. Boys and women were sent to rule over them.

There was nothing that annoyed Darnley more than a reference to his youth. He folded his arms and glared at Knox; but Knox was not the man to be intimidated by a glare in his own kirk.

God justly punished Ahab, he declared, because he would not take order with the harlot Jezebel. In these evil days Ahab joined Jezebel in idolatry.

Darnley, deeply conscious of his new status, could not suffer insults lightly. He stood up and, calling to his attendants that he was going hawking, strode out of the kirk.

Mary was sympathetic when she heard what had happened, and laid no blame on her husband who, so far, could in her eyes do no wrong. Instead–in her new mood of bravado and deeply conscious of the brawny kilted men in their steel bonnets who paraded the town–she sent for Knox.

'Master Knox,' she cried as he stood before her, 'this day you have insulted the King. I therefore forbid you to preach in Edinburgh whilst there are sovereigns in the capital.'

'I have spoken nothing but according to the text, Madam,' answered Knox. 'The King, to pleasure you, has gone to the Mass and dishonoured the Lord God, so shall God, in His justice, make you an instrument of his ruin.'

'How dare you make such wicked prophecies!' cried Mary in panic.

'I but speak as God commands me, Madam.'

'You will abstain from preaching whilst there are sovereigns in the capital or suffer the rewards of treason.'

She dismissed him.

Knox began to harangue the Lords of the Congregation more vehemently than ever, urging them to rise against the Queen. Still Mary did not despair. There seemed little need to, as she surveyed the Highlanders who had pitched their tents about the city. Marching through the streets could be seen the kilted warriors, accompanied by the skirling of the pipes–big men, broad and strong; fierce men who did not know the meaning of fear were rallying to the cause of the Queen.

Bothwell was back in Edinburgh, eager to put his services at the command of the Queen–and there was a saying on the Border that Bothwell was worth an army. Huntley's Highlanders and Bothwell's Borderers made a formidable assemblage; and the Queen's eyes glistened as she watched them.

Knox quailed before the display of might. He had found an adversary, who he had not believed existed, in the Queen herself. When John Knox took a look at the steel bonnets of the North he heard the voice of God advising discretion.

So Mary was now ready to place herself at the head of an army which, it was agreed, could not have a better commander than the Earl of Bothwell.

There was only one who opposed that command, and this was the Queen's husband.

He was peevish, for although he was called King of Scotland, the Crown Matrimonial had not been bestowed upon him. He was furious when he thought he detected a lack of respect in those about him. He resented the arrogant Borderer; he had quarrelled with many of the lords and was fast becoming unpopular even among those who had decided to give Mary their support.

He sulked and, when Mary tenderly asked the reason, he flashed at her: 'Madam, it is a sad thing when rogues and adventurers are preferred to honest men.'

'My dearest, what do you mean?' asked Mary.

'That villain Bothwell . . . to command your army! Are you mad? The man's a brigand.'

'He's the best general in Scotland with the exception of Kirkcaldy–and he is with our enemies.'

'The best general! What of my father?'

'But your father cannot be called a great general.'

'You insult my family and consequently me. Mayhap I had better remove myself from your presence. Mayhap I had better find other friends . . . true friends who love me.'

Mary smiled at the spoilt boy in indulgent exasperation. He was so pretty–even when he sulked–that she could not help softening towards him.

'Henry, come and sit beside me.'

He did so sullenly.

She stroked his golden hair back from his face, but he rudely shook her off. 'What is the use of pretending you care for me, when you insult my family by putting that crude oaf above them?'

'My crown is in danger, dearest.'

'*Your* crown! Yes, that is how it is. *Your* crown which you will not share with me. You promised me all I could wish for, and now that we are married it is a different story.'

Mary sighed. 'It *is* a different story now that we are married. Henry, what has happened to you? You were so modest . . . so gentle . . . before we married. Was it because you were deceiving me, pretending to be the man you were not . . . until we were married?'

A cunning look flickered across his face. He threw his arms about her and kissed her, forcing her back into her chair.

'Mary,' he breathed. 'You do not love me, Mary.' He was smiling secretly. He had power over her through her sensual need of him. He could get what he wanted from his Queen. 'Mary, forgive me. . . .'

'My darling!'

'It is . . . these people about you . . . they do not pay proper respect to me. Mary is the Queen, they seem to say, but who is Darnley? Only her consort . . . of no importance at all.'

'That is quite wrong, Henry.'

'Then show them it is wrong. Give the command to my father. Dearest Mary, please me in this thing . . . just to prove to me . . .'

She was weakening; she was sinking into that mood when her senses were in command, when nothing seemed too much to give in return for all the joy and pleasure he gave her.

The two men faced each other–the adventurer from the Border and the Queen's pretty husband. Darnley was examining the velvet-lined, perfumed gloves–a present from the Queen–which he was drawing on his hands.

'Her Majesty' said Darnley with a smirk which made Bothwell's fingers itch to draw his sword, 'has appointed my father commander of her armies.'

The colour deepened in Bothwell's ruddy face. He had been certain of the command. He knew that the men would follow him to death if need be, because he had the qualities of leadership and men feared him while they admired him. To set weak Lennox at the head of the armies was folly. Moreover, Lennox was not even on the spot.

'I would wish to hear that from Her Majesty's lips before I believed it,' muttered Bothwell.

'Would an order, signed by the Queen, suffice, my lord?'

Bothwell nodded, and Darnley unrolled the scroll he had carelessly carried under his arm. Bothwell studied it.

The foolish woman! he thought. The lives of loyal Scotsmen are at stake, and she can deny this popinjay nothing!

Yet he was too soon returned from exile to risk being sent back again. He bowed his head, but as his eyes met those of Darnley, there was murder in his heart. The strong fingers twitched. He was imagining them, pressing that scented throat until the silly boy had no breath left. He was certain in that moment that the best way any Scot could serve the Queen was by ridding her of the foolish boy she had married.

Never had the Queen lived through such triumphant days. She herself, wearing a light suit of armour under her scarlet, gold-embroidered riding dress and a steel casque under her hood, rode out with her army behind her. Beside her rode her husband, distinct from all others on account of the gilded armour he was wearing; he had not forgotten to put on his scented velvet-lined gloves.

As she rode south, Mary's subjects rallied to her.

'God save the Queen!' they cried. They were enchanted by the youth and beauty of their King and Queen. Compared with them the stern-faced Puritan Moray seemed very colourless.

'Give the Queen a chance,' murmured the people. 'Why should the bonny lass not choose her own husband if she wishes it! And who is behind this rising of Moray's . . . who but the Queen of England!'

There were many who thought often and bitterly of those raids on their homes, of the marauding hordes from beyond the Border. Those raiders were the friends of Moray. Let Moray keep his friends. Scotsmen were rallying in the cause of their Queen.

And so Moray found a lack of the response which had been expected. Few rallied to his standard, and the English, seeing how matters stood, became evasive. Elizabeth held up the aid she had promised, and Moray's rebellion, which was to have brought him control of Scotland, was crushed without bloodshed. He was forced to flee across the Border, for he dared not remain in Scotland; and with him into exile went his powerful helpers–Châtelherault, Glencairn, Kirkcaldy and many others.

Knox, reproaching God, advised Him to do His duty by the exiles and bring them back to power in Scotland. He found some comfort in whispering evil gossip concerning the Queen and Rizzio. The latter, he declared, was a spy of the Pope's; he was the slave of the Roman Harlot; he had corrupted the Queen's mind while he corrupted her body.

'Was it true,' asked the people of Edinburgh, 'that Signor Davie was the Queen's lover?' It was said that he spent long hours alone with her. He was not handsome, but he had beautiful eyes and he played the guitar with great skill. This guitar in itself was believed to be a magic thing; it was made of tortoiseshell, mother o' pearl, ebony and ivory. It could make any who heard it its slave. When Signor Davie played it before the Queen, he cast a spell upon her so that she was eager for his embrace.

Such were the tales which were circulating through Scotland.

Meanwhile heartening news came from London of Elizabeth's reception of Moray, which had been quite different from his expectations. The Queen had received him with great hostility, upbraiding him for daring to question her 'dear sister's rule'. All knew that this was a ruse of Elizabeth's; all knew that she had promised aid to Moray, and that, had he shown signs of succeeding, it would have been given. But it was a heartening sign to Mary and her friends that Elizabeth should consider it politic to scold Moray for daring to rise against his Queen.

The affairs of the Queen of Scots were more satisfactory than they had ever been before. She was strong now and, while determined to be tolerant in religious matters, was celebrating the Mass with less caution than hitherto.

Mary could have been happy but for the fact that Darnley was growing more and more ill-tempered and arrogant. Her own temper–always ready to break out–had on several occasions flared up against him. Bickering had broken out between them; even their sexual relationship was no longer completely satisfactory. He had changed; he was no longer the tender lover, and his one thought was to exert his superiority over her. Her dignity was in rebellion and her sensuality could not subdue it.

Often she reflected: I could be quite happy now if Henry were only as he used to be.

But gradually she became aware of that other menace; the growing scandals concerning Rizzio.

In the Canongate Church Lord Bothwell was being married. Outside the kirk the citizens waited to catch a glimpse of the bride and groom as they passed from there to Kinloch House, where the celebrations would take place.

There was a look of satisfaction on the face of the Border Earl. He was pleased with this wedding of his and with the general turn of events. Here he was, after years of exile and imprisonment, rising and likely to become one of the most important men in Scotland.

He liked his bride–Jean Gordon, sister of the Earl of Huntley–who brought him all he wanted. She was rich, of high birth and a good woman.

At the moment she was pale and a little sullen. She was not as pleased to marry the Earl of Bothwell as he was to marry her; that in itself had provided a certain piquancy, for he was accustomed to being much sought after. Strange that the woman he should honour with his hand in marriage should be one of the few reluctant ones he had ever encountered.

Jean was twenty, very pale, with sandy hair, large eyes and the long Gordon nose. She was proud and cold, he imagined; but that would be a change. Too many had been too warm towards him.

When he had asked her to marry him–having previously obtained the consent of her brother and the Queen–she was cool and distant. Another woman might have been frightened, and he would have known how to deal with such fear; but Jean was too proud to show fear.

She obviously wondered why her brother should have considered a man from the Border, and of such reputation, worthy of her. Only the well arched brows betrayed the thought, but they betrayed it completely.

'I do not see, my lord, how such a marriage could be,' she had replied to his proposal, 'since I have already been promised to Alexander Ogilvie of Boyne.'

'Ogilvie!' Bothwell had cried. 'Let that not trouble you. I will deal with Ogilvie of Boyne.'

'Deal with him? I do not wish you to *deal* with him. I am telling you that he and I are betrothed.'

'I have the consent of your family to the match,' he had told her grimly, and he had taken her proud face in his hands and given her his bold stare. It had not had its usual effect, and the faintest shadow of distaste crossed her face as he kissed her full on the lips with a laugh.

But of course it was useless for her to protest. The marriage had been arranged. The Queen had given her consent and Jean's brother had decided to unite his fortunes with the rising ones of Bothwell.

Bothwell needed this marriage. Lord John Stuart, who had married Janet Hepburn, had died recently, and that marriage, from which Bothwell had hoped much since it brought him the Queen's own brother as his brother-in-law, had availed him little. Now that the Gordons were back in favour Jean was an admirable match, and he was determined that she should be his wife.

So they were married, for Ogilvie was not the man to stand out against the Queen's wishes and those of such a powerful nobleman as Huntley had become. Jean's wishes went for little, and here she was–Bothwell's bride.

Her hand was limp in his. Never mind, he thought. We shall soon change that.

He felt grand and powerful, ready to achieve anything. The Queen had wished the ceremony to take place in the chapel at Holyrood, but Bothwell, declaring that he was a Protestant, had insisted that it should take place in the Canongate Kirk.

The Queen had given way graciously. She was pleased with Bothwell; she had even forgiven him for the slander he had spoken against her, accepting his word that it had been a fabrication of the foul-minded Dandie Pringle.

In Kinloch House the Queen was the guest of honour. The King had accompanied her, but not very graciously. He was grumbling that one of his high estate should be expected to attend celebrations at Kinloch House. It was a large house, a luxurious house, the property of a rich townsman who was a favourite at the Court; but Darnley, newly come to royalty, could not deign to approve of anything that was not entirely royal. Moreover he hated Bothwell for his manliness and for the fact that he would have made a better general than Darnley's father. Darnley knew that had Bothwell commanded the army and acted as he wished, the rebels would now be the Queen's captives and not enjoying their freedom in England, where they were doubtless being encouraged to make fresh plots against the Queen.

Mary found the wedding less enjoyable than others she had attended. The bridegroom made her uneasy. She remembered clearly the first time she had seen him when she was in France, and how his appraising, almost insolent gaze had made her uncomfortable. He had not lost that habit. Now, in his doublet made of gold-coloured silk with its puffed sleeves, its inlets of satin, and with narrow lace ruff about his sunburned neck, he looked more virile in his finery than he did when less splendidly clad, for the colourful, almost womanish garments, called attention to his strength and masculinity. Those powerful shoulders, those strong hands, that hard face engraved with the strains of many adventures which had not always turned out happily, that sensual mouth touched with bitterness which must have consumed him during his exile, made of Jean Gordon's husband a complete contrast to the handsome young man whom Mary had married.

Mary felt a qualm of conscience about Jean, who had wanted Alexander of Ogilvie. Jean had been one of her ladies of the bedchamber since Livy had gone and the Gordons had come back into favour, and Mary knew her well. She was a practical girl, and Mary assured herself that she would not allow her disappointment to warp her outlook. She was calm and would prove a steadying influence on the Borderer.

Jean must be proud, continued Mary's thoughts, to see Bothwell so shine in the jousts. He was undoubtedly the victor of the tournament, which was very satisfactory indeed, since he was the man of the moment on this his wedding day.

What strength! Mary shivered slightly. There was something terrifying about the man. She wondered if the stories she had heard of him were wholly true. Was he really the ruffian he was made out to be? Was it true that he had scores of mistresses?

He was a bold man and a wicked one; she had no doubt of that; yet compared with him, her own Henry did seem somewhat childish and ineffectual.

The Bothwell honeymoon was spent at Seton. To both it was an unsatisfactory honeymoon. Bothwell was bewildered; he could not understand his Jean. She was a Highlander; he was a Lowlander; she belonged to the most important family of the North and her father had been the Cock o' the North. It was clear that she found his manners repulsive; he had laughed at her when she disclosed this, and determined to make no effort to mend them. He had been piqued by her attitude towards him. No woman had aroused his interest so completely before, and she was not even beautiful. Her pale face with its crown of sandy hair was serene beneath the green and gold cap, and the lacey ruff accentuated its oval contours; he found it impossible to disturb that serenity.

She submitted unmoved to his rough love-making. He would have preferred her to protest; then he could have brought into action his famous Border tactics. Her calm expression seemed to say: I am married to you and I will do my duty, no matter how unpleasant that may be.

He had even tried gentleness. Nothing moved her. And once, watching her when she was unaware of it, he imagined by the sadness in her face that she was thinking of Alexander Ogilvie.

'Curse Alexander Ogilvie!' cried the Borderer. 'If I had him here I'd slit his throat, and you would see who was the better man.'

'The slitting of throats cannot decide who is the better man,' she had answered.

'It can decide who is the live one,' he had retorted grimly.

'But we were not discussing life and death.'

She showed no emotion when she arrived at her new home of Crichton Castle. What did she think of those stark stone walls built to stand against the raider from the other side of the Border? How did it compare with the glens and fells, the rushing streams and waterfalls of her beautiful Highlands? She gave no sign. It was as though she shrugged her elegant Gordon shoulders and accepted Crichton as she accepted James Hepburn.

'Well,' he roared, 'do you like my castle?'

'It is my home, so I needs must,' she replied.

He watched her as she busied herself with the alterations she would make. She had brought several of her mother's servants with her and she set them sweeping and cooking, cleaning and sewing. Bothwell was amused; he could see that soon he would have a model home.

This wife of his interested him. Her frigidity was such as he had never encountered. A wife frigidity, he presumed it to be. One would not tolerate it in a mistress. Yet it intrigued him. Here was the first woman who did not melt before his flaming personality.

He had never been faithful to one woman for so long. He might have gone on being faithful, had he not happened to take a short cut through his wife's sewing-room one day.

Seated on low stools were some of his wife's sewing-maids and among them was one who immediately caught his eye. She was small, her face was pale, and her hair the blackest he had ever seen, and so abundant that no amount of restraint could have kept it in order. He was aware of the girl's brilliant eyes fixed upon him as he sauntered through the room. The older maids modestly kept their eyes on their work.

As he passed the girl he stared at her and bodly she returned his stare. He knew then that he had been too long faithful to one woman, and it was a most unnatural condition.

But he forgot the girl until next day when, on his way to the stables, he suddenly remembered that on the previous day he had passed through the sewing-room. He went there again and saw the girl. She was like an inviting goblet of wine ready for the drinking, and he was a man who suffered from the perpetual thirst which only such wine could assuage.

A girl like that in the house! he mused. Why, if I do not . . . then someone else will!

He sent for French Paris whom he had kept in his service even though he knew the man stole from him and had been in that half-jesting, half-earnest plot to poison him.

'Who is the girl in the sewing-room?' he asked.

'The girl, my lord? You would mean Bessie Crawford, for sure.'

'How are you sure, man?'

''Tis the only girl in the sewing-room that would interest your lordship.

Why, I've laid a wager with Gabriel that you would take her before the week was out.'

'You insolent knaves!' grinned Bothwell. 'And when is this week out?'

'Sir, it runs out this very day.'

Bothwell slapped the man's shoulder so hard that French Paris' knees gave way.

'We cannot have that,' said Bothwell.

Paris sniggered. 'Her ladyship, in turning out the rooms, my lord, has discarded furniture which she had sent down to the cellars. It well-nigh killed us. An old couch, my lord, there was among other articles. 'Tis there now . . . old . . . shabby . . . having been in use since before my lady's coming, sir . . . but still a couch. . . .'

'Send the girl down to the cellar to get wine,' said the Earl.

'Yes, my lord. And lock the door and bring the key to you?'

'How well you follow my plans, man!'

'My lord, there have been other times.'

'Do it then. I'd like you to win your wager with sly Gabriel.'

Paris went off chuckling.

Bessie had heard much of the Earl and she never tired of listening to stories of him. They whispered of him that no woman was safe if he fancied her.

'Keep your eyes on your work,' said elderly Nan, who sat stitching beside her when the Earl passed through the room. 'Don't go casting them in *that* direction, my girl.'

Bessie did not reply. She sat still, shivering with excitement.

When she left the sewing-room that afternoon French Paris was waiting for her.

'You're to go down to the cellar,' he said. 'You're to bring up a flagon of red wine.'

'Where to?' asked Bessie.

'To me in the kitchen.'

Bessie went down the stone stairs to the cellar, taking the candle which Paris had thrust into her hand.

'Watch your step,' he called after her.

Bessie did not like the cellar very much. It was dark and damp and there were cobwebs which touched her face as she groped her way forward.

Suddenly she heard the door shut behind her and the key turn in the lock.

'Master Paris!' she called shrilly. 'Master Paris!'

She went up the stairs and tried the door. She was right. It had been locked. It was a silly trick, she supposed. Paris was teasing her. She looked round her. She must not be frightened. It was just a joke; she must remember that. The servants liked to play jokes on one another. Well, she would do as she had been bidden. She would get the flask of wine and then, if he had not unlocked the door by then, she would bang on it and call for help.

She went to where the flagons were stored, and picked up one; but as she turned towards the door she saw that it was open. She laughed with relief.

'A silly trick, Master Paris,' she said. 'Don't think to frighten *me*.'

But it was not Master Paris who had turned and was locking the door behind him. Bessie's heart raced as the tall figure of the Earl came towards her.

She dropped the flagon as she heard him laugh.

'My . . . my lord . . .' she stammered.

Then she felt those strong arms seize her.

'I . . . I do not understand, my lord. . . .'

'You cannot deceive me, Bessie,' he said. 'You understand very well indeed, as you did in the sewing-room, did you not?'

'No, my lord, I . . .'

'No!' he cried. 'Then I shall have to make you.'

With that he picked her up as though she herself were no heavier than the smallest flagon of wine. He put her on the couch. Then Bessie began to understand.

The Queen was humiliated beyond endurance.

She and her husband had been entertained at the house of one of the rich burghers of the city. Darnley no longer attempted to hide from her the fact that he was a heavy drinker and, worse still, a drinker who could not carry his drink.

He no longer bothered to disguise his true nature. She had to agree with others that he was vain, dissolute and despicable. He would pick quarrels with those who dared not stand up to him; he brawled in the streets, accosting women, demanding that his companions did likewise; he boasted of his mastery over the Queen who, he asserted, was so madly in love with him that she would deny him nothing.

Mary watched him, and as she did so her feelings towards him were first lacerated with humiliation and then began to grow colder.

She had begged him this evening to drink less. He had shouted at her before the company that it was no matter for her to decide what he should drink. She should remember that he was her lawful husband. He knew how to punish her, he said with a leer, if she did not treat him with due respect.

This was more than Mary could endure.

She bade goodbye to her host, and, in tears of humiliation and rage, left the house.

Darnley stayed on to drink himself unconscious and be carried back to Holyroodhouse by his attendants and friends.

She was in her apartment when one of them came to tell her that he had been brought back to the palace and put to bed.

She nodded coldly.

There were no more tears; she was no longer heartbroken, for she had made a strange discovery: she had ceased to care for Darnley.

She did not understand herself. That raging passion which had swept over her had turned completely cold. It had died as suddenly as it had flared. She could not understand how she could have imagined herself in love with the dissolute youth. She began to see him in a new light. The blue eyes which she had thought so beautiful now seemed inane, the soft lips weak and foolish. She had begun to suspect that what she had so desperately needed was not Darnley's love but a lover. She was beginning to know herself.

A great sadness came to her. She had dreamed of the perfect union, and she was discovering most bitter disillusion. Darnley's boyish naïvety was assumed; he was hideously experienced; he was full of vice; he had practised every sort of depravity. How he must have laughed at her for falling such an easy victim to his youthful charm.

There was one other factor–a most important one–which had caused her to decide on the measures she would take: she was pregnant.

Perhaps her pregnancy made her less eager for his embraces; perhaps the slackening of desire had given her a chance to see him as he really was. No matter. She saw; and she had made up her mind.

She rose and sent a page to David Rizzio with a message that she wished to see him at once. It was midnight, but he had not retired. Early hours were never kept at Holyroodhouse.

'David,' she said, 'I have something secret to tell you. I wish no one else to know it. I hate Darnley.'

'Madam!'

'Yes, it is true. It has suddenly come to me. I did not really love him. There had been so much talk of marriages, and they never materialized. I suppose I wanted a lover and he was there. He seemed more eligible than anyone within reach. Now I think him loathly. Oh, David, you wonder. I have been so doting, have I not? You wonder if I really mean what I say.'

'Madam, his behaviour to-night was disgraceful.'

'His behaviour every night is disgraceful. He was quite insincere before the wedding. Now we see him as he really is–an arrogant upstart, a drunkard and a lecher. Let us face the truth, David. How has he behaved towards you? Do not speak. I will tell you. He has been insufferable, although when he first came here, knowing the influence you had with me, he made himself most agreeable. That is the truth, is it not, David?'

'Yes, Madam.'

'And you agree with me that my marriage is the biggest mistake I ever made?'

'It was mine too, Madam. I do not forget that I urged you to this marriage.'

'Dear Davie! You did, it is true. But you could not have urged me to the altar if I had not wished to go. The mistake is mine, not yours. We have both been deceived, but let us not ponder on past errors. I have determined to banish him, right out of my heart and from my bed. He shall never share the crown.'

'No, Madam, he should not.'

'It is great good fortune that I have not already bestowed on him the Crown Matrimonial which would have given him powers equal to my own. Then we should have been too late. In future no documents are to be shown to him. We will have a stamp made with his name on it so that his signature will not be necessary on any documents, and you can affix it without consulting him. Consult him! What would be the good of *his* opinion!'

'Madam, he will be infuriated when he hears of this.'

'Davie, his fury matters not at all. I will show him that any power he wields comes from me. I shall never give him another chance to humiliate me as he has to-night.'

David was smiling; he was well pleased. His dignity was dear to him, and Darnley had insulted him time after time. David had known that the Queen must one day grow out of her infatuation, and he was glad that time had come.

'Madam,' he said at length, 'you do well to cut Lord Darnley out of your policies. He has no conception of the important part you have to play in world politics. His own egoism, his own vanity are so large that they obscure his vision and he cannot see beyond them. Madam, never has your position been so secure. These despatches from the King of Spain make his attitude clear. He is delighted with the turn of events in Scotland, and this happy state of affairs, he knows, has grown out of Your Majesty's prompt action against the rebel lords. With Moray and his friends in England, and with Knox subdued, you have so pleased King Philip that he is planning to help you establish yourself even more firmly on the throne of Scotland, with the Catholic religion restored. Madam, I know that the King of Spain sees no reason why an attack–providing our affairs continue to improve–should not be made on our enemy beyond the Border. The King of Spain visualizes the day when the Protestant bastard is robbed of the crown she has no right to wear, and it adorns your own fair brow.'

'Queen of England and Scotland, David!' Her eyes shone. 'That is what I want. If we were one country, then would these wasteful Border raids be discontinued. We *are* one land; we should stand together. That way lies peace, Davie.'

'Yes, Madam. It will be the happiest day of my life when I see you crowned Queen of England.'

'And Philip will truly further this end?'

'He has said so quite clearly . . . or as clearly as can be expected from one so cautious. I beg of Your Majesty to read this despatch.'

They were bending over the table reading, when the door was burst open. Darnley stood watching them; his nightshirt was open at the neck, his hair disordered, his face blotchy, his eyes blood-shot from his recent carousal. He was still very drunk.

'I knew it!' he shouted. 'So you are there then . . . you two together. I knew I'd catch you. I know it's true what they say of you . . . furtively creeping away together. . . . The Queen of Scotland and a low-born music-maker. By God!'

The Queen said haughtily: 'Go back to your apartment at once.'

Darnley laughed, 'Do not think to deceive me, Madam.'

'I have no intention of deceiving you. I will tell you plainly that I am weary of your disgraceful behaviour. Henceforth you and I live apart.'

Darnley reeled and hiccupped. 'Oh . . . so *he* satisfies you, does he . . . this low-born . . .'

Mary rose and strode towards him; she could not control her rage. She took him by the hair and shook him. He stared at her in bleary wonderment.

''Strue . . .' he said. 'He's your lover. That stunted go-by-the-ground, that . . .'

'Be quiet!' cried Mary. 'I will have you taken to the Tolbooth.'

Darnley's mouth fell open. 'Come, Mary,' he spluttered. 'Come to bed . . .'

She pushed him from her and he fell to the floor.

'David,' she said calmly, 'call two of his men. They shall carry him back to bed. Now I shall go to mine. Good night, David.'

She went out, leaving Darnley lying on the floor in his drunken stupor.

Darnley swaggered about the Court. If the Queen denied him her bed, others did not. He was watched–though he did not know this–by many lords of the Court. There was Maitland of Lethington, now affianced to Mary Fleming. He was privy to the secrets of the bedchamber. It was not that Flem wished to betray her mistress's secrets; she loved her mistress second only to Lord Maitland himself. But Maitland was the cleverest statesman in Scotland; he had beguiled the English Queen and the English ambassador with his diplomacy; so it was not difficult for him to discover all he needed from his beloved Flem. Maitland's vanity had been deeply wounded. He had been the Queen's chief adviser, had employed his skilful diplomacy in England, and on returning to Scotland had found another in his place: David Rizzio, the upstart musician.

Clearly Scotland would be a happier place for Lord Maitland of Lethington if Rizzio were no longer there.

There was Ruthven–slowly dying of a wasting disease and determined to enjoy great power before he departed from this life. He too resented the Queen's trust in her musician.

There was James Douglas, Earl of Morton, the most treacherous of them all, the man without scruples, the cruel lecher whose bastards were numerous. He was in touch with Moray who was trying to obtain the Queen's pardon, and return to Scotland. Morton, feigning loyalty to Mary, was also in league with the English. He was fully aware of the Spanish plot to strengthen Scotland before making an attack on the English Queen's throne; Cecil and Elizabeth were also aware of this plot. The unlucky Queen of Scots did not know how many of these gentlemen who surrounded her were spies for the champion of Protestantism, Elizabeth of England.

Moray was waiting to leap back into Scotland. So Morton, Maitland, Ruthven, with Argyle and others, met to discuss the new state of affairs, how to rid themselves of the upstart Rizzio whose foreign policy had led them to this pass, how to restore Moray and the exiled lords to their estates, how, when destroying Rizzio, to destroy also–or at least make impotent–the Queen herself.

Money and support were not lacking from England, for Elizabeth was now genuinely alarmed. Philip of Spain was behind this plot, and he could always alarm the English Queen. Philip sent money to Scotland, but the English, being warned of this through Cecil's clever spy-system, waylaid the ships which carried the treasure, captured it and brought it to London.

Philip's advice to Mary was that, since the operations must be delayed owing to the capture of the treasure, she should feign friendship with Elizabeth and lull the suspicions of the English.

Mary did not know that those noblemen who surrounded her throne were in the main spies for England. These men were Protestants and had no intention of allowing their country to return to the Catholic Faith, but it did not occur to their Queen that they could be so blatantly treacherous.

As for Rizzio himself, clever as he was and faithful to the Queen's interest, he had his weakness. He could not resist strutting a little, each day adding something to his finery. An arrogance had crept into his manner. Were the great lords of Scotland going to endure the arrogance of this upstart? Was a musician, a player of the harp and the guitar, a singer in the Queen's choir, to be set over the chieftains of Scotland?

David Rizzio became even more unpopular than Darnley for while the lords despised Darnley they were forced to admire and envy Rizzio who had risen from obscurity to power.

Morton sat beside Ruthven's sick bed in the latter's Edinburgh house. Ruthven lay back in bed; it was clear that he had not long to live, yet his eyes were brilliantly alive in his yellow face; they burned with a lust for Rizzio's blood. Morton was not surprised, gazing at the strange gaunt face, that many believed Ruthven to be a witch.

Ruthven's hopes lay with Morton. The most ruthless of the lords, it was to Morton's interest to have Moray back in Scotland, and Morton would have no compunction in committing murder to bring that about. He was no newcomer to the art of murder.

'It would be a simpler matter to waylay the fellow,' Morton was saying. 'It would be over in a few minutes. He could be hustled into one of the city wynds and two stout men would make short work of him.'

'Nay,' said Ruthven, rising on his pillows and falling back with exhaustion, 'that is not the way. *She* shall see the deed done. She is heavy with her child now. In less than four months it will be born . . . if she lives . . . if she survives. . . . No! Let him be taken when he is closeted with her. Let her see the deed done. She has insulted us by her preference for the low fellow. Besides . . .'

Morton nodded slowly. 'It may kill her,' he said bluntly. 'Her health is not good . . . and a pregnant woman, seeing her lover done to death before her eyes . . . I see your point.'

'There is the hope that it may prove too much for her. But we shall not turn our daggers on the Queen. No . . . no . . . let her death come through shock, through remorse . . . anything you like. There is one other whom we must implicate in this. Neither my lord Moray nor Cecil and his Queen wish it to be known that this is a political murder. So there must be another reason for the death of our little musician, and we have it to hand.'

'Oh yes, we have it at hand. The Queen's pretty husband must be implicated. We are all agreed on that.'

'The murder of Rizzio,' said Ruthven, 'is to be no political murder. It has nothing to do with bribes and instructions from England. It is a *crime passionel*, you understand.'

'Then he must be with us when the deed is done.'

'He must indeed! You can arrange that. The silly young fool will believe all you tell him. He is like a peevish boy robbed of his toys. She will have nothing to do with him. He whimpers because he finds more pleasure in the bed of a queen than in that of a tavern wench. He'll not be difficult to manage. Then we shall have the whole world shocked by the wanton ways of a queen. And if she does not die of shock, she will be most certainly ruined.'

'And the child will doubtless not survive this.'

Ruthven nodded. 'Go to work, friend Morton,' he said.

Morton had asked to see the young King and to see him alone.

Darnley scowled when he saw his visitor. He was not fond of the Douglases. But Morton was full of flattery–the sort which could not fail to please.

'What a delightful doublet! Never have I seen such a happy blending of colour. Ah, mayhap it is Your Majesty's fair complexion and golden hair which makes the colour seem so perfect. It is small wonder that the Queen is so madly in love with her husband.'

Darnley's scowl deepened. He was recalling the scene which had taken place early that morning. He had waited for Mary in her apartment, had driven out her women and insisted on seeing her alone. She had come at three in the morning, smiling serenely; she had been playing cards with Rizzio. They had supped together, with one or two others as company; and then had settled to the cards. As the game had been so exciting they had gone on playing until early morning.

Darnley had complained: 'It is a shameful thing that you keep your husband waiting while you play cards with a low musician.'

'My shame,' she had retorted, 'is that I have such a husband to keep waiting.'

She cared nothing for him, and now she was unkind to him. She kept all secrets from him. He was never allowed to see any state papers.

He had seized her arm and said: 'Madam, I demand my rights.'

'Your rights?'

'To share your life, your bed, your crown.'

She had laughed and pushed him from her. 'You have forfeited those rights, Henry. Now leave me and send my women to me, for I am tired and wish to go to bed.'

'I will not go!' he had declared. 'I shall stay here. You cannot turn me away.'

'I can and I will.'

'I shall shout to the whole palace that you are turning me out of your apartment.'

'Shout all you wish. You will only be telling what is already known.'

'Mary . . . dearest . . . I love you.'

'No,' she had said. 'It is a good thing that neither of us love each other. Now go or I shall have to have you turned out.'

He had ignobly left the apartment, and the memory rankled.

Now he continued to scowl at Morton as he said: 'The Queen is *not* in love with her husband.'

'The Court knows it,' said Morton, 'and resents it.'

'Resents it?' said Darnley alert.

'Do you think, Your Majesty, that we like to look on at the vulgar intrigue between the Queen and this foreign upstart?'

'So there *is* an intrigue!'

'Does Your Majesty doubt it?'

'I . . . yes . . . no . . . I am not sure.'

'They would be very careful in your presence, I doubt not.'

'Very careful! You . . . you mean . . .?'

'Your Majesty, he is with her night and morning. What are they doing, think you–discussing state secrets all the time?'

Darnley's eyes narrowed. 'It is true. It is shameful. I . . . a King . . . to be treated so! I . . . who have been faithful to the Queen!' He faltered and looked at Morton but Morton was not smiling at the obvious lie. He merely looked sympathetic.

'There are many of us,' said Morton slowly, 'who wonder why you do not do the fellow to death. None could blame you if you did.'

'No!' repeated Darnley. 'None could blame me.'

'I have received news from the Queen's brother in England.'

'Moray! He is no friend to me.'

'But would be. It is a shameful thing, he says, that you should be denied your rights. Not only are you denied the Queen's bed, but the Crown Matrimonial. Lord Moray says that if you will restore to him and the exiled lords their estates which have been confiscated, the first thing he will do on his return to Scotland will be to give you that Crown.'

'How could I bring about his return? How could I restore his confiscated estates?'

'Alas, how could you? A short while ago when the Queen doted on you, it might have been possible for you. But now . . . another holds her favour. David Rizzio is the man who enjoys all her favours . . . every one . . . adviser, secretary of state . . . lover . . .'

'I would I could kill that man!'

Morton smiled. 'Your Majesty,' he said, 'let us leave the palace. Let us be sure that we cannot be overheard. There is something we have to say to each other.'

Bothwell and his household had moved from Crichton to another of his houses, Haddington Abbey. He was finding enough to entertain him in his own household for a few weeks. Jean's attitude towards him had not changed in the least, and he was still intrigued by it. Bessie Crawford supplied the erotic entertainment which he had always found necessary–and life passed pleasantly.

There were matters to be attended to on the estate. Jean was doing for Haddington what she had done for Crichton; she was never idle; even when she sat resting she would have her embroidery in her hands.

He saw Bessie often. Her great eyes would follow him, waiting for the signal. Upstairs in the loft . . . this minute . . . or out in the fields away from the Abbey . . . Bessie would be there–a small, quiet girl who could be aroused at his touch to a passion which equalled his own.

He liked Bessie. Between them they–she and Jean–were responsible for his long stay on his estates. He might have continued to stay but for one thing.

It happened quite simply. He went to the sewing-room because he had been reminded suddenly of Bessie and felt an immediate need of her company. Bessie was there alone; his wife had been with her, for they were working together on the same piece of tapestry; but when he arrived Jean's chair was empty.

He said: 'To the loft! Wait there for me.'

Bessie scrambled up. Her eyes were anxious. She began: 'My lord . . . I cannot . . .'

'Go, my girl. Go up, I say.'

She stammered: 'My lord . . . my lady . . .'

He seized her by the shoulders and pushed her towards the door. She almost fell, laughing on a note of high-pitched laughter that betrayed the rising excitement, that complete abandonment to his will. She picked herself up, dropped a hurried curtsey and ran from the room.

He laughed, and after a few moments followed her to the loft.

Bessie was always inarticulate with him. They had exchanged few words. Words were unnecessary in such a relationship. But now it seemed she was trying to tell him something. She had work to do. She must not be long. He would not listen; he did not want chatter from Bessie. He forced her down on to the dusty floor of the loft. The very fact that she wished to go made him determined to keep her there. He liked resistance; he had come to expect it on the Border.

So he kept her there longer than usual, and Bessie, while she could temporarily forget her anxiety, found that it had returned to her when she was at last released.

She made her way down to the sewing-room. The Countess was there; so were several of the servants.

Bessie, red-faced, her dress dusty, put in a shamefaced appearance.

'And where have you been?' demanded Jean.

'Please, my lady . . . I . . .'

'Look at the dust on your dress. What has happened?'

Bessie stammered: 'I went to the loft . . .'

'You went to the loft when you should have been using your needle! Look at your hands. They're filthy. Go and wash them. You must not do delicate needlework with hands like that. Then I shall want to know why you left the sewing-room to go there.'

Bessie, glad to escape, almost collided with the Earl who was then coming into the room. Bessie ran. The Earl scarcely looked at her. But he was betrayed. His clothes were as dusty as those of Bessie. It was a strange sort of dust. Remains of cobwebs could be seen attached to his doublet as they had been to Bessie's hair.

Jean looked at him sharply. She knew that the servants were looking too. She was aware of suppressed laughter. Knowing the Earl, and understanding Bessie, there was only one conclusion to be drawn.

She said nothing to her husband, but mentioning that she had work for them to do, she commanded the servants whom she would need, to accompany her to the kitchens where she wished to make arrangements for that night's supper.

Half an hour later she returned to the sewing-room where Bessie–the dust brushed from her dress and her hands clean–was diligently working.

'Oh, Bessie,' said Jean, 'your father lives in the smithy outside Haddington town, I believe.'

'Yes, m'lady.'

'That is fortunate for you. Gather your things together and go to him immediately.'

'Go . . . m'lady?'

'Yes, Bessie. I find that I no longer require your services.'

Bessie blushed and stammered, then burst into tears. To leave this wonderful house, to live in her father's wretched smithy, to help at the anvil instead of doing fine needlework, to have as a lover some village lout instead of the great Earl of Bothwell–it was too much to be borne!

'Now, Bessie, it is no use weeping. Get ready. Go at once. I shall expect you to be gone in an hour.'

There was nothing Bessie could do but obey.

Bothwell shrugged his shoulders when he heard what had happened. Then he burst out laughing.

'So you're jealous, eh?' he said. 'Jealous of a sewing-girl!'

'Not jealous,' his wife replied. 'Pray visit her if you wish. I have no objection now that she will be no longer here. It is merely that I cannot have you making demands on her time when she is working for me.'

He was astonished. He had never known such a woman.

After that he had Bessie brought to him on one or two occasions. The tradesmen of the town were obliging, providing rooms where they could meet, and carrying messages to and from the smithy; but he grew tired of such arrangements. His lust always demanded satisfaction without delay. By the time matters could be arranged his ardour had cooled or been slaked elsewhere.

So . . . he returned to Edinburgh.

It was Saturday evening. The March winds howled down the great chimneys as the Queen was taking supper in the small closet next to her bedroom. She was in her sixth month of pregnancy and her physicians had advised her to fortify her strength by eating meat although this was the Lenten season; they had also prescribed quiet for the royal patient. The servants were hurrying into the closet with dishes of meat which they set on the small table. Mary was reclining on a couch and beside her were her bastard sister Jane, Countess of Argyle, and her bastard brother, Lord Robert Stuart. It was a small party in view of the doctor's advice, and the Laird of Creich her master of the household, Arthur Erskine, her equerry, the Queen's doctor, David Rizzio and a few servants completed it.

The beef was delicious, and with it they drank French wine.

'This wine always reminds me of Chenonceaux,' said Mary wistfully. 'Oh, what happy days they were!'

'Would Your Grace go back?' asked Robert.

'Nay, brother. If I went back I should have to return again by the same road, and at times I found the going tedious.'

'Signor Davie looks grand this night,' said the Countess.

David looked down at his damask gown which was trimmed with rich fur. His doublet was made of best satin; and his hose were of russet velvet. There was a fine feather in his cap, and about his neck hung a great ruby, a gift from the Queen.

'Yes, Davie,' said Mary, ''tis true.'

'I should consider it an insult to Your Majesty to appear clad in anything but the best I could assemble,' said David.

'You are right, Davie,' said the Queen. 'I like not drab garments. Sing us something of France, please. I have a longing to hear French songs to-night. Master Erskine, I beg of you pass David his guitar.' She turned to one of the serving men. 'Can you pull the curtains a little closer? There is a draught.'

'The wind is fierce to-night, Madam,' said the Laird of Creich.

The servant had gone to the window. For a few seconds he looked out and saw figures moving about below. They were numerous and they were in steel bonnets with guns, swords, Jedburgh staves and bucklers.

What were these men doing out there? He had heard of no reason why they should be there. They might be troopers. What was afoot to-night? Some exercise, he supposed. He would have mentioned it to the company but, as he turned from the window, Signor David was already playing his guitar and his rich voice was filling the small chamber.

When the song was ended, the servant left the apartment. He was going to make sure that he had interpreted correctly what he had seen. He quickly discovered that there were many–possibly more than a hundred–armed men stationed about the palace.

Almost as soon as he had gone, the door which led to the private staircase was opened and Darnley came in. Mary frowned. He appeared to have been drinking. He came to where she sat and slumped on the couch beside her; he laid a hot hand on her arm.

'Have you had your supper?' she asked coldly.

The company had become silent and tense, waiting for one of those scenes which seemed now inevitable when the Queen and her husband were together.

Darnley had not answered her, and suddenly all except the Queen had risen to their feet, for, standing in the doorway through which Darnley had just come, was Lord Ruthven. His face was yellow above his gleaming armour; his hair was wild and there was a look of death on his face. For a moment they thought they were seeing Ruthven's ghost, as they knew he was near to death and not expected to leave his bed again; moreover he had always been suspected of having magical powers.

No one spoke in those frightening first moments as Ruthven's hollow eyes ranged about the room and came to rest on David Rizzio.

Then Mary saw that Ruthven was not alone. Behind him, through the narrow doorway she caught glimpses of Morton, Lindsay, Kerr and others. Ruthven suddenly lifted his hand and pointed to David.

'Come out, David,' he said slowly. 'You are wanted without.'

David did not move. His great eyes seemed to have grown still larger; his trembling hand reached for the Queen's skirt.

Ruthven began to shout: 'Come out, David Rizzio. Come out from the Queen's chamber. You have been there too long.'

Mary stood up and confronted Ruthven. 'How dare you, my lord, thus come into my chamber? How dare you! You shall pay dearly for this. What means this intrusion? Who are those who follow you here? Why have you come?'

'We come for David Rizzio, Madam.'

'Then go away,' commanded the Queen. 'If David is here it is my wish that he should be.' She turned fiercely to Darnley: 'What means this outrage my lord? Do you know aught of this?'

Darnley did not reply for a second or so. Then he mumbled: 'N . . . no. But it is a dishonour that David should sup with you, and your husband be kept out.'

Ruthven caught the hangings to prevent himself falling from exhaustion. Mary looked round at the terrified company. Catching her look, Erskine and the Laird of Creich started forward. Ruthven cried in a hollow voice: 'Let no one touch me. They will regret it.' He looked supernatural in that moment, and the two men stood where they were as though held there by Ruthven's uncanny powers.

Mary cried out: 'Leave at once! Go! I command you to go.'

'I have come for Rizzio,' persisted the grim-faced Ruthven. And with those words he unsheathed his dagger.

It was the signal. His accomplices rushed into the chamber.

Rizzio gave a great cry and, falling to the floor, gripped Mary's skirts and tried to hide himself in their folds. Dishes were swept aside; the table toppled over. The Countess of Argyle picked up the candelabra in time and held it high above her head.

Mary felt the child protest within her; nauseated, she tried not to faint. Rizzio was clinging to her and she made an effort to put herself between him and those men who, she knew, had come to kill him.

George Douglas had twisted Rizzio's arm so that, with a cry of pain, he released his grip on Mary's gown.

She saw their faces vaguely, distorted with blood lust, and the desire to kill not only Rizzio, she believed, but herself and the child she carried.

'Take the Queen,' someone said, and she saw Darnley close beside her. He put an arm about her and held her; she turned from him in revulsion just in time to see George Douglas snatch the dagger from Darnley's belt and drive it into the cowering, shrieking Rizzio.

Hands were clutching the terrified David who was bleeding from the wound. She watched him as they dragged him across the floor, and his terrified eyes never left her face. She stretched out her arms to him.

'Oh, Davie . . . Davie . . .' she sobbed. 'They are killing you, Davie.

They are killing us both. Where are my friends? Is this the way to treat the Queen?'

'Be quiet!' hissed Kerr. 'If you are not, I shall be forced to cut you into collops.'

She could hear the shrieks in the next chamber to which they had dragged David; she heard the hideous thud of blows. She heard the death agonies of David.

'His blood shall cost you dear!' she cried; and she slid to the floor in a faint.

When Mary came out of the swoon she was aware of Darnley beside her, supporting her. For a moment she was uncertain what had happened to shock her so; then the sight of the room in the light from the candelabra showed her the upturned table, the spilled food and wine and the carpet soaked with David's blood.

She turned to Darnley and cried out in anguish: 'You are the cause of this. Why have you allowed this wicked deed to be done? I took you from low estate and made you my husband. What have I ever done that you should use me thus?'

'I will tell you, Madam,' cried Darnley. She saw his shifty bloodshot eyes; she smelt the wine on his breath and she knew he was not entirely sober. 'Since yonder fellow David came into credit and familiarity with you, you have had little time to spare for me. I have been shut from your thoughts and your chamber. You were with David far into the night.'

'It was because you had failed me.'

'In what way? Am I failed in any sort in my body? There was a time when you were so eager for me that you came to my chamber. What disdain have you for me since you favoured David? What offence have I committed that you should be coy with me? You have listened to David and he spoke against me.'

'My lord, all that I have suffered this night is your doing, for the which I shall no longer be your wife, nor lie with you any more. I shall never rest content until I have made you suffer as you have made me suffer this night.'

She could not bear to look at him. She covered her face with her hands and wept bitterly.

Ruthven returned to the chamber.

He said: 'His lordship is Your Majesty's husband, and you must be dutiful one to the other.' As he spoke he sank into a chair from very exhaustion and called for wine to revive him.

Mary went to him and stood over him. 'My lord,' she cried, 'if my child or I should die through this night's work, you will not escape your just reward. I have powerful friends. There are my kinsmen of Lorraine; there is the Pope and the King of Spain. Do not think you shall escape justice.'

Ruthven grasped the cup which was offered to him. He smiled grimly as he said: 'Madam, these you speak of are over-great princes to concern themselves with such a poor man as myself.'

Mary stood back from him. She understood his meaning. He was implying that they were too great to concern themselves with the troubles of a Queen of a remote country, who could be of little use to them when her nobles had rendered her powerless.

Mary was seized with a great trembling then; for she realized that the folly of Darnley had, by this night's work, frustrated all her careful plans; all her triumphs of the last months were as nothing now.

Others were hurrying into the room. She saw the mighty figure of Bothwell among them, and her spirits lifted. Rogue he might be, but he was a loyal rogue. With him were Huntley and Maitland of whom she was not quite certain, but could not believe they were entirely against her.

Bothwell cried: 'What means this? Who dares lay hands on the Queen?' He seized Ruthven and pulled the dying man to his feet.

'What has been done has been done with the consent of the King,' said Ruthven. 'I have a paper here which bears his signature.'

Bothwell seized it. Mary watching, saw the change in his expression and that of Huntley. They at least were outside this diabolical plot.

Morton, who was with them, cried: 'The palace is full of those who have had a share in this night's work.'

Mary's eyes were fixed on Bothwell, but at that moment there came a shouting from below. The townsfolk of Edinburgh had heard that something was amiss in the palace and had come demanding to see the Queen.

With a sob of relief Mary dashed to the window, but Kerr's strong arms were about her. She felt his sword pressed against her side while he repeated his threat to cut her into collops if she opened her mouth.

Ruthven signed to Darnley. 'To the window. Tell them that the Queen is well. Tell them that this is nothing but a quarrel among the French servants.'

'Henry!' cried Mary. 'Do no such thing.'

But Kerr's hand was over her mouth.

Darnley alarmed and uncertain, looking from the Queen to Morton and his followers, seeing the murderous light in Morton's eyes, remembering the groaning, blood-spattered David, allowed himself to be led to the window.

'Good people,' he cried. 'There is naught wrong in the palace but some dispute among the French servants. 'Tis over now.'

He turned and looked at Mary's stricken face. This was the last act of treachery. He was completely against her now.

She looked for Bothwell and Huntley among those who had filled the small chamber. They had disappeared. Maitland had left too. His loyalty was doubtful but she could have trusted his courtesy and gentleness.

She realized then that she was alone with her enemies. Nausea swept over her; the child leapt within her; and once again on that terrible night, she fell fainting to the floor.

Through the long night she lay sleepless. What now? she asked herself.

There were only a few women in her bedchamber. One of these was old Lady Huntley–Bothwell's mother-in-law. The others had been appointed by her enemies, and her Maries were absent. There was no one to help her then.

She struggled up and Lady Huntley came to her.

'Where are my women?' she asked. 'I wish to get up immediately. I wish to leave the palace.'

'Your Majesty,' whispered Lady Huntley, 'that you cannot do. The palace is surrounded by the armed men of your enemies. My son and Lord Bothwell have left Edinburgh in haste. They could do nothing by staying. It would have been certain death. They were here alone, as you know, with few of their men and only a few servants to do their bidding.'

'So I am a prisoner here? But what of the people of Edinburgh? They will come to my assistance. I know it.'

'Your Majesty, they cannot do so. The King has issued a proclamation. He has dissolved Parliament and commanded all burgesses, prelates, peers and barons to leave Edinburgh immediately. The tocsins are sounding.'

'This is a terrible thing that has come upon me,' said Mary. 'Is there no man in Scotland on whom I can rely?'

'There are my son, Your Majesty, and my son-in-law.'

'They ran away, did they not, when they scented danger?'

'Only because they can serve you better alive than dead. They have hurried away to muster forces to come to your aid.'

'Many have deceived me,' said Mary. 'I trust no one.'

She turned wearily on her side and, being aware of the child, a sudden courage came to her, reminding her that it was not for herself alone she must fight.

The child! She would fight for the child. And in a flash of inspiration she realized that the child might give her the help she needed. They could not deny her a midwife, could they? They could be made to believe that the terrible events of last night had brought about a miscarriage.

She was excited now.

Who could help her in this? Lady Huntley. She was old but she could play her part. Who else . . . when the palace was held by her enemies?

But there was one of uncertain loyalty. There was a foolish gullible one. There was one whose craven mind she understood–her husband, Lord Darnley.

She said to Lady Huntley: 'They cannot object to my seeing my husband, can they? Go at once and see if you can bring him to me. Tell him that he will find a submissive wife if he will but come to me.'

Darnley came, and as she looked at him, her hope sprang up afresh. He was afraid; he was afraid of her and he was afraid of the lords who–now that the murder was done and done in his name–had hinted that he would do as they bade him.

'My lord . . .' said Mary, stretching out her hand.

He took it hesitantly.

'What is this terrible thing which has come between us?' she asked. 'What has made you take the side of my enemies against me?'

'It was David,' he said sullenly. 'David came between us. He has been your lover. Was I to endure that?'

'Henry, you have allowed these men to play you false. They have tricked you. You must see this now. How have they treated you since the deed was done? They command you to obey them. This was no murder of jealousy. This was a political murder. They wanted David out of the way because David knew how to make us great . . . *us*, you too, Henry . . . you who would have been my King. This was not done because you or they imagined David to be my lover. That was how they used you and how they will continue to use you if you allow them. They promised to make you King, but they will make you powerless. And when my brother returns, they will find some means of despatching *you* . . . as they have despatched David.'

Darnley's teeth began to chatter. He was wavering. When he listened to Morton he believed Morton; but now Mary's version of the motives of these men seemed plausible. They had ordered him to dismiss Parliament. Last night they had ordered him to speak to the people of Edinburgh. He had had no say in either matter. Already he could see the gleam in Ruthven's eyes; he could see Morton's tight, cruel lips sneering at him.

'It is my brother whom they will make their leader,' said Mary.

'He . . . he . . . is riding with all speed to Edinburgh,' stammered Darnley. 'He will be here . . . at any minute.'

'Then you will see how they will treat you. You will not live long to feel remorse for what you have done to David. My brother always hated you. It was because I wished to marry you that he went into exile. We defeated him then; that was because we stood together. Now you have gone over to our enemies who seek to destroy me, our child and you too, Henry. You will not escape. Indeed you will be the first whom they will despatch. Who knows, they may let me live on as their prisoner.'

'Do not speak so . . . do not speak so. Do you realize that they are all about us? There are armed men everywhere.'

'Henry, consider this: Help me, and I will help you. You and I must stand together. We must find some way of getting out of here.'

Lady Huntley had come into the room. She said: 'Madam, forgive me for breaking in on you thus, but I thought you would wish to know that your brother, the Earl of Moray, has arrived at the palace.'

Darnley and Lady Huntley had left her, and her brother would be with her at any moment now. Lady Huntley had given her a message brought by one of Bothwell's men and smuggled in to her. It was the most comforting thing that had happened for many terrible hours.

'Do not despair,' was the message. 'Do not think Bothwell and Huntley have deserted Your Majesty. They left Holyrood in order to gather forces to come to your aid. Bothwell will soon have a Lowland force ready to fight for you; Huntley too will be there with his Highlanders.'

The message went on to say that it was imperative for her to leave the palace as soon as this could be arranged, and Bothwell was forming a plan whereby she would be lowered over the walls by ropes to where he would be waiting for her with horses.

She laid her hands on her heavy body, Bothwell seemed to think she was a hardy adventurer like himself, instead of a woman, six months pregnant. Lowered over walls in her condition! It was impossible.

Still, it was gratifying to know that outside these walls her friends were making plans for her safety.

Nevertheless she must find some way to escape from the palace. She must do it, not by following Bothwell's wild suggestion, but in a subtler manner; her plan was already beginning to take shape.

Her brother came into the apartment at that moment. He knelt before her. He lifted his face to hers and there were tears in his eyes when he embraced her.

'Dear Jamie,' she said.

'My dearest sister, I blame myself for this terrible thing. I should never have left you. Brothers and sisters should not quarrel. Had I been at hand I should never have allowed you to suffer so.'

Those tears in his eyes seemed to be of real emotion, but she was not so foolish as she had once been. Did he really believe that she did not know he had been in the plot to kill Rizzio? Did he really believe that she did not understand that he had returned to Scotland to wrest her power from her and take it to himself? It was with pleasure that she would deceive him now as he had so often deceived her.

'Jamie,' she said, 'you see me a sick woman. My child was to have been born three months from now.'

'*Was* to have been born?'

'I am in such pain, Jamie . . . such terrible pain. I fear a miscarriage.'

'But this is more terrible than anything that has happened.'

'You see, Jamie, they have so far taken only my faithful secretary. Now they will take my child as well.'

'You are sure of this?'

She put her hand to her side and groped her way to the bed. Moray was beside her. He put his arm about her.

'Jamie, you will not let them deny me a midwife?'

'No . . . no . . . certainly you must have a midwife.'

'And . . . Jamie . . . it distresses me . . . all these men about me . . . at such a time. I . . . in my state . . . to have soldiers at my door. Jamie, look at me. How *could* I escape in this condition? How could I?'

'I will have a midwife sent to you.'

'I have already asked my woman to bring one. See that she is not kept back, I beg of you.'

Mary turned her head away and groaned. She was enjoying her triumph; she had successfully deceived her brother.

She gripped his hand. 'And . . . the men-at-arms . . . they distress me so. I . . . a Queen in my own palace . . . a poor sick woman . . . a dying woman . . . to be so guarded. Jamie, it is mayhap my last request to you.'

'No . . . no. You will soon be better. Dearest sister, I will do all that you ask. I will have the midwife sent to you as soon as she comes. I will see what may be done about clearing the staircases about your apartments.'

'Thank you, Jamie. This would not have happened, would it, had you been here? Oh, what a sad thing it is when a brother and sister fall out. In future, brother, we must understand each other . . . if I live through this.'

'You shall live, and in future there shall be understanding between us. You will be guided by me.'

'Yes, Jamie. How glad I am that you are back!'

The 'midwife' had come. She was a servant of the Huntleys and knew that her task was not to deliver a stillborn child but to take charge of letters the Queen had written and see that they were despatched with all speed to Lords Huntley and Bothwell.

Moray and Morton had decided that if Darnley would stay in the Queen's bedchamber all night, the guards about her apartments could be withdrawn. They trusted Darnley, and in any case the Queen was considered far too sick to leave her bed.

In the evening all the lords retired from the palace to Douglas House, the home of Morton, which was but a short step from the palace. There they could feast and talk of the success of their schemes and make future plans.

As soon as they had gone and the sentries had been withdrawn, Mary rose and dressed hastily. Darnley had changed sides completely now that she had inspired him with fear and had promised him a return to her favour. After the child was born they would live as husband and wife again. He had learned a bitter lesson, Mary said; she hoped that in future they would trust each other.

She had satisfied him that the lords who held them prisoners represented but a small proportion of the population. Had he forgotten what had happened when they had married and Moray had believed he would raise all Scotland against her! Who had mustered the stronger force then! She assured him that all he had to do was escape with her from the palace and join Bothwell and Huntley, who were mustering their forces at this very time. Darnley would be a fool if he did not join her, for her friends would have no mercy on him if he did not. Those with whom he had temporarily cast in his lot would have no further use for him either.

So, trembling, Darnley agreed to deceive the lords, who were feasting and congratulating themselves in Douglas House; he would escape with Mary from Holyrood and ride away.

'Now,' said the Queen.

She was wrapped in a heavy cloak. She stood up firmly. The child was quiet now; it was almost as though it shared the suspense.

'Down the back staircase,' said Mary. 'Through the pantries and the kitchens where the French are. The French will not betray us . . . even if they see us. We can rely on their friendship.'

With wildly beating hearts they crept down the narrow staircase, through the kitchens and underground passages to one of the pantries, the door of which opened on to the burial ground.

Darnley gasped. 'Not that way!' he cried.

'Where else?' demanded Mary contemptuously. 'Will you come or will you stay behind to share David's fate?'

Darnley still hesitated, his face deathly pale in the moonlight. He was terrified of going on, yet he had no alternative but to follow her, and as he stumbled forward he all but fell into a newly-made grave.

He shrieked, and Mary turned to bid him be silent.

'Jesus!' she cried, looking down into the grave. 'It is David who lies there.'

Darnley's limbs trembled so that he could not proceed. 'It's an omen!' he whispered.

In that moment Mary seemed to see anew the terrified eyes of David as he had been dragged across the floor. Angrily she turned on her husband: 'Mayhap, it is,' she said 'Mayhap David watches us now . . . and remembers. . . .'

'No . . . no . . .' groaned Darnley. ''Twas no fault of mine. . . .'

'This is not the time,' said Mary, turning and hurrying forward.

He followed her across the grisly burial ground, picking his way between the tombs and shuddering as he caught glimpses of half buried coffins.

On the far edge of the burial ground Erskine was waiting with horses. Silently they mounted, Mary riding pillion with Erskine.

'Make haste!' cried Darnley, now longing above all things to put as great a distance as possible between himself and the grim graveyard. He imagined David's ghost had been startled from his grave and caused him to stumble there. Terror overwhelmed him–terror of the dead and of the living.

They rode on through the quiet night, but Erskine's horse with its royal burden could not make the speed which Darnley wanted.

'Hasten, I say!' he cried impatiently. ''Tis dangerous to delay.'

'My lord, I dare not,' said Erskine.

'There is the child to consider,' cried Mary. 'We go as fast as is safe for it.'

'They'll murder us if they catch us, you fools!' cried Darnley.

'I would rather be murdered than kill our child.'

'In God's name that's folly. What is one child? If it should die this night, there'll be others to replace it. Come on, man. Come on, I say. Or I'll have you clapped in jail as soon as we are out of this.'

Mary said: 'Heed him not. I would have you think of the child.'

'Yes, Madam,' said Erskine.

Darnley shouted: 'Then tarry and be murdered. I'll not.'

And with that he whipped up his horse and went ahead with all speed, so that soon he was lost to sight.

Mary felt the tears smarting in her eyes, but they were tears of shame for the man she had married. She was not afraid any more. In moments such as this one, when she was threatened with imminent danger, she felt a noble courage rise within her. It was at such times that she felt herself to be queen in very truth. She had duped Darnley; she had lured him to desert her enemies. she had foiled the plots of Moray and the scheming Morton. Once again, she believed, she had saved her crown.

Oh, but the humiliation of owning that foolish boy for a husband! For that she could die of shame. He was not only a fool; he was a coward.

How she wished that he could have been a strong man, a brave man on whom she could rely. Then she would not have cared what misfortunes befell them; they would have faced them and conquered them together.

After many hours in the saddle, just as the dawn was breaking, Erskine called to her that they could not be far from the safety of Dunbar Castle.

A short while after, he told her that he saw riders. Mary raised her weary eyelids. One man had ridden ahead of the rest. He brought his horse alongside that which carried the Queen. She looked with relief and admiration at this man who reminded her, by the very contrast, of the husband whom she despised.

She greeted him: 'I was never more glad to see you, Lord Bothwell.'

Chapter Four

The June night was hot and the Queen lay tossing on her bed. She had suffered much during the last months, but now her greatest ordeal was upon her.

Her women were waiting now, and she knew that they did not expect her to leave her bed alive.

She was weary. Since the death of David she had become increasingly aware of the villainies of those about her; she could put no great trust in anyone. Even now, in the agony of a woman in childbirth who has suffered a painful pregnancy, she could not dismiss from her mind the thought of those hard, relentless men. Ruthven was dead; he had died in exile; but his son would be a trouble-maker like his father. Morton, Lindsay, George Douglas, Boyd, Argyle were all traitors. Moray, her own brother, she knew, had been privy to the plot, and the plot had been not only to murder David Rizzio, but to destroy her. Maitland of Lethington—her finest statesman, a man whose services she needed, a man who had always shown a gentle courtesy which she had not often received from others—was of doubtful loyalty. He had fled to the Highlands with Atholl–surely a proof that he was not without guilt.

These men were dangerous, but there was one, the thought of whom depressed her so much that she felt she would welcome death. Why had she married Darnley whom she was beginning to hate more than she had believed it was possible to hate anyone?

He was loyal to nobody. He betrayed all those with whom he had worked against David. Now he was in a state of torment lest she pardon those lords who were in exile and they return to take their revenge on one who had turned informer. He sulked and raged in turn; he whimpered and blustered; he cringed and demanded his rights. She could not bear him near her.

It was an unhealthy state of affairs. It was true that with the followers mustered by Huntley and Bothwell she had returned triumphant to Edinburgh, and the lords responsible for Rizzio's murder–with the exception of Moray who, she must feign to believe, was innocent of complicity–had all hastened to hide themselves. Some minor conspirators had been hanged, drawn and quartered–a proceeding which she deplored for its injustice, but which she was powerless to prevent. Bothwell was in command and, although he was the bravest man in Scotland, as a statesman he could not measure up to Maitland or Moray.

So she made her will and thought of death without any great regret.

She had failed; she saw that now. If only she could go back one year; if only she could go back to the July day when she had walked into the chapel at Holyroodhouse and joined her future fortunes with those of Darnley! How differently she would act and how different her life might consequently be!

She would have come to understand that she could have rallied her people to her and deprived her brother of his power. She had to be strong, but there was this terrible burden to hinder her; she had married the most despicable man in Scotland and he had all but ruined her.

But now the pains were on her and it was as though a curtain was drawn, shutting out those grim faces which tormented her; but the curtain was made of pain.

Between bouts of pain she noticed that her dear ones were about her. There was Beaton who suffered with her. Poor Beaton! Thomas Randolph had been sent back to England in disgrace, for he had been discovered to be trafficking with the rebels and exposed–not only as a spy for his mistress, which was understandable–but as one who worked against the Queen with her Scottish enemies. Poor Beaton! thought Mary. Like myself she is unlucky where she has placed her affections. There was dear Flem on the other side of her–heartbroken because Maitland had fled from the Court. Sempill was in disgrace and dearest Livy was with him.

But for the murder of David they would all be happy. And but for Darnley's treachery David would be alive now.

I hate the father of this child! reflected Mary. Evil things are said of me. There is doubtless whispering in the corridors now. Who is the father of the Prince or Princess who is about to be born–Darnley or David? Who is it–the King or the Secretary? That was what people were asking one another.

Darnley might be with them when they whispered, and it would depend on his mood of the moment whether he defended or defamed her.

'Why did I marry such a man?' she asked herself. Now that I am near dying I know that I can only wish to live if he should be taken from me.

Beaton was putting a cup to her lips.

'Beaton . . .' began Mary.

'Do not speak, dearest,' said Beaton. 'It exhausts you. Save your strength for the child.'

Save your strength for the child! Do not fritter away your strength in hating the child's father.

There came to her then that strength which never failed her in moments of peril. She battled her way through pain.

At last, from what seemed far away, she heard the cry of a child.

Mary Beaton was excitedly running from the apartment crying: 'It is over. All is well. The Queen is delivered of a fair son.'

Her son was born–that child who, she prayed, would unite her tortured land with the kingdom beyond the Border; for she knew that there could be no real peace between them until they were joined as one country under one sovereign. Her kingdom must be held for him as well as for herself.

There was one thing she must make sure of immediately. It should not be said that this little James Stuart was a bastard. Rumours of bastardy meant trouble in the life of a would-be king.

Already she had noticed the scrutiny of those who studied the baby. She saw the faint twitch of the lips, the appraising gaze. Now who does he resemble? Is it Darnley? Are his eyes particularly large? I wonder if he will be a skilled musician?

Her first task was not a pleasant one. She must feign friendship with her husband. She must not allow him to pour poison into people's ears, for he would do that even though it was clear that by so doing he injured himself.

She called Darnley to her in the presence of all the people who crowded the chamber and said in a loud voice: 'My lord, you have come to see our child. Look into his bonny face. God has blessed you and me with a son, and this son is begotten by none but you.'

Darnley bent over the child. She was implying that she knew what slander had been spread. He was afraid of her and all that she could do to punish him. He was afraid of those lords who were implicated in the Rizzio plot. They were now in exile, but once let them return, and he feared that his position would be as perilous as David's had been. He was uncertain how to act. At times he felt he must cringe before his wife; at others he wished to show that he cared nothing for her; but when she confronted him with a serious matter such as this, he was always at a loss.

Mary looked from her husband, who had bent over the child, to those lords who stood by watching. She said in a loud ringing voice: 'I swear before God, as I shall answer to Him on the day of judgment, that this is your son and that of no other man. I wish all gentlemen and ladies here to mark my words. I say–and God bear me witness–that this child is so much your son that I fear the worse for him.'

She turned to the nobleman nearest her bed.

'I hope,' she said, 'that this child will unite two kingdoms, my own and that of England, for I hold that only in such union can peace be established between the two countries.'

'Let us hope,' said Moray, 'that the child will inherit these two kingdoms after yourself. You could not wish him to succeed before his mother and father.'

'His father has broken with me,' said Mary sadly.

Darnley stuttered: 'You cannot say that! You swore that all should be forgiven and forgotten, that it should be between us as it was in the beginning.'

'I may have forgiven,' said Mary, 'but how can I forget? Your accomplices would have done me to death, remember . . . and not only me . . . but this child you now see before you.'

'But that is all over now.'

'It is all over and I am tired. I wish to be left alone with my son.'

She turned wearily from him, and silently the lords and ladies filed out of the bedchamber.

While Mary slept the whispering continued through the castle.

She had sworn that Darnley was the father. Would she have sworn that if it were not true? Would she have called God to witness if David had been the father?

Surely not, for her condition was not a healthy one; and the chances that she would die were great.

But whatever was said in the Castle of Edinburgh, and whatever was said in the streets of the capital, there would always be those to ask themselves–Who is the father of the Prince–Darnley or David?

She had two objects in life now–to care for her baby and to escape from her husband. He was constantly beside her–pleading, threatening. He was no longer indifferent. He fervently wished to be her husband in fact. She must not lock him from her bedchamber, he cried. She must not set guards at the door for fear he tried to creep on her unaware.

He would cry before her, thumping his fists on his knees like a spoiled child. 'Why should I be denied your bed? Am I not your husband? What did you promise me when you persuaded me to fly with you? You said we should be together. And it was all lies . . . lies to make me the enemy of Morton and Ruthven. You took their friendship from me and you gave me nothing in return.'

'I give nothing for nothing,' she said contemptuously. 'They never had any friendship for you.'

'You are cruel . . . cruel. Who is your lover now? A woman like you must have a lover. Do not imagine I shall not discover who he is.'

'You know nothing of me,' she told him. 'But learn this one thing and learn it for all time. I despise you. You nauseate me. I would rather have a toad in my bed than you.'

'It was not always so. Nor would it be so. How have I changed? There was a time when you could scarcely wait for me. Do not think I do not remember how eager you were . . . more eager than I.'

'That is done with. I do not excuse my own folly. I merely tell you that I now see you as you really are, and I shudder to have you near me.'

These quarrels were the talk of the Court. Darnley himself made no secret of them. When he was drunk he would grow maudlin over his memories. He would confide in his companions details of the Queen's passion which had now turned to loathing. Sometimes he wanted to kill somebody . . . anybody. He wanted to kill Bothwell who was now high in the Queen's favour, and had been since the death of David. Some said that Bothwell would take David's place; and it did seem that the Earl was more arrogant than ever. Some said Moray would be the one to take David's place. The Queen did not trust him, but his standing in the country was firm.

Darnley was afraid of Bothwell. The Earl had a habit of inviting his enemies to single combat, so Darnley shifted his gaze from Bothwell to Moray. Moray was a statesman rather than a fighter. Darnley felt that in single combat he would be better matched with Moray than with Bothwell.

He began to brood on the influence Moray had with the Queen; he remembered that Moray had been against the marriage in the first place.

He burst in on Mary one evening in August and cried out that he was tired of being left out of affairs, and he would no longer stand by and allow insults to be heaped upon him.

Mary took little notice of such outbursts. She was playing chess with Beaton, and went on with the game.

Darnley kicked a stool across the apartment.

'Your move, Beaton,' said Mary.

'Listen to me!' roared Darnley.

Mary said: 'I've got you, I think, Beaton my dear. Two moves back you had a chance.'

'Stop it!' cried Darnley. 'Stop ignoring me. Come here. Come here at once. I tell you, I'm tired of being treated thus. You will come with me now . . . and we will resume our normal relations. . . .'

'Will you leave this apartment,' said the Queen, rising from the chess-table, 'or shall I have you forcibly removed?'

'Listen to me. If it were not for my enemies I should have my rights. I should be King of this realm. I should be master in our apartments. I would not allow you to turn me out. . . .'

'Oh dear,' sighed Mary, 'this is very tiresome. We have heard all this before, and we are weary of the repetition.'

There was one thing which infuriated him beyond endurance, and that was not to be treated seriously. He drew his sword and cried: 'Ere long you will see that I am not ineffectual. When I bring you your brother's bleeding head, you will know what I mean. He is against me. He always has been. I am going to kill Moray. I shall waste no more time.' With that he rushed from the room.

Mary sat down and buried her face in her hands. 'I can't help it,' she sobbed. 'He fills me with such shame. I wish to God I had never seen him. I would to God someone would rid me of him. Beaton . . . I doubt that he will attempt anything, but go at once to my brother and tell him in my name what he has said. He had better be warned for if aught should happen to James it would doubtless be said that I had a hand in it.'

Mary Beaton hurried to do her bidding while Mary sat back and stared helplessly at the chessboard. She might pretend indifference to him, but how could she be indifferent? All that he did humiliated her beyond expression.

Oh God, she thought, how I hate him!

Moray knew well how to deal with Darnley and his folly.

Calmly he summoned Darnley to appear before him and a company of the most important of the lords at the Court. Darnley, afraid to refuse to appear, went reluctantly and was put through an examination by Moray himself who forced him to confess that he had uttered threats against him. Darnley blustered and denied this, until witnesses were brought who had overheard his words to the Queen.

Always at a loss in a crisis Darnley lied and blustered and was easily proved to be both lying and blustering. He looked at the cold faces of his accusers and knew that they were his enemies. . . . He broke down and sobbed out that everyone was against him.

Had he spoken threats against Moray? they insisted.

Yes . . . yes . . . he had, and they all hated him; they were all jealous of him because the queen had chosen to marry him; and although she appeared to hate him now, once it had been a very different story.

'I must ask you,' said Moray, 'to withdraw those threats and to swear before these gentlemen that you will not attempt to murder either me or any of those whom you believe to be your enemies. If you will not do this, it will be necessary to place you under arrest immediately.'

He was beaten and he knew it. They were too clever for him. He had to submit. He had to ask Moray's pardon; he had to swear not to be foolish again.

They despised him; they had made that clear. They did not think it worth while to arrest him; they did not want to punish him; they merely wished to make him look a fool.

Mary was able to forget her unhappiness for a time. Something rather pleasant had happened. Her dear Beaton, after being miserable on the banishment of Randolph, had fallen in love.

Mary was happy about this. It seemed a charming solution to something which had worried her. She wished she could have overlooked Randolph's perfidy for the sake of poor Beaton. But that could not be, and the man had had to go; but now Beaton was in love again and this time it was with Alexander Ogilvie of Boyne.

This was a particularly happy state of affairs, for Mary had given her consent to the marriage of Bothwell with Jean Gordon, and Jean Gordon had once been promised to this very Alexander Ogilvie. He must have recovered from the loss of Jean, for now he seemed eager to marry Mary Beaton.

She told Bothwell of this. 'I am so happy about it. Mary Beaton is such a charming girl, and I am glad to see her so happy. I shall have the marriage contract drawn up at once.'

'I see, Madam,' said Bothwell. 'Was this Ogilvie not the man to whom my wife was once promised?'

'Did you not remember then? It is the very same. Ah, my lord, I expect you have made dear Jean forget she ever had a fancy for this man.'

She wondered how Jean enjoyed being married to the man. She had heard rumours that he had not mended his ways since marriage. But, she thought comfortably, Jean would know how to deal with trouble of that sort.

She gave herself up to the pleasure of preparing for Beaton's marriage. There was one who was a little saddened by the prospect of another marriage. Poor Flem! Maitland was still in exile. Flem talked of him often, pointing out to the Queen that he was her best statesman, demanding to know if it was not folly to keep in exile a great man whose one desire was to work for his Queen.

'Dear Flem,' said Mary, 'I can understand your feelings. Maitland *is* charming and clever. I know that. But if he were not involved in the murder of poor David, why did he find it necessary to go away?'

'Madam, he knew that Bothwell was his enemy and he also knew that you trusted Bothwell more than any man.'

'Happily would I have trusted Maitland if he would have allowed me to.'

'Dearest, you could trust him. He is your loyal subject and you need him.

You know that none has his subtle cleverness. You know he is the greatest statesman in this country.'

'I believe you are right in that, Flem.'

'Then, dear Madam, forgive him–if there is anything to forgive. Recall him. You know that he was no friend to Morton and Ruthven. Oh, it is true that he did not care for David. Remember he was your first minister, before David took his place in your trust. And why did David take his place? Only because Lord Maitland was doing you good service in England, to which country you sent him knowing that he could serve you at the English Court more wisely than any of your subjects.'

'You are a good advocate, Flem, and I will think about it. I believe it is very likely that I shall recall the fellow.'

'Dearest . . .'

'Oh, I do not think that he is without blame. But you must keep him in order if I allow him to return, and you must warn him that he must be as faithful to me as his wife is, and that it is due to my love for her that I pass over his disaffection.'

Flem kissed her mistress's hand and went on kissing it.

Bothwell heard rumours that Maitland was about to be recalled. He cursed aloud. He did not like Maitland. The suave courtier was too cunning for him. He feared that if Maitland returned to Court it would not be long–with the influence of Mary Fleming–before some charge would be raked up against Bothwell which might result in his falling from the Queen's favour. He did not forget Maitland's share in bringing about his exile from the Court. He also suspected Maitland had played some part–though perhaps a small one–in the plot to poison him. They were natural enemies, and he must do all he could to prevent his return to Court.

He wondered how he should proceed. What he needed was a secret audience with the Queen. He decided that if he could only be alone with her, he could talk more freely and make his arguments more plausible without interruption. The Queen was but a lass, in his opinion–rather emotional and sentimental. He believed that if he could explain how Maitland had always been his enemy, how the fellow had not always been a faithful supporter of the Queen, how he, Bothwell, had never once failed her when danger threatened, there might yet be time to dissuade her from bringing Maitland back to Court.

He knew that in a few days the Queen would be going to the Exchequer House–a small dwelling in Edinburgh which was next to one occupied by a man who had been a servant of his. To this small house Mary was going to check some of her accounts and make arrangements for the clothes which would be needed for her son's christening. She wanted to be alone for a few days–apart from an attendant woman and one servant–so that she could not only go into this matter of accounts but come to a decision as to who should be given the guardianship of the young Prince.

Everything seemed to be working in Bothwell's favour. He believed that at the Exchequer House it would not be a difficult matter to obtain a private interview with Mary.

He would not ask for it in case it should be denied to him. Mary would guess what he wished to say and, characteristically, would not wish him to say it. Doubtless Mary Fleming had swayed her one way, and she would be afraid that he would attempt to sway her another. Mary would wish to please them both and, since she could not in this instance give him his wish, she would do all in her power to avoid seeing him.

He understood her very well–a sentimental lassie who was no match for the wily wolves who prowled about her. Therefore she should have a private interview with him, not knowing that it would take place until it was forced upon her. For his purpose she could not have chosen to go to a better place than the Exchequer House–indeed this idea would not have come to him had she not been going there.

David Chambers, who had been one of his superior servants, was the man who lived next door to the Exchequer House; and the gardens of these two houses were separated by a high wall, but in this high wall was a door which made it easy to pass from one to the other. David Chambers had done good service to his master, and Bothwell had rewarded him well. Many a woman had entertained Bothwell at the house of Chambers; and if Bothwell desired to meet a certain woman he merely told Chambers this, and Chambers arranged a meeting. Chambers' house had proved for some time a useful place of assignation.

Moreover the two servants who were with the Queen at the Exchequer House were the Frenchman, Bastian, and Lady Reres. Bastian need not be considered; he would be lodged in the lower part of the house. As for Lady Reres, by great good fortune, she had been Margaret Beaton, sister to Janet, and on his visits to Janet there had been times when–perhaps he had called unexpectedly–only Margaret had been there to entertain him. Margaret, who was very like her sister, had proved an excellent substitute, a sensible creature, ready for the fun of the moment and not one to bear a grudge. Women, such as the Beaton sisters, were the best friends a man could have. Passionate women, such as Anna Throndsen, could cause a great deal of trouble. He was thankful now that Anna had gone back to Denmark, leaving their son behind to be cared for by his mother's servants. But he need not think of Anna now. All he need concern himself with was the fact that Margaret Beaton, now Lady Reres, was to be the lady-in-waiting to the Queen in the small house, and that he had easy access to that house through his servant David Chambers.

It was all very easy to arrange. He went through the door in the wall and asked Bastian to bring Lady Reres to him and to keep his coming a secret. Lady Reres soon appeared. She was heartily glad–and very amused–to see him.

She wanted to know what devilment he planned.

'Merely to see the Queen. A matter of some importance. What I want is a secret interview and do not think I can get it when she is living in state. So I chose this time when she is living here in seclusion for a few days. Margaret, could you take me to her?'

'I will ask if she will see you.'

'That will not do. She will say no. She will send for the ministers or her courtiers or someone. This is a secret matter, and I wish none to hear it but herself.'

'My lord, you ask too much.'

'Not from you, Margaret.' He pushed her playfully against the wall. 'Remember the good times we had?'

'Well, they are over,' said plump Lady Reres with a laugh.

'Never to be forgotten by either of us.'

'Why should you choose to remember me out of the six thousand . . . or have I been niggardly in the counting?'

'I have not kept the score, but you are one I remember well.'

Lady Reres laughed again. 'I would, of course, help you all I could. But how can I let you into her apartment? I tell you she is alone here, apart from myself and Bastian. What will she say to me when she knows I have allowed you to come in?'

'She need not know. You need not let me in. But leave her alone after supper this evening and leave the door open. I will slip up by the back stairs. You will be discussing next day's supper with Bastian in the lower part of the house and thus not hear me.'

'We are responsible for the safety of the Queen.'

'Do you think I would hurt the Queen? I tell you it is a matter of great importance . . . a state matter. It is imperative that I see her . . . for her sake as well as mine. Now, will you keep my secret? Say nothing to her, leave her after supper, and see that the way is clear for me.'

'I don't like it.'

'But you will do it for an old friend?'

'I know nothing of it, remember.'

'Why, bless you, Meggie, you know nothing of it. The fault will all be due to my boldness.'

He gave her a loud kiss of gratitude, and she went away thinking of him nostalgically as he used to be in the old days when he came to see Janet. He had changed, she supposed. He was more interested in state matters. His marriage had mayhap sobered him. Ah! They had been good times. She felt young again thinking of them.

The Queen had supped in her small bedchamber and the remains of the meal were still on the table. She was very tired and glad to be alone, free from ceremony for a few days.

She was wearing a velvet robe–loose-fitting–and her chestnut hair hung loose for the weather was warm. It was a comfort to be able to dress thus.

Suddenly she heard a step on the stair. It must be Margaret returning. She was thinking: We shall be leaving here perhaps the day after tomorrow, but there is still another day in which to live quietly.

The door opened and she started up in amazement, for Lord Bothwell was standing on the threshold.

'Lord Bothwell!' she cried.

'Yes, Madam.' He bowed.

'How did you get in here? Why did you not give notice of your coming?'

'I will explain,' he said.

She was angry because now in this small room in this small house his arrogance seemed more in evidence than ever.

'I wish to hear no explanations,' she said. 'I will call Bastian to show you out.'

He did not move. He stood by the door as though barring her way.

'Lord Bothwell,' she said, 'what is the meaning of this?'

He did not speak. He was looking at her flushed face, her disordered hair. He was looking at her as he had never looked before. In that moment she was afraid of him. She would have pushed past him, but he caught her. His grip hurt and she cried out, trying to twist her arm free.

She stammered: 'This . . . this unwarranted . . . insolence. . . . How . . . how dare you! You shall suffer for this.'

He had gripped her by the shoulders and bent her backward.

'Shall I?' he said. His eyes were glazed; they looked dazzling in his sunburned weather-beaten face. 'Then there shall be something worth suffering for.'

'You come here,' she panted. 'You come in . . . unannounced. . . . Release me at once. You shall pay dearly for this.'

Bothwell was the Borderer now; the statesman had fled. He had forgotten that he had come to talk about Maitland. He had been in situations of a similar nature before. He had felt this wild excitement, the demand for satisfaction at all costs. But this was different; this was piquant; this was more exciting than those other occasions. Many women had partnered Bothwell in such scenes, but never a Queen before this.

He cared for nothing now but the surrender of the woman. If it meant death, it must go on now. It was the first time he had seen her, stripped of her royalty. It was the first time he had discovered what a very desirable woman she was.

He pulled her towards him and roughly caressed her body. Mary was trembling with rage and sobbing with terror. She knew that this encounter had cast its warning over her many a time. It was the meaning of those insolent looks. He would treat her now as he would any peasant over the Border. He cared nothing for the fact that she was the Queen. There was only one thing that was of importance to him; the satisfaction of his vile nature.

She kicked and tried to bite. It was all she could do for she was pinioned. He had turned and, holding her firmly with one arm locked the door.

She stammered: 'This . . . this . . . outrage. . . . It is the most monstrous thing that ever happened to me. . . .'

'It will also be the most enjoyable,' he said.

'You will lose your head for this.'

'No,' he said. 'You have never had a lover yet, my Queen. Wait . . . have patience. . . . Don't fight . . . and then the sooner will you come to pleasure.'

He had torn her robe from her shoulder. She was conscious of her weakness compared with his great strength. He lifted her in his arms then as though he read her thoughts and would stress the fact that she was impotent to resist him.

'It is no use screaming,' he said. 'No one will hear. They'll not break the door down if they do. How could they? Poor Bastian! That feeble Frenchman? Fat Margaret? Have no fear. None shall disturb us.'

'You have gone mad,' she said.

'It *is* a temporary madness, they say.'

'You forget . . . I am the Queen.'

'Let us both forget it. Queens should not bring their royalty to the bedchamber.'

'Put me down. I command you. I beg you.'

'I mean to . . . here on your bed.'

He put her on to it. She tried to scramble up but he had forced her down. She struggled until she was exhausted. The room was spinning round her. She thought afterwards that she fainted for a while. She was not sure. She was aware of his heart and hers beating together . . . heavy, ominous beating.

She had no strength left to hold him off. She lay passive without resistance, without resentment or anger. There was nothing but this extraordinary, overwhelming emotion–this mingling of fury and pleasure, of a terrible shame and an unaccountable joy.

She lay on her bed long after he had gone.

What has happened to me? she asked herself. Why do I not send for Moray? Why do I not order the immediate arrest of Lord Bothwell? On what charge? The rape of the Queen?

She remembered that she would present a strange sight if Lady Reres came to the room. She got up from her bed. She gazed at her torn clothes which he had thrown on to the floor. How explain them? But they would be part of the evidence she would need to bring him to the scaffold. The rape of the Queen! She could hear the words now. She could hear John Knox thundering them from his pulpit. He would say that she had encouraged Bothwell. 'No,' she said aloud as if in answer to his imagined accusation. 'It is not true. I always disliked him. Now I hate him. How dared he? The shame of it . . . the shame of it!'

She could not shut it out of her mind. Every detail was clear in her memory. His face . . . his eyes . . . his hands, tearing her clothes.

'He forced me,' she murmured. 'He dared . . . and I the Queen! By now he will be speeding for the Border. He will be terrified of the punishment, which can be nothing less than death.'

She took the torn clothes and hid them in a closet. She could not bear that anyone else should see the shameful evidence. Hastily she wrapped a damask robe about her, and smoothed her wild hair. Now she felt a little calmer. There were still red patches on her face, on her neck and her body. She touched her left cheek gently. Would those marks never go?

She began to pace up and down the apartment. The Queen who was dishonoured! The Queen who was defiled! He had planned this thing. He had known that she would be here. Moray had said once that David Chambers was his procurer and was known as 'Bothwell's Bawd'. David Chambers brought women to his house and Bothwell went there to visit them. So Chambers had procured the Queen for Bothwell. He would have lent his house for the purpose. Bothwell had clearly come from Chambers' house and, because she was ill-guarded, he had found a way to her apartment.

She would never be able to look the man in the face again. Indeed she would not need to. He should be imprisoned at once and hurried to execution. He should not live to gloat over his conquest. But how could she proclaim the crime to the world? She pictured herself telling Moray. 'He came to my room. I could not hold him off. He forced me. . . .'

She imagined the smiles, the whispers. 'Why did the Queen go to the Exchequer House? Oh, 'tis next door to David Chambers' and he is Bothwell's Bawd.'

'What shall I do?' she whispered to herself. 'What can I do?'

Lady Reres came up to the room. She should reprimand the woman. She had been careless. She and Bastian must have left some door unlatched. But how could she talk to Lady Reres of what had happened? How could she talk of that terrible thing at all?

'Are you disturbed, Madam?' asked Lady Reres.

'Disturbed?' cried the Queen. 'No . . . no. I am feeling tired. I think . . . that I am a little unwell. I feel coming on one of those attacks which I had so often when I was in France.'

'Should I send for a physician, Your Majesty?'

'No . . . no. Rest will suffice. Leave me. I will go to bed. Rest is what I need. I do not wish to be disturbed. Oh . . . but . . . sleep here tonight. I . . . I have a fancy not to be left alone this night.'

Lady Reres drew the curtains and the long night began. She did not sleep at all. She lived through it all again. The opening of the door . . . every detail until that moment when she had found herself alone with her shame and that excitement which made her heart thunder till her body was shaking.

She returned to Holyroodhouse next day. She could not bear to stay in the Exchequer House, although she had not finished the work she had gone there to do.

Bothwell had the effrontery to wait upon her with the other noblemen of the Court.

As he knelt before her, her heart thundered. He had raised his insolent eyes to her face, and his smile was conspiratorial, as though they had shared a charming adventure together.

Her eyes kindled; her temper flared and impulsive words rose to her lips.

Arrest that man! she wanted to say, and was almost on the point of doing so. In time she pictured the ensuing scene. Moray would ask: 'On what grounds, Madam?' 'On the grounds of rape.' 'The rape of whom, Madam?' 'The rape of the Queen.'

There was nothing she could do unless she would expose herself to greater humiliation, and the cunning rogue, the violator of the innocent, knew it. She was conquered in her own Court as she had been in her bedchamber. She dared say nothing. She was afraid. That was the truth. She could not publicly own to her shame. She dared not face the calumnies of Knox. Consequently it seemed that he who had committed this great sin would go unpunished.

But she would find other ways to make him suffer for what he had done. She would find some other way of banishing him from the Court, for his presence there would be a constant reminder.

Even now she could not prevent her thoughts from going over and over what had happened on that night.

He found an opportunity to speak to her. She was tense as he stood beside her. She could almost feel again his hands tearing her clothes, forcing her on to the bed.

He said: 'Now that we are such friends, madam, I wish to ask a favour. Do not grant Maitland permission to return to Court.'

She turned her back. But that, in the presence of the others, was too pointed a rebuff. He had been in such high favour before today. If her manner towards him so obviously changed people would wonder why. They might even guess. That secret must be kept.

She said in a low strained voice: 'You are no friend of mine and never shall be. You need never again make a request to me, for it shall not be granted. You shall lose your head for what you have done. Do not think that because it is still on your shoulders it shall remain there.' It was difficult to put the vehemence she felt into those words, for she must keep her voice very low in case it should be overheard.

'A pity,' he said. 'I fancied you thought my person rather pleasant when we last met.'

'You fancy, my lord,' she answered, and she forced herself to smile, 'that you have behaved in a clever way. You know that I cannot denounce your conduct because of the great shame it has brought me. But do not imagine that will save you.'

'Madam, do not pretend that last night's encounter brought any less pleasure to you than to me. It was startling . . . unexpected. I myself had not planned it, but how happy I am that it happened. There shall now be no holding back of all the joy we shall bring to each other.'

'I have never heard such insolence.'

'You have never had a lover worthy of you before, madam. Startling, is it not? It would be easier to explain if we were alone.'

'I shall see to it that I am never again alone with you. Moreover I shall require you to swear friendship with Lord Maitland when he returns to Court–which he will very soon do.'

He bowed. 'Madam,' he said, 'your wish is law.'

A few days later she returned to the Exchequer House. It was necessary that she should do so for there was much to prepare for the Prince's christening, and as she had undertaken the work, she told herself that she must finish it. She had thought on that never-to-be-forgotten night that she could never bear to be in that room again, that she could never bear to lie on that bed. Oddly enough that was just what she now wished to do.

She could not settle down to her task. She could not decide what clothes must be bought for her servants. She could not decide what she herself should wear. She could only think of Bothwell. I did the only thing possible, she kept telling herself. There was nothing else I could do. How could I have told anyone what occurred?

On the first day of her return to the Exchequer House Lady Reres came to announce that Lord Bothwell was below and wished to see her.

She turned away that Lady Reres might not see her face. 'No, Reres,' she said shortly. 'I'm busy.'

'He said it was a most important matter of state, Madam. He begs you to see him.'

She did not answer, but she thought: I must show him that I have no fear of him. But this time there shall be no locking of the door.

She told Lady Reres that he might come up and state his business if he could do so with brevity.

He stood before her, insolent as ever, towering above her, reminding her of his strength.

'It is a marvellous thing to me,' she said, 'that you dare come to this room again.'

'Madam, I have a fondness for this room. I shall always remember it as the four walls within which I enjoyed the greatest experience of your life.'

'You are unbearably insolent.'

'I but seek to speak the truth, Madam.'

'Lord Bothwell, I will not endure your insolence. I have decided that you shall not escape punishment for what you have done. I cannot proclaim your latest misdeeds to the world since I myself was forced to play such an unhappy part in them.'

'Unhappy! You do not know yourself. You have a great capacity for loving, Madam. You have not realized how great. But I have. Would Your Majesty cast back your thoughts to that night and be entirely honest with yourself? Will you ask yourself whether, when you ceased to fight and began to relax, you found that what I so ardently desired was not Your Majesty's own desire?'

She stared at him. She put out her hands as though to ward him off. He came towards her, ignoring her outstretched hands. There was nothing of the courtier about him. He caught her to him and laughed. Then he bent her backwards and kissed her. Knowledge of the truth came to her then. There was something in herself which called to that in him which was primitive and barbaric.

'Why did you come back to this house?' he whispered. 'Tell me that! Why . . . why?'

She did not answer. She was breathless with agitation and expectation, for it was clear to her now why she had come back. It was to offer this challenge to him. It was to bring him back here again.

He knew her even better than she knew herself.

She had come back because he had set a torch to that desire in her which had been lying dormant. He had provoked a mighty conflagration. She desired him now with an intensity which equalled his. And when two such as they recognized their needs, nothing could restrain them.

She felt herself lifted in his arms. It was happening again . . . not in her imagination, but in reality.

They were lovers now. She could think of little else but Bothwell–the last meeting, the next meeting. The periods between were irksome times of waiting.

Flem had become Lady Maitland of Lethington; Beaton had married Alexander Ogilvie; of the Queen's four Maries there was only Seton left. Yet it did not seem important; no one was important but Bothwell.

Some already knew of the relationship between them. It was impossible to keep it entirely secret; Bastian, her French servant, knew, and so, of course, did Lady Reres. Seton knew. Others whispered that Lord Bothwell seemed to be in high favour with the Queen and it appeared that he would soon be taking the place, in her counsels, of David Rizzio. David's brother, Joseph, was now at Court and Mary had given him a high place. Yet she was scarcely aware of the young man; she was aware of little but Bothwell.

Darnley watched her. He would stay away from Court, sulking in his father's castle; then he would return, coming to her apartments, demanding his rights. He was more despicable to Mary than he had ever been; he seemed quite repulsive. How could I ever have thought I was in love with such a man! she asked herself again and again. It was inexplicable, especially as Lord Bothwell had so often been there for her to see. She had been blind–blind to life, blind to passion, blind to love.

Now she had miraculously lost her blindness. This was living. This was what she had been born for.

Darnley was frightened. Maitland was back at Court, and Maitland was one of those lords who had felt it necessary to leave Court after the murder of Rizzio. This was but a beginning, thought Darnley. He knew that Moray and Maitland would now urge the Queen to pardon Morton, young Ruthven and the rest of them, restore their estates and bring them back to Court. And when they came, what would be their first action?

Darnley was a fool, but any fool would know the answer.

He had been present at the murder of Rizzio; he had given his support to the murderers; the murder had been done in his name–out of his jealousy of the Queen. Yet he had turned traitor. He had changed sides at the crucial moment, so the plot had failed in some way. Rizzio had died, it was true, but the Queen had escaped. She had gathered her followers about her and, with Huntley and Bothwell, had returned to Edinburgh triumphant; the murderers, in spite of all their elaborate plans, had been defeated and forced into exile. And who was to blame? Darnley!

They would never forget and they would never forgive.

And soon the drama would be enacted all over again; but in place of Rizzio there would be Darnley.

If and when the lords returned, he dared not stay. And Maitland was already back.

He was frantic. He began to make plans. He would get into touch with the Pope; he would write to Philip of Spain. After all, was he not a good Catholic–a better Catholic than Mary with her talk of tolerance. Good Catholics did not talk of tolerance. Why should he not procure the support of the Catholic world? Why should he not usurp Mary's throne? Perhaps one day he would be King, not only of Scotland but of England as well. Moreover he was the father of the undisputed heir.

Lennox, his father, was alarmed on hearing of his plans–for Darnley had to confide in someone, and the only person whom he could trust was his father.

'But, my son,' said the Earl of Lennox, 'this is ridiculous. The Pope would not aid you, and the King of Spain is a cautious man. He would not support a rebel such as you would be.'

'A rebel! I am the King.'

'In name only. The Crown Matrimonial has never been bestowed on you.'

'It is so unjust. I was promised. And first Rizzio frustrated me . . . and now it is Moray and Bothwell. Maitland is back. My old enemy. He will kill me. I know he will. He will bring the murderer Morton back, and together they will kill me.'

Lennox, in great agitation on account of his son's hysteria, wrote to the Queen telling her that Darnley proposed leaving Scotland for Spain.

Mary sent for her husband. He came, ill at ease.

'What are these wild plans of yours?' she demanded.

'I shall not tell you.'

'Henry, I insist.'

'Why should I stay here?' he screamed. 'What am I? You only want me to stay because you fear the scandal my departure would give rise to. Take me back. I demand to be taken back. I wish to be your husband in very truth. Let me stay with you, share your bed and board. Then you shall not have a more faithful servant.' He threw himself at her and tried to put his arms about her. She drew back in disgust.

'Mary . . . Mary,' he pleaded. 'You used to love me. You used to come to my chamber because, you said, you wanted us to be alone even if it was only for a little while.'

She pushed him away. She hated to remember those times; and even now she was comparing him with another. She would never allow Darnley to touch her.

She said: 'If you attempt to put your hands on me I shall call the guards.'

He whimpered: 'What have I done? How have I changed? You used to be eager for me.'

'If you say that again you will regret it.'

'But I will say it . . . I *will*!'

'Go quietly now or I shall call the guards. In the morning you may state your case before the lords of the Court.'

He had no help for it but to go; and in the morning he faced them nervously–Moray and Maitland among them, those two who hated him and he believed sought to destroy him, those two who would not be satisfied until they had brought his enemies back to Court.

Moray did not intend to spare him, nor did Maitland. The cold eyes of Moray, the sarcastic ones of Maitland frightened him. He scraped his feet on the floor and scowled at his toes.

Why was he going to run away? they demanded.

He did not know. He wanted to leave Scotland, that was all. He did not now think he would go after all. It was just to make the Queen understand how badly she treated her husband.

'It would be a treasonable act,' said Moray, 'to leave Scotland for Spain. For what purpose did you intend to go?'

'To . . . to bring the Queen back to her duty. . . . To be received back in her favour. . . .'

'It is hardly the way,' said Maitland suavely, 'to win the Queen's favour–by playing traitor to her.'

'I am not a traitor. I am no traitor!' screamed Darnley.

Mary could bear no more. There was nothing she wanted so much as to be rid of Darnley. She was filled with shame whenever she was forced to look at him.

She said: 'If he gives his word not to leave Scotland, we will pardon him . . . providing he returns to his father's castle . . . and stays there.'

Darnley's face was white with rage, but he trembled with fear as he turned from the watching group and, shouting: 'Goodbye, Madam. You shall not see my face for a long time!' he hurried away.

It was October and the mist lay thick across the land, when news came of Border fighting near the town of Jedburgh. Bothwell left Court and galloped south at the head of his men.

Mary was desolate. She had begged him to let someone else go, for she could not exist without him; but he had laughed at the idea. The Border was his domain. If there were trouble there, who should be at hand but Bothwell? Then she began to understand the difference in their passion. She realized that she did not mean as much to him as he did to her.

He *wanted* to ride away. The excitement of battle called him as lust had called him in the room at the Exchequer House.

She was frantic with anxiety and jealousy. He would doubtless call at one of his castles before returning, and he would see his wife. She visualized Jean Gordon–not exactly a comely woman–oval face, sandy hair, and the long Gordon nose; yet it was said that in the early days of his marriage Bothwell had been more faithful to Jean Gordon than to any woman.

But not now, she assured herself. He would come straight back to the Court. He must. Why had she not made him promise not to go to his home? Because one did not, she had also realized, command Bothwell in such matters. She knew that to have asked him not to visit Jean would have put it into his mind to do so. But if he was not the man to make such promises, neither was he the man to deceive her. If he had thought of seeing Jean he would have boldly said so. It was his arrogant and most disconcerting boldness that she loved. These were a symbol of his independence. It showed her clearly that she, the Queen, needed him, more than he needed her.

How long would he stay? Until he wished to return?

Why did I let him go? she asked herself. The answer was: You could do no other. None could hold Bothwell against his wish.

With what joy she discovered that there was an assize at Jedburgh which she should attend! With what joy she set out on the journey!

She had a perfectly reasonable excuse for going to him, for her duties as Queen demanded her presence in Jedburgh. Fate was being good to her at last.

Seton watched her with some anxiety as they set out.

Never, thought Seton, had she looked so beautiful. She had changed since her association with Bothwell; she had become feverishly gay. But would it last? wondered Seton. Bothwell was not the man she would have chosen for Mary. There was no tenderness in him; there was instead a ruthlessness and a primitive appetite. What did he really feel for Mary beyond his lust? There were times when Seton thought she would like to see the peace of a nunnery because the outside world made her so unhappy.

Meanwhile they rode towards Jedburgh, but before they reached that town the news was brought to them. Mary saw the man as he rode towards them and her heart leaped, for she knew him as one of Bothwell's men.

'What news?' she cried. 'What news?'

'Bad news, Your Majesty.'

Her hand tightened on her reins. 'Bothwell?' she gasped.

It seemed as though the man took a long time to answer. 'It was John Elliot of the Park . . . the notorious highwayman, Your Majesty. My lord heard that he was in the neighbourhood and went out to get him. The highwayman was wounded, but . . . not seriously. . . . He turned on my lord, and . . .'

'And . . . killed him?' murmured Mary.

Seton was beside her, her gentle eyes pleading: Not here . . . do not betray yourself here before these people. You loved him. . . . He was everything to you . . . but do not betray yourself here before these witnesses.

'So Bothwell is killed,' said Mary blankly. She looked at Seton, pleading for help. I am lost. I care for nothing. I wish it were I who had died.

Seton said: 'It is a great shock. Her Majesty has not been well of late. I think we should rest here for a while before continuing our journey.'

Seton escorted her to the chamber which had been prepared for her and lay down beside her on the bed, putting her arms about her; they did not weep; they lay close together while Seton stroked the Queen's hair. At length the Queen said: 'There is nothing to live for, Seton. I wish that I were dead.'

She did not know how she sat through the assize. She supposed she conducted herself with outward calm, for none seemed to realize the tumult within her. The strain was so great that at times she seemed near to fainting. The old gnawing pain was back in her side.

She was lenient as she always was with offenders. She wanted to help all those who suffered. And all the time she was thinking: I wish I were dead instead of him. How I wish it was I who died.

When the assize was over there came a messenger from Bothwell's Castle of Hermitage. He was not dead, said the messenger, though so seriously wounded that death seemed inevitable. Then she was filled with hope. She would go to him at once. She would *make* him live. She tried to hide her joy; she said calmly: 'He has received his hurt in my service, and I myself must see that all that can be done for his comfort shall be done.'

So she set out from Jedburgh to the Castle of Hermitage, and there she saw him. He was wounded in the thigh, the head and one of his hands; and so severe were these wounds that they would have killed an ordinary man. But he bore them with ease. He lay looking at her, and the old insolent look was in his eyes. They seemed to grin at her below the bandage.

'Thank God you are alive!' cried Mary.

Even as she spoke she fell fainting to the floor. The strain of the last few days had been too much for her. She had sat through the assizes believing her lover dead; she had not been allowed to show her grief because their union was not a regular one, and the need for secrecy had made her burden the harder to bear. And now that she saw him lying very badly wounded, yet still with more vitality than that of ordinary men, now that she knew she might not lose him, the tension snapped. In the days that followed she was as near death as he was.

She lay at Jedburgh in the house of Lady Fernyhirst whither she had been carried in a litter, and a terrible melancholy filled her.

I love him, she mused, but what am I to him? One of the thousands who have amused him for a while. I, who am a Queen, am but a light woman to him.

She had a husband; he had a wife. What hope was there that they could ever marry? Marriage with him was what Mary desired beyond all things. Only that could comfort her and give her peace. She longed to end her adulterous association, but she could only end it by making it legal.

During those days at Jedburgh she believed she was dying. So did Moray. He began helping himself to some of the precious silver in Holyrood. For more than a week she lay close to death. Bothwell was brought to the same house, but although he had been severely wounded, owing to his amazing vitality, there was no doubt after the first days that he would live.

Mary lay in the room above his, thinking of him constantly while John Hume, her player on the lute, and James Heron, her player on the pipe tried to beguile her with sweet music. But the music no longer charmed; she could only think of Darnley and Jean Gordon who stood between her and her lover. She planned the new dress she would have when she rose from her bed; it should contain twenty ells of red silk, four ells of taffaty and three ells of finest black velvet; there should be twenty ells of royal Scotch plaid. But what was the use? Such delights could no longer hold her attention.

Darnley came to see her. He was sulky. He had been sending letters abroad. He had reminded Philip that Mary's friends were Moray, Bothwell and Maitland, who were all Protestants. It was Moray who was doing much harm to the Catholic cause in Scotland. Philip would readily understand how different matters would be if Darnley were King and Mary had no power to harm the Church.

He did not care so much that she turned away from him. She would rarely speak to him. She had not wished him to come, she implied. Soon he rode away. There were other women in the world besides Mary; and his head was teeming with plans for his own greatness.

When Mary rose from her bed she went to visit Bothwell. He was unable to move, for the wound in his thigh had not yet healed.

'Ah,' he said, when he saw her, 'so we both came to grief, eh?'

'I thought you were dead,' she answered quietly. 'They told me so.'

'It would take more than John Elliot to finish me. I'll be up and about as soon as my flesh heals.'

'And what of your head?' she asked. 'She lifted the bandage and looked at the head wound. She shivered. 'My dearest. . . . I cannot bear to think what might so easily have happened.'

He took her hand and kissed it. 'I am out of action,' he said. ''Tis a pity.'

'You will soon be well. I shall nurse you myself.'

'Mayhap I should go to Jean for the nursing.'

Mary's face flamed. 'That shall not be. I shall nurse you.'

He grinned.

'Did you go to Crichton?' she demanded. 'Did you see her?'

'I did.'

'And did you . . . ?'

That made him laugh. 'I declare I shall break open my wounds afresh if you say such things.'

'Did you? Did you?' she cried.

'My dear Queen, what do you think? I am her husband, am I not? It is long since I saw her.'

Mary's eyes filled with tears of rage and jealousy.

'Sometimes I wonder how I can go on loving you.'

'You should not wonder. It is very clear why you do. Now you must not be jealous. She is my wife; you are my mistress. I am content that it should be so.'

'But I am not!'

'Alas, how can you change it? By breaking away from me, of course. You could do that.'

'You do not care.'

'You will see. As soon as I am on my feet we will meet again in the Exchequer House as we did on that first encounter.'

'You should not have gone to Crichton,' she insisted.

He only shrugged his shoulders.

'You have a greater regard for her than for me!' she went on. 'Yet I hear that she has no great love for you. She wanted Alexander Ogilvie. She preferred him to you and yet . . . you go to see her!'

'I like her,' he said quietly. 'I'm fond of her. There's no one quite like Jeannie.'

'And there are many like the Queen!'

'No. There is only one Queen and only one Jeannie. I am fond of them both.'

'But I . . . can give you so much more than she can.'

'What?'

'My love . . . myself . . . my honour . . . my . . .' She put her arms about his neck. 'Please . . . do not be so cynical. You must love me. How can you go to her . . . when you know my feelings?'

'She might ask, How can I go to you . . . and with more reason. What can she give more than you can, you ask. She could give me children.'

'Could I not?'

'Not legitimate ones. So you see, she can give more than you can. You are two women. You have two eyes, a nose, a mouth, two arms, two breasts . . .'

'Be silent!' cried Mary tense with emotion. Then she added: 'There is one thing I could give you which she never can. A crown.'

A flame leaped into his eyes, the only sign that she had touched his smouldering ambition. She knew–and he knew–that nothing would ever be quite the same between them again.

Mary sat alone in her chamber. She, with her nobles about her, had left Jedburgh and was travelling by stages to Edinburgh. Bothwell, now well enough to travel, was with them. The wound in his thigh was healed, and that was all that he had been waiting for. His head was still bandaged, but he cared little for that if he could be on his feet again.

They had rested at Craigmillar and it was in the castle there that Mary sat.

She knew there were schemes in Bothwell's head. She knew that his attitude towards her had changed in some ways. He was as lusty as ever; he had wished–as she had–to resume their passionate relationship. But there was something else. She had more to offer him than Jean Gordon had; she had said so and he had accepted that.

She could not get Darnley out of her thoughts. Sometimes, in her dreams, she saw him lying on the floor in the supper chamber at Holyroodhouse, clutching at her skirts; and as she turned shuddering from him, his face would change to that of David.

'Holy Virgin,' she often prayed, 'intercede for me. Let me die now, for I believe it were better so. I am an adulteress. Let me die before I sin more deeply.'

The door of her chamber opened, and she thought it was her lover coming to her. but although Bothwell was there, he was not alone. With him were four of the lords–Moray, Maitland, Argyle and Huntley. They stood before her–five men, relentless in their struggle for power, and it was Maitland–the obvious choice as spokesman, suave and persuasive–who addressed her.

He began: 'Madam, much distress is caused, not only to you but to our country, through the evil conduct of one who can bring no good to any. I speak of your husband, Lord Darnley.'

She bowed her head and, when she raised it, caught the burning eyes of Bothwell upon her.

'It is known,' went on Maitland, 'that he has tried to get into communication with Spain and Rome; and his object is to do harm to Your Majesty who has done nothing but good to him. Madam, shall you tolerate such conduct, even though it is that of your own husband?'

'I am powerless to do otherwise. If we keep him under close surveillance, if we see that he does no real harm, it is the best that we can hope for.'

'Not so, Your Majesty. If you will grant pardon to Lords Morton, Ruthven and the rest who are now in exile, we, your servants, shall find means of making a divorcement between you and your husband. This is necessary, not only for Your Grace's comfort, but for that of the realm, for if he remains with Your Majesty, he will not rest until he has done you–and the country–some evil.'

Mary saw her lover's eyes upon her. They were gleaming as they had gleamed at the time of the rape. But this time was it her body he desired to possess, or was it her crown? She tried to be calm. 'I agree with what you say, my lord Maitland. But if there were a divorce it would have to be made lawful, and I could never agree to anything which would prejudice my son's inheritance of the throne.'

Bothwell said: 'It could be done. It could be done. My father was divorced from my mother but my inheritance was safe.'

'But my son is a Prince, Lord Bothwell.'

'It matters not, Madam. We would arrange this matter to bring no harm to the Prince.'

Moray now spoke: 'The Kirk would be against divorce.'

Bothwell's lips curled; Maitland's eyes were sardonic. He said: 'My lord Moray is a stern Protestant, so we must find a means of ridding you of your husband which will enable him to look through his fingers and, beholding our doings, say nothing.'

Mary caught her breath. What was Maitland's meaning? Was it that Moray was too religious a man to approve of divorce, and therefore murder would be necessary to rid her of Darnley?

She was trembling. She must not look at her lover. Had he persuaded the lords to this action, she wondered; had he started to make plans when she had told him in Jedburgh that she could offer him a crown? She knew now that these ruthless men were determined to murder Darnley. Each had his reason. For some it was because Darnley had betrayed his friends, having agreed to the murder of Rizzio and then turned to the other side and foiled these men's schemes. He was to die for that. But there was one who had been outside the plot. There was one who could reduce her decency, her love of justice, to nothing, and put in its place an overwhelming desire. He wanted to rid Scotland of Darnley, for through Darnley's death he saw a crown for himself.

She was glad there were others present. She must not look at him. She said coolly: 'I wish to do nothing by which any spot might be laid on my honour and my conscience.'

Maitland was smiling subtly. 'Madam, leave this matter in our hands and Your Grace shall see nothing but that which is approved of by Parliament.'

'But remember,' she insisted, 'nothing must be done to cast reflection on my honour and my conscience.'

'It shall be as Your Majesty wishes.'

They left her, and when they had gone she lay in bed, her heart pounding, as she reflected on what lay behind the words of those men.

The baby was christened James Charles with great pomp at Stirling. That was in the middle of December. Darnley, though in the castle, refused to appear. His attitude was giving rise to much gossip; and the castle was full of foreigners, for representatives from all countries had come to Scotland for the christening of the Prince.

Darnley was hinting that he was not the father of the child. He was whispering that each day the boy was growing more and more like the Italian music-maker. On other occasions he would stoutly declare that there could be no doubt that the child was his and that it was shameful that his wife would not live with him.

Oh to be rid of him! thought Mary. Could there be a divorce? Was it possible?

She had made an alarming discovery. She was to have Bothwell's child. She asked herself how she could explain this pregnancy. Something must be done and done quickly.

She told no one. She must keep her secret until she could find a way out of her trouble. She loved intensely. She could have been happy. But her love was bringing her nothing but misery.

It would have been better if I had died before I knew this love, she told herself continually. It would have been far better if I had never lived to sin as I now sin.

How could she confess her wickedness! How could she seek the comfort of her religion when she dared not confess? How could she promise to reform her ways when she had not the power to do so, when her lover could so easily make her his slave?

On Christmas Eve she signed the pardon which would bring Morton, Ruthven, Lindsay and the other rebel lords back to Scotland. She knew that doing so was tantamount to signing Darnley's death warrant.

Darnley knew it too. When he realized what had been done he lost no time in leaving the Castle of Stirling. He made for Glasgow, that territory which was under his father's domination.

Only there could he feel safe from his enemies.

It was January and the weather was bitter. Mary, alone with her thoughts, told herself again and again: I cannot do this thing.

And every time she answered herself: But I must.

Darnley was suffering from the smallpox, and safe in his father's castle he was carefully guarded by his father's men.

When Mary told Bothwell of the child he was by no means displeased.

'There must be no delay,' he said. 'You must see that. Delay is dangerous for us now.'

'Why do you say these things?' she demanded feeling half demented. 'What good could come to us . . . even if we were rid of him? What of you? You are not free!'

He had laughed. 'I'll be free and ready when you are.'

'And Jean?'

'She will stand aside. There'll be a divorce on the grounds of consanguinity. We are related.'

'So, we shall both be divorced and then . . .'

'Divorced! Divorce takes too long where Kings and Queens are concerned. Do not forget the child. It should not be born out of wedlock and it will not wait.'

She closed her eyes and tried to fight free of the spell he laid upon her. She thought fleetingly: If I could go to a nunnery. . . . If I could live out my life there. . . . But he had his arms about her; he was giving her those rough caresses which always brought memories of the Exchequer House.

He said: 'He must be brought from his father's territory. He could stay there for months surrounded by Lennox's men, hiding in safety. He must be brought to Edinburgh.'

'Who will bring him?'

'There is only one who can.'

'No . . . !' she cried.

'Yes,' he said smiling. 'He would come if you went to him. You could bring him from his father's territory. We need him here in Edinburgh.'

'He is sick.'

'All the more reason why you should look after him.'

'I have told him that all is over between us.'

'Women . . . even queens . . . change their minds.'

She said faintly: 'You had better speak plainly.'

'Go to him. Promise him anything. But bring him out of his hiding place.'

'Promise him . . . anything?'

Bothwell laughed. 'It is hardly likely that he will be in a condition to ask you to redeem your promises.'

She turned away. 'I cannot do this.'

He seized her, and forced her to look into his face.

'You will do it,' he said. 'You will consider what it means to us, and you will do it.'

She could refuse him nothing. He knew it, and she knew it. Now she cried: 'No, I cannot do this thing. I never want to see him again, but I cannot do this.'

He did not urge her then. He laughed; he caressed her; reduced her to that state of mind and body when she had no thought or wishes beyond the immediate moment.

'You will,' he said, 'do this for me.'

And she knew she would.

When he had left her she remained alone and in torment.

She picked up her pen and, because she dared not write of the terrible thing which was in her mind, she wrote of her passion for the man who had completely enslaved her. She wrote of the tears she had wept on his account, of that first brutal encounter which had taken place before she had known this overwhelming love.

Riding towards Glasgow in the bitter weather, Mary felt like a woman in a trance. She knew that she would play the part which was desired of her. Her own will was subdued. Her lover had as complete possession of her mind as he had of her body. There was one thing which could help her do this: her hatred of Darnley.

When she reached the castle she was taken at once to Darnley. If he had sickened her before, he did so doubly now. The marks of his disease were on his face and the room was unpleasantly odorous. He wore a piece of fine gauze over his face to hide the disfigurement as best he could. But he was pleased to see her.

'It is good of Your Majesty to come hither to see me,' he said humbly.

'There is much I have to say to you. You are very sick.'

'I shall recover.'

She could not bear to look at him. She said: 'Why have you behaved so badly? If you had not. . . . But tell me why you write letters complaining of the cruelty of "some people". You mean your wife, of course. What have I done to be treated so by you?'

'You will not forgive me. You turn from me. I long to resume our normal married life and you will have none of it. I know that I have acted very foolishly, even wickedly. Madam, I am very young. I am not twenty-one yet. I am younger than you are. Let us try again. There is only one thing I desire: to get back to that happy relationship which was ours. Oh, Mary, you loved me once. Have you forgotten?'

She shuddered. 'It was so long ago. I did not know you then.'

'You knew part of me. I *was* like that. I could be like that again. I have been led astray by my own folly . . . by the folly of others. I think of you constantly . . . as my Queen and as my wife. How could I ever be content without you, having known you?'

'I cannot believe you to be sincere. I know you, remember. If I took you back there would be those hideous scenes . . . that shameful humiliation. I cannot forget what you have said to me, how you have humiliated me–not only in private, but before my subjects.'

'Then you would take me back? You would let me be with you again?'

'How could I trust you?'

'You could! You could!'

'Hush! Do not excite yourself so. It is bad for you. Lie still. Speak calmly.'

'Speak calmly when *you* are here, when you have ridden here to see me?'

'I am uncertain,' she began.

'Mary, I will be a good husband to you. Mary, why should we not be happy together? We have a child . . . a son. We could be happy.'

'If we were different people we might be. I . . . I have brought a horse-litter for you.'

He was pathetically alert. 'Why so? Why so?'

'I wish to take you back with me to Edinburgh.'

'To take me back!' He looked wildly about the room. 'To take me back, Mary? I have too many enemies at the Court. They have sworn to be revenged on me for . . .'

'For David's death,' she said. Her eyes were brilliant as she looked full at him and went on: 'It is just a year since David died.' The memory of David, pulling at her skirts as he was being dragged across the floor, gave her courage. He–this sick and repulsive boy lying in the bed–had had no compunction in sending David to his death. She went on: 'That is what you are thinking of, is it not? You fear them because you plotted with them to kill David and then deserted them and informed against them.'

He nodded slowly and fearfully. He said: 'I hear that they have plotted to do me harm. But I would not believe that you would join them in that. Why do you wish me to go back to Edinburgh?'

'Because so many talk of the strained relations between us. I would have us appear to the world to be living in amity together.'

'Mary,' he said, 'I will come back on one condition. I will rise from my sick bed and come back to Edinburgh if you will give me your promise to be my wife . . . in all things.'

She hesitated.

He went on: 'If not, I shall stay here. I want your solemn promise, Mary. You and I shall be at bed and board as husband and wife. Promise me this, and I will leave with you tomorrow.'

She was silent for so long that he said sulkily: 'Very well then, I remain here. It is far too cold for me to travel.'

'You would be comfortable in your litter. You would have the utmost care. In Edinburgh we should all be together . . . you, I and the child. I would care for you myself.'

'I will come only if you promise me that one thing: we shall be as husband and wife and you will never leave me as long as I live.'

'As long as you live,' she repeated, and the shivering took possession of her again. She went on: 'But it would have to be after you have recovered. We could not be together until then.'

'I will recover quickly,' he said eagerly.

'Very well. We shall start tomorrow.'

'Your promise, Mary?'

'I give it.'

'And never to leave me as long as I live?'

'Never to leave you as long as you live,' she repeated.

'Then let us set out tomorrow.'

Shaken, relieved and horrified, she said to herself: It is done. Soon my task will be over.

Darnley was sleeping deeply, his disfigured face turned away from her. Mary sat in the sick room watching through the long night. She was too distressed to sleep and she could not sit idly; so she took up her pen and wrote to her lover.

'I am weary and sleepy, yet I cannot forbear scribbling as long as there is any paper. . . .'

She had been writing for some time without considering what she wrote but setting down her thoughts as they came into her mind. She glanced back over the paper and read:

'He would not let me go but would have me watch with him. Fain would I have excused myself from spending this night sitting up with him. . . .

'I do a work here which I hate much. . . .

'Excuse me if I write ill. I am ill at ease and glad to write unto you when others be asleep, seeing that I cannot do as they do according to my desire, that is between your arms, my dear life whom I beseech God to preserve from all ill. . . .'

There were tears in her eyes and they fell on the paper.

Will this night never end? she asked herself. She looked at the man in the bed, and she thought of the man whom she loved, and she murmured: 'It were better if I had never been born, better I had died long ago when a child, and so many thought I should, than that I should come to this.'

They left Glasgow next day.

'Are we going to Holyroodhouse or the Castle?' asked Darnley.

'To neither,' she answered him. 'In your state it would not be good to stay at either place. You are sick of a disease which many fear. I have had a house prepared for you, and there you shall rest until you are well enough to come to me at the palace.'

'And share your apartments,' he reminded her.

'And share my apartments,' she repeated.

'Bed and board,' he said, smiling. 'Where is this house?'

'It is one of those on the southern slope of the city. You know the ruins of the Church of St Mary. There are several houses there, and this one belongs to Robert Balfour. He has lent it to us that you may rest there until you are well enough to come to the palace.'

Darnley frowned. 'Among all those worn-out and ruined houses! You would mean Kirk-o'-Field, would you not?'

'Kirk-o'-Field, yes. Close to the ruin of St Mary's.'

'It is an odd place to which to take me.'

'It is near Holyrood, and for that reason it seems suitable. It is an old house, it is true, but we have furnished your apartment royally. When you are within and see the bed I have had set there for you, and the rich hangings I have had put up, you will agree that you are as comfortably housed as in your father's castle.'

'And you . . . will you be at this house in Kirk-o'-Fields?'

'I shall have my bed taken there. I shall sleep in the room below yours, so you will not be lonely. Your man Taylor and a few others will be with you. And I shall be there too.'

He nodded. 'But Kirk-o'-Field! A dismal place!'

'Only outside. Inside it will be as a palace furnished for a king.'

As they came into Edinburgh and Darnley saw the dismal surroundings of the house which had been chosen for him he was uneasy. He looked with distaste at the house itself which had been lent by Robert Balfour, the Provost of Kirk-o'-Field and brother to Sir James. It was a house of two stories. There was a spiral staircase in a turret by means of which it was possible to enter the lower chamber and the upper through two small lobbies. On each of the two floors there were a few rooms which were more like cupboards than rooms–these were the *garderobes* and here the servants would sleep. Sliding panels acted as doors for these *garderobes*. The house had been built over an arched crypt.

'Such a spot!' he said, 'For a King! Ruins all about me and a view of Thieves' Row from the window!'

'Wait until you see your apartment.' She showed him the lower chamber in which was her velvet state bed. 'This is where I shall sleep. I shall be immediately below you. Let me show you your apartment and then food shall be brought.'

He was cheered when he saw his apartment. It was decorated with tapestry and velvet hangings which had been taken from the Earl of Huntley at the time of his disgrace, as had the magnificent bed and most of the furnishings. Darnley could not complain of these.

He lay exhausted on the bed and thought of the future. He believed he had acted wisely in becoming reconciled to the Queen and in showing his trust in her. He would emerge from this sickness a handsome young man again; he would be the Queen's adored husband. He only had to lie in bed and recover his strength and his handsome appearance. Then all that he desired would be his.

Mary had slept in the velvet state bed at the house in Kirk-o'-Field on Tuesday and Friday of that week. On the Friday, late at night, she had heard the sounds of stealthy footsteps close to the house. She had not awakened Lady Reres who had been her companion since she had gone with her to the Exchequer House, but had crept to the window. She had seen French Paris and some of James Balfour's men opening the door of the crypt and carrying in something bulky. She shuddered and went back to bed, wondering what the men were doing.

On the following day when she returned to Holyroodhouse, she had a few moments alone with Bothwell. He had taken her into his fierce embrace.

He said: ''Tis a fine bed you have there in Kirk-o'-Field.'

She looked at him wonderingly. 'I saw it,' he told her. 'I have keys to all doors. A fine velvet bed. I have a fancy for that. We'll share it on our wedding night. Have it brought from the house tomorrow and a less fine one put in its place.'

'Why . . . tomorrow?' she asked.

'Because I ask it, and because you will do anything in the world to please me.'

Darnley said: 'Why are they taking away your velvet bed?'

'It is too fine for such a room as the one below this.'

'Yet . . . to take it away . . . after you took such pains to have it brought here!'

'I wish it to be cleaned and prepared.'

'Prepared?'

'For our reconciliation.'

He was smiling. 'It shall be our bridal bed, for it shall be as though we are newly married. You will be here tonight, Mary?'

'I shall come to see you tonight, but I shall have to return to Holyrood as there is a wedding which I am expected to attend. Bastian is marrying Margaret Carwood. You know how fond I am of Margaret–and of Bastian. I promised Margaret I would dance at her wedding and that I would see that hers was a fine one.'

'Would that I could dance at Margaret's wedding!'

'There was a time when you would have scorned to dance at a servant's wedding.'

'I was so young. I was over-proud! And look to what my folly has brought me!'

She turned away because she knew that if she tried to say more the words would choke her.

After a pause he said: 'This is a strange house. Do you think it is haunted? I hear footsteps. I fancy I hear whispers. There are strange noises in the night. In the crypt, it may be. I seem to hear these sounds.'

'This is such a small house that you would naturally hear noises from without.'

'Perhaps that is it. Mary, I think much of the velvet bed.'

'Yes,' she said faintly, 'the velvet bed.'

'You shall see that I have changed. I was so young, Mary, and the honour done to me was too much. You . . . so beautiful . . . so desired by all, and to be so much in love with me as you were! And then to be the King. Remember my youth. Why do you weep, Mary? Is it for the past?'

She nodded, and she thought: For the past, for the present, for the future.

Robert Stuart, Mary's base-born brother, had come to see his kinsman Darnley. Robert was in a quandary. The Stuart characteristics were strong in him, and the Stuarts, if they were often weak and foolish, hated cruelty and were overwhelmingly tender and generous to their friends.

Robert was disturbed. He had heard rumours and the rumours concerned Darnley.

Why, Robert asked himself, should Darnley have been brought to a house such as this? Darnley was a fool not to see the reason. There was a plot against him and his enemies were all around him. Even the Queen hated him and wanted to be rid of him. Why could not Darnley see what was so clear to others?

'You seem disturbed,' said Darnley.

'I am,' retorted Robert. 'Are you not?'

He signed to the servant to leave them alone together.

'Where does he go when he leaves this room?' asked Robert.

'To the little gallery with the *garderobes*. There are really only two rooms in this house. Mine and the Queen's. It is a very small house.'

'You are isolated here, my lord.'

'I shall not be here long. Plans are being made for removing me.'

That was too much for Robert. 'It is only too true,' he said. 'Plans are being made and you will not be long on this Earth if you ignore them.'

'What do you mean?'

'Think, man. Why have you been brought to this desolate spot? If you are reconciled with the Queen why is it not Holyroodhouse or Edinburgh Castle? Why this little house in ruined Kirk-o'-Field?'

'Because . . . because I am sick. Because . . . because many fear my disease. I shall go to Holyrood with the Queen as soon as I am well. She has had her state bed removed this day, that it may be where we can use it together.'

'Jesus!' cried Robert. 'Is it so then? Her state bed removed! Then man, do not wait another hour in this accursed house. Fly now . . . while you have yet time.'

'The Queen is my friend. The Queen has promised me that I shall be her husband.'

'Listen! Bothwell, Morton, Moray, Maitland . . . all are against you. You betrayed so many after Rizzio's murder. They wish to free the Queen from her marriage with you. A plot to do so is afoot. Do not ask me more. Go! I am warning you.'

'I trust the Queen,' stammered Darnley.

'Then you are a fool. Hush! Someone comes.'

'It is the Queen herself,' said Darnley, rising from his bed.

'Say nothing of what I have told you,' said Robert.

But Darnley had not yet learned enough wisdom.

'Mary,' he cried as she came into the room, 'I have just heard a terrible tale. Robert says there is a plot to kill me.'

The Queen grew pale. She looked at her brother.

Robert thought: Why did I try to help the fool? Let him wait here to die. He deserves death for his folly, if for nothing else. He laughed and protested: 'I . . . ! You have misheard me, brother. I know of no plot.'

'But you have just said . . .' began Darnley.

Robert shrugged his shoulders. He looked at his sister. 'It would seem that he wanders in his sickness.'

Darnley cried out in anger: 'But you have just warned me. Mary, what does he mean? Is there some plot?'

'I . . . I do not know of what you speak,' said Mary.

Robert smiled patiently. 'You misunderstood, my lord. I spoke of no plot.'

'It . . . it was meant to be a . . . joke?'

Oh, you fool, thought Robert. A joke! When the Queen wishes to be rid of you. When there is not a nobleman at Court who does not hate you, who has not some score to settle. Robert said coldly: 'You have completely misunderstood me.'

'So . . . it was nothing . . .' began Darnley.

'It was nothing.'

'I do not like such jokes,' said Darnley angrily.

'Robert,' interrupted the Queen reprovingly, 'you should remember that Henry is very weak as yet. You should not distress him so.'

Robert lifted his shoulders and smiled his charming Stuart smile. He began to talk of Bastian's wedding.

On Sunday evening Mary took supper at the house of Sir James Balfour, and for company she had with her Lords Huntley, Bothwell and Cassillis. Bothwell was anxious that Mary should be where he could keep an eye on her. He had heard that Robert Stuart had warned Darnley. He could see that she was frightened tonight. She knew that her brother Moray had some reason for leaving Edinburgh other than the fact that his wife was slightly unwell. Moray–the sanctimonious man who could not look at evil except 'through his fingers'–had always thought it advisable not to be on the spot when some deed was to be done which, though necessary to him, might earn the condemnation of all decent people. Moray's departure was a sure sign that trouble was coming very near. None knew that better than the Queen.

She rose from the supper table saying that she had promised to call that night at the house in Kirk-o'-Field to see Darnley.

'Your Majesty has not forgotten the wedding?' asked Bothwell.

'Oh no. But I must see him first, for I have given him my promise to do so.'

'Then,' said Bothwell, 'let us all go now to his apartment.'

'Shall we not be intruding on their Majesties?' asked Cassillis.

'Nay,' said Bothwell, 'we three will play dice in a corner while the Queen talks with her husband.'

The party left, and guided by the flare of torches, passed through Black Friars Wynd to Kirk-o'-Field.

Mary was deeply aware of her lover's presence. She knew that what happened tonight was of the utmost importance to him, and therefore to her.

Darnley was pleased to see her, but not so pleased to see her companions.

'We came, my lord,' said Bothwell, 'to escort the Queen.'

'Come, sit beside me,' said Darnley eagerly to Mary.

Bothwell smiled. 'Your Majesties may forget our presence. We shall be playing dice in this corner.'

Mary sat by the bed and Darnley said in a low voice: 'Would you were staying the night.'

'I would, but I must attend the wedding, and there will be dancing till three of the morning. I could not come then.'

'Tomorrow night then?'

'Tomorrow night . . . if possible,' promised the Queen.

He began to talk then of his plans for the future, when he would leave this house and how happy they would be together. Mary listened, yet aware of the men playing in the corner; now and then looking up to find her lover's eyes upon her.

She wondered: Was ever woman asked to play such a part?

She rose at length and said: 'I must not forget the wedding.'

'So soon!' complained Darnley.

She nodded and turned to the players. 'My lords, I would go back now to dance at the wedding.'

They rose, bade farewell to the sick man and left him with his attendant Taylor.

As they came out of the house, Mary noticed with surprise the face of French Paris who was waiting with his master's horse.

'How begrimed you are, Paris!' she exclaimed.

'Yes, Your Grace,' said the man, with an evil grin.

By the light of torches they rode back to Holyrood, where the wedding celebrations were in progress. Mary joined in the gaiety–dancing, singing and seeming as gay as any; but just after midnight she declared that it was a shame to keep the newly married pair from their nuptials, and she would conduct Margaret to her *coucher* at once that she might in person assist in the custom of breaking the benediction-cake over the bride's head, present her with the silver posset-cup and throw the stocking.

When these ceremonies had been completed the Queen retired to her own chamber, and as soon as her women had prepared her for sleep, she lay on her bed, exhausted.

Darnley could not sleep. His room seemed to be filled with gloomy menacing shadows. He kept thinking of Robert's words and of the uneasiness of the Queen. He had noticed the glances which Bothwell had sent in her direction from the dice table in the corner of the room. It was almost as though Bothwell were the King and Mary his humble subject. What had given him that impression? What had given him these uneasy thoughts? Was it this lonely, isolated house? Was it the thought of all his enemies? Was he remembering the hatred he had once seen in Mary's eyes? He could sense evil near him. Those voices in the night–what did they mean? Were there evil spirits in the crypt below the house? Were his enemies hiding there in order to spring upon him in the dead of night? He raised himself on his elbow. He could make out the figure of Taylor lying at the foot of his bed.

'Taylor!' he whispered.

Taylor started up in alarm. 'My lord?'

'I cannot sleep. I hear noises. Taylor, there is someone prowling about the house.'

Taylor was listening. 'It is but the wind, my lord.'

'No, Taylor. I think not. Quiet! Listen with me.'

'My lord, shall I wake the servants?'

'How many are there in this house, Taylor?'

'Only the three, my lord: Nelson, Symonds and my own servant.'

'Have they said aught of noises in the night?'

'No, my lord.'

'They sleep deep in their little gallery. But then . . . any who prowl about the house would not come for them. Jesus! I shall be glad when we leave this house. I like it not. I shall leave it tomorrow.'

'My lord,' said Taylor in a whisper, 'there is someone on the stairs.'

Darnley was out of bed. Taylor had seized his wrap and would have put it about him, but Darnley was at the door.

'Quick, Taylor. We must get out of this house. They come to murder me.'

'Your robe, my lord.'

But Darnley could not wait. He drew Taylor behind the door just as it was being cautiously pushed open; and two men came stealthily into the room.

They did not see the two behind the door and, as they approached the bed, Darnley, with Taylor behind him, speedily ran down the staircase and out into the garden.

Darnley heard someone cry: 'After them!'

He recognized the voice as that of Archibald Douglas.

The cold night air made him gasp as it cut across his lightly covered body; he was wearing nothing but his nightgown. Dark figures moved towards him; he was caught and held in strong arms.

He gasped: 'You . . . you could do this to a kinsman!' He was weak from his illness, but it was surprising what strength there could be in a sick man when he was fighting for his life. A damp rag was slipped across his mouth. He could scarcely breathe. He smelt vinegar as he fell unconscious to the grass.

Taylor was being suffocated by the same methods. Before he died he heard a voice ask: 'Shall we take them back?'

'Nay . . .' came the answer. 'They're too heavy and time is short. We must be well away from Kirk-o'-Field in ten minutes' time. Leave them here. They're near enough to the house and there'll be no trace of them by morning.'

Stealthy figures moved about the house.

The plans had gone awry. Darnley and his man, Taylor, were to have been strangled in their room. There was no time to take them back. There was only time to put a safe distance between the conspirators and the house in Kirk-o'-Field. They started towards Holyrood, but before they reached the palace they heard the roar of the explosion. The citizens were running out of their houses. The guards of the palace saw men with blackened faces entering it; and there was one of these whose bulk betrayed him; and on the night that Darnley was murdered and the house in Kirk-o'-Field blown sky-high, Bothwell was seen by many with his guilt upon him.

The Queen was startled out of her sleep by the explosion. She rose in her bed crying out in terror. Seton was beside her.

'What is it, Seton?' demanded Mary. 'What is it?'

Seton answered: 'I know not.' And she ran to the window. 'It looks like a great fire. The sky is brilliant and there is much smoke.'

'Where, Seton, where?'

Mary was now beside her at the window. She knew before she looked that the explosion had occurred in Kirk-o'-Field. Her teeth chattered and her body shook as with an ague.

Chapter Five

There was tumult throughout Edinburgh. The citizens were in the streets. There was speculation throughout the palace.

Bothwell had to be roused from slumber by his servants. He appeared to be sunk in a deep sleep, though he lay in his bed still dressed and with the grime on his clothes and face.

'Jesus!' he cried, rushing to the window. 'What is this? It would seem as though the city is ablaze. 'Tis an explosion, I'll warrant, somewhere near Kirk-o'-Field.'

He rode out with his followers.

'Keep clear of the fire, good people,' he cried. 'Stand back and keep your distance.'

The good people of Edinburgh looked at him, and looked quickly away. Rumour travelled fast.

The guards of Holyrood had already whispered that one of those who came hurriedly into the palace soon after the explosion was Lord Bothwell himself.

In the dawn light men searched the spot. The house was now a smouldering ruin. How explain the mighty explosion which had rent the place? Was it gunpowder? Explosives could easily have been stored in the crypt. And who had done this? Who would have dared stack gunpowder below a house in which the Queen's husband lay sick?

Two men were certainly suspected of foul play! Bothwell who had been seen returning by the guards, and Archibald Douglas whose shoe had been found, marvellously intact, close to the ruins.

But there was a discovery yet to be made. The charred bodies of three servants had been found by those who searched, but where were the bodies of the King and Taylor? Could they have been completely destroyed?

It was not long before they were found. They were lying in the garden, in their nightgowns. Beside them was Darnley's velvet gown as though it had been dropped hurriedly.

It was certain that the explosion had not touched them, but nevertheless they lay lifeless on the grass–most mysteriously dead. The plot became clear now. Darnley and Taylor had been murdered and the explosion which had been arranged to hide the crime had completely failed to do so.

All Edinburgh was aroused to indignation. Who murdered the King? was the question to which the citizens were determined to find an answer.

The Queen was numb. She did not know how to act. The whole of Scotland was talking of the murder of the King. Soon the whole world would be talking. The murderers must be found, said the people. But could Mary join with them when she knew that the murderer-in-chief was her lover?

Bothwell swaggered about the town with thousands of his men within call. No one dared show his suspicion if he had any respect for his life.

The Queen should have been plunged in mourning; but instead she was merely dazed. She took no measures for twenty-four hours to bring the murderers to justice. How could she? She was too deeply concerned. Edinburgh knew it. All Scotland knew it. And the news was being carried with all speed to England and the Continent of Europe.

'You must do something,' said Seton. Poor Seton was aghast. She knew too much, yet she could not believe that her beloved mistress would have agreed to the murder of her husband. Yet Seton knew that Bothwell could do what he wished with Mary; she knew that Mary was in love with her husband's murderer.

'What can I do?' said Mary. 'I wish I were dead. I wish I were in Darnley's place.'

'You must do something to show the people that you wish for justice,' Seton implored. 'You must show them that you wish this crime to be solved.'

Mary broke into hysterical laughter which ended in sobbing.

The next morning there were crowds at the Tolbooth reading the placards which had been affixed there during the night.

The biggest of these bore the inscription: 'Who is the King's murderer?' And beneath it was a drawing of Bothwell.

There were other placards. One said: 'The King's murderers are Lord Bothwell . . .' and there followed a list of servants–Mary's servants–and among them was David's brother Joseph Rizzio.

The implication was clear. Bothwell was the murderer-in-chief, but the Queen's servants had helped him in his crime.

Bothwell came to see the Queen. Without asking permission he dismissed her attendants. He showed greater arrogance than ever now, being sure of his power. He was the most powerful man in Scotland, for the Queen was his to command. His eyes gleamed with excitement. He was unafraid though he knew himself to be in constant danger. He was ready to face all the lords of Scotland, all the judges. He was completely sure of himself. But they must plan carefully now, he warned. It was inadvisable for the Queen to stay in Edinburgh. The people were growing restive. Darnley should without delay be laid in the royal vault.

'We'll offer a reward of two thousand pounds and a free pardon to any who can give information regarding the murder. And we'll have those servants of yours sent out of the country immediately, for how can we know what they will divulge if they are captured and put to the torture?'

'What of you?' she asked.

'I'll take care of myself,' said Bothwell. He caught her to him and laughed. 'And of you,' he added.

She knew her conduct was wrong but she could act in no other way. She could only live through the weeks that followed by striving to pretend the tragedy had not happened. She did not appear to be mourning. She even attended a wedding. She shocked the citizens by her almost feverish pursuit of gaiety. They did not know that in her own apartments, night after night, she was near to collapse.

Bothwell hurried her off to the Castle of Seton, accompanied by himself, Maitland and a few of the lords. All were on tenterhooks, all uncertain of what was to happen next–with the exception of Bothwell whose intentions were perfectly clear in his mind.

In the streets of Edinburgh the cry against him rose more shrilly, now that he was not there to strike terror into the populace.

'Let Bothwell be tried for murder!' shouted the people. 'Bothwell . . . with his servants and the Queen's . . . killed the King.'

The Earl of Lennox raised his voice. He demanded that the suspected Earl of Bothwell be brought to trial.

At Seton the lovers could be alone together, but Bothwell was more interested in plans for the future than making love.

'Now,' he said, 'you are free to marry. You are free from that troublesome boy.'

'Free!' she cried. 'I shall never be free from him. He will always be with me. I can never forget him.'

Bothwell was impatient. 'He is dead and that is an end of him. Did you not want him dead? Did you not long to be my wife?'

'If we had met long ago . . .'

'Oh, have done with your 'ifs'! We could marry now and there is nothing to stop us.'

'There is your wife.'

'I have told you that I can rid myself of her.'

'Not . . .'

'By divorce,' he said impatiently. 'Jean will agree. There must be no delay. Remember, we have a child to think of.'

'How could we marry now? How could we marry soon? The whole world will know that we are guilty.'

'We must marry,' said Bothwell. 'We shall marry.'

'I dare not. I long to be your wife but I dare not. There is no way out of this. You are accused of the murder. My servants are accused, and that means the people believe they acted in my name. Should we marry, all the world would say that we killed Darnley to bring this about.'

Bothwell took her by the shoulders. He said: 'We shall marry. I tell you we *shall* marry. Whatever happens, I am determined to marry you.'

'Then you must force me to it in some way. I must seem to surrender against my will. That is very necessary or the whole of Scotland will be against me. Oh, my dearest, what have we done! What have we done!'

'What we set out to do–rid ourselves of our encumbrances. What do you wish? To tell the whole world that I ravished you and therefore you consider it necessary to marry me?'

'It is true,' she murmured.

'And that is the only reason why you wish to marry me. Ah! You were no reluctant partner . . . after the first shock!'

She protested: 'You do not love me. You care more for Jean Gordon than for me.'

'I am ready to divorce her, am I not. And all for love of you!'

'Rather for love of my crown.'

He laughed. 'Let us not make such fine distinctions. You are the Queen and royal. Your crown is part of you, and if I would do what I have for the sake of a crown, yet it is for love of you too. You are my mistress, my concubine in private; but in public you must be my Queen. You must be royal. You must distribute the favours. That is how you would have it. When we are alone, I am the master; but when we are in public, you will be the Queen, I the servant.' He paused and seemed to consider awhile. Then he went on: 'Mayhap you are right. Mayhap that is how the people would have it. I will seize your person. I will hold you captive. The whole world shall believe that you are my captive and I ravished you. You therefore feel that the only way in which you can redeem your honour is through marriage, and for that reason you will seek the earliest opportunity to bring it about. You are a widow now. I shall soon be free of Jean. Nothing will stand in your way. That is our next move, my Queen. Leave it to me.'

'There is nothing else I can do,' she said. 'My whole life, my entire happiness is in your hands.'

She would think of nothing but her love of Bothwell. She would put her whole trust in him. He would bring them safely through this danger in which they found themselves. She had sent out of the country Joseph Rizzio and those of her servants who were suspected; she was relieved to know that they were safe. Bothwell and James Balfour would know how to defend themselves.

Bothwell had ridden through the streets of Edinburgh calling on any who accused him to come out and do it openly. He was ready, he declared, to wash his hands in their blood. He had his men–thousands of them in their steel bonnets thronging the streets of Edinburgh–but he would take on any of his challengers single-handed.

Mary wanted to show him how much she loved him; she could not give him enough. She had already bestowed on him the Castle of Blackness; and all the rich furs and jewels which Darnley had amassed were given to Bothwell. She wrote poems expressing her love for him, betraying the depth of her feelings, her desire for him, her bitter jealousy of his wife.

Bothwell himself was ready and eager to face a trial. It was arranged that should do so, and, ostentatiously filling the town with his followers, he prepared to make his journey to the Tolbooth where the trial was to be held.

He was confident of the result. The Justice was that old and warm supporter of his, Argyle; the jury was picked. Every man among them knew that only fools would support Lennox in his weakness against the might of Bothwell.

It was not that the lords did not fear Bothwell; it was not that they were unaware of his rising power. They were suspicious of his relationship with the Queen, but he now had five thousand men in the city, and the guns of Edinburgh Castle were under the command of one of his men. The strength of Boswell was much in evidence and the lords could not but quail before him. Bothwell was in charge of events and they were afraid of him.

The citizens watched him ride to the Tolbooth, magnificently clad in velvet hose passamented and trussed with silver and with his black satin doublet similarily decorated; he wore jewels presented to him by the Queen, and his great figure mounted on a fine horse had all the bearing of the King he was determined to become. His exultation was obvious.

The Queen could not resist looking out of a window of Holyrood to watch his departure. She felt there was no need to pray for his safety; he would look after himself; he was invincible.

The trial was conducted in a solemn manner, just as though it were a real trial. The lords considered the evidence brought forward by Lennox; they retired and after long discussion declared the verdict.

'James, Earl of Bothwell, is acquitted of any art and part of the slaughter of the King.'

Triumphantly he rode through the streets of Edinburgh. He galloped along the Canongate and shouted to the people: 'People of Edinburgh, I have been acquitted of that of which I was accused. I have been pronounced guiltless. If there is any man among you who doubts that verdict to be a true one, let him come forward now. I challenge him to single combat. Let him fortify his accusations with the sword.'

People listened behind bolted doors; no one ventured forth, though there was scarcely a man or woman in Edinburgh who did not believe Bothwell to be the King's murderer.

Up and down the streets he galloped, pausing now and then to call to his accusers to come and fight with him. None came. And at length he returned to Holyroodhouse to tell the Queen that events were moving in their favour.

Mary's life was divided between periods of delirious joy and dreadful remorse. She was more passionately in love with him than ever. He was without hypocrisy, whatever other faults he might have. He would never pretend. He enjoyed their relationship; her passion was as fiercely demanding as his; he found great pleasure in their union, but he was less sentimental than she. She differed from other women in one respect as far as he was concerned; she had a crown to offer him. He would not have been the man he was if he could have hidden this fact. Mary knew it and it caused her many bitter tears.

Often after he had left she would read through some of the sonnets she had written for him. There was one which described her feelings without reserve.

'Pour luy aussi j'ay jette mainte larme,
Premier qu'il fust de ce corps possesseur,
Duquel alors il n'avoit pas le cœur ....'

She read it through again and again, thinking of all the bitter tears she had shed for him. She read that line which was as true now as it had been when she had written it.

'Brief, de vous seul je cherche alliance.'

Within a few days he decided he must go to see his wife.

'I must persuade her to the divorce,' he said.

'I hate your going to her!' she cried.

He laughed aloud. 'I go to ask her to release me. What cause for jealousy is there in that?'

The only comfort she could find was in pouring out her thoughts in verses–verses which he would read and smile over before he locked them into his casket, there to lie forgotten.

But he did not go to see Jean then. He discovered that it would be unwise to leave Mary–not for love of her but because he feared that his enemies might capture her and keep her their prisoner. He talked instead to Jean's brother, Huntley. Huntley, aware that Bothwell was the strongest power in the land, decided that it would be worth while setting aside a sister in order to share in that power.

The divorce must be speedy. Bothwell told Huntley that it could be brought about on the grounds of consanguinity as he and Jean were distantly connected.

It was impossible to silence the rumours. The Queen's husband dead. Bothwell seeking to divorce his wife. The inference was obvious.

Great events were about to burst on Scotland. Danger lay ahead. This was certain, for the Earl of Moray had left Scotland for France. He wanted no part in what was about to take place; he only wanted to partake of any good which might come within his reach through the ruin of the Queen, which more than ever seemed to him inevitable.

Bothwell was triumphant. He had been the chief instigator of Darnley's murder and had gone unpunished. His men swaggered through the streets clanging their bucklers and broadswords. They commanded the fortress. All the nobles were invited–or ordered–to take supper with Lord Bothwell at the Ainslie Tavern.

At the closing of the recent parliament he had carried the Queen's crown and sceptre for her, back to the palace. Now there was not a man among them who dared refuse his invitation, while there was not one who was completely easy in his mind.

The revellers were feasting and making merry in the tavern when they were suddenly aware that the inn was surrounded by Bothwell's men who stood on guard at the doors.

Bothwell called to his guests: 'My very good lords, I thank you for your company, and now that we are all together and you know me for your friend, I would know you for mine. I have a bond here and I shall ask you, one and all, to sign it.'

Only the Earl of Eglinton, who was sitting near a window which was unguarded, managed to slip away unnoticed. The others were caught, intensely aware of the armed men surrounding the inn.

Morton cried: 'What is this bond, friend Bothwell?'

'I will read it to you.' Bothwell stood on a table and taking the scroll in his hand read aloud:

'James, Earl of Bothwell, being calumniated by malicious reports and divers placards as art and part in the heinous murder of the King, has submitted to an assize, and been found innocent of the same by certain noblemen his peers and others barons of good reputation. We, the undersigned, oblige ourselves upon our faith and honour the truth of our bodies, will answer to God, that in case hereafter any manner of person shall happen to insist farther on the slander and calumniation of the said heinous murder we and our kin, friends and assisters, shall take true and plain part with him to the defence and maintenance of his quarrel with our bodies, heritage and goods. And as Her Majesty is now destitute of husband, in which solitary state the Commonweal cannot permit Her Highness to continue, if it should please her so far to humble herself by taking one of her own born subjects and marry the said Earl, we will maintain and fortify him against all who would hinder and disturb the said marriage. Under our hands and seals at Edinburgh this day of April the 19th, in the year 1567.'

The lords were dumbfounded.

They had expected to be asked to stand beside him in the event of his accusers' rising against him, but this proposed marriage with the Queen was a feat of daring which they had not expected, even from Bothwell.

They hesitated. They were aware of the men-at-arms outside. The ferocity of Bothwell's men was well known. And here they were, caught in a trap, befuddled with wine, heavy with feasting.

Morton stepped forward and said: 'It is true that Lord Bothwell was acquitted and therefore every man should stand beside him should he be attacked on this matter of the King's death. I will give my signature to the bond. It is true that Her Majesty is left a widow and that for the good of this country she should marry. If Her Majesty should humble herself and take one of her born subjects and that should be the Earl we see before us, then I say that will be for Scotland's good and I hereby sign the bond.'

Bothwell was taken aback. He had not expected such ready support from Morton.

One by one the lords came up to sign the bond. They knew they must do it or die. Bothwell would have no mercy.

While they were uneasy, Bothwell was triumphant. But there was one who was far from displeased by what he had witnessed in the tavern; he was sly Morton.

By God! he swore to himself, little do these oafs know when they reluctantly sign this bond that they are doing just what they would wish to do; they are signing Bothwell's death warrant. And he, poor fool, is too drunk with ambition to know it. Should he marry the Queen they are both doomed. Such a marriage would expose them to the world as Darnley's murderers. The most foolish step they could take at this point is to marry.

He decided he would send word at once to Moray. It would not be long before James Stuart would return to Scotland to take the Regency.

There was at least one other who agreed with Morton. This was Elizabeth of England. She herself had been in a similar position seven years ago when her lover's wife had been found mysteriously dead at the bottom of a staircase, and Elizabeth with her lover Robert Dudley had appeared to be guilty of the murder. Mary had a shining example of royal behaviour in such a delicate situation. To marry Bothwell now would be to destroy herself, as to have married Dudley at the time of Amy Robsart's death would have destroyed Elizabeth.

The Queen of England had no love for her Scottish rival but she had a strong desire to preserve the dignity of royalty. She wrote warningly to Mary, but her warning meant nothing to the Queen of Scots. The Queen of England was governed by ambition; the Queen of Scots by her emotions which were now concentrated on the passion she felt for one man. Her hand was in that of her lover, and if he were dragging her down to destruction, he was with her and nothing else seemed of any real importance.

On a bright April day Mary set out for Stirling Castle in order to visit her son. She did so at the secret command of Bothwell. He himself had declared his intention of going to Liddesdale where fighting had broken out and his firm hand was needed.

She took with her a small retinue in which were included the lords Maitland and Huntley and Sir James Melville. As she rode out of Edinburgh the people came out to look at her. They were pleased that Bothwell had left the capital; Mary's lovely tragic face softened the hearts of the people to such an extent that they could not believe her to be guilty of murder.

'God bless Your Grace!' called the citizens; but they added: 'If you be innocent of the King's murder.'

If she be innocent! Mary shuddered. What would she not give to be innocent? Everything she possessed but one thing–the love of Bothwell.

Lord Maitland, riding beside her, was filled with fury against her and Bothwell. He saw clearly now how Bothwell had duped the lords, how he had secured their help in the murder of Darnley–not to rid Scotland of an encumbrance, but to remove the Queen's husband that he, Bothwell, might marry her.

That he should have been so used was galling to Maitland. He determined now that if Bothwell married the Queen they should never rule Scotland together. Maitland and Bothwell could never be anything but enemies.

Maitland had wished to serve the Queen. His wife was a very dear friend of the Queen's. He had worked faithfully for her until that time when she had taken Rizzio into her confidence and set him above Maitland. Now he saw that he had, with others, been Bothwell's dupe, and he was determined that he would never accept that man's domination.

Huntley looked sly. Maitland wondered what plans he had made with Bothwell, and as Bothwell was his brother-in-law. Maitland could guess. Bothwell would need Huntley's help if he were to break free from his wife.

Maitland must be on his guard. He had seen too much; he had been too clever. Bothwell, who had so cleverly rid the Queen and himself of Darnley, would have little compunction in being equally ruthless with others who threatened their schemes.

These were uneasy thoughts for Maitland on the road from Edinburgh to Stirling.

The Earl and Countess of Mar, who were the guardians of the little Prince, greeted the Queen with suspicion. News had travelled and they knew of the paper Bothwell had more or less forced the lords to sign. It occurred to Mar that it might be the plan of the Queen and her lover to kidnap the Prince. Mar was not going to lose his precious charge, and he made that quite clear.

Mary held the baby in her arms. He was ten months old, a solemn-faced, wise-looking little boy. He gazed with wonderment at his mother and she, smiling, let his little hand curl about her finger. He was placidly curious as she covered his face with kisses.

If she could take him away with her, live quietly in a nunnery with him, perhaps she would in time forget that she had any desire but to care for him. But such would never be allowed. Already the Earl of Mar was watching her suspiciously; insistent hands were stretched forward to take the baby from her. She was not allowed to be alone in the nursery.

'I am sorry, Madam,' said the Earl. 'The Prince has been accorded to my care and I have sworn to watch over him, night and day.'

'Even when he is with his mother?'

'At all times, Madam.'

So this was the state to which she was reduced–a mother who might not be alone with her child! She told herself fiercely: Soon it will be different. When I marry, my husband will stand beside me and there shall not a lord in Scotland who dares treat me thus.

They left Stirling on the third day. Her spirits were high, for she had always been happy in the saddle and she knew what was waiting for her on the road.

It was arranged between them. He would be there . . . towering above all men, striking terror into her escort, seizing her person, taking her as his prisoner to Dunbar, and there boldly–as the world would think–forcing her to submit to him. All would be well, for her future was in his hands.

But as they came nearer to Edinburgh she grew uneasy. He should have appeared before this. They were within a mile of Edinburgh Castle itself and unless he arrived almost immediately their plan would miscarry. But he did not disappoint her. She heard the sound of horses' hoofs pounding on the quiet earth as she rode into Foulbriggs, the small hamlet between Coltbridge and West Port; and as she was about to cross the foul stream–from which the place took its name and which was swollen with the filth from the city–Bothwell's strong force came into view. Blades gleaming, pikes aloft, they surrounded the Queen's small company. Bothwell rode up to her.

'What means this?' she asked.

'Madam,' said her lover. 'I must ask you to turn your horse and ride with me to Dunbar. You are my prisoner; but have no fear. No harm shall come to you if you obey.'

A young captain rode forward and prepared to do battle with Bothwell for the sake of the Queen.

'Put your sword away, my friend,' said the Queen. 'I command you to do so.'

'I'll take care of the young fool,' growled Bothwell.

'There shall be no bloodshed,' said the Queen.

The young soldier turned to Mary, his eyes alight with that devoted admiration which she so often inspired. 'Madam, I would die to save you.'

She smiled, and her smile was her answer. The young man knew that she was by no means disturbed by this adventure, that she was Bothwell's very willing prisoner.

Maitland cried: 'What means this?'

Bothwell flashed a brilliant smile in his direction. 'Patience, my lord

Maitland. Soon you will know.'

He then dismissed most of her retinue, but kept Lord Maitland, Lord Huntley and Sir James Melville with him; and the journey to Dunbar began.

The Queen rode ahead and Bothwell was beside her.

Mary waited in the apartment at Dunbar Castle which had been prepared for her.

Soon he would join her. She could close her eyes and imagine that she was in the Exchequer House on that evening before it all began. It would be just like that. They would enact that scene once again, and the whole world should believe that it was the first time it had taken place.

Bothwell would stand exposed to the world as the Queen's ravisher, and as his innocent victim she would declare that she must marry him. As for the unborn child–that would have to be explained later. It was imperative that she marry hastily, that the whole world should not be too shocked by her marriage, and that suspicions that she had been an accomplice in her husband's murder should be allayed.

It was a desperate scheme but their position was desperate. When she had glanced at his stern profile as he rode beside her from Foulbriggs to Dunbar Castle, she had revelled in his strength, in that power within him. How willingly would she surrender! How happily she waited for her ravisher!

In a room below, Melville was remonstrating with Bothwell. Maitland stood aloof; he knew too much. He understood that the Queen and Bothwell were already lovers. He knew that this was just another bridge which they had to cross together.

Melville said: 'Bothwell, know you not that this is treason? You are unlawfully detaining the Queen. For what purpose?'

'I shall marry the Queen,' said Bothwell.

'She will never consent,' said Melville.

'I will marry her whether she will or not. And it may be that by the time I release her from this castle she will be willing enough.'

Melville was aghast at the implication of those words.

Bothwell laughed and went to the Queen's apartment.

Melville turned to Maitland. How could Maitland appear so calm? Had he not heard Bothwell express his intention to ravish the Queen?

Maitland's smile was cynical. Should they be perturbed, it implied, because what was about to take place would be but a repetition of what had been happening for several months?

Maitland shrugged his shoulders. He was concerned with preserving his own life. He was secretly convinced that if he could keep alive for a few more weeks, he need never fear Bothwell again . . . nor the Queen.

Bothwell came to the Queen's apartment and he stood on the threshold of the room, smiling at her as he had smiled in the Exchequer House.

She cried out in feigned alarm: 'My lord . . . what means this?'

He smiled. As though she did not know! But he enjoyed the masquerade as much as she did. Of late she had perhaps been over-eager, and a certain amount of resistance had always appealed to him.

So she protested but her heart was not in the protest, and she was glad when she could surrender freely to his passion.

For twelve days he kept her at Dunbar Castle–his passionate mistress and his most willing slave.

At the end of that time the Queen was escorted back to Edinburgh. She rode into the city with Bothwell beside her, he holding her horse's bridle that the city might know that she was his captive.

Maitland was with them, plans forming in his clever mind. They would marry–those two foolish people–and they would ruin themselves. Morton was already in secret touch with Moray. The country was going to be roused against the King's murderers; and the hasty marriage, the threadbare plot of abduction and seduction would be seen through; the Queen would have none but Bothwell to stand beside her. When she took Bothwell she would lose all else.

Bothwell and Mary could think of little beyond their marriage which would make him King of Scotland and her the wife of her lover. Neither of them could look very far beyond their greatly desired goals.

There was one obstacle yet to be overcome. Bothwell was not free to marry; but he had already set in motion negotiations which would bring him a divorce on the grounds of consanguinity. The Archbishop of St Andrews signed the nullity agreement, but Jean was not satisfied with this. She had been truly married to Lord Bothwell, she declared; and that marriage had been entirely legal. She would not have it said otherwise. She would be happy to be free of Bothwell who had been no good husband to her, but she herself would seek a divorce on the grounds of adultery.

This caused a slight hitch. Bothwell had a reputation as a murderer, and all Scotland knew that he was an adulterer, but the whole world including the fanatical Philip in his Escorial, sly Catherine de' Medici in the Louvre, subtle Elizabeth in Greenwich, would now see him brought low through his wife's allegations. Jean was determined to have her revenge for the slights she had suffered. She named Bessie Crawford, the daughter of a blacksmith, as the partner in Bothwell's adultery.

The scandals grew. The story of Bothwell and Bessie became common knowledge. A Haddington merchant explained how he had one afternoon, on the instructions of Lord Bothwell, taken Bessie to the cloisters of Haddington Abbey; there he had locked her in and given the key–on Lord Bothwell's instructions–to his lordship. There Bessie and the Earl had remained together for a considerable time.

Is this the man who would be King of Scotland? people were asking each other. There were many ready to pry into the affairs of Bessie Crawford and Lord Bothwell and ensure that the whole world should know of them.

His enemies were already at work, but the bold Earl cared nothing for this. What mattered it how the divorce was brought about as long as his marriage with Jean was severed? He had the lords' consent on a document; he was free; Mary was free; and they would wait no longer.

John Craig, the preacher who had taken Knox's place in the Kirk when the latter, after the murder of Rizzio, had thought it wise to go to England and remain there, was loth to publish the banns.

Bothwell threatened him, but the man stood his ground. He begged the Earl to consider the Church's law against adultery and ravishment; he warned him of the likely suspicion of collusion between Bothwell and his wife, the too sudden divorce and above all his and Mary's complicity in Darnley's murder.

'Read the banns!' roared Bothwell. 'Or by Jesus I'll have you strung up by the neck.'

But John Craig turned away. His courage was high. 'There is only one thing which would make me do it–a written order from the Queen.'

Bothwell laughed. A written order from the Queen! What could be easier?

But he was disturbed. The preacher had boldly stated what was being said in secret.

According to the law, rape was punishable by death, and it was alleged that as Bothwell had raped the Queen, she felt in honour bound to marry him even though it was such a short time since her husband had died.

There were no ends to the twists and turns which must be made to extricate themselves from the position in which they found themselves.

Now Mary must declare that rape was forgiven if the woman subsequently acquiesced; and this, she declared, was what had happened in the case of herself and Lord Bothwell. To show her feelings for him she gave him fresh honours. He was made Earl of Orkney and Lord of Shetland. But the whispers were becoming louder throughout the land, and all were discussing the loose behaviour of the Queen and her paramour. The Queen was no better than Bessie Crawford, and nothing she could say or do would make the people believe that the man she proposed to make their King was anything but a seducer, an adulterer and a murderer.

The night before their marriage was due to take place, a placard was pinned on the door of the palace. It ran:

'Mense malas Maio nubere vulgus ait.'

It was alarming to be reminded through these words of Ovid's that wantons married in the month of May.

Nevertheless on that May morning, accompanied by Huntley, Glamis, Fleming, Livingstone and others–all of whom attended her with restrained feelings–Mary was, in the chapel at Holyrood, married to Bothwell.

But where was that bliss for which she had looked? He had never pretended, but now he had no time to play the lover. Now he must consolidate his position, and already the lords all over the country were making their animosity felt. He was ready. He loved a fight. And now he was preparing to fight for the crown of Scotland.

Mary began to realize the enormity of what she had done. She had married her lover, notorious as the seducer of Bessie Crawford; she had debased her royalty–an unforgivable sin in the eyes of all those who were royal. Her relatives in France were numbed by the shock. Catherine de' Medici in public declared herself shocked and saddened beyond expression, but in private gave full vent to her delight and satisfaction; Philip of Spain had nothing to offer but contempt, and that he showed by silence. Elizabeth of England, while pleased at the prospects of the inevitable result, was genuinely shocked that the Queen should so betray herself and her crown. Elizabeth could not help but remember how near to disaster she had come in circumstances so similar; but she had been wise; she had known when to draw back.

There was less contentment now for Mary than ever before, since she could not help knowing that her lover was outgrowing his passion. To him she was but a woman with a crown–and now the crown was his. If she could have fallen out of love with him as she had with Darnley she would have suffered far less. But she could do no such thing; his indifference could not turn her from him.

He neglected her and absented himself for long periods, during which she believed he saw Jean Gordon. She would lie awake at night picturing them together. She believed that sly sandy-haired Jean merely pretended not to be in love with him.

She reproached him on his return but he merely laughed at her, neither admitting nor denying that her surmise was correct.

'You can talk of Jean Gordon when we are in such danger!' he cried. 'Do you know that our enemies are massing their forces against us?'

'But you have visited her. I believe you still think of her as your wife!'

'There is that in her which makes me think of her so. You have always seemed as my mistress.'

Did he mean that or was it part of his brutality? She did not know.

She was exhausted from sleepless nights. Darnley's ghost seemed to mock her. 'You have changed husbands. I died that you might do so. But has it proved to be a change for the better?'

She could not bear his indifference, his cold matter-of-fact passion.

Once she withdrew herself from his arms and, half clad as she was, rushed to the door of her apartment calling to Jane Kennedy to bring her a knife.

'A knife, Madam? A *knife*!'

'That I may pierce my heart with it. I cannot endure to live this life. I would rather be dead.'

Then she flung herself on to her bed and gave way to passionate weeping.

All over the country the lords were gathering. Moray was watching from some distance, waiting to leap forward and seize the Regency when the Queen was defeated. Morton called together Argyle, Atholl and Mar, and told them that Kirkcaldy of Grange was ready to lead an army against Bothwell and the Queen; and that Glencairn, Cassillis, Montrose, Caithness, Ruthven, Lindsay and others were with them. Maitland was still at Holyrood, but waiting his opportunity to escape and join the rebels. Maitland had made up his mind. Mary was unfit to rule. Her conduct of the past year had shown that clearly. The woman who had gathered an army together at the time she had married Darnley and marched against Moray with the country rallying to her, was not the same woman as this love-sick creature. At that time Mary could have risen to greatness; her future might have been assured; but alas, steadily she had taken the downhill road which could only lead to eventual defeat.

Bothwell was aware of the forces gathering against him. He left Sir James Balfour holding Edinburgh Castle and departed with Mary for Borthwick.

It was not for love of her that he was with her constantly now, but because he feared that the rebels might seek to capture her. She reproached him for this, but he made no effort to console her.

Before they had been many days in that solid fortress which was built on a steep mound, surrounded by a moat, and possessed towers so strongly fortified as to discountenance invaders, Lord Hume arrived and demanded the surrender of Bothwell. Awaiting the arrival of his Borderers the Earl roared forth his defiance, but as the days passed and his men did not come he began to calculate how long he could withstand a siege. The castle, with its central fortress, its winding passages, its low arches, its windows which were thirty feet from the ground, was a stronghold, but he had no intention of starving to death. He decided he must break out of the castle.

'Take me with you,' begged Mary.

He shook his head. 'Impossible. One of us might get through. Two would surely be caught. If I can break through the guards I shall ride with all speed to Dunbar. Then I shall muster my men, and, by God, I'll have Hume's head. I'll have the heads of all rebels.'

'Oh my dearest, make sure that it is not they who take your head.'

'My head and shoulders are as firmly wedded as we are!' he cried.

She clung to him, all tenderness, begging him to take care.

He put her from him and, in spite of the enemy guard surrounding the castle, he managed to break out.

Those who had been set to guard the castle, on discovering that Bothwell had eluded them, were afraid to touch the Queen, and they started off towards Edinburgh believing that Bothwell had returned there. Then, dressed in the clothes of a boy–for she dared not attract attention to herself, Mary was lowered from the window of the banqueting hall on to the grass some thirty feet below, and hurried down the mound where she found a horse, saddled and waiting for her. Then began her ride through that wild country of glens and swamps, moorland and mountain. It was many long hours before she reached Dunbar. Bothwell, hearing of her approach to the castle came out to meet her. He lifted her from her horse and held her at arms' length.

'You make a bonny boy!' he said. And he slung her across his shoulder and carried her into Dunbar Castle.

For the rest of that night she was ecstatically happy. Everything seemed worth while. They made love and afterwards they made plans, and then made love again.

He said at length: 'We cannot remain here. We shall have to ride forth to meet them.'

'We shall win, my dearest,' she cried. 'We shall win and be happy together. You could not fail. Anything you desired you would win.'

'Thrones are not such easy prey as queens.'

'Queens are not easy prey,' she answered, 'except for those whom they love. And to those whom Fortune loves, thrones may come more easily than the love of a queen.'

He kissed her and they were fiercely passionate lovers again. She wondered whether it was because he feared there would be little time left for loving.

She determined to ride with him at the head of the army.

She had come to Dunbar dressed as a boy and there was none of her own garments at Dunbar Castle. No women's clothes could be found for her except that of a citizen's wife. She put on a red petticoat; and the sleeves of her bodice were tied with points; a black velvet hat and a scarf were found for her. And so, dressed as a tradesman's wife–she rode out to meet those who had rebelled against her. Her spirits were high, for beside her rode Bothwell.

The armies met at Musselburgh and the Queen's encamped on Carberry Hill close to that spot where some twenty years before the famous battle of Pinkie Cleugh had been fought; but now that the two armies were face to face they both appeared reluctant to fight.

For a whole day inactivity reigned, each side anxious not to have the sun facing them during battle, and now that they had come to the point, the rebels had no wish to fight against the Queen nor had the Queen to fight against her own subjects.

So the long day passed–each side alert and waiting, watching each other from opposite hills across the little brook which flowed between them.

In the afternoon Du Croc, the French ambassador, rode to the rebels and declared his readiness to act as mediator between the two forces.

'We have not,' said Glencairn to the Frenchman, 'come to ask pardon but to give it. If the Queen is willing to withdraw herself from the wretch who holds her captive, we will recognize her as our sovereign. If, on the other hand, Bothwell will come forth between the two armies and make good his boast that he will meet in single combat any who should declare he is the murderer of the King, we will produce a champion to meet him, and if he desires it another and another, ten or twelve.'

'You cannot seriously mean me to lay these proposals before the Queen,' protested Du Croc.

'We will name no other,' said Glencairn, and Kirkcaldy and Morton joined with him in this. 'We would rather be buried alive than not have the death of the King investigated.'

Du Croc then went to the Queen. Bothwell was with her.

He cried: 'What is it that the lords are at?'

Du Croc answered: 'They declare themselves to be willing servants of the Queen but that they are your mortal foes.'

'They are sick with envy,' said Bothwell. 'They wish to stand in my place. Did they not all sign the bond promising to make good my cause and defend it with their lives and goods?'

Mary said quickly: 'I would have all know that I espouse my husband's quarrel and consider it my own.'

Du Croc then told her of the suggestion that Bothwell should engage a chosen champion in single combat. Mary looked fearful. She could not agree to that, she declared. There should be no single combat. What man was there on the other side who was of high enough rank to fight with her husband?

'Unless this is done,' said Du Croc, 'there will be bitter fighting.'

'Stay and see it,' said Bothwell. 'I can promise you fine pastime, for there will be good fighting.'

'I should be sorry to see it come to that for the sake of the Queen and for both armies.'

'Why, man,' boasted Bothwell, 'I shall win the day. I have four thousand men and three pieces of artillery. They have no artillery and only three thousand men.'

'You have but yourself as general,' said Du Croc. 'Do not forget that with them are the finest soldiers in Scotland. Moreover there is some discontent I believe among your people.'

When he had gone Bothwell and the Queen looked round them at their army and, to their dismay, they saw that Du Croc had spoken the truth. Many of those who had marched behind her banner were now visibly deserting to the other side. They did not wish to serve under the banner of an adulteress and a woman who had, they all believed, had a hand in the murder of her husband.

Bothwell then rode forward shouting: 'Come forth! Come forth! Which of you will engage in single combat?'

Kirkcaldy stepped forward.

Terrified for her lover, Mary galloped up to his side.

'I forbid it!' she cried. 'There must be someone of rank equal to that of my husband. I will not have him demeaned by this combat.'

Bothwell cried: 'Let Lord Morton step forth. I will do battle with him.'

But Morton had no wish for the fight. His friends rallied to his side and declared that such a man as himself must not face the danger of combat. He was worth a hundred such as Bothwell.

Bothwell had no desire to fight any but Morton, and when others were offered he declined to accept them as opponents. And while this farce was in progress Mary saw with dismay that her force was dwindling so fast that there were scarcely sixty men left to support her cause.

She asked that Kirkcaldy should come to her and, when he came, she asked him what terms he would give.

'That you leave your husband, Madam, and the lords will submit to you.'

'You mean that he will go free if I return to Edinburgh with you?'

'Yes, Madam. Those are our conditions.'

She looked about her in despair. Bothwell stood apart with a few–a very few–of his Borderers. She knew that there were two alternatives. She must part with her lover or see him slaughtered before her eyes. She asked that she might be allowed to speak to him.

Drawing him aside she said: 'We must part. It is the only way. You will be allowed to ride off with your men unmolested.'

'And they will take you back to Edinburgh. For what, think you?'

'I am their Queen. They will remember that. I shall force them to remember it.'

'You place too much trust in them.'

'I can do nothing else.'

'Mount your horse. Pretend to bid me farewell . . . and then . . . we will gallop off to Dunbar. There we will fortify ourselves. We will defend the castle while we raise an army.'

'They would kill us. That is what they mean to do. They mean to part us. They will do it either by our willing separation or by death.'

'I demand that you do as I say.'

But she shook her head and gave him her tragic smile. She was the Queen and he could no longer force her to his will. She longed to ride with him, but greater than her desire for him was her fear for his safety.

'I shall go with them.' she said.

Kirkcaldy rode up to them. 'The time is up, Madam,' he said. 'Unless you make an immediate decision I shall be unable to hold my men.'

Bothwell held her in his arms. In those last moments she was aware of an exasperated tenderness. She had decided, and he was opposed to her decision. He believed that once more her emotions had played her false and that she was delivering herself defenceless into the hands of her enemies. His last kiss held a plea. Do not trust them. Leap on to your horse. We will snap our fingers at that mighty army. We will ride together to Dunbar.

But she, who had been so weak in love, could also be strong.

Let them do what they would with her, let them deceive her; he had an opportunity of riding away unmolested. He would find his way to safety.

One more kiss; one last embrace.

A terrible desolation came over her, for she had a sad premonition that she would never see his face again. She wavered and clung to him afresh. But Kirkcaldy was impatiently waiting.

He helped her into the saddle and she turned her horse.

Bothwell had shrugged his shoulders; his spurs pressed into his horse's flanks and he was away.

She turned her head, straining for the last glimpse of him; but Kirkcaldy had laid his hand on her bridle and was leading her away.

How right he had been! How wrong she was to trust them!

She knew that if she lived twenty years she could never live through such horror, such shameful humiliation, as now awaited her.

Seeing her thus, mounted on her jennet, stripped of her royalty, a conquered queen in a red petticoat, the rebel soldiers, remembering and repeating the rumours they had heard of her, inflamed by the vilification of years which had been hurled against her by John Knox, jeered as they gloated on her humiliation.

The whispering first started among the low soldiery. 'Who murdered the King?'

The rest took up the cry. 'Burn the adulteress. Burn the murderess.'

The soldiers crowded about her and Kirkcaldy had to hold some back with his sword.

'Bring her to the city–the scene of her shame!' they cried. 'Let her see what the citizens of Edinburgh have to say to her.'

So she was led towards her capital, and two soldiers, bearing a banner extending between two pikes, marched before her; the banner was turned towards her that she might read the crude inscription thereon. On this banner had been painted a figure of Darnley lying murdered, and beside him was a smaller figure which was meant to represent Prince James, Darnley's son and hers. The little Prince was on his knees praying: 'Judge and revenge my cause, O Lord.'

'Make way! Make way!' cried the soldiers. 'Good people of Scotland, we bring you the murderess. We bring the woman who, with her lover, slew her husband. We bring you the whore of Scotland. Make way for the adulteress.'

She was alone; she had lost her strong man and had given herself over to traitors, but as always in terrible adversity she found great courage.

She took the hand of Lord Lindsay of the Byres who was beside her and cried: 'By this hand which is now in yours I swear I'll have your head for this outrage.'

'Madam,' said Lindsay, 'look to it that you do not lose your own.'

For hours it lasted, that terrible ride. She was exhausted and only pride kept back the tears of heartbreak. Never had a queen been treated so. If her lover had been with her now, how different it would have been. Then they would not have dared to treat her so. She should have obeyed him. Then he and she would now be riding to Dunbar . . . together.

She kept her eyes fixed on the hideous banner. She had lost everything–her lover, her child, her throne.

It was twilight when they came to Edinburgh. Crowds thronged the Canongate to watch her pass; and there was not one friend in the city to give her a word of comfort.

'Here comes the murderess,' they cried. 'Let us burn the whore.'

Morton had arranged that the procession should take an indirect route through the city. Mary did not at first understand why. Then suddenly she realized what they were doing; they were taking her along the road which led to Kirk-o'-Field. They halted for a moment before the ruins of that house in which Darnley had been murdered. There the banner was brought close before her eyes, and the people crowded in on her.

'Burn her! Burn her! Now . . . *now*! Why do we wait? She betrays her guilt.'

'Good people,' cried Mary, 'I beg of you let me speak.'

But her words were lost in howls of derision. And as the people closed in on her Kirkcaldy once more drove them off with his sword. Lindsay, Morton and Atholl were forced to join him.

Almost unconscious with strain and exhaustion she was taken to the provost's house and there put into the strong room, the window of which looked straight on to the street. About the window the rabble clustered and the banner was set up outside so that every time she lifted her eyes she could see it.

But for Kirkcaldy she could not have lived through that night. Kirkcaldy had not foreseen what would happen; he was a general who had promised safe conduct to the Queen, and since he had given that promise he meant it to be kept. Morton had no such scruples and had it rested with him he would have let the people have their way. He knew that Moray was on the way back from France. It was true that Huntley, with some of his Catholics, was half-heartedly preparing to rally to the Queen, but the people were all against her. They believed her to be guilty of adultery and murder, and they cried: 'Take her to the stake. That is the place for sinners such as she is, be they queens or commoners.'

There was no food for her in the provost's house; there was no bed; she had no means of bathing her face or changing her clothes.

She paced the room, moaning softly to herself, worn out with fatigue, distressed and hysterical. All through the night people thronged the streets and the fiery light of torches filled the room.

Again and again she tried to speak to them; she tried to win their sympathy. She stood at the window, her hair loose about her shoulders; in her great agitation she plucked at her bodice until it was in shreds and her breasts bared. She beat against the walls; she wept; and at last she sank to the floor, moaning and whimpering.

Outside the cry of 'Burn the adulteress! Burn the murderess!' was chanted through the streets.

Another day came. She went to the window, her long hair covering her bare shoulders.

'Good people . . .' she cried. 'Good people . . .'

But their only answer was: 'Burn her. Burn the murderess of her husband!'

The dreadful banner was before her eyes. She wept and stormed. Then she saw Lord Maitland passing along the street. She called to him. He would have looked away but the sight she presented was so terrible that out of pity he was forced to turn back.

'Come here, Maitland,' she cried. 'Come here.'

He knew that if he followed his inclination to hurry away he would be haunted by the memory of her eyes for ever.

She looked at him–the husband of her dear Flem–and one of those who had betrayed her. How wicked was the world, how cruel!

'So you are with them now?' she called. 'So you are with my enemies, Maitland?'

'Madam,' he answered, 'I served you well until you chose others who you thought would serve you better.'

He had never forgiven her for supplanting him with David. He would never forgive her for her marriage with Bothwell.

She cried: 'Did *you* not know then of the plot to murder Darnley! Were you not in the plot, my lord?'

His answer was: 'Madam, you destroyed yourself when you took Bothwell for husband. Had you not become his slave and the slave of your own passion, you would not now stand guilty of murder.'

The crowd roared: 'Burn the murderess!'

Maitland averted his eyes and passed on.

In that moment she knew that all who had planned to murder Darnley were against her. They would–as Maitland would– revile her, doing their utmost to put all the guilt on her shoulders and those of her lover, that investigations should not be made concerning themselves. The murder of Darnley–like the murder of Rizzio–would be shown to the Scots and the world not as a political murder, but as a *crime passionel.*

She was lost. She knew it. Maitland had had some honour in the old days. He had been one of those whom she could trust; but Maitland was ready to save his own life and his political rewards at the cost of the reputation, and perhaps the life, of the Queen.

She lived through another day of torment, and that evening, because they feared for her reason, they took her from the provost's house to Holyrood. She was forced to walk as a captive with Morton on one side of her, Atholl on the other, while the soldiers marched with them to protect her from the murderous rabble. As she walked the odious banner was held before her eyes and she prayed for death.

But in Holyrood some comfort awaited her, for there she found some of her women, and among them those two loved ones, Mary Seton and Mary Livingstone.

She wept in their arms and they swore that they would not leave her; they would die with her and for her if need be.

But her captors did not intend her to stay at Holyroodhouse. Late that night she was hurried out of the palace and, hysterical and exhausted with misery and fatigue, she was taken through the darkness to Lochleven where her jailors would be the Douglases–Sir William and his wife who was Moray's mother.

And there, in the ancient castle on an island in the centre of a lake, Mary Stuart came to the end of her turbulent reign, for that night she passed into the half-light, a prisoner. She was twenty-four years of age and had many years left to her, but her life as Queen was virtually over.

Mary, Queen of Scotland and the Isles, had become Mary, the captive.

It was the month of February, and in her apartment in Fotheringay Castle the Queen was dividing her possessions into separate piles. There was a little money and some trinkets–not very much left after twenty years of prison–and there were so many to whom she wished to leave some token, some memory of herself.

She was very tired; she had lived little more than forty-four years but it seemed twice as long.

She looked at that dark corner in which one of her ladies–her dear Jane Kennedy–sat silently weeping, rocking her body to and fro in the agony of her grief.

Elizabeth Curle, another of those who had been with her in many of her doleful prisons and who loved her, did not weep, but her grief was manifest in every line of her body. The others had run from the chamber, for they could not control their sobbing.

'My children, my children,' said the Queen softly, 'it is not a time to weep. You should rather rejoice to see me on a fair road of deliverance from the many evils and afflictions which have so long been my portion.'

They did not answer her; and her thoughts travelled back to that road along which she had come. So many years ago it had been since she had said good-bye to her lover. Twenty years! And she had not seen him since that day. He had become but a memory to her, a memory that was both sweet and bitter.

Life had been little kinder to him than to her. He had escaped to Denmark, but not to freedom. Anna Throndsen had forgotten the love she had once had for him and had sued him in the courts for money she had given him in the past. Mary's family, the Guises, would not allow a man who had ruined their niece to regain his freedom. They had arranged with Denmark that he should be imprisoned in the Castle of Malmoe, and there he had spent ten weary years. He had died at length, of melancholy, it was said; half mad with frustration, he, the strong man, confined within four walls would dash his head in very desperation against those walls; he too had been glad to die. And before he had died he had written a confession declaring her innocent of Darnley's murder although he himself had played a large part in it. That confession had brought great comfort to Mary in Chatsworth–where she had been imprisoned at that time–for it brought with it a vivid reminder of that immense strength which was without fear. Poor Bothwell! Poor lover, who had once believed the world was his to conquer and subdue. Ambition had ruined him as certainly as passion had ruined her.

But that was all long ago, and there was no need to dwell upon it, for soon she would be past all earthly pain.

Memories of Lochleven came to her–of George and Willie Douglas who had loved her and sought to help her escape from her prison. It came back to her in clear brief pictures: Lochleven where she had been forced to sign her abdication and had known that her son had become the King of Scotland: Lochleven where she had given birth to twins–hers and Bothwell's–still-born and so tragically symbolic: Lochleven from where she had all but escaped dressed as a laundress, and had been betrayed because a boatman had seen her beautiful hands which could never have belonged to a laundress. But it was at Lochleven that George and Willie Douglas had loved her and had determined to give their lives if need be for her sake, so that eventually, with their aid she had escaped, but alas! only to Langside and utter defeat at the hands of her brother Moray's troops.

She had known then that her only hope was flight from Scotland, but where could she seek refuge? She must be a fugitive from her own land; her son was lost to her, brought up by her enemies to believe the worst of her; her own brother was determined on her defeat and offered her nothing but a prison or death.

Could she go to France? she had asked herself. She thought of her family there. But France was ruled by an evil woman, a woman who had never shown herself to be Mary's friend. How could she throw herself on the mercy of Catherine de' Medici?

There was only one to whom she could appeal for mercy–the Queen of

England; and so for more than eighteen years she remained the prisoner of Elizabeth. She had asked for hospitality and had been given captivity. And during those years there had been one subject which had always been raised when her name was mentioned: the subject of the Casket Letters.

She often thought of those letters, which had been read by all the important people of England and Scotland; the whole world discussed them. There were some who declared they were the actual letters and poems Mary had written to her lover; others insisted that they were forgeries. If they were authentic, then Mary was exposed as an adulteress and murderess; if they were false, then Mary's story remained a mystery which none could ever solve. The testament of tortured men could count for little. Such confessions gave satisfaction to none but those who extorted them, and were worthless.

How clear it all became when she looked back on it. Moray, Maitland, Morton–they were the leaders and they were determined to destroy her. They would show her to her subjects as a murderess and adulteress, for only thus could they rouse the people against her.

Those men, who had certainly been more deeply concerned in the murder of her husband than she had, now banded together and self-righteously sought to force her–with Bothwell–to take all the blame. It was necessary to their policy that she and Bothwell should do so; they had sought to write her epitaph for her own generation and all generations to come: Mary Stuart who was involved with her lover in her husband's murder for the sake of an adulterous passion.

Would they succeed? How could she know? She could only hope that after she was dead there would be those who sought to sift the truth from the lies and at least do her justice.

'Oh God,' she prayed aloud, 'have mercy on me. The thief on the cross was forgiven; but I am a greater sinner than he was. Have mercy on me in this hour of my death as You had on him.'

Would her story have been different, she wondered, if Geordie Dalgleish had not produced the silver casket? Would it have been possible for her to return to her country and reign as its Queen, but for those incriminating letters?

Geordie had been arrested when all Bothwell's servants had been taken up and tortured with the object of making them confess that Bothwell and Mary–and they alone–had been responsible for Darnley's murder.

Geordie had been Bothwell's tailor and, as a servant of the Earl, suspect. Perhaps to curry favour with his tormentors he had shown them the silver casket which he said had been found beneath his master's bed.

Those revealing sonnets were exposed to the world. She had written to her lover of her innermost feelings; and now the whole world was reading what she had written for his eyes alone. She had written letters to her lover, and those letters must have conveyed her great passion for him; but she surely had never written those cruel words, those brutal words, which were said to have been penned while she sat by Darnley's bedside!

How angry she had been, how shocked, how humiliated! She had wept tears of rage when she had heard that the poems and letters were being publicly read; but now even that seemed of little moment.

In those early days of captivity her hopes had been high. She had been taken from prison to prison–from Carlisle to Bolton, Tutbury, Coventry, Chatsworth, Sheffield, Buxton, Chartley and finally to Fotheringay.

Buxton held a bitter-sweet memory for it was at Buxton that the last of her Maries to be with her–Seton–had come near to marriage with Andrew Beaton.

A sad little story theirs had been. Mary Seton had had one great love in her life and that was for her mistress and namesake. Of the four Maries Seton was the one who had loved the Queen best. Andrew Beaton had fallen in love with the quiet and gentle Seton and had spent seven years trying to persuade her to leave her mistress. Mary had watched them and had longed to see her faithful Seton happily married, as she knew she would have been with such a man as Andrew. Why should Seton spend her life in captivity because her mistress must?

Seton made excuses. She would not marry. She had solemnly vowed herself to celibacy. She would never leave her mistress.

But the Queen wished to see the love-story brought to a happy conclusion against the grim background of her prison. It had been a pleasant occupation, during the long evenings, to plan for those two.

It was her idea that Andrew should go to Rome to have Seton's vow nullified. Andrew had left, and what a sad day it had been for her as well as for Seton when the news had come of Andrew's sickness and death.

So Seton's vow was not broken and Seton remained with her mistress seven years after the death of Andrew; but by that time Seton herself was in danger of dying, for the cold and damp of the prisons she shared with the Queen had affected her health so severely that Mary had to command her to go away and save her life.

'I *must* bear these hardships,' Mary had said. 'But there is no need for you to. I would rather have you living away from me, dearest Seton, than staying here a little longer to die.'

So Seton had at last been persuaded, but only when she was too sick for argument, to go to Mary's Aunt Renée at the Rheims convent. How overjoyed Mary would have been could she have accompanied her! But not for Mary was the seclusion of the nunnery; she must endure her damp prisons. She had come near to death through rheumatic fever and, after a miraculous recovery, was often attacked by such pains that she could not walk for days at a time.

And at last she had come to Fotheringay. There were only a few more hours left to her in this last of her prisons before she passed on to another life.

The long weary years had gone; but many of them had been filled with hopes. There had been suitors for her hand. Norfolk was one, and he had lost his head because he had become involved with her. Did she bring bad luck to those who loved her? Don John of Austria was another. He was dead now–some said he died by poison.

There had been many plots which had filled her with temporary hopes; plots with Norfolk, the Ridolfi plot, and, last of all, the Babington plot.

It was six o'clock on the morning of February the 8th, 1587.

Turning to her women, Mary said: 'I have but two hours to live. Dry your eyes and dress me as for a festival, for at last I go to that for which I have longed.'

But she had to dress herself–her women's fingers faltered so. They could not see her clearly for the tears which filled their eyes.

She put on her crimson velvet petticoat, her green silk garters and shoes of Spanish leather. She picked up her camisole of finest Scotch plaid which reached from her throat to her waist.

'For my friends,' she said, 'I shall have to remove my dress, and I would not appear naked before so many people who will come to see me die.'

She put on her dress of black velvet, spangled with gold, and her black satin pourpoint and kirtle; her pomander chain was about her neck, and at her girdle were her beads and cross. Over her head she wore white lawn trimmed with bone lace.

'Watch over this poor body in my last hour,' she said to her weeping women, 'for I shall be incapable of bestowing any care upon it.'

Jane Kennedy flung herself on her knees and declared that she would be there to cover her dearest mistress's body as it fell.

'Thank you, Jane,' said Mary. 'Now I shall pray awhile.'

She knelt before the altar in her oratory and prayed for the forgiveness of her sins. 'So many sins,' she murmured. 'So many foolish sins. . . .'

She prayed for poor Anthony Babington who have given his name to the plot which had finally brought her to this . . . a young man in her service who had loved her as so many had done. Poor Anthony! He had paid the price of his devotion. He had suffered horrible torment at Tyburn, that cruellest of deaths which was accorded to traitors.

And now she herself faced death.

She took the consecrated wafer which the Pope had sent her, and administered the Eucharist herself–a special concession from the Pope which had never before been allowed a member of the laity.

Then she prayed again for courage to face her ordeal, and remained on her knees until morning dawned.

Too soon they came to take her to the hall of execution.

She rose from her knees but she found it difficult to walk without aid, so crippled with rheumatism were her limbs.

Her servants helped her but, when she reached the door of the gallery, they were stopped by the Earls of Shrewsbury and Kent and told that the Queen must proceed alone.

There was great lamentation among her servants, who declared they would not leave their mistress. Mary implored the Earls to grant her this last request.

'It is unmeet,' said the Earl of Kent, 'troublesome to Your Grace and unpleasing to us. They would put into practice some superstitious trumpery, such as dipping their handkerchiefs into Your Grace's blood.'

'My lord, you shall have my word that no such thing shall be done.'

Finally the two Earls gave her permission to take with her as escort, two of her women and four of her men. She took Sir Andrew Melville Master of her Household, Bourgoigne her physician, Gourion her surgeon, and Gervais her apothecary for the four men; and the two women were her beloved Jane Kennedy and Elizabeth Curle.

As she was assisted slowly and painfully down the staircase to the hall, she saw that Andrew Melville was overcome by his grief.

'Weep not, Melville,' she said. 'This world is full of vanities and full of sorrows. And fortunate I am to leave it. I am a Catholic, dear Melville, and you a Protestant; but remember this, there is one Christ. I die, firm in my religion, a true Scotswoman and true to France. Commend me to my sweet son. Tell him to appeal to God and not to human aid. Let him learn from his mother's sorrows. May God forgive all those who have long thirsted for my blood as the hart doth for the brooks of water. Farewell, good Melville. Pray for your Queen.'

Melville could not answer her. He could only turn away while the uncontrollable sobs shook his body.

Into the hall of death she went. Melville bore her train, and Jane and Elizabeth, who had put on mourning weeds, covered their faces with their hands so that only their shaking bodies betrayed their grief.

Mary saw that a platform had been set up at the end of the hall. A fire was burning in the grate. She saw the platform, covered with black cloth; she saw the axe and the block.

She reached the chair–also black-covered–which had been provided for her, but she could not, without aid, mount the two steps to reach it.

As she was helped to this, she said in a clear voice: 'I thank you. This is the last trouble I shall ever give you.'

The death warrant was read to her. The Dean of Peterborough pleaded with her to turn from the Catholic Faith while there was yet time. To both she preserved a dignified indifference.

The moment of death was drawing near. The executioner was, in the traditional manner, asking her forgiveness.

'I forgive you with all my heart,' she cried.

Looking about her she prayed silently for courage. It was not her enemies who unnerved her. It was Jane Kennedy's quivering body, Elizabeth Curle's suppressed sobbing, Andrew Melville's tears and the sad looks of the others which made her want to weep.

Her uncle, the great Balafré, had once told her that when her time came she would know well how to die, for she possessed the courage of the Guises.

She was in urgent need of that courage now. Her two women had come forward to help her prepare herself. She kissed them and blessed them, but they could do little to help her remove her gown; their fingers trembled, but the Queen's were steady. She stood calm and brave in her camisole and red velvet petticoat, while Jane Kennedy fumbled with the gold-edged handkerchief which she tied over her mistress's eyes.

Now Mary was shut away from the hall of tragedy; she could no longer see the faces of those who loved her, distorted with grief; she was shut in with her own courage.

Jane had flung herself at her mistress's feet and was kissing her petticoat. Mary felt the soft face and knew it was Jane.

'Weep not, dear Jane,' she said, 'but pray for me.'

She knelt there on the cushion provided for her, murmuring: 'In thee, Lord, have I hoped. Let me never be put to confusion.'

Groping, she felt for the block; the executioner guided her to it. She laid her head upon it saying: 'Into Thy hands, O Lord, I commend my spirit.'

Bulle, the executioner, hesitated. This was his trade; his victim had forgiven him, knowing this; yet never before had he been called upon to wield the axe for one who affected him so deeply with her grace and dignity.

Every eye in the hall was upon him. He faltered. He dealt a blow. There was a gasp from the watchers, for the axe had slipped and though the blood of Mary Stuart gushed forth, she was merely wounded.

Trembling, Bulle again raised his axe; but his nerve was affected. Again he struck, and again he failed to complete his work.

It was with the third stroke that he severed the Queen's head from her body.

Then he grasped the beautiful chestnut hair, crying: 'God save Queen Elizabeth! So perish all her enemies.'

But the head had rolled on to the bloodstained cloth which covered the scaffold, and it was a wig which the executioner held up before him.

There was silence in the hall as all eyes turned to the head with the cropped grey hair–the head of a woman grown old in captivity.

And as they watched, they saw a movement beneath the red velvet petticoat, and Mary's little Skye terrier, who unnoticed had followed his mistress into the hall, ran to the head and crouched beside it, whimpering.

The silence was only broken by the sounds of sobbing.

The Queen of Scotland and the Isles had come to the end of her journey–from triumph and glory to captivity, from joy to sorrow, from the thrones of France and Scotland to the axe in the hall of Fotheringay Castle–and to peace.

The Goldsmith's Wife

Jean Plaidy

Author's Note

It is unfortunate that Shakespeare's play, *Richard III*, with its misstatements and distortions and exaggerated character-drawing of the central figure, should be generally accepted as history. But such is the case, so that if Richard is written about from any other angle an explanation seems advisable.

Handicapped as he was by living under Tudor rule, Shakespeare naturally dared not contradict the historians of his day, whose concern it was to vilify Richard in order to applaud the Tudor usurpation, and in so doing lay the blame for the foulest crimes of the period upon Richard.

Since the Tudors guiltily destroyed any state papers which might confound their falsehoods, it is not easy to discover the truth of what happened during Richard's brief reign. The evidence obtainable has been sifted and analysed, and I am sure that the fair-minded will agree that the picture of Richard as presented in *The Goldsmith's Wife* is a balanced one.

As for Jane's discovery of Anne Neville, that is entirely fictional. How Richard discovered his future wife is a mystery; but, taking into consideration Jane's adventurous and warm-hearted nature, together with the fact that, owing to her upbringing in Cheapside, it is more likely that she, rather than any other at court, would have been in touch with the humbler citizens of London, my theory of Anne's rescue seems plausible.

The books to which I am indebted are too numerous to set out here in detail, but the chief of them are:

History of England, by William Hickman Smith Aubrey.
The Lives of the Queens of England, by Agnes Strickland.
Life of Richard III, by Sir Thomas More.
Richard III, by Caroline Halsted.
History of the Life and Reign of Richard the Third, by James Gairdner.
Life and Papers of Richard III, edited by James Gairdner.
Prejudice and Promise in the Fifteenth Century, by C. L. Kingsford.
Historic Doubts on the Life of Richard III, by Horace Walpole.

J.P.

Cheapside

Down in the cellars under his house in Cheapside, Thomas Wainstead was instructing his servant, Jeffers, on the drawing of good Malmsey which would be needed for supper. Thomas, a round and plump man, his face rosy with good living, his clothes plain but of the very best material to be bought, looked what he was–a successful mercer of Cheapside. He was God-fearing, zealous in the carrying out of his duties, an honest tradesman, a good citizen, a man of substance. Yet, as he talked to Jeffers, there were signs of uneasiness upon his face; and Jeffers, twenty-eight, and good-looking enough to make many a housemaid, serving wench, or even a citizen's wife turn to take a second look at him, knew full well the cause of his master's uneasiness; for Jeffers also felt this apprehensive elation which, since yesterday, had filled the house.

The reason was tangible enough. Upstairs in her room, with the help of her maid Kate, Thomas Wainstead's daughter Jane was preparing herself for this evening's company. When Thomas and his servant came up from the cellars to the ground floor it would doubtless be possible to hear the young voice of Mistress Jane singing as she made her toilet. She was a gay young girl, and her speech was ever interrupted with laughter that set even her father's lips twitching, in spite of his determination to be stern and suppress those lively spirits, which, together with the most uncommon beauty of the child, were driving him, so he told himself, to an early grave.

Jane, but yesterday returned from Northamptonshire, had, in twelve hours, made a different place of this house; and, in spite of his pride in the girl, Thomas was far from pleased. He had hoped that a year or so in Northamptonshire might change her, for the country should have a quietening effect. Thomas mourned afresh his gay and pretty wife, who had died when Jane was but a child. Perhaps she would have known the right way in which to treat their daughter. Yesterday, when the girl had returned home, he had known immediately that he would have to find a husband for her, and that speedily. Jane was irrepressible. She was sixteen now, and lovelier than she had been at fifteen when he had sent her into Northamptonshire; and at fifteen he had seen troubles ahead.

She was very beautiful, with her sparkling blue-grey eyes, her abundant yellow hair and her delicate colouring. People spoilt her. The servants and apprentices–even when she was a child–had risked scoldings and whippings for the sake of young Jane. For she, though so beautiful and in full knowledge of her grace and charm, was warm of heart and easily moved to compassion. Quick of wit, she was no respecter of persons. Once he had found her helping an old woman with the water she was carrying from the conduit–a lousy, dirty old woman with whom she should have known it was not meet for a mercer's daughter to converse. He remembered that day well–a hot day, and the stench from the Fleet, into which the tanners and butchers flung their refuse, had come drifting down Cheapside. He had demanded an explanation of her conduct. 'She was so old,' said Jane. 'And it was little to me.' 'And did you not know that had you asked my permission to do such a thing it would have been refused?' Her laughter had rung out, clear and sweet, like the bells of St Mildred's. 'But how could I have asked the old woman to wait while I ran home and asked your permission, Father?' Yes, she had always been ready with her answers, and Thomas had known only one way of dealing with undutiful daughters. He had given her such a blow that she was sent from one side of the room to the other. And what had she done? Shrugged her pretty shoulders and tossed her pert head, and given him to understand that she would do the same again should the occasion arise.

Thomas, by no means a calm man, grew hot at the memory. The girl had the power to infuriate him, yet fill him with pride. Not that he had ever let her know by word or gesture that he was proud of her; there had been more blows than smiles, more whippings that soft words.

Thus had she been a constant anxiety to him. He had hoped to beat the boldness out of her, but she was not the sort to lie passive under punishment, and he had often found it necessary to tie her to the whipping post he used for his servants. She hardly ever wept, but at times she looked at him with hard hatred in her eyes. But her hatred passed speedily for she was incapable of bearing resentment for long. And what happened after these beatings? The entire household lined up against him. Not that any of them would dare utter an audible protest; that would have been to ask for the whip to be laid about their shoulders, and they had wisdom enough not to risk that, for when Tom Wainstead laid it on he laid it on sharp. All the same, when he sent Jane to her room, and gave instructions that she was to stay there on bread and water, he knew full well that, between them, the cook and Kate would see that all the daintiest titbits were smuggled up to her. As for Kate, she adored the girl. Kate was a fool, and he should never have taken her into his house. And, by the Holy Virgin, he thought, the first sign of any mischief from her, and out she'll go.

But it was a vain threat. He knew he would not turn the woman out. Ravaged by time and adventure Kate certainly was, but she had been a little beauty once. And well, a man is but a man, even though he be a respected mercer; and a widower of some years' standing may be allowed a lapse or two.

'Hold the candle higher, you fool!' he shouted at Jeffers. 'And don't drop tallow all over me.'

Jeffers looked hurt, but he was not really alarmed. The whole household knew that the master's sudden outbursts of seeming anger were due to his own thoughts rather than the faults of those he scolded.

Wainstead's eyes beneath his bushy brows looked into Jeffers's mild ones. 'And when we are at table see that Mistress Blague's glass is kept well filled. She's one to like her liquor as well as a little pressing to take it.'

'Yes, master,' said Jeffers; and the two men enjoyed a smile at the expense of Mistress Blague.

'As for my friend William Shore,' said Thomas, 'we must give him of our best. I believe him to be a man who will know the quality of good wine, though it may well be that he'll not take over much.'

'Yes, master.'

The mention of William Shore's name had brought a return of good humour to the mercer's face. His reason for cultivating the goldsmith's friendship had not been an idle one; and a good deal depended on tonight's supper party. Thomas had given much thought to it. There would be just four of them–Shore and Mistress Blague, himself and his daughter. And during the meal, and after, Thomas would keep his ears and eyes open.

He wanted a good marriage for Jane; and he wanted to hand her over, a virgin, to her future husband. He wanted to say, 'The responsibility of Thomas Wainstead is done with. Now, Will Shore, it belongs to you.'

Shore would be, without doubt, a perfect son-in-law. Had the mercer looked a little high? Perhaps. But then he had good merchandise to offer. Goldsmiths, like Shore, were important men in the City; they were the richest and most respected of the tradesmen; they came into contact with the nobility, and now and then with royalty. Shore, with his fine house in Lombard Street, with his flourishing business, was a man of means and standing. He was also a pious man, and though he had passed marriageable age, being every bit of twenty-eight years, he was not a man to indulge in light living; therefore it was time he took a wife.

If Shore was willing, Jane should marry him, even it she had to be beaten or starved into submission. For her beauty and her wit, Shore must immediately desire her; but her saucy, merry ways, and her rebellious thoughts, which she did not hesitate to translate into conversation, might not please him so well.

'Get along up,' he roared at Jeffers. 'What are you standing gaping at, man?'

His thoughts, returning to the waywardness of his daughter, had brought the anger back to his mind. He was remembering now what had happened when he had taken her to see the coronation of Queen Elizabeth Woodville. As they had stood on the edge of the crowd, a man who was obviously of the quality had sidled up to them in order to stare at Jane. Then had come to the mercer some glimmer of the fears which would later be his. In this wicked City there abounded unscrupulous men ever ready to seduce innocent girls. The King himself set an example of immorality. 'Citizens,' was the cry of the townsfolk, 'hide your wives and daughters, for the King comes this way!'

There had been yet another occasion, and this more alarming than the first. It was another of those processions in which the Queen, lifted from comparatively humble status to the throne of England, liked to indulge. Through the streets of London had come the knights and squires in cloth of gold and crimson velvet, riding on their stately horses; and one of them, a handome man of obvious nobility, had let his eyes rest on Jane; the man had smiled, and Jane had returned the smile, with all the freedom, gaiety and charm she would have bestowed with equal generosity upon the lowliest stall-holder in Candlewick Street.

'Who is that man?' he had whispered to his neighbour in the crowd, taking good care that his daughter should not hear the reply, and at the same time assuring himself that she should be whipped soundly for throwing her wanton smiles at the nobility.

'Know you not?' was the whispered answer. 'It is Lord William Hastings, favourite of the King, and married to the sister of the Earl of Warwick.'

Married! Then he should not be casting his eyes on the daughters of good citizens. But marriage, by all accounts, did not stop these court gentlemen from seeking amusements other than in their legitimate beds.

Jane had had her beating; and as he had turned from her and gone to the window, he had seen, standing in the very courtyard of his own house, a person who walked off hastily as the mercer appeared at the window; and this person was of the same handsome proportions as Lord Hastings.

The next day Jane had left for his relatives in Northamptonshire; and while she was in the country her father had made his arrangements for her future.

He and Jeffers had reached the big dining hall, and Jeffers carried the wine into a little parlour which led out of it. Thomas's mood had changed again. He had made his plans well. Tonight was the sequel to the smiles Jane had bestowed upon my Lord Hastings. Tonight Jane should smile at a man of her own class, and he at her; and their smiles should give Jane's father no cause for apprehension, but good reason for delight.

The house of Thomas Wainstead was one of the grandest in Cheapside. It was built, as were most of its neighbours, round a courtyard; on either side of its gates, and overlooking the street were the quarters of his servants and apprentices; looking out on the courtyard were his own and his daughter's chambers. The great hall dominated the house, and most of the main windows looked out on to it. It was the custom for all to take their meals in this great hall. Thomas would sit at the head of the table, his daughter on his right hand; and farther down the table sat the apprentices and servants in order of seniority. Opposite the great hall, on the other side of the courtyard, were those premises in which Thomas pursued the business of a very successful mercer, and the apprentices lived over these offices. Below the house were vaults where Thomas kept his merchandise, well locked up against robbery; and the keys of those vaults never left him. There were also his wine cellars, for he loved a good wine, and liked to keep a generous table. He was a benevolent master to those who served him well.

But this evening five o'clock supper was not to be served in the great hall, but in the more intimate parlour at a table set for four only. He did not wish Will Shore and Mistress Blague to sit down with his rough serving people, for Mistress Blague was very genteel, and Will Shore, being a goldsmith, doubtless lived in grander style in Lombard Street than Thomas Wainstead could afford in Cheapside.

He saw that the table had been well prepared, and that the floor of the parlour had been strewn with fresh rushes. The appetising smell of flesh roasting on spits in the kitchen could be detected; and there was a hush throughout the house, as though everyone in it was aware that this was an important occasion.

It was half-past four and his guests should be here at any moment. Ah! He could hear a disturbance in the courtyard now, and looking through the window, saw Mistress Blague arriving. He went out to meet her, frowning because Jane should have been at his side; she would have to learn better manners if she were to grace a goldsmith's house.

Then he smiled, for Mistress Blague amused him somewhat. She was, he guessed, every day of thirty, but she liked to be thought younger. Her small sly eyes and pinched mouth may have been acquired through over-much gentility. She was greatly respected in Cheapside as the King's lace-woman, and she was certainly to be admired for her craft. No one in London could make better lace than Mistress Blague; but the silly woman liked it to be thought that the King honoured her with his patronage because of a certain tender interlude which once passed between them. She would make a pretence of keeping secret about her past, but was always hinting that the King had played a part in it. Of course the King had so many love affairs that Mistress Blague might easily have been the heroine of one of them.

He kissed her on the mouth after the fashion of the day.

'How well you look, Mistress Blague,' he said, and she smiled, well pleased.

And indeed she did look well in her stiff dress, the skirt of which would have swept the courtyard had she not held it up daintily at one side, court-fashion; and her steeple hat was inches taller than most of those one saw, and the soft cascade that over-flowed from it reached almost to the hem of her gown.

'You also, Mr Wainstead. And where is this pretty daughter of yours of whom we have heard so much?'

'The girl's in her room, dressing. She should be here to greet you. But, believe me, Mistress Blague, it is solely on account of her desire to look well in your eyes that she spends so much time on her toilet. I had taken the liberty of telling her that a lady of fashion was coming to supper.'

He had well repaid any slight which Jane's lack of courtesy might have brought about. Mistress Blague was all smiles and simpers.

'I fear she will be greatly disappointed when she sees me.'

'Doubtless she will be smitten with envy. *She* will want such a gown. *She* will want such a hat.'

This pleasant conversation was interrupted by the arrival of Will Shore, who came riding into the courtyard, and Thomas was gratified to see how his head groom sprang forward to take the goldsmith's horse and lead it away while Will came towards his host.

'This is indeed a pleasure,' said Thomas warmly.

'The pleasure is with me,' said the goldsmith in his quiet voice.

'You know Mistress Blague, of course.'

'Indeed I do. And right glad I am to meet her once more.'

Mistress Blague smiled and the goldsmith murmured that rarely had he seen her look so well. Thomas was faintly alarmed. What if Will Shore liked the woman so well that he decided she would make a better wife than Jane Wainstead! Thomas studied Will afresh. The man's clothes were more sombre than one would have expected a wealthy goldsmith to wear. Will was a quiet man, a cautious man, devout and farseeing. Would such a man wish to take to wife a flighty creature like young Jane? And how would Jane feel about him?

Be still, he admonished himself. If Will wants Jane he has her, even if I have to whip her insensible and carry her to the altar.

He was all impatience now to get inside, to call Jane and see the effect she would have on the party.

Will Shore was saying: 'So your daughter is back, Thomas?'

'Aye. Back, and as lovely as ever she was when she went away.'

Mistress Blague's eyes narrowed. 'We are all eagerness to see so much beauty.'

There again he had been wrong. He should have let Jane's beauty burst upon them. That was always more effective than preparing people for some dazzling spectacle.

They went into the house, and as they entered Jane came down the staircase. They all stood looking at her. Even her father was taken aback by her beauty. She herself was smiling, seeming unconscious of it. Her dress, like Mistress Blague's, was blue, but blue seemed a different colour on Jane from what it did on Mistress Blague. The blue of the dress was reflected in Jane's eyes so that today they seemed more blue than grey, and more beautiful than the colour of the dress; they seemed longer, merrier than Thomas remembered them; her lips were parted to show her even teeth; she was a little flushed with excitement, for she loved gaiety, and the prospect of a party always set a greater sparkle on her. The bodice of her dress was low-cut, and trimmed with white; it was laced across her breasts; she wore a simple lace headdress, and her bright hair streamed over her shoulders. She was a small and dainty creature, and when she lifted her skirt and showed her fashionably pointed shoes as she came downstairs, Mistress Blague suddenly seemed clumsy and crude.

'So you are come,' said Thomas. 'Methinks it would have been more seemly had you been down to receive your guests.'

She bowed low. 'I am sure, Father, that you are more able than I to greet them with that courtesy which is their due.'

Neither Mistress Blague nor Will Shore could take their eyes from her.

'You have recently come from the country, Mistress Jane?' said Mary Blague.

'But yesterday.'

'And doubtless,' said the goldsmith, 'you find Cheapside a little strange after the country?'

'Not strange,' answered Jane, 'but delightful. I have longed to see Cheapside again.'

'You should not get too attached to it, my dear,' said Mary. 'Methinks you will not spend many days in the street, unless you marry a neighbour.'

'I see,' said Jane smiling, 'that you think I shall soon marry and go away from all this. That may be so. But I should miss it sadly.'

'Come,' said her father. 'Let us go to the parlour where I will have supper served at once.'

It was certainly a good idea to have supper served in the parlour, thought Thomas, as he watched his daughter and his guests. Will was obviously taken with Jane; but being taken with a girl did not necessarily mean marriage. That sad fact was at the very root of all his fears for Jane. He listened to their talk.

'So you are a goldsmith, sir?' said Jane. 'That must be interesting.'

'I am, Mistress Jane, and it is not without interest. You must call on me in Lombard Street . . . you and your father.'

'I shall like that and look forward to meeting your wife.'

'I have no wife–yet.'

The blue-grey eyes were mischievous. 'You speak as though you intend to remedy that lack, sir.'

Thomas all but choked with anger. That was no way for a modest girl to speak to a man.

'Holy Mother of God!' he cried. 'Where are your manners, girl? An you show sauciness to my guests you'll smart for it.'

Will Shore wriggled uncomfortably, but Jane merely smiled reproachfully at her father.

'But was I saucy?' she asked.

'I fear,' Will put in hastily, 'that the fault may have lain with me. It did seem to me but a natural reply.'

'It was,' said Jane.

'Be silent, girl,' retorted her father, but without much ire, for Jeffers was bringing in roasted peacocks, their bodies decorated with their own feathers. The cook had done well, Shore was taken with Jane; so how could Thomas feel anything but mellow? He turned his attention on Jeffers. Was the man filling Mary Blague's glass? He was. Was he looking after Shore? Shore did not appear to care what he ate; he had no eyes for roast peacocks, ox nor lamb; nor had he taste for Muscatel and Malmsey while he could feast his eyes on Jane and drink in her silly chatter. Tomorrow Thomas would talk to Jane and let her know his will.

Kate came in, her fat face beaming and the sweat of exertion running down her cheeks. Her bodice, thought Thomas, was too low cut; it was laced across the bosom as was Jane's, but Kate's great bosom seemed to threaten to break the lace in its eagerness to be free of such restriction. Kate was a temptation and a menace in the house. Thomas knew that she had been a light woman, a camp follower with the Lancastrian army when it came south. She had come to him and told her story and he had taken pity on her. That had happened nearly ten years ago. She grew older, but he fancied not less wanton. And, he . . . ?

Well, there had been just one small lapse in ten years. No, be honest, Thomas Wainstead . . . more than one. The woman was a constant reminder as well as a constant temptation. Still, being a man of high morals, he could not turn her out simply because she reminded him of his own sin; and he must keep her there that he might be constantly tempted and resist. He believed that she crept into Jeffers's bed now and then; and that Jeffers, an upright man like his master, suffered the same torment of perpetual reminder and temptation.

Jane was smiling at Kate, and Kate returned the smile. He would talk to Jane. There, he would say, is a result of immorality. Had Kate been a good woman, she might have been a wife and mother now. But no. For if he said that, Jane would doubtless remind him of the good women who starved in the streets in winter and begged for alms at the City's gates, while over the river, in the narrow streets of Southwark, there were women whom her father would not call good, yet they could be sure of their food, aye, and fine clothes to put on their backs.

He frowned across the table at Jane. She had ever known too much, and she had ever retorted too sharply. She was far too attractive for the peace of mind of a man so preoccupied with his virtue that immorality, by its very contrast, must be continually in his thoughts.

The conversation had now been led by Mistress Blague to court matters. Jane leaned her elbows on the table and her eyes sparkled as she listened.

'And, Mistress Blague, do you really believe that the Queen's mother is a sorceress?'

'A sorceress she undoubtedly is. Why, my dear, at Grafton Castle she had her own room with its crucible and charts, mixtures and potions, and in it she practised black magic . . . *black* magic, I tell you. If ever a man was led into a trap that man was Edward the King.'

'How *I* should love to be able to weave spells,' cried Jane.

'Tush, daughter,' admonished Thomas. 'You know not what you say.'

'But think, Father, if one were such a spell-binder, there is nothing–nothing one could not achieve. Do tell us, Mistress Blague, how His Grace the King was caught. Was it a love potion?'

'A love potion! That came after.' Mary Blague's eyes were narrower than ever. There was a flush under her skin. She was very angry. Did she believe, wondered Jane, that, had she possessed a mother who could weave spells, she herself might be the King's wife at this moment and not merely his lace-woman?

Mary Blague had started on her favourite subject of conversation. 'He was riding up north to quell a rebellion. Oh, the sight of him! The handsomest man in all England. He stands well over six feet, and his lovely face is irresistible to all. And there, hunting in the forest of Whittlebury, he found standing beneath an oak the widow and her two fatherless sons. It was—'

'Elizabeth Woodville,' cried Jane.

'It was,' said Mary Blague. 'And what did she do but throw herself upon her knees and plead with him to restore her lost inheritance!'

'And he,' said Jane with mock-wisdom, 'finding all women as irresistible as he is to them–at least, for the first week of acquaintance—'

'You presume too much, girl,' interrupted her father. He didn't entirely trust Mary Blague. What if she should pass on what she heard to some person at Court? Many a man's ears had been struck off for saying less than Jane had said just now.

'The King is a gentleman,' said Mary reprovingly. 'It is true that he has a fondness for our sex. It is part of his manhood. And so was he lured to Grafton Castle where Elizabeth lived with her mother.

'The sorceress,' said Jane.

Thomas noticed that Will Shore was looking at Jane and laughing, as though he thought everything the girl said was sheer wit.

'The sorceress indeed,' said Mary, thrusting her head forward. 'His Grace the King must be entertained at Grafton. How simple, while he was at table, to slip a potion into his wine. He had not been there an hour or two when he fully believed that he desired Elizabeth Woodville more than any woman he had ever met. And she a widow, admitting to seven years of life more than his. 'Tis nearer twelve I'll swear. "Oh," says she, "I am not worthy to be your wife, but I am too good to be your mistress." And so, refusing him her bed and aided by her sorceress mother, she at long last made him agree to a secret wedding.'

'It's a charming story,' said Jane.

'And a romantic one,' agreed Shore. 'Why should not the King marry to please himself and not the lords about him?'

Jane leaned forward, smiling. 'Why, sir, are you also enamoured of His Grace the King? I knew the women were. I had yet to learn he could draw such devotion from the men.'

'Be silent, girl,' growled Thomas. 'How dare you, at my table, speak disrespectfully of your King?'

'But, Father, it is well known that His Grace incurred the displeasure of many noble lords by his marriage. It is only women who sigh and smile and say he is so handsome and charming, and curse the ill fate which did not give them sorceresses for mothers"

Will Shore laughed outright at this, and Thomas allowed his lips to turn up at the corners.

'I ask you, Will,' asked Thomas, 'what would you do with such a one as this beneath your care?'

'I should be very proud,' said Will; and his pale eyes seemed to take on a warmer glow.

So, thought Thomas, for all the girl's forwardness, the evening is taking a good turn.

'I should like to see the King,' said Jane.

'You shall when he next rides through the City,' promised Mary.

That she shall not, thought Thomas, if she still be under my care. What if my Lord Hastings should be in the throng?

'There is grave news in the City,' said Will, sobering. 'Warwick never took kindly to this marriage of the King's. He was all for marriage with a French princess and alliance with the French.'

'And not a bad thing either,' said Thomas. 'Wars, wars, wars! Let's have peace for a change.'

The two merchants frowned as they talked of past events and looked gloomily into the future. The threat of war hung over the country still; and surely no war was so terrible as civil war. Looking back over the last ten years there had been nothing but battles–and battles wherein Englishmen fought Englishmen. Now, with Edward on the throne, while they feared war they could hope for peace. Edward was the most magnificent soldier of the day, but by reason of his pleasure-loving nature was not wedded to war. Edward believed in trade and the good things that peaceful trading brought; therefore London merchants supported Edward and had no love for fiery Margaret of Anjou who stormed about the country trying to persuade Englishmen to put her husband, poor, mad Henry the Sixth, back on the throne.

Jane, leaning her elbows on the table, was not listening to them. She knew, of course, why Will Shore had been invited tonight. She had for years been able to read what her father considered his most subtle thoughts. She was being shown off to the wealthy merchant as though she were a bale of fine linen or a roll of silk. Jane studied the goldsmith and shuddered.

Never, she thought, could I find it in my heart to love him.

She was only momentarily depressed by this project of her father's, for it was not in Jane's nature to suffer depression for long. She would find some way of escaping from the goldsmith when the time came, and the time had not yet come.

She was fascinated by Mary's gossip. All the woman's talk of court life was doubtless hearsay, but it made enlivening conversation.

'They say,' said Jane provocatively, 'that the Queen still rules the King. He has many mistresses, but there is not one of them that can wean him from her for more than a week or two.'

'Huh!' Mary's eyes flashed. 'What chance have ordinary decent women against a witch?'

'How does one become a witch?' wondered Jane.

Mary was shocked. 'To say such things! Wickedness is born in a woman. There is plenty of wickedness and to spare at the court. It makes me shudder to contemplate it.'

'Yet also does it delight you to contemplate it,' pointed out Jane; and she added quickly: 'And so does it me. I would I were there to see it.'

'It is not the lot of the merchant class to go to court, my dear.'

'Nay, but I would it were.'

Mary tittered. 'Now and then, of a certainty, a humble girl finds means of spending a week or two in court circles.'

'You mean she attracts the attention of . . . shall we say some personage of high eminence. She becomes his mistress and—'

Mary was coy. 'It has happened, you know.'

'But I hear the King has acquired a most distressing habit,' said Jane. 'He goes among the common people disguised as one of themselves. He has his love affairs and departs. I call that unfair. How wretched to lose the glory of royal favour as well as one's virtue!'

Jane's voice broke on a laugh and Mary frowned. Thomas looked up from his conversation with Will Shore. Jane was irrepressible. Heaven knew what he was going to do with her.

Mary said: 'Methinks they taught you much in Northamptonshire.'

'One does not need to go to Northamptonshire to learn that the sun shines or the rain falls. And the King's love affairs are accepted as is the weather.'

Thomas banged the table, for really the girl had gone too far. 'You will leave us, Jane. I will talk to you later.'

Jane rose while Shore intervened. 'The evening will be dark without your daughter's bright beauty and sparkling wit.'

Jane gave him a grateful smile which made him flush a little. Thomas noted it, but all the same Jane had to go. She needed a good talking-to before she was allowed to mix in company.

'Nay,' insisted Thomas, 'I have been over-lenient already. Up to your room, girl.'

Jane said a decorous good-night to the guests and went.

Her room overlooked the courtyard. It was by no means an up-to-date room, for Thomas did not believe in pampering his household. The hall was pleasantly furnished, so were the offices where he received his customers, but the bedrooms were simple. There were rushes on the floor, and he had not introduced the new fashionable beds. Jane slept on a kind of mattress on the floor. She had a mirror on a table and a rough stool on which to sit at it. There was a cupboard in which hung her clothes, yet the table was untidy with ribbons, a strip of lace and a horned hat.

She came in and shut the door, went to the glass and looked at herself, grimaced at what she saw, and sitting down began removing her headdress.

There was a faint tap on her door, and Jane swung round on her stool, smiling, for she knew who this was. She was right. Kate came in, her eyes wide, her lips parted. She stood leaning against the door in an expectant attitude. She wanted to know why Jane was in her room and not downstairs with the guests.

'I was sent up,' explained Jane, 'for talking too much and without respect for the King.'

Kate was shocked, for, like Mary Blague, she was devoted to the King. 'That was wrong of you, Mistress Jane.'

Jane laughed. 'Oh, I know he is the most handsome man on earth, but all the same his love affairs are numerous. My father knows it, and as for Mary Blague, she would have us believe that she has the most intimate knowledge in that direction. And yet am I sent to my room for stating a simple fact.'

'You'll have no sympathy from me,' said Kate. 'He is a man, and a man will be a man.'

'Even though he be a King. Tell me, Kate, is manhood measured by mistresses then?'

'I'll not hear a word against him. And could you but see His Grace I'll warrant you'd change your tune.'

'Indeed I'd not.'

'If he turned his bonny smile upon you, you would.'

'I'd not be proud to walk in such a crowd, Kate.'

'Shall I comb your hair, my love?'

'Yes, Kate. Please do.'

They were silent for a second or two and silence was something which rarely existed between them. Kate was thinking of the past in which, strangely enough, the King himself had played a small part. She saw Ludlow Castle, rising gracious and pleasant above green Shropshire fields. She had lived in the castle, for her father had been head groom to the Duke of York, father to King Edward, and now and then she had caught glimpses of His Grace the King–only then he had yet to win his crown–and in those days he had been known as the most handsome and irresistible man in all England. Kind he had been to his serving men and women–particularly to the women–and also to his brothers, George and Richard and his little sister Margaret. Kate was thinking now of a certain October day ten years ago, when she had been a young and innocent girl engaged to marry Walter who had worked at the castle under her father. But on that October day soldiers, led by the enemies of the Duke of York, had ransacked the castle, stealing its beautiful furnishings and ornaments, raping its women, killing its men. Kate had seen Walter lying battered and bloody in the castle grounds. She herself had fallen to the lot of an uncouth Scotsman. She saw herself afterwards tramping behind the Lancastrian army on its way to London, a dirty, wheedling camp woman, eager to please this man and that.

Jane was thinking of the smile about her father's mouth and the glint of something of which she was not quite certain in the eyes of William Shore.

Seeking to escape from unpleasant memories, Kate spoke first. 'So you were sent up. This will mean a whipping, as sure as I stand here.'

'I hope not, Kate.'

'Mind you,' went on Kate soothingly, 'your father's not so strong in the arm as he was.' She stroked Jane's shoulder. 'It's a shame to bruise your lovely skin.'

Jane burst into the sudden laughter which was characteristic of her. 'Perhaps he won't. I've a notion that I'm something more than a daughter now, Kate. I'm a piece of merchandise, and it may well be that I shall never be whipped again. For I am to be offered to a customer, Kate. The company downstairs has been gathered here for a very special reason. Can you not guess?'

Kate blew a shrill little blast between her lips. 'Goldsmith Shore!' she cried. She smiled. 'He is a very rich gentleman, I have heard.'

'He has cold hands. They are like the skin of a fish.'

'Holy Virgin! You can get him to warm his hands before he touches you.'

'I don't want to marry Will Shore, Kate.'

'Why, he is one of the richest men in the City. It does not surprise me that your father has chosen him. You would be wise to listen to your father, that you would. There are not many Will Shores in London to be had for the asking, I do assure you.'

'I'm rather frightened, Kate. I seem to have grown up so suddenly. I've got to marry. I've got to let him take me to Lombard Street–and I don't want to go, Kate.'

'It's the strangeness of it, lovey.'

'But, Kate, I want to wait a while.'

'You are too fair for waiting.'

'You understand though. You've told me how you loved Walter all those years ago in Ludlow. You wanted to marry him. You loved him.'

'Yes, and much good did it do me.'

'It would have done much good if you had married Walter.' She was silent for a second or two; then she said: 'Kate, when you were a serving maid at Ludlow, you saw the King. What manner of man is he, I wonder, that can make Mary Blague's eyes sparkle when she speaks of him? And you are the same, Kate.'

'As you would be–should you see him. Heads turned to watch him; eyes followed him. The whole household doted on him–even the cold and haughty lady Duchess, his mother.'

'He must have been very conceited.'

'Not he. It was all so natural that he should be admired. Wasn't he the strongest, the gayest and most handsome wherever he went!'

'Oh, Kate, what grand circles you have moved in! You have served the King; you have lived under the same roof as his brothers the Dukes of Clarence and Gloucester. Kate, how can you bear a mercer's household after that?'

'You mock me.'

'I did not mean to mock. I just long to see the sparkle in your eyes which the memory of the most charming, the most beautiful and the most amorous man in all England can put there.'

'I'm not sure that isn't treason,' said Kate primly.

'Alas, treason and truth may often go hand in hand.'

'It does not surprise me that your father would hand you to another. Come, let me comb your hair and get you to bed, for mayhap if you are sleeping when your father's guests are gone, the whipping will be put off until tomorrow.'

Kate combed the lovely golden hair.

The saints preserve this lovely child, she thought. Let her never know the like of what happened to me.

Dusk was falling over the City as Kate hurried back to Cheapside. Kate was anxious not to be out after dark; there were too many ruffians abroad who would be ready to slit the throat of a defenceless woman for the sake of the few coins she might possess. Kate understood the needs of these poor men, old soldiers most of them, who had drifted to London with the Yorkist or Lancastrian armies. Kate had not followed the camp without learning something of the hardships which befell soldiers in time of peace.

Thomas had sent her out with a piece of silk to one of the great houses beyond Ludgate and towards Temple Bar. It should have fallen to the lot of one of the apprentices to deliver the silk, but Thomas had come upon Kate, idling, as he said, in the kitchen, and as the order was urgent he had despatched her at once.

Kate was worried, for a gloom had settled on the Wainstead household during the last few weeks. Thomas had declared that his daughter should marry Will Shore, since the goldsmith was more than willing; but his daughter had refused; and although Thomas might stamp and rage and swear his daughter should give him obedience, although he might force her to go to church, he could not say the words which would make her the goldsmith's wife. In the meantime, there was Jane, confined to her room and kept there for nigh on three weeks with nothing, so the mercer thought, to nourish her but bread and water. And what objection, Kate asked herself in exasperation, had Jane to the goldsmith? He was rich and he loved her truly. Shore's servants had whispered to Kate that the goldsmith kept good house in Lombard Street; and there was, Kate had ascertained, a most personable gentleman who reigned in the kitchens there. Many scullions worked for him; he was a mighty man in height and girth; he had the merriest of twinkles in his eyes which had not grown less merry when they rested on Kate.

She had come through Ludgate and was hurrying into St Paul's Churchyard when a horrible fear came to her that the footsteps which she had heard behind her for some minutes must have been following her. Kate started to run, and whoever it was behind her started to run also. There was no doubt about it: Kate was being followed.

She began to sweat with fear. With dusk, lawlessness came to the City. Thieves and ravishers lurked in dark alleys. How many bodies were found in narrow byways! How many were flung into the cold waters of the Thames! Kate ran through the churchyard. She dared not look round. He who followed uttered a curse and she could hear his heavy breathing. The houses rose darkly beside her, for she had reached Cheapside. She saw the Cross loom up before her. Very shortly she would be past Friday Street and have reached her master's house. But even as she turned into its gates a hand shot out and caught her arm. Kate screamed as she was pulled round to face a cloaked figure.

'Be silent,' said the man. His was a cultured voice and in it was a hint of laughter; but Kate was not to be fooled by that. She stared up into the face which was peering down into hers. She could not see it clearly, but she did see the jewels at his throat; and life with the family of York, and later in the mercer's household, had taught her to recognise a nobleman's style of dress when she saw it.

'Greetings, sweetheart,' said the man; and he kissed her full on the lips. He was no sweating old soldier, and Kate waited breathlessly for what should happen next.

'What do you want of me?' gasped Kate.

'Do not speak so loud, girl. Is it *your* master who has a daughter–the most beautiful girl in London?'

Kate told herself she ought to have known it was Jane whom he was after. 'The mercer has a daughter who is beautiful,' she said.

'And she is your mistress?'

'Yes.'

'Then you shall help me to have a word with her.'

'I could not. Why, my master—'

'Your master pays you well to keep a strict eye on his daughter, I doubt not. What if I pay you better?'

'Think you I would betray my mistress for money?'

'If you would not you would be the first maid in London to refuse such easy earnings.'

'Pray release me.'

'Not yet. Tell me your mistress's name.'

'You hurt my arm.'

'Her name, woman?'

'It is Jane.'

'Which is her room?'

'The third from the gate on the left side. It looks out on the courtyard.'

'So. Now listen to me. You are to go to your mistress now. Beg her to bring a lighted candle to the window. I would look on her face, for it is long since I saw it.'

'I dare not.'

He brought a coin from his pocket, but Kate turned away.

'You are a foolish wench.'

'I am true to my master and my mistress.'

'How do you know that it would not please her to come to the window?'

'She does not know you, sir.'

'She would be very happy if she did.'

'She would not.' Kate never could stop her tongue running on. 'She is to be married to a goldsmith–when her father can force her to it.'

'Force her, eh? So would her father force her? I'd have his head off his shoulders.'

'There's no law that I know to take a man's head off his shoulders for arranging his daughter's marriage.' Kate had lost her fright now and was enjoying the adventure.

'You're too saucy, girl. You must do as I say and you'll not be sorry. What's your name?'

'Kate.'

'Kate, tomorrow at this hour you will come to Paul's Churchyard and there I will give you a message for your mistress.'

'I do not promise.'

'It will be the worse for you if you do not. Help me and all will go well with you. Betray me to that old scoundrel and one dark night when you come home from meeting your lover . . .'

'I do not go out at night to meet my lover.'

'Do not tell me the old rascal allows you to have him in the house! Now listen. You will come to St Paul's Churchyard tomorrow night or . . .'

'I–I will come. There can be no harm in it, for she will not listen to you.'

Kate was released. 'Go now,' he said. 'I will wait here. Tell her I wait. And tomorrow, Kate, at this hour, we meet. Remember now. Do not betray me. I am a person of some import in this City. I could have you put in the pillory or taken as a harlot. My servants shall waylay you.'

'No!' cried Kate.

'No,' he said soothingly, 'it shall not be, for you are a wise wench. Go now, and remember what I have said.'

Kate ran into the house and went up to Jane's room.

Jane was lying on the bed, disconsolate and defiant. She raised herself and leaned on her elbow to look at Kate, for it was obvious that Kate was agitated.

'What has happened, Kate?'

'I cannot tell you yet.' She went to the table and with trembling hands took up the lighted candle which stood there.

'Kate!' Jane leaped up and stood beside her. 'You look so strange. What is it that has frightened you? Tell me quickly.'

'Come with me,' said Kate; and she took Jane's hand and led her to the window.

'What are you looking for?' demanded Jane. 'Why–there is someone down there. Kate!'

Jane turned from the window, dragging Kate with her. 'What does this mean, Kate? You were showing me to someone down there. Oh, Kate, how dare you! It was a man–was it not?'

'It *was* a man, mistress.'

'How dare you! How dare you! First my father will show me off as though

I am a roll of silk; and now you will show me off as though I am a harlot and you a procuress.'

'That,' said Kate with dignity, 'is no talk for a young girl.'

'Talk is not important. It is action that matters. And you have acted most unwisely. You had better tell me all about it.'

'He followed me. It was in Paul's Churchyard that I heard his footsteps behind me. I have not been so frightened since Ludlow. And then–as I turned in at the gates–he caught me and held me, so that I could not escape an I would.'

'An you would!' cried Jane scornfully. 'You know full well you had no wish to escape.'

'Well, I will admit to a little curiosity as to what he wanted. There were jewels at his throat and the cloth of his garments would have made your father's eyes glisten.'

'It made yours glisten too, Kate, I'll warrant.' Now they were laughing together like two schoolgirls. 'What said he, Kate?'

'He asked about you. He is very handsome. His voice is beautiful and he said things that frightened me. I have to be in the churchyard tomorrow for a message he has for you. Then we shall know who he is.'

'Quiet, Kate! You're shouting.'

'Oh, mistress, suppose he be a noble lord, and suppose he is so smitten in love for you that he will marry you!'

'The love that smites these noble lords for merchants' daughters does not carry them as far as marriage, Kate.'

'There are many wonders in the world.'

'But nothing so wonderful as that. If my father gets to know of this . . .'

'He shall not.'

'If you continue to shout to the housetops he will.'

'But it is so beautiful.'

'What is beautiful? The man? His clothes? His brutal way of frightening you?'

'I was not really frightened. I have prayed the Virgin to show us a way out. I have prayed that you might have your will and not fall to the goldsmith. This is an answer to my prayers.'

'Wait a while before you see too much in this. To me it would appear just another gentleman in search of adventure. Rest assured he will not find it here.'

'You would shut yourself away from the world,' grumbled Kate. 'You wait for someone you can love. One does not *wait* for love, but goes out to meet it.'

'I shall not go out to meet it in the form of this swaggering fellow who dares accost you in the street. I hope he did not think I went freely to the window. But he will, of course. These creatures are puffed out with conceit. Oh, Kate, Kate, you have a lot to answer for.'

They looked at each other solemnly for a moment, and then fell to laughing; they laughed so much that they feared the mercer would hear; then they were quieter, whispering in the darkness.

In the great dining hall Thomas Wainstead nodded over the table. In a moment or two he would snore. The apprentices dozed; even the chatter of some of the servants sounded sleepy. Among the rushes the dogs were still gnawing the bones which had been thrown to them, and giving little grunts of satisfaction as they came upon gobbets of fat and gristle which had been spat out by the diners.

Jane looked along the table. She was no longer on bread and water diet. Her father had become frightened by her pallor, and he said she was to come down to eat good flesh and drink some wine. He would rather have a disobedient daughter, thought Jane affectionately, than a dead one. He worried too much about her and she did wish that she could please him. She was ready to admit that she was wayward and daring, but at the same time she would insist she knew how to take care of herself. For instance, in exactly five minutes' time she was going to slip out into the courtyard and there by the stables meet the mysterious nobleman who was infatuated with her. Kate had brought her several messages in which he had declared that he was deep in love with her, and that he could not sleep nor eat until she consented to listen to his pleading. It was all very exciting and exhilarating after her imprisonment, and as there was a spice of danger in the adventure it was irresistible to Jane. Her father had said that she might take a turn in the courtyard, although she was not to go into the streets unaccompanied by himself. There, again, Jane must smile for him. Poor dear foolish man, did he not know that it could be equally daring to venture into the courtyard as the street?

Kate came in, her lips pursed, her eyes betraying that something was afoot. Jane put her fingers to her lips and looked cautiously along the table. Thomas was snoring, and Jane rose and tiptoed lightly out of the room.

Kate whispered: 'He is come. Outside, he awaits you.'

Jane drew round her the cape which Kate had brought with her and went speedily out. A dark figure came swiftly towards her.

William Lord Hastings was dressed in the most exaggerated fashion, for although he wished to keep his identity a secret, he wanted Jane to know that he was of the nobility. He would have told her that he was Hastings, friend of the King, but since he was well known all over the country, that would not do, for Jane would surely know–or soon discover–that he had a wife, no less a person than the sister of the great Earl of Warwick. He must content himself therefore with wearing such clothes as could only be worn by the highest in the country. His shoes were long and very pointed. His short jacket exposed the shape of handsome legs and thighs, and this jacket was trimmed with rich fur, while its wide hanging sleeves were so exaggerated as to be ridiculous. His hat was feathered and there were jewels at his throat.

'Jane!' He put his hands on her shoulders, kissed her, and would not release her.

'Enough,' she said. 'What is it you wish to say to me?'

'Say to you! That which I have said a thousand times already. Leave this squalor and come with me.'

'My father would not be pleased to hear you speak thus of his house, my lord.'

'Nevertheless, Jane, if you could but see the house I would give you, you would be unable to resist it.'

'My lord, if you would keep your hands from touching me, I should enjoy your company the better.'

'You are cruel, Jane.'

'Nay, only curious.'

'So you keep me dancing to your tune in this manner simply because–you are curious?'

'I am too curious. You are too amorous. Now, if I weren't curious and you weren't amorous, all this would never have arisen.'

'Mean you that there is naught in it but curiosity for you?'

'How could there be aught else when I scarce know you?'

'Jane you are amused to tease me. Come here and kiss me. Let me show you what life with me would be like.'

She laughed. 'That I know full well. Life with you would doubtless be lived in an apartment in one of those grey houses on the other side of the river, whither you would take me; and there, after a week or so, leave me.'

'Leave you!'

'Aye, leave me. I might ask, "And where are you going now, kind sir?" And you would say, "To find another simple maiden like yourself." That is, if you were truthful. Dost think I was born yesterday? No. Do not come near me. If you do I shall scream. My father is in the dining hall. He will loosen the dogs. . . .'

'Why do you wish to humiliate me? By God's Holy Virgin, I have never been made to suffer such indignity. Doth that not show how I love thee?'

'It does but show what a mighty conceit of yourself you have.'

'Listen to me, Jane. . . .'

'Listen to you when you will not even tell me your name!'

'You shall learn that ere long. Then you will be sorry that you have treated me with such indignity.'

'Tell me,' she mocked, 'you are not His Grace the King?' He hesitated, for the desire to have her believe this was so great that he was reluctant to deny it. 'I hear,' she went on, 'that he doth love to go among his female subjects. Here in the City they say, "Hide your wives and daughters, for the King comes this way." But you are not the King.'

'You are sure of that?'

'I am indeed. For it is said that there is not a woman in the world who could say no to him. Well, am I not a woman, and so easily do I say No to you. Therefore must it seem that you are not His Grace.'

'It pleases you to tease me.'

'Just as it pleases you to pursue me.'

'Jane, could you not love me a little? I would give you everything you desire. Jane, think of it . . . beautiful jewels . . . a life at court . . . everything.'

'Everything but marriage.'

'I did not say I would not marry you.'

'Nor did you say you would.'

'Why, look you, Jane, should you insist . . .'

'I insist! But it is you who are insistent.'

'Have done with this banter. I adore you, Jane.'

'The truth would be more pleasing than your adoration. If you are ready to make honourable proposals, why do you not go to my father's house, and not to his stables? The answer is easy. You wish to seduce me and then desert me. Mayhap you have already a wife.'

'I swear . . .'

'That you have not? Then I have solved one mystery. You are not the King. And methinks I have had enough, for there is a chill in the air, and my father will beat me if he finds me here talking to an amorous gentleman, whatever his rank at court. Good-night to you, sir.'

'Jane!' He caught her hand.

'Let me go.'

'I will not. Do you think you may come out here and tease *me* thus? I will have your lips. By Christ's Holy Mother, you are fairer than I ever dreamed. Why, Jane, come with me and you will never regret it.'

She was frightened now, realising her folly in giving way to her love of excitement. He held her fast while she banged her fists ineffectually against his chest, making him laugh.

'And what shall you do now, think you? See! I could sling you across my shoulder thus. I would make off with you.'

'Put me down.'

'What? Now I have you in my power? I shall not put you down until I have had my will of you, and after that mayhap you'll not be so eager to be put aside.'

'I hate you,' she cried; and she kicked him as he held her.

He gave a sudden cry of anger, and, seizing her opportunity, she pulled his feathered hat over his eyes while she gave him yet another kick which made him release her as he doubled up with pain. She ran towards the house.

Panting, laughing, she fell against Kate, who was standing at the door in case it should be necessary to warn her that her father was coming.

'Shut the door, Kate. Bolt it. Holy Virgin, that was a near thing! He had me slung across his shoulder. Why, he might have run off with me there and then. I was a fool, Kate. It was my own fault.' She was half laughing, half serious. 'Oh, Kate, he was comic. I asked him if he were the King, and he tried to make me believe he was.'

''Sh. Your father is stirring. Better slip upstairs, dearie, or my back'll be sore, and so will yours if he gets wind of what we're at.'

'Do not ever allow me to go out and meet him again!' said Jane. 'He's dangerous.'

'I ever liked a man to be bold,' said Kate wistfully, 'and 'tis my belief he loves you true.'

William Lord Hastings was far from pleased with the progress he was making with the mercer's daughter. The whole affair was maddeningly undignified. He was no adventurous young boy to indulge in the romp that this was turning out to be. The girl was unusual; she could make a fool of him; and it was a preposterous situation wherein the Chamberlain of the Royal Household and Master of the Mint, a baron and associate of the King, a man of sober years–for he was approaching forty–should have to hang about in a mercer's courtyard at dusk, there to be trounced by that mercer's daughter.

He was weary of the chase. He had decided more than once that he had had enough of it, but he found it impossible to forget the girl. He was a rake, a profligate; he obeyed the fashion of the day, and promiscuity was the fashion. He was not the man, however, to admit himself beaten, but was determined to subject himself to no more indignity. He had hoped for help from the woman Kate. He had threatened to have her whipped through the streets for harlotry or put in the pillory for thieving. 'Or,' he had said, 'I'll set my men upon you . . . lusty fellows and a whole dozen of them.' That had terrified her more than anything, so that he felt he could be sure of the help he would need from her.

His plan was simple and he was going to set about it immediately. He wrapped a long gown about himself–for he had clad himself in his plainest garments for this purpose–and setting out from his apartments in

Westminster Palace, he went swiftly to the river where he hailed a waterman to row him to Southwark.

He sat in the boat, listening to the splash of the oars, glancing along the river towards the bridge and beyond where the great stone walls of the Tower of London reached up to the sky. Along the north bank he saw the lovely old houses with their gardens and orchards running down to the river's edge; but it was not with the gracious north bank he was concerned; his business lay with the squalid south, and as soon as the boat touched land he had leaped out, tossed a coin to the man, and was hurrying up the steps towards the streets of Southwark. He lifted the side of his mouth as he walked along. In a very short time Mistress Jane would be not quite so haughty. In Southwark she would learn docility as many a woman had learned it before her.

As he walked through the narrow streets he knew that eyes watched him through the discreetly curtained windows. A woman with lewd eyes and naked, he saw, beneath her cloak, for she allowd the cloak to fall open as she came towards him, smiled invitingly. He waved her aside with nonchalance, for he was no newcomer to Southwark.

He stopped before a tall house about which there was a cleanliness lacking in its neighbours. He mounted the steps and knocked at the door which was opened almost immediately by a fat girl in her twenties. She wore a cap with ribands and a low-cut gown. She curtseyed, knowing him for a nobleman and patron of the house; she expected at least a kiss, but his preoccupation with Jane Wainstead made him ignore her.

He said curtly: 'Conduct me to your mistress.'

The girl, pouting, bid him enter.

He was taken to a small room which might have belonged to a well-to-do middle-class home. There were clean rushes on the floor, and the hangings were not of common worsted, but of tapestry woven to represent scenes from the French wars which Henry the Fifth had conducted to the satisfaction of his countrymen. Harfleur was represented, together with Agincourt. Hastings did not spare them a glance. He had seen them before.

A woman came into the room. She was middle-aged and very neatly and simply dressed; hanging on a chain about her neck was a silver cross. There was about her a puritanical look which her surroundings seemed to stress. She was called Madam by all who had dealings with her; and it was known that, under the mysterious Mistress Bee who owned this place and had never been seen here even by its most honoured patrons, she was the head of this establishment.

Now she smiled ingratiatingly. She was eager, she said, to know the requirements of the noble lord. But first she would tell him that there was a very charming acquisition to the house. A girl not more than fourteen–a Venus and almost a virgin.

'Nay,' said Hastings. 'I have come to ask you to reserve an apartment for me.'

'An apartment, my lord?'

'Come, come,' said Hastings impatiently. 'It will cost much, I know. I am ready to pay. The apartment is to be of your best. It is to be in readiness for me and a lady.'

'You are bringing the lady, my lord?'

'I am. It may be tonight. It may be tomorrow. But you must be ready for me. It is understood?'

'It is, my lord, but . . .'

'Bother not your head about money, good woman. I will pay now.'

'Ah,' said Madam, 'you shall have the very best apartment in the house. It shall be made clean and sweet. And how long shall you be needing the apartment, my lord?'

'That, I do not yet know.'

'Until further orders shall we say, my lord?'

'It is enough,' said Hastings. 'And another matter . . . The lady may be . . .'

'A little indisposed when she arrives?' Madame patted her prim collar. Madam had genius. She made the most lecherous adventure sound puritanical; abductions, left to her, seemed as dignified as the ceremonies of the Church.

'I see you are going to help me,' said Hastings; and he laid his money on the table.

'My lord,' said Madam, 'it is the custom of this house to satisfy our gentlemen.'

He came out humming. It was very simple. He hailed a boat and in a very short time was across the river; he hurried northwards and did not pause until he reached Bucklersbury. He stopped now before a shop whose window was full of brightly coloured bottles. He stepped down three stone stairs, pushed open a door, and went into the dark little shop which smelt of musk and herbs.

Leppus, the dried-up little apothecary, hearing the door open, emerged from the darkness behind the shop. He took one swift look at Lord Hastings and bowed obsequiously. He had served many gentlemen of the court and recognised one when he saw him. Leppus's skin was brown as walnut and his teeth were yellow; his nose was long and artfully hooked; his eyes were black and bright; and his eyebrows hung over them half-concealing the cunning that lay in them. It was said at the court that he was more than an apothecary. His love potions were true love potions inasmuch as they could be relied upon to rouse the most sluggish to amorous revelry. He could supply poisons, and it was said of him that he never asked questions, merely high prices. The King himself was reputed to patronise Leppus; and Leppus was suspected of being very rich. He was, it seemed, a master of magic. He could produce herbal drinks to make women fruitful; and if they were unwillingly with child, potions to terminate their pregnancies. He had sleeping draughts which, he would remind his patron with a leer, if taken in double doses would produce death. He had herbs to make the complexion good, lotions to make the eyes bright; he had aphrodisiacs to rejuvenate flagging desires; he could make wax images to resemble the enemies of his patrons and supply pins with which to pierce the waxen bodies; he had the tears and sweat of martyrs which he sold in costly containers, ând which were holy charms against plague and disaster. Now Leppus recognised my Lord Hastings and muttered that he was eager to know how he could serve such a noble lord.

Hastings followed the old man into an inner chamber and sat down. Leppus stood with his back to the light watching the nobleman's face. Was it a strong sleeping dose for a rival? Leppus would know. An aphrodisiac for a reluctant maid? He was amused by these matters which occupied these men of the gay court, and pleased to wield the power he did over them. What mattered it to Leppus who sat on the throne? Edward or Henry, he would still have customers glad to use his brains and buy his goods.

'Leppus, I want a sleeping draught.'

Leppus nodded. 'A not too strong sleeping draught, my lord?'

'A sleeping draught that could be slipped into a glass of wine and none be the wiser.'

'I know. I know. I have the very thing.' Leppus went to a bench at one end of the room, drew up a stool, took from a shelf a bottle containing white powder, and spread on the bench before him a piece of paper on to which he ladled out a small quantity of the powder.

'How long will the effect of this last, Leppus?'

'For two or three hours, my lord.'

'That is what I need. She–the one who takes it–cannot possibly wake, even though . . .'

'Even though she'–Leppus corrected himself with some elaboration–'even though this person were, shall we say, carried on horseback across the City; even then this–er–person would not wake until the draught had had its way.'

It was uncanny, thought Hastings, frowning at the old man's back, how much Leppus knew. One would feel like murdering him if one did not know that he held similar secrets regarding half the men and women of the court.

'And have you some little potion–a love potion–something that would change the—'

'Something that would change the heart of an icy maiden? Oh, I have that also my lord. Now, here is your sleeping draught. Slip it in the wine. It will only take a few minutes to work its effect.'

'You are sure that—'

'It is absolutely safe, my lord. And now for the love potion.' He had turned his back to Hastings, who knew that his ugly old face was creased in smiles and that the seduction of Jane Wainstead in Mistress Bee's Southwark rooms was being enacted before his eyes. Others had said old Leppus made them feel like that. How gratifying it would be to take the old man by his shabby coat and cut out his tongue so that he might never make his sneering remarks again, to put out his eyes so that one need not feel he saw things not intended for him. But if old Leppus was hated, he was certainly respected. He was too wise, too useful to be treated badly.

'Now,' said Leppus, 'a little charm, I think, to bring you luck with the lady.'

'I think the draught and the potion will be sufficient.'

'You must have a charm for luck, my lord. Now look. Here is a little figure. It is an ancient god of some foreign land. Set it on a table where it can see you and smile on you and bring you luck.'

He wanted five shillings for the charm; the potion and draught were another five. The figure had a look of old Leppus about it, and Hastings imagined it propped up in some conspicuous spot in the apartment Madam had reserved for him. It would seem as if that repulsive old man was looking through the ugly eyes of the god. Hastings believed that was possible. He would have liked to destroy the thing but he dared not. If he did, Leppus, with his obscene magic, might destroy the potency of both those small neat packages.

Hastings paid the apothecary what he asked, and Leppus leered after him as he left the shop and hurried away.

Jane lay back in bed watching Kate fidgeting at the table. Kate seemed strange tonight. She was flushed and nervous.

'Kate,' said Jane, 'you seem ill at ease tonight. Have you been to St Paul's Churchyard this day?'

'Yes, I have then.' Kate spoke defiantly.

'And did you see him?'

'I saw him.'

'And what said he?'

'He said that you were cold and cruel and would doubtless dally until it was too late to find a man to marry you. You knew not, he said, when life was offering you something good.'

'So *he* is something good? I doubt it, Kate. I doubt very much that he is something good. And, Kate, you had better be careful, for I have a fancy that my father has grown suspicious of late.'

'No!' cried Kate, shivering suddenly.

'Indeed, yes. He looked at me most oddly. I believe he has seen your gallant gentleman lurking about the house.'

'*My* gallant gentleman!' cried Kate.

'Well, 'tis you who have so many dealings with him. Have I not told you that I will have none of him?'

Kate leaned against the table and spread her trembling hands over her skirt until her fingers touched the pocket. In that pocket was a neat little package. She looked wistfully at Jane. Kate had assured herself that the noble lord had spoken the truth when he said he meant to marry the girl and make a great lady of her. Jane was too young as yet to know what was good for her; and once the dangerous business was done with, how grateful would Jane be–and so would he–to clever Kate who had made it all possible!

What she had to do was perfectly simple. There was nothing evil in the little package which she carried in her pocket. It would merely produce a pleasant sleep. She was to give it to Jane last thing tonight, just before the girl was ready to sleep. That would be in a few minutes' time; and then, when the household was asleep, all Kate had to do was tiptoe downstairs, let in the man who loved Jane so romantically, conduct him up to this chamber, and let him carry out the sleeping girl. As for Kate, she was to be in Paul's Churchyard at midday on the morrow and there she would be told where Jane was and when she might see her; and then as soon as Jane was in her new grand home–at court most likely–Kate would be sent for to act as maid to her newly elevated mistress. It seemed like a dream coming true; but, of course, the dangerous part had to be lived through first, and if she and the gentleman were caught, she knew she would be thrust out into the streets; but this she would risk for the sake of what would come after. No wonder she was trembling now.

She said: 'You do not want to marry Will Shore, so why are you so cold to this noble lord? You will not even stand at the window that he may see you.'

'Assuredly I will not. And at least Will Shore is an honest man.'

'You think the noble lord is not?'

'I think, Kate, that he is not.'

'He is very fascinating.'

'Doubtless he is, Kate. I will take your word for that.'

'Have you no desire to see him again?'

'I have no desire to be his mistress for a week.'

'The jewels in his clothes . . .'

'I do not care so much for jewels. Nor do they mean an assurance of honesty.'

Kate thought, This is driving me mad. How do I know what I ought to do? Sooner or later her father will force her to marry Will Shore, and then she will be unhappy.

'Enought of this noble lord,' said Jane. 'Give me a cup of wine and I will settle down to sleep.'

There were shadows in the room. The single candle cast a flickering light upon the table.

It is now I must do this, thought Kate. He said she would not taste it. He said it would do no harm. It will be a sweet peaceful sleep and she will wake up in his arms. Well, I promised and I will do it.

Kate shot the powder into the wine and took it to Jane, almost spilling it, so much did she tremble. Cold sweat ran down her back. What should she do? Snatch the cup from Jane and confess what she had done? But it was for Jane's sake that she did it.

It was too late now, for Jane had drunk the wine. She had noticed nothing. She lay back; her face had grown pale and her eyelids drooped already. Kate sat, watching her.

The minutes passed and Kate did not move; she listened to those sounds which meant that the household was retiring for the night. She heard Thomas go to his room; she heard the servants first making their beds in the great hall and then settling down to sleep. They would not remark on her absence, for they would think she was sleeping in Jane's room. Moreover, they were usually so fatigued that they fell into their beds as soon as they were ready and were quickly asleep. Later she must creep down to the hall, and in the morning she must pretend that she had spent the whole night there. Time enough for that. Kate rarely thought of more than one thing at a time.

She waited until she could hear no sound but the creaking of the oldest boards in the staircase before she crept to the window and stood there waiting. She did not wait long. From below came a long low whistle. That was the signal. All she had to do was creep downstairs and let him into the house. He would do the rest.

But now that the moment had come Kate was filled with a great doubt. She was about to give this helpless girl into the hands of a man of whom she knew very little. Quite suddenly Kate knew she dared not do it.

She could never recall what happened during the next few seconds. She did know that she ran screaming along the corridor and started to hammer on the door of her master's room. It seemed that she stood there for a long time before he flung open the door and stood before her in a coat he had picked up in a hurry; his face was purple, his lips sagging.

'What means this, woman?' he demanded; and Kate fell sobbing against him.

'He is there, master. He is there. He is coming to take Mistress Jane away. He gave me stuff to put in her wine.'

'What's this? *What's* this? Who is where?' The mention of his daughter's name had set fear stirring in Thomas. He knew enough of the nature of those adventures indulged in by promiscuous young men to get, even from Kate's incoherent words, some idea of what was afoot. He seized Kate by the arm and dragged her along to Jane's room. He stared in horror at his daughter's face; it was so unnaturally pale and still.

'Jane!' He dropped Kate's arm to lean over his daughter. 'My little Jane.' He felt her heart and an immense relief showed in his face. He understood.

Jane was not the first to be drugged before an abduction. He turned to Kate, gripped her shoulder, shook her violently, and then flung her on to the floor, where she lay staring up at him with terror in her eyes. He leaned over her, took her by the throat and shook her afresh.

'You had better tell me everything, before I kill you,' he said.

It came out in jerks, the whole story–Kate's meeting with the man in St Paul's Churchyard, the messages, Jane's indifference, and finally the plot. As Kate talked she was shaken and beaten, but there was on her face a vacant smile of relief. She would be beaten as she had never been beaten, but she did not care. She had saved Jane.

Thomas left her lying exhausted on the floor. He went downstairs and unlocked the front door. For one wrathful second he stood face to face with Lord Hastings. Hastings recovered himself first. He turned and walked rapidly away. Thomas followed him, calling scoundrel, commanding him to stop; but Hastings had leaped on to his horse and was away, leaving the furious mercer, barelegged and barefooted, to shake a trembling fist at the fleeing figure.

Now the whole household was astir. Apprentices had gathered on the stairs; they whispered with the serving men and women. A robbery? Someone trying to break into the vaults?

'Back to your beds, all of you!' Thomas shouted; and they slunk away, while their master stamped barefooted back to his daughter's room. Kate was on her knees by the bed, sobbing, while Jane still slept her deep unnatural sleep.

Thomas leaned over Kate, gripped her by the ear, and pulled her up.

'Go to my room and get me a wrap. Bring it back here at once.'

Kate went and was back in a few seconds. He snatched the robe from her and wrapped it round himself while Kate stood trembling before him.

'How long will my daughter remain like that?'

'I–do not know.'

'You do not know, you wicked, wanton woman! And *you* gave her the drug, did you not?'

Kate nodded. 'I wish I were dead, master.'

'Wish you were dead! You're going to wish you'd never been born before I've done with you. Stop snivelling, I tell you. By God's Holy Mother, you shall pay for this.'

'I would wish that,' cried Kate. 'I will welcome every stroke, for now I see how richly I deserve it.'

'Stroke! Think not that a mere beating will be your reward for this night's work. You'll be out on the street this time tomorrow.'

Kate was shocked into silence. Out on the street, no home, nothing to eat but what she could beg. Who would take her in after the way she had repaid Thomas Wainstead for his goodness?

He made her tell the story over and over again. What had the man said? What had Jane said? He was satisfied that his daughter had not had a hand in this sordid intrigue and he was inclined to be more lenient with Kate on that account.

There they sat through the long night, Thomas occasionally roaring out a question; Kate moaning softly, contemplating a dreary and most wretched future.

Not until dawn came did Jane begin to stir. Thomas leaned over the bed. 'Jane,' he whispered. 'Daughter.' His voice was tender.

Jane opened her eyes and looked at him.

'All is well, daughter. Your father is here with you.'

'Father . . . I feel . . . so strange. I . . .'

Thomas put an arm about her. 'Bring a cup of wine,' he shouted to Kate. 'Quick, woman.' And Kate ran, eager to obey, to make up in every small way for the great harm she had done.

Thomas snatched the wine from her and held it to Jane's lips. Jane sipped and a little colour came into her face.

'That's better,' said Thomas with relief.

'Father . . . what happened . . . to me?'

Thomas said viciously: 'You were drugged by that drab.'

'Drugged?'

'Aye. Drugged by that slut, that sloven, that harlot there. Working for a scoundrel she was. Eating my meat, drinking my wine and working for a scoundrel. By God, by Christ, she'll wish she'd never been born!'

'Kate!' cried Jane.

'Oh, mistress,' sobbed Kate. 'I never thought . . . I never meant to. . . .'

'Kate,' said Jane; and she held out her hand. But Thomas struck Kate as she would approach the bed, so that she staggered across the room and fell, cutting her head against the table. This violence seemed to lift Jane out of her drugged stupor.

'Father . . . no . . . no.'

'But yes,' cried Thomas. 'Get up, you harlot,' he shouted at Kate; and Kate got up.

'Come here, you strumpet,' he said; and Kate came. 'Nearer,' he roared at her, and pulled her by the hair, which was hanging loose about her shoulders.

'Now, daughter,' he said. 'Understand this: This woman, whom you trusted, sought to betray you. She drugged your wine and she had schemed to hand you over to a scoundrel.'

'Kate!' said Jane in shocked horror.

'Nay,' screamed Kate. 'I did not do it. It is true I put the powder in your wine, and when I saw you sleeping . . . I knew it was wrong. Believe me, mistress. At first I thought it would be right for you. I thought he would marry you, make a grand lady of you and save you from the goldsmith. But then . . . suddenly I knew it was wrong, and, instead of letting him in, I called your father.'

Thomas eyed her narrowly. It was true. At least she had had the sense to do that. He felt the rising of uncontrollable anger. Everything he had done to shield his daughter was of no avail. This brought home to him how easy it was for her to deceive him. If he had lacked peace before, how much more would he lack that happy state now. He thought longingly of what his daughter's marriage to the goldsmith would mean.

Jane was making a great effort to rouse herself from the stupefying effects of the drug. She herself was safe, so all her thoughts were for Kate. She saw the blood on Kate's face and the terrible fear in her eyes as she visualised her future. She understood Kate well enough to know what had gone on in her mind. Kate was a simple woman, for all she believed herself to be so wise. She had genuinely believed that she was helping her mistress to a happier life. Poor Kate!

'Father,' she said weakly, 'Kate meant no harm.'

'Meant no harm!' cried Thomas. 'No, she only meant to pass you over to a rascally fellow.'

'But she repented in time, you see, Father, for here I am in my own room, and all through Kate.'

Kate had brightened, and Jane was deeply moved to see the hope which came into the woman's face.

'Father,' persisted Jane, 'you will not be hard on her . . . for my sake.'

'For your sake! What have I had but disobedience from you? Let me tell you this, daughter, tomorrow I go to William Shore and tell him you have come to your senses.'

'No,' said Jane, 'you will not do that.'

'Oh, yes I will. Tomorrow you will be betrothed to Shore. Aye, and married to him as soon as I can manage it. And that slut'–he pointed at Kate with a trembling finger–'gets out of my house, and I never wish to look into her wicked face again.'

'But, Father, where will she go?'

'She'll go over to Southwark most like. That's where her bawdy friends live and where she belongs. The harlot! I knew from the moment I took the drab into my house that I was making a mistake. "I was turned out of Ludlow Castle when the soldiers came," she said. "There was naught I could do but follow the camp to London." Followed the camp of her free will, I'll swear. Well, back she goes to where she belongs–and that's not in the house of an honest merchant.'

'But, Father, what will become of her if you turn her out?' asked Jane. 'She has nowhere to go.'

'Mayhap the scoundrel she was about to let into my house will do something for her.'

'She did not let him into your house.'

'I'll hear no more now. Get you to sleep.' He turned to Kate. 'As for you . . . you'll go straight out of this house . . . now. And don't let me see you whining at the back door or I'll have you flung into Ludgate.'

'Father!' cried Jane.

'I said I would hear no more.'

Jane roused herself from the effect of the drug which seemed to chain her to the bed. 'You shall hear me,' she said.

Relieved by her improved appearance, Thomas shouted at her: 'Think you it is your lot to command me, girl? You have been pampered enough already. Another word from you and I'll put a whip about your shoulders.'

'Do so,' said Jane, 'but still I shall speak.'

He advanced towards the bed. Jane smiled at him. She felt light-headed and very weary, but she could not rest while Kate had that look in her face, for Kate was obviously more frightened than any living creature should be.

'Father,' she said, 'you want me to marry Will Shore, don't you?'

'A foolish question. You know well my wishes.'

'Then, Father, I will marry him.'

Thomas smiled. 'So you have come to your senses at last. Right glad I am, girl, for it gave me no pleasure to shut you up and starve you.'

'There is a condition, Father.'

'A condition?'

'Yes. I marry Will and Kate stays with me.'

Thomas narrowed his eyes and looked from Kate to Jane; then slowly his mouth began to turn up at the corners.

There was something gloomy about the house in Cheapside after that night, although the mercer went about whistling gaily.

Kate's part in that night's abortive abduction had not gone unpunished, although the mercer kept his promise to his daughter, and Kate stayed on in his house. Thomas had lashed her to the whipping post and given her a beating she would never forget. She had screamed, then groaned and become unconscious, sagging there at the post before the mercer had done. She had to keep to her bed for three days after the beating, while a pale-faced Jane–grown quieter and more serious–fiercely condemned her father for what he had done.

Thomas smarted under his daughter's tongue, and wondered why he allowed her to call him a savage. But at the same time he could congratulate himself that it would not be long before Will Shore must be the one to deal with her waywardness.

Jane rubbed ointments into Kate's wounds, and herself waited on her maid during those three days; and both maid and mistress were more subdued than any had ever seen them before.

Kate would bear the marks of that beating on her body for as long as she lived. But it seemed that Jane suffered more than Kate from that night's adventure, for she had become betrothed to Will Shore, the goldsmith.

Lombard Street

The goldsmith was bewildered. For nearly two years Jane had been his wife, and yet that complete satisfaction, that fulfilment, which he had thought must be the natural outcome of his marriage, was denied him. He loved her with all the passion of which he was capable. He loved too his fine house, his business, all the beautifully wrought and valuable articles which made up his stock; he was proud of his standing in the City; but the pride and love he felt for Jane were greater than he felt for any other of his possessions. The love of the goldsmith for all his treasures was bound up in the esteem in which he wished all men to hold him. He longed to be a strutting giant, feared for his strength, a wit admired for his ready tongue. Instead he was a man of small stature, of gentle almost timid manners. He had grown rich, though, through saving the groat here, the shilling there. But for all that he was a small man, and he knew it.

Being unable therefore to attract attention to himself through his own personality, he sought to do it through his possessions; and thus had he become an acquisitive man. He liked to go into his vaults and to handle the precious metals there; he liked to stroke Jane's golden hair, caress her lovely limbs. 'The gold is mine,' he could gloat, and know that men envied him. 'Jane is mine,' he could tell himself; and for Jane he was also envied.

He should have been satisfied, but he was not, for he did not understand the lovely high-spirited girl whom he had bought with his own treasured gold and his years of hard work and shrewd dealing. He had heard her laughing with the woman, Kate, whom she had insisted on bringing with her. It worried him that when she was alone with him she rarely laughed. He disliked Kate. She was not the sort of woman he would have had in his house but for Jane. She was, he suspected, lazy. He suspected certain revelries in his kitchens. Belper, his fat and clever cook, loved women almost as much as he loved food. Belper had been a disturbing element in his house even before Kate had come into it; but Belper was worth a little inconvenience. He was one of the best cooks in London, and a goldsmith often found it necessary to entertain those of the quality who were his customers; therefore it had been necessary to forget Belper's second love, since he had such a way with his first. Kate was of no such value.

On this particular day he was going the round of his house, locking up all doors, except the front one, for they would have to go out by that and lock it afterwards. All the servants had already gone, except Kate, who was helping Jane to dress. They were late already and should have been in Cheapside by now. He shook his head. He should scold Jane for her lack of punctuality; he would prepare to scold and because she was so beautiful he would forget his impatience and know only pride.

He wished they could have a child. He saw in a child a new treasure; he would like a child that looked exactly like Jane but had his shrewd ways—a child that laughed and was witty and yet had a head for business. So far, there was no sign of a child. It was a continual irritation. He wondered if men and women whispered behind their hands as he passed: 'The goldsmith cannot have a child.' It was a slight on his manhood.

He went to the front door and opened it. A roar of voices that shrieked and laughed seemed to fill the house. The crowd was already gathering, and he and Jane would not find it easy to get to her father's house in Cheapside, from where they intended to view the procession. Jane took too long in decking herself out in her finery. The goldsmith shook his head uneasily. He doubted not that Jane would attract as much attention as any riding in the King's procession.

It was comforting, though, to contemplate that for a time at least there would be an end to war. As a serious-minded merchant, Will knew that only out of peace could prosperity grow. He rejoiced that King Edward had prevailed, and that the trouble-making Earl of Warwick was dead. Pray the saints, thought Will, that this is an end to civil war. Let Edward reign in peace from now on, and good times will lie ahead. There would be pageantry and revelry in place of discomfort and death. Small wonder that the citizens of London were gathering in their thousands to welcome the return to his capital of victorious Edward.

But he and Jane must be gone or they would not get a glimpse of the pageant, thought the goldsmith, as he made his way upstairs. The women were laughing, and Kate was saying: 'We are frail creatures indeed, but if we do aught wrong, is it not because some evil spirit leads us to it? Can we be blamed? Mayhap when we think we sin most it is but the will of God that we should do so.'

'Why, Kate,' said Jane, 'that is a comforting creed. You should preach it at Paul's Cross. I'll swear you'd have half London following you.'

Will opened the door and their frivolity was curbed. Kate started to straighten the things on the table busily, as though she was the sort who could not let her hands remain idle for a moment. Did she think to deceive him? Jane gave him what he knew to be a false smile of welcome.

'We are very late,' he said harshly. 'I doubt if we shall get a view of the King.'

He laid a hand on her arm and he looked at her in that appealing way which never failed to move her or fill her with self-reproach. 'Tell me where I fail, Jane,' said the meekness of his eyes. 'Mayhap I could change.' But how could she tell him? How would she say, 'I do not love you, nor can I ever love you. I like not the heavy way you breathe; the way you pick a bone as though you will get every scrap of meat off it–not in hunger but in fear of waste. I like not the way your hands pat and caress me as though you feel there is something shameful in this, and yet, having bought me in marriage, you have paid for the privilege of being shameful. There are thousands of things about you that I do not like, and though I have tried to like them, though I have prayed that I might like them, I never can.'

She got up, trying to smile affectionately at Will; and in a short time they were walking briskly out of Lombard Street past the Stocks Market into the Poultry. Here the crowd was thicker than ever. Men had climbed posts to see over the heads of others. They were shouting and whistling to one another. Some of the traders from the cookshops were pushing their way through the crowds. Trays hung from their necks by means of straps, and the trays were loaded with pieces of meat, bread and cakes, mead and wine. People were eating, laughing and shouting; and every now and then there would break out the cry of 'King Edward!'

Too many people cast their eyes on the goldsmith's radiant wife. It disturbed his peace of mind, for much as he liked to see her admired, he did not care that it should be by the rabble of the Poultry.

He scolded her. 'You see, you have made us late. How shall we now reach your father's house? We must watch the procession from the streets here–among this mob of people. I declare the stench of them is past bearing. And all because you would not be ready in good time.'

'But is it not good to see so many people enjoying this day?' said Jane. She was laughing now at a tumbler who was performing for the benefit of the crowd.

'And what your father will say when we do not arrive, I cannot imagine,' went on Will.

'I can,' said Jane. 'He will fall into a rage.'

'And that amuses you? I declare I like it not that your father should think me so inconsiderate. . . .'

'Never fear, Will! the entire blame for this will be laid where it belongs . . . on my shoulders.'

There was a sudden shout from the crowd. The shouting grew louder, and in the distance the sound of trumpets could be heard.

And now, thought Jane, I shall see the King himself. I shall see this man who is supposed to be so irresistible that virtuous maidens discard their virtue at his command. I shall see the Queen who so enchanted him that, profligate though he was, he could not resist her. Small wonder, that wherever they went people turned out in their thousands to see this romantic King and his Queen.

Now came the first of the brilliant cavalcade–men bejewelled and dazzling in their gorgeously coloured clothes. Then came a chariot surrounded by guards, and a sudden hush fell on the crowd, for the two women in this chariot were enemies of the King and not to be cheered. One was the hated Margaret of Anjou, who had been captured at Tewkesbury where her son Edward had met his death. The other occupant of the chariot could not but excite the pity of all who saw her; and it was her presence which prevented the crowd from actively displaying its hatred. She was a very pale, sad-faced girl of about sixteen, and her name was Anne Neville. She was the younger daughter of the Earl of Warwick, and had been betrothed to Margaret's son who had recently been killed at Tewkesbury. She had spent most of her childhood with the King's youngest brother, Richard of Gloucester, and it was said that, although she had been forced into betrothal with Margaret's son, it was Richard whom she loved. Therefore did it seem sad to these Londoners that this girl, pale as a primrose, must ride as a prisoner, while that very Richard whom she was reputed to love rode in a place of honour near his brother the King.

The chariot rolled on, and as Jane gazed at those gloriously apparelled knights, at the brilliant trappings of the stately horses, she saw among them a face she knew; and as she looked, the handsome head was turned towards her. It was the man who was responsible for that terrifying night when she had been nearly abducted, the man who was responsible for her marriage to Will Shore. The glance he now gave her conveyed his pleasure at seeing her again. There was in it, too, a look of confidence, of arrogance, which seemed to say, 'Do I seem the man to accept failure?'

Was it fear or the crowd pressing round her that made her sway towards Will? She felt as though she were about to faint.

'What is wrong?' asked Will anxiously.

'I feel . . . too hot.'

'It's the crowd. We should have viewed this from your father's windows. Come. We'll get home before the crowd begins to move.'

She felt better as soon as she entered the house, but she let Will take her up to bed. He left her while he went to get some wine. When he brought it back he watched her closely for a few seconds, and then he said with a great hope in his eyes: 'Jane, could it be . . . You were so suddenly faint that . . .'

'No,' she said quickly. 'No.'

He smiled in an embarrassed fashion. 'I was hoping that you would tell me you were with child.'

'I am sorry, Will. But it is not so.'

They were both sorry about that, she thought, after he had gone. A child would have made such a difference to them. If only it had been a child, and not that man on horseback. He had brought trouble before; she felt certain he would do so again.

The wine had made Jane drowsy. Through her window she could hear the shouting of the people. The procession was ended, but the crowd was still bent on pleasure. She had, from her father's house in Cheapside, often watched the people after pageants. She had seen their wild dances, their frantic merry-making. Often she had looked from a window on to strange scenes, fantastic, lurid in the glow from lighted torches. She had heard screaming laughter that seemed scarcely human; she had seen men and women fighting together, making love; she had seen them stretched out drunk on the cobbles below the house. Her father had had to bolt his doors and barricade his windows on such nights as these; he must have the apprentices ready with staves in case it should be necessary to protect the house again rioters, for thieves were abroad, and all that was evil in the hysterical drunken crowds was let loose on such nights.

This was another such night, a night for rejoicing, since King Edward, after a few months' exile, was back on the throne; and it seemed that there were many of his subjects who wished to emulate that beautiful profligate, their handsome, popular, lecherous King.

Jane dozed and dreamed she was back in the crowd. She saw again the man on horseback; but in her dream, instead of riding on, he came swiftly towards her, picked her up from beside Will, and slung her across his horse. Jane screamed, and the scream awakened her.

Kate was standing by the bed staring down at her.

'Mercy on us! That was a bad dream, mistress.'

'I'm glad I awoke,' said Jane.

'So you all but fainted in the street, lovey?'

'It was the heat and crowds, Kate.' And when Kate's eyes narrowed knowledgeably, Jane burst out: 'Pray do not look sly and secret because you think I ought to be with child. I am not, I tell you.' Kate pursed her lips and Jane went on: 'Did you see the King?'

'I did; and the Queen was with him. She is very beautiful. I saw her in her litter, that was carried on poles. The horses were splendid creatures.'

'Were the horses as beautiful as the Queen?'

'They were not. The Queen has the most lovely yellow hair I ever saw . . . next to yours. She wore it loose and flowing; and they say the King is much in love with her after their long separation. And all the Princesses were lovely, as for the little Prince . . . he is just a baby. You should have heard the people cheer when they saw *him*.'

'Kate, you've something on your mind.'

'On my mind, mistress?'

'You know that it is useless to deceive me. You know something and you are waiting to tell me.'

'I saw *him* in the procession, mistress,' said Kate. 'I learned his name. He is Lord Hastings.'

Jane caught her breath. She had heard of Hastings. He had distinguished himself at Barnet and Tewkesbury, and he was a close friend of the King's.

'Then,' said Jane sharply, to hide her fear, 'it is a pity, methinks, that my Lord Hastings does not behave in a more seemly fashion.'

'Indeed it is,' said Kate, but she could not hide the sparkle in her eyes. She was convinced that life was meant to be a gay affair, and nothing would have pleased her more than to see her beautiful mistress deep in a secret love affair.

'How did you learn who he was?' demanded Jane.

'I asked a man who stood beside me in the crowd.'

'He may have been mistaken.'

'Nay. There were many who said it. Think of it, mistress. He loves you, and he is the King's closest friend and favourite.'

'He would never be friend and favourite of mine.'

'That is what you say now.'

Jane jumped off the bed and caught Kate by the wrist. 'Kate, you have not been . . .'

'No, mistress. No. I have done nothing.'

'Because if you ever betrayed me as you promised him to do that night, I should not save you again.'

'I would do nothing–nothing without your consent.'

There was a sudden knocking at the door. 'Who is there?' asked Jane, while Kate hastily began tidying the things on the table for fear it should be the goldsmith.

But it was not the goldsmith, and Kate stopped working at once. It was merely Bess, one of the kitchen girls.

'Yes, Bessy?' asked Jane kindly, while Kate glared at the girl, for they were rivals for the attentions of the fat and affectionate Belper.

'If you please, mistress, there is a gentleman below who says he must have speech with you. It is a matter of some importance.'

'A gentleman? Did you not ask his name?'

'Yes, mistress, but he did not give it. He said to ask you to come at once; and he spoke most pressingly.'

Jane stood up. 'Very well, Bessy. Where is he?'

'I left him in the parlour. He had stepped into the house before I had time to ask him.'

'I will go at once and see who it is,' said Jane.

She went down, and, opening the parlour door, saw, looking jaunty and very sure of himself, Lord Hastings. He came towards her and would have laid his hands on her shoulders while he kissed her mouth in greeting, had she not held him off.

'Sir,' she said haughtily, 'I know not why you have come here.'

'You know well,' he said gravely.

'I must ask you to go at once.'

'Has not the goldsmith's lady better hospitality to offer me than this?'

'There is no hospitality for you in this house.'

'I am sorry for that, Jane,' he said sadly, 'for, by my faith, you are more fair than I had thought you.'

'How dare you come here!' You should be shut in the Tower for what you tried to do to me.'

'Speak not of that, Jane. It grieves me.'

'I am glad of that. Mayhap there is some decency in you then.'

He smiled whimsically. 'You do not understand me. It grieves me that I did not succeed in carrying you off.'

There was something overpowering about the man that robbed her of her calm. He was very handsome in his fine garments, and though his mouth was firm, his eyes twinkled. He stepped towards her. She was terrified that his intention was to pick her up and walk out of the house with her.

'Will!' she screamed. 'Will!'

Hastings was taken aback. His face flushed angrily. 'Are you mad? You would call your husband?'

'Will!' called Jane. 'Oh–quickly–quickly!'

There followed the sound of running footsteps. Will had heard her cries.

'Jane, where are you? Where are you, Jane?'

'Here,' called Jane wildly. 'Here in the parlour.'

She tried to run past Hastings but he caught her and held her fast. She tried to kick herself free.

'You foolish girl,' muttered Hastings. 'Be still.'

'Foolish!' panted Jane. 'Is it foolish to despise you? *I* call it wisdom.'

Hastings was furious. He had expected that such daring he had displayed in calling on the woman in her husband's house would be applauded and win her admiration immediately. He had believed that Jane was like other women of his acquaintance who would wish the wooing to be arduous, but who would be ready enough to fall to him after a while. Being absent with the King, he had been unable to continue his pursuit of her since his attempt to abduct her from Cheapside had been foiled, but now he was ready, and the waiting had been long enough. He felt foolish. He had suffered sufficient indignity for her already. He was determined to endure no more.

'This is the last time I'll come courting you,' he said.

'That is the best news I've heard for a long time,' she flashed back.

Then the door opened and Will, followed by his steward, came in. 'Jane!' cried Will.

'Oh, Will, praise the saints you've come. This–man–has dared to come into your house. He is the man who tried to abduct me.'

Hastings, having released Jane on the entrance of the goldsmith, stood, his arms folded, looking scornfully down on Will Shore.

'You knave!' shrieked Will. 'I'll have you tried for trespass. How dare you force an entry into my house!'

Hastings laughed. 'Be silent,' he said shortly. 'It is clear you do not know whom you address.'

'He knows he addresses a knave and a liar,' said Jane hotly.

Hastings continued to look at Will. 'I would have you know, fellow, that I am Lord Hastings.'

'I care not if you are the King himself,' said the goldsmith recklessly.

'Bravo!' cried Jane.

Hastings flashed an arrogant glance in her direction. 'You speak rashly,' he said. 'Now stand aside, goldsmith, unless you care to feel the point of my sword through that brave heart of yours.'

He pushed past Will, and, reaching the door, turned to look at him and Jane.

'Think not,' he said, 'that I shall forget this day.' His eyes went to Jane. 'Methinks, madam, that this husband of yours will, ere long, regret that he dared to insult Lord Hastings.'

He went out. They were silent in the parlour as they listened to his footsteps on the cobbles in the courtyard.

Then Will turned to Jane and put an arm about her.

'Have no fear, sweetheart,' he said. 'I will protect you.'

Jane smiled at him. She wished she could believe that he had the power to do so.

For the next few days Jane was afraid to go out for fear she should meet Lord Hastings. When dusk fell she did not care to stray far from the side of Will or Kate. She could not forget how vindictive Hastings had looked when he had said they would regret their treatment of him. She wished she could believe that his talk of revenge had been an idle threat, but she knew that terrible things could happen to those who opposed powerful men such as he was. But two days after the incident the King and his court left London abruptly, and Jane's peace of mind returned.

There was a hush over London during those days. King Henry the Sixth, whom the conquering Edward had made a prisoner in the Tower, died mysteriously. He had been murdered, some said, by order of the King. People remembered that, ineffectual as he was, mad as he was, he had been a pious man who had never cared to wrong any, and they began to look upon him as a martyr. His dead body was paraded through the streets, so that all might see it was really the deposed King Henry who was dead; and in view of the attitude of his people, even popular King Edward had thought fit to leave the capital for a little while. It seemed to Jane then that there was some good in all evil, since when the court removed from London, Lord Hastings must go with it.

The goldsmith was almost as relieved as his wife, and when in a few weeks the court returned to Westminster Palace, both Jane and her husband were thinking a good deal less about the threats of Hastings.

Business was good, and rich men came to the premises in Lombard Street; the apprentices were kept running up and down to the vaults to bring up the most precious of their master's goods for the inspection of customers. And Will was almost content, seeing trade flourishing and his wife quieter than he had ever known her.

Then one day there came to the house a handsome merchant who told Will that he wished to buy much gold and plate and would see of his best. He was a tall and well proportioned man, and he had a charming and confiding manner which immediately won the goldsmith's heart.

'I have heard,' said this man, 'that, an I wish to buy the best gold plate in London, then to William Shore of Lombard Street must I come.'

It was not only the words, it was the charming smile that accompanied them that made the goldsmith almost over-eager to please. He could not help feeling oddly flustered as the big man sprawled on a tapestry-covered stool, his long, well-shaped legs thrust out before him. Will sent two apprentices down to the vaults to bring up the very best of his stock that it might be displayed for the rich merchant's approval.

'My name,' said the merchant, 'is Long. Edward Long.'

'At your service, sir,' said the goldsmith, 'and I trust you will find here that which pleases you.'

The merchant selected several pieces. 'I will send my servant to collect them,' he said. 'I verily believe I have found some of the really finest pieces in the town.'

'I think so too,' said the goldsmith. 'Your friends will envy you, good sir.'

'I was indeed right to come to William Shore, I see. Odd how men will talk. They said to me, "William Shore has the finest plate and the handsomest wife in London." Men talk, sir.'

The goldsmith was so pleased that he was filled with a desire that the rich merchant should admire not only the plate but his wife.

'My wife, sir, is considered more beautiful than my plate.'

The merchant looked disbelievingly at the plate and gave no indication that he wished to see the woman whose beauty had given rise to such discussion.

'I will call her that you may see her for yourself,' said Will.

The merchant lifted his shoulders. 'I shall, of course, be delighted to meet the lady, but, alas, I have little time . . .'

His reluctance made the goldsmith more eager. He sent one of the apprentices up to tell his mistress she was wanted below. Jane came down at her husband's bidding. Her morning gown was of her favourite and most becoming blue, and embroidered on it were flowers which had been worked in gold thread. Spangles glittered as she walked; and her long yellow hair hung over her shoulders.

The merchant looked at her, and Jane looked at the merchant. He was very good to look at, she decided; and she liked the steady gaze of his eyes, liked his admiration the more because he attempted to conceal it.

'Wife,' said Will, 'this is Merchant Edward Long who has bought some of my finest plate this morning.'

'I am glad to hear it and to meet you, sir,' said Jane.

Edward Long put his hands on her shoulders and kissed her on the mouth. It was a strange and startling kiss; yet a kiss was the habitual greeting between men and women, and since she was a child Jane had been kissed thus in greeting.

'Tell me,' said Edward Long, 'what think you of the choice I have made?'

'I think you have chosen of my husband's best. That is so, is it not, Will?'

'It is, wife. Pray order one of the servants to bring refreshment to our friend. You can stay a short while, sir?'

The merchant hesitated. 'I do confess to being somewhat fatigued. I should like the opportunity of judging whether your wine is as good as your plate.'

The goldsmith rubbed his hands with pleasure, and Jane hastily sent the apprentice who was hovering at the door to the kitchen to have refreshment brought. She felt the colour heighten in her cheeks. This merchant had aroused her curiosity. There was about him an air of great dignity, and he was an exceptionally handsome man; she found it pleasant not to be stared at in a crude fashion, and at the same time stimulating.

When the wine arrived she poured it out and took it to him. Over the goblet their eyes met and his were inscrutable.

'I thank you, good mistress.' He lifted his goblet. 'To good business.'

'To trade,' echoed Will. 'May it continue as it is going on.'

'There is an improvement these last weeks, good Shore? Trade has been more brisk since . . .'

'Since the King came back and put his enemies to flight.'

'To the King,' said Edward Long.

'To the King,' said Will Shore.

The merchant leaned towards Jane. 'Tell me, Madam,' he said. 'I have heard that the merchants' wives in this City are devoted to the King. Is it true?'

'They say he is very handsome,' said Jane.

'What? Have you never seen him?'

'Nay.'

'Were you not in the City when he rode through?'

'Yes,' said Jane.

'And you would not walk a yard or so to see his handsome face?'

'We joined the crowds,' explained Will, 'but my wife was overcome by the heat.'

'But,' said Jane, 'we saw the first part.'

'Mayhap you do not care for these processions?'

'I did not care to see the King's enemies, those two women, in their shame.'

'Love you the King's enemies, mistress?' asked the merchant.

'Indeed she does not, sir. Jane talks over-wild and always did. She is a woman to speak before she has thought.' Will frowned at Jane. 'It makes foolish talk often enough.'

'But interesting talk,' said the merchant. 'I would hear more of it, for pleasant it is to find someone who does not say exactly what everyone else is saying.' He and Jane exchanged smiles. 'Tell me,' he went on, 'have you some affection for Margaret of Anjou?'

'I like not her methods,' said Jane, 'but methinks that once having been in possession of a throne, it is but natural to make some effort to regain it. Moreover, I felt it was unnecessarily cruel to make her humiliation public.'

'Kings are often cruel,' he said.

'I fear so. Glad I am to be but the wife of a humble citizen.'

'*Are* goldsmiths so humble?'

'They are tradesmen, I thank God; not courtiers.'

'You like not courtiers, Madam?'

'I cannot say. I know none. But it seems to me that a man whose opinions must be adjusted to keep his head balanced on his shoulders lacks the dignity of . . . shall we say, a goldsmith?'

'You think then that those about the King adjust their opinions to keep their heads on their shoulders?'

'Assuredly,' said Jane. 'Whereas with us merchants it is just a matter of "The old King is gone; long live the new one." As the distance from the throne grows greater, so diminishes the danger. I had rather keep my head in its rightful place than live too near kings.'

'Nor does that surprise me; if you will forgive my forwardness, Madam, I would say it is a most beautiful head.'

'Thank you,' said Jane, and found herself flushing.

Shore said: 'So, sir, you think my wife is to be admired as much as my plate?'

'More so. Much more so. I take away my morning's purchases with an easy conscience, knowing I leave behind the greatest of your treasures.'

'You are most gracious, sir,' said Will.

'I am most interested,' said the merchant. He smiled quizzically at Jane. 'In her views about Queen Margaret I am very interested. I believe the lady thinks the King something of a monster to imprison the woman.'

'Nay, she does not,' said Will quickly. 'Jane knows, as we do all, that Queen Margaret was a menace to the safety of our country. There is not a citizen in London who does not sleep more peacefully at nights knowing King Henry and his son are dead and Margaret a prisoner.'

'But your lady wife is kind of heart, I see. She regrets the King's conduct in exposing Margaret to public shame. *I* forget not the death of the King's father. It is not so long ago that he was killed near Wakefield. Mayhap it is forgotten that Margaret's men cut off his head and set upon it a paper crown before it was placed in mockery over the gates of York. I am inclined to think a public ride was little to ask in exchange for that.'

'That was a terrible thing,' said Jane, 'but I do not think that one act of cruelty needs another to balance it. Revenge is not only evil; it is stupid. There is no good to grow out of it. To forgive one's enemies is not a good thing only, but a wise one also.'

'Methinks, sir,' said the merchant, draining his glass, 'that your wife should be first adviser to the King.'

They all laughed.

'It pleases you to mock me,' said Jane. 'I care not. I know I am right.'

The merchant laughed afresh, and he had infectious and delightful laughter. 'Forgive me,' he said, 'if I say that from what I have heard of the King he would lend a willing ear to a lady as charming as yourself should she deign to advise him.'

'They say,' said Jane, 'that for all his grandeur he is very easily led.'

'By women,' said Shore.

'Ah, yes,' said the merchant, 'I hear His Grace is most susceptible to the ladies.'

'Which shows,' put in Jane, 'that he is not strong.'

'Think you then that he is a weakling? They tell me that he stands well over six feet and that without his boots.'

'Giants may be weak,' said Jane, 'and dwarfs be strong men.'

'He was certainly said to be weak over that marriage of his,' said Will.

'I liked him for it,' declared Jane.

'Did you indeed, Madam?'

'I did. And how I should love to see the Queen!'

'And the King?'

'Yes. But more the Queen. I think she must be truly wonderful to have tamed such a . . .'

'Notorious lover of women?' said the merchant.

'Such a rake,' said Jane.

'Hush, Jane. You talk too wildly.'

'Why must the truth always be wild?'

'Doubtless,' suggested the merchant, 'because the truth is often dangerous. Lies are so comforting, so easy. Therefore are lies safe.'

'I scorn such safety.'

'I see you do, Madam. Never fear, sir, I shall whisper nothing of this to the King.'

They laughed afresh, and after a short while the merchant said he must go. 'I will send my servant to collect my purchases. He will bring the money. Such pleasant wine . . . and company.'

'Good day, sir,' said Will. And, 'Good day, sir,' said Jane. Will added: 'I trust we shall have the pleasure of seeing you again, sir.'

'That may well be.'

'A most profitable morning,' said Will, when he and Jane were alone. 'Was he not a charming man?'

'He was indeed,' said Jane; and she went upstairs smiling; it was not easy to get the handsome merchant out of her thoughts.

'My dear Will,' said Mary Blague, the satin of her gown crackling, her narrow eyes smiling, 'I would you could lend me our dear Jane for this afternoon. I know you are busy with your accounts. Therefore, thought I, it would be a small favour to ask you to give up your wife's company. I am doing a new pattern–a beautiful lace it is. I swear the King will like it when he sees it. I want to show it to Jane.'

'My dear Mary,' said Will, 'you must ask Jane herself.' He went to the door and called Jane who soon came running in.

'I want you to spend the afternoon with me, dear,' said Mary. 'Now you must come. I'll have no refusal. Please, Will, plead for me.'

'There is no need to plead,' said Jane, who enjoyed any outing. 'I will gladly come.'

'Mary wishes to show you a new pattern,' said Will.

Jane was surprised at that, and wondered why Mary Blague should want to show *her* a new pattern. Jane herself had never excelled in such womanly arts as lace-making and embroidery; it seemed strange that Mary should be so excited and seem to dread a refusal. But perhaps she was a lonely woman.

'You'll come after dinner?' said Mary.

'After dinner,' agreed Jane.

Mary left them and Will, seeing Jane thoughtful, said: 'Did you not wish to go, my dear?'

Jane shrugged her shoulders. 'I find her amusing, though I cannot like her very much. But I do like her gossip about the court, and I must confess I delight in her sly suggestions of that remote and most romantic friendship with the King.'

'There is a streak of mischief in your nature, Jane. I should pray for strength to resist that.'

'But I enjoy my streak of mischief, Will. I should miss it sorely.'

'You should also pray that your frivolity might be subdued.'

'And pray too that God will strengthen my desire for you,' she retorted.

'Wife! What sort of talk is this!'

She was immediately repentant. 'I am sorry, Will, but you angered me. You have said that I am over-cold and you wished me warmer, and as I have so many sins, I thought that was very likely one of them.' She put her arm through his. 'Forgive me, Will. I am unkind to you who are so good to me.'

He patted her arm. 'Now, Jane, no tears.'

She put her hand to her eyes; there were tears there. Why am I so unhappy? she asked herself. What have I to be unhappy about?

'I think a little prayer . . .' said Will; and she wanted to scream at him, though she managed to smile and quickly left him.

After dinner Jane set out to see Mary Blague. Quickly she left Lombard Street and came past the Stocks Market into the Poultry and on to Cheapside where, close to the corner of Bucklersbury, stood Mary's house. That house was like Mary herself; its windows were heavily curtained as though it was necessary to keep from the prying eye what went on behind them.

Mary was in the courtyard waiting for Jane, and she greeted her guest not only with affection but with something like relief. She took Jane into the shop, and when they were there she opened a drawer in which she kept her laces.

'Which is the one you wished to show me?' asked Jane.

Mary held up a piece of beautifully made lace. 'It is for the King's exclusive use,' she said.

'It must be gratifying,' said Jane slyly, 'to continue to please the King.'

'I can think of no greater pleasure than to serve His Grace,' answered Mary primly. 'But come, let us to my sitting-room, where we may talk in peace.' She took Jane's arm and led her from the shop into a dark passage behind it. 'Ah–Danok,' said Mary, as a huge man appeared suddenly in the darkness of the passage.

Jane started. She had seen Danok before, but the sight of him never failed to make her shudder. Jane's father had once said that the creature was not in full possession of his wits, but Jane did not believe this; the eyes beneath the shaggy brows were sane enough, though they seemed to look back at experiences which, the saints be praised, were not known to all men. He had been a prisoner in the Tower years ago, and there he had engaged the attention of the torturers. He was without a tongue, and Mary had hinted that other parts of his body had been mutilated. She called him rather coyly her Eunuch. Danok was a strong man for all his disabilities. He worshipped her, Mary said, because when he had been released from prison she had found him wandering along the river bank, bewildered and starving; she had taken pity on him, brought him to her house and made him her servant. Now, she said, he would protect her with his life's blood if need be.

'Danok,' said Mary, 'go and bring Doll to me.'

Danok inclined his head and went off silently; and as Jane mounted the stairs with Mary, an elderly woman of neat appearance, but who was grotesquely disfigured by the King's evil, came into the passage and looked up the stairs towards her mistress and the guest.

'Doll, guard the shop. Let me know if anyone of importance needs me. I shall be in my sitting-room with Mistress Shore.'

'Yes, madam,' said Doll; and she went hurriedly to do her mistress's bidding.

'Now,' said Mary, 'we shall be comfortable. How nice it is to see you, dear. There–sit there where I can see your pretty face. Every time I see you I declare you grow bonnier. I will show you how I draw my patterns. Mind you, there is not another soul in London I'd show these to. What if my patterns were copied, eh? And taken to the King's Master of the Wardrobe! Ah, you think the King would be sure to take mine. Mayhap. There are some who remember old friends and some who forget them; but methinks His Grace is of the first kind. My dear, would you like to try a little of my special wine?'

'Thank you, no. It is too soon after dinner.'

Mary went to the window, drew aside the heavy curtain and looked down into the courtyard. 'I do hope none will come to demand my attention this afternoon. But if that should happen–you will understand, dearest Jane?'

'Assuredly I will.'

'Why–bless my soul.' Mary looked over her shoulder and frowned. 'Why–yes. He *is* coming here.'

'Who is it?' asked Jane.

'No one you would know, dear. A friend–a rather special friend. Now had I known he was going to call this afternnon . . .'

'I'll go,' said Jane. 'You know I can come any afternoon, and as he is a special friend . . .'

'Indeed you will *not* go, my dear. He is going to the side door. If you will excuse me just a moment, I will go down and let him in myself. It is rather an important merchant friend whom I supply.'

'Then if it is business . . .'

'No matter. No matter. We will see what it is he wants. I will bring him up. I am sure you will like to meet him. He is a very charming and amusing man.' She went out murmuring apologies and in a few minutes returned, accompanied by a tall richly dressed merchant. Jane and the merchant looked at each other in astonishment.

He spoke first. 'By God's blessed Virgin, it is Mistress Shore.'

'And you–are the merchant . . .'

'Who came to your husband to buy plate.'

'So you know each other already,' said Mary. 'Well, that is a surprise. A pleasant one, I can see, for you both.'

'For me most certainly,' he said; and now he was different, bolder than he had been that morning in Lombard Street. Jane felt an exhilaration which manifested itself in the hot blood in her cheeks and the thumping of her heart.

'It is a pleasure,' she said, and he kissed her lingeringly in greeting.

He settled himself on the couch very near to Jane. His personality filled the room, which seemed suddenly tawdry and unworthy of him. He crossed his well-shaped legs and let his eyes rest for a second or two on his pointed shoes, but only for a second or two; then they were back on Jane's face. 'Indeed,' he went on, 'I remember well our last meeting. It was our first, too. Pray God there will be many more. I remember well the views you expressed, madam. I remember your criticism of the King.'

Mary gasped. 'My dear Jane, you could not have been guilty . . .'

'Most guilty,' he said, laughing, 'but, I suspect, most just. And I told her, Mistress Blague, that she ought to be chief adviser to His Grace.'

Mary went off into laughter which seemed exaggerated to Jane.

'I am sure,' said Jane coolly, 'I should be most unfitted for the post.'

'Doubtless,' said Mary, 'His Grace would take upon himself the task of schooling you.'

The merchant leaned forward in his chair; he took Jane's hand and stared down at her palm. 'I see great things for you in life. Riches, fame and happiness.'

'Do you jest?' asked Jane. 'Or do you know of such matters?'

'One does not need to look into your hand to see that joy awaits you. It is writ in your face.'

'Jane receives so many compliments,' said Mary, 'that they mean little to her. She accepts them and forgets them, and remains, withal, the most virtuous lady in the town.'

'I read that also,' he said.

'In my hands or my face?' asked Jane.

'In both,' he told her.

'I will bring refreshment,' said Mary; and she went out, leaving them together.

'Did you ever think to see me again?' he asked.

'I did not think I ever should.'

'I trust you were saddened at the thought?'

'Mayhap I was. It is often sad to meet someone, to laugh awhile and then never to see that person again as long as one lives.'

'But you would have to have some esteem for the person, would you not, to feel so sad?'

'Esteem?' She shrugged her shoulders, no longer embarrassed now that the shock of meeting him was over, but only stimulated. 'Scarcely. One might have been amused merely.'

'Surely people esteem those who amuse them?'

'It depends, I dare say, on what they set a value.'

'How glad I am I came to Mary Blague's this day.'

'I could see that you were as surprised as I. But I shall leave you soon as I understand you have come to discuss business.'

'I shall be desolate if you do. Jane . . .'

'I think we have known each other scarcely long enough to indulge in the familiarity of Christian names.'

'We know much about each other. What matters it if it has taken us a short time to learn it?'

'I know little of you, sir.'

'You know you like me. Therefore must you know a good deal.'

'You assume a good deal.'

'Come, Jane, I am sure you do not smile so sweetly on those you hate. If you do I must think you a hypocrite; and that I could never do.'

'Did I then smile so sweetly?'

'Delightfully and in most friendly fashion. I'll warrant you were not displeased to see me. I'll swear you thought when I entered the room, "God be praised, here is someone to enliven the gloomy hour I must spend with Mary Blague."'

'Did I show that?'

'You did.'

'It was wrong of me.'

'It was, and for penance you shall call me Edward and I will call you Jane.'

Mary returned, carrying a flagon of wine. Jane noticed that her face was flushed patchily. Mary was behaving oddly this afternoon. Jane saw that she was serving her very best wine. She seemed to have great esteem for Mr Edward Long, and at the same time to be a little afraid of him. As for the man himself, he was perfectly at ease, charming to both of them, but showing most decidedly that it was Jane who interested him.

Mary turned the conversation to court matters and asked Edward Long what was the latest dance.

He explained to Jane: 'I serve the court, and therefore know much of what goes on.'

Jane laughed, for the wine and the man's company were making her feel very gay. 'Then must you have been vastly amused when I told you what I thought of the court and courtiers.'

'No. I would not say that you were wrong. As for the dance . . . Well, I discover a little of these matters. Let us try a step or two.' He stood up, towering over Jane.

'In the room adjoining this one I have a lute,' said Mary. 'Shall I play for you? I am sure that Jane would learn the steps more quickly than I.'

Dancing with him, laughing when she made a false step, Jane thought, After this afternoon I shall not see him again. I must not see him again.

There was a sudden knock on the door, and when Mary laid aside her lute and went to it, Jane heard her say: 'A customer? I will come down at once.' Mary turned to the dancers with a 'Pray forgive me. I must go down to the shop. I trust I shall not be kept long.'

'We understand perfectly,' said Edward, 'and we will entertain ourselves until your return.' When the door shut on Mary, he went on: 'I trust she will be long, though however long she may be, I fear that it will seem to me but a short time.' He took Jane's hand. 'Jane! Dost know that ever since I set eyes on thee I have thought of little else?'

Jane withdrew her hand. 'That will not do, sir. Why, when you left my husband's house you thought nothing of me until you came into this room this afternoon.'

'Why do you think thus, Jane?'

'Had you been so eager, would you not have come back to admire the goldsmith's plate–and his wife–and not waited until by chance you were confronted with her?'

'Ah! I did remember that you were the goldsmith's wife, and, thought I, 'If only it were as easy to possess his wife as his plate!'''

"You are over-forward, sir, and I like it not.' Jane's manner was very cool now.

'Then pray forgive me, for, believe me, I am not myself this afternoon.'

'I trust you are not. I do not like these professions of affection on such short acquaintance. But mayhap you go to court and there learn your manners.'

'Yet would you like court ways, did you know them.'

'I shall never like the light and easy way in which court manners assume it is possible, nay simple, to seduce the honest wives of honest citizens.'

'I am heartily in agreement with you, Jane.'

'Then shall we talk of other matters?'

'Pray let us. What shall it be? The recent wars? The weather? Will the plague return to London this summer, think you?'

Jane laughed. 'Can you not think of more pleasant subjects?'

'The only subject I can entertain, with you before me, is such that, while wholly pleasant to me, may offend your pretty ears.'

She regarded him shrewdly. 'When you were in my husband's house you played the merchant to perfection. Your eyes said you were a thousandfold more interested in his goods than in his wife. But now, in another house you play the . . .'

'What would I play?'

'Am I being presumptuous when I say you would play the lover?'

'It is a matter of simple logic, I fear, Jane. Why, even the most hard-headed merchant must long to do that when he is face to face with Jane Shore.'

'And it would seem to me that it is a part familiar to you.'

'What gave you such impression, Jane?'

'I cannot but believe that the merchant who, before he met me, had never had the time nor inclination to play lover, would stammer a little, would not express himself in such a practised way.'

'But you must see that I am no ordinary man. Look at me and tell me that you do.'

'I see a man with merry eyes which like to laugh. I see a man who loves good wine–and Mary Blague's best is hardly good enough for you. You love gaiety and pleasure.'

'Ah, I see I must tread warily with you.'

'You must tread as you please.'

'Then I will, Jane.' He was laughing as he seized her and bent his face down to hers. She was angry–not, she realised, because he wished to make love to her, but that he should do it casually on this their second meeting.

'I beg of you to release me at once,' she said with dignity.

He was quick to see that her anger was real. 'I pray you will forgive me,' he said meekly.

'And I pray that you will tell Mary I had to leave at once.'

'Allow me a few words of explanation.'

'There can be no explanation.' She went into the next room where she had laid her cape. He followed her and stood watching her almost humbly.

'I never wish to see you again,' she told him. She was trembling, for decidedly this was not true. He had changed her from the moment she had first seen him. She felt that if she had never known him she might eventually have learned contentment; now she never would. She would remember him all her life–his handsome face, his great figure and his merry laughter. She knew she was in great danger. She knew her own weakness; he had made her aware of that in the last half-hour. She must run quickly, while she had the power to run. His virility, his overwhelming manliness, could not belong to one indifferent to women; such grace and charm, such an easy way of saying the things one wanted to hear, could only grow out of long practice. He was as profligate as Hastings. But he was more dangerous, for already, after a small taste of his company, she was finding her will to resist him growing very weak indeed.

He had laid a hand on her shoulder and was saying: 'I have been over-forward. Believe me when I tell you I had no intention of being so. You must forgive me if the sight of you threw me momentarily off my balance. Say you'll be friends or I shall die of melancholy. Put aside your cape and give me one more chance.'

'Chance for what?'

'That we may know each other better. That we may be friends.'

'What good could it do us to be friends?'

'Think you then that you could quickly feel something stronger than friendship for me?'

'If that were so, what good could it do?' She turned to him suddenly, searching his face for some hint of laughter; there was none, only a deadly seriousness.

He said: 'Jane, I would be honest with you. Had I only but seen you before you met the goldsmith! But what is to be, will be. Yet cannot a poor man take the crumbs which fall from the rich man's table?'

'I understand you not.'

'Lovers we cannot be, for I see you are a virtuous woman. I also would be virtuous, but alas! my flesh is weak. Jane, give me your friendship. That I will cherish.'

Jane let her hood fall on to the stool where she had laid it when she came in. She said: 'Let us return to the other room, or Mary will wonder why we left it.'

'I am forgiven then?'

'You are. But pray remember that I will not have a repetition of such conduct.'

'I will remember it, Jane.'

They looked at each other suddenly and burst into laughter. Jane did not know why she laughed, except that being with him had such an effect upon her that she wanted to laugh for sheer happiness.

'This is no matter for laughter,' she said, with an attempt at severity.

'Of a certainty it is,' he assured her. 'For it was the laughter of happiness, Jane. I am happy because I am forgiven.'

'Doubtless you think me a prudish woman?'

'I could never look into your eyes and think that. There is great warmth in you, Jane, for the lucky man who could kindle the fire.'

'Once, before my marriage, I had a most unhappy experience,' she said. 'It might well have proved disastrous. I was all but abducted; and ever since that day I have felt the need to tread cautiously.'

'You poor child! The blackguard should have been shut up in the Tower.'

'That is what I think. But it seems he is a gentleman of the court.'

'Would I knew his name!'

'It would avail you little if you did. He was of high rank.'

'Pray tell me, Jane.'

'I believe him to be Lord Hastings.'

'The knave!'

'So say I, and still tremble to think of what might have been my lot had his plans succeeded.'

''Tis the penalty of so much beauty.' He went on gently: 'Have no such fear of me. I would not undertake such knavery. Were I so blessed that you should come to me, it should be willingly or not at all.'

'There is no question of what you suggest. You forget I am already a wife.'

'I would I could forget it.'

'So now you understand my recent anger. That experience has put me on my guard against all seducers.'

'There is a world of difference between lust and love.'

'One can be born in a moment,' she said slowly. 'The other needs longer and more arduous labour.'

'There you are wrong, Jane. There are times when love is born more swift than lust.'

'They are twins, then, and mayhap it is difficult to tell the two apart. Mary Blague returns, methinks. Now I shall go.'

'Then I shall escort you back to Lombard Street.'

'Pray do not.'

'I would obey your wishes in all things, Jane.'

'Then I will go alone. It is only after dark I fear the streets.'

'Jane, we shall meet again.'

'I think this should be our last meeting.'

Mary was hesitating at the door; she coughed, waited a while and then came in.

'Mary,' said Jane, 'it grows late and I must go home.'

Mary looked from one to the other.

'She would go alone,' said Edward.

'And leave you two to discuss your business together,' said Jane.

Hurrying through the streets, she felt bewildered; and when she was back in Lombard Street, Kate's inquisitive glances irritated her; and when the goldsmith laid his hands upon her she found it difficult not to implore him to leave her alone.

Mary Blague came hurrying out of the house near the waterfront. A cape, with an all-concealing hood, covered her from head to foot. She must quickly find a waterman to row her across, for she was always relieved when she reached the other side of the water. Time after time she had asked herself why she did not go out of business and live the life of a lady, perhaps in some village well out of London, such as Bethnal Green or Brentford–or mayhap farther out still, into Sussex or Surrey. But she knew that, had this really been her wish, she could have set about doing it tomorrow. She could not, however, bring herself to give up her profitable business. Lace-woman to the King? Well, yes; and there was money to be made in lace if you had the patronage of those of high rank. But there were other and more easy ways of earning money; and Mary Blague was first a business woman whatever else she might be.

In Cheapside she was the respected lace-woman, almost as highly placed as the mercers and the grocers, though, of course, not as the goldsmiths. But Will Shore himself could scarcely be more wealthy than she was. In Cheapside, then, Mary Blague dined out and entertained all the most respected of her neighbours. But it was in Southwark, as Mistress Bee, that she wielded a greater power. To her belonged the roomy house, the girls who worked for her. There was not one of them who, on the orders of Mistress Bee, could not be turned out on the streets to starve. She liked to reflect on that, for, almost more than money, she loved power.

At fifteen Mary had come to London from the country home where she was the twelfth child of needy parents. She was to be the companion of an aunt who had a little money laid by, and Mary had hoped that one day the money would come to her. But when her eyes had been opened to City ways, she had learned that there were more speedy methods of acquiring wealth than awaiting the death of an old lady whose capital was only large in the eyes of Mary's needy parents.

Matters had not gone well at first. There had been a love affair, a lover who fled, a child born in a house very like the one she now owned in Southwark, a spell of working for a while in that house; and then had followed a clever stroke of business involving a little blackmail. Mary did not like blackmail, for she knew it to be dangerous; but this was so simple. It was the case of a rich young merchant with a newly married wife. 'Give me the money to set myself up in little lace-shop, and you shall never hear from me again.' This was done and the lace-shop prospered, and then the Southwark house had come into being; and the latter gave her greater pleasure than the former. It brought greater sums of money and greater power. She derived much pleasure from shaping the lives of those about her. Many a young girl came to her house in Cheapside to learn lace-making; some came as servants. How simple to put temptation in their way! And how quickly they responded to her sympathetic advice! 'I know of a way to help you. There is a house in Southwark . . .' And what life had done to Mary Blague all those years ago, Mary would let it do to these girls. She was for ever on the lookout for victims. And now–Jane Shore.

It was an interesting life Mary led. Cleverly she kept her two existences apart; it was amusing to be two different people. There was only one person in Cheapside who knew the connection between the lace-woman and the brothel-keeper. This was Danok, and he could never speak of it to any.

A waterman came towards her; he brought his boat to the stairs and she got hurriedly into it; very soon she was on the north side of the river. She loosened her cloak. She had left Mistress Bee on the south side of the Thames.

She was smiling, for she was thinking now of the attractive man who had asked her to help him with Jane. For none other, she thought, would I have allowed my house in Cheapside to be used to such purpose.

Her eyes were wistful; she was wishing she had Jane's youth and beauty, just as though she were a foolish sentimental girl. Well, he would soon tire of Jane, and then when the goldsmith learned of his wife's frailty and mayhap turned from her, that good business woman, Mary Blague, would be waiting to help her.

She turned into Bucklersbury and drawing her cloak round her, as though by so doing she could transform herself once more from Mary Blague to Mistress Bee, she went quickly down the stone stairs and into a shop.

She and Leppus knew each other. Perhaps he wondered why she should make so many strange purchases in his shop. It did not matter. Let Leppus look to his own affairs. There was doubtless much he might wish to hide.

He came forward as she entered. A hideous little black beetle, she thought him. His hook nose twitched.

'Good-day to you, lady. What can I do for you this day?'

She followed him through to the room behind the shop. He sat on his high stool and peered at her.

'I want some of your elixir of life,' she said.

'The rejuvenating mixture! My elixir of life! For life is love and love is life, lady. My elixir costs good money, and it is of greater worth than money, is it not? It makes the aged young.'

'Yes, yes. Let me have it, please.'

'I will. But first tell me, is it for a lady or a gentleman?'

'Does that make any difference?'

'But how can I whisper the magic into it if I do not know? It is different for a man and a woman.'

'It is for a woman, then.'

'Is she young or old–or is she getting to that state when we may not ask her age?'

Was he insolent or was it necessary that he should know?

'She is young,' she snapped.

'Is it not sad that we should force in the young that which should come naturally?'

'Give me the powder, please. I am busy and must hurry. Here is the money.'

But it was useless to try to hurry him. She sensed in him that love of power that she understood so well because she shared it.

'Money!' he said, flashing his beady eyes upon her so that they peered between the drooping eyebrows which hung over them like a creeping plant over the windows of a deserted house. 'What is money to an artist such as I am!'

He was powerful, she knew. He was the possessor of many strange secrets. She wished him to know that she understood his power and respected it; but at the same time she wished him to respect hers.

'This is for a person of some importance.'

'Ah, good lady, to the starving dog the beggar with a crust of bread is of importance. To the apprentice, so is the humble tradesman. Importance is relative, and you must know that I have served His Grace the King.'

Mary's cheeks flushed suddenly. A retort came to her lips, but she repressed it.

'Come,' said Leppus slyly, 'you are angry with me. Have I said aught to distress you? Why, from the look of you one would think the little love drink was for another who charms your lover.'

Was it true that he saw with the eyes of a wizard? She liked the uncanny atmosphere of his shop even less today than usual.

'I will pay you and take up no more of your time,' she said.

'As you will.' He stretched out his hollow palm.

She felt hot and flustered as she turned into the Poultry and hurried towards Lombard Street; though it was not with Leppus she was angry, but with Jane Shore. The sly creature, she thought, I hate her. All the same, she is the fairest female I ever clapped eyes on, and one day she is going to be very useful to me.

Will was just riding out when she reached his house. He dismounted to greet her. 'This is unfortunate,' he said courteously. 'I have to ride out to a customer. You will find Jane in.' When Mary said she would go in to see her, Will hesitated for a while and then added: 'She seems listless of late. I wonder if aught ails her. Mayhap you could do something to cheer her.'

'Be assured that I will do my best,' she told him.

Jane received her in the parlour. The girl was pale. No wonder! Doubtless she had suffered many a sleepless night. Well, well, my chuck, thought Mary, you cannot have your pleasure and keep your virtue, though doubtless a little beauty such as you thinks there may be some way of doing it.

'It is long since I saw you,' said Mary. 'Why did you not come yester eve? I was expecting you.'

'Mary–I cannot come.'

Mary sat on a stool and arranged her cape about her. 'I would not wish to ask what you might not wish to tell,' she said. 'But is it because of a certain person that you stay away?'

Jane burst out: 'Every day I come he is there.'

'He is there every day in the hope of seeing you. I am sorry–sorry that mine should have been the house where you should meet. It places me most awkwardly.'

'Oh, Mary, it was no fault of yours. It was the purest accident. Tell me–how is he?'

'Sad of heart because you do not come to meet him.'

'I cannot meet him, Mary. I dare not. You are my friend, Mary, and glad I am that none but you knows–nor ever shall.'

'Your secret is safe with me. You love him, do you not?'

'I do, Mary. If I had never gone to your home that day . . .'

'It is sad, when love comes, to say it nay. But you are right, my dear. You are a wife. There is naught to be said. You will not see him again.'

'I must not. The other day I took up my cloak and all but ran to your house. Oh, Mary, I am a wicked woman. I think of him continually. I see his face. I hear his laughter. Oh, Mary, what am I to do?'

'My dear child, you are overwrought.'

'There is so much wickedness in me, I fear. This day I all but confessed this wild and unreasoning thing. . . . I almost confessed it to Will.'

'What good would that do you or Will? Now listen. Come to me tomorrow. Come early. If he comes also we will not let him in. There you can unburden your heart to me and I will give you my advice for what it is worth.'

'Mary, you would promise not to let him in?'

'For shame! You look at me as though you are begging me to let him in.'

'I dare not see him. I dare not listen to him. Mary, try to understand what has happened to me. It is true I have met him but three times at your house . . . and once here, and yet . . .'

'Hush! Come tomorrow and we will talk.'

'You are a good friend to me, Mary.'

Aye, thought Mary; and to him also. She touched the little packet in her pocket, and a deep frustrated rage swept over her. Why should Mary Blague have to accept the insults of old Leppus for the sake of this girl? She was in no need of the old magician's elixir. Never mind. Mary Blague could wait, and one day there would be no need for her to accept insults on account of Jane Shore.

In Mary's parlour she and Jane sat looking at one another. Each was tense and waiting. Jane was thinking, Will he come? If he does, I shall not see him. Mary thought, There she sits feigning primness. She will say Nay with her lips and Yes with her eyes. I know her sort. And doubtless he doth too.

'You will take a little wine, my dear?'

'No, thank you. Listen! Mary! Someone is in the courtyard.' Jane jumped up and went to the window. She stood there looking down on him. How unfair that she had been married so early to the goldsmith!

Mary said in an exasperated voice: 'I will go and send him away. I told him not to come.'

'Yes,' said Jane, 'send him away.'

Jane turned from the window. She thought wretchedly over the past. She hated afresh the man Hastings who was responsible for her marriage, for never would she have married Will but for that planned abduction. More than anyone on earth she hated Hastings. But for him she would be free now. It would not be necessary to send her lover away. Surely it would do no harm to see him once more.

'Mary,' she called; but Mary had already gone.

She thought of him, how he had looked the last time they had met here in this very room; he had talked to her very earnestly then; that was after he had dismissed Mary with such gay assurance, such charming arrogance, that it might have been his house they were in instead of Mary's. And Mary had gone meekly, though she had been perplexed and doubtful. Then he had pleaded with her; he had wished her to leave Will, to go away with him. She had wavered and all but agreed, so was she bewitched by him; and then, wrenching herself free, she made a vow that she would not see him again. He was below now, and so weak was she that in spite of that vow she was saying to herself, Just once more!

The door opened and he came into the room.

'So you would conspire with Mary Blague to keep us apart?' he demanded reproachfully. He lifted her in his arms.

'Put me down,' she begged. But he did not, and she was still in his arms when Mary came in.

'Jane, you must not blame me,' said Mary.

'I do not, Mary.'

He smiled, first at Jane, then at Mary. 'Blame? Who is to be blamed for love such as this? And listen. I'll not be kept away again, I swear it.'

'Let us have some wine,' said Mary faintly.

'Yes, good friend,' said Edward, 'let us have some wine.'

Mary poured it out, watching them.

'Drink this,' she said. ''Twill help you to discuss your troubles.'

'Since when was love a trouble?' asked Edward.

'You are right,' said Mary quickly. 'Love is no trouble . . . only a joy . . .'

While it lasts, she thought. Let him tire of her quickly. Then, Jane Shore, it will be my turn.

'A joy indeed,' he said. 'What folly it is to love and not to love!'

'Please do not speak of it now,' pleaded Jane.

'Mary knows, does she not? You know, Mary, of this that has happened to us.'

'I do. I reproach myself that it is in my house that you have met.'

'You may cease to reproach yourself,' he told her. 'Rather rejoice with us.'

'I cannot forget what I have done in allowing . . .'

'Depend upon it, we shall not forget you.' He went to the table and poured more wine. He said: 'You may go now.'

Mary went. Jane hardly noticed her going, for a strange light-headedness was stealing over her. Her eyes were dilated, her body tingled.

He sat close to her and took her hands. 'Jane, you know I'll not let you go from me.'

'But you must,' she said weakly.

'Why? Can you say you do not love me?'

'No, but . . .'

'Then that is enough.'

'You forget I have a husband. He is a good man and kind to me.'

'I will be kind to you.'

'I could not hurt him.'

'Then will you hurt me? You cannot, I tell you. When my arms are about you, you'll not be able to.'

'You frighten me. You look so strange.'

'It is my love for you that you see in my face.'

'It is great, is it not?'

'So great that there is no denying it. Listen to me, Jane. We will go from here together. . . . You need never go back to his house. I will give you such a house that . . .'

'Say no more. I must go now, Edward. I begin to feel so strange. . . .'

'Strange, dearest?'

'So light-headed, so gay . . . and very happy. I must go. I know I must. This must be the end of our friendship. I will say goodbye now. Do not look at me. Do not touch me.'

She heard his laughter close to her ear as he lifted her up.

'Look at me,' he commanded. 'Look at me, sweet Jane, and then tell me that I must never see your face again.'

'Oh, Edward, I cannot. You should have let me go.'

'And now that I have not done so?' He laid his lips against her cheek. 'What now, Jane?'

She thought wildly, This is what I always wanted. This is why I fought as hard as I could against marriage with Will. If only I had waited!

But this was no time for regretting the past, for the present was filled with joy and pleasure waiting to be explored. She knew now that she had gone too far to turn back. She had not the will to turn back.

'Jane,' he said, 'you must not be afraid. You would not wish to escape now!'

She shook her head; his voice, low with passion, seemed to fill the room. 'No, you must not be afraid, Jane. There is nothing but this, our world inside the four walls of this house, which has become more beautiful than any palace because it holds us two.'

He kissed her, and his kiss was slow and gentle; it warmed swiftly, and then it was as though she were scorched with the white-hot passion that was in him.

'You cannot say No to this, Jane,' he said. 'You cannot say No to me.'

Will Shore knocked at the door of Mary Blague's house. Danok let him in and conducted him to the parlour beyond the shop. Will waited there nervously until Mary appeared.

'My good friend,' cried Mary, 'how pleasant to see you! But you look worried. What ails you?'

'I am going out on business,' explained Will, 'so I looked in on my way. It is about Jane. You are her friend. I thought that you might help me.'

'I will tell my servant to bring us wine. Then we will talk in peace.'

When the wine was brought, Will said: 'Methinks Jane is ill. Of late she has behaved with such oddness that is beyond my understanding.'

'Since when was this?'

'For some weeks. But of late her malady seems to have taken a different turn. It seemed to start a few days ago, after she had returned from your hospitality. She came into the house, and I thought at once that she was sickening for something. She went straight to her bed. She seemed so wild, and when I asked her if aught ailed her she said she felt very sick indeed. I wanted to send for a physician, to which she said she thought there was little a physician could do for her. I tried to soothe her but my caresses seemed but to aggravate the malady. She has grown melancholy. I swear it is a fever that besets her. What can I do?'

'Does she weep much?'

'She does. Then I have heard her laughing with that maid of hers. It is a wild sort of laughter. I seem to upset her. She trembles beside me when abed at night, and if I would as much as touch her, she bursts into tears.'

'And it has gone on for a week. It is indeed too long.'

Indeed it was too long, she thought, for Jane's lover was an impatient man, apt to be angry with those to whom no blame should be attached; and Mary was fearful of his anger.

'It seems to me that Jane needs a little gaiety to forget her melancholy. Will you forgive my forwardness if I say what is in my mind?'

'*Your* forwardness, Mary! You are the most reserved of ladies.'

'Then you will know that what I say now is but to help you. What Jane needs is a child. It is a strange need that comes to women. Give her a child and she will forget her melancholy. But first we must try to cheer her. Now, you know that I have friends at court. There is to be a ball, and I–as the King's lace-woman–have an invitation to go. I may take one friend, and I suggest it shall be Jane. You will see that the thought of a grand occasion will cheer her. And then when you have her gay and happy . . . forgive my lack of discretion, dear friend . . . well, what I mean is this: I have heard it said that a contented woman is more likely to conceive. . . .'

The goldsmith was grateful. 'You are indeed a friend, Mary,' he said fervently.

'Let us hope that I may be fortunate enough to help my friends when they need me. Now if you will excuse me, I will go to your house and see Jane at once. I will tell her of the ball, and doubtless you will see a change in her when you return.'

The goldsmith left, and Mary, slipping on her cloak, thought, I should have been a diplomat so cleverly do I manage the affairs of others. I had to get Jane to the ball, and now I have without the least difficulty obtained her husband's consent.

She found Jane in her bedroom with Kate, who was at once dismissed.

Jane wept when Kate had gone. 'It is such a relief,' she said, 'to be with someone who knows me for what I am. You have seen him?'

'He comes every day and asks for you. He regrets that he ever let you go.'

Jane smiled wanly. 'He would have had me leave there and then with him. Oh, Mary, I must talk of it to someone, or I shall go mad. I cannot think what happened to me. I love . . . Of course I love him, but I believed myself capable of remembering my duty to Will and my marriage vows. And then . . . I was so strangely without resistance. I never thought of the wrong I was doing Will . . . until afterwards.'

'I believe,' said Mary wryly, 'it is often thus. It *is* afterwards that realisation comes. But,' she added maliciously, 'you will never see him again, will you? You betrayed your husband once and are determined not to do so again.'

'Oh, I am,' said Jane sadly.

'That is very commendable. Now you cannot live all your life in melancholy. How would you like to go to a court ball?'

'A court ball? But how could I?'

Momentarily, thought Mary, she has forgotten her lover.

'You know, my dear, that I have connections at court. I have been invited and may take a friend.'

'It . . . it would be interesting, but I have no heart for it.'

'Then you shall come with me.'

Jane's eyes had begun to sparkle. Had he not said that he had business at the court? 'Mary . . . what could I wear . . . if I went?'

'You have many beautiful dresses in your cupboards.'

'But for the court!'

'We will see what can be done. A stitch or two here, a touch there . . . and one of your gowns will pass at court.'

'Mary, you are a good friend to me.'

When Mary left she met Will coming in.

'How did you leave her?' he asked eagerly.

'Excited at the prospect of a ball. Depend upon it, all will go as it should.'

'May the Virgin bless you, Mary,' said Will.

And Mary went on her way, smiling.

In Mary's bedroom Jane was dressing for the ball. During the last few days she had been constantly in Mary's company. They had taken the grandest of her dresses and with some of Mary's fine lace had renovated it into something worthy of the court. Mary had been filled with an inner excitement which bubbled over now and then into bursts of laughter which she did not seem to be able to control. Jane thought she knew the reason. It was because Edward would be at the ball. He would have received an invitation just as Mary had.

A chariot, Mary had explained, would call at the house and take them to Westminster Palace.

'A chariot!' Jane had cried when she first heard of this. 'Mary, you must have great influence at court.'

Now here they were, Jane magnificent and beautiful in her gown, and Mary slightly more magnificent but much less beautiful in hers. When the chariot arrived, the driver and footman treated them with great respect, and Jane had never felt such a grand lady in all her life.

As they drove into the Palace yard, men in royal livery ran to their assistance. What would they say, wondered Jane, if they knew that these seemingly great ladies were but the King's lace-woman and her friend the goldsmith's wife?

It mattered not, for now they were in the great hall, and never in all her life had Jane seen such magnificence. The hangings were of richest velvet and cloth of gold. Jewels sparkled on the clothes of brilliantly clad men and women. Ah, thought Jane, overawed and feeling very insignificant now, they could not have mistaken us for anything but the lace-woman and goldsmith's wife.

But people looked at Jane, for her beauty was remarkable.

'When shall we see the King and Queen?' she whispered.

'Ere long, I think,' whispered Mary in her turn. 'Look about you at the great. See you the fair frail lady yonder? That is the Duchess of Clarence and with her her husband the Duke.'

'She is very lovely,' said Jane.

'She looks not long for this world. She is pale as a lily.'

'And he is red as a peony.'

'He is overfond of the wine. But do not talk so loudly, Jane.'

'I had forgotten. We are at court, and must keep our eyes open, our ears alert and voices unheard. Tell me, who is the pale slender young man?'

'Where?'

'There, next the Duke.'

'That is Richard Duke of Gloucester, brother to Clarence and the King.'

'I wish the Queen would come. I long to see her.'

'You will. Ah–they are coming now.'

The rumble of voices had been replaced by silence, startling in its suddenness. It was broken sharply when the heralds at the door blew three blasts on their trumpets.

'Bow your head,' whispered Mary. 'They are coming now.'

Jane bowed, but could not resist peering upwards to see them. The Queen was tall, and her classical features were perfectly moulded; she had a cold face and her yellow hair was her greatest beauty.

And with her–the King. Jane stared at the great figure which dominated the hall. She swayed a little towards Mary, but Mary was waiting for her, and caught her arm to steady her. The hall seemed to swing round Jane, and she was but vaguely aware of the blur of faces and the brilliant colours. It could not be, she told herself again and again. It was just a startling resemblance.

'Mary,' she stammered. 'I–I—'

Mary hastily put a finger to her lips. 'Hush!' warned Mary.

Jane turned her eyes once more upon that magnificent figure that was sparkling with the costliest jewels. Every eye in the hall was upon him. There were diamonds in his coat and rubies at his throat. Jane, bewildered, had turned to Mary. She looked into the woman's face and understood. Mary knew. Mary had known all the time. Jane remembered how he had said to Mary in her own house, 'You may go now.' She remembered Mary's sycophantic laughter. Jane was dizzy with this sudden, frightening realisation.

A moment ago she had felt she would faint; now she was angry. The deception he had practised on her was cruel and humiliating. She wanted to run out of the palace and hide herself. She felt now that she would never be able to escape the shame which enveloped her. Her lover had turned out to be the notorious rake, the man who had but to beckon to the women of London–or York or Leicester for that matter–to have them run to him willingly. How she had despised those women–and now she had discovered that she was one of them. The King had come disguised to Jane Shore as he had to dozens before her; he had beckoned and willingly had she gone to him.

Her cheeks flaming, she remembered their conversations. What had she said of the King? Enough to send her to prison doubtless. She was glad. She had meant every word of it. She hated him now as fiercely as she had loved him. He was not only a rake but a liar; and she had allowed him to amuse himself as lightly with her as he had with so many others.

She turned to Mary angrily. 'You knew all the time. You lied to me.'

'Lower your voice, Jane. People look your way.'

'I wish to go home,' said Jane. 'I wish to go home at once. How do you think I can endure to stay here when . . .'

'Dear Jane, be sensible, you cannot go now.'

'I must and I will. I wish never to see him again.'

'There is no shame in being loved by the King. There is scarce a woman here who would not give all she possesses to change places with you.'

'He ordered you to bring me here tonight, did he not?'

Mary nodded.

'He commanded you to lure me to your house?'

'He thought it would make a good meeting place.'

'What a King is this,' cried Jane bitterly, 'who spends his time planning the seduction of his subjects!'

'Hush! Hush! You attract attention with this wild talk.'

'Oh, Mary, I know you are not to blame. You were helpless. He just used you. I hate him.'

'To hate the King is treason. You must be silent, Jane.'

'I wish to go home.'

'Wait! The King will start the dance. None can leave now. We should be noticed. Besides–he comes this way.'

It was true. People drew back as he passed. He was going to choose a partner with whom to start the dance–and he was coming towards the spot where Jane and Mary stood.

'Bow,' whispered Mary. She herself curtseyed low. Jane bent her head.

He laughed his easy pleasant laugh that Jane knew so well.

'Well, Jane,' he said, 'there was no other way, you know. It had to be.'

Jane was too hurt and bewildered by her discovery, too humiliated, too wretched in her newly found knowledge of his real character to be overawed by him. She did not think of him as the King, but simply as the man who had deceived and betrayed her.

She looked at him coldly. 'I am about to leave,' she said.

'No. You will stay. I command you to stay.'

He was the same man who had made love to her in Mary Blague's house, yet there was a difference. He had put on a new arrogance; his eyes were tender but there was a ruthlessness about his mouth even while he smiled at her. Her mood had softened, for he had taken her hand, and at his touch she realised afresh that it mattered not who he was–King or commoner–she loved him, and to be with him brought her such happiness as she could never know away from him. He saw her hesitation and smiled, certain of his power over her.

'Come,' he said, 'we will start the dance, you and I.'

'I–to dance with you–with the King?'

'Do not think of me as your King, Jane, but as the man who most humbly loves you.'

She allowed him to lead her to the centre of the hall. The whole court knew what this scene meant, for Edward had never been reticent about his love affairs. Obviously this lovely girl had been brought to court because the King had found her somewhere and she had caught his fancy. It had happened before; it would happen again. No one was very surprised, only amused and interested. This time though, it was whispered, she was indeed a beauty. They made bets as to how long she would hold the King's favour. Three months, some suggested, for she was indeed a charming creature. *Three* months? To whom had Edward the Fourth ever remained constant for more than one?

Edward was whispering passionately as they danced: 'Jane, why did you stay away so long? Why do you turn your face from me?'

'I never meant to see you again,' she answered. 'I never shall–after tonight. I wish to go as soon as I can. Mary was wrong to bring me here. Perhaps you will be so good as to release me after this dance.'

'You are very angry, are you not?' he said sadly. 'It is the first time I have ever seen you angry.'

Her voice trembled. 'I would not have believed you could have so deceived me.'

'It was necessary, Jane.'

'Necessary? To come to my husband's house disguised as a merchant, to–trap me as you did?'

'But, Jane, I am your lover. I will be your lover for ever. And you were willing, were you not?'

'To my shame, yes.'

'Nay, to your delight and mine. Know this: I have scarce slept at all since that day when you and I were truly lovers. You shall not leave my side again.'

'You could not make me stay. You could not do that.'

He laughed. 'What if I command it? I remember well, Mistress Shore, you have said some treasonable things of me.'

'And right glad I am of it,' she flashed at him. 'I declared my abhorrence of the King's light manner of living, and I do so again.'

'It would not have been light had he met you years ago. He was seeking you, Jane. Do you not understand that?'

Jane laughed, for that stimulating excitement was creeping over her. She must face the truth. She cared for nothing except that she might stay beside him.

'You do not expect me to believe that–Your Grace. I suppose I must remember to call you that now, must I not?'

'If you should forget the respect due to us,' he said in a tone of affected dignity, 'rest assured we should not find it in our hearts to send you to the dungeons. The rats would make indifferent bed-fellows, and, by the Virgin, I know of a better one for you.'

'You are different,' she said sadly. 'You now speak lightly of what was once a sacred matter.'

'If I seem light,' he answered soberly, 'it is but because I fear to have lost your esteem, and I joke to hide my fears. Jane, you loved a merchant. Cannot you love a King?'

'You seemed so sincere,' she said, 'and it is alarming to discover you but played a part.'

'I but put on airs with garments of state. Divest me of these and beneath them you will find the same man who loved you so completely. But we cannot talk here. We will slip away together where we may be quiet.'

'I do not wish to go,' cried Jane in alarm. 'I will stay here, and when this dance is done—'

His grip on her fingers tightened. 'Nevertheless, Jane, you *shall* come. I shall not let you go until you have listened to me. Come this way.'

His eyes glittered as they met hers. She was afraid of him, yet the fascination of him was as strong as ever. He held her fingers firmly and drew her towards a door which led out of the hall. She was hot with shame, for she knew that everyone in the hall was watching their withdrawal. What thought the Queen? The beautiful Queen whom he had met so romantically in Whittlebury Forest, whom he had loved so blindly that, against the wishes of his counsellors, he had married her–what did she think of this unconventional behaviour with the wife of a goldsmith?

He drew her into a small room hung with rich tapestry. On the floor was a carpet of deep blue embroidered with golden thread. Even in her present state of mind Jane was not insensible to the extreme luxury of this room. On the deep window seats were exquisitely embroidered cushions; and the tapestry-covered seat with its ornate canopy led her to believe that this was one of the King's less formal presence chambers. The room was perfumed with musk and sweet herbs.

The King shut the door and leaned against it, watching her closely. 'Here,' he said, 'we may have peace for a while, but first I will kiss you.' This he did with great warmth. 'Now you must tell me that you love me,' he added.

She shook her head in distress. 'I cannot say. I have just discovered that you have deceived me.'

'You shall forget that discovery in another. You shall learn, my sweet Jane, that no matter who I am, you love me.'

'You have been led by many to believe yourself irresistible, I know,' she told him coolly.

'You were one of them,' he retorted. He ran his hands caressingly over her. 'Do not blame me for my birth, Jane.'

'It was a cruel thing to do and I cannot forget it. To you it seemed amusing. It has not been so to me. How can you ask me to love you–*you* of whom they say, "Citizens, hide your wives and daughters, for the King comes this way"? That is you–the King. The seducer of women. And I despised them for falling so readily to your will. Do you not understand? I am so shamed–so humiliated. I want to go away–and die.'

He said gently: 'They fell in love with my rank, dearest Jane. There is no shame in what you did, sweetheart. I beg of you to forget my past sins, for I love you truly. It will be different now. What need of other women? Dost not know that while I flitted hither and thither like a butterfly testing the flowers, 'twas for Jane I searched?' He kissed her bare shoulders. 'Forget all that has gone before. 'Tis over and done. I have found you, Jane.'

How she longed to believe him! How plausible he was! Common sense whispered, 'To how many has he said those words before?' But the passion which the touch of his hands could arouse in her answered, 'What matters that? What matters anything as long as you can be with him even for an hour?'

She drew away from him. 'It must not be.'

'Nevertheless it shall be.'

'You mean–you would force me?'

'Never have I forced a woman yet. Should I begin with her I love best of all?'

'Then I shall never see you again after this night.'

'Believe it not, Jane. Tomorrow morning, the first face you shall see will be mine beside you on the pillow. Thus shall it be throughout our lives. Apartments have been prepared for you here in the palace, for in truth I cannot live without you.'

'I will not stay.'

He smiled at her. 'You cannot still doubt that you and I were meant for one another.' He laid his hands on her shoulders. 'See how you tremble at my touch. Your lips say, "I must go home." But what say your eyes? What says your trembling body? "Take me, Edward. Take me." That is what *you* say, Jane. No matter what those sweet lips falsely utter. And so shall it be. I will kiss the Nay from your lips, until they cry Yea. Then wilt thou be all mine.'

'You will release me at once,' she said with dignity.

His dignity matched hers. 'Never fear that I shall do aught but at your will.'

'Then I shall go home this night.'

'It shall be as you say. But you shall wait until the ball is over. Then a chariot shall take you back with Mary Blague. You may stay the night in her house instead of in your lover's arms. It is for you to say.'

'I could never be happy with you now, my lord.'

'Call me Edward as you did when you lay in my arms. Say that again, only call me Edward.'

'I could never be happy with you now, Edward.'

'You will never be happy without me. So you will go back to your husband. It is not for virtue's sake. For what virtue is there in giving him your favours as the price he asked for marriage? You sell yourself to him, Jane; to me you would give. Let not your eyes be blinded. Love is not for sale. Think on that, Jane.'

'He tries so hard to please and I have made my vows.'

'And did you make them willingly? I swear you never loved him.'

'None but thee have I ever loved.'

'Why, bless you, Jane. That's true, I know. Cast away your doubts. Come to me and be my love for ever. What joy we will know! There is nothing in this kingdom you could ask and I would not give it. Deny me not, Jane, for if you do, a most melancholy man must sit upon the throne of England.'

'You charm me with your words, your looks, your smiles. But I cannot. I *will* go tonight.'

'I have said a chariot shall take you back as it brought you. But listen, Jane. Tomorrow–just before the hour of five, another chariot will wait outside a certain house in Lombard Street, and in it will wait a very anxious lover. An you come not to him tomorrow, then on the next day will he wait–and the next and the next–so humble is he, so longing for you. Can you disappoint him, sweetheart? Can you stay in the dull house and sell yourself to one so unworthy? Jane, it is immoral.'

They laughed together. 'You make me forget you are the King,' she said.

'I make you remember that I am your lover?'

She nodded. 'I would I knew what I should do. But you bewilder me. You make me wretched and happy in turns. I shall never know true peace again.'

'I promise you shall find it in my arms.'

'I must go tonight.'

'It is for you to decide. Come, we must return to the hall. You may forget I am your King; others will not.'

Every eye was on her. Smiles came her way. She was at first embarrassed, but Edward's ease of manner brushed embarrassment aside. He took her first to the Queen, who was graciousness itself. It was difficult to believe she knew that she was being introduced to her husband's mistress.

'Mistress Shore, Your Grace,' said Edward with nonchalance. 'Methinks you will like each other well.'

The Queen smiled a cold smile and begged Jane to rise. She said she hoped Jane was enjoying the ball.

Jane looked into the face of the woman who seven years before had enchanted Edward. There was no sign of jealousy in the cold blue-grey eyes; there was only appraisal. Elizabeth Woodville was accustomed to her husband's mistresses; their presence at court did not worry her, for she had kept her own influence over him since their first romantic meeting. She had bent him to her will then, and she continued to do so. It was of no lasting importance that she shared her influence with the various women of his fancy from time to time.

She liked the look of Jane. It was more gratifying to be supplanted by a real beauty than by a woman whose attractions she could not understand; and Elizabeth liked to understand the King. Besides, it was obvious from the sweet expression on the lovely face of Edward's latest mistress that she was no scheming woman and obviously not of the nobility. No serious rival here. Let others enjoy Edward's body as long as Elizabeth kept her sway over his political acts.

The Queen was therefore charming to Jane.

'Now, sweetheart,' said Edward, 'I'd have you meet some members of my family. My favourite brother first, for he will be your friend as he is my friend.' He called: 'Richard! Come hither. I would speak with you.'

Richard, Duke of Gloucester, came to his brother. He was a pale-faced young man of about nineteen, short and slender; and it was only when his rather cold eyes smiled at her that Jane saw the resemblance between him and his brother. One of his shoulders was slightly higher than the other, but this was scarcely perceptible.

'This is Mistress Shore, Dickon. And, sweetheart, my brother Richard, the best friend I ever had. Love each other well, you two.'

The Duke bowed low and Jane returned the bow.

'We have not met before, I think,' said he gravely.

The King laughed. 'Assuredly you have not. Think you, young Dickon, that you could have met my Jane and not remembered her?'

'I could not, for never saw I face so fair.'

'Now that is good, Jane, coming from Richard. For, let me tell you, he is not over-fond of complimenting the ladies.'

Jane was warmed by the sight of these two together, for the looks they gave each other told her clearly that there was deep love between them.

'Bring George and Isabel,' said the King.

How different was George from his brothers! He was fattish of body, purple-red of face, and he had the bloodshot eyes of a man who is overfond of wine. He looked at Jane with some slyness. She did not like George; nor, she sensed, did Edward; and she marvelled greatly, remembering the talk she had heard between Will and her father, of how this man had played traitor to his brother the King. There must be much kindliness and family feeling in Edward. Isabel, George's wife, was a fragile girl of some beauty; and to her Edward spoke very kindly.

He would introduce Jane to others of his court. And now, listening to these people, finding herself answering them, even allowing a little of her natural gaiety to seep through her shyness, she was suddenly appalled to realise that she, Jane Shore, was no longer a humble person; she was here at court; and the King was commanding these important people to like her and to be her friend.

'And here,' said Edward, 'is my good friend Hastings. Come hither, man, and pay your respects to Mistress Shore.'

Hastings bowed low. Jane inclined her head. Not a sign, beyond an almost imperceptible lifting of his lips, did Hastings give that they had met before. Jane was trembling. She moved closer to Edward, who took her hand and pressed it. 'A good friend of ours,' he said, smiling. 'A very good friend indeed is Hastings.'

At the banquet which followed, Jane must sit on the left side of the King, the Queen being on his right. He would talk to Jane, pat her hand, declaring by every look and gesture that he loved her. Everyone present was now eager to please her. It was, 'What is your opinion, Mistress Shore?' and, 'What do *you* say to that?'

As for Jane, she could not help being exhilarated; she could not help being happy. And if the wine was a little intoxicating, the close presence and the soft looks of the handsomest man in England was more so. She would not have been Jane if she had not thrown aside all thought of what must follow. Let the future take care of itself. She forgot her shyness. Edward had made her forget that this was the court and he was the King. He was her lover, and because she was his mistress she was the most important lady of the court, next to the Queen. She sparkled; she did not attempt to curb her merry tongue. It was pleasant to receive applause instead of scolding. Laughter echoed round the table.

'Holy Mother!' it was whispered. 'Did we give her three months? I'll give her ten. And look you. My Lord Hastings has his eyes upon her. The King–then Hastings. This Jane Shore has a future.'

There had never for Jane been such a night of triumph.

'Never have I loved as I love thee,' whispered Edward.

Jane thought, I'll remember this day all my life. For never shall I look upon his face again.

And when the ball was over she stepped into the chariot and rode away with Mary Blague to Mary's house, where it had been arranged that she should spend the night.

It was almost noon before Jane returned to Lombard Street next day. She had not slept until dawn and then had fallen into a deep sleep which was troubled with a jumble of dreams. Mary Blague, her eyes veiled, her lips drawn tightly together as though to hold in her smiles, awakened her. It was eleven o'clock.

As though she still dreamed, Jane dressed and made her way back to her husband's house. She hurried in and went upstairs, hoping she would not see Will. She felt that last night's burning experience must be written on her face.

Kate heard her come in. The inquisitive creature quickly found some pretext for coming to her mistress's room.

'Did you see the King, mistress?' A court ball would seem bliss to Kate.

Jane nodded.

'Tell me true, did you not think he was the handsomest man on earth?'

'He is very attractive,' said Jane blankly.

'And saw you the Queen?'

Jane nodded. 'She is also very attractive.'

Kate watched her mistress slyly. Something had happened; and Kate guessed what. It was certain to happen sooner or later. A noble lord? Could it be Hastings?

'Tell me what you did eat, mistress? And what were the dresses like? And did you dance then? A thousand pities it was old Mistress Blague you went with. You should have had a handsome gentleman to take you.'

'Oh, Kate, be silent,' said Jane. And then: 'I'm so tired. We were late and I scarce slept.'

'Too much good food and wine, I'll warrant.'

Then Kate was really silent, for the goldsmith had come into the room. She picked up Jane's cloak and put it into the cupboard. The goldsmith looked at her impatiently, and she, interpreting his look, made off as quickly as she could.

Will sat on a stool and watched his wife.

'And how liked you the ball, Jane?'

'It was wonderful.'

'And how was the dress?'

'Very simple compared with the others. It looked splendid enough at home, but you should have seen it at court!'

'I'll warrant your face made up for the plainness of your gown, Jane.' She shrugged her shoulders and he stood up, and, coming to her, laid a hand on her shoulder. 'What ails you, wife?'

'What should ail me?'

'You have changed. Yet you enjoyed the ball–I see that. Tell me, there was none who made too free?' She shook her head swiftly. 'Jane, it seems long since I kissed you.' He laid his lips against her hair. She could not endure it.

'Will–please.'

'What's wrong with you?' He spoke irritably. 'One would think you were not my wife. Come, enough of this folly. Have you not had a comfortable home? Am I not good to you? Why, when you were in your father's house he did not hesitate to whip you. Have I ever raised my hand against you?' He went to the door and turned the key in the lock. She felt herself go cold with horror. He went on with a burst of nervous laughter: 'That girl of yours comes bursting in. Why, Jane, I love you. You grow lovelier than ever. I swear I never saw you look as beautiful as you do today. Court balls suit you, wife. You would have made a lovely court lady, but don't forget you are my wife–*my* wife.'

She saw a pulse beating in his throat; she saw his hands reaching out to her; and she could not bear it. She seemed to hear Edward's voice. 'A chariot will wait outside a certain house in Lombard Street . . .' She must hold Will off. She could not bear to feel his hands upon her. It was only until five that she must hold him off. She found her voice. It sounded shrill. 'No, Will. *No!* Not now.'

He smiled; there was a glazed look in his eyes which she had never seen before. Was it because he had always waited to douse the light before making love to her? Had he always looked like that? She could not bear him. There was only one man in the world who must love her.

'Nay, sweetheart,' Will was saying. 'What matters the hour? We are man and wife–we have God's blessing.'

'Kate will come. I know she will.'

'Then she will find the door locked on her.'

'She will wonder, and spread a tale abroad.'

That made him hesitate, for he was always susceptible to people's opinions of him.

'The servants would whisper together. Wait–Will.'

His hands dropped to his sides. 'You are right, wife.' He hastened to unlock the door.

She was still shivering long after he left her. Five o'clock! And it was not yet past midday. She put a few garments together, and then laid them back in the cupboard. I dare not go, she thought. I cannot stay.

She threw herself on to her bed and tried to pray. Kate came in and found her thus.

'Kate, shut the door. I must talk to someone or I shall go mad.'

Kate was only too willing. She shut the door and set a stool against it and sat on it, eagerly awaiting confidences.

'Kate, I am in love. Oh–so much in love. You cannot know.'

'That I can,' said Kate.

'I cannot stay in this house. I am leaving this afternoon. You betrayed me once, Kate. Yet I trust you. I know you will not breathe a word of this to any.'

'I'd let them cut my tongue from out my mouth before I would utter a word. Oh, mistress'–Kate's face puckered suddenly–'what will become of me? The goldsmith will not keep me, and your father will not have me back.'

'I hadn't thought of that. Mayhap I could take you with me.' Kate looked radiantly happy. 'Kate, at five of the clock a chariot will be in this street. It will be waiting for me. Let me know when it comes. Let me know the minute it comes. Oh, Kate, I am very wicked, but I cannot stay longer in this house. I must go to him I love. I believe I was born wicked, because now I am overcome so easily, so naturally. . . .'

'Love's not wicked,' declared Kate. 'No amount of sermons at Paul's Cross would make me believe that.'

'I think you're right, Kate.'

'You're sure he'll not send me away, mistress?'

'I am sure of that, Kate.'

'Shall I put our things together?'

'No. We take nothing of mine. When the chariot comes we slip our cloaks about us and walk out . . . just as though we are going to the market.'

'No clothes?'

'Nothing from this house, Kate.'

'Not your jewels?'

'Nothing . . . nothing at all.'

''Tis a mistake, mistress.'

'I do not care.' Jane threw herself into Kate's arms and began to sob.

'There, my pretty,' soothed Kate. 'Stop crying. Stop grieving. Love's to make you happy, not to make you cry . . . just at first in any case.'

'Oh, Kate, I could not help but love him. He is so different from all others. Kate, you will love a court life, and so shall I.'

'A court life, mistress! I know. It is . . . my Lord Hastings.'

'No, Kate. It is . . . the King.'

Kate's mouth fell open. She stood up and laid her hands across her breasts and tears ran down her cheeks. She was back in Ludlow Castle, watching from a window while the handsomest man in England rode into the courtyard.

Five o'clock. It would never come. The weary afternoon wore on. Could she trust Kate? Would Kate go to the kitchen for a last farewell with Belper?

She could smell the roasting meat from the kitchens. She heard Will below with a customer. Five o'clock was the supper hour. A difficult time, and there must be no false steps. They must be ready to slip out unnoticed.

At a quarter to five Kate was panting up the stairs.

'Mistress, mistress, a chariot has just drawn up.'

'Oh, Kate, are you sure?'

'I have been watching this last hour.'

'Have you your cloak?'

'Yes, mistress.'

'Then now . . . *now*.'

Down the familiar staircase–she would never see it again–past the parlour where Hastings had dared wait for her on the evening of Edward's ceremonial ride through the City . . . out through the porch.

'Run, Kate! Hurry!'

The door of the chariot was flung open. Jane stepped in, Kate at her heels. Jane was drawn into Edward's arms; she heard his quiet laughter.

'I knew you'd come, sweetheart. I knew you'd come.'

She said breathlessly: 'I have brought Kate. I had to bring Kate. She is my maid, and I could not leave her or he would turn her out. Say I may bring Kate. . . .'

His laughing eyes went beyond Jane to the plump figure that crouched there in the chariot eyeing him with wonder and reverence.

'Greeting, Kate,' he said. Then he shouted to the driver: 'Whip up and be gone.' He turned to Jane and kissed her loudly on the lips. 'May you bring Kate? Why, my beloved, bring all the wenches of Lombard Street–what matters it, an Jane Shore comes with them!'

The chariot rattled over the cobbles of Lombard Street, on to Westminster.

Westminster Palace

Jane, lying away in the big bed with its magnificently carved legs and cornices, watched, through an opening in the curtains, the first streaks of red in the early morning sky. She had awakened suddenly after a restless night, and for a moment had thought she was in the room she shared with Will Shore in Lombard Street. But how different was this room in her apartments in Westminster Palace! How different from Will was the man who lay beside her! It was barely a month since Jane had taken up residence at the palace, but what a lot she had learned in that month!

Her eyes travelled across the familiar splendour of the room. There were no common rushes on the floor, for it was tiled, and here and there covered by brightly coloured carpets. There was one chair only in the room–an elaborate affair of velvet and tapestry which was reserved for the use of the King. There were several stools with tapestry-covered seats and beautifully carved legs; and in one corner was a small wooden structure which was curtained off from the rest of the room and which was shaped like an altar. Above this was a crucifix, and before it a velvet rug on which to kneel and say prayers. The bed itself was luxurious. It was set in a square compartment separated from the room by gorgeous curtains suspended from the ceiling.

Peacocks in red and blue and gold were embroidered on these curtains and the cushions on the bed were coloured to match.

Jane turned to look at the handsome face of the man who lay beside her on the feather bed; his fair hair was disarrayed, and his face half buried in the fine linen of the sheets. Gently, she removed the sheet and looked at him with uneasy tenderness. Her eyes went to the full lips which betrayed their owner's love of sensuous pleasure; and she wondered how many women had, waking as she had this morning and looking upon his sleeping face, asked themselves, 'How long shall I keep him? How long before some other takes my place?'

Her thoughts went back over the four gay and wildly exciting weeks. Balls, masques and banquets; she had enjoyed them to the full for Edward was beside her. Merry Jane Shore she was called, and the King was proud of her wit. But in this dawn light she must face the truth. Basking in the King's pleasure was like dancing in the summer sunshine, and the summer did not last throughout the year. But I love him so much, thought Jane illogically. That must make a difference. None of the others loved him as I do.

He stirred and murmured something in his sleep. Did he dream of her? She was no fool; and a month at court had taught her that she was a small part of his life. Jane pressed her face into the pillow and tried to forget the faces of some of those who were now sleeping in this great palace; she tried not to think of their moving lips as they asked each other, 'How long? A month is a long time with the same woman.'

She could not stop thinking of Hastings. Whenever he was present his eyes seemed to watch her unceasingly, as though he waited for some sign that the King was tired of her. She could not forget the waiting sultry desire in the man's eyes.

The Queen troubled her also. What was the meaning of the cold calm smiles bestowed on her by the Queen?

Jane shuddered, for everything at court was gayer, fiercer, more cruel than in the simple homes of Lombard Street and Cheapside. The lavish banquets, the entertainments, the dazzling garments, might have belonged to an eastern court. Here was licentiousness that appalled; lovers were taken in an afternoon and discarded by evening, exchanged, discussed. Amorous adventuring was the main business of the court; and how could she shut her eyes to the fact that the King set the fashion! Just now he was deeply in love with herself. Now she was back at the question which had begun to dominate her life. How long?

There was another side to court life–grim instead of gay, filled with horror instead of colour, hate instead of love. A carelessly spoken word and men and women were despatched to the Tower, their lands confiscated, and perhaps they would never be heard of again. This was a strange life, a life of pleasure and fear. And in the centre of it all was Edward, the most brilliant member of the brilliant court, the most loved and the most feared. For this man, who, it was said, changed his loves as he changed his garments, had Jane left the peaceful security of her husband's house.

Each day she learned more about him, and learning found a different man from the handsome merchant to whom she had given her love. His vanity was extreme enough to be naïve. He would strut in front of the mirror, admiring his person; he would bid her stand beside him, and while he feigned to admire her would in truth be studying himself. His rages were what she feared most. They did not occur often for he was by nature easy-going; but when they did come they could be terrible. She had seen him angry with a tailor who had spoilt the coat he was making; she had heard him threaten to have the tailor flogged. It was she who had saved the tailor. He liked women to plead with him; she was beginning to understand that he wished to see himself as the strong man, weak only where his love was concerned. There was little he enjoyed as much as granting favours to women.

The story of the tailor spread. People in trouble were for ever seeking her out, begging her to intercede for them. Only yesterday a woman had come begging an audience. It was a Mistress Banster of East Cheap who kept a pie shop there. Her son Charlie was in trouble. He had spoken against the King and had been taken to the Tower. She feared they would cut off his ears. He was but fourteen.

She seemed to hear the woman's voice now. 'For pity's sake, lady . . . For pity's sake. . . .' The boy had but said what many said before him: Edward had had King Henry murdered, and King Henry was a saint.

Last night Jane had tried to tell Edward that she wanted him to save the boy's ears, and she had chosen a moment when he lay temporarily satisfied beside her.

'Edward,' she had said, 'there is something I would ask of you.'

'Yes?' His voice had been slurred and sleepy.

She had told of the woman, and the boy who was to have his ears cut off. She waited for an outburst of horror. None came. Edward had survived too many bloody battlefields to be disturbed by the cutting off of an unknown boy's ears. He had drawn her towards him and sleepily bitten her ear. 'You have pretty ears, Jane. What if I bite them off? You should not tempt me with your talk of ears.'

She had been deeply shocked, and rashly had not attempted to hide her feelings. 'How can you, when that poor boy–he is but a child–lies in the Tower? Edward, you must listen to me. I cannot sleep for thinking of him.'

'That's treason. You must think of none but me.'

'Edward, would you not do something for me?'

'Anything for you, sweet Jane.'

'Then let this boy go free.'

'What did he then?'

'He but repeated some idle gossip.'

'Concerning me? Well, then, when he has no ears to hear idle gossip, 'twill be the better for me, will it not?'

He had rolled over and she saw then the cruelty of his mouth.

'But, Edward, if I asked you . . .'

'What said he?'

'It was something about King Henry's death.'

That had been a mistake. She had seen the change in his face. She had recognised the look of guilt. He wanted to be good; he wanted to be benign; he wanted laughter all around him and people to adore him; he did not care to see himself as a brutal murderer. A murderer? she had thought. Is my Edward then a murderer?

'My dear Jane!' His voice had been ice-cold. 'You must not meddle in such matters. The boy deserves his fate. We cannot allow our enemies to speak thus against us. Rebellions grow out of such talk. You must not ask us to forgive our enemies.'

They had lain, a small but hostile space between them. Was this the end then? Jane asked herself. If not, how long?

The discovery of cruelty in him could not kill her love. She was completely fascinated, unable to resist him. She longed now to creep up to him and beg his forgiveness, to tell him that she would never interfere again; she loved him unconditionally.

He awakened suddenly and reached for her. 'Jane!' His voice was sleepy, yet it held desire. He drew her to him. 'Why, your cheeks are wet! What ails thee, Jane?' The old tenderness was in his voice, melting her fears, wiping away all emotions but this rising, thrilling joy.

'I feared I had offended you.'

He laughed. 'Nay, you could not do that. You are soft and small and sweet and I love you.'

'Then . . . all is as it was before?'

'Give me your lips, my little love,' he said, 'and I'll give you that boy's ears. How's that for a bargain?'

But afterwards she lay awake, and fear returned. She had saved the boy, but she had had a terrifying glimpse of kingly power and kingly cruelty.

Yet, there could be no happiness for her without this man. She must continue to please him. She would wrap her love so closely about him that he could not escape it; it should be a net to hold him, yet so fine and flexible that he should not be irked by the sight and the feel of it.

She heard the first stirrings of morning in the palace before she fell asleep.

In the corridor leading from her apartments Jane came face to face with Hastings. It was the first time since she had come to the palace that they had been alone. She would have hurried past him, but he barred her way.

'Please allow me to pass.'

He did not move. 'How long now, Jane?' he asked.

'I understand you not, my lord.'

'I think you do.'

'If I do understand you, Lord Hastings, I can only consider you a fool.'

'Any man is a fool who allows himself to get caught in love as I have.'

'Were I you, I should talk of such matters to those who are interested to hear them.'

'You are not interested in my love affairs because you are deep in one with the King, but when that is done with . . .'

'I find your manners as objectionable in Westminster as they were in Lombard Street.'

'And I find you a thousand times more desirable in Westminster than I did in Lombard Street. More's the pity.'

'It surprises me that the Lord Chancellor should so demean himself.'

'There is much that I do that surprises me, Jane,' he said sombrely.

In spite of her hatred, her interest was aroused. What a strange man he was! Edward had said he was one of his cleverest ministers, and yet he conducted himself like a schoolboy. She asked him if he did not realise that were she to tell Edward he had accosted her thus he might find himself in a dangerous position.

'I know it.' He came closer, and his eyes were earnest. 'But I cannot help myself. You say I am a fool. You speak truth. I know now that I should have approached you in a different manner. And now . . . but for me you would never have come here.'

'But for *you*?'

'Who do you think told Edward of the goldsmith's lovely wife? Revenge it was to be, revenge on the goldsmith who dared insult me.'

'So *you* sent Edward to Lombard Street?'

'One does not send Edward. I merely whispered that I had seen the loveliest girl in London. That was enough. Ah–but perhaps I was not foolish. In a little while, in a month–or perhaps a week . . .'

'Have you not yet learned that I hate you?'

'You shall learn to love me. A Chancellor is not such a bad exchange for a King. Many of Edward's mistresses have had to be content with less.' She turned abruptly from him, but he caught her wrist. His eyes glittered. 'My lovely Jane, I will make you happy. It will be you first, not for a week, nor a month–but always. That is how I love you, Jane.'

'You mock me.'

'Nay, I speak the truth.'

'I shall tell the King of this.'

'Yes, do. It may put the idea of a change into his head. It cannot be too soon for me.'

She ran from him, and Hastings, shrugging his shoulders, made his way back to his apartment. He was wondering how Edward had succeeded with her. When Edward was in the midst of a love affair he always deluded himself, as well as his partner in the adventure, that it was the most important in his life. Therein doubtless lay his success.

He found his wife, Catharine, stitching at a piece of embroidery. She looked at him coldly. There was no love between them, and never had been, though both had desired the marriage. He was the great Hastings, and she was the sister of the Earl of Warwick; they came from two of the richest families in the country; they were two aristocrats, each gaining wealth and power from the other.

She looked at him coldly now because she considered him a fool to cast longing eyes upon the King's newest mistress while the King was yet enamoured of her.

There was one thing they shared in common, though–and that was hatred of the Queen. The Hastings-Warwick alliance was meant to unite two great families and so add to their power. But now, through the Queen's habit of marrying her upstart relations into the richest and oldest families in the land, the Woodvilles were fast becoming very powerful and dangerous. It was therefore the duty of every noble house to stand against them.

Hastings sat on a stool and smiled at his wife. 'I am thinking of bringing my cousin to court,' he said. 'I have spoken to the King of her already.'

Catharine thought of the girl of whom he spoke. Fifteen, a charming age. Primed by Hastings she might easily please the King. It was well for a house when the King was amused by one of its women. But did he think to deceive her? Was he bringing the girl to court that she might influence the King for the good of their family? No. He was bringing the girl to court that she might lure the King from Jane Shore!

And he thought to deceive her. Queer, thought the countess, that one so skilled in war and politics as her husband could scheme so clumsily for his women.

Edward was walking in the gardens of the Palace of Westminster with his brothers when he looked up and saw the Queen at her window. Her maid was combing her hair and it shone like gold coins.

Across the King, his brothers argued. He was weary of the continual strife between these two. He hated displays of temper; if any was to lose a temper, that should be himself.

They were quarrelling about Anne Neville, who had a short while before been a prisoner of state and had now mysteriously disappeared. Edward guessed George was responsible for the girl's disappearance. With Isabel, George's wife, she was co-heiress to the Warwick fortune; and George had no intention of sharing that fortune with Anne Neville. To complicate matters, Richard wanted the girl, wanted to marry her.

'Enough! Enough!' cried Edward. 'Take your quarrels elsewhere. By God, if I wanted the girl I'd find her! Go, Dickon, be a man. Find the girl and marry her, if that's what you want.'

'You would give your consent to such a marriage?' demanded George.

'I did not give my consent to your marriage with her sister, but you married her all the same. By God's Holy Virgin, George, I wonder at my clemency towards you!'

That silenced him. Watching him, Edward grew hot at the thought of George's treachery. With Richard it was different. Dear Richard, but a boy for all his cleverness. He was romantically in love with this Anne Neville. Let him enjoy the girl–if he could find her. Richard had been put under her father's care when they were children and they had grown up together. Let Richard find where George had hidden her and then he could marry her, for with her sister she was the biggest heiress in the country. Pray the Virgin there had been no foul play. He wanted no more trouble between his brothers.

But the glint of the Queen's hair in the sunlight was pleasant. He left his brothers and went up to her apartment. The tiring maid curtseyed as he entered. He signed for her to leave him with the Queen. When they were alone he went to Elizabeth and kissed her. 'Well, my Lady Bessy, I swear you grow more beautiful every day.'

'I saw Your Grace walking with your brothers. I trust nothing is wrong.'

'There will always be wrong between those two.'

'And how fares Mistress Shore? I declare I have not seen her these last few days.'

With some women the question might have been the beginning of reproach and recrimination. But he knew that Elizabeth had no desire to quarrel with him. He told her Jane was well.

'A pleasant and a lovely girl,' said Elizabeth.

Now he was momentarily angry with her. She had always had the power to anger him, and how furious she had made him during their courtship! 'Your mistress I cannot be.' The tight red lips had meant that. Her acceptance of Jane and his other mistresses, while it pleased him, irritated him. It was so unnatural. But then, his Elizabeth, as he had always known, was an exceptional woman; and he did not regret his romantic marriage. He remembered afresh the excitement of the first weeks with Elizabeth. Strange that she should have attracted him so strongly. She was different from all other women, so perhaps that was the reason; though he had never before liked cold women, in her case the attempt to arouse passion in her had the charm of the unattainable. Elizabeth had a love, however. It was love of the power the King brought her, not of the King himself.

'You're thoughtful,' she said.

'My thoughts were of you, Bessy.'

'I trust they were pleasant, my lord.'

'Very pleasant.' He sat on the table and, leaning forward, kissed her lips. they were cold against his own. He thought of Jane's soft warm ones. Jane was a loving little thing, but so many had been loving.

'I was recalling that day at Grafton,' he said. 'Seven years ago, and here I am as deep in love with you as ever. There have been others, 'tis true, but back I come to my lovely Bessy.' He laid a hand on her breast; she did not draw back, nor did she respond. 'And she,' he went on, 'is like one made of marble. But no matter. . . . Do you remember that day? Your mother, a priest, and a gentlewoman or two. What secrecy! Oh, Bessy, what were your thoughts when I rode away and left behind me the Queen of England?'

She smiled slowly. 'I was very happy, Edward.'

'You were indeed, for were you not the Queen? Remember how I would come to stay at your mother's house–a guest for a night or two–and after the retiring hour you would slip along to my apartments?'

Elizabeth nodded. She was not likely to forget the days which had carried her to the summit of her desires. She had become Queen, and after years of widowhood and being forced to live on her mother's bounty, that was pleasant. Now, this talk of their secret marriage could be leading up to one thing only. Could he never be satisfied? God knew he had mistresses enough. He had the virility of ten men. That she discovered in that brief period when she had been the only one to occupy his thoughts. The Virgin be praised that he loves variety, she thought, for did his fancy rest long on one he would kill her. Well, she had children enough now, but perhaps there should be a second boy. It had taken them long enough to get young Edward. Three daughters and then a son. There should be more sons. The times were perilous, and it was dangerous for a woman who set such store upon a throne to have only one son.

She sought now to make what she could out of the situation. Edward was the sort of man who liked to give. She knew him better than did anyone else; she could always choose the most proper moment to press for a favour. Edward would have been kindhearted if he were not utterly selfish. He would have been benevolent if he were not so quick to anger. He would have been great if he had not loved pleasure so completely. He would have been a great lover of his country if he had not loved women so much. That was how she saw Edward–near-great, a man of contrasts, so that every good quality was balanced by its exact opposite. Even his good looks were beginning to be impaired by a life of excesses. Elizabeth guessed that in time his beauty and grace would be lost in grossness of body and manners.

'Edward,' she said, for seeing his brothers with him in the grounds had set an idea working in her mind, 'have you any knowledge of what happened to the Neville girl?'

He was tired of the Neville girl. She had disappeared, he said testily. That was all he knew.

'One of the richest girls in the country and she disappears! Where to? Someone must know.'

'Then that someone is assuredly not I. All I know is that George, as her brother-in-law, would take charge of her, and one day she disappeared from his house.'

'George has had something to do with that disappearance. He has hidden her, because he fears Richard will marry her and take her share of the Warwick fortune.'

'And you have other plans for the Warwick fortune, eh? You want Anne for one of your many uncles and cousins.'

'I should feel it my duty to find a husband for the girl,' said Elizabeth primly. 'She is not to be blamed for her father's treachery. The sooner she is married the better.'

The King laughed. 'Oh, Bessy, Bessy, you'll be the death of me with your marriages. What a woman! What a maker of marriages! Can you not be content with marrying yourself to the King? Surely you have no more penniless brothers and cousins. I thought you had found monied marriages for the lot by now. I don't forget your brother, Bess. How old was he when you married him to the old Dowager of Norfolk? Eighteen was it, Bessy? And the old lady turned eighty! Bessy, is there no end to your matchmaking?'

'Edward,' she said, laying her hand on his coat and smiling at him, 'you will do what you can to find her, and when she is found you will let me arrange a marriage for her?'

'Why, Bessy, have I ever refused you anything yet?' He laughed, and grasping her golden hair in either hand pulled her gently towards him. Seven years of marriage, and she could still attract him! There was not a woman like her in the kingdom–with the exception of Jane. He would throw Anne Neville to her as, a short while ago, he had thrown her to Richard. She should at least have the pleasure of thinking the Neville fortune was all but in the hands of her greedy family.

She was smiling, but she was as cold as ice. That was what he wanted, for it reminded him most pleasantly of his wedding night.

Jane was heartbroken, for the King no longer loved her. It was three days and nights since he had been to her apartments. Kate, busying herself with the wardrobe, kept her frightened eyes downcast. Where would this end? Was the brief period of glory over?

It was due to a tall, slender, black-haired girl–a protégée of my Lord and Lady Hastings. She was the exact opposite of Jane, being tall where Jane was short, dark where Jane was fair. The King, it was said, was very gracious and very merry with everyone who came his way, which was a sure sign that he was preparing to embark on one of his major love affairs.

Jane knew that Hastings had done this, for the man was an evil shadow hanging over her life.

'I hate you! I hate you!' she told him fiercely when he waylaid her.

'I have heard that hate and love are very close, sweet Jane. Today you hate; tomorrow you will love.' There was a sudden tenderness in his voice. 'Jane, how can you be such a little fool! Have you not learned yet what folly it is to love the King? His affections are here today and gone tomorrow. Come with me. I have plans for us.'

'I remember other plans of yours!'

'I have changed. You have changed me. We will leave the court if you wish it. If you will only trust me.'

'As well trust a serpent!'

'I would do anything in the world to make you happy.'

'So you plotted against me?'

'It is for your good. I am not a careless boy who knows not what he wants.'

'You are an evil man, and I hate you. I hate you.'

'But, Jane, what is to happen to you? Where will you go? You must come to me then, for I shall be waiting for you.'

'I would rather starve.'

'You say so because you have never starved. You know not what you say.'

'I know well enough that I hate you.'

She ran from him into her apartment. She threw herself on to the bed, drew the curtains and gave herself up to bitter weeping. Life was so cruel. The man she had idealised was a philanderer–and worse, yet he had the power to break her heart. She herself had changed from that innocent girl of Cheapside, that young woman of Lombard Street. She had become capable of fierce love for the King, fierce hate for Hastings.

Oh, God, she thought, if only I had a child, then I could bear this. Edward had numerous sons, some in high, some in obscure places–why could she not have one? She had made the acquaintance of the royal children. They were charming, and all with a look of Edward. Elizabeth, the eldest, was proud, but Cecily and Mary were sweet, though Jane's favourite was the baby, who was just a year old and named after his father. But what was the use of thinking of the child! Perhaps she would never see him again. Perhaps she would have to leave the court, and there would be nothing left but memories.

Kate drew aside the curtains of the bed, her eyes wide with excitement. The Queen's woman had brought a message. The Queen would speak with Jane at once.

When Jane reached the Queen's apartment Elizabeth dismissed her women and told Jane she might sit. That in itself was significant, for it was rarely that Elizabeth allowed any to sit in her presence. She could never forget the years of indignity, and they had made her ever conscious of her present power. Often she kept her ladies on their knees for as much as three hours at a stretch; even her own mother, who had been largely responsible for Elizabeth's present glory, must kneel in her daughter's presence and wait until permission was given to rise. But Jane might sit and listen to what the Queen had to say. Elizabeth came quickly to the point.

'Mistress Shore, you are unhappy, thinking to have lost the King's favour?' In spite of her misery Jane found it difficult to suppress a smile, for it seemed so odd for the King's mistress and the King's wife to be discussing such a matter together. 'She who has temporarily supplanted you,' went on Elizabeth, 'and, mind you, I say temporarily, has not a tenth of your beauty, nor, I understand, your wit. But His Grace the King is susceptible to youth and beauty . . . and above all to variety.'

'Your Grace is kind to me,' murmured Jane.

Elizabeth inclined her head. 'I like you, Jane Shore. And may I say that most of the women with whom the King amuses himself are not to my liking. What I would say to you is that if you lose the King's affection you will have none but yourself to blame.'

'I . . . do not understand, Your Grace.'

'That, methinks, is because you have been but a short time at court. The King has been mightily taken with you. Indeed, I would go as far as to say that none but myself has ever taken his fancy as you have. I have kept his affection for seven years. I shall continue to do so until one of us shall die. And because I love the King and because you also love him, I know that it is better that he should betray me with you than with the many wanton creatures who would seek to attract him. I will now tell you how you may keep his affection.' Elizabeth laughed and her laughter was icy. 'Come, my child. You look bewildered. It is simple enough. You have more beauty than any other at court. You can make the King laugh. There is no need for you to throw these gifts into Hastings' waiting arms. The King loves me; he loves you also; he is capable of loving many. But because a man likes roast peacock it does not mean he does not also like a good slice of homely bread. Never fear. He will come back and back again, if you are clever enough to let him. Go back to your apartment, and when the King comes to you, as assuredly he will, smile at him, behave as though this interlude had never been; if refer to it you must, refer to it as some trifling incident, too small to be regrettable. What the King hates more than anything is a weeping and reproachful woman. He will run from your tears and run towards your smiles. If you follow my advice, I venture to say that this is not the end of the pleasant attachment between Jane Shore and His Grace the King.'

'You are too kind to me, Your Grace. I cannot understand . . .'

Elizabeth smiled at her. If she did not understand then she was indeed a little fool and doubtless she would lose Edward sooner or later. But perhaps she had not yet learned that the Queen must keep the King from indulging in more than the lightest affairs with the female relatives of her enemies.

'Do not forget what I have said,' she commanded, and dismissing Jane, congratulated herself on this day's work.

The Queen was right. The King soon came back to Jane. He felt ashamed and was prepared to be critical of Jane therefore. But she was waiting for him, dressed in the same shade of blue, her yellow hair rioting over her shoulders. He noticed at once that she wore a jewelled ornament which he had given her on an occasion when he had sworn eternal fidelity. Her smile was warm and she seemed merrier than ever.

She ran to him. 'Edward, how wonderful to see you!'

He held her at arm's length and looked at her shrewdly. No reproaches. Just a welcome. And she was more beautiful than ever. Why had he ever thought that other one more attractive? He kissed her and his relief changed to passion. He did not know that Jane was fighting to keep back her tears, that her laughter was forced, that she was facing the sad fact that if she could learn to share him he was hers perhaps for always. She felt unclean, humiliated, yet her need of him was as urgent as ever.

'My little one,' he said, 'there is none on earth to stand against thee.'

There was now no need for him to play the faithful lover as he had been doing for so long. It was a great relief. He could be natural with Jane, for in spite of her sweetness and loving ways she had learned the reasonable manners of the court.

He did try to explain at first though. 'I think I must have been bewitched. But here I am, back again, and eager to make up for every minute spent away from you.'

'Remember it not. 'Twas but the habit of a lifetime doubtless.'

Merrily he laughed, and Jane laughed with him, though never had she felt less like laughter.

The story spread through the court. The King is back with Jane Shore. Hastings heard it. He was frustrated and sick at heart.

Lady Hastings laughed at her husband. 'Your little plan has failed, my lord,' she taunted him. 'It would seem your cousin's brief moments with the King did naught but rob the girl of her virginity.'

Hastings hated his wife and his cousin; he hated the King. He knew that everyone was laughing at him, and he could not bear to be laughed at. Yet even more than the loss of dignity did he feel the loss of Jane. He could not forget her. She had changed his life. For the first time was he truly in love, and finding it a wretched state to be in. He endeavoured to forget Jane. He left the palace, and, going down to the river, hailed a boat and savagely told the boatman to row him over to Southwark. There, he thought, in those dark rooms where every vice that the devil had put into the minds of men could be practised, there would he forget Jane Shore.

But he found it was impossible to forget her.

After the King's brief love affair with Hastings' protégée, Jane's position changed subtly. Next to the King and the Queen, she had become the most important person at court. Nobody now speculated as to whether she would retain her position as the King's favourite mistress; it was taken for granted that she would.

Jane was deeply conscious of a change in herself. She was worldly; it was no use denying that she loved the gay court, the good living, the erotic excitements to which Edward introduced her. She knew now why she had longed to escape from the sober life of Cheapside and Lombard Street. She was kind of heart, and it was the easiest thing possible to arouse her pity, but she knew herself to be a courtesan, and she could not forget it. She was treated with great respect, and even the King's brothers, Clarence and Gloucester, cultivated her acquaintance. She was ready to plead with the King for any cause she considered just, and it was rarely that she asked for anything for herself. But always she must scheme to please the King; she had learned even that to plead another's cause she must use wit and laughter, never tears. She must act a part continually.

Outside the court the Town talked of her. The woman Banster and her boy Charlie could not praise the King's favourite too much; there were many like them. Jane knew this and it pleased her.

Always she tried to face the truth; she must hold her place, and she did not see how she could do this unless she saw life as it really was. She was disillusioned. She had learned that Mary Blague, the respected lace-woman of Cheapside, had connections with a house of ill-fame across the river. Kate, who was enjoying court life and all its intrigues and adventures, had on one occasion followed Danok from Cheapside to the house in Southwark, and on another she had followed Mary Blague. Jane was aware, through court gossip, that the house in Southwark was a brothel and that there was a mysterious woman who owned the place. She believed that woman to be Mary Blague. And had not Mary arranged for her seduction in the lace-making establishment? Whom could one trust?'

And I, thought Jane, am as wicked as any, for I am one of those harlots they speak of at Paul's Cross; and were I not the King's harlot I should be forced most likely to do a penance in the streets. Yet, how could she wish that she were back in Lombard Street? How could she wish she were anywhere but where she was? She had the love of the King, and if it was born of the senses–she must be truthful–so was hers for him.

Yet, in their new relationship there was a difference. They were companions, and he enjoyed talking to her. He told her of those desperate days when he had been almost constantly at war, of the terrible weeks of exile which he had endured more than once in his stormy journey towards the throne. She understood then his urgent desire to live life fully, to plunder from it every conceivable pleasure. The times were perilous. He must enjoy everything that his power could bring him, while that was possible. They were of a kind, he and Jane.

He told her of his brothers. Clarence, he confessed, was at the root of his biggest worry. 'I must keep him close to me, Jane, for I swear that when he is out of my sight I tremble to think what he may be plotting.'

'Think you not that he has learned his lesson?'

'George will never learn his lesson. That is his great failing.'

Jane thought constantly of the girl Anne Neville, for her strange disappearance was discussed often. She tried to talk to Edward of her, but Edward was weary of the subject.

'The girl's a tiresome creature, Jane. By the Virgin, I fear murder between those two brothers of mine, one day.'

'If only she could be found!'

Edward turned on her, frowning. 'If she is found there will be trouble.' He shrugged his shoulders. 'Let her stay in hiding. She is safer there. Picture the strife, Jane, if she were found. Richard wants to marry her, and the Queen has already marked her for one of her relations. There'd be trouble between Richard and Bess. And what of George? By my faith, methinks there'll be trouble saved if the girl stays in hiding.'

'But have you thought what she may be suffering, Edward?'

'Enough!' He was lazy; he liked life to run smoothly. Anne Neville was unimportant while she remained hidden. She would be a nuisance if she were found. It did not matter to him that a gently nurtured girl might be suffering hardship.

Indeed, he was a different man from the merchant who had seemed perfect to Jane. But I am different too, Jane reminded herself.

'Let us talk of other matters,' said Edward, and kissed her. It was easy for Jane also to forget Anne Neville . . . for the time being.

But Jane remembered Anne again when Kate brought news to her. Kate had witnessed something very strange and had hastened to tell her mistress. Waiting for a lover, in a secluded part of the gardens, she had witnessed a meeting between . . . whom did Jane think? She would surely never guess, so Kate would tell quickly. None other than the Duke of Clarence and Mary Blague! Surely if the Duke was indulging in a love affair it could not be with Mary Blague!

'No,' said Jane, 'it could not have been a love affair.' She warned Kate to say nothing of this meeting, but she herself could not forget it, and because she thought of Mary Blague as an evil woman, a procuress, a woman who had strange connections with an evil house in Southwark, she began to see a reason why this woman should secretly meet such a person as the Duke of Clarence. Might it not concern the missing girl?

She would go to Edward. But what was the use? Edward would shrug his shoulders. Let the girl remain hidden, he would say. That was the more peaceful way.

Yes, let the girl remain hidden, for on no account must Jane Shore anger the King. But Jane found she had not changed so much as she had thought. A pale, frightened face came between her and whatever she was doing, and there was no peace for Jane. She could not forget the girl she had seen riding in the chariot with Margaret of Anjou. The daughter of a man who had been one of the highest in the land, might now be a prisoner in a brothel.

She would have to risk Edward's displeasure; and so the day after she had the news from Kate, she was making her way to the apartment of the Duke of Gloucester.

Richard was working, and before him on the table lay a pile of documents. He was conscientious, and matters of state interested him far more than the pleasures in which his brothers indulged. There were times when he would have liked to take over the burden of kingship in name as well as in deed. There were so many schemes in his head; had he been the King he would have spent less time feasting and would have enjoyed making laws rather than love. Everything in life would be subordinated to the good of his country; and now, as the King's chief adviser, matters of state occupied a large part of his thoughts.

He looked up as Jane entered, and flicked a speck of dust off his elaborate sleeve. Like his brothers, he loved fine clothes, and he was always careful to wear something about his neck that might hide the fact that one shoulder was higher than the other. He smiled, for he did not dislike Jane Shore. He thought her a graceful lovely creature, but he deplored Edward's lack of wisdom in doting on her so utterly. Still, he guessed that had she not genuinely loved his brother she would have remained a virtuous wife.

'Richard,' said Jane haltingly, for they had been commanded by Edward to dispense with ceremony and call each other by their Christian names. They did this, but never without a certain embarrassment on both sides. 'Richard, I have some news which I feel may be of interest to you. I hesitate to tell you because there may be nothing in it; yet, on the other hand, there may. It is about Anne Neville.'

He laid aside his pen. Only the pulse beating furiously at his temple showed her that he was moved. She looked over her shoulder. He rose swiftly, went to the door and looked out. 'We are quite alone. Pray speak.'

Jane was afraid now of the wildness of her suspicions, for she saw that this pale, cold-seeming young man was truly in love with the missing girl. She was glad she had come to him. No matter what was to follow, she was glad. Weeks at court had made her conscious of danger, but had done nothing to curb her reckless generosity.

'I fear I may be wrong,' she said, 'but mayhap it is worth while following this up, and I thought I should come to you.'

'Yes, yes.'

'My maid was in a secluded part of the gardens when she witnessed a meeting between your brother the Duke and a woman–who has connections with a house in Southwark.'

'I have heard of that house.'

'I wondered if their meeting had anything to do with—'

'Holy Mother! Anne in such a house!'

'The woman lends herself to any dark and evil business and—'

'I shall go at once. I shall take some men with me. I shall search the place. By the Virgin, I'll kill George for this!'

She had never thought to see him so moved. She tried to restrain him, to explain that it was but an idea that occurred to her, but he would not listen. He had gathered up his papers and locked them in a box. It was characteristic of Richard that he could at such a moment think of doing that.

Jane silently prayed that he might find Anne Neville in that house in Southwark, and find her unharmed. Richard would make a good quiet husband, she thought; and thinking of her own exciting and unaccountable lover, she was both sorry for and envious of Anne Neville.

Jane was terrified. She who had merely thought to reunite a pair of lovers had stumbled into danger. She had dared interfere in a desperate game which was being played by ruthless princes.

She had heard from Richard what had happened at the Southwark house. He had knocked at the door, and when Madam opened it, he, with seven well-chosen men, had stepped into the hall. 'I believe,' he had said, 'that you harbour here a certain lady. If that should be so, I ask you to deliver her up to me at once.'

The woman had shown surprise and indignation until she discovered Richard's identity. Richard had then been allowd to search the house, but he had not found Anne.

'How sorry I am!' cried Jane. 'I fear I but raised your hopes pointlessly and so made you more unhappy than ever.'

'It was no fault of yours,' answered Richard. 'And I thank you for telling me. If you should discover anything further . . .'

'Depend upon it,' Jane warmly assured him, 'I shall come straight to you.'

The matter might have rested there but for Kate, but Kate could never resist gossiping. She whispered to her lover that the Duke of Clarence and the King's lace-woman had been meeting secretly. The story was whispered round the court, with the result that it reached the Duke's ears. He lost no time in tracking it to its source, and Kate was summoned to the presence of the Duke.

When the Duke's anger was roused he lost all sense of dignity. He was angry now. Kate stood before him, shivering with terror. She was the sort who would not need the rack nor the thumbscrews to make her talk; nevertheless he threatened her with them. And out came the whole story. She had seen him with Mistress Blague and she had told her mistress. So it was Jane Shore who had taken the tale to the Duke of Gloucester. The friends of Gloucester were the natural enemies of Clarence.

'Throw the woman into the Tower,' cried George; and the weeping, terrified Kate was led away.

George sought out Jane, and such was his anger that he threw all caution from him.

'Mistress Blague, the brothel-keeper, is a friend of yours, madam?' His insolence was intolerable, and Jane understood at once that the Duke was her open enemy. She was in a dangerous position, but when she was actually face to face with danger she was always stimulated by it.

'How dare you speak to me thus!' she cried. 'I do not wish to see you again until you have learned your manners.'

George laughed in her face. 'Sluts give themselves airs, do they not? Come, tell me, did the brothel-woman procure you for my brother? 'Tis what I had from that slut of yours who spies into the affairs of your betters for you.'

'You will allow me to pass.'

'Not before I have said my say. And I advise you, madam, to show more respect to me. Think not that I shall disregard such conduct. A day will come when I shall sit upon the throne.'

Jane quickly saw her advantage. 'You speak treason, sir,' she said.

George's face was purple, his bloodshot eyes rolled. 'By Christ!' he cried. 'I'll not be treated thus by harlots such as you–even if they be the King's harlots.'

'Then it was true that she was hidden in that house,' said Jane. 'It is true that you took that poor girl and subjected her to such horrors . . .'

'Hold your strumpet's tongue!' he cried.

'Your anger leads me to believe my suspicions are correct.'

'Be silent, or I'll have you thrown into the Tower along with your maid. I'll set the guards on you. I'll have you racked.'

Jane was pale and sick suddenly. 'My maid–in the Tower?'

''Tis where she should be. God's Holy Virgin, I, the son of my father, to be treated thus by my brother's harlots!'

'You will release my maid at once.'

'Release her? Not before we have racked the whole treasonable truth out of her. You too, madam, if needs be.'

He laughed in her face and left her. Thus was she terrified of what she had set in motion. Kate in the Tower. Anne Neville undiscovered. And, if Kate were to be rescued, it would be necessary to tell Edward the entire story. Had he not told her she must not meddle in such matters? She held him to her by such flimsy threads. She must set Kate free though, even at the risk of incurring Edward's anger. Experience had taught her to wait until he was in an acquiescent mood before asking favours, yet how could she wait–while Kate was in the Tower? What a fool I am! she thought. Why do I rush in and act before I think? As well ask herself why she had left the security of life with Will for the thousand risks and dangers of life with Edward. She had done these things because she was herself.

There was no help for it. She must confess what she had done, and she must beg Edward for Kate's release; she must beg with more courage and more tact than she had ever used before.

She went to her apartment and put on her most becoming gown; she set her hair in loose curls about her shoulders. She must chaffer with her beauty, for that was all she had to offer. She thought of a proud young girl who had lived with her father in Cheapside. How low have I fallen! she thought. But I am what I am, and my kind must beg for favours thus.

Edward was occupied with matters of state. He was sitting alone in his privy chamber when she sought him. Busy as he was, he looked up and smiled.

'I have something to say to you,' she burst out. 'Something that will not wait.'

'Say on.' His eyes grew warm at the sight of her.

'Edward, did you know that Richard has been to Southwark in search of Anne Neville?'

The warmth died out of Edward's eyes, and he brought his fist down sharply on the table. 'And brought her back?' he demanded.

'Nay. But he had word that Anne was in Southwark and went there in all haste.'

'Had word? What meddlers there are to disturb our peace! Who brought word to Richard that the girl was in Southwark? That is what I would like to know.'

'Edward, I fear . . .' She moved nearer to him and laid a trembling hand on his shoulder. 'I fear you are going to be angry, for it was I who told Richard that I thought Anne might be there.'

He stood up. He towered over her, scowling. '*You!*'

'I discovered that George and Mary Blague had been meeting, and I connected this fact with the disappearance of Anne Neville. I told Richard of it.'

His eyes narrowed. 'Did I not beg of you to leave this matter alone?'

She nodded. 'You did.' She was sickened now, not by her fear but by the thought of herself currying favours with her charms. She saw herself in her apartment, slipping into her most becoming gown, arranging her hair over her bare shoulders. Her eyes blazed suddenly. 'You did,' she cried, 'and I cared not!'

'You cared not!' His voice was dangerously cold.

'No. Because, no matter what you say, it is wrong to leave that girl alone and friendless. It is wrong–wrong, I tell you. I care not what you do.'

He said: 'You disregard my order. You are a meddlesome woman. Know you not what happens to those who disobey me? You try me too far. You bring your woman's sentiment into those matters which you understand not. You are a fool, Jane; and I suffer not fools about me. It is better for a girl to die a thousand deaths than that civil war should break out in this country. Richard and George will be at each other's throats over this Neville girl. If you were not such a fool you would know how quickly trouble starts. A quarrel is picked, sides are taken and there is the beginning of endless trouble. My brothers have their followers. Know you not . . . But of course you know nothing of these things. My brother George plans for one thing, and that is to throw me from my place and take it himself. And you, because I have shown you favour, will meddle. Go from me now, and if you would please me, listen to what I say. Meddle no more.'

'I will go, Edward. But first I must tell you why I came. Kate, my woman, is in the Tower.'

'Kate in the Tower? By whose orders?'

'George sent her there.'

His anger was more violent; his eyes bulged with fury and the veins were like blue cords upon his temples. He said through half-closed lips: 'So George has sent the woman to the Tower!'

'He threatens her with torture. Edward, oh, please–punish me for what I have done, for it is true I did meddle–but please release Kate.'

Edward was not listening. He was at the door shouting for an attendant. When the man came he roared at him: 'Send the Duke of Clarence here to me instantly.'

Even George dared not disobey such a command. He came in, nodded with some insolence to his brother, and scowled at Jane.

'Carrying tales already, I see,' he muttered.

Jane looked in terror from one angry brother to the other. The resemblance between them was now very marked. Both faces were distorted with rage, both purple with fury.

'Since when has it been your habit to issue orders as to who shall be sent to the Tower?' demanded Edward.

'The Tower is the place for traitors, brother.'

'A traitor to me might well be a friend to you.'

'This wanton wretch has carried tales about me,' screamed George. 'I said, "To the Tower with her," and I meant it.'

'I would have you know that you have no power to issue such commands.' Edward raised his clenched fist as though he would strike his brother. 'Would you take the crown from me and wear it yourself?'

'You surround yourself with these insolent wretches,' said George. 'You surround yourself with those who would spy on my privacy. I will not have it, I say.'

'You will regret this day's work while there is blood in your veins. Brother, learn your lesson. Much have I endured at your hands, but my patience is wellnigh at an end. If you have aught of which to complain, bring your complaints to me. If any has sinned, let him be tried first and then imprisoned.'

'Is it Your Grace's custom then to try all those he sends to prison?' sneered George.

Edward's hand went to the hilt of his sword. He said slowly: 'Have a care, George. I am your King, remember.' His rage suddenly burst out into a string of oaths. 'By God, if you wish to keep your head on your shoulders, have a care!'

Jane cowered against the hangings, subdued and frightened. Never had she seen such hatred in any face as she now saw in that of Clarence. She knew that if Clarence could have safely murdered the King there and then he would have done so.

'Get you gone!' cried Edward. 'Before I do you some injury, get you gone!'

'Right willingly,' said Clarence. 'And though you are my elder brother and the King, and therefore must be obeyed, think not that I will brook such insolence from your whores and their serving wenches.'

'Be silent! You will now give an order for the woman to be released. Do it quickly or, by Christ's blood, I'll have you sent to the Tower in her stead.'

George threw a look of hate at his brother, in which Jane was included; then he bowed sardonically and went out. Edward looked after him for a second or so before turning to Jane. She saw the anger fade from his face, and she knew that he had been badly upset by the scene.

'Jane,' he said quietly, and when she went to him he put an arm about her. There was something protective in the gesture. 'Why,' he went on, 'you love me, Jane, do you not?' She nodded, and he laid his hand on her hair. 'That is well. You have just witnessed an ugly scene. My brother lusts to kill me. Such is the curse of kingship. But when a man has one to love him as you love me, then it seems he should be grateful.'

'Edward, I fear it is my meddling which has caused you this pain.'

'Nay, suppress your sorrow on that count. His hatred was smouldering in him before this happened. This but brought it out. 'Tis better to know what malice one may have to face than to come upon it in an emergency unaware. There are times when I despair of George. He was ever a difficult boy–vain, strutting, bombastic. Sometimes I can say, "Poor George!" For poor he is who grasps at the unattainable. Jane, there are times when you have thought me cruel. Nay, deny it not. Let there be truth between us two. Have I not seen a shuddering discomfort in your eyes at times? Know this, Jane: I live on the edge of a volcano. I am most unsafe. And you, living near me, are in danger also. There is room in my life for little softness. He is my brother, yet I should hate him. But hate him I cannot. Jane, do you know what I should do, were I a wise man?'

She shook her head and he put his mouth to her ear that he might whisper. 'I should hire some men . . . men who are ready to do aught they are bid for a price. Tomorrow my brother should be found dead in the waters of the Thames.'

'Oh no, Edward. No. That cannot be the way.'

'I all but lost my crown for softness once. You would not wish me to do so again? Months of exile! You cannot guess what such a man as I would suffer at such a time. A King . . . and not a King. My Queen in sanctuary. My son, the heir of England, born in that place without the comforts a mere tradesman's son would enjoy. The bitter, bitter experience! He was my enemy then . . . that wicked brother of mine. But because he is my brother I forgive him. I remember him as a bright-eyed boy, a boy without those drink-sodden dreams that make him see himself the King of England.'

'Edward,' said Jane solemnly, 'I trust you will do nothing that will haunt you with remorse.'

He kissed her tenderly. 'Remember, I live in constant danger, and that danger must be shared by those whom I love.' His face hardened. 'Meddle not in matters that concern you not, Jane. Keep from them, that I may come to you for rest and peace. Now I will send a messenger to the Tower to discover whether good Kate has been released. And if she has not . . .'

'Oh, if she has not, Edward . . . ?'

'George shall feel my strength. My brother must tread warily in future.'

Edward had a new mistress with whom he was delighted. All his light loves would be cast off now. Not Jane Shore though; she was as permanent as the Queen herself. It was not surprising. She was the gayest, the wittiest, the most good-natured creature at court. She could, it was true, fly into a temper, but her indignation was more often than not in someone's cause other than her own.

Behind the curtain of her bed Jane wept bitterly. He will come back, she told herself. He had come back before and he would do so again. Now that she was alone at night her dreams were troubled. Hastings figured largely in them. She had Kate make herself a bed on the floor because she was afraid to be alone.

They were sad days, and at night she would lie awake listening to Kate's deep breathing, while she was filled with remorse, remembering old days in Lombard Street; then she would pray for forgiveness, until she laughed at herself. It was only the deserted woman who had time to repent. When Edward returned she would be as lighthearted as ever.

Time hung heavily. Often she and Kate donned the sober garments of some of the serving maids, and with their hoods well over their faces went into the streets. On such expeditions they would laugh and giggle together, and Jane would forget her jealousy of the King's new mistress.

Once they wandered into East Cheap and there came face to face with a woman who recognised Jane in spite of her concealing hood.

'I should know your sweet face anywhere,' said Mistress Banster. 'Dost think I should ever forget what you did for my Charlie? You must come to my back parlour for a cup of wine.'

Jane saw that the woman would have been hurt had she refused, so she allowed Mistress Banster to conduct them into the parlour by means of a side door. 'For, good gracious me,' said the woman, 'if I took you through the shop they'd stare you out of countenance. I swear they've never seen such loveliness.'

It was a fusty little room to which she took them; the smell of greasy cooking hung about it and the flies kept up a continual buzzing. Through the narrow smudgy window it was possible to see a small square of backyard in which the rats foraged over refuse heaps.

Charlie came in; he kept touching his ears in such a way that moved Jane deeply. 'You must always count me your friend,' she told them impulsively.

It was a great day for them, Mistress Banster told her; she and Charlie had never thought to entertain Jane Shore in their back parlour. If ever Jane and Kate were in East Cheap and in need of refreshment, the Bansters would deem it a great honour if they came to this shop parlour to take it.

After that Jane often slipped on the sombre cloak, and she never passed the cook-shop without going in. Sitting in that frowsty parlour she felt she could regain her self-esteem. It was so pleasant to slip a little money into the hands of poor people; and their adoration of her was gratifying, smarting as she was under Edward's neglect. When she passed the house in Lombard Street she would suffer deep depression, and feel heavy with the weight of her sins. She would face the truth then. She had deserted her duty that her wild passion for a man might be gratified. She had grown to love the brilliance and excitement of court life. When Edward's eyes were on her, admiring, desiring, she felt as though she were engaged in some mad dance which she could not stop, though she felt it might be leading her to destruction. Sometimes, wrapped in her concealing cloak, she would stop to listen to a preacher at Paul's Cross. 'The wages of sin is death,' said the preacher, and although he dared not talk openly of the licentious court, she knew he preached against it. And was she not one of the brightest lights of that court–the chief courtesan–passionate, sensuous, as eager for love as Edward himself! Though she was faithful to him and he was unfaithful to her, she believed she sinned as deeply as he did. But when she went to the humble cookshop in East Cheap, her mood was lightened. To these people she had done good service. And not only to them. How many people had been made happier because Jane Shore was the King's mistress! How many had escaped torture and death! Watching the stern-faced preacher, she could reason, 'I may have lost my own soul, but I have saved the bodies of others.'

And these visits to East Cheap had their sequel. Mistress Banster, sipping her wine one day, talked of her neighbour, a certain Mistress Clack, a rival of hers and a woman for whom she had no great liking.

'A hard creature and barely feeds them that work for her. Some of the scum of London she keeps in her kitchens. Poor starving things, they come and look into my rubbish heaps for what they can find. And, my word, I heard a story the other day . . .'

Jane was alert, listening to the story Mistress Banster had to tell. It seemed that a certain Lottie, who had at one time worked at Mistress Clack's, now pursued a different trade in Southwark, and came along now and then to visit Mistress Banster.

'Lottie has changed. A poor shivering thing she used to be. I caught her once picking over my refuse. I brought her in and gave her a crust. We were friends after that. Well, Lottie ran away. I know where she went and I didn't blame her. A girl can't live on Clack's food. She's in a house now . . . over at Southwark. Well, that's another story; and what she told me is past believing. Mind you, I've seen this poor thing in their backyard . . . a little wisp of a thing. 'Tis hard to believe she might be a lady of high rank, and Lottie swears she's mad. But, says Lottie, there was such a to-do when she got away that Lottie can't but think she is this Lady Anne Neville she thinks herself to be.'

'Lady Anne Neville!' cried Jane.

'So Lottie says. She was kept in that house, you see . . . and Lottie talked to her, and she talked to Lottie. Stark, raving mad, Lottie thought she were.

Lottie told her a girl could get her food and a bed at Clack's place, and to Clack's place the poor thing came when she ran away from Southwark. She's begged and prayed of Lottie not to tell a soul who she is. Lottie, you see, was in my back when out comes the poor thing to Clack's back . . . and they just stared at one another, and this poor thing goes white as a ghost. She's not in her right senses, she ain't.'

Jane gripped her stool. Could it be that unwittingly she had found Anne Neville, and that it was within her power to end the poor girl's suffering? She thought of Edward, eyes narrowed, while the purple blood flooded his face. Edward would be terribly angry if she meddled again. She dared not. She had to think continually of pleasing Edward, and now that he desired someone else more than he desired her, her position was precarious. She would go away and forget this story. That was the wise thing to do.

But one thing Jane had never learned was wisdom. How could she ever be happy again if she did not do all she could for Anne and Richard? She could not shut out of her mind the picture of a poor starving girl, escaped from a brothel, picking over refuse in the backyard of an East Cheap cook-shop.

'I must see this girl,' she said. 'Would it be possible for you to bring her to me?'

Mistress Banster said she could but try. But the girl was timid, for she had already been frightened out of her wits. If she knew someone wanted to see her she would probably fly out of Clack's and never be heard of again. It might be possible to lure her in with the promise of a crust or a little soup.

Jane sat in the Banster parlour while Mistress Banster went into her backyard and waited for someone to come out, whom she might ask to bring the girl to her.

It was a wretchedly miserable hour for Jane. She kept reminding herself how easy it would be to call Mistress Banster in; to go from the shop and forget all about Anne Neville. But that was something she could not bring herself to do.

It seemed a long time before Mistress Banster brought the girl in. Anne's eyes were sunken and there was an unhealthy flush on her cheeks; her hair, which should have been lovely, hung lank and greasy round her gaunt face; she was dressed in dirty rags that scarcely covered her thin body; but Jane recognised her as the girl who had ridden captive in the chariot with Margaret of Anjou.

Anne was terrified at the sight of Jane and turned to run, but very gently Jane took her hand, and in Jane's face was all the kindness of her heart, so that it was impossible even for one as fear-haunted as Anne Neville to doubt her good intentions.

'I am your friend,' said Jane. 'I want to help you. Will you sit here beside me?'

Anne looked down at her dirty garments and shuddered; but Jane put an arm about her and drew her down beside her. 'I am Jane Shore,' said Jane.

'I have heard of you,' said Anne. 'You are good, the poor people say.'

'Let us talk of you. There is one who loves you dearly and who has sought you long. He still seeks you.'

Anne's face was illuminated suddenly: 'Richard?' she said.

'He came to search for you in Southwark.'

'Then it was he who came.' She began to cry weakly. 'How can I tell who is my friend when my own sister's husband . . .'

'George is wicked and cruel,' said Jane vehemently. 'But you love Richard and Richard loves you. I will bring him here to you. And then you will know you are safe.'

Anne collapsed into hysterical weeping. She reiterated that she did not know whom she might trust. Her brother-in-law had taken her into his house; and from there he had had her despatched to an evil house in Southwark.

The thin claw-like fingers clutched at Jane's cloak.

'I was a prisoner there. I discovered what sort of house it was. The girls told me. They told me that when I was well enough, what had happened to them . . . would happen to me. It is a terrible house. I heard horrible laughing . . . and sobbing. Babies are born there . . . but those babies never live. They throw their bodies in the river. I thought they were bringing someone to me . . . and I ran away. The woman who looked after me told me I must run away, or what had happened to them would happen to me. And it was Richard who came; Richard . . . who came to find me! I ran away though . . . and so I came to Mistress Clack's. You are good. I know you are good. You would not betray me. I think George meant to kill me. But you would not lie to me, Jane Shore. You have a kind and lovely face and you would not lie to me. . . .'

Jane wept with her. What terrible things can happen to women! thought Jane. And she did not care that she had jeopardised her position with Edward; she did not care that she had placed herself in greater danger than before.

Dazed, Anne went back to the kitchen behind Mistress Clack's cook-shop. Mistress Clack, puffing as she walked about because she was so fat, cursed her as she came in. Mistress Clack was eating . . . she ate all the time . . . and grease ran down her chin. She picked continuously at the food with her dirty, greasy, food-stained fingers as she cooked it.

'And where have you been? Missing nigh on an hour. There'll be no dinner for you. Them that don't work gets no food, I say.'

Food! Who wanted her greasy food? Richard was coming. Jane Shore was bringing him. Richard would protect her from George, and Jane Shore would protect her from Edward.

Now she must wash the floor. Usually the task sickened her, but today it mattered not at all. She must go down on her hands and knees and pick up the greasy bits of chewed gristle spat out by Mistress Clack. Some cleanliness there had to be or the rats would have become unmanageable. This she had endured for weeks–the hot, fetid atmosphere of the kitchen, the cuffs that had come her way; for there was none, declared Mistress Clack, as incompetent to work in her kitchen as Anne, and Anne knew there was justice in the remark. Still, she preferred this to that frightening Southwark house. This was hard labour in exchange for scraps of food which were flung to her as though she were a dog. Indeed, the dogs under her father's tables had fared far better than she did in the Clack kitchen. But this she had to endure if she were to eat and be able to throw herself down on to her straw every night, her limbs aching with the day's fatigue. Nights held their terrors as well as the days; she was worried by lice, and rats that pulled at the coverlet; and those poor miserable half-starved people who worked with her laughed at the way she spoke and her dainty manner of eating; they cursed her and threw things at her when she coughed at night. Then she was glad of the hard work that tired her so completely and gave her some nightly hours of oblivion.

And now . . . it might well be ended. There was about that courtesan, the King's favourite, such an air of kindliness as Anne had never come across in the whole of her life. She had even feared Richard a little, and, although she admired him, was never completely at ease in his company. Yet Jane had been different, gentle and yet hot in her indignation at the suffering of others. She had heard Jane Shore's name mentioned often in the Clack cook-shop, sometimes accompanied by obscenities, but often spoken of with something like reverence. Anne cared not what Jane had done, for Jane was good. Jane had given her new hope and faith. She would trust Jane; and in spite of everything that had happened, she believed only good could come through Jane.

'Mistress Banster's asking for yer,' whispered one of her fellow-workers who was more kindly than the others. 'Run orf now. P'raps it's a plate of soup she's got for you.'

Anne took one last look round the kitchen. She knew she would never see it again; she wanted to remember it in every detail; she would never forget the stale, greasy smell of cheap roasting flesh, the smell of dirt and decay.

She ran out of the room and to the street. Outside the Bansters' was a chariot. Jane was at the side entrance. She had been crying and her smile was very tender; and the way in which she looked at Anne made the girl forget her terrors.

'He is here,' whispered Jane.

And there he was, coming towards her, hardly changed at all. His features twisted oddly when he saw her. 'Anne!' he cried. 'Anne!'

Then he held out his arms and she ran into them. They embraced–the man elegant in his fur-embroidered garments, the girl in her filthy rags.

Jane watched them, silently weeping.

The King stormed up and down the Queen's apartment.

'A pretty kettle of fish, I'll swear. Warwick's girl found in a cook-shop and brought to Sanctuary! Now we shall have trouble. George is swearing she is his ward and none shall marry her without his consent. Richard was the one to find her–and how, I should like to know. Hath my noble brother formed a habit of visiting the cook-shops of East Cheap? Richard swears he will marry her whether I give my consent or not. Would to God the girl had been left to rot in her cook-shop!'

'My lord,' said Elizabeth, 'there is one way out of this. Give her to Richard, and George's anger might lead to–anything. Let her stay in Sanctuary until something can be done.'

The King's anger faded; he went to the Queen and put his hands on her shoulders, laughing down at her. 'Clever Bessy will look after the girl, eh? Bessy will find her a pleasant husband.'

'You mock me. I think it our duty . . .'

'That's the trouble, Bess. Your sense of duty towards your family is a little too strong at times.'

'I want Anne's happiness and security.'

'Together with half the Warwick fortune for the Woodvilles. I am weary of the girl. How *did* Richard find her? He must have had help in this matter. I wish I could find his helpers. They should repent through every vein in their hearts.'

The King's anger frightened Jane. She knew he was most disturbed by the importunings of his brothers. The court kept out of the way of all three as much as possible. An ominous quiet hung over the court. This affair, it was whispered, might well lead to more serious trouble. Grave events had started from less inflammable matter. Next to the King these two men were the most powerful in the country, and here they were, ready to fly at each other's throats.

Edward must give a bold and prompt decision without delay, but Edward was undecided. Clarence was on one side of him, Gloucester on the other, pulling him this way and that; and in the background was the Queen, who said, 'Give the girl to neither; give her to the Woodvilles.'

Edward did what he always did in times of stress: he went to Jane. There was none, he knew, who loved him as disinterestedly as she did.

'My head feels fit to burst,' he told her. 'By the Virgin, Jane, there's trouble brewing.'

She would have him lie back on her couch while she applied sweet-scented unguents to his temples. Her fingers were cool and soothing.

'There are times,' he said, 'when I think there is none in this kingdom I can trust save you.' He put an arm about her and drew her down beside him. 'There is no peace for me. Richard wants the girl; George wants her. What can I do?'

'Give your consent to her marriage with Richard. Let her be brought from Sanctuary, let the wedding be celebrated–and there is an end to the matter.'

'An end, Jane? That would be but a beginning. Then would start the real fight between my brothers.'

'How so, if she be Richard's wife?'

'It is not the girl they fight for; it is her fortune.'

'That may be so with George, but not with Richard.'

'Still, Richard was ever one to demand his rights.'

'Edward, think not of Anne's fortune, but of herself. She loves Richard and Richard loves her. Let them marry. Do not we ourselves know what it is to love?'

He laughed. 'Assuredly we do. And so well that methinks we but waste time in discussing the affairs of others.'

'Give your consent to her marriage with Richard.'

'You are a fervent advocate.'

'Is it such a big thing to ask?'

'It is indeed. Why do you not ask for the things it is easy to give–as do some? Your pleas are all for others. Do this for them, you say, when what I wish is to do some good to you.'

'Richard has been true to you always and George has been your enemy. Why should you now seek to please George at Richard's expense?'

'There is no need to placate one's friends, only one's enemies.'

'That is cowardly, surely.'

'When there is trouble for this land in sight, verily I am a coward. I would to God the girl had never been found!'

'You cannot say that,' she cried passionately. 'A cook-shop! A foul, stinking place–and she Warwick's daughter! What she must have suffered we cannot know Edward, you must let her be happy now.'

There were tears in her eyes, not only for Anne, but for herself and perhaps for him. She sensed that there was no pity in him. Anne was nothing to him but a nuisance; and Jane trembled to contemplate the blindness of that love she had given to such a man. She had been bewitched by too much beauty, too much charm of manner. She had seen the brilliant shell, not the man he was, until too late. She was frightened, too, because it was not the real Jane whom he loved; it was *her* brilliant shell–the lovely oval face, the soft white skin, the merry laughter.

'By the Virgin,' he was saying. 'I would I knew how Richard discovered her. *That* he refuses to tell. But this I know–someone found her and carried the tale to him. If I could lay hands on that man I would make him repent it.'

She buried her face against the jewelled surface of his coat.

'What would you do to him, Edward?'

'He should die a traitor's death.'

Jane closed her eyes, saw the yelling mob, herself dragged to Tyburn all through the streets of London. She imagined rough hands laid upon her, the coarse shouts of the crowd–and the horrible death.

''Twould not be just,' she said, 'for such a little thing.'

'A little thing!' How quickly his anger came. She did not look into his face, but she knew the colour would have flamed up under his skin and behind his eyes, and that his mouth would be ugly. There would be little left of that gay and charming merchant who had captured her heart and even now refused to let it go. 'A little thing to cause me such uneasiness? You understand not such matters. I have enough of trouble. Is not George waiting–seeking an opportunity to rise against me? In such breeding ground are wars spawned.'

When he was calmer she said: 'Yet, 'twas wrong that that gentle girl should suffer so. And Richard, who has ever served you well, should be well served by you.'

'You are over-soft to lovers, Jane.'

'Might that not be because I am one myself?'

'Ah,' he said. 'I also. And you are the one I love, Jane.'

Her heart was beating fast with fear. How much did he love her? How deep did his love go below the senses? That recklessness of hers, which she had never been able to curb, swept over her. She was in a mood now to throw away everything in order to learn the truth.

She knelt up on the couch. Her eyes looking dark and big.

'What ails thee, Jane?'

'I have something to say to you, Edward.'

'Say it quickly and come down to me again.'

'It was I who found Anne Neville–I who found her for Richard.'

'*You* found Anne Neville! *You*–again?'

She bowed her head and closed her eyes, an awful numbing fear taking hold of her. He struggled up; he had her by the shoulders and his grip was fierce. What a fool I was! she thought. Why did I do it? Why did I give Anne to Richard and lose Edward for myself? Or, having done it, why did I tell?

'I would know more of this,' said Edward.

She flung up her head, her cheeks flaming and her eyes flashing. 'I care not what you say!' she cried. 'He loved her. He was unhappy. She was unhappy too. I found her–and I sent him to her. What is it to be–the traitor's death?'

He looked at her flushed and lovely face. 'Holy Mother of God!' he exclaimed, and, bursting into sudden laughter, he pulled her down to him and kissed her fiercely. His loud booming laughter shook them both. She laughed with him.

'What is this?' she said at length. 'Is it the last rites before the traitor's death?'

'So–it was you, Jane. My sweet and lovely meddling Jane. You shall tell me all about it. But not now.'

There was relief in her laughter now. While she had beauty, while she could arouse his desires she had nothing to fear, for his amours were more important to Edward than anything else.

'My loving Jane,' he said, 'who was so kind to those who loved!'

'Edward!' She caught his face and held him from her for a breathless second. 'Edward, promise me–your consent to their marriage.'

'What?' he cried. 'You would bargain?'

'Yes, I will bargain.'

'And you so kind to those who love?'

'I could never resist you, as you well know. Thus it was in the beginning; thus will it always be. Whatever you refuse me, whatever you give me, I can but love you.'

'My dearest Jane,' he said, 'there is nothing I could deny you.' His face was close to hers; his voice grew faint and blurred. 'Richard shall have his Anne. Let them enjoy each other–as we do. As we shall . . .'

The Tower of London

Part One

From Fickets Fields to London Bridge the people were assembling. From the Abbey at Westminster to St Giles's in the midst of green fields, from St Clement Danes without Temple Bar to St Peter ad Vincula within the precincts of the Tower of London, the bells rang out.

In the gardens of the Palace of the Tower Jane sat with Anne, Duchess of Gloucester; and with them were the two little Princes, the King's sons, young Edward who was now five years old and his brother Richard who was two years younger. Jane had been reading aloud to the children from Malory's *Morte D'Arthur*, which William Caxton had recently printed and presented to the royal household; but now the book had been laid aside and the children played on the grass while the two women talked desultorily; and there was about women and children an air of expectancy.

It was three years since Anne Neville had married Richard, and she had now a son–another Edward–who was just two years old. She was, Jane knew, calmly happy, but her terrible experiences had left their mark upon her. She was nervous and timid; and she did not like staying in this palace; but that was an aversion she shared with Jane, who could not forget, as she walked in the shelter of the ballium wall or rested in the gardens and saw the weather-washed walls of the White Tower and the solid strength of the Beauchamp, that this was a prison, and behind those great white walls men suffered torment too terrible to be thought of.

Young Edward looked up from his play. 'I wonder what time my father will come.'

'We cannot be sure,' answered Jane, 'but we shall hear the shouting and the trumpets long before they reach the Tower.'

'One day,' said Edward, 'I shall ride at the head of the cavalcade as does my father. One day the people will shout for me.'

'One day!' echoed Richard, who adored his brother and repeated everything he said, for he had been taught that young Edward was to be King of England.

'Do you think my father has conquered all France?' asked Edward.

'I doubt whether the conquest was as complete as that,' Jane told him. 'We must wait to hear what he has to tell.'

'Four months since they went away,' said Anne. 'It might have been years.'

'Jane,' said young Edward, 'when the feasting is ended, how long before we return to Westminster or Windsor?'

'You do not like this old palace?' said Jane.

'I like Windsor,' said Edward.

'I like Windsor,' echoed Richard. 'And I like Baynard's Castle with grandmamma.'

'This is beautiful,' said Jane quickly. 'Why, the gardens are lovely. I thought you loved the paintings in the great hall. Did you not tell me the story of Antiochus pictured on the walls there?'

'I like the paintings,' said Edward. 'But this is a prison–more than a palace. If you walk along by the Beauchamp you see faces at the windows.'

'You should not wander about alone.'

'I am not afraid to wander alone,' said Edward with dignity. 'But I like not prisons. I have heard people say that when this place was built years and years ago they buried people alive in these walls–built them in–to bring good fortune to the place. Oh, Jane–Aunt Anne–it was children they built in–like myself and Richard and Elizabeth and Cecily . . .'

'You must not listen to such tales,' said Jane quickly. 'Shall I read to you?'

Jane read, but the boys were too excited to listen; they wandered off.

'I thank the Virgin,' said Anne, 'that my little Edward will never wear the crown.'

'There are some,' said Jane, 'who reach up greedily for it, and others who turn away from it.'

'King Henry was one to turn away.'

Jane found she was shivering. Just beyond this garden in which they sat was that very Wakefield Tower in which, long ago, King Henry the Sixth had been stabbed to death.

Jane hastily changed the subject, and after a while she stood up, declaring it was time they prepared themselves to receive the men.

'Where are the boys?' asked Anne.

'They should not wander off alone. They see sights not meant for their young eyes. Their nurses will be looking for them.'

But Jane was not thinking much of the children; she was contemplating the return of Edward with apprehension as well as excitement. It was four months since he had left England to wage war on France; she wondered what those four months had done to change him, for even before he left Edward was rapidly changing from a young and handsome man into a corpulent old one. But his charm had not abated. She remembered how, to raise money to take the war into France, he had gone about the country demanding what he called Benevolences. He had visited even the outlying villages, wheedling money from the pockets of the people, and it was astonishing to see them come to him, reluctant, even sullen, and go away smiling. The sight of him and the words he had spoken were worth every coin the people had pledged themselves to pay him. The women longed to be called before him, to be kissed and complimented and smiled upon; the men talked in the inns, for long after, of what the King had said and how he had shaken them by the hand. The country adored him; he could carry it into war and his people might grumble, but when he appeared with a smile or a kiss they were ready to worship him.

He had sailed with his brothers George and Richard; Hastings was with them too. Jane had wondered if she would ever see any of them again.

And as she was about to make her way to her apartments, Kate came running out of the palace and with her was one of the nurses of the young Princes. Both women looked distraught.

'Mistress,' said the nurse, 'I cannot find the young Princes anywhere. They will not be ready to greet their father.'

'I have searched the palace,' cried Kate. 'They are nowhere to be found.'

'But they were here a short time ago,' said Anne.

'Let us all go and look for them,' said Jane. 'It will not be long then, I swear, before we find them.'

They left the palace gardens and wandered off in different directions–Kate went one way, Jane and Anne another; and the nurse in yet another.

Kate, rather more plump than she had been a few years ago, as gay as ever, called to a warden whom she saw making his way towards one of the towers. He had seen the little boys, he said; they had wandered towards the cook's place. If Kate went through the postern gate, she would see a flight of stairs. That was where the warden had last seen the little boys.

Kate lost no time in hurrying through the postern and down the flight of stairs. She came to a heavy door which was ajar, and, pushing it open, heard someone singing a jolly roystering song. She paused to listen to it, and smelt the appetising smell of roasting flesh.

She was standing on the threshold of a big kitchen with a low ceiling and a floor of stone. In one of the biggest fireplaces she had ever seen a great log fire was burning, sending up cloud after cloud of smoke through the great chimney. Before the fire a huge carcase was roasting, and a poor little scullion, who looked as though he had been scorched and shrivelled by the intense heat, was seated on a stool watching it. At the end of the room was a huge table laden with great pies, cold meat, and fish as yet uncooked. There were several people in the kitchen–warders, jailors, scullions and lower servants of the royal household; but Kate scarcely paused to look at them, for sitting on the table, where the food had been pushed aside to make room for them, their faces flushed with excitement, their legs dangling, sat the two little Princes. Kate dashed at them.

'My lords! My lords!' she cried. 'What do you here? Your nurse is looking for you. Your noble father will be waiting.'

'Look about you,' said Edward. 'Is this not a wonderful place?'

Now Kate was aware of a man who was standing beside her, a mighty man who towered above her so that she had to lift her head high to see his jolly face that was topped by his white cook's cap, and as she looked Kate's astonishment was replaced by a great bounding joy. 'Belper!' she cried shrilly.

Belper dropped the ladle he was holding on to a pie of savoury meats with such force that it broke the top crust of pastry. He took a pace towards her and let out a mighty roar of recognition. 'Kate! Merry hell! And looking as bonny as a fresh roast peacock.'

Then was Kate held fast against the great white-clad body that smelt of good wine and delicious food, while she received a great smacking kiss on the mouth. 'Now, Kate, what do you here?' he demanded when he released her. And what joy it was for Kate to see his face, fat, red and shining, and his eyes creased up with delight!

'My fortune changed,' she told him. 'I followed Mistress Shore to court.'

'Fortune changed for me also,' he told her. 'I have been here ever since I left Goldsmith Shore. It suits me. Every soul in this place depends on me for what he eats. What a life it is! I eat till I can eat no more. Most work to fill their own bellies, but I work to fill those of others as well as mine own.' Belper had always roared with laughter at the lightest joke, but when the joke was his own he was particularly pleased with it. He nudged Kate in case she had missed the point; but Kate was in no need of nudges. Now everyone in the kitchen was laughing, and Kate was remembering Belper's infectious enjoyment.

'Sit down, Kate!' roared Belper. 'What'll you have? A slice of peacock or a wedge of wild boar? I have a fine roasted ox.. . .'

Weak from so much laughter, Kate shook her head. She had been sent in search of the Princes that they might be ready in time to greet their father. 'I dare not stay . . . much as you tempt. Another time . . . mayhap.'

'Another time it shall be, good Kate. Another time! *Any* time. Ask for me. Belper. Here you shall feast, sweetheart, and if you should at any time of the day feel the need of a mouthful and a tankard to wash it down . . . then come to Belper. Belper has just what you need.' He nudged her, his twinkling eyes showing that he was about to go off into anouther bout of choking laughter. Kate would have been glad to have stayed, but she turned away from the fascinating cook to the two little boys.

Belper paused in his laughter. 'Now after the banquet tonight there'll be a feast in these kitchens. . . .'

'After the banquet,' said Kate, her eyes glistening.

'Tonight,' said Belper in a whisper which could be heard throughout the kitchen.

'Tonight,' whispered Kate, and hurried the Princes out of the kitchen, feeling that if she did not go quickly she would never be able to tear herself away.

'I like Cook Belper,' said Edward.

'I like Cook Belper,' said Richard.

'Ah,' put in Kate fervently, 'and well I like him also, my little lordships.'

At the head of the table in the great hall sat Edward the King. He was in a deeply contented mood as he looked along the laden table at the brilliantly-clad people assembled there. The stained glass windows threw a warm and cheerful glow on the table and the velvet hangings and those wonderful pictures which had been painted on the walls added comfort and bright beauty to the ancient and noble room.

Many oxen, sheep and pigs had been roasted to provide this banquet, together with swans, pike, porpoises, pheasants, peacocks, calves and boars. Edward had given orders that this banquet was to be more lavish than any other, for he was anxious that his people might know that it was given to celebrate a most successful campaign. He would have them know that the French business had been satisfactorily concluded.

Edward frowned as his gaze fell on Richard. Richard looked grim, for he was not pleased with the way things had gone in France; he had gone so far as to dissociate himself from those dealings between Edward and the crafty old French King. Richard, thought Edward impatiently, had too many scruples. Why be ashamed that there had been no real war? Why be ashamed to take French bribes? Better to spend wealth in good living than to squander it on fruitless wars. Naturally Louis was ready to pay so that English soldiers might be removed from French soil. Richard had painstakingly pointed out that the people of England had paid the King their 'benevolences' that lost territory in France might be regained. Richard could be a young fool at times with his talk of honour. The King and his nobles were richer by many thousands of French crowns, and Edward's eldest daughter Elizabeth was betrothed to the Dauphin. If Richard refused his share of the French bribe, that was his folly.

The minstrels were coming into the gallery. A year ago Edward would have been the first to dance, either with the Queen or with Jane. He smiled affectionately from one to the other. They had scarcely changed at all, and one of his greatest pleasures in coming home had been to see them again. How lovely Jane was! Louis had insisted that he should make the acquaintance of the most attractive women in France, and this he had quickly set about doing with his habitual skill and conquering charm; yet he had not found one to equal Jane. She had grown plumper, but he liked plump women.

Jane returned his smile. She was fighting hard not to show that the King's appearance shocked her. The purple in his face had deepened, and there were heavy bags under his eyes. He had left his radiant youth behind him in France. He had caught a fever there, an unpleasant ailment that shook him every now and then with returning fits of ague. He was no longer the beautiful Edward.

'Dance!' he cried and sat back watching. Elizabeth the Queen sat with him, for she did not care to dance, fearing it impaired her dignity. But Jane danced. How Jane danced! Jane looked but a girl still; the years had done little to change her. She was now dancing with the elder of his two stepsons, Thomas, Marquis of Dorset. A handsome man, young Thomas, and even the most casual observer could see that Thomas was Elizabeth's boy. Edward wondered idly about Elizabeth's first husband and the marriage which had produced Thomas and his younger brother. Had Elizabeth been warmer to her first husband than she was to her second?

But his attention was back with the dancers. He was not sure that he liked to see Jane and Dorset together. They were much of an age, and the young man had already the reputation of being one of the most profligate at court. He was as haughty as his mother, and doubtless as ambitious, but he certainly had not inherited Elizabeth's cold blood.

Dorset was saying to Jane: 'It is a great pleasure to be home again. Give me good English fare and English women. The French! Bah! Their cooking is over-greasy, and their women over-warm.'

'It surprises me,' said Jane, 'not that you find cause for complaint in the former, but that you do also in the latter.'

'There you are mistaken, Madam. Warmth should be kindled by the one who desires it.'

'You mean it is more pleasant to hunt the wild boar than the tame peacock?'

His beautiful eyes lingered on her. 'Indeed, yes. And how exciting it can be to hunt in forbidden woods!'

'But surely none is forbidden the King's stepson?'

'The King's stepson is not the King, alas!'

'Indeed no. And methinks that the King remembers that, though his stepson may appear to have forgotten it.'

It was reproof, for he was too bold, and she would have him know that it was unwise to be so. But she was excited and exhilarated; she was susceptible to his handsome charm. Life had been dull these last four months and there was nothing Jane loved so much as gaiety. And now the King was home, but he was a different man from that Edward who had left England four months ago. She had looked forward to a passionate reunion; she was deeply shocked to realise that she could no longer feel passion for the King. That was why she was faintly alarmed by the bold glances of this attractive young man.

She sought now to change the subject. 'What think you, my lord Marquis, of this French affair?'

Dorset smiled. He thought very well of it indeed. He was one of those who were richer for the venture. 'The people want glory,' he said. 'They want to hear names like Crécy and Agincourt again. They are bewildered now, but, never fear, Edward will subdue them. What a King! He has but to smile, to lure money from their pockets.'

'The people will surely be glad to see their men safe home.'

'Rest assured they will, and give not a thought to the money they paid to the King. Edward can melt the heart of a nation as easily as he melts the reluctance of his women.'

'The war in France has changed him. He looks ten years older than he did.'

'Too much good living in Paris. And then . . . his fever. It pulls a man down when he begins to climb up his thirties, and Edward has always partaken too freely of the good things of life.'

The dance was over, another had begun. To her dismay Jane found herself unable to refuse the partnership of Hastings.

The face of Hastings was haggard, his eyes in their deep sockets were mournful. He still watched Jane with brooding desire; she wondered now why she had ever been afraid of him. She told herself she hated him still, but she found that even her dismay was partly feigned, for the man's devotion was truly flattering, and it was stimulating to have the men home again. She needed gaiety; she needed to exchange bright words with Dorset, cruel ones with Hastings . . . for the King had come home a different man from the lover who had gone away.

She saw that Hastings was angry now, and that was because he had been watching her with Dorset.

'Well, Jane,' he said, 'this is the happiest moment of four long months.'

'You did not enjoy your stay in France?'

'You know I could not when a stretch of water separated us two.'

'I'll warrant you found much to amuse you.'

'I thought of you continually.'

'Enough of such talk, for I like it not.'

'Mayhap you like it better from Dorset?'

She flushed. 'You are insolent, my lord.'

'I would warn you that Dorset is the biggest rake at court.'

She was angry now. She had been foolish. She had let him see that she was attracted by Dorset. 'Since when, sir,' she said, 'did you resign the title to him?'

'Since I became so enamoured of you that none other could please me.'

Jane laughed. 'Deceive yourself not. 'Twas cruel age not faithfulness that forced you to give way to Dorset.'

Hastings was angry as only she could make him angry. 'One day you will be sorry for this.'

'So you still continue to plot against me?'

'I plot only for your happiness.'

'That has been very clear to see, right from the moment you planned my abduction.'

'Will you never forget a youthful folly?'

'Never! If I ever have a chance to repay you, rest assured I will.'

'You are so kind to others, so cruel to me. Why?'

'Because I hate you. Because I have always hated you.'

'It is a relief to know you are not indifferent. One day you will come to me, and on that day you will have become a wise woman.'

'You may not be the biggest rake at court, but you certainly are the biggest coxcomb.'

'I must be proud, Jane, because I am the man you will one day love. The King grows old, and you grow out of love with him.'

'How day you!'

'You give yourself away, Jane. Will you never learn to be wise? Dorset has nothing but a beautiful body . . . and misery to offer you. I grow old, but I can love you deeply and tenderly. Jane, forget me not.'

'I shall never forget you . . . never forget my hatred of you.'

'You should not have danced with Dorset for so long. The King's eyes were on you.'

'I see they are on me and Hastings,' she retorted. 'I will take your hint and see that I do not dance over long with you.'

She sat long beside Edward and together they watched the dancers.

'I saw you dance with Dorset. Have a care, Jane.' His fat hand, with the rings embedded in it, patted hers. 'That young stripling hath a reputation as evil as . . .'

'As evil as your own,' laughed Jane. 'Nay, my lord, there is none at this court to be compared with that of its King.'

He laughed, but he was quickly sobered. 'But, Jane, 'tis a handsome fellow, that young stepson of mine.'

'You have brought jealousy back from France as well as a fever. There is none in this court to compare with yourself. Ask any, and you will be told that is so.'

'There will always be those to tell a King what he wishes to hear.'

'When I pass the lad I will avert my eyes, if that is Your Grace's pleasure.'

'It is our pleasure,' he said seriously. 'Nay, our command.'

The two little Princes were playing together in Jane's apartment. They often came, for Jane encouraged them; she had longed for children of her own, and since none had come to her it seemed natural that she should give her attention to Edward's sons. The Princes were lonely children. The Queen was fond of them, but she had little time to spare for them. Elizabeth Woodville would always be Queen first, mother second. So to Jane they came.

They were shouting at her now. 'Come on, Jane. You're not the warder now, you know. You are the King of France. All you have to do is to sit on your throne and look wicked. Oh, Richard, look at Jane looking wicked!'

Richard rolled on the floor in his amusement at Jane's impersonation of the French King.

Sitting on her stool, looking sly and crafty as the French King, Jane's thoughts ran on uneasily. She was out of love with the father of these children. Strange that she should be the one to be tired first. He must never know it, of course. He seemed so old nowadays. At this moment he was in his room in the castle–for they were at Windsor–poring over his charts and crucible, for now he was obsessed by the thought of changing base metal into gold. And Jane, although she was twenty-six, was young still.

She must not complain, for life had been good to her. She was rich now in her own right. Edward had given her a small but delightful house with beautiful gardens which ran down to the river; it was a charming place, luxurious enough for the entertaining of a King. But her friends told her she was a fool. She could have been the richest woman in the country, for Edward would give her all she asked. Ironical it was that now she had ceased to love him he seemed to love her more.

'The treaty is signed,' said Edward shrilly. 'We're back in England now.'

'Let's play prisoners,' said Richard. 'I like that better than French treaties. That happened long ago.'

'Not so long,' said Edward. 'Two years.'

'But that *is* a long time ago, and there are always prisoners.'

'Richard, you shall be prisoner,' said Edward; 'and Jane, you will have to challenge us as we come through the Traitor's Gate.'

'Holy Mother,' cried Jane, 'can you not play a more cheerful game?'

'Be ready,' insisted Richard.

'I will. Now. In the King's name!'

Her thoughts had gone back to the King. It was two years since he had returned from France, and as each week passed he grew less like the man she had loved. He was very fat, diseased and often violent; it was true that that inimitable charm was still with him, but the change was tragic. She had lost Edward, not to another woman as she had always feared she would, but to age and disease. Edward had grown old, and Jane had stayed young. She tried not to see too much of Dorset.

Everything was changing about her. Kate had left her; she had married Cook Belper and lived with him in his quarters at the Tower of London. Anne of Gloucester had left the South and was living with Richard in her old home at Middleham Castle.

The boys were looking at her expectantly.

'In the King's name I challenge you!'

'A dangerous rascal,' said Edward. 'It will be the torture chambers for him.'

They were both pleased with Jane's shudder; it was so realistic.

'Let me see the warrant,' said Jane severely.

'Here it is; and I would have your acknowledgment of the prisoner.'

'Take care how you ascend the steps,' said Jane. 'They are very slippery, and many a prisoner has fallen and broken his bones.'

'Ha,' said Edward, 'they'll be broken fast enough on the rack, never fear.'

'Speak not of such matters,' said Jane in earnest.

'Bah!' said Edward, while Richard squealed with delight. 'Thou art over-squeamish, man.'

'You may rack me to death and you'll not draw my secrets from me,' cried Richard proudly; and at that moment there was a tap on the door, and, being bidden to enter, Thomas Grey, Marquis of Dorset came in.

'Thomas!' shrieked Edward in delight, while Richard ran to his half-brother and began climbing up his legs.

Dorset smiled at Jane over the children's heads. 'What ruffians are these?' he cried. 'I declare these crude manners cannot belong to the future King of England and His Grace the Duke of York.'

'You must forgive them, my lord,' said Jane. 'They have so recently played a pair of blackguards that they need a little pause before they remember their rank.'

Jane saw the adoration in the boys' eyes as they gazed up into the handsome face of their half-brother; she herself was uneasy as she always was in this man's presence. He reminded her so vividly of long ago days; he made her feel as she had felt in the shop in Lombard Street when her lover had come courting her. But the courtship of Dorset was a secret thing. She knew he was an ambitious man and could not forget that she was the King's mistress; he would remember too the sudden violent rages of the King; he had no wish to cause them. Always, it seemed, he waited for a sign from Jane. She gave none. At least, she had given none so far. He had now come to this apartment not to see the Princes but to see her. Standing there, he regarded her with his slow smile, whose meaning, except that there was a good mixing of desire in it, she did not completely understand. She guessed his intentions; his reputation was known to all, so how could she be ignorant of it? He was not the type of man any wise woman would have chosen for a lover; but when was Jane ever wise? His attraction was of a peculiar nature, for while he fascinated he repelled; but he excited madly; and Jane longed for excitement.

She said now: 'I had not noticed the lateness of the hour. I must retire.'

His smile was almost sardonic. 'Is it not a strange thing,' he said in mock sadness, 'that when Dorset comes in Jane Shore must go out? Why must it be, I wonder?'

'The King will be expecting me.'

'The King is closeted with my grandmother,' said Dorset. 'They consult the stars. The King does not miss you. But the King's sons and the King's stepson would miss you sorely if you went away.'

'You shall stay, Jane,' said Edward imperiously, for Edward, in his preparation for kingship, was often imperious.

Richard supported his brother. 'You must stay for my execution, Jane. You have to be my mother watching with the crowd. Jane cries beautifully, Thomas.'

'Cry or laugh, I'll warrant she does either . . . beautifully.' Dorset took Jane's hand and as she would have withdrawn it he seized that of young Richard. 'I like not this game of execution!' he said. 'I know a better. It is a court banquet, and at the table all the old and sick are nodding, for they have eaten too much and drunk too freely. The minstrels have come into the gallery and all the young and beautiful have risen to dance. You are the young, brothers, and Jane is the beautiful. Come.' He began to sing as he seized Jane. The children stood by watching breathlessly for a moment or two, then they joined the dance.

'Be not afraid,' said Dorset.

'Afraid? Why should I be?'

'Methought you feared the wicked Marquis.'

'Are you wicked then?'

'As wicked as you are beautiful. I ought to warn you, Jane, that when I set my heart on something I usually get it.'

'What does Thomas say?' called Edward.

'Nothing of importance,' retorted Jane. 'He but repeats the idle chatter of the court.'

The King had half an hour to spare before he went into conference with his French ambassador, so he went to Jane's apartment. He was very worried, and as usual the cause of his worry was his brother George. He had just left the Queen, and there was no tongue that clacked quite so fast as the Queen's when there was something she wanted. She never upbraided him; but she went on and on until she got what she wanted. And now what she asked was the imprisonment of George. She was right doubtless, but Edward was a family man, and he shrank from the task. From imprisonment to death could be a very short step. Edward had no wish to fall into that temptation.

He stretched himself out wearily and looked at Jane; he smiled because she never failed to delight his eyes nor his ears. It was a good day when he had gone to the goldsmith's place. He never regretted it.

Jane came to the couch and stretched herself out beside him. 'It is George again, is it not?'

'It is always George.'

Jane nodded. She knew that since his wife's death George had been trying to bring about an advantageous marriage for himself, and that his choice had fallen on Mary of Burgundy. George could never be allowed to have Burgundy, for his first plan would be to lead an army against England and try to win the throne for himself. Edward had refused to allow the match, and foolishly, at the Queen's request, had tried to persuade Mary to marry Lord Rivers, the Queen's brother. This was absurd, of course, for Rivers would never be considered as a suitable parti; but Edward, under the Queen's influence, had given way. George was furious that he should be slighted while the low-born brother of the Queen was promised what he himself desired. George was out to make fresh trouble.

'There will be no peace for me while he lives,' said Edward slowly.

Jane looked at him in alarm. 'You do not plan . . .'

'Does he not deserve anything that I might plan for him? Do you not know that had he been able he would have despatched *me* long ere this?'

'Yes . . . I believe he would.' Jane laid a hand on his arm. 'But, Edward, I beg of you, do nothing which you would regret all your life.'

'Regret!' Edward made an impatient movement. 'Why should I regret . . . whatever I might do?'

Jane watched him uneasily. Anger made of him an old man; the veins at his temples stood out like knotted string. She felt a great tenderness towards him.

'You promised your father to look after him, and it was a sacred promise which you will never forget. Whatever he does to you–and I do not deny that he has deserved the worst you could do to him–you must forgive him, because he is your brother, and your father made you promise to look after him.'

'Yes,' he said slowly, 'I promised. But how weary I am of the miserable affair! I would to God that brother of mine would catch a pox and die. Sit at my feet. I like to touch your hair. It looks as it ever did, as if it were sprinkled with powdered gold.' She sat at his feet and his fat sparkling fingers fondled her hair. 'You heard doubtless,' he went on, 'that George caused two of his servants to be hanged at Warwick. He trumped up a charge against them of poisoning his wife and child. I cannot allow him to usurp my power thus. He presumes too much.'

'I fear the drink destroys his mind.'

'Drink and his ridiculous opinion of himself will destroy his body, should he go on in this way. Were he any other he would have gone to the block long ere this. He turns his drunken bloodshot eyes towards the throne, Jane. I must act soon against him. The Queen . . .' He stopped and smiled wearily. 'There is nothing that will please her but to see his head on London Bridge.'

Now Jane understood. The Queen was urging him to get rid of Clarence. Elizabeth would not care how, as long as it was done. Edward was plagued by the Queen. He wished to remove his brother, but he was superstitious, and he could not forget a promise he had made to a dying father. So he came to Jane–tender-hearted, sentimental, unambitious Jane. She would plead for her worst enemy, because she was a soft-hearted little fool. Jane could be relied upon to beg Edward to have no hand in murder.

And that was what Edward wanted. Pleasing his women had become a habit.

Now she said: 'Try reasoning with him, Edward. Try to make him understand you wish him no ill.'

'You talk like a fool, Jane. While I would reason with him he would set a dagger at my throat.'

'Yet would you be haunted all your life if aught happened to him through your orders.'

He sighed. 'Well you know me, Jane. But there is a new turn to this affair of my brother Clarence. A servant of his, a certain Thomas Burdett, has become involved in a charge which has been brought against him and two others.'

'What charge?'

'They have worked for my death and that of my sons by magic and necromancy.'

'And this man . . . is a servant of George's?'

'Who,' said Edward flushing purple, 'doubtless arranged this matter. This man has talked of my early death and that of my sons. Of a certainty this is George's doing. And you ask me to forgive him! I tell you, you are a fool, Jane.'

'And what will happen to this servant of his?'

'He has already been found guilty and hanged. And even then George would not let well alone. After I had left for Windsor he rode hot-foot to Westminster, and there in the council chamber, before the councillors, had a declaration of the innocence of this man read aloud . . . a man, mark you, who had perished at my command. The Queen is right. There'll be no peace until George's head rolls on the straw at Tower Green. And Jane, you would have me lenient! Always it has been your habit to come to me and beg forgiveness for this man, mercy for that.'

Jane rose and, going to him, put an arm about him. He feigned to ignore the caress but he liked it.

'Mercy brings friends, not enemies,' she said.

'And softness leads to disaster.' He turned her face up to his. 'You are very lovely, Jane, and I fear I give way to you overmuch.'

She hid her face in his jewel-encrusted jacket. She did not want him to see the pity in her eyes. She understood him too well. He did not want trouble; he wanted only to indulge his love of luxury; he wanted to see his coffers filling up; he wanted to enjoy his mistresses; he wanted wealth, and peace that he might enjoy it. He had had strife enough in his youth. She longed now more than ever to recapture the passionate love she had once had for him.

He kissed her and remembered it was time he went to the audience chamber. Relations with France were friendly; Louis was paying regularly to keep the peace, but today the French ambassador had evil tidings. He had heard that the Duke of Clarence was involved in a plot to raise an army on the Continent that he might march against his brother.

Edward did not trust the French, and the motives of wily Louis were so twisted that it was not easy to unravel them. He thanked the ambassador and decided to set fresh spies in his brother's home at Warwick Castle. These spies soon had news for him. They brought an incredible story, but then everything that George did was incredible. In the dungeons, below Warwick Castle, George kept a boy–probably a bastard of his or even Edward's–who was remarkably like George's own son. This boy was being trained to act and speak exactly in the same manner as George's son, so that George might send his own boy to the Continent to lead the army to England, while none would be aware that he had gone. It was a crazy plan conceived doubtless in a drunken dream. It was preposterous, but typical of George. And there was danger in it.

Edward commanded George to come immediately to Westminster, and when the two brothers stood face to face, Edward accused George of treason.

The result of that interview was that George found himself committed to the Tower of London.

Richard, the little Duke of York, was feeling bewildered, for though he was but five years old it was his wedding day.

There was a great fuss about this matter. He had been told what he must do, and his mother had talked to him for a very long time yesterday. He was a little afraid of his mother.

'You must remember that you are the son of the King,' she had said. 'You must remember that, when you are married to Anne tomorrow.'

'Yes, gracious mother,' he had said; and he had knelt when she talked to him, for although she was his mother he must never forget that she was also the Queen.

'Every eye will be upon you tomorrow, Richard. You must rememer that, when you walk into St Stephen's Chapel. You must remember that Anne is your bride.'

He was a little afraid of Anne. She was two years older than he was and seemed very grown up. He felt that it was all very well to be married when you were seven, but when you were five it was a very different matter.

His brother Edward had been nonchalant enough.

'Why must I marry before you?' Richard had asked.

'I shall marry a princess, naturally, for I am to be the King. *You* are just my brother. *My* marriage will be a very grand affair.'

'I wish I were seven,' sighed Richard, for he was sure he would not in the least mind being married if he were but seven.

But now his mother said something startling to him. She bid him stand,

and laying her hand on his shoulder looked solemnly into his eyes. 'Richard, you must never forget that one day *you* may be King of England.' He stared at her. 'It is not impossible, my son. Your brother Edward is the elder, but if aught should happen to him, then the burden of kingship would fall upon this head.'

She kissed him and bid him depart and not forget all she had told him of the importance of the morrow.

If aught should happen to Edward! The words made him shiver. There was so much in the world that he did not understand. A short time ago he had not known of marriage, and now he was to be married. His father–his big father who rumbled when he laughed and had the purplest face Richard had ever seen–poked him in the ribs and laughed at him. 'So you are to have a wife, eh? Well, I'll tell you a secret. See that you always get your own way with her.' His father laughed loudly at that, so Richard laughed too, for although he did not know what his father meant he supposed it was very funny.

He had repeated what he had to do, and very soon his nurse would come to dress him. His ceremonial garments were laid out waiting for him. He looked at them, touched the soft scarlet velvet and ran his finger over the cloth of gold. It was to be an important day, his nurse had told him, and he was to be the most important person of the day. 'You must not forget that you are the Duke of York, the son of the King.' How many times had that been said to him? He must not forget. . . . He must not forget. . . . He was not a little boy merely; he was the Duke of York, the son of the King.

Suddenly his face puckered. It was all very well for them to say there was nothing to worry about, and all he had to do was walk beside Anne and repeat the words the priest told him. But suppose there was something about marriage they hadn't mentioned! Life was full of so many surprises, and there was much he had yet to learn.

He ran to the door, and he did not stop running until he reached Jane's apartments.

Jane was sitting on a stool at her mirror and two women stood beside her; one was dressing her lovely hair while the other did something to her gown. She did not look round when he entered, but one of the women cried: 'Why, 'tis the little bridegroom!'

Jane swung round then. 'Richard!' she cried, and he ran to her, scrambling up on to her lap, his wide frightened eyes studying her face. She did not ask questions. She seemed to understand, as she always did understand, exactly what was troubling him. She put her arms round him and held him tightly as though he were merely a little boy–any little boy. It was undignified, but he didn't care. He wanted to be undignified; he wanted to forget what they were always insisting he should remember.

'Why,' said Jane suddenly, 'it is going to be great fun this day, Richard. I hear they have decorated the chapel in most magnificent fashion–and all for you. Beautiful carpets are hanging on the walls. You will walk under a canopy which, I dare swear, will be the colour of gold. Oh, this will be a day to remember.'

'Jane,' he said, in a whisper that only she might hear, 'I do not want to get married.'

'But you will,' she whispered back. 'You will like it. Anne is excited. She will love getting married.'

'But she is nearly seven, and seven is different. Edward is seven.'

'But you will be seven soon.'

'Why, yes.' He brightened. 'So I shall.' He buried his head against Jane's soft breasts. 'Jane, what does it mean? What shall I have to do?'

'You will walk to the altar and Anne will be there, and you will say what they tell you to say. And afterwards there will be a wonderful feast at the palace and everyone will drink your health–yours and Anne's–and you shall eat as much as you wish.'

'Yes,' he said, admitting with a nod that all that was very exciting. 'But what–after, Jane?'

'After? Oh, after that you will go back to your lessons and you will do all the things you do now. It will be just as though—'

'Just as though I am not married?'

'Just like that.'

His relief was apparent in the deep breath he took. 'But then,' he demanded, 'why do they want me to be married?'

'Well, when you are fourteen you will go and live with Anne–or Anne will come and live with you. Anne will come to Baynard's Castle if that is where you are living, and there you will have a lot of children and be happy for ever after. You will like that, Richard.'

'How old did you say?'

'Fourteen.'

'It is years and years away.'

The women wiped their eyes, and Jane laughed and said his nurses would be missing him, for it was time he dressed, so she carried him to the door and kissed him tenderly. 'There is nothing to fear, dear Richard,' she whispered. 'Shall I come back to your room with you?'

He wished he need not go, for he was deeply in love with Jane. He wished he could stay, resting his head on her soft bosom, talking about when he would be fourteen; but of course he must remember that he was the Duke of York.

'Thank you, Jane,' he said. 'I will go alone.'

He was not frightened after that, and when his mother held his hand and led him up to the altar of St Stephen's Chapel he was almost happy. His mother pressed his hand reassuringly. She was very pleased about his wedding because, so his brother had told him, Anne was the richest little girl in England, and as heiress to the Duke of Norfolk she was considered worthy to marry into the royal family.

Richard listened to the service; he repeated what he must. He heard Anne whisper her responses as she stood beside him, her little chest naked, her long hair flowing over her shoulders, her rich skirt trailing the ground so that there was so much more of velvet and cloth of gold than there was of Anne Mowbray. He wanted to tell her not to be frightened, for after this all would be just as it had been before.

In this little chapel, with its magnificent decorations all in honour of his wedding, were the highest people in the land. First his father, looking bigger and more sparkling than ever; then his mother, smiling and gracious because she was so pleased. Uncle Richard and Aunt Anne had come down from the North to be present at his wedding. Uncle Richard was pale and stern-looking; and Aunt Anne was pale also and looked very ill. Their little son Edward was with them. Poor little cousin, he looked very tired. Richard wondered when he would have a marriage.

His other uncle was not there. Richard wondered why, and at the same time he was glad. He did not like Uncle George any more than he liked Uncle Richard. They both frightened him in their different ways; they were not a bit like Richard's father, who, although he was King, was really very kind. Still, it did seem strange that Uncle George and Cousin Edward and Cousin Margaret were not at the wedding.

There was little time for these reflections, for they were leaving the chapel now, and he heard the shouts of the people who had come to see him and Anne. Uncle Richard was scattering gold coins among the people. There was great rejoicing throughout the land, his mother had told him, for there was nothing the people liked so much as a royal wedding.

And, once the ceremony was over and the celebrations began, Richard was happy. All the guests drank his health –his and Anne's–while they stood together, hand in hand.

'Do you like being married, Anne?' he whispered.

She said she did; but he knew she rather despised her bridegroom because he was younger than she was. She would have preferred Edward. He forgot that, though, as he watched the jousting and sat down to the banquet just as though he were grown up. Then he felt there was a good deal to be said for getting married.

On and on went the laughter and the music so that it seemed to Richard it would never end. It was the longest day of his life, he thought; and then suddenly it faded away. His head sunk on to his jewel-trimmed jacket, and at the height of the festivity which was to celebrate his wedding the little bridegroom fell asleep.

The court was in residence at the royal palace of the Tower of London, and for days there had been banquets, jousting and pageantry, for the King wished to entertain his brother Richard before the latter's return to his duties in the North.

There was little the King liked better than pageantry and to know himself the centre of his gay court, more dazzling than any member of it. And at this time he needed distraction, for he could not forget that while he fêted one brother the other was a prisoner in the Bowyer Tower. The eyes of his father continued to haunt him. Surely, he told himself, if his father had foreseen what George would try to do he would have understood the predicament in which his eldest son, the rightful King, now found himself.

He could not enjoy the feasting nor the jousting; he could take no delight in the performance of the wild beasts from his menagerie. All about him people were applauding, crying out appreciation of some particularly daring feat of his bearward; but the King did not see the performing bears nor the artful tricks of the monkeys; he could think of nothing but his treacherous brother and the promise he had made to his father. Sitting there, staring moodily before him, he decided this could not continue. He would release George, since that was the only way to ease his conscience. If George made more trouble doubtless he would be able to deal with him, for George was, praise the saints, the most stupid man in England.

When the display was over, Edward hastily distributed a few purses of gold to those responsible for its arrangement and made his way alone to the Bowyer Tower. At his approach the warders sprang to attention, but Edward waved his hand and said: 'I would be conducted to the apartments of the Duke of Clarence.'

He was led up a spiral staircase, along corridors, and right to the top of the

Tower, which had been deemed the safest place for one who might prove a slippery prisoner. The door was unlocked and the warder stood aside for the King to enter. 'I will have the key,' said Edward. 'You will receive it later.'

He took it and went in, locking the door behind him. George started up when he saw him. George's eyes were bloodshot and he had been drinking even more heavily than usual.

'Now, George,' said Edward, in a conciliatory voice, 'this is a sorry state of affairs.'

George laughed; when he was with his brother his jealousy and hatred of him stifled every other emotion, even ambition. If he had a dagger he would have attempted to kill him there and then. Edward knew this and had come well armed.

'Sorry indeed,' snarled George, 'when out of his jealousy one brother must trump up a charge against another.'

'Let us have none of this folly,' said Edward sternly. 'You know full well that any less soft than myself would have had you despatched long ere this. But for the promise I made to our father I myself would not have endured your insults and your treachery as long as I have. You should have died with your traitor-accomplice Warwick. But you are my brother–and for this reason I have forgiven you.'

'Forgiven me! So that I may suffer the indignity of confinement in this place with low rascals to guard me!'

'You have been treated with great mercy, and you know it.'

George, inflamed by wine and jealousy, threw himself on to his bed and pummelled his pillow. He was working himself up into a mad rage. 'You stand there,' he shouted, 'you–good King Edward! Everything is as you will have it. Was it not always the same? Our mother–our father–all of them bowing down and worshipping you. The handsome one–the eldest son–the King. Every man ready to follow you to death. Every woman begging the favour of sharing your bed. Edward the magnificent.'

'Be silent, you fool,' said Edward.

'I will not be silent. You are a cheat. You are a liar. You practise black magic. It was sorcery that gave you the throne, and through sorcery you keep it. The Queen is a witch. Jane Shore is a witch. And you—'

'Pray calm yourself, or I shall go away.'

'The Queen is a witch–a witch and a harlot.' George was losing all control now. 'A harlot–just as Jane Shore is a harlot. Burn them all, I say. But save the biggest faggots and the brightest flames for the Woodville harlot. She is no Queen.'

'What are you saying, you knave?'

'Only this, brother. The Queen is your harlot just as Jane Shore is. The Queen is no wife to you.'

'Enough of this folly, for you tempt me sorely.'

'It is not for you to say "enough." What of Eleanor Butler, eh? She was your wife–aye, and alive when you went through a ceremony of marriage with Elizabeth Woodville.'

'You are drunk, George.'

'Drunk–drunk–drunk on Malmsey. And you are drunk with power–too drunk to see what goes on around you. Good Bishop Stillington can bear me witness. King Edward has not long to live–and then God save King George!'

Edward said calmly: 'This story is yet another of your foolish fabrications. I advise you not to speak of it further, if you value your life. I had come to speak to you in friendly fashion, but I see I must put that off until I find you influenced more by good sense and less by good Malmsey.'

George had slipped back on to his bed, murmuring insults against the Queen. Edward went out and locked the door. He made his way out of the tower, called a warder and gave him the keys. He asked that the Constable of the Tower be conducted to him without a moment's delay. When the man came to him, Edward said: 'My lord Stillington, Bishop of Bath and Wells, is to be arrested immediately. Place him in solitary confinement in the most inaccessible part of the Tower.'

The Constable hastened to do the King's bidding.

Edward was furious with a fury born of fear. Out of the past a ghost had risen up to threaten him. He scarcely remembered what Eleanor Butler looked like, for it was years since he had known her. She had died, he had heard, in a nunnery; and that must have been ten years ago. How had George come to learn of that incident from his past life? Stillington knew. Who else? Some of Eleanor's family. But they would not dare do anything about it. Edward was sweating under his heavy garments in spite of the January cold.

George could only have recently acquired the information. The story had been smuggled in to him. By whom? Stillington? Well, Stillington was under lock and key, and he would not know freedom again until he learned not to speak of matters touching his betters. But what of George? George was never to be trusted; as long as he breathed he would think treason and act treason if he had a chance. The throne was now unsafe for Edward's sons. And who would have thought that Eleanor, mouldering in her grave, could have brought him to this! She had been a widow–just as Elizabeth had. He had a fondness for widows, mayhap. Shrewsbury's daughter–and her husband had been a son of Lord Butler of Sudely. It had been one of those passionate affairs in which he had indulged so lightly during his youth. Eleanor had been as determined to get a promise of marriage from him as Elizabeth had been. 'Your mistress I cannot be.' How many times had he heard that? And in every case he had managed to get round it, to make vague promises which he had no intention of keeping. Elizabeth Woodville had been too clever and too attractive for him to resist. Eleanor, it seemed, had been clever also, for while Elizabeth shared his throne, Eleanor returned from the grave to assert her rights.

It was no use pretending to himself that this was not a serious matter that had come to the knowledge of his greatest enemy. It was true, every word of it. He cast his mind back to a young and ardent man, an unwise man where his desires were concerned. 'Why, then, I will marry you,' he said. Then he had not been the King, merely the Earl of March with the promise of kingship; and he had desired Eleanor Butler so urgently that he had made his rash promise and been fool enough to make his vows before Stillington. That had been her family's work, but when he had later, as all-powerful monarch, refused to recognise the marriage, they had been wise enough to keep silent on the matter. There had been a child who had died, and Eleanor had, most obligingly, disappeared into a nunnery. When he had heard of her death, some years after his marriage with Elizabeth, he had dismissed the matter as done with.

And now here it was–and because it deeply concerned Elizabeth, he went to her and told her what George had said. He had never seen Elizabeth so frightened. She felt her throne shake under her. Her dignity, her power, and the future of her children were in danger. She did what he had rarely seen her do: she lost her calm.

'It is a lie,' she cried.

'It is the truth,' said Edward.

'How could you have been such a fool as to promise her marriage–to go through a form of marriage? You must have been mad.'

Angry lights appeared in the King's eyes. 'No more so than when I acted similarly with you.'

'This marriage cannot be legal.'

'According to the law it is.'

'And that means . . .'

Alarmed as he was, he could not resist baiting her. In some small measure it made up for all her coldness to him. 'It means,' he said, 'that it might be difficult to prove that you and I are married, in which case the people would declare you no longer Queen.'

Her eyes looked black in her drawn face as she clenched and unclenched her hands. 'It is false.' Suddenly she turned to him and flung her arms about him. 'Edward, our children! Little Edward and Richard. This must not be!'

No, of course it must not be. He was too old to get more children by a new wife. He had too many illegitimate sons already; he did not wish to add Edward and Richard to the tally. This thing had to be fought; Eleanor was dead; let her story die with her.

'George must die–at once,' said Elizabeth, and she was cold and calm once more. As he was silent, she cried: 'Will you let him live now to destroy your children's future?'

'He is a prisoner. No harm can come while he is a prisoner.'

'Prisoners escape.'

'He shall not.'

'Have you forgotten he is in the Tower on a charge of treason? Why–oh, why . . .'

'Because it is not easy to kill one's brother.'

'Kill! Kill! You talk as though you were asked to wield the axe yourself.'

'Whoever wielded the axe, it would be at my command that he was struck down.'

'Edward, you are a fool!' She had lost control again, so great was her fear. 'First you get involved with a woman. How could you be so soft?'

He turned on her, his eyes blazing: 'You should know, madam. She tried the same tricks as you did, and–as with you–they worked.'

She shrank from him, but quickly regained her poise. 'Edward, I implore you to think of our children. George must die, and with him Stillington–or let his tongue be cut out and his hands cut off that he may not speak or write this thing.'

'Your ambition is great,' said Edward coldly. 'Have a care. It would be well to remember that it is for me to say what shall and what shall not be done.'

He left her then, remembering with relief that his brother Richard was in the palace. He sent for him, and when he was sure they were alone he told him everything that had happened.

Richard looked grave. 'You say Stillington is already a prisoner. And who knows about this but Stillington and George?'

'None of import, or we should have learned something sooner. Richard, what am I to do with this brother of ours?'

Richard bit his lip. He walked to the window and looked out, though he did not see the lawns and the grey walls of the Cradle Tower. He was thinking that to Edward, egoistical in the extreme, this was but a personal problem; it astounded Richard that Edward did not realise its significance to him–the very man in whom he was confiding. George was in the Tower on a charge of treason, Edward had no legitimate son living, and as for Edward himself, that corpulence, that heavy breathing, those recurring fits of fever–all these things could mean but one thing: Edward could not live much longer. Was he blind? Did he not see what a dazzling prospect he had opened up for his brother Richard? What Edward was saying was this: 'You, Richard, in a few short years–or mayhap months–will be the rightful King of England.'

To wear the crown, to hold the reins firmly in one's own hands, to dedicate oneself body and soul to the country one loved better than anything else on earth, better than wife or child or even one's own life!

Richard sought to control himself. He must hide his emotion. He must listen to what Edward had to say. He must advise.

'Is there no reasoning with him?'

'Reason with George? As well talk to a tiger. If this story be bruited abroad . . .'

'Ah,' said Richard, his eyes gleaming, 'then the people will not have young Edward on the throne after you.'

'It was not a true marriage,' said Edward quickly. 'I made a few promises. There was no church solemnisation.'

'Nay, but such vows are considered binding nevertheless.'

Edward was in despair. 'Dickon, what can I do? I see only one way out of this. Is he not in the Tower on a charge of treason? Death is the reward of traitors.'

'And justly so.'

'I have suffered much sleeplessness over George. The sensible way is to rid myself of this false brother.' Edward looked round sharply. 'What was that?'

'Only the wind stirring the hangings.'

'I promised our father,' said Edward, and he continued to look over his shoulder. It seemed to both men that their father's spirit was in the room. Neither could meet his brother's eye, for each was afraid the other would see his guilty looks. George dead and I would be safe; my children would be safe, thought Edward. George dead–and the way to the throne is cleared for me, thought Richard.

Richard spoke first. 'You have told the Queen?'

Edward nodded.

Richard's lips curled. 'She trembles for her children?'

'She does, brother.'

Holy Mother! thought Richard. Even now he does not see. He thinks his secret safe with *me*. Had he, carelessly possessing these things, forgotten that there was no sight more beautiful than a glittering crown, and that power was the most cherished gift earth had to offer. Yet–there was honour.

Did the hangings stir? wondered Richard; and he remembered clearly his father's noble face. How simple it would be to say to Edward, 'Destroy George.' That was what Edward wanted him to say.

Never had the Duke of Gloucester experienced such mixed feelings. Never had his love for his brother been so great and never before had he so despised him as a fool. Never had he been so elated, never so depressed. And all the time he had the uncanny feeling that his father was in the room watching them.

It was a great struggle, but his sense of honour overcame ambition.

''Twould be murder,' he said at length. 'If you kill George because you fear he will speak against you, then you betray the trust our father fixed upon you.'

Edward laid a hand on his brother's shoulder. 'You are right, Dickon. I thank the Virgin you were here when I most needed your counsel.'

Richard hurried away, and no sooner was Edward alone than he was again beset by doubts. It seemed to him that he heard the laughter of women–women whose names he had forgotten, women who, in that vast crowd, were now merely a remembered laugh, a voice, a flash of a smile, a shudder of ecstasy. Now they mocked him. He had had his way with so many; he had been the conqueror, they the vanquished. Now it seemed they banded together to mock him, to whisper: 'But were we the defeated, Edward, or were you?'

He could not endure to be alone, so he went to Jane, and to her blurted out the whole story. 'The Queen says there is one way out and one only,' he finished.

'But you could not do it, Edward. You must not do it.'

He smiled with relief, and holding her against him kissed her with great gentleness. 'You are my good angel, Jane. I cannot do it. Richard agrees with me. He advised me not to do it.'

'He advised you not to do it,' said Jane slowly. 'Yet if you did–then he would be heir to the throne.'

Edward's face was purple suddenly. 'Richard, heir to the throne! What nonsense you talk! Have I not two sons?'

'But if your marriage to their mother was no true marriage . . .'

He put her from him and she saw the veins stand out on his temples. 'It shall not be said!' he thundered. 'It shall never be known. I tell you this affair with Eleanor Butler was nothing–nothing.' He strode to the window, then he swung round to face her, and she saw that his eyes had grown fierce. She felt suddenly tender towards him, remembering the greatness of a love that was past. He was begging her to help him, to agree that George must die. But she must be true to herself; she must be as she had always been, bold and reckless, but truthful. She went to him and looked up into his angry eyes.

'Edward, nothing is gained by turning from the truth. Whether your marriage with the Queen is legal is not what we have to talk about. The urgent problem is whether you shall have George executed because he has learned your secret. If you kill him because of this, you will have murdered one who was put in your care.'

'You are too bold, Jane.'

'If I had not been I should never have left my husband and come to you.'

'There's truth in that.' He smiled suddenly and charmingly. 'And if you were not bold you would not speak truth to me when others lie. Tell me, Jane, why should I stop at this? Are my hands so clean? I have killed before.'

'This man is your brother, Edward.'

'I would to God I could forget it,' said Edward bitterly.

There was no rest for the King. He could not sleep, he could not eat. There were voices in his ear all the time. 'Kill him! Kill him! It is the only safe way.'

And then: 'My son, look after your brothers. I leave them in your care.'

He felt he had lived through ten years in two days. Every time a messenger came to him he was startled. What now? he would wonder. Has it leaked out, then?

The Queen's eyes appealed to him. They cursed him for a weak fool. 'Kill! Kill! Kill!' said the Queen's eyes.

Never had sons seemed so fair, so promising; never before had he known how he loved them. Their mother's eyes followed them yearningly. 'And what sort of a father are you, my lord,' she asked bitterly, 'thus to expose your sons to treachery?'

If he could but forget the solemn vow he had made! If he could feel young again, young, bold and careless of death! He *was* young, but his body had enjoyed too many experiences not to have aged beyond his years. He was grossly fat and the tertian fever he had caught in France had never left him. He had enjoyed too much rich food, too much good wine, too many strange women. Now he asked for peace and comfort and it was denied him. There came a time when a man must make his peace with God; his sins should be committed in the flush of youth; age was the time for repenting old sins, not for the committing of new ones.

I could not do it, he would tell himself; and then he would see the Queen's eyes, dark with misery, hear her lips murmur: 'It is so easy. Kill, kill, kill!'

Would this night never pass? wondered Jane. She had never before known Edward so disturbed. He lay beside her in the elaborate bed, but he did not sleep. His face had lost its rich red-purple colour; it looked a dark and smudgy brown in the light of the candles. He had insisted on lighting them. This night he could not bear the dark.

'Edward,' she whispered, 'you must try to sleep.'

'It is no use, Jane. There is no rest for me this night.'

She smoothed his hair back from his forehead. 'It is because you have as yet made no decision about George. Edward, decide now . . . that you will do what is right. Decide, and let matters run their course.'

'Jane,' he said, catching her hand and holding it firmly, 'you do not understand. You cannot understand.'

'I can and I do.'

The candles flickered, and it seemed to the King that the room was more full of shadows than was usual. 'How dark it is!' he said. 'It is the darkest night I ever knew.'

'Shall I light more candles?'

'No, stay here with me. Stay close, Jane.'

They were silent for a while. Then his arms tightened about her. 'Jane,' he whispered. 'Saw you something?'

'Where?' she asked.

'There by the door. Methought . . .'

''Tis nothing but the hangings.'

'Methought I saw a figure standing there.'

''Twas but the wind stirring the hangings.'

''Tis a gusty night, Jane, a dark and gusty night.'

Again there was silence, then he said: 'Jane, you do not sleep either.'

'It has deserted us both this night.'

'I am glad, for I would talk with you. You know what those two boys mean to me. They are my sons. I have made great plans for them.'

'It is natural that you should, Edward, but . . .'

He interrupted her sharply. 'Why do you say "But"? What means that "But"?'

'If your son has no right to the crown it would be better if some other wore it.'

He laughed suddenly. 'You consider not what you say. With my brother George on the throne none would be safe. England herself would be in danger. Better if I broke the vow I made my father. . . .' She noticed that he was staring at the hangings by the door. 'I say,' he said in a louder voice, 'better if I broke my vow to my father than that George should sit upon the throne.'

She knew now what was in his mind; she guessed now what he had done. She lay beside him shuddering.

'Try to sleep, Edward,' she whispered. 'In the morning can you think on these things.'

But there was no sleep for either of them. They lay still, feigning sleep, both conscious that just beyond their window the grey walls of the Bowyer Tower rose up to the February night sky.

A butt of Malmsey. George hiccoughed and surveyed it with satisfaction. Sent in by Edward. Edward was trying to propitiate him. And no wonder! To think that in George's hands lay the power to crush his greatest enemy; for his enemy, he had always insisted, was not his brother, but his brother's wife. What joy to see her pride humbled! She, who had made others kneel before her, should kneel until she fainted with fatigue. As for her precious little bastards . . . well, no matter. That could wait until Edward was dead and George upon the throne.

The Malmsey was good. It had ever been his favourite wine. What pleasant dreams it could conjure up even in a prison cell. How long could Edward last? Edward was over-fat, rotten with disease. A different Edward now from the brother of George's childhood. 'The King is dead,' he muttered. 'Long live the King! Edward is dead. Long live King George!'

He drank to King George. The son of George, Duke of Clarence, not Edward's son, would one day be Edward the Fifth of England.

He drank more wine. He grew very drowsy and he did not see two men come into his cell. They were clad in dark and inconspicuous garments, and as they looked at the drunken man they talked in whispers and they avoided looking into each other's faces.

The solitary lantern which stood on a ledge in the wall threw a feeble light round the room. On the bed the Duke snored and groaned in his sleep. His face looked yellow in the lantern light; his rich coat was sodden with wine.

The two men came silently to the bed and looked down at him. Then one seized his feet, the other his head, but as they would have lifted him George opened his eyes. 'What's this?' he asked sleepily.

Both men immediately took their hands off him. One said: 'Your Grace, a thousand pardons. We did not mean to disturb you.'

'We thought Your Grace asked for another drink,' said the other.

'Drink? Bring me a drink . . . here now. . . .'

The man who had been holding his feet came to the head of the bed. He bent over and whispered: 'Alas Your Grace, the Malmsey is in the butt. We can assist Your Grace to it.'

George was very drunk, but the mention of Malmsey revived him a little.

He nodded, closed his eyes and began to snore.

The men whispered together.

'He is very far gone in drink.'

'That is good. I counted on it. Try again.'

The man bent so that his mouth came down to the Duke's ear. 'Your Grace, we will assist you to the wine.'

George protested only mildly as the men lifted him from the bed. He was not even surprised when he found himself looking into the butt of wine. He bent over it. It was nectar; it was an opiate that brought beautiful dreams. He could taste the wine now. There was nothing but wine. He could not breathe; he was slowly choking. He could not raise his head, for two strong men were holding it down that he might take his fill of his favourite wine.

He gasped and struggled, but what were the feeble struggles of a drunken man against two intent on murder!

It was not long before George, Duke of Clarence, ceased to struggle. Then did his murderers lift him and tip him into the butt so that his head and shoulders were deep in the wine.

The Tower of London

Part Two

Once again the plague stalked the City of London. Through the riverside alleys it came, striking down men and women and children; it left them groaning on the roadside, calling for help which none dared give. From the narrow streets with their refuse-laden gutters stinking in the hot air, it spread to the main thoroughfares. The polluted Fleet, alive with flies that fed on the filth thrown into it by the butchers and tanners, carried it onwards, until the entire City lay groaning under the death-dealing invader which saw fit to invade its streets every few years.

The court had moved to Windsor, and into the great castle there had seemed to creep a tension which did not diminish with the passing weeks. The King's attacks of fever had become more frequent and people were asking each other, 'How long will he last?'

Jane's feelings towards the man she had loved so passionately were peculiarly mingled. It was saddening to see him who had been so magnificent surpassing all others, grown so fat that he could scarcely move with ease. Edward had been Nature's darling; he had come into the world equipped with every quality and opportunity which should have made him great. But what a bad fairy it was who at his christening had given him that deep sensuous love of pleasure, that self-indulgence which was to grow to such magnitude that it had strangled every virtue. To see him now, aged beyond his years, pitiably trying to regain that virility he had squandered, was heartbreaking. The handsome irresistible man had become the repulsive roué.

The great change in him had come with the death of his brother George, who, it was said, had been drowned in a butt of Malmsey, but Jane, who had lain awake with the King on the night of George's death, could not believe that it had been an accident. She knew that every time the Duke was mentioned the King was shaken, and his bloodshot eyes looked beyond the company as though he thought he might see something which was invisible to others. Jane believed that Edward had ordered the murder of his brother.

'I will always love you,' she had cried passionately to the handsome merchant in Mary Blague's house; she had believed it, and in a measure there was truth in that cry of hers. The man she had loved was a different man from the Edward of today. The charming witty philanderer had become the murderer of his brother, prematurely old while Jane was young.

Wandering in the Great Park among the noble oaks and the wide-spreading branches of the beech trees, Jane fought a battle with herself. She would walk the great avenue and survey one of the finest panoramas in Europe; she would climb the tower of the third Edward and look across the green and pleasant countryside which was cut in two by the gleaming river; and she would try to suppress the wild and raging passion that was in her for the man who was bewitching her as once the King had done.

She thought a good deal about Hastings too. She enjoyed her meetings with him, enjoyed reviling him, so great was her hatred of him. She did not know that she thought more of him than she had ever done before, and that when she was not occupied with thoughts of Dorset, Hastings filled her mind.

One gusty March day as she was walking in the Home Park, Dorset saw her from a window of the castle and hastened out to her. She saw him coming and leaned against the trunk of an ancient oak to steady herself, for the sight of him never failed to disturb her.

He seized her hands and kissed them. 'Why, Jane,' he said, 'you must be a witch, for I declare you look more beautiful in a March wind than you do at a court banquet.'

She was frail, she knew, and life with Edward had taught her to need the frequent excitement of physical love. Dorset in his handsome garments reminded her poignantly of Edward when she had first known him. He smiled at her, sensing the effect he had upon her. It was no novelty to him. He charmed with his very brutality, with his evil reputation. 'Dorset is a brute,' women said, 'an attractive, irresistible brute.' It was his virile masculinity that attracted, not his character.

'Why do you keep me waiting, Jane?' he said.

She pretended not to understand. 'When have I kept you waiting?'

'You know my meaning. You know for what.' He thought it was fear of the King, and not loyalty, that made her hold back. 'Who is your lover now? Do not say Edward. How does he spend his time? He looks into the future; he seeks the philosopher's stone. Oh, Jane, the present would be good enough for me, if you would share it; and I know more pleasant things to look for than a non-existent philosopher's stone. Jane, you were not meant to be neglected thus.'

He seized her roughly, and was amused to find her trembling. He laughed at her feeble struggles. 'You know you do not want to escape. Be truthful.'

'*You* to tell me to be truthful! Do you, who so sadly lack the virtues, look for them in others?'

He put his handsome face close to hers. 'I do not need to be anything but truthful, Jane. It is true that I have no virtues. What of that? Vice is so much more attractive than virtue.'

'More fashionable, you mean.' There was evil in him, she knew, and she was fighting hard to suppress the longing he aroused in her. Part of her wanted to escape, but part wanted to stay with him. 'I will be truthful with you,' she said with a touch of her old spirit. 'There are many at court who find it difficult to refuse you, but do not make the mistake of thinking that because some do, all must.'

She saw the flush under his skin. His eyes gleamed at her. 'Mayhap not all,' he said, 'but methinks Jane Shore is among them that do.'

Jane, pressing her hands against him, held him off. 'Then think again, Thomas.'

But he was forcing her back against the tree, kissing her mouth.

'Not yet,' she pleaded. 'Thomas . . . not yet.'

'Holy Mother, have I not sought you long enough?'

'If the waiting grows wearisome,' she responded tartly, 'then, my lord, you should seek elsewhere.'

He raised his eyebrows, mocking her. 'You would send me to others then?'

She beat against his chest. He was a big man; Jane was a small woman. 'You haven't a chance, Jane,' he said, and his laughter was quiet and mocking.

'You have the laughter of a demon,' she told him.

'That is what I am. A satyr to waylay you in the forest, to make you a bed among the bracken. Once you have tasted the joys I know of, you will never have the will to say Nay to me.'

'I could not deceive the King,' she said faintly.

'Can you then so rely on *his* fidelity? He grows old. He would not know that you, as you put it, deceived him.'

'But *I* should know, and it would make uneasy knowledge.'

''Twould be forgotten in the joys that I should show you. You may well look alarmed. Do you think I do not know you long for me? I will beckon and you will come. And if not . . .'

'If not?'

'What I cannot have by asking I will take by force.'

'You *are* a demon, Thomas Grey.'

His eyes were laughing. 'Mayhap you are right, and you will sell your soul to me when I take your body. In this forest demons are abroad. We will go to Herne the Hunter's blasted oak, and there I will make you a bed of bracken.'

'You will not. I wish to return to the castle now.'

'And if I do not choose that you should return to the castle?'

'You find it amusing to tease me, but I do not share your amusement. Pray stand aside.'

She was afraid, for he had laid the palms of his hands against the trunk of the tree and she was imprisoned; but in her, mingling with her fear, there was a longing that he might take her by force, that she might satisfy her senses and say, ''Twas no fault of mine. I had no choice.'

He seemed to read her thoughts for he laughed and said: 'You are wise, Jane. When submission is inevitable, 'twould be foolish not to relax and enjoy.'

She felt her anger rising to meet her passion. 'You are mistaken in me. . . .'

'I think not, Jane,' he said. 'I think not. . . .'

They both heard the shout; they both turned their heads and saw Hastings. Jane could not understand her emotions. She was filled with a wild unreasoning joy because Hastings had found her with Dorset thus. She was glad that he could see the wild disorder of her dress, and the red patches on her throat and chest where Dorset had roughly kissed her. Hastings glowered angrily, while Dorset smiled insolently at him, though his hand had come to rest on the hilt of his sword.

'I heard your call for help,' said Hastings, 'and so did hurry to rescue you from this man.'

'I gave no call,' said Jane maliciously. She knew that he was jealous of Dorset's youth. Dorset was thirty, Hastings fifty-three. Dorset had won honours effortlessly through his mother; Hastings was a clever statesman, a brilliant soldier, and he had fought beside the King. Hastings had desired Jane for many years and his desire for her obsessed him. He could not bear that Dorset, notoriously light and cruel in his love affairs, should succeed where he should fail.

'My Lord Hastings,' said Dorset, 'can you not see that we do not require your company?'

'I heard Jane's protests,' insisted Hastings.

'I assure you, my lord,' said Jane quickly, 'I can defend myself should the need arise.'

'That may be, but to my mind you need protection from this man.'

Dorset swaggered towards him, drawing his sword. 'I would know the meaning of such words.'

Hastings' sword was out. 'Methinks you do know, Marquis.'

Dorset was young and lithe; he had parried the blow and they stood, swords crossed, glaring into each other's eyes. Jane forced a way between them. 'Put away your swords at once,' she cried. 'My Lord Hastings, you have no need to fear for me. I can take care of my own affairs. I beg of you both, if you would please me, to put away your swords.' They did so, but with reluctance. 'I am going back to the castle,' said Jane; and she turned and walked from them. Dorset and Hastings, silently hating each other, each vowing that before long Jane should become his mistress, walked on either side of her towards the castle.

The King opened his eyes. Dark shapes were in his room. This was the end, he knew. He was old and tired, and death was beckoning. News had been brought to him that the King of France was deceiving him; the Dauphin, promised to Edward's daughter, was to marry the heiress of Burgundy. The shock had been too much. The King had fallen into one of his violent rages. He had been carried unconscious to his bed.

He was sure that he would not rise from it again and there was much to be done. He must make the future secure for his little son; he must make his peace with God, for he feared he had lived a sinful life.

He saw Jane at his bedside and he remembered her as she had been when he first saw her in the goldsmith's house. He remembered that he had deliberately gone to that house with the intention of taking her from her husband. Then it had seemed an amusing adventure; in the face of death he knew he had done an evil thing.

'Jane,' he said. 'Jane . . . I took you from . . .'

She knew what troubled him; he felt her tears upon his hands. 'We were so happy,' she whispered. 'I would not have had it different.'

He thought of all the light women who had amused him temporarily and lured him from her side. He tried to tell her that he was wishing he could go back to the beginning of their union.

The Queen came to him. He must not let her influence him now. There was his son to consider, for very soon the thirteen-year-old boy would be King. He declared his son to be under the protection of his brother Richard. 'Into his care I deliver my son, the Prince.' The Queen was displeased. Was she not his mother? 'No, no, Bessy,' he murmured. Didn't he know her family? They were bloated with the power which he, at Elizabeth's request, had bestowed upon them. No. Young Edward must be in firm good hands, and there was only one pair of hands he trusted for this duty.

He asked that Dorset and Hastings might be brought to him. Edward could not see them clearly, but he knew that the tall glittering figure was his handsome stepson, and the more soberly clad, shorter, older man was his friend and counsellor, Hastings.

'William,' he said; and Hastings knelt by the bed and kissed the fat hand that was now clammy and turning cold. 'I–I have sent for you two–because there is enmity between you.'

The dying Edward knew that Jane was involved in that enmity; but it was not Jane only; they were natural enemies. Dorset was one of the main pillars of the Woodville party, and Hastings had never liked the Queen's family. If there was trouble after his death, Hastings would be with Richard, Dorset against him.

But there must be no trouble, for what could a boy of thirteen do against such cunning warriors as these? There must be friendship among the nobles if there was to be peace for little Edward.

'I beg of you–with my dying breath–I beg of you–be friends. Let me see you shake hands across my bed. William, my old friend; Thomas my son–I command you. Peace between you two.'

Jane watched the two men, saw them shake hands as Edward bid them. She saw genuine grief in the eyes of Hastings, but the face of Dorset was inscrutable.

Edward was satisfied. He lay back, watching the shadowy shapes about the room. Everything was fading. His lips moved. 'Jane–Jane–we have been happy. No, George . . . Father–Father . . . I did not want to do it, Father. Forgive me. I did it for my sons. It was the only way. Bessy was right. . . . It was the only way.'

Then he forgot Bessy, forgot George, forgot Jane. He had sunk into unconsciousness.

The dead King lay in state, his once beautiful body covered only from the navel to the knees, for all to see, so that none might doubt that Edward the Fourth was indeed no more. Mourning for its most loved King hung over the City. There was much to recall of him–the charm, the gaiety, the gracious beauty. In the streets the sentimental recalled him in the glory of his youth; the more practical turned their eyes towards the palace and wondered what mischief the King's death would set afoot.

In her apartments Jane sat numbed, thinking back over the past. Dorset saw her wandering through the park. She would be easy game now, he reckoned; but let her wait. She was sentimentally mourning the man she had ceased to love long ago, and she would, as yet, make an inadequate mistress. Moreover, his head was full of plans which were of greater importance than dalliance with Jane Shore. So he did not seek out Jane, but went to his mother's apartments. Elizabeth welcomed her son warmly; they shared each other's interests and there was no need for her to choose her words carefully.

'Think not,' she said, 'that I shall allow Gloucester to rule this land. The King is but a child, but *I* am his mother.'

'Mother,' he reminded her, 'we are fortunately placed, the King being at Ludlow, in our hands, while Gloucester is in the North.'

'And you, my dearest son, as Constable of the Tower are in a happy position. Was I not right to get you so placed? Should the occasion arise we could hold all London against any who might assail the City.'

'Aye, Mother, and who rules London rules England. Gloucester has not a chance.'

'He is a crafty man, Thomas, as fine a soldier as his brother was.'

'Never fear, everything must be settled before he reaches the South.'

'He has powerful friends in London.'

'Hastings for one.' Dorset smiled slyly. 'I would not care to have Hastings against us. He is an enemy of mine for more reasons than one. I never thought to wish him my friend. But were he with us, and not against us, I should say certain success was ours.'

'Could we not win him to our side?'

'Bribe Hastings! You do not know the man, gracious mother. He is a strange man–not one man but two. Debauchee in his youth–and mayhap still is. To women he will lie and scheme to rob them of their honour. That is one Hastings. But the statesman, the soldier–he sets honour high. Methinks you could offer him the crown in return for treachery to Gloucester and he'd refuse it.'

'We should certainly not do that,' said Elizabeth grimly. 'But to my mind all men have their price.'

Dorset laughed suddenly, for he had caught sight of Jane in the grounds. 'Even Hastings has his price perchance,' he mused. And then: 'There goes Jane Shore. She mourns the King more deeply than does Your Grace.'

'Poor Jane! She has lost all.'

Dorset smiled at his mother. Edward had been merely a source of power to her, and she could not undertand that he could be anything more to Jane.

'Mother,' he said, 'if we need Hastings we shall win him to our side.'

'You think we could achieve that, Thomas?'

'There would be ways, I doubt not.'

They talked for a long time of what they planned to do; and as they talked the citizens of London filed slowly past the dead body of the most handsome King who had ever sat upon the throne of England.

Dorset did not let many weeks pass before he sought out Jane. He had marked the hungry looks of Hastings. Dorset's eyes were sly. It was stimulating to link passion with ambition. He dressed himself with the utmost elegance in his doublet, which was trimmed with cloth of gold and cut short to show his beautifully moulded legs; he wore a ruby at his throat and another in his cap, and he sprinkled himself with the musk with which Leppus supplied him regularly. He was a fine fellow, he assured himself; what other man would be setting out to seduce the most beautiful woman in the court and be thinking of–Lord Hastings? The beauty of Jane and the power of Hastings. He thought of little else. Hastings was a power in London, for the City was faithful to the strangest people. Why had it taken Hastings to its heart? He did not know.

Boldly he went to Jane's apartments. It was a simple matter to overcome her resistance. Weakly she pleaded, as he had expected, that the King was so recently dead.

'Fear not the dead, Jane,' he had said, slipping her gown from her shoulders and laying his burning lips against her skin. 'Holy Mother, there is more to fear from those alive than those who moulder in their graves.' Throwing himself down beside her he had laughed in his triumph. 'This is the end of your reluctance, Jane. We shall change roles, you and I. You shall be the suppliant. You shall not say, "Not yet." No, Jane, not that. You shall say, "Now–for I cannot live without you."'

That was the beginning. Loving Dorset was like slipping into a quicksand, and Jane slipped fast. Her purely physical need of him dragged her down; she would be submerged very soon, powerless, his completely.

She felt at times ashamed, degraded. This was passion without love–a burning flame that scorched her spirit, no gentle warmth. He would lie beside her and talk casually of his affairs with others with a frankness that hurt and shocked her. He meant to shame her; he meant to degrade her. She tried to break away. She had the house which Edward had given her; she would leave the court. And then he would come to her and she would sink deeper and deeper into the quicksand.

Hastings was furious. People were laughing at him. It was said that for years he had waited like a hungry dog for the King's titbit; and now Dorset had pounced on it before he had had time to seize it.

'You are a fool,' he told Jane when he waylaid her. 'Dorset is the very devil with women. To think that you should join that sorry crowd!'

'I do not need your pity. Keep it for others,' she said angrily.

'You will need it ere long. Think not that when he has done with you, you can come creeping to me. I would never take one of Dorset's cast-off mistresses.'

'I'll not tolerate your insolence,' she cried, and hurried from him that he might not see her tears.

Jane moved to the palace of the Tower. Dorset had his duties there and he would have her near him. She told herself and him that she would not go, for good sense said, 'Retire from court life. Regain that dignity which was yours while Edward lived.' But passion overruled good sense.

It was pleasant to have Kate near her again. Kate longed for confidences, but she did not get them. There was no one to whom Jane could talk of the terrible fascination of the Marquis. So Kate talked instead about the happenings at the Tower. 'Messengers come and go the whole day through,' she told Jane. 'What they are about, Heaven may know, but I can only guess. Why, 'tis as though we are preparing for a siege. There's more soldiers about the courtyards every day, and now they've fixed a cannon on Tower Hill. The arms are being brought out from the armouries.'

Kate was right; and the whole of London was uneasy; but Jane could think of little but her lover.

A hooded figure stepped into the boat and asked to be rowed across the river. The boatman was eager to obey instructions, for in these days of uncertainty, when those who had been great yesterday were no longer great, a poor boatman could never be sure what influence a patron might have. This was a lady with a soft and gentle voice; she showed little of her face, but enough for him to see that it was of great beauty. He wondered what her business across the river could be. She looked sad and was silent, and he did not like to see one of her sort making her way to Southwark. She paid him well and thanked him graciously, and he watched her make her way along the waterfront until she was lost to his sight.

Jane was going to see Dorset. She felt guilty and ashamed, yet exalted. She could scarcely wait to feel her lover's arms about her, and she had to remind herself over and over again that she must go cautiously, and that even now there might be someone following her, someone who would discover her lover's hiding place, and betray him and Jane with him. For Dorset was in hiding. His plot and that of his family had failed. Richard of Gloucester, riding South, had been warned in time by the Duke of Buckingham, and now the little King was in the charge of his Uncle Richard, as his father had intended he should be; and Lord Rivers, his uncle, and Richard Grey, his half-brother, were the prisoners of Gloucester. London, largely due to the intervention of Hastings, had received Gloucester and the little King with a warm welcome, and the Queen had had to fly to Sanctuary with her family. As for Dorset, he could only hide until he or his friends could gather strength and men to fight.

Running, and glancing over her shoulder to make sure she was not being followed, Jane came to a short and narrow street. She stopped before the largest of the houses and hastily knocked at the door, which was opened after a few moments, just an inch or so, and a man with hollow eyes and an oddly twisted mouth looked out at her.

'Oh, Danok,' said Jane, 'let me in quickly.'

Danok undid the heavy chain which prevented him from opening the door for more than an inch or two, and Jane stepped quickly into the house. The door was promptly shut behind her and the chain fixed in its place.

She was shivering, partly from relief at having reached the house unobserved, partly with the horror the place never failed to inspire in her. It was an evil house, and its quietness was more horrible because occasionally it was broken by strange noises–the soft padding of feet, the low rumble of voices, the faint moaning of some young creature in distress, and sometimes the agonised shriek that might come from a woman in labour. Jane felt this house to be full of all human evils–of lust and avarice, of misery, pain and death. She hated coming here, yet come she must, for Dorset commanded her.

A door opened and a woman glided towards her. She was dressed in dove grey, and about her neck, on a heavy chain, hung a silver cross.

'Would you be so good as to step in here before you are conducted to his lordship?' asked Madam quietly.

Jane nodded, and followed her into the room she indicated.

'Your ladyship must be very careful on your journey here.' The woman let her heavy lids fall over her eyes. 'I thought I should warn you. His lordship was one of our most frequent guests . . . in the days of his prosperity. It might be that his enemies would expect him to be with us. It is true that, in the ordinary course of events, it is the gentlemen who come here to visit ladies . . . but there are some who might suspect such an illustrious lady as yourself. . . .' Madam smiled as Jane flushed hotly. She shrugged her shoulders and went on: 'We have the reputation of being most accommodating to our gentlemen. Nothing, many realise, is considered beyond our power to provide for them.'

Jane's anger flared up suddenly. 'And as,' she said caustically, 'refuge in time of trouble is as expensive as pleasure in time of peace, there are some who would suspect *you* of helping his lordship at this time?'

'You get my meaning exactly. Some little matter came to light last evening. One of my ladies was asked by a visitor some very unusual questions about the company of this house.'

'Should that appear so very distressing and uncalled for?'

'Indeed yes, when I tell the questions concerned his lordship. And I took the precaution of looking into the inquiring gentleman's background. He was of the household of His Grace, the Duke of Gloucester. That is why I suggest you show even greater care than usual.'

'Never fear, I shall be careful. And now may I be conducted to his lordship?'

Madam went to the door and clapped her hands. A bold-looking girl of about sixteen, whose face was already marked with debauchery, came in answer to the summons. 'This is Kitty,' said Madam. 'She waits on his lordship, and I hear he is very pleased with all she can do for him.'

Kitty led the way down two flights of stone stairs, through a dark passage which was flanked on either side by walls in which were several doors, all shut. Moisture trickled down the walls and the stone floor was slippery. Dorset was so situated that he could, at the first signs of danger, slip out of the house through a back way which might not be suspected of belonging to this house.

Kitty knocked at the door before which she had paused. Dorset's voice said: 'Who's there?'

''Tis Kitty, my lord,' said the girl. 'With a lady to see you.'

Dorset unlocked the door. 'Jane!' he cried. And to Kitty: 'Be off with you. And if I find you listening at the door I'll have you whipped.' He shut the door and stood leaning against it. 'That will settle the slut. She knows I mean that. Now Jane, what news?'

The first thing he thought of was news. There were plenty in this house to amuse him, but only Jane could bring him news from his friends outside; none but Jane could take messages from him to the Queen.

She said: 'There is little news. Gloucester is at Baynard's Castle, and the King is to leave the house of the Bishop of London for the palace of the Tower.'

He kissed her then, but calmly. 'What news of my mother?'

'She stays in Sanctuary with young Richard and her daughters.'

'She should not have fled there. It was a confession of guilt. She could have been more useful elsewhere.'

Jane tried to soothe him, to turn his thoughts from his ill-fortune to herself. She said: 'Gloucester does not want trouble. He is glad that the affair has been settled without bloodshed. I think that when he is assured that your family is prepared to accept him as Protector of England and guardian of the King, he will forgive you.'

'Forgive us? It is not for him to forgive. Think you we shall ever accept him as guardian of the King? You talk like a fool, Jane.'

'Better to talk like a fool than to act like one!'

'Now, Jane,' he said soothingly, for he did not forget how useful she could be to him, 'you did not come here to quarrel, I'll swear.'

'I did not. Oh, how I hate this place!'

'Yet you come to see me.'

'I cannot stay away.'

'Sweet Jane. You are mine . . . absolutely and unconditionally.'

'It would seem so, Thomas. Were you to retire from court, I am convinced Gloucester would be your friend.'

'What! Should I seek friendship with that ill-favoured pig, that traitor. . . .'

'He is not a traitor. Edward left his son in his care, and he has come to London to perform his duties.'

Dorset's face was purple with fury. 'So you are on the side of Gloucester. You are for your friend Hastings. Holy Christ! Have you become his mistress then?'

It was Jane's turn to grow hot and angry. 'I hate the man, and well you know it.'

'But he does not hate you; and would not Hastings, the friend of Gloucester, make a better protector than Dorset in hiding?'

'I do not seek protectors. Nor have I ever.'

'Did you never put yourself under the protection of the King?'

'I left my husband for Edward because I loved him.'

He took her hands. 'Forgive me, Jane. I am overwrought. Here I am in this place, bribing whores and a procuress to keep me hidden.'.

She softened at once. 'I understand what you have suffered.'

'There is so much to bear. But for that traitor Buckingham this would not have befallen us. Buckingham and Hastings . . . together they proved our undoing.'

Jane found herself defending her old enemy. 'Hastings did what he thought right. He was loyal to Edward, and he will be loyal to Gloucester and the King. Come, rest a little. Let me pour some wine for you.' She went to the table and poured out some wine.

'Jane,' he said soberly, 'you run great risk in coming here, particularly as you go about the court and bring me news. There would be short shrift for you were you caught. Why do you do it? Why do you not find a more agreeable lover? The great Hastings is panting for you. Yet, you wrap a cloak about you and come to this place. If you were caught even Hastings might not be able to save you. Why do you do it, Jane?' She stood over him with the wine and he drew her down beside him. 'I'll tell you why. You come because you cannot help yourself. You'd follow me to hell, Jane, an I beckoned. You'd follow me to damnation.' He stroked her hair. 'You cannot resist me. Well, you are very fair and you are very loving, and I love you truly. And while we love, what should we care for what happens outside these four walls! That is the glory of love such as ours. You can forget all else in me . . . and I in you. That is the very essence of its appeal for you and for me. I'll warrant Gloucester never found a woman to love his miserable deformed body as you love mine.'

Once more he was battling down her resistance. She could not escape his fascination.

Later, when he lay quietly beside her, he began to talk of Hastings once more.

'Often as I lie here thinking of my ill-fortune I remember this, Jane: Had Hastings been with us, and not against us, there might have been a different story to tell. What odd favourites London chooses! The old City took Edward to its heart for his charm and his beauty, and because he was a fine fellow who liked to seduce its citizens' wives. And when he grew fat and lazy and demanded his benevolences, London still loved him. So with Hastings.

Hastings followed his royal master's habits and London loves Hastings. London listened to Hastings, Jane, when she ought to have listened to me.'

'What good can all this bitterness bring you?'

'Why does Hastings support Gloucester, think you?'

'Because he considers it his duty so to do.'

'You have a high opinion of the man you pretend to despise.'

'I should not have thought you cared so much for me, Thomas,' she said sadly, 'as to be so jealous on my account.'

He covered her face with kisses, but she sensed a lack of warmth in them. 'Ah,' he whispered. 'He is an upright, honourable man, but the most upright and the most honourable can be seduced from their duty.'

'What do you mean?' asked Jane.

But Dorset did not answer. He laughed wildly, caressing her, kissing her; and then he began his love-making all over again.

Later, when Jane looked back on that period of her life, it seemed to her that her passion for Dorset was a madness that possessed her and blinded her to everything but the need to satisfy it.

One day when she went to the house in Southwark she found him in a passion of fury.

'Shut the door,' he commanded, as soon as she entered; he took her by the shoulders, but there was nothing lover-like in the gesture.

'You have news, Thomas?' she asked, startled.

'News of treachery and betrayal. Holy Mother! We have to act now and act quickly.'

'What is this news?'

'It is a lie. It is an evil fabrication of that hog Gloucester. What news, say you? Just this, Jane. He has forced Bishop Stillington to tell the wildest, wickedest lie before the Council that was ever told.'

'Bishop Stillington?' said Jane, her memory stirring.

'He says my stepfather was never truly married to my mother. Edward, he says, was precontracted to a woman who bore him a child and died in a convent, but who was living when he married my mother.'

'Yes,' said Jane slowly, 'I remember.'

He seized her by the arm and shook her. '*You* remember! What nonsense is this? What do you remember? It happened long before you came to court.'

'But Thomas, it is true. Stillington was in the Tower for talking of it. It was . . . about the time that the Duke of Clarence was . . . found dead. I shared Edward's confidences. It is true that he was married before he married your mother.'

Dorset lifted his hand as though to strike her. 'If you ever say that again,' he said, 'I . . . I'll kill you.'

She looked at him; her eyes were cold. He cared nothing for her; he cared only for ambition. He smiled suddenly, seeing in her eyes that which he knew he must dispel.

'Forgive me, Jane. Forgive me, sweetheart. It is this fresh disaster. Do you not see that if this is bruited abroad it is the end of us?'

'The end of the Woodvilles,' she said coldly.

'Then of *us*, Jane, for you are one of us. You and I have been too close for aught else, my dear.'

She was softening towards him already. 'Clarence discovered this,' she said. 'He taunted his brother, the King, with it.'

'Who else knew beside yourself?'

'The Queen and Gloucester. Edward said the secret was with those whom he could trust.'

'Those whom he could trust! That pig and viper Gloucester. And Stillington knows. My father was a fool to let him go free.'

'He was ever one to shelve unpleasant matters. Stillington promised secrecy, so he freed him.'

'On payment of a handsome fine, I'll warrant. My step-father could be trapped into folly with the utmost ease. In his youth it was women; and as he grew older, gold.'

Jane turned to him appealingly. 'Look at the truth, Thomas. Your mother was not truly married to the King, and the Princes are not truly Princes. Therefore is Richard of Gloucester King of England.'

'Be silent! I'll not have it said.'

'It is the truth.'

'So you are against us also? Whom can one trust?'

'I am not against you. How could I be when I love you? But Richard is true King of England.'

'Where is your loyalty, Jane? To me . . . to Edward? You owe something to Edward if not to me. He trusted you, Jane. Are you going to turn against him? It was his wish that young Edward should sit on the throne. Richard of Gloucester is a traitor, for did he not know his brother trusted him and so believed him to be the last man to turn against the little King, that he left the boy in his charge?'

Watching Jane, Dorset saw her troubled eyes. What a fool Jane was! She was too emotional, too generous, too goodhearted. She had come into the world with great gifts–beauty and charm; but she was soft and foolish, too careless of herself. She would come to an evil end one day when her beauty had faded and with it her charm; she would find herself destitute in a careless world.

She wanted to believe Dorset was right. She was thinking of Edward, and how easy it was to think–when it was what she wanted to think–that Gloucester was a traitor, inasmuch as he had promised to care for his brother's son and as soon as his brother was dead set about trying to put himself on the throne.

'Jane,' said Dorset, 'you will help Edward's boy?'

Help young Edward, whom she loved as though he were her own child? Indeed she would. No matter what was right and what was wrong. Love was more important in Jane's eyes than right. For the sake of Edward the King for whom she had abandoned her virtue, for the sake of Edward his son, and for the sake of Dorset, who bound her to him with the bonds of physical desire, she would help.

'You love those children, do you not, Jane?' went on Dorset. 'Not only Edward, but little Richard too. What will become of those poor innocent children if Gloucester takes the throne? They would have their supporters. There would always be those to doubt Stillington and Gloucester. There would be some who would try to put little Edward back upon the throne. And Gloucester? Have you ever looked into those fish's eyes of his? What would Gloucester do, think you, to two innocent boys who stood in his way?'

Jane's eyes were wide with horror. 'But what can I do, Thomas? Richard is truly King of England. Oh . . . but I cannot bear to think what might befall little Edward.'

His face was alight with enthusiasm, and he was very handsome thus. Enamoured of that beautiful face, Jane found it easy to believe in his sincerity.

'This marriage was but a promise. Shall those innocent children suffer for that? Shall all England suffer? Jane, you can help. You must.'

'How?'

'You could rally people to our cause. There is one who, doubtless, could be persuaded to do aught you asked him.'

She stared at him in horror, for Hastings was never far from her thoughts. 'I could do nothing of that nature, Thomas,' she said quickly.

'Why not? Hastings loved Edward. He loves Edward's son.'

'He is Gloucester's friend, and you know that well.'

'He is more eager to be your friend than Gloucester's.'

'I understand you not.' Jane was trembling, and although her eyes flashed, her face was very pale.

'A word from you, Jane, and Hastings would listen. You could talk to him.'

'And what should I say?'

'With soft words you could bring Hastings to our side.'

'I could not do that, Thomas.'

He could have struck her, but he kept his control. He had dominated her before; he would do so again. 'Does it mean nothing to you to see me brought low?'

'It breaks my heart to see you thus.'

'You have a proud look for one who suffers from a broken heart. You condemn me to death; for let me tell you that will be my portion when Richard is on the throne, unless I can escape to France. You condemn the little Princes to the same evil fate. And yet would you but give a word and a smile to a man who would do anything you asked of him, you could save us.'

'You think Hastings would desert Gloucester for you–because I asked him?' She wished she could subdue her excitement; she wished she could stop thinking of Hastings as her lover. Afterwards she would say to him, 'There! You would have betrayed *me* once. Now I have betrayed *you*.'

'You could bring him over–if you were his friend.'

'His *friend*! What do you mean by that?'

He did not answer, and she turned fiercely on him. 'How dare you suggest this! What have you ever cared for me? Be his friend, you say. His friend! I hate you.'

'You are behaving like a child, Jane.' Dorset's lips were coldly prim. 'And, by the Virgin, you mistake me. I said, "Be his friend"; and I meant "Be his friend." You say you hate me. By God, you shall retract that statement in a very short time.' He took her by the shoulders. 'I declare you relish him. You are a shameless harlot. You are weary of me. You long for Hastings.'

Jane beat her fists against his chest in such anger as she had never known in the whole of her life. 'I hate you,' she said, half sobbing. 'I think I've always hated you.'

'How like you, Jane! You say you hate me when you love me. But you say you hate Hastings also. Can it be that you do not know the difference between love and hate?' She had grown quiet, and he drew her to him and touched her hair with gentle fingers as he talked. 'Am I not the most jealous of men? Would I not rather suffer the torment of obscurity and certain death than that you should do–that which it came into your mind to do?' She stirred, but he would not release her. 'But you could speak with him; you could even promise him–for what are promises when one is desperate? You could tell him that between themselves Stillington and Gloucester have concocted this story of a marriage. I'll warrant loyal Hastings would be truly loyal and ready to fight for his little King–should you ask him.'

'But they did not concoct this story, Thomas.'

'Very well. Let Gloucester continue with his evil purpose. What do I care? I cannot live my life in this place. I shall try to escape and doubtless be caught. I shall be thrust into the Tower and tortured, and when to torture me further would be to kill me, they will lead me out to Tower Green, and you will be there, Jane, looking on, to see my head, streaming blood, roll in the straw. You will shed a tear and be sorry then that you did nothing to save the head you once loved, for love me you did, Jane.'

'I still love you,' said Jane.

'No. You love me not. I know it now. Misfortunes, I have learned, come not singly.' He kissed her and drew her on to the couch. He wanted to be sure he had lost none of his power over her. 'Jane, I have asked too much. You must not come here again. It is too dangerous.'

He bent his handsome head to kiss her throat, gently at first, then deliberately he let his kisses grow more passionate. Her eyes were half closed and she was returning his kisses. The moment was approaching for them both when there was nothing but their fleeting need of each other.

'Jane, sweetheart,' he said, 'you will bring Hastings to our side?'

She said then that she would do anything he asked of her. She would talk to Hastings and see what it was possible to do.

'Bless you, Jane,' said Dorset. 'I knew you loved me truly. I knew you'd not fail me.'

Jane was dressing herself with great care, and rarely had she looked so beautiful. She was wearing her favourite blue and her lovely hair was flowing about her shoulders. She was excited, glad that she had decided to bring about the betrayal of Hastings. She had changed, she supposed, since she had come to court. She, the kind-hearted, the most easy-going woman in London, was planning revenge and finding the thought of it sweet. How delicious to play a trick on him, as he had tried to trick her all those years ago!

I am wicked, she thought. I am as bad as the preachers at Paul's Cross say I am.

This morning, as if by accident, she had met him as he made his way to Baynard's Castle, whither he was bound for conference with Gloucester. He had bowed, and his face had lit with pleasure at the sight of her.

She had said to him: 'Good day to you, my lord.' And she had spoken in a more gracious voice than she had ever used towards him before.

'Good day to you, Jane,' he had answered. And then: 'You look distraught. Is anything wrong?' A tender line played about his mouth; a look of yearning was in his eyes; he longed to help her.

'I have much on my mind, my lord. I am a foolish woman, and there is none with whom I can discuss my troubles.'

It was a direct invitation and he had seized upon it. 'Could I be of any help?'

She had been filled with exultation at the eagerness of him. She was no longer important, and yet he was as anxious to please her as anyone ever had been. He did not taunt her with her fall from power. Doubtless there was some good in Hastings; but she was not going to let herself be deceived. She would not forget the past; she would not let her hatred soften.

'It would mean a waste of time, my lord.'

'A waste of my time!' She caught the warmth of his eyes as they rested on her; the longing of years had been in that glance, brightened by such hope as she had never seen there before.

'When, Jane?' he had asked.

'You mean, my lord, that you can spare the time to talk to me?'

'Would you come and sup with me today? That would give me the greatest pleasure.'

'You are good to me. I feel that in view of everything . . .'

'Nay, Jane, forget what went before. That is what we have to do. Forget the past. Shall I see you at four of the clock?'

She had faltered, her sense of shame making her recoil.

'Please, Jane,' he had insisted. 'It will give me the greatest possible pleasure.'

He had had to hurry off then, for he could not keep Gloucester waiting.

Jane had then gone to her house near the river, where, since Dorset had been in hiding, she had lived. The encounter with Hastings had disturbed her deeply. What have I become? she asked herself again and again. She was like an animal that altered its skin to resemble the environment in which it lived. Beside the might of Edward the King she had been serenely comfortable, never dabbling in affairs of state, begging favours for those in trouble; gentle, kindly, witty Jane Shore. But now, through her love for the scheming Dorset, she herself was deep in intrigue. Where was the gentle, forgiving Jane Shore in this woman who now found such pleasure in contemplating revenge for a long-ago injury that had come to nothing? Was it revenge she sought? But what else should she want of Hastings?

She must be wily, cautious and brave. Spies watched her, the spies of Gloucester, the most important–some said the most ruthless–man in England. Danger was stimulating, and so she tingled with excitement as she prepared herself to visit Lord Hastings.

She reached his apartments in good time. One of his attendants, in the brilliant Hastings livery, ushered her ceremoniously in; and immediately she was surrounded by bowing men and women who had evidently been told to expect a person of great importance to their master. She saw then a man she knew to be a certain Catesby, a friend of Hastings. He recognised Jane, bowed to her and went out of the house. Jane wondered then how long it would be before the court was whispering that Jane Shore and Hastings were on terms of intimacy.

Hastings himself had now appeared and was coming forward to greet her; immaculately dressed, he looked very distinguished. The years had softened his face, and the tenderness in his smile made him pleasant to look upon. He was very pale, and Jane saw a nerve twitching in his cheek.

'Jane, it was good of you to come.'

'Nay, my lord, it was good of you to receive me.'

He waved a hand to dismiss his attendants, and they were alone. He said: 'Could you not call me William, since we are to be friends?'

She laughed. 'Friends! After how many years is it–William?'

'Many weary years. Too many to count.' He led her into a small but elegantly furnished room. 'But they have dealt kindly with you, Jane,' he added.

'And not unkindly with you.'

'It is gracious of you to say so; but let us go to the table and I will have supper served immediately.'

She sat down and he went to the bell rope. Menservants came hurrying in to serve the meal. Everything was of the most luxurious. It was as though he said, 'See. I can entertain you even as did the King.'

She could see that he could not stop comparing himself with the late King; she could see that his hopes were high and that he considered this *tête-à-tête* supper to be an introduction to that relationship he had always desired should exist between them.

Peacocks, feather-decorated, were brought in by silent-footed men and maids; there were quails and roast pheasants, ducks and chine of beef. He had been most careful in selecting the choicest of his wines. It was as though he, the epicure, spread his talents before her.

As they ate he talked lightly, and it was not until after they had had their fill, and the serving men and maids were dismissed, that he, leaning his elbows on the table and watching her earnestly, asked if she were not lonely, living as she did.

'Living as I do? How do you know how I live?'

'I draw conclusions. Tell me, there is no . . .'

'Protector?' She laughed lightly. 'Nay, though England has one, I have not.'

'I am glad of that, Jane. I had hoped . . .'

She steered him away from the subject. 'My lord–William–these are troublous times.'

He shrugged his shoulders. 'The Protector is a strong man; and England, like you, Jane, has need of a strong man.'

'But England has a King, has she not?'

'A little boy. Jane, there is much I would say to you and have been trying to say to you ever since you came, but it is not easy. You know my feelings for you. Right from the beginning . . .'

'Oh, William, how that takes me back! Right from the beginning! It reminds me of the time when I was a little girl and my father took me to see a procession.'

'I rode in that procession.'

'You looked at me–and that was the beginning of everything.'

'You would not have supped with me thus unless you had meant to be my friend, Jane?'

'I am your friend, William?'

'You know it is more than friendship that I need from you.'

'Then let us speak frankly, William.'

'That is what I would wish.' He had risen and came over to fill her glass. He rested his hand on her bare shoulder; it was feverish and its touch was a caress. She lifted the hand from her shoulder and put it from her.

'Yes,' she said, 'let us talk.'

He pulled a stool up close to hers and leaned his elbows on the table, watching her face. 'This night,' he said, 'is the happiest of my life since Edward brought you to court. You must believe me, Jane, for I have never ceased to reproach myself for what I did. Jane, will you forgive me?'

She touched his hand lightly, and he seized hers and held it. 'If you ask forgiveness of me,' she said, 'then must I ask it of you. I have been spiteful to you–for years I have taunted you. So please do not let us speak of forgiveness.'

'You were wont to hurt me with your tongue,' he said, 'but I did not forget that you had other powerful weapons which you did not use against me. Some would have ruined my career. Edward's ear was yours, was it not? People used to say that more court was paid to you, in Edward's time, than to any other in the land. You could have had me sent from court–banished–ruined. Oh, Jane, you are not only the fairest, but the sweetest of women.'

Her eyes filled with sudden tears. 'Nay,' she said swiftly; and she was at once miserable and ashamed.

'But yes,' he insisted. 'There is not a soul in London who would not agree with me. You are the dearest of women, and I love you.'

She could not look at him. 'There is much to say,' she stammered. 'Remember, William, it is I who came here to talk to you.'

'You came here to tell me of your loneliness, Jane. I am lonely also. Why should not you and I give each other the comfort we need?' He laughed suddenly. 'That is an ill way of expressing what we could give each other. Comfort! Is Heaven to be spoken of in terms of comfort? Let us forget the past, Jane.'

'We were different people in those days, William.'

Yes, she thought, we were very different. I would never have come here to him for this purpose in those days. I had some sense of honour then, some dignity. But I have changed, even as he has; but he has changed for the better; I for the worse. Dorset has changed me, brutalised me; a woman cannot allow herself to be used as he used me without such treatment leaving its mark upon her.

He went on talking, making excuses for that Hastings who, in his reckless adventuring days, had sought to abduct her, and had laid wicked plans for so doing. He covered his face with his hands. 'And so did I lose you, Jane, for many years. My cruelty was to blame, my vindictiveness towards the goldsmith. How often have I tortured myself with the reflection that it was I who gave you to Edward! I–who willingly and most stupidly gave away that which I longed to possess and cherish.'

'It is done with and forgotten,' she said gently. 'We are no longer young and foolish.'

'And being no longer young and foolish, let us grasp at that which offers delight to us both.'

'Such matters cannot be hastened. I did not come here to talk of myself. There is something else, and I wish to ask your advice. I am distracted. Please, William, help me in this matter, and then–mayhap we can think of–ourselves.'

She saw the hope leap into his eyes. Had she said, 'Help me in this and I will be your mistress'? Had she said it as crudely as that? What had happened to her to make her tremble at the thought of this man's embrace?

'Tell me what troubles you, sweetheart,' said Hastings.

'It is the little King, William. He is nothing more than a little prisoner in the Tower.'

'No, no, Jane. He is no prisoner. He is lodged in the state apartments, awaiting his coronation.'

'While his mother, his young brother and his sisters are kept in Sanctuary?'

'Kept in Sanctuary? They stay there, remember, of their own accord.'

'Because they fear to come out.'

Hastings shrugged his shoulders. 'The Queen was guilty of a planned rebellion. That much was made clear by her hasty retirement into Sanctuary as soon as she knew the plan was foiled.'

'A plan for rebellion?' Jane's cheeks burned. The wine was exciting her; it was more potent that she had guessed, and she suspected Hastings of knowing this. She thought of the sleeping draught which he had induced Kate to give her. She must remember that, for it hardened her against him 'Rebellion against whom? Against the King? Or his uncle? There is a difference, you must know.'

'No, Jane, there is no difference. I pray you, sweetheart, if you will talk of these matters keep your voice low. There are spies everywhere. And, remember, you were once on most friendly terms with one of the chief members of the Queen's family.' She flushed, and he hurried on: 'Forgive me, Jane. That is over and done with, is it not?'

'Do not speak of it again.'

'Nor will I. But remember this, my dear one: you would not be suspected unless you talked with indiscretion. His Grace of Gloucester is most friendly disposed towards you. We have talked of you.'

'You have talked of *me*?'

'With the utmost friendliness on both sides. He forgets not what you once did for him and the Duchess. There is much I have never forgotten–nor ever will.'

'You do well to warn me. I speak without caution. But I will repeat, William my friend, that to side with the little King is not to side with the Duke.'

'What have you heard, Jane?'

'That he conspires with Stillington to take the crown from Edward's son.'

Hastings was astounded. 'How knew you this, Jane?'

'Such news travels fast. Soon all London will be talking of it.'

'I did not know that it had leaked out.'

'I have heard that Stillington proclaimed it at the Council. William, what has happened to Edward's friends, those who swore loyalty to him? They swore to protect his son. Edward never thought his own and trusted brother would turn against the boy.'

'You are hot in defence of the boy, Jane.'

'Because I love him, He and his brother were often with me. I longed for children–and they *were* my children. Do you believe this story Stillington has brought to the Council?'

'I know not what to believe. But if it can be proved, then Richard of Gloucester is rightly Richard the Third of England, as the son of Clarence, through his father's treason, has been attainted.'

'Richard swore allegiance to his brother's son, did he not?'

'He did, but if this can be proved, it is not Richard who owes allegiance to young Edward, but Edward to Richard.'

Hastings is right, she thought. But what of little Edward, whom she loved as if he were her own child? What of Dorset? But during this meeting with the man whom, she must constantly remind herself, she hated as she had never hated anyone before, Dorset was becoming more and more remote. When she did think of him she saw the cruelty of his mouth, and she compared it with the gentleness of Hastings' smile. She had longed for gentleness; she had always wanted love with passion. She knew suddenly that she was doing now what she had longed to do for some time–that was, escape from Dorset. She was bewildered, not knowing what she wanted, to love or to hate, to tease or to surrender. These foolish men, she thought, with feminine logic. A pox on their quarrels! What does it matter who is King–Edward or Richard? Why cannot we all be kind and loving to each other?

Hastings was saying: 'There is good evidence that Stillington speaks truth.'

'But would it not be easy for Gloucester to concoct such a story?'

'If he were of such mind, doubtless it would.'

'And do you believe him to be of such mind?'

'I believe him to be a man of honour.'

'Honour? What is honour? That which is evil to some men could seem good to others. Gloucester swore to his brother to protect the boy, and did he know of this matter before his brother's death? My lord, might it not be that Gloucester seeks to take the crown from that innocent boy's head and wear it himself?' She laid a hand on his shoulder and noted with pleasure that by a touch she could drive all thought of Gloucester from his mind. 'William, you promised loyalty to Edward. Your loyalty has been that quality which I most admired in you. If you desert the King now, how can I go on believing in your honesty?'

Hastings seized her suddenly and swung her off her feet. Her face was on a level with his. 'What do you mean, Jane? Tell me truly. What do you mean?'

'You promised loyalty to Edward,' she said. 'If you desert his son I could never trust you.'

'These are matters in which you should not become involved.'

'Then put me down, my lord, and I will go.'

He shook his head. 'You are not going, Jane. You will stay here with me. You will stay for ever.'

'No,' she said; but she knew she was going to stay, and she knew she wanted to stay. 'How could I, when you are preparing to betray Edward's son–the little boy I love!'

He pressed his mouth against hers. 'What have such matters to do with us? God in Heaven, how I have wanted you! How I have dreamed–and at last you are come to me.'

She thought: I have dreamed too. Nightmares. Did I really want him all the time?

'You must hate me, William,' she said slowly, 'for what I have said to you. Gloucester is your friend and you love him well. You will be faithful to him, unto death–more faithful than you would be to me.'

She heard his voice, slurred with passion, yet soft with tenderness. 'Hate? Sometimes I have thought I hated you, but that was only because I loved you. You are right when you say that Gloucester is my friend; but what are friends set side by side with lovers? What could Gloucester ever be to me beside Jane Shore? My Jane, my own–whom I have yearned for and dreamed of these many years. But now you are come to me, and now you shall stay. You shall never leave me again.'

'I do not know,' she said weakly. 'I cannot say . . .'

'You are a madness in me,' he told her, 'a madness that has been chained to my heels for many long years. This was meant to be, Jane. I have always known it. I loved Edward well until he brought you to court and showed so clearly that he meant to keep you there; then I longed for his death. Such was my love for you.'

'It was not true love,' she insisted. 'If it had been I might have loved you when you came to me in Cheapside. It was because you played false that I have hated you ever since.'

'You would have loved me then, had I acted differently all those years ago?'

'We promised we would not speak of the past. I trust you now. I have drunk of your wine, though in view of what once happened I might so easily have been afraid.'

'Everything that happens now between us must be with your most willing agreement. I am not such a fool as I once was.'

'Then I think I should go home.'

'I beg of you to stay. I have not said all I wish to. You came to me because you were distressed on behalf of the King. What did you hope that I would do about this matter?'

'I hoped that you might see the boy–comfort him. I hoped that you might bring your powers to work for him and not against him.'

'I had hoped you came because you were lonely and sought my company.'

'Mayhap there was something of that in it.'

'Stay with me, Jane.'

'I cannot think clearly. Let me go now–and another time . . .'

'You slipped away from me before, and I cannot let you do so again. You no longer hate me. You never did hate me. Confess it, Jane. You never did.'

'It was not hatred then. I do not know what it was–but it had the look of hatred.'

'When I kiss you,' he said, 'you tremble. Jane–you need me.'

She did need him. She was lonely and she wanted to be loved, not cruelly but tenderly. She must escape from Dorset, and Hastings would show her the way. She needed the devotion of Hastings to heal those wounds she had received through Dorset's brutal treatment.

She lifted her face to Hastings. If this is hatred, she thought, it is peculiarly stimulating, exciting–and deeply satisfying.

Hastings smiled, and his smile was one of triumph.

Was she acting a part–the part of Hastings' mistress? How easy, how delightful it was to play! How pleasant to run to him when he returned to her, to beg him to take care when he went out, to return his kisses!

One day, she thought, I shall laugh scornfully at him. I shall say, 'Now, my lord, this is how you would have made me suffer. I wonder how many of your victims have felt as you do now!'

Yet she would weep real tears when he went to one of those council meetings. She would start with terror when she heard a commotion at the door. For they were more than lovers now; they were conspirators. How easy it was when he lay beside her, indolent after satisfied passion; shorn of his power like Samson of his locks, how simple to win his loyalty for little Edward! How easy to let him believe that between them Stillington and Gloucester had concocted this story of Eleanor Butler! Hastings was deeply in love. What did he care for Gloucester? He cared only for Jane Shore. He was completely happy; he had attained that goal for which, over many years, he had strived.

The excitement of her relationship with Hastings soon made Jane impatient of politics. Her thoughts were concentrated on Hastings the lover; Hastings the statesman, now head of the new secret party, was remote. She did not realise the immensity of this matter for which she was largely responsible. Hastings was winning more important personages to his side; they came secretly to his house and were shut in with him for hours at a time; Jane did not think of what they might be planning; she was only angry that they took him from her side.

He would talk to Jane of what he had done, this day and that, until she would stop her ears and refuse to listen. Then he would laugh and kiss her, and tell her he was glad she kept aloof from these quarrels: he would forget everything then, but themselves; and they would enjoy their love together.

She had finished with Dorset now, for not since her early days with Edward had she known such happiness.

Hastings said: 'Sometimes I fear I have dreamed all this, and that I shall awaken and find you not beside me. For in truth, Jane, this happiness you have brought me makes my days pass as though I dream.'

He was right. It was like a dream. An odd, exciting, fascinating dream of hate–or love.

There was one man who watched the lovers with calculating eyes. He was a man named Catesby; of great ambitions, he had been a close friend of Hastings and enjoyed his confidences. He had come a long way, largely owing to the help of Hastings, but he looked ahead to greater achievement. He knew, as Hastings' friend and confidant, that the noble had recently changed sides. This was folly, reasoned Catesby, and Hastings was surely bewitched. How could Hastings succeed when his opponent was the cleverest, subtlest man in England? Catesby had decided on which side he was going to be. He had to choose, and he chose Gloucester.

Not that he told Hastings this. Why should he? It was simple to go to Hastings' meetings, to listen to his plans. The Protector had already noticed him and commended him. How much more warmly would the great man commend him if he disclosed the Hastings plot to him.

Hastings was a fool–a love-sick fool. He seemed hardly aware of the danger he was in. If ever Catesby had seen a man being led to disaster, that man was Hastings; beckoned on, he was, by beautiful Jane Shore. What a fool he was to let a woman lead him to oppose the mighty Gloucester, for Gloucester would have no mercy; he cared nothing for his friends; he only cared for England.

One would desert one's patron for the future King of England if one were wise, and Catesby was wise. It was hardly a week after Jane's first visit to Hastings that Catesby strolled along to Crosby Hall and begged an audience with the Protector, stressing that it was of the utmost importance that the interview be granted. He was conducted to Richard at once.

Richard had changed in the last weeks. He was paler than ever; his eyes were alert and he seemed almost furtive in his watchfulness.

He was deeply shocked as he listened to Catesby's story. His cold eyes kindled into such heat of anger that Catesby seemed to shrivel before it.

'You dare accuse–*Hastings*–of treachery!'

'My lord, Your Grace, I know it to be so. Hastings has taken me into his confidence. He has been bewitched by Jane Shore, who, Your Grace knows, was mistress to Dorset. She is with him night and day. She is a witch, Your Grace, and witches can seduce strong men from duty. He will go whither she beckons, and she beckons him to treachery.'

Richard was full of anxiety. He had looked on Hastings as his most reliable friend.

'This must be false,' he said sadly.

'I would it were, Your Grace. I had loved Hastings. It is the woman who has bewitched him.'

'Good men are not bewitched, Catesby, nor lured from honour. How can I know you speak the truth?'

Richard closed his eyes. The heat was oppressive today. He felt tired and sick. Whom could he trust if Hastings failed him? He could never trust any again. He would have trusted Hastings with his life.

'There are many of his household who could be questioned, Your Grace.'

'You are right, Catesby.'

'I trust I pleased Your Grace in coming.'

'You did the only possible thing, Catesby. When traitors are abroad 'tis the duty of every right-thinking man to expose them. Go now and speak of this to none. I trust you, Catesby.'

'Your trust is not misplaced, my lord Duke.'

'You may leave this to me. I will attend to it.'

He watched Catesby depart. His face puckered suddenly. Not Hastings! Not his old and trusted friend! Hastings had been Edward's friend–one of his ablest statesmen, one of his most admired friends. Richard had thought he had inherited that friendship. But if Catesby had spoken the truth Hastings was at this very moment plotting against him.

Anger surged up and drowned his sorrow. Hastings should regret this day. There was no time to lose. He must test the truth of this story, and if it proved to be true, he would know how to act.

In the privacy of their chamber Jane helped Hastings prepare himself for the meeting of the Council. Now she must help him into his coat; now she must fetch his shoes, and flick imaginary dust from his garments, for the joy of touching him.

She knew the truth now. She loved Hastings. She wanted to explain to him her wanton wickedness, how she had meant to lure him to love her, and then turn from him and laugh at him, as he would have laughed at her all those years ago.

It was no use trying to explain. There was no time for explanations; there was only time for happiness. They had wasted so much time, he said. They must waste no more. Every moment must be a joy to her as it was to him, for his heart's desire had come to him, and what more of life could any man or woman ask?

Sometimes he was afraid of so much happiness; then Jane would laugh at him. Jane was ready to snatch at all the happiness about her, as her due. She showed him how to do the same.

And now, as she fluttered round him, they would pause and smile in this delightful intimacy, laughing now and then, not at anything in particular, but just because they were happy.

'Jane,' he said reluctantly, 'I must hurry, or I shall be late.'

'You'll not be late. Your barge is waiting at the steps.'

'It will not do to keep Gloucester waiting.'

'Oh–he is easy-tempered enough.'

'Easy-tempered when things go well, but he does not care to be kept waiting.'

'But, my lord, you are so clever; most graciously would you excuse your lateness.'

'What should I say? "My Lord Duke, I beg your pardon for my lateness. But Your Grace himself would have been late had he to bid farewell to the loveliest lady in the world." '

They laughed, with the quick delight of happy people.

'Make me not your excuse, sir,' laughed Jane, She was sober suddenly. She put her arms about him and scanned his face. 'William, sometimes I grow uneasy.'

'Uneasy? Why, bless you, Jane, there's naught to fear.' He kissed her tenderly. 'I'll be back shortly. You will see. Watch for the barge. I'll come straight back to you.'

'But you go to the Tower, and I never liked the place. There is an overpowering melancholy about it. I remember little Edward's saying that young children were built into those walls years ago. I am foolish, I know, but I wish this meeting was not at the Tower.'

'You must not be uneasy, sweetheart. I swear I'll be back soon. 'Tis nothing–a meeting fixed weeks back.'

She looked at him solemnly. 'Before you changed sides?'

He laughed. 'Listen, Jane! We are right. We plan no treason. We fight for the rights of Edward the Fifth. Only traitors need fear the Tower.'

'Only traitors? Many an innocent man has passed through the Traitor's Gate, William!'

' 'Tis unlike you to be morbid, and I'll not have it.' He lifted her and kissed her. 'Come, kiss me, Jane. I'll be back with you by midday.'

She kissed him and went down with him to the barge.

'Turn and wave to me, William,' she said. 'Do not forget.'

'Forget you, sweetheart? 'Tis something I could never manage, as you well know.'

He was gone. She watched the boatmen row him down the river . . . down towards the Tower. Hastings waved his hand. She continued to stand on the bank watching. In the distance she could see the fortress that seemed to brood like a great sentinel over the City. She shivered and wondered if Anne Neville was watching Richard set out for the Council in the Tower.

Hastings sat back in the boat, thinking of Jane, impatiently longing for the time when he could return to her. Strange, this fever in his veins. Love had soured his life for many years and at last had sweetened it. He could see the flower gardens along the river banks. The roses were beautiful, for it was the month of roses. He smiled at the yellow flowers of the St John's wort that grew in such profusion, tangling itself about the frailer stems and strangling the life out of them. The grass was more green this year; the trees were more beautiful and abundant in their foliage. Never before had he realised how very beautiful was this City. Perhaps, though, it had never been so beautiful as it was now. Perhaps this year, which he would always remember as the first of his union with Jane, was indeed a glorious year, not only for him but for all London.

He thought of the years stretching out before him; they were to be the happiest of his life, for Jane had brought him such deep peace and pleasure as he had never thought to enjoy. Tender devotion, tempered with passion and the weight of experience to give deep understanding to one another–that was what they had come to. He had built up a pretty story about himself and Jane. It was a delightful romance of sadness and misunderstanding. They had loved right from the beginning; but he had not known it then. Young and hot-blooded, he had imagined that what he felt for her was the same as he had felt for others; and he had disappointed her so that she had turned to Edward. That was easy to understand. Glittering Edward had been the most powerful man in the country, charming and irresistible. And all the time it was Hastings whom she had truly loved. A pleasant thought. But now the great grey towers were throwing their reflection on the sunlit waters; the boat shot rapidly along, and then the boatman was tying it to the ring, and Hastings was swinging out of the boat, mounting the damp and slippery steps, and walking swiftly to the council chamber.

He glanced towards the palace to see if there was any sign of the little King. There was none. He met Lord Stanley and Bishop Morton, and they went in together.

It was cold inside those thick walls after the warmth of the sun. In the big room the men seated themselves at the council table and waited. The Duke of Gloucester was late. Hastings drummed his fingers on the table. Where was the Protector? It rarely happened that he was late; it was a nuisance. His lateness would prolong the Council and it might be that Hastings would not be with Jane at midday as he had promised.

He was lost in a sensuous dream. He was not in this gloomy chamber, but in his own comfortable quarters. He saw his bedroom, made delightful now with the evidence of Jane's presence about it. Jane was sitting on a stool, combing her hair as it glinted like real gold in the sunshine.

The councillors had risen, for the Protector had entered the room. Richard was smiling, though he looked pale, and there were deep shadows under his eyes, which suggested sleeplessness. Hastings was sorry suddenly for the Protector, pitying his frail body; there was something inherently unlovable about Richard of Gloucester. Hastings laughed at himself–Hastings, the crafty statesman, thinking of love at a council meeting called by the Protector, the man he himself was plotting to overthrow!

In the presence of the Protector he felt unsure. It had always been so. Unlovable, cold and distant, Richard might be, but he inspired respect. There was a certain icy nobility about him. If he was accepting the Stillington story, thought Hastings, it must be because he believed it to be true.

Richard was exchanging pleasantries with Morton now, complimenting the Bishop on the fine strawberries he had seen growing at Ely House when he was last in Holborn. The Bishop must send him some, for he was fond of strawberries. Sly old Morton, who hated Gloucester as a mouse hates a cat, was obsequiously bowing and promising the best of his strawberries. He declared he would immediately despatch a servant to gather them for the Duke.

'My lords,' said Richard, 'would you excuse me for a while? Continue with your deliberations. There are matters which require my attention in this place. I pray you therefore proceed. I will be with you ere long.'

He went out. Strange, thought Hastings; he scarce looked my way.

It was almost an hour before Richard returned. His face was grey, his hands trembling, and from the working of his mouth and the glitter of his eyes it would seem that this trembling was an indication of anger.

He strode across to his seat in the council chamber. There was silence, awed and tense. He sat down, and still the silence lasted. He seemed to be struggling within himself to find words.

Suddenly he stood up and, in tones most unlike those it was his custom to employ, he began to shout.

'My relationship to His Grace the King,' he cried, 'is close. It was I whom my brother entrusted with the administration of this country.'

The Council, puzzled, could only murmur its agreement. A silence of some seconds prevailed, then Richard cried: 'And what punishment, think you, my noble lords, should those deserve who seek to bring about my destruction?'

Nobody spoke, but Hastings felt an icy coldness grip his body.

'Answer me!' cried Richard, banging on the table.

But none dared answer. Some looked to Hastings, for he was the Protector's oldest friend. If any dared speak, then must it be Hastings.

He stood up and faced the Protector. 'My lord, surely they deserve to be punished as traitors, whoever they be.'

'Whoever they be,' said Richard; and he laughed suddenly and bitterly. 'Then shall I tell you who these traitors be! I shall tell you who they be who plot against me. There is my brother's widow. And for another . . . she who was his mistress. You know which I mean . . . Jane Shore. Both of these have worked together to destroy me.'

At the mention of Jane's name Hastings had turned pale. He knew that every member of the Council was watching him, for there was not a man there who did not know the relationship he himself bore towards Jane, nor that he had come straight from her that morning.

'Your Grace,' began Hastings; but now Richard had turned on him, now he was coming to the great moment towards which he had been working.

'Well, my Lord Hastings?' he asked; and his voice seemed suddenly shot with malice and contempt.

'If they have done such things, Your Grace, and if it can indeed be proved against them,' began Hastings.

Richard silenced him. 'And do you answer me with your "ifs" and "ands"?' he shouted. 'I tell thee, traitor, that they have done it.' Every man round the table caught his breath as the word 'traitor' fell from Richard's lips; every eye was now on Hastings. 'And I,' continued Richard, very slowly so that not one word was to be lost, 'I swear by St Paul that thou hast joined them in this villainy.'

Richard was indeed sick at heart, for he had known for certain from the moment he had mentioned Jane Shore's name, that Hastings was a guilty man. Hastings . . . whom he had thought to be his friend. He looked at the man standing before him, bold and defiant. And I thought he loved me, thought Richard, even as he loved Edward my brother. What is it that Edward had and I have not? Edward was a light liver, a man who did not always keep a sacred promise; yet men loved Edward, as they never love me.

There came to him an inclination to say: 'Hastings, go your way. I cannot see the death of one who, though he may have changed, was once my friend.' But that was fools' talk. A man would indeed be asking for failure if he allowed a traitor to live. He must lash himself to fresh fury. He must see this man, not as one he had loved, but as the traitor he was; and there was one state and one place in which traitors should be–and that was headless on Tower Green.

He turned from Hastings.

'I swear I'll not dine before your head is brought to me, traitor!' he said; and as he did so he struck on the table with his fists which was a sign for the guards waiting outside, to enter.

'Treason! Treason!' cried the guards, rushing into the council chamber.

'You know your duty,' said Richard. 'Every one of these men is to be placed under arrest.' With scorn he watched the members of the Council. He saw Stanley resist arrest, and watched the blood streaming from his mouth as a consequence. The guards did their duty. And, as Richard watched, it was of Hastings he thought. Hastings he had almost loved; and he had believed Jane Shore to be his friend. Morton he had never liked nor trusted. But that Hastings should betray him! False friends were more to be feared than lifelong enemies. He would deal with Hastings expeditiously. There should be no softness for Hastings.

'Ha, traitor!' he said, looking straight into Hastings' face. 'You are under arrest, and by the Virgin, I'll not dine this day till your head and body have parted company!'

The guards had heard. They hurried the members of the Council to cells awaiting them. Their arrest was precautionary. It remained to be seen whether they were all guilty. But Hastings had had Richard's trust. There should be no leniency for Hastings. They faced each other. Two stalwart warders gripped the arms of Hastings; another held his halberd at Hastings' chest. They awaited the Duke's commands, for had he not said, regarding this man, that he would not dine until his execution, and was not His Grace of Gloucester ever a man to keep his word?

'Let him be taken to the Green at once,' said Richard.

'At once!' cried Hastings aghast. 'I have never heard the like of this. Am I to have no trial? No chance of proving my innocence?'

'You are already proved guilty, my lord,' said Richard.

'Is this a new law the Protector would impose on England?' asked Hastings haughtily.

'It has ever been the law of England that those who plot against its government shall die the traitor's death.'

'Without being proved guilty?'

'I have proved you guilty, my lord. Your perfidy is well known to me . . . and that of your mistress.'

'I implore Your Grace that, whatever you do to me, you will spare Jane.'

'I do not take revenge on foolish women. She shall be punished but . . . My lord, I refuse to discuss this matter with you.' He shouted to the guards, 'Take him away! Take him to the Green!'

'You cannot mean this,' said Hastings. 'There was never execution such as you propose since England promised a fair and honest trial to all. The block must be prepared and . . .'

'Doubtless,' said Richard grimly, 'a piece of wood which will serve as a block may be found.'

'You would deny me a priest then?'

Richard hesitated.

'Take him to the Green,' he ordered. 'See that a priest is sent for. Let him make his peace with God. And hurry . . . for I have made a vow I will not eat while Hastings lives.'

Jane was uneasy–restless. She longed for the return of Hastings. When he returned she decided she would tell him everything; she would try to explain the madness Dorset had wrought in her. She wanted Hastings to know that he had rescued her from enslavement.

She went into the garden and back and forth to the river's edge; she could not keep her eyes from wandering towards those grim grey towers.

But at length she could not bear to stay there longer, watching and waiting for his return. She went into the house and tried to occupy herself with reading, but her thoughts wandered out to the garden, to the river, to the Tower; and on the page before her she saw the river glittering in the sunshine, the fields of red sorrel and white moon daisies stretching out beyond the City, and brooding over the scene, the Tower of London.

And because she could not shake off her fear, she tried to pray. She was disturbed at her prayers by an attendant, knocking urgently on her door. She bid the woman enter.

'There is someone below who begs to see you, Madam,' she was told.

'Who is it?'

'A woman, Madam. She says that the matter is urgent. She is very distressed.'

'Then bring her to me quickly,' said Jane.

Kate came running in. She was breathless and there were tears on her cheeks.

'Kate, Kate, what is wrong? You have come from the Tower. . . . Is it . . . my lord?'

Kate nodded.

'What, Kate . . . oh what?'

'If you would see him before he dies, there is not a moment to lose,' said Kate.

The room seemed to sway. She could not be hearing aright. Before he . . . died? But only this morning he had been in this room . . . so much alive . . . so much in love with her and with life.

'Perhaps even now,' said Kate, 'it is too late. But he was promised a priest.'

'Kate, Kate, what are you saying?'

Kate was weeping bitterly. 'I heard it was to be, just before he was arrested. Come, my little love, or you will never see him alive.'

She let Kate lead her from the house, down across the soft grass to where Kate's boat was waiting. How slowly they moved towards the cruel fortress!

'I heard it from the guards,' said Kate. 'It was at the council meeting. My Lord Gloucester was in a fury. He had discovered a plot, 'twas said.'

Jane stared unseeingly at the lovely banks, at the flowering shrubs and the fruit trees that marched down to the sun-dappled water. After this, she thought, I shall hate all summer days.

She knew she had betrayed Hastings. Her revenge was complete. He had given her to Edward and now she had given him to Death.

They left the boat; they ran along the path between those oppressive grey towers; past the Beauchamp, past the White Tower. . . . She saw the church on the Green through her tears; and then the Green itself, with that little group of men.

'Stand away there!' called a voice; but she did not heed it. Her running footsteps carried her on; her streaming eyes sought those of Hastings. She saw the colour rush into his face, which previously had been grey as the weather-washed walls of the towers.

'Jane!'

'William, my dearest!' She flung herself at him.

'You should not have come,' he said.

'I had to come. There is so much to say. I must confess it all. I love you, William. What will my life be without you?'

'You have made my last days happy ones, Jane,' he said.

She shook her head. 'William . . . I came to you . . . I came to you . . .' The words would not come, but she fancied he understood.

'Nothing matters now, Jane. Forgive all I tried to do to you.'

'There is nothing–nothing. It was I . . . I did not come–to you in love. But now that is changed. I love you, and I have brought you to this. . . . Oh, God in Heaven, could we but go back a few short days! It is I, who love you, who am taking your life.'

Hastings put her from him. 'You must go from here. Go now, Jane. Go quickly. Stop for nothing. Hide yourself–and stay in hiding. In a little while it will be safe for you to come forth. But now–you are in danger.'

'It matters not.'

A guard stepped forward and touched Hastings' shoulder. 'My lord . . .' he began.

Jane, shuddering, turned her eyes back to the Green, where a piece of wood, hurriedly taken from the chapel, where repairs were in progress, had been laid on the grass to do service as a block.

Hastings nodded. His eyes seemed to look beyond the walls of the Tower, beyond the river, into eternity. Already he had taken on the look of a man who has left the world behind him.

Somewhere on the river Jane could hear the splashing of oars. The ravens came close and croaked hideously.

'Goodbye,' said Hastings. 'Remember this. You made my last days the happiest of my life. Go now. You must not see the end.' He appealed to Kate. 'Take her away–quickly. And look after her.'

'I will, my lord,' sobbed Kate.

They took him to that rough piece of wood, for there must be no delay. The Protector was an impatient man, and he must not be kept from his dinner.

Kate was pulling Jane away from the tragic Green. Hastings shrugged his shoulders. This was the end; the end of ambition, the end of love. He had had fifty-three years of adventure and a whole week of love.

He scorned to have his eyes bandaged. He stood erect taking in the scene. One last look at the sparkling river; one last look at the grey towers. Goodbye, London! Goodbye, Jane! Goodbye to love and life!

Calmly he laid his head on the rough wood. Swiftly and silently the axe descended. His head rolled on the straw; there was a short and horrible stillness everywhere before the ravens resumed their croaking.

Ludgate

The procession wended its way slowly through the streets of London. Measured was the tread of the pious churchmen; they walked, chanting, the palms of their hands pressed together, their eyes turned heavenwards. There was one among them, white-robed and scornful of face, who carried the great cross, holding it high as he walked, and chanting with the rest. And before him, her feet bare, and with nothing to cover her except a plain kirtle of rough worsted which fell from her waist to her feet, walked a woman. Her beautiful golden hair spread itself about her shoulders to cover her nakedness, and she carried a lighted taper in her hand. This was no common harlot of the streets; it was Jane Shore, King's favourite, judged guilty of harlotry by the Lord Bishop of London, who had sentenced her to do penance that she might make amends for the sinful life she had led.

The cobbles were hurting her feet; already they were sore and bleeding; the sun was hot upon her naked skin that gleamed white as milk, through the yellow of her hair. Merchants and apprentices, housewives and prostitutes, rich men and beggars had lined the streets to see the greatest show for years. Jane Shore, rich and powerful–to whom in the days of King Edward more court had been paid than to any noble in the land–was brought as low as the commonest harlot from the stews of Southwark.

But Jane did not feel the contempt of the churchmen; she did not hear the tittering murmurs of the crowd; she scarcely felt this shame, for there was no room in her heart for anything but bitter remorse. What mattered it that she must parade thus, half-naked, through the streets of London? What mattered it that she was branded Harlot? What mattered anything? for Hastings was dead, and she had sent him to his death. 'Oh, God,' she murmured as she stumbled on, 'would that I had died with him!'

It was hot, and the stench from the Fleet stream was polluting the air more evilly than usual on this Sunday morning. Many pairs of eyes watched the beautiful woman, eyes that scorned and eyes that pitied; and many that followed the unconscious grace of her looked longingly and lecherously upon her, even as they called her 'harlot'. But only vaguely did Jane hear the mutter of their voices; she was not aware of the scorn and lust, the indignation and the pity; or of the quirking lips that professed their horror that such shame could befall a woman, and showed so plainly that it delighted them to behold such shame. Jane's downcast eyes did not see her cut and bleeding feet; she saw nothing but the eyes of Hastings as he had looked his last on London's river.

Her eyes were hard and bright, and the crowd marvelled at her dignity.

'See how proudly she walks! Has she no shame, then?'

'Shame? Shame on them that would shame her, I'd say.'

'And I. And I. When I was a-starving in the plague year it was Jane Shore who saved the lives of me and my fatherless little ones.'

'Aye, a good woman, for all her harlot's ways. Our good King Edward loved her. God rest his soul.'

The procession had halted, for it had reached the cathedral. The pious ones had grown more pious, the scornful more scornful.

Jane was lifted temporarily out of the misery which thoughts of Hastings must bring her, for she realised that the moment had come when she must enter the cathedral and offer her lighted taper to the images of the saints.

She could say to herself, 'I am sinful. I sent the man I loved to his death, and I no longer care to live.' What a mockery was this! These men about her with their chants and their prayers and their secret lusts–for there were few who were guiltless–would now see her do penance; they would enjoy her shame while pretending to deplore it. They, who had paid court to her while the King lived, who had dared show nothing but respect, now drew their robes closer about their bodies as though fearing contamination. 'Purge this woman of her sins,' they prayed. And they thought: 'Thank God I have the good sense to keep my secrets.'

How she and Edward would have laughed at these men, could they have seen into the future! What would Edward have said, had he seen his fat bishops who had done such honour to his favourite mistress, now condemning her for having loved him too well? But Edward was dead; Hastings was dead; and Jane envied them.

The heat in the cathedral was stifling, and the faces of the images looked back blankly at her. She threw back her hair and caught the glistening eyes of sweating priests upon her, and, flushing, quickly covered herself with her veil of hair.

A penance, she knew, was a lucky escape, for she might have been sentenced to death. Swift death would have been sweet. She thought lovingly of the clean cut of the axe. One last moment to look over the sparkling river, to sense the sweet beauty of a summer's morning with that clarity which she knew had come to Hastings. The grey towers, the blue sky, the warm sun–and then a quick stroke, a firm cut–and one stepped from all that was familiar into the unknown. She had longed for it. But Richard of Gloucester had decided to be magnanimous. He had washed his hands, reserved his judgment, and handed her over to the Bishop of London. And so the Bishop had, most righteously deploring that immorality to which he had turned a blind eye during Edward's lifetime, sentenced her to this penance. Disgrace instead of death. The familiar streets instead of the unknown. A crowd of sightseers instead of her Maker.

The respite was short. Now she must leave the cathedral and face the crowds once more. Now she must go to Paul's Cross and there make public confession of her sins, as the Bishop had said she should. She must be a warning to those women who might fall into temptation, as she had fallen. She was to be an object of ridicule and shame to the poor of London who, as a result of the many services she had been able to render them when the affection of the King had been hers, had come to see a virtue in her sin, and had condoned–nay, admired her–in her evil life.

She heard the hush that went through the watching crowds as she came out into the sunshine, and she longed again for death. She folded her hands across her breasts and made her way to the cross.

In the crowd someone murmured a curse on the Protector for subjecting good and beautiful Jane Shore to such public indignity. The bishop had sentenced her, it was said. Well, bishops did what their masters told them, and the Protector was to blame.

There was one person standing on the edge of the crowd who was watching with great interest. Mary Blague, as fashionably dressed as ever, had aged, her skin had grown more wrinkled, her eyes more sly. How she had hated Jane Shore! Loved by Edward. Loved by Dorset. Loved by Hastings. Who would be her next lover?

She turned to the man beside her; his lips were slack, his eyes glazed as he kept them on Jane Shore.

''Tis a pity, sir,' said Mary, 'to see a woman brought so low.'

His face hardened, his eyes grew cruel and his lips tight. 'So should all harlots confess their shame,' he said in anger.

'You speak truth,' said Mary; and inwardly she laughed and thought, Look your fill. She is not for you.

There were few in London that morning who were not thinking of Jane Shore. In Baynard's Castle the Duchess of Gloucester wept for her. Even the Protector could not get her out of his thoughts. He had been lenient with her. He wished the people to cast aside the glorified pictures they had made of her in their ignorant impious minds. They must see her now, evil and lewd, with the lighted taper in her hand; they must see that she was no better than any slut from Southwark. He must destroy her influence with the people. She had earned death, for she was as treacherous as Hastings; but his wife had pleaded for her, had bid him remember what Jane had done for them; nor did he feel real anger towards her. But she must suffer, as all must, who worked against Richard of Gloucester.

His good friend Catesby came in to report to him.

'Your Grace, the woman has done her penance. I never saw such a crowd in all my life.'

'What think the people now of their goddess?'

Catesby was silent.

'Answer me!' said Richard.

'Methinks, my lord, that though some were glad to see her shame, there were many to pity her.'

'Pity! They should congratulate her on her good fortune.'

He knew in his heart that this was another example of the love and respect which these charming people managed to win from others. Jane Shore, the harlot, was loved; and people were sad to see her disgrace. Richard of Gloucester, who sought nothing but his country's good, was not liked at all. He glanced shrewdly at Catesby. The man had not said there were murmurings in the crowd against himself; but were there? He suspected that if he pressed Catesby he might discover the truth. But why should he? He knew without asking.

Jane was free. She had been tried by the bishop; she had listened to his diatribe on her wickedness; and she had done her penance and might go now and mend her ways.

A concealing cloak wrapped about her, she came out of the bishop's palace into the streets, those streets which had formed the backcloth of the stage on which she had played so many parts. She could never pass Lombard Street without remembering her life with Will; and in Cheapside she must recall her father's household. It was in Bishopsgate that she had first seen Hastings; and now she could turn her eyes towards the fortress and think of days spent in the palace there when Edward was her lover, and that other day just behind her when Hastings was taken out to the Green to die.

The rain was beginning to fall and a mist was floating up the river. She hurried on. She was tired of the streets which held so many memories. She must remember that now she had to start a new life; and as she did not know what sort of life it was going to be, she must get away from the streets and think about it.

She went towards that house which Edward had given her some years before his death. Edward had filled it with treasures when he had given it to her. The richest plate was hers; the hangings on the bed itself were worth a fortune; but now the place looked dark and gloomy. She knocked at the door, but no one came to answer it, and turning the handle she found that the door was open. She went in slowly, wonderingly. The hall had been stripped of everything it had contained.

She called to her maids. 'Janet! Bess! Anne! Where are you all?' Her voice echoed through the house in a hollow fashion.

She ran across the hall and pushed open the door of her favourite parlour. All the rich hangings had been removed, the carpets had been taken from the floors.

'Janet!' she called again, and listened to the echo of her voice through an empty house.

Understanding came to her. Her servants had gone; her goods had been taken from her. Mayhap the house itself no longer belonged to her. It would have passed with its rich contents to the Crown, for had she not been guilty of treason to the Lord Protector? She went slowly to the staircase and sat down on the bottom stair. She covered her face with her hands and laughed. She who had been so rich in love and wordly goods was now unloved and penniless. She was crying now, hysterically, telling herself that she would stay in this empty house until she died.

She was not sure how long she sat there, but dusk had begun to creep into the house when she was suddenly aware of a movement outside. Someone was standing on the other side of the door which she had left ajar. Jane stared at the door. It moved, half an inch at first, then it was pushed open. A woman stood there looking at Jane; and as Jane stared at her she shut the door behind her as she came into the hall.

'Good evening to you, Jane Shore.' The voice was expressionless, and in this light Jane could not see the woman's face, but she fancied she had heard the voice before, and though she could not say to whom it belonged yet a great uneasiness came to her..

'Good evening. I think I know your voice. Who are you?'

'Of a surety you know me, Jane. I am an old friend.'

Jane struggled to her feet, and as she did so her cape fell open, betraying the fact that she wore nothing but the kirtle in which she had done her penance.

'So they took your clothes as well,' said the woman.

'They have taken everything–everything I had.'

'Then right glad I am that I came.' The woman came closer and opened her cape. Jane looked into her face, and at that moment ceased to think of death and was filled with an urgent desire to protect herself against the evil she had come to associate with this woman.

'Mary Blague!' she cried.

'None other.' As Jane moved away from her Mary extended a hand and caught her arm.

'Please leave me,' said Jane quickly. 'I . . . I can fend for myself. I have friends in London.'

'And here is one who has come to you, guessing that here she would find you.'

'It was good of you, but . . . I have those to whom I can go.'

'I was in the crowd,' said Mary.

'It seemed all London was there.'

'I came here to offer you help.'

'It is good of you . . . but I cannot accept your help.'

'Come, Jane. You are half faint with lack of food and exposure. You grow hysterical. You remember against me that it was I who, in my house, arranged that you should meet the King. But he asked it, Jane, and who was I to refuse him? You are sick and ill and you have not eaten for days. Let bygones be bygones. It is true I acted wrongly with regard to you and the King. It is true, as you know, that I own a house of ill-fame in Southwark.

Oh, Jane Shore, have you not yet learned of the terrible things that can happen to a woman who is alone and friendless? If she has money . . . that is another matter. Come, Jane. I am human. I wronged you once. Give me a chance to repay that wrong.'

Jane was swaying. Mary Blague's talk of food made her feel dizzy. She had scarcely eaten since the day they had executed Hastings. She felt light-headed, and had to keep reminding herself that the penance was over; she was here in a house which had once belonged to her, and Mary Blague was standing before her, offering assistance.

Mary had an arm about her; Mary's small eyes seemed half-closed. 'Come, Jane, you are dizzy. Come home with me. Oh, do not shrink from me. Of course I do not mean to Southwark. I mean to the house where I make my lace. Oh, there was a time when your eyes would dance at the thought of coming there. What the years do to us!'

'I cannot go with you,' said Jane.

'Oh yes, my dear, you must; for believe me it is the wisest plan. With me you can rest awhile. You are sick and ill, and have need of rest. But come with me you must, for, look, I am here, waiting to succour you.'

'I do not care what becomes of me.'

'Your sadness is too close to you, my dear. It is ever thus when tragedy stands close. But remember it is behind you now. You have passed it, and every day will carry you farther from it.'

Jane turned from the woman to the emptiness of the house. What did it matter where she went or what became of her? But she could not go with Mary Blague–not that evil woman. Her thoughts turned fleetingly to Kate. But dared she go to Kate? She must not forget that she was under suspicion and by the grace and mercy of the Lord Protector had been given a reprieve from death. What might happen to Kate if she were suspected of treason through her friendship with Jane Shore! She must not go to Kate.

The woman was speaking soothing words. 'Come, dear Jane. Know you not how it has been on my conscience all these years that I helped ruin your marriage with Will? Give me a chance to expiate my sin.'

'I know when Edward commanded you to do what you did it was not in your power to refuse.'

'Then you'll not hold it against me, Jane?' pleaded Mary. 'You will be my friend?'

Friend? That was impossible. Yet her very dislike of the woman was helping her to forget that tragic morning on Tower Green. She was wavering, Mary saw, and she smiled triumphantly.

'Come, Jane, come. Hot food, clothes, rest, friendship. I offer them to you, my dear.'

And so did Jane allow herself to be led out of the bare cold house to that in which she had first known the passionate love of Edward the King.

Nothing was too much trouble for Mary Blague if it contributed to the comfort of her guest. Jane must have the best of everything; good food, excellent wine, and a wardrobe worthy of her.

'Never forget, my dear,' said Mary more than once, 'the King loved you. It is something of which a woman should always be proud.'

Listlessly Jane accepted this hospitality. It was characteristic of her that she should suppress her doubts even in the face of what she knew of this woman. Jane could never learn any lesson from life. It was so easy to forget the horrors she had glimpsed in that house where she had visited Dorset; it was so easy to forget what Anne Neville had whispered to her in those days when they had been friends. Mary Blague had given her food and shelter, comfort also; and surely no human being was wholly bad.

Mary waited. The silly little fool, thought Mary. How easily duped she is! No wonder Dorset decided to use her. No wonder she is in her present position. Good fortune was heaped into her lap, and for her uncontrollable lusts she threw it all away. She is stupid and deserves her lot; which, considering her idiocy, will be very good indeed. And what a treasure she will be to me, for from far and wide will come the richest in the land to enjoy the intimate friendship of the beautiful and notorious Jane Shore!

But Mary was a business woman and did not intend to keep Jane in idleness for many more weeks. She came in one day, professing deep distress and went straight to her guest.

'My dear,' she declared, 'I have today seen that which grieves me greatly. Pour out a little wine for me, please do.' Mary sipped her wine and turned her sly eyes on Jane. 'It was outside your house . . . the house that was once your house.'

'Yes?' said Jane.

'There was a crowd.'

'Looking for me?'

'Alas, I fear so.'

'They had come . . . to arrest me?'

'The idea does not seem to disturb you!' said Mary tartly.

'It does not. I do not think I greatly care.'

'You talk like a fool. Life has much to offer you. You are beautiful. You had wit once. Do not tell me that you have forgotten how to amuse and charm the great. Do not forget that many still will long to talk with and . . . admire Jane Shore, who was the King's favourite for as long as his life lasted. You are most richly endowed, my friend.'

'They were Gloucester's men you saw this morning?'

'Indeed they were not. They were merchants to whom you owe money. They sought payment.'

Jane turned pale. 'I had forgotten. I must owe a great sum.'

'You do. And it is money you will have to find somehow, or you will go to Ludgate Jail.'

'What curse has come upon me?' cried Jane. 'My wealth has been taken from me . . . everything I possessed. They might at least have paid my creditors before they robbed me of my possessions. Oh, Mary, tell me what I should do now.'

'You must remain hidden until you can pay your creditors.'

'But how shall I ever be able to pay them? These debts were incurred when I had no notion that I might not be able to settle them. I still had much until . . .'

'Until you played traitor to the Protector and so incurred his displeasure.'

'I have none but myself to blame,' said Jane, looking back on those fantastic months of her servitude to Dorset. But for that folly she and Hastings might have been happy together now.

'No,' said Mary briskly, 'you have none but yourself to blame. Yet I will help you. There *is* a way in which you can remain hidden for as long as you wish. I will look after you. I will protect you as carefully as ever did your lovers. And while you remain hidden you can earn money, you can pay your creditors; you can pay me for the comforts I have showered upon you. My dear, you look startled. What do you imagine it has cost me to furnish you with the fine clothes you now wear?'

'Oh,' said Jane faintly. 'I'm afraid I did not think. . . .'

'Mayhap it is not your way to think overmuch. Have there not always been others to think for you? First your father, then Will Shore, the King, Dorset, Hastings . . . and now . . . Mary Blague.'

Jane stood up, realising suddenly what Mary Blague had planned for her. 'So . . .' she began.

But Mary had also risen. 'The answer to your problems, Jane Shore, is my house across the water.' She laid a hand on Jane's shoulder, but Jane brushed it aside so angrily that Mary staggered back.

'I will leave your house at once.'

'Indeed, and why? I can assure you my house in Southwark is the most luxurious of its kind. You were glad enough to come to it once to visit Dorset. I offer you a more dignified position. It shall not be you who come to visit your lovers, but they who come to visit you.'

'Be silent!' cried Jane.

'You forget, do you not, that you are not now the King's mistress. Edward is mouldering in his grave. God knows what has happened to Dorset. And rest assured he has long tired of you. Hastings is buried. And you do naught but flout one who has some hope to offer you.'

'I would never for a moment consider accepting your offer.'

They faced each other in silence for a moment, then Mary said: 'Be sensible. You have nothing between you and starvation. What will you do? Beg in the streets? You'll not be allowed to. As a fine lady you incurred debts which the miserable creature you have become cannot hope to pay from what she will get by begging. The very clothes you are wearing do not belong to you. At least, shall we say, my dear, they have yet to be paid for?'

Jane was furious–more with herself than with Mary Blague. How could she have been such a fool? She undid the girdle about her waist and let it fall to the floor. She slipped the dress off her shoulders while Mary went into shrieks of mocking laughter.

'Very fine! And so you would scorn the shelter I offer you . . . you who have walked the streets as a harlot with a lighted taper in your hand? You will go forth into the streets clad only in a cloak and kirtle! Very noble!'

Jane took Mary by the shoulders and shook her until she was gasping for breath. 'Be silent, you wicked woman, or I will kill you.'

'So you would practise murder as well as harlotry. Well, perhaps you are well versed in the art. They say the King ever took your advice, and there were some mysterious doings in the Tower of London.'

Jane's hands dropped to her sides. The woman seemed to be urging her to more acts of wanton folly.

'I shall leave this house at once,' she said.

'You will not forget that you are deeply in my debt. I have a little bill for you. It is rather high. You see, I thought that nothing but the best was good enough for Jane Shore.'

'You are the most evil thing that ever touched my life.'

'You did not think that when I so skilfully managed your affair with the King. Then it was, "Good Mary Blague." "*Dear* Mary Blague." You are a fool. If you were not, you would jump at my offer. You would say, "Bless Mary Blague," as you did once before.'

'I shall never say that. I will find some way of living . . . of paying my debts.'

'But you have never worked . . . except to please your lovers. You are fair enough still, I grant you; but these last weeks of your life have scarce added to your charm. Be reasonable.'

'There is no point in talking further. I shall leave your house at once.'

'You shall not take those garments with you. They are not paid for, remember.'

'I shall take nothing but what I brought.'

'And there again you are wrong, my headstrong girl, for you shall take another debt with you. But you'll come back to me ere long.'

'I never shall.'

Jane ran up to the room which Mary had said she might use during her stay in this house; she threw off the garments with which Mary had provided her; she put on her kirtle and wrapped her cloak about her. Mary was waiting for her on the stairs.

'Do you think you can go like this?' she demanded. She caught Jane's arm, but Jane twisted herself free. 'Where will you go? blustered Mary.

'You cannot imagine I would tell you that?'

'I demand payment of my bill.'

'You shall be paid in time.'

Speculation shot up in Mary's eyes. 'You know where Dorset is, do you not?'

Jane smiled. Let her think that she knew that. Let her think that Jane Shore was not completely alone and helpless.

'You will be steeped further in treachery towards the Duke of Gloucester,' cried Mary. 'Do you think a man like Dorset will ever succeed against the Protector?'

She sought to detain Jane, but Jane threw her off.

'I never want to see your sly face again,' said Jane; and she ran downstairs and out of the house.

Janet, Mary's maid, stood gaping after Jane.

'After her . . . quickly,' cried Mary. 'Don't dare come back until you have found out where she has gone.'

Jane, running swiftly through the streets, had one thought, and that was to get to Kate. Kate would know where to hide her; there were more hiding places in the Tower than anywhere else in England. As long as her disgrace did not reflect on Kate there was nothing to fear. From Kate she would get food, clothes, temporary shelter and friendship.

Janet watched her turn in at the Tower gate and then went back to her mistress, and told her what she had seen.

Mary smiled grimly, reminding herself that it was better to be Mary Blague, rich brothel-keeper, than beautiful Jane Shore fallen on evil times.

Jane felt temporarily at peace in the room over the kitchens. It was a small room, thick-walled, and its narrow windows, deep set in the thick stone, did not let in much light. Kate had brought her some clothes, and Belper had plied her with as much food as she could eat in a week. They were glad and proud to have her. She tried to warn them of possible danger, but they would not listen. They would keep her coming a secret, they said, although there was not a man or woman in the Tower who would give her hiding place away.

Kate was excited, and delighted that it was to her that Jane had come.

'Why, bless you,' she said, 'I know the underground passages of this Tower as I know the palm of my hand. I was very good friends with one of the jailers, and he showed me . . . well, perhaps a little more than he should have showed me. But that was all to the good. I could put you in a place where none would think to look for you.'

'Kate, you're a comfort.'

'We always stuck together, mistress, and that's a pleasant thing to do. A pity you didn't come straight to me instead of getting into the hands of that creature.'

'It was a pity, Kate, but don't let's think of that now. I am here, and only my friends know it. I cannot see what is to become of me, for I cannot stay here for ever. And I have nothing . . . nothing at all.'

'Shame and pity!' cried Kate. 'What His dear Grace the King would say I don't care to think.' Kate crossed herself and looked up at the ceiling of this room, which was so like a cell. 'To make *you* parade the streets in such fashion. . . .'

'It is over and done with,' said Jane, 'so let us not speak of that. Times change and we change with them. I, who was so beloved, am now almost alone; but I have you, Kate, and I do not forget it. I have you and kind Belper, and doubtless many a good friend could I but find them. Perhaps life will be gay for me again. Dry your eyes, Kate.'

Kate was ready enough to dry her eyes. 'Ah, yes,' she said, 'for you are so beautiful. There will be one near as handsome as His Grace was. I swear it; I know it.' She was pensive suddenly. 'This is like old times. I could almost believe we were together in Cheapside or Lombard Street or the palace. I have been thinking where I will hide you. There is a chamber of fair comfort between the White Tower and the Beauchamp. We shall furnish it with as much comfort as we can manage, and hide you there. You'll not be afraid?'

'I do not think so. I used to fear the dead, but so many I have loved are among them. Edward? Hastings? They would do naught but help me. I do not believe my father would wish me any harm. And Will? Oft-times I wonder what became of Will.'

'Doubtless he found himself another wife.'

'I hope so. And with her, happiness. Kate, do you ever see the little King?'

'Hardly ever.'

'Yet he is still here, in the Tower, is he not?'

'Yes, he is still here. But I hear they have brought his little brother to him to bear him company.'

'Little Richard! How glad I am! He will enjoy having Richard with him.'

'So now both the little Princes are in the Tower. Oh, I know one is the King and one the Duke of York, but people speak of them as the little Princes.'

'How I should love to see them!'

Kate's eyes sparkled. 'Mayhap we could arrange the matter.'

'Do you know where they are lodged?'

Kate shook her head. 'But I could discover. I am rather friendly with one of the attendants.'

They began to laugh together as they had in the old days. They would find a way of communicating with the boys. With excitement, the colour was returning to life.

But as they sat in that room, planning, they heard a shout from below which was followed by the tramping of many feet. Kate, turning pale, ran to the window and looked out. The face she turned to Jane was sufficient to show what she had seen.

'They have come for me?' asked Jane.

Kate nodded. 'Oh, Holy Mother of God!' she whispered. 'They are here . . . and it is too late to hide you.'

Jane had never known that there was such misery in London, until she entered Ludgate Jail. During her first days there she scarcely noticed the passing of time. She lay on the stone floor, overwhelmed by the terrible plight in which she found herself. The foul smell of decaying flesh floating in through the narrow barred windows from the nearby fly-haunted, disease-ridden Fleet, made her retch, until after a few days it ceased to disturb her. She turned in disgust from the filthy walls down which trickled the accumulated slime of ages. She was appalled by the men and women who shared the great common hall in which they ate and slept and passed their miserable days and nights. They were like hideous effigies of real people–unkempt, terribly gaunt, some ferocious, some meek; many, suffering from horrible diseases, lay dying on the cold stones. Through the apertures the flies came in thick black streams and with them the wasps that were bred in the filthy refuse on the banks of the Fleet. And mingling with the terrible smell that came through the windows was another as hideous, that of diseased, unclean humanity.

Most of the inmates of Ludgate prison had little hope of regaining their freedom. Many were in for debts which their captivity gave them little hope of paying off. Jane's offence, she heard, was more than debt; she was accused of conspiring, by sorcery, against the life of the Protector.

The weather was hot; the loathsome wasps and flies buzzed continually; children, some of whom had been born in the place, wailed in their misery; others ran about and fought each other for the crusts of bread which some poor prisoner had been too sick to eat.

It was difficult for Jane to understand at first the very depth of this degradation to which she had sunk. She had never in her wildest imaginings conjured up such a horrible invention. Often she had passed the prison near the gate. Then it had seemed just an ancient edifice, a rather charming addition to the landscape, rising as it did beside the wall of the City and the old gate. When she had been a child she had often begged to be allowed to fill one of the baskets which the poor prisoners lowered down as they called their piteous pleading cries through the barred windows, but her father had never allowed this, In the jail, he had said, were lepers and people suffering from plague. One should keep well away.

Now she could smile at the memory of that admonition, smile with great bitterness. Now, *she* was one of those who must be avoided. She had never known that such brutality and indifference to suffering could exist. The jailers had been respectful to her on arrival. She was well dressed–in Kate's clothes–for a prisoner; she had a gentle, cultured voice. A lady, thought the jailers. Here is a chance of making money.

So was the whole iniquitous business of bribery laid before her. Her food, it was explained, would be bread and water, and not over much of that, unless she liked to pay. Why, then, a roast duck? A thick wedge of succulent beef? Good wine? Nothing was too much trouble for a jailer to bring to a prisoner who paid him well. There were many in Ludgate who lived like the quality. A good table. Their own quarters. Lady friends to visit the gentlemen, and gentlemen to visit the ladies. A nice little gambling game to pass the time. Nothing was too much trouble. But a jailer had to live, just as luxuries had to be paid for.

Jane said quite simply that she had nothing at all. Then did they shrug expressive shoulders. No money? Then she must go back to the common hall. So back she went to listen to the growling, quarrelling human voices, to the miserable groans and the obscene jests; she watched the weary old prostitute, who had wine sent in every day, lying on the floor in a state of maudlin drunkenness; she listened to the crazy parson, who had never been able to get over the disgrace of being sent to Ludgate, preaching, as he did continually to the crowd of people who sometimes roused themselves from their indifference to jeer at him; she saw an old thief instructing a new thief how to pick pockets; she saw an emaciated mother feed her newly born baby; she saw an old man die while a man and woman cast aside their rags and attempted to satisfy their lust; she listened to the continual cry of beggars. And she could not realise that this had become her world, in which she must live out the remainder of the days left to her.

'Pity the poor prisoner! My lords and ladies . . . free men and women . . . pity the poor prisoner!'

Try as she might, Jane could not shut out the tired and hopeless voice. If only the woman would stop. Listening to her, Jane forgot her indifference to life in her anger against those who could pass by, ignoring that poor plea. What hope, she thought grimly, that any passing Ludgate jail will give a thought to a prisoner, let alone the requested alms?

Anger and pity welled up in Jane. She could hear the drop of the basket; now it would be dangling outside the walls, and some passer-by might look up at a hopeless face that would seem like that of a caged animal, shudder and turn quickly away. The woman who held the basket was old; her hair hung about her head like verminous, writhing grey snakes; she was a sad sight with her twisted mouth and sunken red-rimmed eyes.

The huge black flies cruised about gaily in the stifling air. They were the only gay things in Ludgate Jail. Odd, therefore, that they should give only additional annoyance and irritation.

'Pity the poor prisoner. . . .'

Beside Jane, on a bed of dirty straw lay a woman whom Jane had noticed before because there was a look of respectability about her. Jane had seen her shudder at some of the sights which it was necessary for them to witness, and try again and again to preserve some decency. Jane had tried to be friendly, but the woman would have none of her. She knew who Jane was, as did most of them, for it was impossible to be oblivious of such bright beauty even in this dim hall. People would stare at her, round-eyed; some jeered and made their obscene remarks, but many were over-awed, for Jane's habit of giving help to the poor was known throughout the London jails. This woman had a daughter, Bet, who could not have been more than eleven years old, and in spite of dirt and lice, inadequate food and such environment, she was not an unattractive creature. She was often missing from her mother's side, and to see the poor woman's frantic search for her moved Jane deeply. She was terrified that some evil would befall the girl, as indeed it might.

Now the girl was by her mother's side, and they both watched the beggar at the grating. Glancing at them, Jane saw their faces grow suddenly alert.

The reason was obvious. Someone outside had put something in the dangling basket. The woman at the window looked furtively over her shoulder; saliva dripped from her toothless mouth; her red-rimmed eyes gleamed. That was all, but it was sufficient to show many who watched her what had happened.

'Holy Virgin help her,' prayed Jane.

Wheezing with excitement, the poor old woman was hauling up the basket which was evidently heavy. There was silence except for the buzzing of the wasps and flies. Now the basket was up, and immediately there was a sudden stealthy movement towards the old woman. Jane turned away. She had seen many horrible things in the few days she had been here, but this she could not bear to look at.

She heard the scuffle, the snorting rage, the wild shrieks, the wail of frustrated anger, followed by a sudden silence; and turning, she saw the crowd of starving people who had been fighting for the contents of the basket, huddled together and staring at it, for it lay on the floor, its contents scattered.

Jane shared the horror of all those who looked, for the basket had contained nothing but three large stones. Someone in the world of freedom had thought it a fine joke to put those stones in the beggar's basket, and let her haul it up.

The silence was broken by the old woman who, squatting on her knees, began to wail. The mad parson, seeing a crowd gathered together, began to cry: 'Repent ye, for the Kingdom of Heaven is at hand.'

Someone turned on him and kicked him violently. He yelped. 'Blessed are ye when men shall revile you. . . . Repent! Repent! Ye have need of repentance.'

Life had returned to normal.

Jane saw now that the woman who had interested her had been hurt in the fight and was near to fainting. Bet was missing, and the woman sat propped up against the slimy wall, blood mingling with the dirt on her tattered sleeve.

Jane went over to her and said in that musical voice which had charmed so many: 'You are ill. You must let me help.'

The woman did not answer, but she smiled faintly when Jane tore a strip from her petticoat.

'We will wash the wound,' said Jane, and took her into the yard. The air did the woman good, and Jane kept up a stream of conversation as she bathed the wound. 'Fortunate we are to have this water. Twenty years ago, had we been here, it would have been denied us. I remember my father telling me that some lady paid a lot of money to have fresh water in this prison . . . fresh water for the prisoners, and without payment. Doubtless many would tell us we should be grateful.'

The woman was not listening, but as she felt better the anxiety came back into her eyes.

'Did you see my girl?' she asked.

'No. I missed her after the fight.'

'I fear for her. This place . . .'

Jane nodded.

'She is young,' said the woman in a burst of confidence. 'She is comely. People notice. The gamblers give her scraps . . . for waiting on them. I am afraid. . . .'

'I understand.'

They were silent; but the frightened mother was glad to confide her fears in someone and Jane was glad to have found a friend.

They went back to the hall. Bet was there. She came and sat down beside them.

Evening fell. They heard the drunken singing of the prostitutes who came by night to those who could afford to pay for them.

'Is it nothing to you,' called the mad parson, 'all ye that pass by?'

The old beggar woman sat dismally at the grating until the daylight faded.

'Pity the poor prisoner! My lords and ladies . . . pity the poor prisoner!'

Each summer's day spent in the fetid atmosphere of the jail was like ten.

'You have friends outside,' said the jailers. 'Money's what you want. Money will buy everything you can desire. Why, there's people as come in here for a rest. It can be as comfortable as that.'

Jane shook her head. She had a good friend outside. Kate had paid money that she might have a word with her; and Jane had seen the horror leap into Kate's eyes when they met. She could not stop herself from staring at Jane. She had brought rye cakes and bread and meat pies from Belper's kitchens; but Jane could not ask Kate for money. Kate would come again she assured Jane; and she was as good as her word; Jane need not fear starvation while she had Kate and Belper outside, ready to serve her.

Every other day Kate came, and Jane would hide the food she brought; then she would take it into the yard where Bet and her mother and some of the poor sick children would share it with her. Jane's was the smallest share, and while she ate it she would think constantly of the poor creatures in the hall to whom she could not offer a part of what Kate brought.

Kate's visits were the only brightness to lighten these days. To Kate, Jane would talk of Bet. Could Kate find a place for the girl? She might hear of someone who needed a kitchen girl, for Bet would be able to leave since she was in jail through no fault of her own, but because her mother had got into debt when her father died, and there was nowhere else the girl might go. But people were not anxious to take a girl from Ludgate Jail. And now the mother was doubly worried, for there had come to the prison a terrifying creature of evil habits and possessed of much money. He was known throughout the jail as Highway Ned, because he had grown rich by robbing travellers on the highway. He had taken the best quarters in the prison since he was a man of means, and it was said that he had got himself arrested for debt that he might hide for a while from some confederates whom he had cheated and who had sworn to have his life. Ludgate had often proved a refuge for such men, since it could provide a safety that would have been difficult to find outside.

Ned had his friends in every day to visit him; thieves and prostitutes gambled and sang bawdy songs in his quarters; and there was nothing that was too much trouble to be done for Highway Ned. His coming had made a difference to the entire community. Several of the women sought to attract his attention, without success. Why should he look at the poor starved creatures when he could have his pick from outside? Hot food came to him regularly every day. Some of the prisoners loitered in the quadrangle merely to smell it as it was brought in. Jane had never seen Highway Ned, but she disliked all she heard of him, and her indignation on behalf of the prisoners was intensified.

Three days after the arrival of Ned, Bet caught his eye. He called her to him, asked who she was and gave her a savoury meat pie. She ate it, and ran to her mother to tell what had happened. Sick with apprehension, Bet's mother confided in Jane. 'Highway Ned would never give something for nothing, now would he?' said the woman.

It was heartbreaking to watch her; she would rise up from her sleep and grope for the girl. Every time she heard Highway Ned and his friends carousing in his quarters she would shake as if with the ague. Jane knew she must do something to help her.

On several occasions she had seen a man pass through the quadrangle. He was middle-aged, soberly but very well dressed. He had dignity and was obviously some person in an important position. Jane had seen that, as he walked through the prison, sniffing his nosegay, he scarcely glanced at the prisoners. This she construed as meaning he had a kind heart and did not care to look upon so much misery; and if he were kind as well as important, might he not be prevailed upon to do something for Bet? Jane decided that the very next time she saw him she would speak to him. She did not have to wait long.

She hurried towards him and stood before him. 'Good day to you, sir.'

Her hair had lost much of its sheen; she was pallid and had lost her plumpness, but her smile was still dazzling.

He stammered an acknowledgement of her greeting. 'You will let me speak to you, will you not?' begged Jane. 'I wish to ask your help. Oh, do not be alarmed; it is not for alms that I wish to beg.'

'I . . . I am not a rich man,' he said.

She smiled. 'There are many here who would consider you wealthy as a king. Perhaps I was wrong to ask you. Would you be so good as to tell me to whom I speak?'

He hesitated, gave a quick look at her, and surrendered to her charm. 'I am the King's solicitor.'

She smiled. 'Oh . . . tell me, please, how is the little King?'

'The *little* King?'

'Edward. Little Edward.'

He shook his head. 'You are shut away from events, Madam. I speak of King Richard.'

'But . . . what of Edward?'

'He stays in the Tower with his young brother. His Grace the King has behaved with wondrous kindness to his brother's bastards. But . . . may I ask who *you* are, Madam?'

'My name is Jane Shore,' she said.

She fancied she saw horror creep into his eyes. He stammered uneasily: 'I see. Good day to you.' And he left her.

He will never come near me again, she thought.

Thomas Lynom, the King's solicitor, came out of Ludgate Prison and walked through the City's gates. He was thoughtful, and even as he crossed the Fleet Bridge he forgot to bury his face in his nosegay. He sauntered along Fleet Street and stared unseeingly at the clumps of trees which dotted the Strand; he looked past the gardens and orchards to Fickets Croft and the meadows beyond. The little brooks were sparkling in the sunshine, and the view which stretched out beyond Temple Bar was fair indeed, but he did not see it, for he was in a deeply thoughtful mood. What a strange encounter that had been! What startling eyes the woman had! They had glowed like lamps in her emaciated face. He could not forget the charming line of that face; and her long hair, unkempt though it was, was the most beautiful he had ever seen.

A beggar . . . nothing more. 'I would ask your help,' she had said. And then: 'It is not for alms I wish to beg.' But did not they all say that? Was it not the beggar's plaint? Oh, it is not for myself, but for a sick child, an aged mother, a crippled father . . . anyone . . . anything, but not for myself.

But she had a beautiful face . . . a *good* face. Yet how could it be good since it belonged to Jane Shore? When she had spoken, though, she had made him believe her; he had found her beauty and her charm engaging. And then he had understood; she was Jane Shore –a prisoner, a harlot who had walked the streets barefoot, a taper in her hand. He would have none of her. If he saw her again during his visits to the prison–and he must make an occasional visit there in the course of his duty–he would turn away.

'"I would ask your help,"' he said aloud. 'Indeed you would, Madam. "It is not for alms I beg." Indeed not, Mistress Shore. I know your sort. I'll have none of you.'

But he continued to think of her, while he assured himself he would have none of her. His master would be displeased if he befriended the woman and it got to the royal ears, for Jane Shore had proved herself an enemy to King Richard; and Thomas Lynom valued the patronage of the reigning monarch too much to disturb the favour he enjoyed.

He would not give the woman another thought.

He went his way until he came to the small but pleasant house which was his most proud possession. He had done well for himself. He had followed his father's profession, but how far had he outstripped his father! His father had been a solicitor; Thomas Lynom was the King's solicitor. He was a quiet man, a man who had worked hard and whose life had been uneventful; he had not sought adventure and adventure had not come to him. What should he want with the woman? What happened to the adventurous? Sometimes they won a crown as Richard had done; sometimes they lost heads, as Hastings had done. But a humble man, such as a King's solicitor, could be dragged to Tyburn and hanged by the neck; or he might have his ears nailed to the pillory, his tongue cut out; he might find himself in Ludgate Jail. Adventure, he was sure, was best left alone.

But what had adventure to do with a Ludgate prisoner? Nothing at all. Just because the woman had a dazzling smile, just because there was beauty in her eyes, he must not forget that she was an enemy of the King. He would do well to keep clear of Jane Shore.

His housekeeper bustled towards him. She was a comely enough creature, round as a tub and purple-rosy as a plum. She kept the serving men and maids in right order, and she ran his house to perfection.

Now he could smell his dinner and it made his mouth water. Chine of beef. A pie with savoury meats. Good wine and plenty, to wash them down. It was ready and waiting. He sat down to enjoy it and his needs were anticipated as they always were. The rushes on the floor were clean and sweet. He would have perfect order, as much cleanliness as possible in his house, for visiting prisons in the name of his royal master had given him a taste for such things. He had them; he had everything he wished.

He drank a good draught of elderberry wine and smacked his lips appreciatively. He cut himself a wedge of beef, good and succulent, done to a turn. But after the first mouthfuls his thoughts strayed from his table. He wondered what Jane Shore would say to such a meal. He pictured her, sitting opposite him, leaning her elbows on the table and smiling at him.

'I want to ask your help. Oh, it is not alms I want. . . .'

'I wonder,' he said aloud.

But his appetite was gone; it was replaced by a desire to know what it was she had wished to ask him.

The next day Jane saw Thomas Lynom in the quadrangle. She smiled at him and he flushed a little, for her smile was more dazzling than he remembered it. He felt ashamed of the good breakfast he had had; then he shook himself free of such folly. It was prisoners who should feel ashamed before honest men.

'Good day to you,' said Jane. 'There is a sharpness in the air. It was not here yesterday.'

'That is true,' he said, and moved closer to her, while the good sound common sense he had inherited from his father bid him take care. But her smile was so pleasant, and there could be no harm in exchanging a word or two with her.

He said: 'You wished to ask me something when I encountered you yesternoon.'

'Yes.' Her smile had grown warmer. The sun brought out some of the colour of her hair; her lovely eyes had softened. Ludgate had only dimmed her beauty; it could not obscure it completely. 'It is a girl here. A poor young girl. She is but eleven years old.'

He raised his eyebrows and looked away from her to where a part of the prison building loomed up beside the City gate. 'A girl of eleven. I do not know what I can do about that.'

'She has done no harm. Nor has her poor mother who is here because she is in debt.'

She has lived beyond her means,' he said sternly.

'Yes, but . . .'

'Then, Madam, she has deserved what has befallen her.' His own household accounts were always neatly balanced. He had ambitions; he had been tempted to live beyond his means, but he had seen the folly of such a course, and he despised those who did not see with his own clear vision.

'But it is so hard when one is poor,' she said.

'That is no excuse.'

'But how do we know the temptations! How can we judge until we know all?'

'Madam,' he said, 'I do not see what it can be that you wish to ask of me.'

'I will tell you. You are a man of means, of influence. I see that.'

'He was more gratified than such a simple remark should have made him. 'Well, I would not say . . .'

'Oh, but *I* would.' She laughed and he thought, So must she have laughed for King Edward. 'You *are* a man of influence, I know, sir. And you have sought me out that you might help me.'

'I can promise nothing. Why, I do not even know. . . .'

'Then I will hasten to tell you. This poor child should not stay in this place. She is young, and the air is infected not only with hideous disease, but with cruelty and wickedness. It is not right that children should grow up in such an atmosphere.'

'I agree with that, but what can I do?'

She moved closer to him. 'Mayhap you could find . . . some work for her to do . . . outside. There is no reason why *she* should stay here. She is free enough to go.'

'Work?'

'Doubtless one of your friends . . . or mayhap you yourself need a good serving maid. She is a strong girl. She would do well, I am sure, could we but get her away from this foul place.'

'Madam, I could not consider the matter. Dost think my friends would want a girl from such a place as this?'

'She has done nothing wrong.'

'There are too many honest girls looking for a living.'

'I see.'

'Good day to you, Madam.'

He looked into her face and saw that there were tears in her eyes, and the tears unnerved him. He did not understand her. He had thought she must be a brazen woman; one did not expect a woman, who had left her husband to become the mistress of the King, to shed easy tears over a fate which must necessarily befall many. He wanted to think of her as brazen and unscrupulous; and he could only be interested in her.

He strode away, but before he had reached the end of the quadrangle he was turning back to her. Jane smiled through her tears.

'It is a hopeless case,' he said gruffly. 'But I might see what can be done about it.'

'Thank you,' said Jane. 'I thought you would. You have the look of a good man.'

He went on his way. He had the look, she had said, of a good man. He kept repeating that to himself as he went towards his home.

Of course he had no intention of doing anything about the matter. How could he ask one of his friends to take in a girl from Ludgate? The idea was absurd, and he would dismiss it from his mind. He did not think he would have occasion to visit the prison for some time to come. Therefore would he put Jane Shore from his mind.

But as he entered his beautifully ordered house he found himself wondering whether he could take in another kitchen maid. His housekeeper was a good, sound, just and honest woman; she would be the right kind to look after a high-spirited girl who had already come into touch with evil things. But what was he thinking? He would have no jailbirds in his house.

He had work to do, and this afternoon he had an audience with the King. He worked hard all the morning before he set out for the palace; and in the King's presence it was impossible to think of aught else but his royal commands, for the pale, slender young man with the unhappy eyes had an undeniable presence.

But when he left the King and came home again he was still wondering whether there might not be a place in his household for the girl.

He called his housekeeper to him. She came, her plum-coloured face creased in respect, her capable hands spread over her stomach.

'Mistress Browner, there is something I wish you to do for me. You are a most excellent and capable woman, and that is why I am asking your help in this matter.'

She was flatteringly eager to serve such a good master. He realised afresh how far he had come and how foolish it would be to mix himself in some unsavoury matter. But what unsavoury matter was this? Let Mistress Browner take the girl into her kitchen. Then he need never see the woman Jane Shore again.

So he told the housekeeper about the girl. She pursed her lips. Did her master realise the wickedness that grew in jailbirds?

He found himself repeating Jane's words. 'But how can we judge, Mistress Browner, unless we know everything?'

'She comes of bad stock, master.'

'She has done no wrong. It is true her parent is getting her just deserts, but the child . . . for she is little more . . . has done nothing. No, Mistress Browner, we must not judge. You can use an extra girl in the kitchen. Oblige me by taking this child. The example of a woman such as yourself, a woman of sound good sense and much virtue, I am sure will be the making of her.'

It was done. He was very eager to go and tell Jane Shore what he had arranged.

After he had taken Jane's protégée into his household, Thomas Lynom did not, as he had intended, curtail his visits to the prison. He began to call every day.

There were other matters that disturbed him now. He could not sleep at night for thinking of Jane in that wretched place. He could not enjoy his food for thinking of Jane's living on bread and water.

He made a habit of taking in a basket of good things for her to eat. She was grateful, and he was delighted until he discovered from the mother of young Bet that she shared everything she received with her fellow prisoners. She was a strange woman. Of course he had heard tales of her when King Edward was living. The poor of London had always looked upon her as a sort of saint, which had seemed to him ridiculous in view of the life she was living. Now, he began to understand.

He paid for special quarters for her, for he could not bear to think of her sleeping in that filthy hall with those wild creatures all about her. She accepted his help with a natural grace. He learned that she shared the quarters, which he had provided, with sick children whom she fed and looked after.

He began to dread and yet to long for his visits to the prison. He knew those dreadful creatures whispered together about him and Jane; that was shocking and horrible to a man such as he was. Sometimes he swore he would never go back, but he always did.

He would dream of Ludgate Jail. The cries of the prisoners would penetrate his dreams; he would hear the coarse singing of the prostitutes and the mad shouts of the crazy parson; sometimes he dreamed of Jane.

As for Jane herself, she was growing fond of him; she said so in her natural easy way.

'It is so good of you to come, Thomas. Your visits enliven my days. How dreary they would be without your coming!'

She longed to hear news of what was happening outside the jail, and he stored up all the information he could get, that he might have something of interest to tell her.

A few weeks after the beginning of their friendship he asked her to walk with him in the quadrangle. The air was fresh and there was a faint drizzle falling, but neither of them minded that.

He said quietly: 'We live in terrible times, Jane.'

'What has happened?' she asked eagerly.

'There is trouble brewing in this country. The King has many enemies . . . they are everywhere . . . all over the country; and there is trouble brewing on the other side of the Channel.'

'You mean . . . with the French?'

'Worse than that. With the Earl of Richmond, Henry Tudor, who, it is whispered, prepares himself to attack the King and to wrest the crown from his head.'

'He will never succeed . . . against Richard.'

'He never will,' said Lynom, wondering what would happen to the King's solicitor if the King fled into exile, or, worse still, lost his head. 'But that is not all I have to tell you.'

'You have worse news?'

'News which will disturb you greatly, I fear. I regret that I should be the one to bring it to you, but you have asked me to tell you all that happens.'

'You do right to bring me news. I starve for news. But pray tell me quickly.'

'It is but a rumour. Mayhap there is no truth in it.' He hesitated, then rushed on. 'It is . . . the little Princes in the Tower. They . . . it is said . . . they are no more. They have been . . .'

He looked about him and it was Jane who said the word. 'Murdered?'

'So it is whispered.'

'But who . . . ? The . . . King! Oh, I cannot believe it of him. He would not do such a thing. They are his little nephews and he loved them. I swear he did.'

She thought of little Richard at his wedding to Anne Mowbray. 'Early wed, early dead,' said the old proverb. But how could she think of that bright little boy . . . dead! She broke down and began to weep bitterly. Lynom was beside her, his arm about her, comforting her. 'Jane, Jane! Sweet Jane, you must not weep. 'Tis but a rumour. Doubtless there is little truth in it.'

'How could such rumours grow out of nothing? Something is there . . . I know it. Oh, Edward . . . dear Richard . . . I would I could have kept you beside me.' She lifted her face to the man who stood beside her. 'I loved them. They were as my own. All their childhood I was there. We played together. I might have been their mother.'

He winced. He did not like her references to her life of sin. There were so many times when he must remind himself that she was a sinful woman. But how he tried to forget it!

He could not comfort her; he could only repeat: 'It is but a rumour which runs round the town.'

She said: 'Kate will know. I can find out from Kate. It cannot be true. Why should the King kill his brother's children?'

'Speak not so loudly. If any should hear . . .'

'Thomas,' she insisted, 'why should he? Tell me that. He has the crown. He has taken that; why should he want their lives as well?'

'The crown is his by rights, for there is proof that the Princes are bastards.'

'That is true, and why, therefore, I ask you, should it be necessary to take their lives?'

'Ask me not. I know not the ways of kings.'

'I do not believe it,' cried Jane passionately. 'I will not believe it.'

'I was wrong to bring you such news.'

'Nay, you were right. I pray you will always bring me news. Think not to spare me, for I would not wish to live in ignorance.'

He would have kissed her hands, but she held him off. Jane, in tears, was irresistible, and even while he regretted that she restrained him, he knew he should feel relief lest he be betrayed into saying something which might prove fatal to his future.

She said: 'Leave me now. I can think of little else but this. And I long for you to come and tell me that it is not true.'

She stayed in her room, weeping bitterly, and when at length she emerged her eyes were red-rimmed and dark with misery.

'Bad news from outside?' she was asked; she nodded, for she could not speak.

She must comfort herself by assuring herself that it was but a rumour. Why should Richard murder the Princes when they had been proved illegitimate, and did not stand in his way? There was no reason why he should.

She awaited Kate's coming; and what relief Kate brought!

''Tis a lying rumour,' declared Kate. 'The Princes still live. I have seen them this very day.'

'Thank God! Praise the Virgin!' cried Jane.

Everyone marvelled at her gaiety; and afterwards she looked back on that day as one the happiest of her life.

Lynom was in love and everyone knew it but Lynom. His housekeeper knew it, though she was far from guessing who might be the object of his passion. Quite a number of the prisoners knew it, but they were not in the same ignorance. It was a mighty joke to consider the King's most dignified solicitor in love with Jane Shore. Jane knew it; she thought a good deal about the man; she was fully aware that there had been many occasions when he had been on the point of declaring his passion and devotion. Jane could not help thinking of all he could do for her. There was a possibility that he might even obtain her release; he could certainly pay her debts; and was he not favoured by the King? The thought of freedom was very sweet, but with it came the bitter memory of Hastings. I could never love Thomas Lynom, thought Jane. How foolish was it to be unable to love a man who could promise so much! But then, had she not always been foolish? It was her folly that had brought her greatest happiness and her greatest sorrow. Yet sometimes she thought, I would give anything in the world to be able to leave this place.

The jailers were full of respect for her now that she had become the cherished friend of one of the most important men who ever visited the prison. And how much more would he do for her? Yet, he reminded her of Will Shore. I had no mind for Will, she thought. I would have no mind for Thomas. And when he would seek to declare his feelings for her she would divert him from the purpose.

As for Thomas, he thought of little else but Jane. He had taken to picturing her in his house, giving orders to Mistress Browner and entertaining his friends. There would be a certain amount of scandal, of course, for Jane Shore was notorious, but he would have to endure that! Yet how could he marry Jane Shore? The idea was preposterous. She was a prisoner–the King's prisoner, and he would have to get the King's consent, and what would His Grace have to say if his quiet and trusted solicitor suddenly explained that he wished to marry Jane Shore? Thomas had gone over this again and again.

One October day, going to the room it had been his privilege to provide for her, he found her gay and radiant. Her happiness restored some of that great beauty which had been hers before she came to the prison, and he was struck afresh by her grace and charm.

'Thomas,' she cried, and held out her hands, for she was more friendly and demonstrative than any woman he had ever known, 'I have heard from Kate that the Princes live.'

He knew that she was the most kindhearted of women; he caught her emotion.

'I rejoice with you, Jane.' And then suddenly, she being close to him, he put his arms about her and gently kissed her forehead. 'Jane,' he said, 'you know my feelings?'

'Why yes, Thomas.' He was taken off his guard; he had not expected her to admit that.

He stammered: 'Why, I love you, Jane. I want . . . if possible . . . that you should be my wife.'

His wife! She had not thought of that. Was she not still the wife of Will Shore?

She said gently, 'But, Thomas, I am already a wife.'

His legal mind had already considered this problem. 'How many years is it since you left the goldsmith?' he asked.

She told him.

'And where is he now?'

'I do not know. It may be that he has left the country.'

'It may be that he is dead. Indeed–and I trust you will forgive my referring to this painful matter–the penance you were forced to do might well be considered in the nature of a divorce. We will verify these matters, and believe me, Jane, I have no doubt that we shall succeed in settling them to our satisfaction.'

Jane felt he was carrying her along too far. She liked Thomas. He was the kindest of men. But marriage! She shook her head.

'Jane, I beg of you. Think what marriage with me will mean.'

She did think. What did the future hold for her? She seemed to see Mary Blague's cruel eyes leering at her. She saw again the people thronging the City's streets to see her do penance.

She felt the importance of this decision. She was offered a comfortable life, a chance to go back to what she had left all those years ago; only instead of a goldsmith she would have a solicitor for a husband. She would know kindness and eventually obscurity . . . and with it Thomas. And, if she did not accept, what would become of her? Even if she should come out of this foul prison, whither should she go? She was alone and penniless. She had a few friends, but how could she throw herself on their mercy? How could she keep herself? And here was Thomas offering so much. But she did not love him, any more that she had loved Will Shore.

'Jane,' he was murmuring, 'I will arrange it. You must leave this to me. Never fear . . . I will arrange it.'

He would have put his arms about her, kissed her, but she held him off, for in the dim light he reminded her so much of Will. She had not loved Will, and she had betrayed him. What if she, not loving Thomas, betrayed him also?

'No,' she cried. 'Not yet. Not yet, Thomas. I must have time to think.'

After he had gone she laughed at herself. You are a fool, Jane Shore, she told herself. This is a chance that will never come to you again.

But I do not love him.

Love! What did love bring you? Great happiness with Edward; but Edward died, nor was he faithful to you. And what misery did you suffer on those occasions–particularly in the beginning–when you discovered his infidelity. Dorset? That was not love; that was lust and torment. Hastings? Brief as a summer's day, and on a summer's day it ended in such tragedy that pray you'll never meet again. That much for love!

And Thomas Lynom? He is a man of some position, but not too much. A hard-working and conscientious man, a man who will love you and rescue you from the terrible plight into which you fallen, care for you, make you happy in your middle and old age. You are a fool to hesitate for a moment.

But remember Will.

Then you were hot-blooded, and there was Edward to come courting you. Edward is dead and you are no longer young. You are a poor, penniless prisoner in Ludgate from where you will never emerge without the help of some powerful person such as Thomas who loves you.

But to marry Thomas seemed in some small measure like going to Mary Blague. That she had scorned; she had never faltered in her determination to turn her back on that way of life.

But it was not the same. She would be a good wife to Thomas and he loved her. A good wife to the solicitor as she had been to the goldsmith?

To be free again, to walk the streets, to stroll out to Fickets Croft on a summer's evening, to walk along the river bank, to glance towards the grey towers of London's fortress and to remember so much that was gay and happy and so much that was best forgotten!

Thomas came next day, eager as a young man in love, awaiting her answer.

'Thomas Lynom,' she said gravely, 'you are a man of some years and good sense. Why do you do this thing?'

'Because I love you,' he said.

She was moved. It was so good to be loved again. She would marry him. She would be true to him. Here was a chance to be the good wife she had not been to poor Will.

'Jane, you will marry me?'

'I do not think that is possible.'

Thomas Lynom in love was a giant in achievement. 'You will see, Jane. I have the ear of His Grace the King and I fancy he is not displeased with me.'

'But he is displeased with me, Thomas.'

'Not in any great seriousness. I will sue for his mercy, and then, Jane . . .'

She felt the fire of his love warming her. He was picturing her, the grime of the prison washed from her, sitting at his table, discreetly jewelled, becomingly gowned; and the picture made him very happy.

'Jane,' he said, 'you will?'

'If it be possible . . . then mayhap I will.'

It was only after he had gone that her elation left her. Freedom she sought, but would she be free? In a charming, well-ordered house, she might be a prisoner just as she was in Ludgate Jail. Such a prisoner had she been in Lombard Street . . . until she had flown.

'It must not be,' she said; and her indecision began again.

The King was astounded when he heard from Lynom that the man wished to marry Jane Shore.

'You are bewitched, man,' he cried; and he meant it. He had persuaded himself that Jane, in company with Elizabeth Woodville, had tried to work her black magic upon him. That had been necessary to ease his conscience. He had wanted to destroy Jane's popularity with the people; he had hoped her penance would have done that; but her beauty and charm, together with the dignified way in which she had undergone the ordeal had, if anything, aroused the sympathy rather than the scorn of the people. Therefore had he felt it necessary to keep her out of sight until she was forgotten. This he had done, and now she was attempting to seduce Thomas Lynom, an honest and sober solicitor.

He saw the firm set of the man's jaw. He liked Lynom; he trusted him; and Richard longed to keep his friends. Moreover, Anne talked often of Jane and was disturbed that he had been the one to send her to Ludgate. If good came to Jane, Anne would be pleased; perhaps, after all, Jane was just a foolish woman, to be watched because of the effect she could have on men of importance.

He laid a hand on Lynom's shoulder. 'You are acting like a fool, good Thomas,' he said. 'But if a man will act thus . . . and is set on marriage . . . we would not wish to stand in his way.'

Lynom knelt and kissed the hand extended to him.

'Your Grace is good to me.'

Richard laughed grimly. 'Ah, my friend, it may be that in a short while you will not think so. It may be that then you will wish I had said you nay.'

'Your Grace is bountiful, and it is my greatest ambition to serve you well.'

Richard was pleased with these expressions of devotion. 'I doubt that not,' he said. 'But, good Thomas, I would have you wait awhile. Because I know you for my friend I would first make certain of the good conduct of this woman. I shall write to my Lord Chancellor of Lincoln on this matter. Mayhap he will speak to you, and if, after that, you are still of the same mind . . . and if the matter may stand the law of Holy Church . . . well, then, it is your matter, my friend; and I wash my hands of it.'

'And if I should pay her debts, Your Grace . . . ?'

Richard waved his hand. 'Then she would have our free pardon. But I pray you, be not hasty. Wait until this matter has the sanction of the Church, and until Lincoln has spoken with you.'

Lynom was dismissed.

There should be no delay, he assured himself. He was aglow with plans for his rosy future. Mistress Browner should indulge in a great cleaning of his house. He was longing for the moment when he would take Jane home. How delightful it would seem after Ludgate Jail! But he must not forget that she had lived in palaces.

But something was happening which was to delay matters.

The King had a few friends whom he thought he could trust, and the chief of these was the Duke of Buckingham. There was one thing Richard had forgotten, and this was that in Buckingham was a strain of royal blood, which worked like a fever in his veins. He could not forget it. Who would have thought, he asked himself continually, that Richard of Gloucester would come to the throne? A dead man here, a bastard there, and one whose hopes had seemed small could grasp the crown. Buckingham was several moves from the throne, and there was one, alive and ambitious, itching to grasp it. This man, it would be said, had a claim prior to Buckingham's. Well, Buckingham could wait. The man he was thinking of was Henry Tudor, Earl of Richmond, now in exile in Brittany.

Buckingham was a weak man. He recognised the strength of Richard, and thoughts of treason would never have come into his head if Richard had not made the great mistake of putting Bishop Morton in his care.

Morton, Bishop of Ely, had been a member of the Council, and had been arrested at the time of the execution of Hastings. Richard had been lenient with the Bishop, for he liked to stand well with the Church; he had, instead of sending Morton to the Tower, put him in the charge of the Duke of Buckingham, in whose castle at Brecknock he would be treated more as a guest than a prisoner. It was simple for wily Morton to sum up the character of Buckingham, whom he considered vain as a peacock, as ready to crow as a bantam, and as eager to chatter as a monkey. The Duke was malleable material in the hands of the clever Bishop.

Morton knew the whereabouts of Dorset; he knew how to get into touch with Henry Tudor. But these men, including the Bishop, were prisoners or outcasts. They needed help from someone who could give it unsuspected. And who should that be but the man whom Richard in his folly had delivered up to the Bishop!

How easy it was to sow the seed of discontent!

'My lord Duke, you have the look of a King. It surprises me not, for you are of royal descent, are you not?'

The Duke strutted about his room, seeing himself as the King of England. Why not? Did the Bishop know he was descended from Edward III?

'Indeed, an I did not, I could see it in Your Grace's face.'

The Duke became a frequent visitor to the Bishop's apartments. How easy it was for Morton to drop the words of criticism of the King!

'I am not one to labour against what God hath pulled down. You, my lord Duke, are an honourable man. The fate of our country means much to you. But what do I say? I am a foolish old man. Forgive me. It is my wish to retire from politics and devote myself to God and my books. Even so, to see our beloved country groaning under–under a . . . But my tongue runs on.'

'Have no fear,' said the Duke, 'that what you might say would go beyond these walls.'

They had done with subterfuge.

'The King is a usurper. He has taken the crown from its rightful place and put it on his own head,' said Morton.

It was well to vilify Richard, but such was not without its complications, for if Richard was the usurper, then was not young Edward the true King? And if he died, or disappeared, there was still his young brother Richard who must succeed him.

The two little boys were undoubtedly a nuisance. They crept into the best-laid plans. For how, thought Buckingham, could I sit upon the throne whilst those two lived? For though they might be proved illegitimate, are not my claims based on what took place on the wrong side of the blanket? And unless we declare them the true heirs to the throne, how can we accuse Richard of usurping it, since he has but taken that which is his by right?

Morton's thoughts worked on similar lines. If Henry Tudor were to come to the throne, how could he enjoy the people's approval while the Princes lived? Richard must be proved a knave, and he could only be thus designated if the Princes were the true heirs; and if they were, then would the people say: 'Let young Edward have his coronation at once.' No, the Princes must be proved legitimate and at the same time they must not be allowed to stop Henry Tudor's passage to the throne. Therefore they must be removed. They must be declared the rightful heirs and–removed.

It was an uneasy matter to speak of, even for a clever Bishop who feels he has a vain and silly Duke in his power.

'The Princes . . .' began the Duke, and averted his eyes.

The Bishop stared at the ornate ceiling of his luxurious prison. 'They are young,' he said. 'They can scarce know the meaning of life. It will be necessary to remove them when . . .'

'. . . when the usurper Richard has been removed,' said the Duke, who was more blunt of speech than the Bishop.

'Let us remember the deaths of men who have crossed him. Hastings comes to mind. One more crime laid upon him . . .'

The Duke nodded. 'But, my lord Bishop, how could this matter be laid at Richard's door? What motive could he have for murder? With the aid of Stillington he has proved the Princes illegitimate. Whether they live or die the throne is still his.'

'If this story of Stillington's was proved to be false, a motive for the murder would be supplied, would it not?'

'But will the people believe it?'

'We must make them believe it. We will see that posterity believes it. I assure you it is not an impossibility. Have you forgotten that I am writing a history of these times? The Princes must die . . . but not yet. Richard must go first and they must follow him. But if we will have the people believing that Richard was responsible for their removal, why then, *before* Richard's death, the rumour must go forth that the Princes are dead. And then, when there is no longer a King Richard, must the deed be done.'

'My lord Bishop, I like it not.'

'My lord Duke, your scruples do you credit. Two innocent children, you say. But remember England. For England I would die this night; and so would you.' The Bishop brought his face close to that of the Duke. 'And so must they.'

The prostitutes brought the news into Ludgate Jail and the rumour spread. There was trouble outside, and terror stalked the streets of London. Few dared go out after dark. Thieves and murderers had grown overbold. During the day people hurried along with downcast eyes, hardly daring to speak to one another for fear they should be tricked into expressing an opinion and find themselves accused of treason.

There was tension inside the prison. If there was fighting and it spread to London, the prison gates might be flung open, and the prisoners of today might be the free men of tomorrow.

There was many a fight in the jail during those days of suspense. The prisoners were taking sides.

'I am for the rebellion. A Dorset! A Buckingham! A Tudor!'

'Take that, you traitorous cur! I am for the King. King Richard–and England.'

The mad parson screeched excitedly until he was hoarse. 'A house divided against itself. . . . Oh, God, have mercy on these miserable sinners.'

Jane shared the excitement and the tension. So Dorset was alive and involved in this rebellion. She thought of him dispassionately and wondered who was his mistress now. Did he ever give a thought to poor Jane Shore? She hoped he did not. The Dorset episode was one she would always remember with shame, and she did not wish to be remembered by him.

And, thinking of Dorset, she began to see how impossible it was that she could ever marry Thomas Lynom. Always when she was alone she felt thus. It was when he came to her full of plans, looking into the future with a serenity which could not fail to move her, that she wavered and let herself take a part in these plans. Sometimes she thought she would rather stay in this place for ever than marry a man she did not love. But would she? She would never grow hardened to the miseries of others; her heart was too soft, her imagination too keen. And yet what would it be like when the winter came? 'I must marry Thomas,' she would murmur, and so was her mind continually changing.

Then again she would remember the frustration, the humiliation of her life with Will Shore. To marry Thomas would be like completing an ugly circle. 'I cannot do it,' she said.

She was relieved that the matter must necessarily be shelved for the moment.

One day, when Thomas came to see her, pleasure was written on his face and in his manner.

'The rebellion is over,' he said. 'The King has victoriously quelled his enemies. Long live King Richard!'

There was cheering now through the prison. 'Long live King Richard!' Those who had itched to take up arms against the King either slunk away or shouted louder than the rest: 'Long live the rightful King!'

'And Dorset?' asked Jane of Lynom.

'Has fled. Doubtless to France. And with him Morton and others. Buckingham is dead. He lost his head, as he well deserved. God was on our side.'

The mad parson took up the story. 'If ever we wanted proof, God has given it to us. He has shown us the right. Down with all traitors! Down with mock marriages! Down with these bastard slips! God has shown us.'

The mad parson went about all that day marvelling at the power of God.

Later Lynom brought in more news. Henry Tudor, he had learned, had turned back to France before landing, because he had heard of the defeat of his friends. After the captured Buckingham's head was severed, Richard rode in triumph to Exeter, acclaimed wherever he went.

'Once more,' said Lynom, 'has the King saved the throne for himself and England from civil war. God save him!'

In the little room which he had acquired for her in the jail, Jane faced Thomas Lynom.

'I cannot do it, Thomas,' she said. 'It is not in me to do it. I should wrong myself and you if I did.'

His face twitched with emotion. 'You cannot mean it, Jane. This is pardon for you–and a new life.'

'Thomas, my dear, try to understand me. Long ago I married the goldsmith. He was a good man and he loved me truly. My father wanted the marriage; I did not; but I yielded. You know that I wronged my husband, that I left him for the King. He left Lombard Street soon after that and I do not know what became of him. But I know this: it was wrong to make such a marriage. Nor will I do so again.'

'You will live on here in this foul place? Do you not see–this is a way out?'

'I cannot do it, Thomas.'

'You do not mean it.'

'Alas, I do. I would I could give you the love you deserve. I loved others who loved me not as you do. I fear I am a foolish woman, but somehow I know that this marriage could never bring happiness to either of us.'

'To me it would. And you too, Jane.'

'It must not be. Go away from here, Thomas. Forget you ever knew me. Find some woman more worthy.'

'But, Jane, in marriage is your freedom.'

'There is no price that can be paid for love, Thomas. I have loved–sinfully–but always it *was* love. And as I see it, there was more sin in my life with Will Shore than with any other; for the others I loved, and Will I did not love. I was married to him for a secure future, and that is why you would have me marry you. I cannot do it. And you must consider what this would mean to you, Thomas. People know of me.'

'I care not for that.'

'I was a wanton. So said my father; so said the Bishop. But I never sold myself. It was my father who sold me to Will Shore. Please, Thomas, leave me now. I have made up my mind because I see this thing clearly.'

He left her then because he could see it was useless to try to persuade her.

She went out into the courtyard. The prostitutes from outside were just coming in. On her straw in a corner a sick woman lay dying. The mad parson was preaching to an imaginary congregation. Somebody began to sob wildly; it was a newcomer. The miserable life went on.

Jane sank down in despair. She had shut herself in with misery. Thomas, good man, respectable citizen, had offered her escape and she had refused it. She had none but herself to blame.

Oh, Jane Shore, she thought, what a fool you are! What a fool you always have been!

Out of the gates of Ludgate Jail walked Jane Shore. In her pocket was a purse that was full of coins. She was a free woman. Thomas had paid her debts and sent her this purse; and the King had given her his pardon.

She was a free woman; and her freedom was a gift, something she had not had to buy.

Thomas had written to her: 'Your debts are paid. Here is some money to help you along. And if you should ever change your mind I shall be waiting.'

The fresh air after Ludgate air was breathtakingly strong.

She walked along by the river, wondering what she should do.

How beautiful was the City with the sparkling sunshine on it! It would soon be November and the mists would hang over the spires and rise up from the water. November. And in June she had thought she had found happiness.

How deceitful was life–promising much and offering no fulfilment of her promises!

A new life was waiting for her. She must not stand here all day staring at the river. She must get on. But whither should she go?

East Cheap

The little room over the Bansters' shop, which was now Jane's was mean and almost bare of furnishings. It contained little beside a table and a stool; and every night Jane made herself a bed of straw in that room. There were no hangings to disguise the ugly walls; the one window was without glass, but it had a shutter, which either excluded all light or exposed the room to the weather. The rushes on the floor were none too sweet, but the room seemed luxurious after Ludgate Jail; and, living thus, Jane reckoned that the money which Thomas Lynom had given her would last for a year or more.

The Bansters had been good to her. They would insist on feeding her and would take only the smallest rent for the room, which they had given up to her while the whole family were crowded into the room behind the cook-shop.

When Jane considered the kindness of her friends her self-pity would evaporate. There were times when she would remember Edward in all his splendid manhood or the fleeting beauty of her week with Hastings; and then she would bitterly lament her ill fortune. But she was by nature ebullient, and when she thought of the horrors of the jail from which she had been so recently freed, she would rejoice at the good fortune which had brought her friends like Thomas Lynom, Kate and Belper and the Bansters.

On a day soon after her release she sat at her window looking down at the crowds thronging through the flesh market of East Cheap, and her thoughts must necessarily go back to that day when she and Will had set out to see the King.

Have done with the past, she scolded herself. Remember this is the beginning of the year 1484, and the year that has gone has been the most tragic of your life.

Today King Richard and Queen Anne would ride through the streets of London, showing themselves to the people after the quelling of the Buckingham rebellion. Jane was going out, but not to see them. She would make her way to the Tower, and her visits to the Tower were what she lived for these days.

What a comfort it was to make her way through the great gate and turn her steps towards the Belper kitchens! She was never challenged. The guards and warders knew and respected her. They knew she but came to visit her friend Kate Belper, and Kate, like Jane, was well liked throughout the Tower.

It seemed to Jane, in her love for Edward's two boys, that they grew daily more like their father. They were always delighted to see her. It was dull, they said, living as they did. Of course, they were not prisoners as poor Jane had been in Ludgate; their surroundings were luxurious indeed; they were the nephews of the King even if they were bastards, for no one could deny that Edward the Fourth was their father; but their lodgings in the Garden Tower were dull indeed, and the small conspiracy which the coming of Jane must necessarily mean was very welcome. They were boys still–thirteen and eleven years old.

Jane looked at her face in the old mirror as she put on her cape. It was true that the mirror was mottled with age, but the Jane who looked back at her was sadly different from that Jane of a year ago. Her skin was yellowish; she doubted whether she would ever regain the healthy delicate colouring which had been one of her greatest charms. She did not need a mirror to show her that her long hair, luxuriant as ever, had lost that look of powdered gold. Kate's clothes hung loosely on her, for she was very thin. Was it really necessary to hide herself beneath the hood? Would any recognise her as the once dazzling Jane Shore?

She shrugged her shoulders. She had left her youth behind her in Ludgate Jail. What mattered that? Most of those whom she had loved were dead, and the Princes did not notice that her beauty was fading. To them she was Jane whom they had loved dearly when they were very little boys, the two most important little boys in the land.

Jane started to descend the spiral staircase. The wood was broken and it was necessary to tread warily. A strange contrast this to Windsor Castle and the Palace of Westminster, which but a short year ago she had considered her homes.

Mistress Banster met her at the bottom of the stairs.

'The streets are filling.'

'They'll not be going my way,' said Jane. 'I shall slip through Candlewick to Tower Street. The procession will not pass that way.'

'Be in before dusk,' advised Mistress Banster. 'There'll be roystering in the streets this night, I'll swear. We're boarding up the front of the shop. We don't want rogues and vagabonds breaking in. A good journey to you. And don't forget: be home by duskfall.'

'I will, never fear.'

Out in the streets Jane caught the excitement. She pushed her way through the crowds. The air of East Cheap was filled with the smell of meat and the cries of the butchers. The cook-shops were doing good trade. People stood about eating and drinking. Beggars whined and showed armless and legless bodies, declaring they were old soldiers. Jane dropped many a coin she could ill spare into an open hand.

She was thinking as she went on along East Cheap of the extraordinary twists of fortune. Here she had found Anne Neville all but starved to death in Mother Clack's cook-shop. Mother Clack had left East Cheap now and Anne Neville was Queen of England. Jane paused. She would take the opportunity of seeing Anne again. The little Princes would like to hear something of the procession and would be disappointed if she had nothing to tell them.

She retraced her steps. In a very short time the cavalcade would be passing through the Poultry and into Cheapside on its way to Ludgate, when it would go along Fleet Street and on to Westminster. Jane could hear the trumpets now. The church bells were ringing out. The royal pair could not be far off.

Jane took her stand close to the old Cross and waited. From here she could see the walls of her father's house. There was another mercer living there now and she was saddened recalling her father. Thank the Virgin he was not alive now to see her brought so low!

First came the heralds, the knights and the squires. She recognised Catesby, and near him rode Sir Richard Ratcliffe and Lord Lovel with the Duke of Norfolk–all the strongest adherents of the King. They had passed, and a special cheer went up, for here was the King, ablaze with jewels; the King was on horseback, and the Queen in her litter was equally dazzling.

The royal pair passed, the cheering died down and the people talked together.

'How sick looks the little Queen! And so pretty, poor lady.'

'It is well that she has already borne the King a son.'

'I dare swear she is not long for this world, poor soul.'

Poor little Queen! thought Jane; and was assured of her own strength. She could take care of herself. She had been bred in these colourful streets with their yelling townsfolk, and she knew she would never be entirely unhappy while she was free to roam them.

She hurried eastwards, turning into Tower Street. As she approached the Tower one of the warders called to her merrily, and she stopped to exchange a word with him. Then she went through the postern gate and down the stairs to the kitchens, where Kate was waiting for her.

'I had expected you earlier,' said Kate as they embraced.

Jane explained that she had stopped to see the procession. Kate herself would have liked to see it, but she did not complain that she had stayed behind that she might conduct Jane to the Princes.

'You'll have a bite to eat before we go?' asked Kate; but Jane was eager to be gone and said so.

Kate wrapped her cloak about her and they came out into the grounds and made their way towards the Garden Tower. Jane was always afraid at such times that there would be someone to bar their way and to tell them that these visits must be stopped. It was pleasant to reflect that almost everybody was busy merry-making on this day. Besides, the Princes were not so carefully guarded as they had been in those days when people still called young Edward, King. Richard was firmly on the throne now; but doubtless he still considered it wise to be in full knowledge of the whereabouts of his nephews.

They entered the Garden Tower. It was cold, and the bells of St Peter ad Vincula that were pealing to welcome the procession seemed to take on a mournful note.

Jane shivered, and Kate said slowly: ''Tis always cold inside these towers–winter and summer alike.'

There were guards outside the Princes' apartments. Kate grinned at them saucily, and they returned the grin.

'Visitors for the young gentlemen,' said one to another; and when Jane smiled at them they bowed and stood aside.

Jane and Kate went into a small antechamber and knocked on a door.

'Enter,' said a boy's voice, which Jane recognised with emotion as being young Edward's.

The two boys were seated at a table by the window, poring over a book. They did not look up for a second or two, thinking it was but an attendant with more logs for the fire which burned in the great fireplace. But when Jane called them by their names they leaped up and ran to her. Richard flung himself at her; Edward was more dignified. Richard was still a child, but Edward had–though very briefly–tasted the honours of kingship.

'My dearest ones!' cried Jane. 'How fare you today?'

'We are weary of this place,' said Edward. 'But your coming has brightened it. Your hands are cold, Jane. Come–you too, Kate. Come to the fire and warm yourselves.'

Jane went with them to the fire, where Edward sat at her feet and Richard leaned against her. They plied her with questions and she told them how she had just seen the procession. And, as she talked, she looked about the apartment which had been the little Princes' home for so long, and she wondered when the King would see fit to let them leave it.

The walls were hung with rich cloth and the big room was furnished in a manner suited to the apartments of the sons of Edward the Fourth; but there was a gloom about the place that depressed Jane. From where she sat she could look out on the Green, and she wished that it was not to this room that she must come to see her beloved boys, for never did she look through that window but she must remember seeing Hastings stand there with a faraway look already in his eyes. She preferred the southern end of the room, which was fitted as a bed-chamber. The bed was beautiful and its curtains richly woven; it was a big bed for two little boys to sleep in. She wondered if they were afraid as they lay by night in that great gloomy chamber, and whether they drew the curtains close so that they might not see the window in that inner partition which faced the bed. Young Richard had been a fanciful child. She was glad, though, that the two boys were together.

'Jane!' Edward seized her hands and looked earnestly into her face. 'Do you think my uncle is ever going to let us leave this place?'

'Assuredly I do. But you must know that he has been very busy of late. He will remember soon that you are here, and then he will send for you to go to court.'

'Mayhap I shall join my wife,' said Richard, 'for I am a married man, you know.'

The two little boys laughed. 'It is odd indeed,' said Edward, 'that Richard should have a wife while I have none. They thought to make a very grand marriage for me–and now it may be that I shall never marry.'

'You will, my little lord,' said Kate. 'I see it in your face.' She took his palm and looked at it while the boys watched her face gravely. 'A long life and a merry one!' cried Kate. 'I have visited a wise woman in Shoreditch, and that is what she promised me. Rest assured if Kate is to have these things, how much longer and merrier shall be the life of Princes.'

They all laughed. That was how it was when Kate and Jane visited them. Laughter ran high; and so did hope. It was impossible to be with these two and not believe that some day, soon, everything would come right.

'What of our mother?' asked Edward gravely. 'We never see her now, nor our sisters.'

Richard's lips quivered. He was only eleven and he longed for his mother. Elizabeth Woodville had been more tender to her boys than to any of her children.

'I do not believe my mother wished me to come here,' said Richard. 'She would rather we were both with her and our sisters in Westminster Sanctuary.'

'Oh, Jane, how long must our mother stay in Sanctuary?'

'Not long now, you will see. Why, now that your uncle has put down the rebellion he will be able to give thought to your family. Doubtless in a few short weeks you two will be riding in processions.'

They laughed at that. They saw themselves on white horses, richly clad; they pictured reunion with their family.

'Jane,' said Edward suddenly, 'what would have happened to us if the rebellion had not failed?'

Jane and Kate exchanged warning glances, for they had seen hope leap up in the little boys' eyes. The two women thought–just as the boys did–that if the rebellion had been successful, little Edward would have mounted the throne.

'You will not speak,' said Edward. 'But I know.'

'Yes,' said Richard. 'Edward knows.'

'It is not wise to speak of it,' said Jane. 'You never know who listens.'

They were silent for a while; then Richard, who forgot these matters more easily than did his brother, said: 'Edward, let us show Jane our little room. The one we discovered the other day.'

'Yes,' said Edward; and the two boys jumped up.

'We found it a week back,' said Richard. 'It was hidden by the hangings–this door was.' He went to the east side of the room, drew back the curtains and disclosed an old door.

'At first it did not seem to open,' said Edward.

'We spent hours trying to make it,' added Richard. 'I do not think it has been opened for years and years. Look. There. It hardly seems like a door at all.'

The four of them stood close together looking down at a dingy staircase that wound out of sight.

'Whither does it lead?' asked Kate.

'To a small vaulted chamber,' said Edward. 'We were disappointed. It just leads to the chamber and stops.'

'Yet it is fine to have our own little room,' said Richard. 'Our secret room.'

'Well,' said Kate, 'I hope your little Graces will deign to show it to us.'

'Come, follow us,' said Edward; and he led the way.

They descended the short staircase to a small chamber about which there was a smell of age and dust.

Outside, the bells of St Peter ad Vincula stopped momentarily, and when they started again it seemed to Jane that there was a melancholy foreboding in their pealing.

Elizabeth Woodville was not the person to remain tranquilly in Sanctuary. It was not a year since the death of Edward, and yet she had become almost as insignificant as the widow she had been when Edward had first met her in Whittlebury Forest. She did not intend to stand by and wait for ever. She had made plans, and her children were at the centre of these, though not of course the two little boys in the Tower, for Richard was firmly on the throne and it would take a successful war to dislodge him. And who would fight for two fatherless boys?

She believed, though, that there was one man who might take the throne from Richard, and that was Henry Tudor, who was now on the other side of the Channel awaiting his opportunity.

One day in early March she sat with her daughters as they stitched at their embroidery. The five girls were talking together, as they often did, of the old happy days when their lives had seemed so full of promise and their father the King had arranged such grand marriages for them. Listening to them, Elizabeth Woodville's eyes rested on her eldest daughter, that other

Elizabeth, who, she hoped, would, through her mother's cleverness, restore her family's fortunes.

'What hope have we of ever marrying?' Cecily was saying. 'We shall stay here for ever.'

But Elizabeth was looking at her mother and had caught a glint of something in her eyes. 'Mother,' she cried, 'you know something. Oh, pray tell us, gracious Mother.'

Elizabeth Woodville nodded and plied her needle thoughtfully. 'As I see it, my children, our troubles are beginning to end.'

'Our troubles ending! Our cruel uncle is stronger than ever.' That was Elizabeth–an ambitious girl, her mother's own daughter, she longed to make a match worthy of her, and she could not forget that she had been promised the Dauphin of France.

'Kings and Queens are never safe, my children. Why, even a man such as your father had his troubles. Why, your little brother, King Edward the Fifth, was born in this place, and I was kept alive and tended by poor citizens of London who believed in your father's cause.'

'I know,' said Elizabeth the younger. 'But I never thought we should come to this–now. And in those days none could keep my father from the throne for long. But now he is dead, and I–who was to have been Queen of France–am betrothed to a poor exile.'

Elizabeth Woodville smiled slyly. 'Never fear. Your father was once, as you call it, a poor exile. Poor exiles, daughter, can become kings.'

'You think Henry Tudor will ever be King of England?' Elizabeth laughed scornfully. 'There is a rebellion and he does not even land. He lies off Plymouth and scuttles back to France.'

'Often there is wisdom in flight.' Elizabeth smiled at her daughter. 'Listen, foolish girl. I gave my consent to your betrothal to Henry Tudor, did I not? What have we to lose? Nothing. And what to gain? One day, depend upon it, Henry Tudor will come to England, and when he does there will be those to rise against your uncle. Henry Tudor has sworn to marry you. Could you hope that he would do that were he already on the throne? Remember your false uncle has set all England calling you bastards.'

'Gracious Mother, mayhap you are right.'

'There is no knowing what will happen, and I feel good things in the air. I have felt much lightness in my heart ever since I was approached to make this contract with the Tudor.'

There was a sudden knocking on the door, and when Elizabeth gave permission for whoever was there to enter, a messenger came in carrying a scroll in his hand. This he handed to Elizabeth the ex-Queen, saying that his royal master awaited her reply when she could conveniently give it. With great dignity Elizabeth accepted the scroll, and when the messenger had withdrawn proceeded with all eagerness to read it. When she had done so she tapped her eldest daughter with it, and said with some severity: 'Daughter, you were a short while ago wondering at the wisdom of my conduct.'

'Oh no, gracious Mother, I am assured that whatever you did was right and proper for us all.'

'It is well that you have as much good sense. Now, children, listen to me. I gave my consent when our friends across the water wished your eldest sister to be formally promised to Henry Tudor. That was at Christmas time in Rennes when, as you know, the young man took the oath that if ever he came to the throne of England he would marry Elizabeth of York. This matter has now come to your uncle's ears, and, as you can imagine, he likes it not. And here is evidence of it. In this paper is a statement that if we leave this Sanctuary and put ourselves in the care of the King, we shall suffer no hurt and husbands shall be found for you all. For me there is an allowance. Now what think you, children, of your mother's strategy? Your uncle does not like it that I should have betrothed my eldest daughter to Henry Tudor. He offers us a bribe–doubtless to stop the match. Never fear, we shall rise again. Look, dear daughters, look at the signature on this document. Even you, Bridget, can read that, can you not?'

'Ricardus Rex,' read Bridget in her high piping voice.

Elizabeth Woodville burst into laughter. 'Let him call himself King if it pleases him.' She laid a hand affectionately on the shoulder of her eldest daughter. 'Mayhap it will not be for long, eh, daughter?'

That year slipped away quickly for Jane. The money Thomas Lynom had given her was gradually disappearing, but Jane had never been concerned about money. All her life there had been someone to provide for her; in her heart she believed there always would be, for even when she was desperately poor and alone in Ludgate Jail, Thomas Lynom had come to succour her.

She was beginning to recover from the weakness which the events of the last year had put upon her. She was growing healthy again, adapting herself to the life which was hers. Her thoughts of the two men she had loved were less frequent and painful now, and she no longer wished for a lover, for she had left her passionate youth behind her, and her affections were now in the possession of the two little boys in the Tower. How pleasant it had been to be able to tell them that the King had already made a move in their favour, since their mother and sisters now had apartments in Westminster Palace! She was sure, she said, that it would not be long before the little boys joined their mother and sisters. But the weeks passed into months and the Princes continued to be lodged in the Tower.

She had heard with great sorrow of the death of the King's only son. Poor Anne Neville would be heartbroken, she knew; and in the streets they were saying that the Queen was too sick to bear the King another child.

Elizabeth Woodville's emotions on that matter were quite different from Jane's, for no sooner had she been installed at the palace than she sought to improve her position. She began to feel that in affiancing her daughter to Henry Tudor she had not been so clever. What had Henry Tudor but ambition!

At the palace, living close to the King, it was possible to realise the power of the man. He was no Edward, who had surely been every handsome inch a king, but he had power and presence, and many feared to have the cold eyes of Richard turned on them in anger. Unlike his brother though he was, King Richard bore the stamp and mould of Plantagenet.

Elizabeth slyly watched her daughter, for the girl was old enough to have hoped for much from life. She still yearned to be Queen of France, but how much more gratifying to be Queen of England!

'My dear,' said Elizabeth Woodville one day, as they looked through the window of their obscure apartments out to the grounds of Westminster Palace where the King walked in earnest conversation with his friend Lord Lovel, 'your uncle is a man of some attractiveness, I think.'

'Attractiveness? He is too short of stature, and I admire a man more of my father's girth.'

'There is a look of your father in his brother, I declare.'

'You may see it, gracious Mother. I do not.'

'You would an you looked for it. Methinks, daughter, that the King hath a fondness for you.'

'For me?'

'Why should he not? You are comely enough. Holy Mother, there is much a woman can do for herself and her family.'

At last the daughter understood. 'But he is my uncle!'

Elizabeth Woodville shrugged her shoulders, sweeping away difficulties as eagerly now as in the old days when she had wanted something from Edward which it had not been easy to obtain. 'Uncles . . . nieces . . . what of that? In certain circumstances His Holiness the Pope can be most obliging.'

'You have forgotten my aunt.'

'Anne Neville is half dead already and it is the King's duty to get sons. . . .'

Elizabeth Woodville smiled. She had seen the hope leap up in her daughter's eyes. The girl was now looking at the King with a new interest.

Christmas came and Jane spent it with the Belpers in the kitchens of the Tower. Belper had surpassed himself, and his table was loaded with the choicest foods. He entertained warders, jailers and soldiers, and even the sworn tormentors and the executioners crept in.

Jane set the table laughing as she had done in the banqueting halls of palaces. These people were glad to have her in their midst, and she was glad to be there. In the morning she had visited the Princes, who were now assured that their captivity would soon be over. Everything was coming right, Jane felt; but when the talk turned to the King and his Queen she was saddened.

'The King,' said merry Belper, 'may be a king, but a king is a man for all that he is a king.' Everyone laughed as they always did at Belper's remarks. 'Why, bless us all,' he went on, 'the Queen is nothing but a sick invalid, they say; and a man may be a king . . .'

Someone ventured: 'They say the King has cast his eyes upon the Lady Elizabeth.'

'I do not believe it,' said Jane. 'She is his niece.'

'A niece is a girl for all she is a niece,' pointed out Belper, chuckling as he stood up to carve the boar's head.

'It is a rumour . . . an evil rumour,' said Jane. 'Why, I remember well a rumour that the Princes were dead . . . murdered. But was there any truth in that?'

'Nay. 'Tis odd how rumour starts.'

'The poor Queen is sick and ailing,' said Kate. 'She has lost her son and there is no heir to the throne. So rumour will supply the King with a new Queen. . . .'

Belper pointed his knife at Kate. ''Twill take more than rumour to give the King an heir!'

Everyone laughed and Belper had to lay aside his knife to wipe his tears of mirth. Jane laughed with them, but her thoughts were mixed, for she had known intimately these people who were just names in Belper's kitchen. What did it mean? How far would the ambitions of Richard take him? And what did that cunning woman, Elizabeth Woodville, plan for her daughter?

Richard was strange and cold; and none knew him well. But Jane remembered his face when she had taken him to East Cheap and he had seen

Anne, ragged and dirty; then had he, the exquisitely clad dandy, held out his arms to her, and into that pale face of his had come a glow of love.

'I do not believe he contemplates marriage with his niece,' said Jane. 'Why, if you could have seen him with his Queen, and how he loved her . . . you would not believe these rumours.'

They were silent as they always were–silent with respect–when Jane Shore gave her accounts of life at court. There was nothing they liked better than to listen to a tale of great ones; and who was better equipped to tell than Jane Shore?

So now she told them of poor Anne Neville whose fortune had tempted that Duke of Clarence who had died so mysteriously in the Bowyer Tower. And they listened to how the Duke hid the girl, and how she escaped to the squalor of an East Cheap cook-shop, until she was found and became the Queen of England.

'And Richard came to her,' said Jane, 'and dearly he loved her. I know it, for I was there to witness it. Nay, listen not to evil rumours.' She lifted her glass and cried: 'Long live the Queen!'

'Long live the Queen!' echoed those around the table.

All along East Cheap people stood in little groups. Jane had drawn back the shutters of her room to look down on them, and friends and acquaintances called up to her as they passed.

'There is something of the devil in this,' called an old market woman; and Jane nodded as she looked along the fast darkening street. It certainly seemed that the devil was at work up there in the sky. What did it mean? Was it the end of the world? There was an uncanny feeling in the cold March air.

Mistress Banster called up for Jane to come down.

''Tis the end of the world. 'Tis Judgment Day. Come down, and let us all stand together against the forces of evil.'

Jane took her cloak and wrapped it round her. Charlie was with his mother, and several people were standing inside the shop, some covering their eyes, some praying, and every now and then peering up furtively through the window to the sky.

''Tis getting mighty dark,' said Mistress Banster.

An old beggar woman, who had come in to shelter with them, whispered: 'And methinks when the sun disappears we shall never see it again.'

'It is the wickedness of us,' said another. 'We have brought this on ourselves.'

'The wickedness of *some*,' said Mistress Banster significantly.

The March wind penetrated the shop and the air grew colder as the darkness increased.

'Day into night,' said the beggar-woman. 'God has turned day into night to show His displeasure. An evil omen, this. I had it from a friend in Shoredith that there was bad times a-coming.'

'Mayhap it is a sign of good times,' said Jane.

'Good? What good could there be in the sun's hiding its face?'

'When it emerges from the darkness it will be like good coming out of evil. If it is a sign . . .'

'Who said it will come out? I never knew the like. 'Tis the devil up there.'

'Take another look, Charlie,' said his mother.

''Tis too bright to look, Mother. Wherever I look I see the sun . . . though my eyes be shut.'

'Devil's work.'

'Ah,' said the beggar-woman. 'Mayhap when the rightful king sits on the throne times will change.'

'Be careful what you say,' whispered Jane. 'You know not who may overhear you.'

'Bah! What matters it? You will see this darkness is but a beginning. Terrible things will happen. I feel it in my bones, lady, and my bones don't lie. Where's the two little boys, eh? The two little Princes? The rightful King and his little brother? Strangled, some say . . . and their innocent bodies dropped in the river!'

'That's a lie!' said Jane. 'I saw them but lately. Only last week I saw them.'

The old woman shook her head, refusing to allow such a firmly rooted belief to be dislodged.

''Tis the truth I speak,' insisted Jane. 'I tell you I saw them but a week ago. They were well and happy, awaiting reunion with their mother and sisters.'

As they were speaking the sky had grown darker. An old woman had taken her beads in her hand and began to mumble her prayers. Others followed her example. A darkness like that of night was over the earth. Looking through the glazed window of the cookshop, Jane saw faint pinheads of golden light springing up on the black background of sky. Greatly daring, she turned her eyes towards the sun. A great terrifying black shadow all but obscured it.

Outside in the street a woman screamed and lay fainting on the cobbles. Others knelt down, covering their faces, waiting for a terrible vengeance.

'This is the end!' screamed the beggar-woman. 'This is the Judgment Day.'

Minutes passed and the darkness grew deeper, and then someone whispered: 'It is growing lighter. I swear it.' And looking through the window Jane saw the sun emerging from that dark shadow. Out in the street the crowds had noticed too.

'The Virgin be praised!' shouted a man. 'It is over and done with. The vengeance of the Lord has been turned from us.'

In the cook-shop everyone began to talk at once.

'The sun has been given back to us.'

'This is another chance.'

'We have not lost the sun.'

'Praise to Christ! Praise the Holy Mother!'

People stood about long after the eclipse of the sun was over. They marvelled and speculated as to its meaning. That it was a display of divine omnipotence was admitted by all. It was a warning, most agreed.

And before the day was ended the bells of London were tolling dismally. From St Clement Danes within the Temple to St Clement's in East Cheap, they gave out their mournful tidings. The news was whispered from mouth to mouth as it spread through the City.

'The Queen is dead.'

'God have mercy on us, she must have died at the very moment when the Almighty in His wrath hid the sun's face from us.'

People were asking strange questions.

'Why should God show His displeasure by covering up the sun's face at the very hour when the Queen was dying?'

'How did the Queen die?'

'The Queen could have no sons, and they say the King is enamoured of his niece the Lady Elizabeth.'

The old rumour regarding the Princes was revived, and, although there were many who declared the Princes still lived, people shrugged their shoulders. Why were the boys kept in the Tower? Why did God hide the sun's face on the day the Queen died?

These were questions which swept like a murmuring wind through the City's streets.

The saddest man in England was its King. He was really alone now. There were one or two men about him whom he thought he could trust, and in whom he must believe, yet how could he help it if suspicions leapt into his mind? He never had a whole night's rest. Dreams troubled him. In them he would see Hastings' guilty eyes looking at him across the council chamber; and perhaps those eyes would become blurred and would seem to change to those of Lovel . . . or Ratcliffe . . . or Norfolk. No, these men were true friends. Yet had he said at one time, Hastings is my friend. If only Anne had been strong! If only she had not died but had borne him many sons! If only he had Edward's personality and charm! But Anne was dead, and there were some of his subjects who suspected him of killing her. There was no happiness for England's King.

Thoughts of a marriage with the daughter of Elizabeth Woodville, like the whispering of evil spirits, were in his mind.

'I must have a son, Anne,' he murmured. 'Understand this. I must have a son.' She would understand; she always had.

He had been glad when Catesby and Ratcliffe had opposed the marriage on the grounds that it would not please the people. The matter had been laid before his counsellors. If he did not marry Elizabeth himself, might she not consider her engagement to Henry Tudor binding? What if she escaped to Brittany and married his enemy? Would that not strengthen the Tudor rogue's chances? Would not more be ready to flock to his banners if he should effect a landing in England, once he was married to the daughter of Edward the Fourth, a lady whom many still believed to be a legitimate Princess?

'Let the girl be removed,' advised Catesby; and she had been removed to Sheriff Hutton Castle–the ambitious Princess who had hoped to marry her uncle! That was a good move and should do much to stop the pernicious rumour that the Queen had met her death by poison.

There was discontent everywhere. Enemies were all about the King. Dorset was in France waiting to spring, and the King must prepare for war. It was almost two years since he had taken the crown and there had scarcely been a happy moment in the whole of that time.

In London the people murmured against him, for he was taxing them heavily in his preparation for war. A silly rhyme was stuck on the door of St Paul's Cathedral, which was a direct insult to the King and his councillors.

'The cat, the rat, and Lovel our dog,
Ruleth all England under a hog.'

No one could fail to understand its meaning. The cat was Catesby; the rat, Ratcliffe; the dog was Frances Lovel's badge; and the boar was Richard's own cognisance.

Hating violence, Richard had nevertheless been forced to resort to it.

Weakness was folly, and he would never be accused of that. The writer of the lines was found and subjected to the horrible death accorded all traitors. Crowds gathered to see him suffer on Tower Hill.

The King's popularity was at its lowest when news reached him that Henry Tudor had landed at Milford Haven.

It was hot August at Bosworth Field. In the shadow of Ambeame Hill was the traitor Tudor's army encamped. Opposite them, eager for the fight, the archers and billmen of the King made ready.

Richard was exultant. He had dreaded this so long, and now that it was upon him he had at least rid himself of the suspense. He was a great statesman, but perhaps a greater soldier. He had come successfully through many campaigns. Here was his chance to settle the Tudor for ever, for Henry Tudor himself was there in that opposite camp; and that was a matter for rejoicing, since so elusive had the fellow so far proved, that although his supporters had been routed many times, he had ever managed to escape his deserts.

There was a fear that haunted Richard now. Of his own will, of his own bravery, of his ability to look death unflinchingly in the face he was sure; but as he looked at those men who stood beside him and professed their friendship for him, he must wonder, Can I trust them? Will they be true? Norfolk, Catesby, Lovel, Ratcliffe–these, my friends, will they follow the example of Buckingham and Hastings? Lord Stanley was on the flank of Richard's army–and Lady Stanley was the mother of Henry Tudor! Could Stanley be trusted?

Agonies of doubt beset the King as the sun rose to a brilliance that made the armour plate and basinets shine like silver. Pikes and swords gleamed in the light of day. The battle was about to begin.

The King, small and slender though he was, looked mighty on his grey horse. His steel suit was polished to a shining brilliance and any deformity was lost in the magnificent way he sat his horse. His courage made of him a giant, and men remembered his successes on the fields of battle. Over his head flew the red-embroidered banner of England; and Parker, his standard bearer, held it bravely, a smile curving his fine young lips. How could brave Richard fear the cringing Tudor, the crafty schemer who had no military prowess and who, it was said, was not over-eager for the fight?

Richard addressed his men. The moment was at hand. With eager fingers the archers were bending their bows, the soldiers were buckling their helms. Soon the trumpets and kettle drums would give the signal for the battle cry. 'For England! For Richard! Death to the Welsh traitor!'

A fair hot day, and the most courageous leader in England was a King who had never lost heart on the field of battle. His eyes gleamed in his pale face beneath the basinet. But in his mind, as he scanned the ranks of waiting men, there was the haunting doubt. Treason. Could he trust Northumberland? Could he trust Stanley?

His horse was rearing with impatience. Now–to the fight.

Soon he was too much occupied to notice the aloofness of Northumberland's men, who, under their treacherous master, were standing by, waiting to see how the battle went before allying themselves with Henry Tudor. As for the traitor Stanley, he had changed sides before the battle began; and so the King's army had an enemy beside it, in its very lines, where it was thought to have a friend.

The confusion wrought by this was terrible, for soldiers beneath the red and white banner of England were fighting each other, not knowing who was friend and who enemy.

Richard was now aware that what he had feared most had come to pass. There was treason in the very heart of his army, and men, fearful of Tudor revenge, were deserting him now.

Ratcliffe was slain, fighting beside the King. There went one true friend. Lovel, Norfolk and Catesby, too, stood firm beside him. His spirits rose. Praise the saints, I have some true friends, then!

'The day is not yet lost, Francis.'

Francis Lovel laughed, his eyes gleaming. Thank God for Lovel, true friend and loyal subject.

Lost! Indeed it was not lost. Nor should it be if courage could prevail over cowardice, true men over traitors. The smile that passed between these two friends brought new hope with it. Richard knew now that it was victory or death.

Norfolk was down, mortally wounded. Surrey, Norfolk's son, was taken prisoner. Lovel was fighting on. The King shouted, rallying his men, and the men took up the battle cry.

'A Richard! A Richard! England and Richard! Death to the Welshman!'

And the King, swinging his bloody battle-axe, hacked his way onward through his enemies.

His men were falling all about him, and he, good soldier that he was, sensed their lack of faith in victory. They had been betrayed and many were deserting the King and going over to the enemy before it was too late. The day was all but lost, but superhuman courage might save it yet.

The King had such courage; and there had occurred to him a daring plan. It was the only way in which to win this battle. Could he but slay the traitor Tudor he had won the day, for what was an army without a leader, and would not those who had deserted the red and white banner for the green and white as readily turn back to the King as they had an hour before turned to the Tudor? And somewhere, not far off, was this man whose death or capture alone could save the day for Richard.

'Fix my crown upon my head!' cried the King. 'For by Him that shaped both sea and land, King of England this day will I die!'

His courage was a flame which lit that of those around him. There were not many left, but those that remained would follow him to death if need be. The King was godlike in his glittering armour. The sun's rays caught the circlet of gold about his helm. There was no fear in him. He was staking his crown, his life, on this.

Parker held the standard above the King's head as Richard, his axe in his mailed fist, rode forward, straight towards that spot where, surrounded by a few supporters, Henry Tudor cowered in terror.

Richard laughed with desperate relief. The day was not lost. Once Henry Tudor lay dead, all those who supported him would turn back to Richard. Stanley and Northumberland should go the way of all traitors.

As for the Welshman, Richard could laugh–the crafty Welshman, cunning as a monkey, was timid as a mouse before the roar of the English lion.

This was not merely the foolhardy bravery of a desperate man; it was high strategy. The routing of the Welshman's army was impossible–but man to man, courage against cowardice must prevail. The English line of kings should not be thrust aside by a cunning Welshman.

He was almost upon the Tudor now–but what a bloody way he had come! He must hack his way through flesh and bone, and even as he cleared his path others rose up to defend the Welshman. Richard had split the head of the Tudor standard bearer and the red dragon worked in white and green silk went down into the blood and dust. But brave Parker held the standard of England aloft over the head of his fighting King; even though Parker had lost both his legs he could still sit, a fixed smile on his bloodless face, holding high the flag of England.

England's King was superhuman. None could fight as he fought. Henry Tudor was slipping behind his supporters, his little eyes wide with terror; but always there was some brave man to leap forward and defend him and then to fall to Richard's axe.

But Stanley, the traitor, hearing what was happening, and knowing what his fate would be if the King won the day–knowing, too, that if it was a matter of single combat, Henry Tudor would not put up any fight at all–came galloping to the spot with three thousand men behind him.

The battle was over. One by one the true knights of England fell beside their King. Richard fought to the end. He would never surrender. His standard bearer had gone down now, but the King still sat his horse, mortally wounded, brave and bleeding from too many wounds. No surrender! No surrender! And victory would have been his but for the treachery he had dreaded ever since he had worn the crown.

They were surrounding him now, and he could see nothing for the blood in his eyes; but he went on fighting.

'Treason!' he cried. 'Treason!'

He slipped from his horse, and only then did his crown roll from his head.

'Treason!' he murmured; and so bravely died the last English King.

The woman who walked down Tower Street towards the Tower of London was subdued in manner; and people, passing her, recognised her and wondered why she, who was always so ready to laugh and chat, was now preoccupied. She was beautiful yet, although she had never recovered from the ravages of Ludgate Jail. Today the serenity of her eyes had disappeared.

She walked across London Bridge and, looking down on the grey waters, she was thinking of all the colourful personalities she had known and who now were no more. She herself lived on, but what a different Jane Shore was this thin little woman in cheap worsted from that glorious jewelled creature who had graced the court of King Edward!

She was thinking now of Richard, that cold, pale man, whom neither she nor any–not even Edward–had really understood. She had heard men talk, with tears in their eyes, of Richard's glorious last hour. She pictured him, the circlet of gold flashing on his basinet, going into battle, hacking his way towards the cowardly Henry Tudor; weak from his wounds, his horse jaded, but his courage burning brightly, a glorious example to all who beheld him. And then–defeat, through the teachery of those who called themselves his friends. It saddened her to think of the man in death, his body dirty and bloodstained, lying on the battlefield, where his enemies found it; they had stripped him of his armour and flung him naked across a sweating horse in the vain hope that they might dishonour him who, but a short time before, had ridden in glistening steel to shame the shivering man whom they now called King of England.

What would this mean to the citizens of London? wondered Jane. How could one know what a new dynasty would bring? Who were these Tudors? Henry Tudor, it was said, had shown poor prowess on the field of battle. How would the English like a Welshman and a coward on their throne?

But to humble folk, what did it matter who sat on the throne? There was still poverty, and taxation meant little to those who had not the wealth to make taxation worth while.

Yet what was it going to mean to those two boys in the Tower? That was what worried Jane. That was what had set the furrows on her brow.

Henry Tudor had already ridden into London. And what a disappointment awaited the assembling crowds, for the man came in a closed carriage! A victorious King should come in splendour, like a hero, magnificent in scarlet and gold. London wanted another Edward, but it had got something very different in Henry Tudor. Was this the beginning of a new age?

As she reached the Tower, Jane noticed that the grass on Tower Hill was dry and brown. How soon would that grass be stained with blood? Defeat in civil war must mean many an execution, for these were savage times. Jane shivered, for Henry Tudor's claim to the throne lay by way of illegitimacy, so how could he take it from little Edward? How was he going to reconcile with justice his seizure of the throne while those two little boys lived? He was going to marry their sister, and already she was on her way to London from Sheriff Hutton; but how could he marry an illegitimate girl? And if Edward's daughter was not illegitimate, neither were his sons. And if those two little boys were the legitimate sons of Edward, how could Henry Tudor mount the throne?

Jane's head ached with the problem; she had had no sleep because of it. Horrible fears beset her, for the ambitions of men were unbounded and there was no foul deed they would not do to win a crown. Love of money? Love of women? What were these things compared with love of power?

There was excitement in the kitchens. There would be grand doings, prophesied Belper. Had Jane heard that the new King was to be united to the Princess Elizabeth? This would mean great doings at the Tower Palace, for the new Queen, in accordance with royal tradition, would come to the Tower of London.

Kate, in private, turned up her nose at the new monarch. 'Call him a King! Holy Virgin, an old-young man who shuts himself up in a closed carriage! Knows he not that his subjects would have a look at him? Doubtless he knows he is not worth looking at. There are those among us who remember great King Edward in his prime.'

'Silence, wife!' said Belper. 'There'll be many heads to grace London Bridge ere long, but I'd not have yours one of them.'

Then were both Kate and Jane sad with their memories of other days, until Jane said: 'Kate, I would you could take me to the Princes. What think they of this change?'

'All mad with excitement, I'll tell you. They think this is going to alter things for them. The little boys have no grief for their uncle. That's how it is in royal families. . . .'

'Let us go to them.' As they left the kitchens, Jane said: 'Kate, I have a horrible fear that we shall soon not be allowed to mount the stairs to the Garden Tower unmolested.'

'Why, whatever has come over you? It would seem you have seen a ghost. You haven't, have you?'

'No, no. My thoughts but run on. I am mistaken. Who would stop our visits? What harm can we do?'

'No one will stop our visits, lovey. I'll see to that. Jemmy, the chief warder, is a special friend of mine. He'd not stop us.'

'But he would have his orders,' said Jane, and her teeth began to chatter.

'Why, you're cold.'

'It is this place. I never did greatly care for it. There is little sunshine in it and too much gloom and shadow.'

Jemmy was on guard. He gave Kate a smacking kiss on either cheek and bowed to Jane.

'All's well then?' said Kate.

'All's well,' said Jemmy.

The Princes were glad to see their visitors. They were changed. It seemed to Jane that new life had come to them, for their eyes sparkled and they laughed more loudly and frequently.

'It will not be long now,' said Edward.

'We shall ride in the procession,' added Richard. 'We have been playing at processions.'

'It was a silly game,' said Edward, 'but it helped to pass the time. Soon we shall leave this place and shall not have need of so many light pastimes. There will be important things to do.'

'When our sister is the Queen!' cried Richard. 'Odd, is it not? We thought Edward would be the King, and now it is Elizabeth who is to be a queen.'

'There is no knowing what will happen to any of us!' said Jane.

'Jane,' said Edward earnestly, 'when we are out of this place . . . when we have what is due to us . . . then shall you come and live with us.'

'Yes,' agreed Richard. 'We have talked of it often, but it did not seem worth while to mention it to you before. Now it is different. Soon we shall be free. We shall not be prisoners in the Tower. We shall have a place at court and much influence, for, after all, we shall be brothers of the Queen. Then shall you come and live with us. You, too, good Kate.'

'Well, I have a husband,' said Kate.

'If he were to die, you shall come.'

'Let us not talk of death now that everything is becoming bright,' said Jane quickly. 'Tell me, have you heard any more news?'

'None but that our sister is soon to marry the new King.'

'Ah, yes,' said Richard, 'and Jemmy has said that he has heard it whispered that he is to go away, he and his men . . . And that we are to have other attendants . . . men of greater importance such as are due to our new rank.'

'Your new rank . . .' began Jane, suddenly turning cold.

'Of a certainty,' said Edward. 'Now that the King is to marry our sister, we shall be brothers of the Queen, and until a lodging at court can be found for us, we are to have new guards. That is what Jemmy said. Why, Jane, what ails you?'

'Nothing,' said Jane.

'You seem to be staring oddly. You see nothing do you?'

'There is nothing to see. I wish the bell would not toll so dismally.'

'We have grown accustomed to it,' Edward said. 'Have we not, Richard?'

Richard nodded. 'It tolls so often.'

It seemed to Jane that the entire chamber was full of the dismal note. She shivered for, as it echoed through the room, it sounded to her like a passing-bell.

Never, it seemed to the two Princes, had a day passed so quickly. It was full of excitement. It was the day after Jane's visit, and they were awakened as usual by the sunlight streaming on to their bed through the window in the alcove which was just opposite it.

Richard said: 'We forgot to draw the curtains last night.'

Edward nodded. Why should they draw the curtains? Simply because Richard had had an unpleasant feeling that someone . . . the departed spirit of one of the many who had suffered in this place . . . might look through the window at them. Edward had not been without fears, but being older than Richard he had not voiced them.

But last night they had forgotten to draw the curtains. It was because they had been too excited, too excited for fear. They knew that they were not to spend many more weeks in this room which they had come to regard as a prison. Glorious events awaited them, for their sister was to be the bride of the new King. The glittering power which they had been brought up to believe would one day be theirs was lost to them, but that did not matter now. The only important thing was escape . . . escape from the Garden Tower, not to be watched, to be allowed out for more than a short while each day to exercise their limbs, to be the free brothers of the Queen.

Small wonder that they had forgotten to fear the shadowy ghosts of the Tower. They laughed now, pleased that they had forgotten. They would never draw the curtains of their bed again. What folly it was to fear the dead! Ah, soon they would leave the Garden Tower for ever.

Their food was brought to them by a new attendant, a black-browed, dark-haired man with deep throaty laughter and a manner which might, to some, have seemed over-hearty, but to the two boys seemed merry indeed.

'Good morrow to you, gentlemen,' he cried. 'I'm your new attendant. Will Slater by name. Called Black on account of the colour of me. Black Will, my lords, at your service.'

Black Will laid beef, beer and bread on the table.

'Got from the kitchen of Master Belper, my lords. Eat hearty; and if your appetites should not be satisfied, nor your thirst content, then will Black Will down to Belper to replenish your platters and your tankards.'

The boys exchanged smiles. Life was changing.

After breakfast came Sir James Tyrell to see them. Tall and handsome, he bowed low before them. Did they guess why he had come? he wanted to know.

Edward answered. 'Yes, it would seem to me that you come, sir, because those who heretofore had charge of our needs are now considered too lowly, for our sister will shortly sit upon the throne, and thus should we, her brothers, be treated with the respect now due to us.'

'That is so, my lord Prince. I am sent here by His Grace King Henry the Seventh to do honour to you, and to assure myself that you are receiving treatment in accordance with your rank. Now would I show you those whom I have ordained shall serve you . . . until a better lodging may be found for you. There is one John Green, a good and honest man. John, come hither and honour your gracious masters.'

John Green came forward. A short man with thick hands and feet, he bowed low and his light eyes beneath their sandy lashes looked full at the velvet-clad figures before him.

'Rise, John,' said Edward, who never forgot the dignity that had become second nature to him.

'I thank Your Grace,' said the man. 'I vow that I will serve you faithfully.'

'There is one other I would bring to your notice, my dear lords,' said Tyrell. 'He is a man I have selected on account of his trustworthy nature–in short, my own groom, John Dighton. Go, Green, and bring Dighton that the Princes may know him.'

Green went out and Tyrell looked about the room. ''Tis a comfortable lodging your Graces have here in the Tower.'

'We are weary of it,' said Richard.

'Say you so?' Tyrell turned to the boys and smiled. 'Methinks 'twill not be long ere you change it for a better.'

'Pray tell us when we shall leave,' begged Richard.

'That I cannot say.' Tyrell had gone to the window in the alcove and looked out; he stared down at the path which ran alongside the apartment. Then he swung round and smiled at them. 'Rest assured, the matter shall be dealt with as speedily as I can arrange it.'

'Then we shall indeed be indebted to you,' said Edward.

'Ah, here is Dighton,' said Tyrell as Dighton, tall and spare and wearing the clothes of a groom, entered, and bowed awkwardly before the Princes.

'At your service, fair sirs,' he muttered.

'Dighton will clean your apartments and do anything you ask of him.'

'That is well indeed,' said Edward.

'Dighton, you may go now,' said Tyrell. When he had gone, Tyrell added: 'It is the King's wish that you shall have every attention worthy of your rank. If there is anything you desire . . .'

'There is nothing we desire,' said Edward.

'But doubtless we shall think of something,' said Richard.

'Then I shall see you tomorrow, my lords.'

'Mayhap tomorrow you will bring us news of when we may be permitted to leave this place,' said Richard.

'Who knows, my lord!' said Tyrell, and he smiled wanly. 'Methinks, fair sirs, that you will not much longer sleep in yonder bed.'

'That is the best news we have heard for a long time,' said Edward.

'Since the death of our father the King,' began Richard, but Edward signed to him to be silent. Tyrell saw the sign and was unexpectedly touched, so that he was seized with a great desire to be out of the chamber.

'Your lordships will forgive me if I hasten away. I have much to attend to. I shall call tomorrow to see if your wishes have been carried out. You may trust my servants to do what is expected of them.'

He bowed and kissed a hand of each Prince before he went out.

Richard was so excited, he began to dance a merry jig.

'Ere long, brother,' he cried, 'you and I will ride through the streets of London.'

'On grey horses,' said Edward.

'At the wedding of our sister. . . .'

'To the King of England!'

They began to prance round the room as though they rode their horses, seeing–instead of the thick walls, the alcove and the great embrasures–the cheering people, the London streets.

Edward stopped suddenly and looked out of the window.

'What ails you?' asked Richard, stopping also.

'I was but thinking.'

'Thinking what?'

'That when you have thought to be a King, it is not such a merry thing to find you are but the brother of a Queen.'

'That is certainly a far-from-merry thought,' agreed Richard. 'But is it not a good thing, when you have been a prisoner, to know that soon you will be free?'

That was certainly a pleasant thought, and soon both boys were prancing round the chamber on imaginary steeds.

All through the afternoon they heard the strange noises. A banging, a tapping, and then a sound as though a great slab of stone had been dropped. They could not understand it.

'Some repairs in progress,' said Edward. 'I think I know. They are doing them before our sister's triumphant entry into the Tower.'

'Everything must be in order for that,' said Richard happily.

They sat at their books, but it was impossible to concentrate. The banging and the tapping went on.

'It sounds close,' said Richard, and he went to the door and opened it. 'It may well be coming from our chamber . . . our little one we found.'

'Nonsense! Who would wish to repair that? No one ever goes there.'

'Except us. Let us go and see for ourselves.'

Edward was not very interested, for his thoughts were far away in the future, but he rose and followed Richard down the narrow staircase.

'I am sure the noises come from behind that door,' said Edward, but he found that the door was locked.

'It was not locked before,' said Richard.

They knocked on the door and the banging and tapping ceased. Edward knocked again, but the silence persisted, although on the other side of the door they heard the sound of very heavy breathing.

'Who is there?' cried Edward; and there was no answer.

Richard began to tremble, for he had always been a little afraid of that chamber with its smell of dust and age, and he would never go to it unaccompanied by his brother. Edward was bolder.

'Open this door, I say.'

There was still no answer and Edward banged on it with his fists. 'Do you hear me? I demand that you should open this door.'

A voice answered then. 'An you wish, my masters.' The door opened and Dighton stood before them. There was dust on his eyebrows and it clung to his cap; the air was so full of dust that the boys began to cough and splutter.

'What means this?' asked Edward, and he would have forced his way into the room, but Dighton put out a hand, very respectfully, to stop him.

'My lord, go not in there. It is most unsafe.'

'Unsafe?'

'Yes, my lord. My master, Sir James Tyrell, has examined this chamber. He sent me to work on it at once. You must not go in there, my lords. It would be most unwise.'

'I see,' said Edward. 'Come, Richard.'

They returned to their apartments.

'How did Dighton get into the chamber?' wondered Richard. 'He did not go through the door we used, and down the stairs.'

'Doubtless there is another way in.'

'We did not see it.'

'When the repairs are done we shall be able to find the other entrance. That is, if we are still here.'

'How concerned Sir James seems for us,' said Richard. 'Already he notices the unsafeness of the chamber.'

'Ah! Once we were of small importance, now it is a different matter.'

Richard shivered. 'Edward, how terrible if we had been in that unsafe chamber . . . and something had fallen on us. We might have been buried there.'

'It is well,' said Edward, 'that there are now those to be concerned for us.'

All through the afternoon the sounds could be heard.

The boys lay in bed. They had not drawn the curtains about their bed, for why should they be afraid of evil spirits? All the same, they could not sleep on a night that had followed such a day. They had got to know Black Will rather well, they believed. He was amusing, and he had told them of his adventures in the wars.

'I like not Dighton, though,' said Richard.

'That was because we found him in our room. He looked so queer with the dust on his face.'

'I like him not,' insisted Richard.

'Well, we need see little of him. We could ask Sir James to have him removed. We need not have attendants whom we do not like. Remember we are brothers of the Queen.'

'Mayhap tomorrow I will ask him. Though the man would be hurt, and he has done naught of which we could complain.'

'And Tyrell would be angry with him as he has failed to please us.'

'Edward, Tyrell has a cruel face. Let us not tell him that we like not Dighton.'

'We will not. So you thought the man had a cruel face?'

'At first I thought there was much kindness in him. It was afterwards–when he turned from the window, I think–there was a wolfish look upon his face.'

'Nay. He looked like a man, not a wolf. Still, there are men one does not like, even as there are wolves.'

They laughed together; then Richard said: 'What shall we wear at our sister's coronation?'

'Cloth of gold and ermine.'

'We shall ride grey horses.'

'Magnificent horses.'

'Shall we ride ahead of the King and Queen?'

'Mayhap.'

'Edward, what manner of man is this new King, I wonder?'

'I wonder also, Richard.'

'I hope he will not prove stern like Uncle Richard.'

'I doubt there was ever man so stern.'

'He is related to us doubtless.'

'Doubtless.'

'Then, Edward, if he be related to us, why is it that you, who are our father's eldest son, are not the King?'

'You know they call us bastards.'

'Then is Elizabeth, our sister, also a bastard?'

'We are all bastards. So said Uncle Richard, did he not?'

'The new King does not mind that our sister is a bastard—' Richard stopped abruptly. 'Edward! Did you see? Did you see that, Edward?'

'See what?'

'There–I saw it. It was a face that did look in at us through the window.'

'A face? I see no face.'

Richard was shivering. 'It has gone. It was there but a second. I was talking–and I fancied a movement there. I looked up. It was there but a second.'

'You have always feared to see a face there.'

'This night I did see a face.'

Edward said: 'I will go and see.'

'I will come with you.'

The two boys got out of bed, Edward disbelieving, Richard white and trembling, certain that he had seen a face. He kept behind Edward as they approached the window. Edward looked out on to the path that ran just beneath it.

'There is none there, Richard.'

'I swear I saw a face.'

'What sort of face?'

'I know not. It was there–and gone. The cap was drawn down over it. But I know it was evil.'

Edward soothed his brother, but he did not really believe Richard had seen a face. It was so easy to imagine faces in this chamber. One thought of others who had occupied it, and grisly pictures rose in the imagination. Richard was over-excited, for Richard was easily over-excited.

As they lay in bed Richard kept close to his brother.

'Edward, do not go to sleep first.'

'No. I will wait for you.'

'Edward, who was it, do you think, who looked in upon us?'

'It was a fancy, Richard.'

'Was it? I hope it was. It seemed so evil.'

'We will not speak of it. Let us talk of the coronation.'

'Oh yes.'

'And afterwards, Richard, we shall have fine apartments at court. Elizabeth will see to that.'

'We shall see our mother. It seems so long since we last saw her.'

Richard was forgetting his fright. They both shut their eyes and continued to talk of the splendours that awaited them. It was not long before they slept.

And as they lay there sleeping a face appeared at the window. It remained there for several seconds; then it disappeared, and cautious footsteps might have been heard going swiftly along the path outside the window.

The footsteps continued along the path. They stopped at a door which led to the Garden Tower. The man who had looked through the window was joined by another, who whispered: 'Well?'

'Jesus Christ! I thought they would never sleep.'

'Then all is ready?'

'All is ready. Dighton waits below.'

'Come then.'

Green and Will Slater crept up the staircase, and at the Princes' chamber they paused.

'Quietly now. I should not like it if they were to waken.'

'Bah! Afraid, Will?'

'Afraid! Me–who's cut the guts out of many a man!'

'And yet . . .'

'Come! Let the deed be done.'

The door was opened very softly. The two men, in stockinged feet, crept across the floor. There was nothing for them to fear. The walls of the room were thick and a few screams would not be heard; and yet they were consumed with an anxiety not to awaken the boys.

They stood by the bed, looking down on the youthful figures. The younger was gripping his brother's garment and his face was hidden in the pillow as though he wished to cover his eyes. Edward lay sleeping on his back, and his lips were curved as though his dream was pleasant.

Green nudged Slater. Why did the man wait? The moment had come and the sooner the deed was done the better. Green went to one side of the bed and Slater to the other. Why did they hesitate? Perhaps because it was easier to cut out the guts of a man in battle than to murder two sleeping boys.

Green's eyes met those of Slater, and both were determined not to show the other his softness. Slater took the cushion he had brought with him and pressed it over Richard's face. The little boy gasped–struggled–then struggled no more.

Edward lingered only a second or so after his brother.

It was done, and there was ghostly silence in the gloomy chamber. Almost shamefully, and stumbling in their eagerness to finish their evil task, each man took one of the boys and slung him over his shoulder. They carried them down to the grave in the little chamber, which Dighton had been preparing for them all that afternoon.

At the spot where East Cheap joins Candlewick Street a little old beggar-woman sat, day in, day out, summer and winter alike. Her hair was long and grey; there was hardly any flesh on her bones, and so small and wizened was she that she looked like a shrivelled doll. Her face was brown and wrinkled; but there were some to take pity on her and throw alms to her that she might just keep alive.

She was such an old woman–surely one of the oldest in London. All those she had known in her youth were dead. It was said of her: 'She once knew great splendour. She declares she is none other than Jane Shore, and they say that she was the favourite mistress of Edward the Fourth.' But it was scarcely possible to believe that this old woman was beautiful Jane who had charmed a King.

Jane knew they doubted her. What mattered it? She would shrug her thin shoulders and smile sadly. There was nothing for her to do but sit and beg as she dreamed of the past and waited for death.

All those she had loved were dead. Kate had died of the sweating sickness which had ravaged the City soon after the disappearance of the Princes. Even the memory of the Princes scarcely moved Jane now, for it had happened so long ago. Jane guessed what had been the fate of the boys. They had been murdered at the order of King Henry the Seventh, for they had stood in his way and they had to die. She had heard that Sir James Tyrell had gone to France with a big pension from his royal master, and later when he foolishly returned to England he was imprisoned in the Tower and executed suddenly without a trial–a dangerous man because he held a dangerous secret. Elizabeth Woodville had been banished to a nunnery. Was that because she demanded to know what had happened to her boys? It was possible to understand these matters if one had lived near the throne and could piece together the small events to make the picture complete.

She had seen so much in her life; and she had lived so long that her mind was full of pictures. She had seen the coronation of Edward's eldest daughter and the risings of Lambert Simnel and Perkin Warbeck; she had glimpsed Will Shore on his way to Tyburn, where he had been executed for clipping gold coin. She had heard the whispering of the people. ''Tis Will Shore, the goldsmith. 'Tis said that years ago he was the husband of Jane Shore.'

But the years passed over her and she forgot that day which was made sad by remorse.

Bishop Morton, now a Cardinal, was writing the history of the last years. She saw him now and then walking through the City with his protégé, Thomas More. Not only did the Cardinal write history, but he sent forth false stories of what had happened in the past. People believed him, for was he not a great Cardinal? The young man with the noble countenance, whose name was Thomas More, believed him. Why should he not? He had not the experiences of the old beggar-woman on the corner of East Cheap.

Nothing was too ridiculous for the Cardinal to say of brave Richard. How simple it was to accuse him of poisoning his wife, and of the murders of Henry the Sixth and the Duke of Clarence! He was even accused of murdering the little Princes, for this was simply a matter of altering the date of their disappearance to that time when Buckingham and Morton put forth their rumour. But who would listen to an old beggar-woman when all the Cardinal's lies were endorsed and applauded by a grateful King! The old dynasty must be discredited to bolster up the new. The silly tale that Richard had been two years in his mother's womb was circulated; it was said that she had suffered hellish pains in his delivery and that he had come into the world feet first, with all his teeth, and a head of hair that reached to his shoulders. Rumour turned the slight deformity into a crooked back, so that to all those who had never seen him Richard came to be known as Crookback. It was said that he was a monster, hideously formed, and that his left arm was withered; and such rumours, spread by a lying Cardinal and a cowardly King, came in time to be accepted.

The years slipped by. Jane saw the coming of the Spanish Princess, Katharine of Aragon, and her marriage with Prince Arthur. She saw the funeral of Arthur and marriage of Katherine to his brother Henry.

She saw the coming of the new King–big, ruddy, golden of hair and of beard–with such a look of his maternal grand-father that Jane felt young at the sight of him.

More years passed and still the old beggar-woman continued to sit on her corner.

One day, when she was so old that she had ceased to count her years, she saw a lovely girl ride through the streets of London, and she heard the people say: 'The King is deep in love with her. So much so that they say he will rid himself of his Queen to marry her.'

And, crouching on the pavement, Jane felt herself slipping away from this Tudor-governed land. She thought it was years ago, when the House of

York was triumphant and that the lovely laughing girl who passed through the streets was Jane Shore, not Anne Boleyn.

'Poor old woman!' said those who carried her body away. 'She's been begging here for as long as we can remember. 'Tis a happy release, for the lot of a beggar is a hard one. And doubly hard, it would seem to her, for if she spoke truth she was once the wife of a goldsmith. From goldsmith's wife–to beggar-woman! What terrible things can happen to us in this cruel world!'

Perdita's Prince

Jean Plaidy

Perdita's Prince

BIBLIOGRAPHY

George IV, *Shane Leslie*
George IV, *Roger Fulford*
George, Prince and Regent, *Philip W. Sergeant*
The First Gentleman, *Grace E. Thompson*
Portrait of the Prince Regent, *Dorothy Margaret Stuart*
Memoirs of George IV, *Robert Huish*
Life and Times of George IV, *The Rev. George Croly*
The Diary and Letters of Madame D'Arblay, The Great Corinthian, *Doris Leslie*
The Good Queen Charlotte, *Percy Fitzgerald*
Life of George IV, *Percy Fitzgerald*
George III, *J. C. Long*
The Four Georges, *W. M. Thackeray*
The First Gentleman of Europe, *Lewis Melville*
Memoirs of Mary Robinson, *edited by J. F. Molloy*
Life and letters of Lady Sarah Lennox, *edited by the Countess of Ilchester and Lord Stavordale*
Loves of Florizel, *Philip Lindsay*
Memoirs and Portraits, *Horace Walpole*
Memoirs of the Reign of George III, *Horace Walpole*
George III, Monarch and Statesman, *Beckles Wilson*
George III, His Court and Family, *Henry Colburn*
In the Days of the Georges, *William B. Boulton*
The Four Georges, *Sir Charles Petrie*
The House of Hanover, *Alvin Redman*
The Dictionary of National Biography, *edited by Sir Leslie Stephen and Sir Sidney Lee*
British History, *John Wade*
National and Domestic History of England, *William Hickman Smith Aubrey*

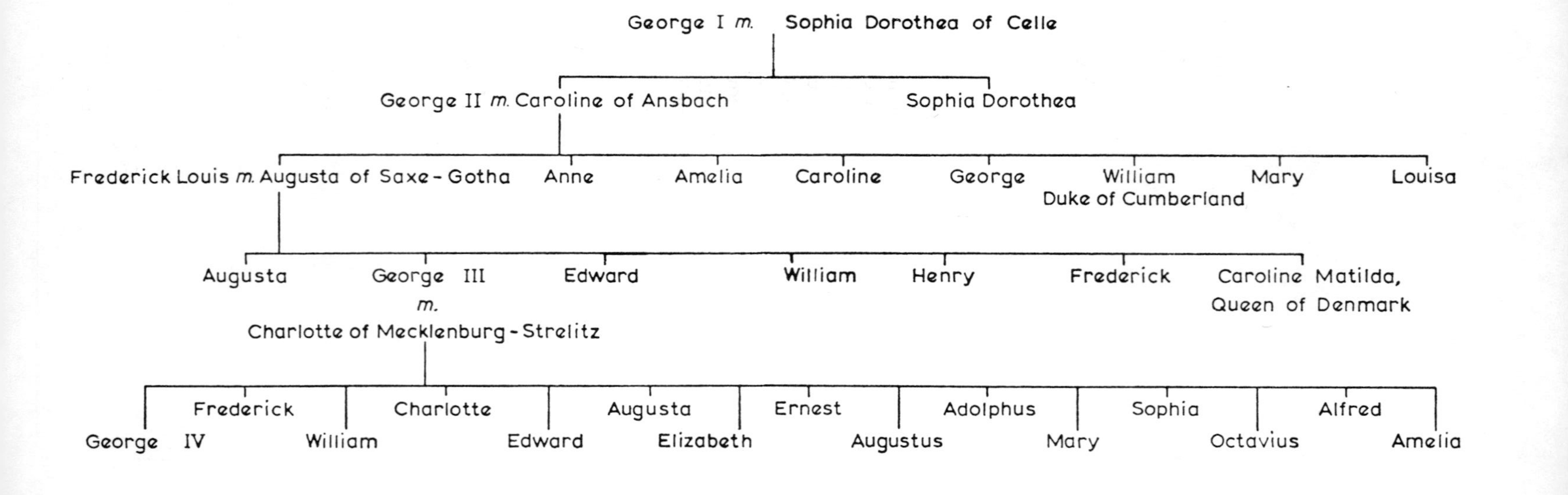

George I m. Sophia Dorothea of Celle
George II m. Caroline of Ansbach
Sophia Dorothea
Frederick Louis m. Augusta of Saxe-Gotha
Anne
Amelia
Caroline
George
William
Duke of Cumberland
Mary
Louisa
Augusta
George III
m.
Charlotte of Mecklenburg-Strelitz
Edward
William
Henry
Frederick
Caroline Matilda,
Queen of Denmark
George IV
Frederick
William
Charlotte
Edward
Augusta
Elizabeth
Ernest
Augustus
Adolphus
Mary
Sophia
Octavius
Alfred
Amelia

The Queen's Maid of Honour

The Prince of Wales stalked up and down his apartments in the Dower Lodge on Kew Green and aired his grievances to his brother, Prince Frederick.

'I tell you this, Fred,' he declared, 'I have had enough. The time is now coming to an end when we can be treated like children. Like children, did I say? Why, bless you, Fred, we are treated like prisoners. Our father, His Majesty . . .' The Prince made an ironical bow which brought a titter to Frederick's lips '. . . is the slave of his own passionate virtue. God preserve us, Fred, from virtue such as that practised by King George III. And our mother? What is she but a queen bee? There in her hive she grows large, she gives birth and, by God, before she has had time to walk a dozen times through her Orangerie or take a pinch of snuff or two, she is preparing to give birth once more. I thought Sophie would be the last, but now we are to have another little brother or sister despite the fact that we have eleven already.'

'At least His Majesty does his duty by the Queen, George.'

'I doubt not that our noble mother would wish him to be a little less dutiful in that direction–although giving birth has now become a habit with her. Really, they are a ridiculous pair. What has the Court become? It is small wonder that people mock. Have you heard the latest?'

Frederick shook his head and his brother quoted:

'Caesar the mighty King who swayed
The sceptre was a sober blade;
A leg of mutton and his wife
Were the chief comforts of his life.

The Queen composed of different stuff,
Above all things adored her snuff,
Save gold, which in her great opinion
Alone could rival snuff's dominion.'

'You see . . . that is the popular verdict on our King and Queen!'

'Kings and queens are always targets for public ridicule, George.'

'Criticism, not ridicule. *I* shall commit sins . . . royal sins, Fred. But I shall never be accused of doting on a pinch of snuff and caper sauce. Oh, when I look back I wonder how I have endured it for so long. Do you remember the frilled collars I used to be made to wear until only a short time ago? Frilled collars, Fred! A man of my age . . . a Prince . . . a Prince of Wales!'

Frederick put his head on one side and regarded his brother. Ever since he could remember he had admired George–the elder brother exactly one year his senior, seeming wise, bold and brilliant–everything that Frederick would like to have been; but he bore no malice, no resentment, because George would beat him to the crown by exactly twelve months; George, in Frederick's eyes, was all that an elder brother should be, all that a prince and king should be; the English, in Frederick's opinion, were going to be very fortunate to have George as their king.

He pondered this now. By God, he thought, for he imitated his brother's mode of speech as everything else, they are going to find George IV a mighty change from George III. George III, The Prince of Wales was contemptuous of their father–so would Frederick be. Caper sauce! thought Frederick with a smirk. When the Prince of Wales became king it would be very different. He would not have a plain wife; he would have a beauty, and perhaps mistresses. Kings should have mistresses; and George was constantly talking of women. He would sit for hours at the windows watching the maids of honour pass by, even though they were not a very exciting band. Their mother had seen to that. George had imitated her taking her pinch of snuff and murmuring in her German accent: 'Nothing that can tempt the Princes!' But there was one pretty one the Queen seemed to have overlooked. George had noticed her. Trust George.

But George was now thinking angrily of frilled collars, and he began to laugh, and so did Frederick, recalling that occasion when George had taken the frilled collar from his attendant's hand and flung it at him, his pink and white cheeks suddenly purple with rage as he cried: 'See how I am treated! I'll have no more of this.' And he had proceeded to tear the collar into shreds.

'You were at once reported to our Papa,' Frederick reminded him.

'That's my complaint,' went on George, narrowing his eyes. 'We were surrounded by spies then and we still are. I should have an establishment of my own. But they are too mean. That's the point, Fred, too mean!'

'I heard it said the other day that the Queen's only virtue was decorum and her only vice avarice.'

'There! That's the way they are spoken of. They live like little squires, not like a king and queen. I'm heartily tired of this state of affairs.'

'Still, they don't flog us now.'

'No. I put a stop to that.'

'Every complaint that was taken to our father brought the same answer: "Flog 'em".'

'It makes me fume to think of it.'

'But I remember, George, the day you snatched the cane from Bishop Hurd just as he was going to use it on you and how you said very sternly: "No, my lord Bishop, have done. There shall be no more of that!"'

'Nor was there,' said George, laughing, 'which makes me wonder whether if we had not stood out earlier against these tyrannies they might never have continued.'

The two young men began recalling incidents from their childhood. George could remember being dressed like a Roman centurion in a plumed helmet and being painted, with his mother and Frederick, by Mr Zoffany. Poor Fred was even worse off because when he had been a few months old they had made him Bishop of Osnaburg, which had so amused the people that the child was represented on all the cartoons in his Bishop's mitre. George was particularly incensed by the wax model of himself at the age of a month or two which his mother still kept on her dressing table under a glass dome. This doting sentimentality went side by side with the stern way of bringing up children. 'Completely Teutonic,' said George. 'By God, can't we forget our German ancestry?' Hours of study; shut off from contact with other people; the King's special diet–meat only a few times a week and then with all the fat pared off; fish served without butter; the fruit of a pie without the crust, all specially worked out by the King who might appear in the nursery dining room at any time and discountenance poor Lady Charlotte Finch, who was in charge of them, if these rules were not carried out to the letter.

'What a life we led!' sighed the Prince of Wales. 'And still do!'

'Worst of all,' added Frederick, 'was growing our wheat.'

'Farmer George would make little farmers of the whole family.'

George shivered distastefully, remembering their father's taking them out to show them the little plots of land which he had allotted to them.

'There,' he had informed them as though, said the Prince of Wales, he were offering them the crown jewels. 'There's your own bit of land. Cultivate it, eh? Grow your own wheat . . . make your own bread. Nothing like tilling the land, eh, what?'

Nothing like tilling the land! Going out in all weathers; preparing the soil, sewing the corn, while the cold winds chapped their hands. The Prince of Wales was proud of his beautiful white hands. The heat of the sun spoiled his complexion. He was proud of that, too, because in spite of a tendency to develop pimples–which would pass–he had a beautiful soft skin, pink, very pink and white. And this precious skin must be burned in the summer sun while the Prince of Wales worked like a farm labourer. They had even been obliged to thresh their own corn and supervise the baking of their bread.

The indignity of it all! But it had to be done otherwise the cry would go up: 'Flog 'em.' And their parents–the King and Queen of England–would inspect the little loaves of bread that had been made with their own wheat and the Prince of Wales had been infuriated to see that George III paid more attention to this bread produced by his sons than to matters of state.

'I must have an establishment of my own,' declared the Prince.

'It's ridiculous that you should be denied it,' soothed Fred.

'I shall demand it.' The Prince rose and was about to strut across the room when his eye caught a dainty figure crossing the Green on her way to the Queen's Lodge. He was immediately at the window. 'By God,' he cried. 'She's a beauty.'

Frederick murmured agreement.

She was small, dainty and dark; and suddenly it seemed as though by instinct she raised her eyes to the window where the two Princes stood watching her.

George immediately bowed. She stood still for a moment, dropping an enchanting curtsey and then turning away, sped across the lawn.

'One of our mother's maids of honour,' said George.

'How did our mother allow such a charmer to get in?'

'Like Homer, she nodded,' laughed the Prince. 'And let us be thankful for it.'

'Us?'

'I, because I intend to know more of the lady; and you because you will be so delighted in my good fortune.'

'Do you think, George . . .'

George looked astonished. Of course he would succeed with the lady. Wasn't he the most handsome, the most desirable young man in England?

Wasn't he the Prince of Wales?

Frederick hastily agreed: 'Yes, of course, George, but our father . . .'

'By God,' cried the Prince, 'I thought I'd made it clear to you that I have had enough of this treatment. Everything is going to be different from now on. I am seventeen years old.'

Frederick, at sixteen, looked suitably impressed.

'Time, dear brother, to have left childhood behind and if our miserly parents will not allow me an establishment at least I shall have a *life* of my own.'

In the Queen's drawing room the royal family was assembled for the evening concert. These concerts took place twice a week, on the King's orders, and every member of the family was expected to attend or the King would want to know the reason why. Only baby Sophie, not yet two years old, was spared. Even three-year-old Mary was there, seated on a footstool at her mother's feet while Queen Charlotte, pregnant with the child who would shortly make its appearance and bring the number of royal offspring to thirteen, industriously worked on her embroidery.

The King was comparatively content on occasions like this. It was while he sat with his family–all outwardly docile–while he listened to the excellent performance of some piece by Handel, that he could forget his anxieties. There were many of these. The trouble growing steadily worse over the American colonies; the conflict among his ministers, the growing truculence of the Prince of Wales; and worst of all the voices in his head which would not leave him alone, which mischievously mocked him, starting a train of thought and suddenly snatching it away so that he could not remember what had been in his mind a moment before, malicious voices which whispered to him: 'George, are you going mad?'

But here in the drawing room with his family seated quietly about him and the Queen looking placid, as she always did when pregnant, listening to the mastery of Mr Papendiek with his flute and Mr Cramer at the harpsichord and the Cervettos–father and son–miraculously performing on their violins, he felt more at peace than at any other time.

He let his eyes linger on the younger children; he sometimes wished that they did not have to grow up. The arch-trouble maker was his eldest son and as Frederick was his intimate companion that made a pair of them. Young William was only fourteen; he would get him off to sea as soon as possible; that would provide some necessary discipline. Twelve-year-old Edward should go to Germany–as should the other boys, except the Prince of Wales of course. There would be an outcry if he were sent out of England; and he had heard that his son had expressed very strong opinions about that too. George was anxious to forget that his great-great-grandfather, who had become George I, was a German who could speak no English. The Prince of Wales was trying to win the approval of the English people already. The King looked uneasily at his eldest son. A tall, good-looking boy, quite handsome, fair and fresh-complexioned; his only physical imperfection being the family tendency to fat. The King wondered whether the Prince had cajoled his attendants into leaving the fat on his meat or to giving him crust with fruit pies. The King was coming to the conclusion that his eldest son was capable of anything.

Why had George turned out so differently from what he had hoped? The rod had not been spared. He himself had had a hand in those beatings–and well deserved punishments they were–but he carried a memory with him of the flushed angry face of the Prince of Wales, and much resentment at the outrage to his dignity.

'Necessary,' murmured the King to himself. 'Disobedience has to be beaten out, eh, what?' And there was young Augustus with his asthma. That had to be beaten out of him too. He was six years old, but he was already well acquainted with the cane; and it certainly seemed to help him get his breath better.

A family could be a great trial–particularly a royal family. But when they were small they were charming. A great solace, thought the King, particularly the girls. He wished there had been more girls. Dear little Sophie was a delight; and as for Mary sitting there so solemnly at her mother's feet, she looked like a little doll. It would have given him great pleasure to have picked her up and caressed her while he explained to her that Mr Handel's music was the best in the world. But he must observe the decorum of the drawing room.

His feet tapped in time with the music, but his mind had darted from his children to the situation in America. They'll capitulate, he was telling himself. They'll sue for peace . . . the rebels! Lord North was uneasy and wanted to give up the Ministry, but he wasn't going to let him. Who else was there but North? Chatham dead. Charles James Fox was making a nuisance of himself–he was even more of a menace than his father had been. Nothing went right abroad . . . and at home there was the intransigence of the Prince of Wales. Why could he not be at peace in the heart of his family? Charlotte was dull, but he was accustomed to her by now; it was true he looked with pleasure on other women . . . women like Elizabeth Pembroke, of course, but his emotions were so much in control that he never went beyond looking. His subjects sneered at him for being a good husband. They laughed at his interest in making buttons; in his liking for the land. 'Farmer George' they called him, and 'The Royal Button Maker'. There was scorn rather than affection in these appellations. The people forgot that when he was not with his family at Kew he was closeted with his ministers making decisions on how the campaign against the American rebels was to be conducted, making decisions as to how the armies were to be deployed; discussing naval tactics. Even now he was urging Lord Sandwich to hold the West Indies at all costs. How could we continue to meet our commitments if we lost our revenue from the sugar islands? And what of home defence? What about the aggressive French and the Spaniards?

Problems everywhere he looked, and the voices every now and then whispering in his head: 'George, are you going mad?'

And why shouldn't a king be a virtuous husband? What was there to sneer at in virtue? It seemed to George that whatever a king did he displeased his subjects if he were no longer young. Everywhere that young rascal, the Prince of Wales, went he was cheered. What will become of him, I cannot think, mused the King uneasily. Ideas chased themselves round and round in his head; like mice, he thought of them . . . fighting each other for his attention and when he tried to look closely at them they disappeared; they turned into mocking voices that reminded him of that dreadful time when he had been ill and had lost control of his mind. Pleasant things like his model farm at Kew, his buttons, his gardens, his baby daughters represented safety. If he could have escaped from all his troubles and lived quietly, the voices might be stilled. He glanced at Charlotte . . . good Queen Charlotte, unexciting but safe. Sometimes he was tormented by erotic dreams of women. Hannah Lightfoot, the Quaker girl with whom he had gone through a form of marriage when he had been very young and foolishly romantic, long since dead–for which ironically he must be grateful; for while she lived she represented a threat to his marriage with Charlotte, and that was a matter to shake the whole foundations of the monarchy, for if his sons were bastards . . . well, it did not bear thinking of and set the voices in his head working faster than ever. And then there was Sarah Lennox–Sarah Bunbury as she had become–whom he had wanted to marry, for whom he had as he had told Lord Bute 'burned'; but he had been obliged to marry his plain German Princess because all Hanoverian Kings married German Princesses; it was a duty they must observe and when the time came young George would have to do the same. So instead of his dear Hannah Lightfoot whom he had so dangerously loved in his extreme youth, in spite of flighty Sarah Lennox for whom he had so burned, he was married to Charlotte.

He was a faithful husband, but there were times when his senses were in revolt. Why, he would demand of himself, should he be the one member of the family who observed a strict moral code? His brothers . . . his sister Caroline Matilda . . . He shuddered at the memory of them. Poor Caroline Matilda whom he had dearly loved and longed to protect was now dead–and he could not be sure that her death had been a natural one–after being involved in a storm of intrigue. Married to a near imbecile she had taken a lover and with him had been accused of treason. The lover had died barbarously and she, the Queen of Denmark, had come very near to the same fate, and would have succumbed to it but for the intervention of her affectionate brother–himself, the King of England. He had been deeply disturbed by the death of Caroline Matilda. Such events haunted him in nightmares. Poor Caroline Matilda had paid a high price for her follies.

With his brothers it was a very different matter.

William, Duke of Gloucester and Henry, Duke of Cumberland, had defiantly made their scandals and brazenly shown their indifference to disgrace. Yet they did not arouse half the resentment and mocking scorn which was poured on the King for being a good husband.

Cumberland had been involved in a most disgraceful affair with the Grosvenors because he had seduced Lady Grosvenor and had–young fool!–written letters to the woman which gave no doubt of the relationship between them. George remembered phrases from those letters which made his face burn with shame–and something like envy–even now. Accounts of intimate details when they had lain together 'on the couch ten thousand times'. His brother, who had been brought up so carefully by their mother, watched over, never allowed to meet anyone but the immediate family in case he should be contaminated, had written those words! And as soon as they escaped from Mamma's apron strings, there they were running wild, getting into scandals like that of Cumberland and the Grosvenors. And Lord Grosvenor had had the effrontery to sue a royal duke and to win his case. The jury had brought in a verdict of £10,000 plus costs of £3,000 against the Duke of Cumberland which George had had to find with the help of Lord North . . . out of the King's household expenses.

And as if that were not enough, Cumberland had tired of Lady Grosvenor by the time the scandal broke and was having an intrigue with the wife of a timber merchant–a very wealthy one it was true and fortunately for the royal purse, the timber merchant was too flattered by the royal Duke's attentions to his wife to make trouble; but no sooner had that affair been freely discussed in the coffee and chocolate houses than Cumberland had a new love and this had turned out to be the most serious matter of all, for Mrs Anne Horton, who was the daughter of Lord Irnham, was intent on marriage, and as she had according to that gossip, Horace Walpole, 'the most amorous eyes in the world and eyelashes a yard long', Cumberland was fool enough to marry her.

This had caused the King so much anxiety that he had done what his mother had urged him to do before her death; he had set about bringing into force the Royal Marriage Act which forbade members of the royal family to marry without the King's consent. Too late for Cumberland . . . and for Gloucester it seemed, for no sooner was the Marriage Act passed than Gloucester came forward to announce that for some years he had been secretly married to Lord Waldegrave's widow–a mésalliance if ever there was one, for the lady was not only the illegitimate daughter of Sir Edward Walpole but her mother was said to have been a milliner!

'Banish them from Court!' George had cried. And Charlotte had declared that she would receive no daughters of milliners. So there was an unsatisfactory state of affairs with his brothers; and since his sons were so wild, the King did wonder what trouble would come through them.

Worry, worry, worry! thought the King, whichever way one turned. Oh, if only life were just living at Kew with Charlotte and the little ones, what a happy man he would be! Well perhaps not happy; he would always think of women like Hannah and Sarah and Elizabeth Pembroke with longing, but while he remained a faithful husband and lived according to his code of honour he could be *serene*.

The Queen was not listening to Mr Handel's excellent music; she was thinking how handsome her eldest son was looking in his frogged coat and hoping the King would not notice how elegant he was and question the price of his garments. Charlotte was alarmed when she saw the light of resentment against his father flare up in her son's eyes. She had to face the fact that the relationship between them was scarcely harmonious. She had adored the Prince of Wales from the first time she had first held him in her arms–'A perfect specimen of a Royal Highness, your Majesty . . .' Oh yes, indeed. He had bawled lustily, this wonder infant, and his health had always been of the best–except of course for the customary childish ailments. At the age of four it was true he had given her a great scare by contracting the smallpox. But he was such a healthy little rascal, he had even shrugged that aside. She liked to tell her attendants how when he was kept in bed someone asked if he were not tired of lying abed so long and he had replied: 'Not at all. I lie and make reflections.' The brilliance of the child! There was no doubt that he was a genius. He was clever at his lessons. He spoke and wrote several languages, French, German and Italian, fluently; he was familiar with Horace and delighted in Tacitus. He learned with ease and had a command of English which astounded his mother and dumbfounded his father on those occasions, which were becoming more frequent, when they were involved in verbal battles. The Queen was a little anxious about this beloved son and his relationship with his father. Oh dear, she sighed, I hope they are not going to follow the family custom and yet another Prince of Wales is going to quarrel with the King. Not George, she assured herself, not her handsome son George.

She often looked at the wax image on her dressing table and thought of him as a baby. He was no longer that. She sighed, wishing that he would visit her more often and now and then ask her advice.

What would she advise him on? On the sort of shoe buckle he should wear? He was mightily interested in shoe buckles. Or on the colour of his coat? Or about those matters which her woman Schwellenburg was always hinting at–his amours. 'De Prince very much interests selfs in *mädchens* . . .' declared Schwellenburg in her execrable English. 'Nonsense, Schwellenburg, he is a natural gentleman.'

Was he *too* interested in young women? No, of course not. She refused to believe it. She refused to believe anything against George; and though she deplored the passing of his childhood when she had had some control over him, she was glad in a way that he was too old for whippings, for she had suffered to think of that delicate flesh being slashed with a cane.

Oh, George, come and speak to your mother, she implored silently. Not just as a duty. Not to bow, kiss the hand, murmur a few meaningless words and be off as quickly as you can. Not that, George, speak as a son to a mother.

She thought of the next child she would bear; but such happenings were commonplace with her. The thirteenth!

A boy or a girl? she wondered. What did it matter now? She already had seven boys and five girls. No one could say she had not given the country heirs. But she had not felt so well with this pregnancy. Perhaps it was time to give up child-bearing. The King would never agree to that, she was sure, and yet what had she been doing in the nineteen years since she came to England?–Bearing children, was the answer. Thirteen of them. Oh, yes, the time had certainly come to call a halt. Not that she could bear to part with any of them. But with fine strong boys like George, Frederick and William at the head of the family–surely they had enough.

The Prince of Wales was pensive tonight. Was he wrapped up in the music? Frederick was beside him. They were inseparable those two and it was pleasant to see two brothers such friends. They seemed now as though they were sharing some secret. They were both watching one of the maids of honour who was in attendance. The Queen heard an echo of Schwellenburg's voice: 'De Prince very much interests self in *mädchens*.' Oh, no, thought the Queen. George is a boy yet. He has always been taught such restraint.

George did not hear Mr Handel's music, though he shared the family fondness for it. He was thinking: She is exquisite. So dainty. Such little hands and feet. He pictured her delight when he made known to her the fact that he was in love with her. He had discovered her name. It was Harriot Vernon. Harriot, Harriot, he murmured.

Fred nudged him gently with his foot because he had spoken her name aloud.

The music had stopped. The King led the applause and, under cover of it, George threw a glance at the young maid of honour which made her lower her eyes and smile. It was enough for the ardent Prince. His invitation was accepted. They must meet. Where?

'You are watched,' whispered Frederick.

'Always, brother,' sighed the Prince.

He turned to his equerry and friend, Lord Malden, heir to the Earl of Essex.

'I wish you to take a message to a lady,' he murmured.

'At Your Highness's service.'

'Come to my apartments,' said the Prince. 'I will give you all instructions there.'

Frederick listened with admiration. This time George was about to involve himself in a real love affair.

'And how?' asked Frederick, 'can you possibly meet Harriot Vernon? You would be noticed. And you know we are forbidden even to speak to the maids of honour.'

George laughed.

'Trust me,' he said. 'I already have an assignation with the lady.'

'Can that be true, George?'

'Indeed yes. Malden has taken a message for her from me and brought one back from her. We are going to meet in the gardens tonight.'

'Where?'

'Why do you wish to know, brother?'

'Because I fear you will be seen.'

'Not us. We shall meet in the most secluded spot . . . not far from the river. You know where I mean. We were saying only the other day few ever go there and you remember I remarked it would be a good spot for a lovers' meeting.'

'You think she will come?'

George drew himself up to his full height and looked most princely. 'I *know* she will come, Frederick. I have her promise.'

'And when she does . . . ?'

George threw a kiss to his reflection in the mirror.

'She can no more wait with patience for the encounter than I can.'

'So tonight . . . at sunset . . .'

'Tonight at sunset,' echoed the Prince of Wales.

Mr Papendiek was playing the flute in the Queen's drawing room at the request of the King. Not all the family were present. The Prince of Wales for one was absent. Frederick, seated next to his brother William, was thinking of George sneaking out to that remote spot in the gardens not far from the river. He was going to wear a great coat of Malden's to disguise himself and there he would await the coming of Harriot Vernon and then . . . Frederick's eyes glistened. He hoped that all would go well and George would not be discovered. He wondered what would happen if he were. He looked at his father caught up in the music, and the Queen sitting placidly by. The child's entry into the world could not long be delayed. It has been going on like this for years, thought Frederick; the family assembled here listening to the King's favourite piece of music; the only difference being that there was a new addition to the family. A new child to sit on the footstool at the Queen's feet while the child who had just vacated it would sit upright on a chair and try not to fidget. So dull! thought Frederick. No change at all.

But a change was coming. He and his brother were growing up. William would soon be sent to sea. And because of this William was half excited, half apprehensive. 'At least,' William had said, 'it'll be an escape from Kew and Buckingham House.' Lucky William, thought Frederick.

The King was in fact giving only half an ear to the music. He was thinking that soon he would have to leave Kew for London. He could not enjoy the sequestered life for long at a time. The dark, clever, rather gross face of Charles James Fox came into his mind. Always plaguing him. The Foxes always had. As though they bore him a grudge for not marrying Sarah. Charles James Fox was her nephew and if ever there was a trouble-maker it was that man.

And the American affair . . . and the French and the Spaniards . . . and the Government . . .

I'll put them from my mind, he told himself. I'll feel all the better for a little respite from affairs. Work all the better when I do get back to business, eh, what? Ought to be on better terms with young George. Can't have trouble in the family. He didn't want to *talk* to George. George was too smart with words. Had an answer for everything. A pleasant game of chess, that was what he would like. Even so, George invariably beat him nowadays. Nevertheless they could get a good game.

Where was George? George ought to be present on a family occasion like this.

Mr Papendiek's solo was over; the King led the applause and when that came to an end and the musicians waited for his further instructions he declared: 'I should like a game of chess. Tell the Prince of Wales that I wish him to join me in a game of chess.'

Frederick was dismayed. They were going to search for the Prince of Wales and would be unable to find him, unless they went to that remote spot in the gardens and then . . . what would they discover? He had feared something like this. He had wanted George to make some provision for such an emergency, but George had merely shrugged aside the possibility of discovery. And now . . . it seemed inevitable.

'Where is the Prince, eh, what?' the King was already demanding as the chess board had been set out and he himself was putting the ivory pieces in their places.

One of the Prince's attendants came in looking harassed.

'Well, well, where is he? eh? eh?' demanded the King.

'Your Majesty, the Prince is not in his apartments.'

Frederick waited for no more. He slipped out of the drawing room and out of the Lodge and made his way with all speed to that remote spot in the gardens. It was dark now, but there was enough light from the moon to show Frederick the two figures embracing.

'George! George!' cried Frederick. 'For God's sake . . . George.'

The lovers parted and George, seeing his brother cried: 'Good God, Fred, what is it?'

'The King is demanding your presence immediately. He wants a game of chess.'

George cursed chess vehemently and stopped himself in time cursing the King. Harriot, trembling with anxiety, looked appealingly at her lover.

'There's nothing to be done but return with all speed and play this game of chess,' muttered the Prince. 'Here, Fred, take this.' It was Lord Malden's great coat with which he had disguised himself. He turned to Harriot and embraced her warmly. George would be a lover in any circumstances, thought Frederick admiringly. Even now while he was on the verge of exposure he was charmingly protective to the lady. 'Fred, see that Miss Vernon reaches her apartments in safety.' Frederick bowed. If he were involved in this affair he would not blame George. It had always been thus between them. They had always protected each other, at whatever cost to themselves, and took loyalty for granted.

So with Lord Malden's overcoat over one arm Frederick conducted the lady to a back staircase of the maids' house while George hurried to the Queen's drawing room where the King was impatiently glowering at the chess board.

'Takes you a long time to get here, eh, what?' He looked into the flushed face of his son. The elegant boots were just a little muddy. Many eyes noted this. There was a whispering behind fans, a few quietly spoken words among the attendants.

The Prince had for some time been ogling the only pretty maid of honour in his mother's entourage and already someone had reported seeing Prince Frederick sneaking out of the King's presence to warn his brother and later conducting the lady back to her apartments.

The Prince played a reckless game of chess which gave the King the advantage. But the latter did not enjoy this. What's the young blade up to, eh, what? the King asked himself.

And all through the household they were whispering of the Prince's love affair.

The next day in the same spot the Prince successfully accomplished the seduction of Miss Vernon; but by this time the affair was palace gossip.

Harriot Vernon went about her duties with the rapt expression of one who may have lost her virtue but had gained the whole world; and when the Prince of Wales was not seeking private interviews with the lady he was in his apartments writing verses to her.

How could Charlotte have allowed such a charmer to appear in the Prince's orbit, people were asking each other. Because she was about to give birth? Nonsense, this little operation was as normal to her as breathing. Still, she had slipped, and there could be a real scandal if the reckless Harriot should prove to be fertile as well as romantic.

Schwellenburg bustling about her apartments, tending the frogs and toads of which she made pets and kept in glass cages, grumbled to herself about the Prince of Wales. 'Ah,' she muttered, 'you willen zees tricks do.' And she tapped her snuff box and listened to the croaking which followed. She was proud of having taught her little darlings to croak at the tap of a snuff box. 'They vise little frogs,' she would say. 'Very vise frogs. Good little toads . . . not like the Prince of Vales. Must talk to the Queen of bad Prince, little frog. Not talk to self.'

And she did talk to the Queen. The Prince of Wales was having a love affair with that wicked young woman Harriot Vernon whom she had never wanted in the royal apartment, and if the Queen had listened to her would never have been there.

Charlotte was not fond of Schwellenburg, but one must have someone to whom one could speak German now and then. Schwellenburg had been with her ever since she had come to England and in any case was a habit now. The woman was arrogant; she made trouble; she was the most unpopular servant in the royal household . . . yet she remained in the Queen's service, bullying the Queen's women, disgusting them with her 'pets', and insisting on their playing long and tedious games of cards with her.

But she was under the delusion that the Queen could not do without her and that she was in charge of the Queen's household.

'Harriot Vernon is in dream . . . forget all . . . remember nothing. Makes loff with Herr George . . . in the gardens and in his bed. Disgusting.'

The Queen said: 'There is some mistake.'

'No mistake,' contradicted Schwellenburg with the boldness of an old servant. 'Haf seen with self's eyes.'

Charlotte thought: 'Of course it is true. And what will the King say? There'll be trouble . . . great trouble. Of course he is growing up . . . and so handsome. Surely there never was any young man as handsome as my George. It's not his fault exactly. He is so attractive. Oh, why doesn't he tell me what he is doing. He never comes to see me as a son should to his mother. He confides in Frederick . . . and perhaps William . . . But never his mother. This must not come to the ears of the King.'

She was loth to believe the affair had gone very far. He was a boy still. He may have been casting eyes on the girl; but that was as far as it had gone, she was sure.

She sent for her son, who came reluctantly and looked a little sulky, she noticed. He had the Hanoverian rather heavy jaw which unless the Prince was smiling, gave a sullen look to an otherwise charming face.

'I don't see enough of you,' she told him. 'I daresay you are very occupied.'

'Your Majesty knows the plans laid down by my father. It gives us little time to do anything but follow his orders.'

Oh, yes, he was resentful. She wondered whether she dare tell the King that the boys were growing up and they should no longer be treated as children. When had George ever taken any notice of her? When she had first come to England George's mother, the Dowager Princess of Wales, had made it very clear that no interference was expected from her. And George had supported his mother. Bear healthy children and that is all that will be expected of you. And they could not say she had not fulfilled their expectations. But listen to her advice on any subject, treat her like an intelligent being? Never. The only place in which she had any power was her own intimate circle. She could dismiss her maids; she could go over the accounts and find them too great; she could make economies and take her snuff and look after the younger children. There her duty ended. That had been made clear to her. So it was no use her thinking she could speak to the King about George.

But she could speak to George–and she was going to find out if these rumours were true.

'So you have no time to visit your mother,' she said wistfully.

'Very little, Madam, very little.'

How haughty he was and how she loved him! She had difficulty in assuring herself that this glorious young Apollo was the fruit of her plain little body. She and George between them had produced this beautiful creature! Stolid George and plain Charlotte. It seemed incredible to her. If he would confide in her, if he would show a little affection . . . she would do everything in her power to give him what he wanted.

But he showed so clearly that he had no need of her. Yet she would have to prevent his quarrelling with his father. He would have to be made to realize that even he must not indulge in a love affair under their very noses.

'You find life a little . . . monotonous?' she asked.

He inclined his head and suppressed a yawn.

'I have often thought,' went on the Queen, 'that our maids of honour lead very dull lives.'

'I agree with Your Majesty,' said the Prince. 'How dull merely to be one of a formal procession from the presence chamber to the drawing room and never allowed to speak unless one is spoken to.'

'Some may have nothing worthy to say.'

The Prince had warmed to his subject. 'Poor ladies! What a life! To make an occasional one of large hoops in a royal coach. I believe they make two new Court suits a year and now and then appear in a side box in a royal play.'

'But she does not have to pay for her seat at the theatre,' the Queen reminded him.

He looked at her slyly.

'Save gold, which in her own opinion
Alone could rival snuff's dominion.'

he thought. Trust his mother to think a *free* seat compensated for a good deal.

'I agree, Your Majesty, that a maid of honour goes to concerts and plays . . . and oratorios *free*. Your Majesty will no doubt remind me that she does not have to pay her physician and gets her medicines for nothing.'

'You have forgotten one important thing.'

'No doubt, for the acts of maid of honour formed no part of my education.'

'I will tell you one,' replied the Queen. 'Perhaps you have recently had experience of this. She may flirt with Princes and go to meet them in the moonlight. Is that also . . . free?'

The Prince was for once discountenanced, and his mother was certain now that Schwellenburg's hints were true. The Prince *had* been meeting Harriot Vernon in the moonlight. Heaven knew how far this affair had gone, but if it reached the King's ears His Majesty would be furious. She was terrified of the King's anger; it took him so oddly nowadays and she was always afraid of where it would end.

She must act quickly, and for once she dismissed the Prince. It was usually he who pleaded his duty to the King and departed as speedily as he could.

As soon as he had left her she sent for Harriot Vernon. The girl stood before her–beautiful, radiant and–guilty.

'I have sent for you, Miss Vernon,' said the Queen, 'to tell you that your services are no longer required at court.'

'But Your Majesty . . .'

The Queen looked surprised. 'Call Madam von Schwellenburg,' she commanded.

'Your Majesty . . .'

'I have said, call Madam von Schwellenburg.'

Schwellenburg, listening at the door, had little need to be called. She swept in.

'Your Majesty calls of me,' she said.

'Miss Vernon is leaving us . . . at once,' said the Queen. 'Pray help her to leave . . . immediately.'

'Vill see to selfs,' promised Schwellenburg, and Harriot had no recourse but to leave with her, and the German woman stood over her while she packed her bags and herself ordered the carriage.

Within an hour of that interview with the Queen, Harriot Vernon had left Court.

Encounter in Hyde Park

George mourned the departure of Harriot for a few days and then found a new mistress. He did not have to seek far. He soon proved what he had never doubted; not only was he extremely personable and completely charming, but as he was also the Prince of Wales he was irresistible. More than this his youthful exuberance, his discovery that the most exciting and alluring prospect in life was women made him completely fascinating to that sex; and as he embarked on the lightest of love affairs with the conviction that his partner in the adventure was the one woman in the world to whom he could remain faithful for the rest of his life, even shorn of the trappings of royalty, he would have been a successful lover.

The Queen had given birth to another son, christened Octavius, who was not so strong as his brothers and sisters and almost immediately, to her consternation, she was pregnant again.

It had been impossible to keep the scandal of Harriot Vernon and the inclinations of the Prince from his father, who declared that his eldest son's conduct gave him many a sleepless night.

But George was impervious to scandal. He had discovered the whole meaning of life; he reiterated constantly to his brothers, equerries and anyone interested that if his parents were too mean to give him his own establishment, no one was going to prevent his living his own life.

His confidant continued to be his brother Frederick, who listened avidly to accounts of George's adventures and began to have a few of his own.

The awkward situations which often accompanied these adventures bothered the Prince very little. There were scandals about him; he had discovered a taste for women older than himself–even Harriot had been a few months older–and his fancy often alighted on those who were married. This could mean jealous husbands, for there were some men who failed to appreciate the honour done to the family by the Prince's favouring one of its women. There was no lack of aspirants for his favours and this meant that envy prevailed among those whom he passed over towards those whom he favoured.

After the dullness of his boyhood he found life full of excitement–and he determined to enjoy it.

There were several people who had their eyes on him–apart from women. It was natural that politicians who were out of favour with the King and were extremely ambitious should have the notion of forming a rival faction. It would not be the first time there had been a King's party and a Prince's party; and now that the latter was growing up the time seemed to have come to make plans. Moreover, no one could deny that the Prince was intelligent. There had never yet been such a cultured member of this branch of the royal family. The Prince had taken to learning with alacrity. Perhaps because there had been so little excitement in his boyhood he had sought it in books. The fact remained that he was well versed in the classics, was a good linguist, had a ready wit and was clearly of a very different intellectual calibre from his father.

One man who was watching him with the greatest interest was Charles James Fox. Fox was perhaps one of the most brilliant men in politics and it was galling to him to see the King and Lord North throwing away the American colonies through policies which, it seemed obvious to Fox, were misguided and foolish.

'The King,' Fox had said, 'lowers his head like a cow and goes on chewing the cud, regurgitating over and over again: "They'll come to their senses." If only he would come to his.'

Fox was thirty years old–leader of the Whigs, distrusted by the King–and not only for his political opinions. Fox knew the story of Sarah Lennox. He could remember the consternation in the family when the King's marriage to Charlotte was announced. His mother had been Sarah Lennox's sister and the whole family had naturally hoped the King would marry Sarah. That it was largely Sarah's own fault that he had not, did not relieve the family anguish. Sarah was a foolish girl–her conduct now was proving that; but she could have been Queen of England with a little careful manoeuvring, for the Foxes would have been a match for the Dowager Princess of Wales and Lord Bute at any time. But Sarah had lost her chance and George had married Charlotte. And this was something for which George could not forgive the Foxes. Every time he set eyes on Sarah's nephew he thought of Sarah, and quite clearly was resentful because he had had to take the plain dull Charlotte instead.

'Why he should dislike me,' Charles James told his friends, 'would be inconceivable but for the fact that to do so is in accordance with accepted human behaviour. I, with my parents and the rest of the family, would have been delighted to see Sarah Queen.'

But the King was a simple man and not accustomed to delving into the innermost recesses of his mind to understand his own motives. He merely said: 'I can't abide that fellow Fox.' And never asked himself if his dislike had anything to do with the loss of Sarah.

Charles James knew that he would never be the leader of the House if the King could help it, and although the King was dependent on his ministers, the King's favour was of the greatest importance to the members of his government.

So the wily Fox had turned his eyes to the young man who was just emerging into the limelight. If the King would have none of him, why not cultivate the Prince? Why not *educate* the Prince in politics. Why not revive the old custom–so prevalent in the Hanoverian dynasty–of setting son against father. There could be, as there had been before, the King's party and that of the Prince of Wales; and as every wise man knew it was more intelligent to attach one's waggon to the rising rather than to the setting star.

The Prince was breaking out of his shell; he was indulging in amatory adventures to the tolerant amusement of the cynical members of the Court, and although a small part of these rumours reached the ears of his parents and their staid supporters, very little could be done to prevent the princely exploits. The Prince was as much a prisoner now as they could make him–still he managed his secret intrigues. But when he was eighteen they could scarcely treat him as a child of twelve. The people would never allow that. And George was only a few months from his eighteenth birthday.

When he did appear in public the people cheered him wildly. George was all they expected a prince to be. With his powdered hair setting off the pink and white of his complexion and making his eyes look more blue than ever he was indeed a Prince Charming. Silver buckled shoes, coats of blue and pink satin, white buckskin breeches . . . He was a joy to behold. And while he was young and handsome the people would love him; and was it not always the case that after a period of Puritan rule the people adored a rake? And young as he was, George was showing all signs of fast becoming that.

'Reflect,' said Charles James Fox to his friend Edmund Burke, 'how the people welcomed the restoration of Charles the Second. How they adored him when he promenaded in St James' Park a mistress on either side and more following behind. And how they loathed poor dull Noll Cromwell because he was a faithful husband and a Puritan. So do they feel about His virtuous but oh so dull and just a little stupid Majesty.'

Burke agreed with Fox, but Fox was not going to leave it at that. He had an idea, and like most of his ideas it was a brilliant one.

It was natural that since the King showed no favour towards him he should be on good terms with those who had a grudge against His Majesty and his mind immediately went to the Cumberlands.

Henry, Duke of Cumberland had, under the influence of his Duchess, the lady whose eyelashes had brought her fame and fortune, smarted under the King's neglect. The King did not wish to see his brother Henry. Whenever he thought of him he remembered the disgusting affair with Lady Grosvenor, and phrases from those very revealing letters which Cumberland had written to the lady, and which betrayed such eroticism as the King had scarcely known existed, haunted his nightmares in which to his dismay women figured so prominently. No, the King could not bear to see Cumberland. It was different with his brother William, Duke of Gloucester, who had made another mésalliance, it was true, by marrying Lady Waldegrave, but although this lady was illegitimate and a milliner's daughter, Gloucester's life was comparatively respectable. Moreover, the King had always been very fond of Gloucester.

This state of affairs made the Cumberlands even more resentful, and it was to them that Charles James Fox decided to turn.

He called at the Cumberland House where he was always a welcome guest. Fox was a witty conversationalist, a high liver, a gambler, an amorist–in fact he indulged freely in all the fleshly vices. At the same time he was the cleverest politician in the country and while the Cumberlands could attract such men to their house their parties could be the most amusing in town. Moreover, they could give not only offence but anxiety to the King.

Fox, a stubble on his double chin, for over-indulgence in food and drink had made him fat in spite of the fact that he was only thirty years of age, his coat slightly splashed with grease from his last meal, for he made no concessions to royal dukes, arrived at the Cumberland House, his mind full of the project.

The Duchess, fluttering her long lashes, received him boisterously. There was nothing regal about the Duchess. Her conversation was amusing and droll and not untouched by coarseness, but she was a very beautiful woman.

The Duke was with his wife–a small man with the loose Hanoverian mouth and the rather bulging blue eyes. Charles James had little respect for his intelligence–the Duchess had more–but his position as uncle to the

Prince of Wales made him important.

He believed that Fox had come for a gamble, for the politician was a gambler by nature and could never resist a game of chance, but Fox quickly disillusioned him.

'I have come to talk to Your Highness of your nephew.'

'George!' cried the Duchess. 'There is no talk of anything but George. What a rascal the boy is becoming! He'll soon be a rival to his uncle.'

The Duke grinned at her.

'I hope someone will warn him not to write letters,' continued the irrepressible Duchess. 'Love letters can be costly when those who receive them are no longer in love.'

The Duke laughed at this reference to the Grosvenor case. 'Is everyone going to go on talking of that forever?'

'I'm sure it is what His Gracious Majesty holds against you . . . far more than your marriage to me.'

'The Prince will need guidance,' said Fox.

'He'll get it,' laughed the Duke.

'Never fear, dear Mr Fox,' went on the Duchess. 'Papa keeps him in his gilded cage and Mamma has tied his reins very firmly to her apron strings.'

'All's very well while he's a minor. Your Highnesses forget he will soon be eighteen. Then we shall see changes.'

'Changes!' mused the Duchess. 'He has shown very clearly the way he will go. Ladies, short and tall, fair and dark will lead him by the hand. And, Mr Fox, is it not charming of him to prefer beautiful English women . . . not like his ancestors who like ugly German ones.'

'He is behaving . . . naturally,' said Charles James. 'Of course he is up in arms against his father.'

'Which does not surprise me,' put in Cumberland.

'It would surprise me if it were otherwise,' said the Duchess. 'The King has treated our Prince like a naughty child in the past and is continuing to do so . . . in spite of the fact that he has shown the world so clearly that he is in possession of his manhood. I don't know the number of seductions to date . . .' She glanced at the Duke. 'Perhaps you do, my darling. But they are too many for a boy. Our Prince is a man.'

'The last one is a rather amusing story,' said the Duke. 'It concerns a certain married lady of the Palace. Yes, His Highness is finding married ladies very much to his taste.'

'Preferring experience to innocence,' added the Duchess. 'Wise young man.'

'There very nearly was a mighty scandal over this affair,' said the Duke.

'There very nearly always is a mighty scandal. Don't look so disappointed, Mr Fox. We'll have our mighty scandal pretty soon, I promise you.'

'It'll come,' agreed Fox. 'And then he must have someone to turn to . . . someone to help him.'

'He'll get his reproaches from the Queen and a lecture from the King, who'll tell him he wishes he could use the cane on him as he did when he was a bad boy.'

'Alas for the dignity of the Prince of Wales!'

'You've heard what happened, eh?' asked the Duke, and when Mr Fox and the Duchess declared they had not he proceeded to tell them.

'The Prince's affaire with the lady was proceeding according to the usual pattern. The lady was living on amicable terms with her husband who–unlike some husbands–had no notion of the honour His Royal Highness was doing him by way of his wife. Indeed, he was that kind of a fool of a man who might have resented the honour, so the Prince and his lady refrained from informing him. One day the husband told his wife that he would be away for the night on Palace business, which made an excellent opportunity for the lovers. Alas, the inconsiderate man completed his business that evening and returned at midnight. He was heard knocking at the locked door of his apartments by the Prince who by chance happened to be sharing the connubial bed with the lady.'

The Duchess burst out laughing and cried in delight: '*In flagrante delicto*, I'll be bound. Our future king is such a lusty young dog.'

'Exactly,' went on the Duke. 'But what could he do? Escape was impossible even if he could have scrambled into his breeches in time. Fortunately for the Prince he has loyal attendants, and being of an open nature is apt to confide in them during the various stages of his love affairs. Consequently, one of his gentlemen was aware of the husband locked out and the lover locked in, and knowing precisely what the husband would find if he burst in, took upon himself the duty of releasing his young master from a very embarrassing situation.'

'A good servant,' said the Duchess. 'What was his name?'

'Cholmondeley. You know Cholmondeley.' The Duchess nodded and the Duke went on: 'Cholmondeley went to the husband, told him that the Prince was in some difficulty and he had been asked to summon him to the Prince's apartments immediately on his return that he might be made aware of the Prince's dilemma. Having conducted the fellow to the Prince's apartments Cholmondeley then went to the lady's apartment and released the Prince who hurried off; then Cholmondeley returned to the husband, told him the Prince had retired and that the matter must rest until the morning. And in the morning he told the husband that the matter had been settled and his help would not be required.'

'That is the sort of servant required by all young men who stray into other men's beds while they are away from home,' cried the Duchess. 'Fortunate George. It would be interesting to know what would have happened if Cholmondeley had not been in his confidence and on the spot.'

'Scandal, scandal, scandal and the King would have stormed at his son and suffered more sleepless nights on his account.'

'So all was for the best,' sighed the Duchess. 'The Prince remains blissful in his enjoyment of the lady and the husband in his ignorance.'

Charles James Fox who had been listening without much interest to the story said: 'This brings me to the point of my visit to Your Highnesses. The King cannot long delay giving the Prince an establishment of his own. And when he does, the young man will have his friends . . . not only ladies. He is witty, possessed of intellect and a contrast to his royal father. We will not find our George growing wheat and making butter and buttons. Young George is of a different calibre. When the day comes we should be ready.'

'We?' said the Duchess, her startling black fringed green eyes wide open.

'Yes,' said Fox. He waved his hand. 'Here should be the centre of the Prince's party.'

'You think he'll be a Whig?'

'Certainly, Highness. Is not old George a Tory?'

The Duchess clasped her hands. 'Of course. It is inevitable.'

'His uncle should show an interest in his welfare.'

'And what will H.M. say to that?'

'It will not be the first time Your Highness has acted without the approbation of His Majesty.'

'We'll do it,' cried the Duchess. 'We'll cultivate the acquaintance of our nephew.'

'It will be necessary to go warily.'

'Very,' agreed the Duchess. 'The King won't have us at Court, you know.'

'I know it full well, Your Highness. But the Prince will choose his own friends. He will, I believe, find more to interest him in his uncle's residence than in his father's royal palaces.'

'We should be heading for a real family quarrel.'

'History,' said Mr Fox cynically, 'has a rather endearing way of repeating itself.'

'A Prince's party to set itself against the King's party,' cried the Duchess. 'We'll do it.'

'I thought Your Highness would wish to,' said Mr Fox demurely.

George was in love once more. He had found the new paragon in the apartments of his sisters when he had gone to visit Charlotte, Augusta and Elizabeth. He had scarcely been able to talk to them so overcome was he by the charms of Miss Mary Hamilton.

Mary was wonderful. Of all the women he had so far loved there was not one to compare with this new charmer. She had all the virtues and being six years older than he was seemed to him ideal. Nor was she a foolish, simpering girl–as he now thought of Harriot; nor was she a blasé married woman cynically breaking her marriage vows. Mary Hamilton was a pure woman and his love for her was pure.

He confided to his brother Frederick, to Cholmondeley, to Malden. This was different from anything that had ever happened before. This was a pure affection.

'Do you imagine,' he demanded of Frederick, 'that I wish to seduce this lady?'

Did he not? asked Frederick in surprise.

'Oh, no, you must understand, Fred, this is a *pure* love. But for my station in life I should immediately offer her marriage.'

Was this not a little rash?

In the circumstances, no. This was quite different from any of those other adventures of his.

'Yet at the time . . .' Frederick tentatively pointed out.

'Oh, be silent, Fred. What do you know of love? I have written to her.'

'George, you remember Uncle Cumberland's letters. They cost our father thirteen thousand pounds.'

'Don't mention my Mary in connection with my Uncle Cumberland, I beg of you.'

'But there were letters.'

'Do you think that Mary would ever use my letters against me. Not that I could write as our uncle did. My love for Mary is pure. It will remain so.'

'But will that be very satisfactory?' asked Frederick, who had come to expect a certain line of action from his brother.

George sighed and went on: 'I have written to her telling her that I am in love with a lady of the Court. I have mentioned no names. I have begged her not to be offended by my confidences.'

'Why should she be?'

The Prince of Wales was too blissfully happy to be angry with his brother's obtuseness. If Fred could not see that this was different from anything that had gone before, it was because he was too young to appreciate this strange and wonderful thing that had happened to him.

'I have written to her. You shall read the letter, Fred. I fancy I have a way with a letter.'

Frederick took the paper and read:

> 'I now declare that my fair incognito is your dear dear self. Your manners, your sentiments, the tender feelings of your heart so totally coincide with my ideas, not to mention the many advantages you have in person over many other ladies, that I not only highly esteem you but love you more than words or ideas can express . . .'

Frederick said: 'But how do you know about her sentiments and the tender feelings of her heart?'

'I spoke with her when I was in our sisters' apartments.'

'But only briefly.'

'My dear Fred, one can fall in love in an instant. I have assured her of my friendship.'

Frederick glanced down at the paper.

> 'Adieu, dearest Miss Hamilton, and allow me to sign myself him who will esteem and love you till the end of his life.'

Frederick whistled, but George impatiently snatched the paper from him, sealed it and summoned Lord Malden to take it to the lady.

The Duke of Cumberland rode out to Kew, and when he demanded to be presented to the King, none dared dismiss him.

George, being told that his brother was asking for an audience, was uncertain how to act. He thought he had made it clear that he had no wish to receive his brother who had so disgraced the family. And yet how could he send Cumberland away? He shouldn't have come of course. He should have written and ascertained first that the King would see him.

George paced up and down his chamber. He thought of Lady Grosvenor and the letters Cumberland had written to her. No, he'd not see his brother. Cumberland lived riotously with that Duchess of his and she was a woman he would not receive.

It was sad, of course, that there should be quarrels in the family, but sadder still that members of it should behave as disgracefully as Henry had.

Then George thought of his mother, who had dominated him and with her lover Lord Bute put him into leading strings until he had broken free of them. She had loved him, though; he was certain of that. And she had died so bravely hiding the fact that she was in terrible pain from the cancer in her throat.

'Forgive your brothers, George,' she had said. 'Don't have quarrels in the family if you can avoid it. Your father and his father . . . Your Grandfather and his . . .' Quarrel, quarrel, quarrel . . . Father against son. And it was no good to the family; no good to the monarchy.

Yet he had refused to receive Cumberland although he had accepted

Gloucester–but not his duchess.

He called suddenly: 'All right. All right. Tell the Duke I'll see him.'

Cumberland stood before him, a little sheepish, a little truculent. He should be ashamed, thought George, writing those disgusting letters to Lady Grosvenor . . . and making me pay thirteen thousand pounds damages to the woman's husband. And now he had this woman with the fantastic eyelashes. Eyelashes, eh what? thought the King. Who but a fool would choose a wife for her eyelashes?

'Well,' said the King, 'so you've come here to Kew, eh, what?'

'Yes, George. I thought we should make an end to this quarrel.'

So it was George, eh? The brother not the subject. As though it were for him to decide such a matter.

'I said I'd not receive you at Court and I meant it. You understand that, eh, what?'

'At Court, yes. I understand that. I've been involved in scandal, but I am your brother, George.'

'H'm,' grunted the King. 'A regrettable fact.'

Cumberland looked hurt and the King was immediately sorry. 'Scandalous,' he said gruffly. 'Don't you know that? Eh? What?'

'Yes, of course. But it's in the past.'

'And then to marry without consulting me. And those letters.' The King blinked his eyes as though trying to prevent himself seeing those lurid phrases.

'It's over, George. Grosvenor's had his pound of flesh.'

'Yes, at whose expense?'

'You've been a wonderful brother and a wonderful king to me, George.'

The King grunted.

'I've thought a great deal about you. You're a lucky man, George. When I think of your family. Octavius is the thirteenth and the Queen will soon be presenting you with another. A lucky man, George.'

'H'm,' said the King, and thought of young George. What was he up to now? One never knew. And rising eighteen. Something would have to be done when he was eighteen. He'd have to be given a little freedom. And when one considered what tricks he could get up to without it–that was an alarming proposition. Still, he was fortunate to have such a fertile wife even if she lacked eyelashes a yard long.

'I feel deprived, George, not to know my own nephews and nieces. I'd give a great deal to be allowed to visit them.'

Oh, no, thought the King, you are not going to contaminate the children.

'I will conduct you to the Queen,' he said. 'I don't see why you should not pay your respects to *her*.'

Cumberland ostentatiously wiped his eyes. He was succeeding beyond his hopes. He had always known old George was a sentimental fellow. He had told Fox so. It was only because he had made no special effort at a reconciliation that there had been none.

'George, it would give me such pleasure . . .'

'Come this way,' said the King.

Charlotte was sitting at her embroidery, her snuff box beside her, a few of her ladies working with her. She looked startled when she saw her brother-in-law and at a sign from the King dismissed her women.

Cumberland approached her and kissed her hands. 'This is a very happy day for me, Your Majesty,' he said.

'My brother called on me and so I brought him to you,' said the King.

And even as he spoke he noticed how plain she looked and he kept thinking of his brother's wife who, he had heard, was one of the most beautiful women in the country. Charlotte never looked her best during pregnancies–she was so small–and one scarcely saw her otherwise!

It was wrong of him to criticize her for doing her duty. He should be grateful. Cumberland might have a beautiful wife but he did not possess thirteen children and a fourteenth on the way.

'I am constantly hearing of the Prince of Wales,' said Cumberland.

Startled lights appeared in the Queen's eyes. What had George been doing now? What new scandal?

Cumberland saw their alarm and delighted in it.

'The people dote on him. He is so handsome. That is what I hear.'

The Queen breathed more easily. 'He is a very good-looking boy.'

'And a scholar too.'

'He was always good with his books. He speaks several languages fluently.'

'German is one, I hear. Our ancestors all spoke that fluently, but George is fluent in French, Italian and English too. And a classical scholar.' Cumberland raised his eyes to the ceiling. 'How did we produce such a genius, George?'

The Queen looked pleased. A discussion of the Prince's perfections always delighted her.

'He's apt to be wild,' murmured the King.

'In that he does not take after his father . . . nor his mother. But it's youth, George, only youth.'

'Then the sooner he grows up the better, eh, what?'

'I am so looking forward to being presented to him.'

The King's lips were set in stubborn lines.

'You cannot see the children,' he said.

'Oh, but . . .'

'I make it clear, eh, what? You cannot see the children.'

Cumberland looked downcast and bewildered. But the King repeated: 'I said you cannot see the children. You heard, eh, what? You cannot see the children.'

Cumberland remembered what a stubborn old mule George had always been. Let him get an idea and there was no moving him. There was something adamant about the way he spoke. So he could do nothing but take his leave and report to Mr Fox that in spite of being received he had made little headway.

The Prince was developing a great fondness for his sisters and could not let a day pass without visiting them.

'It is pleasant,' said the Queen, 'to know that there is such affection between them.'

Even the King grunted when she told him and said he was glad George was at last realizing his responsibilities.

If they could have seen the Prince's absorption in his sister's attendant they would have felt less satisfaction; but Mary Hamilton was no Harriot Vernon.

She had told the Prince as much.

'No matter what my feelings I should never do anything which I considered detrimental to my honour, Your Highness.'

The Prince had seized her hand and cried passionately: 'Do you think I should ask it? Your honour is more important to me than my own life.'

Chivalry was now the rule of his life and those adventures which had gone before seemed crude and coarse. Pure love was the only true love; it was much better to dally on the road of romance than to reach the climax, for when one did romance very often fled.

Mary was beautiful and so wise, being twenty-three years old, six years his senior. She had enormous eyes, a slightly tip-tilted nose and plump cheeks. She laughed often and infectiously. She was perfect. She admitted to a fondness for the Prince. Was it love? he asked eagerly. Yes, it was love. But not gross love. She would not allow him to demean himself nor her.

Several of the ladies in the Princesses' apartments reminded her of Harriot Vernon.

'The Queen sent for her one afternoon. Within an hour her bags had been packed and she was gone. Be careful, Mary.'

Mary needed no warning. She was going to be careful.

'All that I have to offer you,' she told the Prince, 'is pure, sacred and completely disinterested.'

'I know,' he answered. 'If it were possible I would ask you to marry me.'

'We know full well *that* is impossible,' replied the practical Mary. 'Perhaps you will not be content with what I have to offer.'

The Prince was on his knees. He was fond of extravagant gestures. He asked nothing . . . *nothing* . . . but to be able to serve her for the rest of his life.

'You will forget me in time,' Mary told him sadly.

'Never, never.'

She shook her head wisely. 'If you did forget me I should regret that we ever formed a friendship, but I should not complain.'

'I shall never allow you to leave me,' he declared. 'How could I endure to be parted from one whom I not only love with enthusiastic fondness but dote on and adore beyond everything that is human.'

'It delights me to hear Your Highness express such sentiments, but I must tell you that I could never be your mistress. My honour is dearer to me than my life . . . even than you are to me and . . .'

The Prince interrupted her.

'You need say no more. I would sooner go to immediate perdition than attempt to do anything that would be detrimental either to your reputation or your honour and virtue.'

Mary sighed with happiness.

'Then you truly love me.'

'You could not doubt it. But I must have something. A lock of your hair in a plain setting and on this shall be engraved the date of that most important event . . . your birth. You shall have engraved a message to me and I shall have one engraved to you. Shall I tell you what mine shall be, "*Toujours aimée*".'

'I think this would be unwise.' Mary was imagining the lock of hair falling into the hands of Madam von Schwellenburg and being carried to Queen Charlotte. The thought of Harriot Vernon had become an obsession with her. People were dismissed from Court within an hour if they became a nuisance; and the Queen had shown clearly what she thought of those unwise women who allowed the Prince of Wales to become enamoured of them.

The Prince was going on rapturously: 'And you must allow me to present you with a bracelet. Please . . . just a plain one and on it I shall inscribe a message for you. I have decided on it. "*Gravé à jamais dans mon cœur*".'

'This could be dangerous.'

'Dangerous.' His eyes sparkled at the thought. 'I would face the whole world for your sake.'

Maybe, she thought, but he would not be called upon to do so. Possibly only the King, who would reprimand him and tell him to mend his ways. Whereas for Mary Hamilton it would be banishment and disgrace. She did not remind him of this, for she had no wish to spoil the idyll by mentioning such practical matters; but she must never be carried away by the charm of the Prince unless she wanted to rush headlong to ruin.

A passionate but platonic friendship would be delightful, but there it must end.

'You must not be too impetuous,' she warned him.

'Impetuosity. Ardour. No word is too strong to express my feelings. I see beauty, accomplishments . . . in fact everything in you that could make your Palamon happy.'

In his romantic way he had called himself her Palamon and she was his Miranda. And when she thought of the passionate letters–and he loved to write letters, for no sooner did he find a pen in his hand than he must use it, and he enjoyed the flowery sentences which he wrote with ease–she was terrified.

'You must write to me as your sister,' she told him. 'Only then can I receive your letters.'

'No matter what your Palamon calls you, my Miranda, you are the love of his life.'

So fervently did he speak that Mary was deeply touched and a little afraid of her own feelings.

She knew that it was going to be difficult to keep her friendship with the ardent young man on the only possible plane which could ensure her remaining at Court.

The King's mood had lightened a little. He had been at odds with his government for some time and the friction between them was all due to the disastrous affair of the American colonists.

'I would accept any ministry,' he had said, 'that would keep the empire intact, prosecute the war and treat me with the respect due to the King.'

North was continually pointing out that times had changed. North was a weakling. Always in the background of the King's mind was that blackguard Charles James Fox. Up to no good, thought the King. He likes to plague me. There was a distant kinship between them, because through his mother, Fox was connected with the royal family, on the wrong side of the blanket it was true, for Fox's mother, Lady Caroline Lennox, was the great-granddaughter of Charles II by his Mistress Louise de Quérouaille; and sometimes Fox reminded him of pictures of his royal ancestor.

It was all very disturbing, but he had received news that Admiral Rodney had defeated the Spanish fleet at Gibraltar and that Sir Henry Clinton had had some success in the southern colonies. Fox and his supporters might declare that these were no major victories and it was true that there was nothing decisive about them, but the King was pleased to have news of them and it set his mind at rest a little.

He could go to Kew with a good conscience and give his mind to domestic matters.

What a joy to visit his model farm, to stroll in the country lanes and receive the curtsies of the country women while the men touched their forelocks as they would to any country squire; to visit the nurseries and see the little ones and make sure that Lady Charlotte Finch was obeying his orders with regard to their eating habits; to take the babies on his knee and caress them. Mary and Sophia were adorable; and the elder girls were charming. There at Kew he could be at peace. He could rise early in the morning and light the fire which had been laid for him the night before and then get back into bed and wait until it warmed the room. His servants might laugh at his simple habits but he did not care.

Then he would talk with Charlotte and perhaps walk a little with her in the gardens. She would talk about the children and her Orangerie and how she had found a new way of saving the household accounts.

It was all so . . . soothing.

Of course there was one subject which gave them cause for alarm–the Prince of Wales–and they must talk of him frequently.

As he sat in the Queen's drawing room alone with her like a simple married couple–he spoke to her of the Prince.

'He is much less wild lately,' said the Queen happily. 'He has become so attached to his sisters. It is most touching.'

'H'm,' grunted the King.

'It is truly so. Augusta tells me he is constantly in their apartments. He is so fond of her and Elizabeth–and so interested in all they do.'

'No more chasing maids of honour.'

'That is all over.'

'I'm glad to hear it. It gave me some sleepless nights.'

He thought of those nights when his imagination had not let him rest, when he had dreamed of women . . . Cumberland's women, Gloucester's women and the Prince's women.

'It was just a little youthful folly, I am sure. He is over that. After all he is so brilliantly clever. Everyone says so.'

'They'll say these things of princes, eh, what?'

'It is true,' insisted the Queen.

'He'll be eighteen soon . . . agitating for his own establishment . . . fancying himself a man. He'll not get it.'

The Queen thought that was a matter for the Parliament to decide, but she refrained from commenting. Long experience had taught her that she was not expected to offer opinions on any political matter–and her eldest son's coming of age was certainly that. All that was expected of her was that she bear children. She might keep her household accounts and had the power to dismiss her maids. That was all.

Perhaps, thought the Queen, if I had not been so busy being a mother I might have insisted on having some say. But it was too late now. George would never allow it; and she was becoming increasingly afraid of upsetting him, for when he was upset his speech grew faster than ever, the 'ehs' and 'whats' multiplied and that queer vague look came into his eyes.

Charlotte was sure that the most important thing was to keep the King calm; and today he was calmer than she had seen him for some time. She must keep him thus.

'We should be seen about together,' said the King. 'Best place to be seen would be the playhouse. We'll have a royal command performance, eh, what?'

'With George accompanying us. That would be an excellent idea.'

'So I thought. I'll send to that fellow at the Drury Lane Theatre. Sheridan, eh?'

'You mean you would command a performance of his play.'

'I don't like the name of it, and I hear it's immodest. The title's enough to tell you that: *The School for Scandal.* It'll have to be Shakespeare, I dareswear. Sad stuff, Shakespeare. Never could see why there had to be all this fuss about it. But it would have to be Shakespeare. The people expect it.'

'Well, you will ask this Mr Sheridan to submit some plays for your choice.'

'Yes, I'll do this. And we will have a family party, eh, what? Good for the Prince to be seen with us. Friendly, family party . . . I'll send for this Sheridan and when I've chosen the play we'll go to the playhouse. It'll show we're a united family, eh? And the Prince of Wales is but a boy yet, what?'

'I think,' said the Queen, 'that it is a very pleasant idea.'

The Prince had shut himself into his apartments in the Dower House to write to Mary Hamilton.

There was one little doubt which was beginning to worm its way into his mind. It was a most romantic love affair this–but he did find that his eyes kept wandering to other personable young women. Not that his eyes had not always thus wandered; but there was a difference. A very disturbing thought had come to him. Would it be very unromantic, while devoting himself to his soulful love, to have a little fun with young women who did not set themselves such a high standard as Mary did?

He dismissed the thought as unworthy. So, this love affair must be perfect. He must stop thinking of indulging in light frivolity with other women. The only one in the world who mattered was Mary Hamilton.

He looked at his reflection in the ornate mirror. It really was a very pleasing reflection. In his blue velvet coat which brought out the blue in his eyes, he was undoubtedly handsome. No one could look more like a prince.

He sat down to write a description of himself to Mary. It would amuse her, he was sure:

> 'Your brother is now approaching the bloom of youth. He is rather above normal size, his limbs well proportioned, and upon the whole is well made, though he has rather too great a penchant to grow fat. The features of his countenance are strong and manly . . .'

He rose and looked at himself again changing his expression several times, laughing and frowning, looking pleading as he would to Mary and haughty as he would when entering his father's presence.

> '. . . though,' he continued, 'they carry too much of an air of hauteur. His forehead is well shaped, his eyes, though none of the best and although grey are passable. He has tolerably good eyebrows and lashes, *un petit nez retroussé cependant assez aimé*, a good mouth, though rather large, with fine teeth and a tolerably good chin, but the whole of his countenance is too round. I forgot to add very ugly ears. As hair is generally looked upon as beauty, he has more hair than usually falls to everyone's share, but from the present mode of dressing it, from the immense thickness necessarily required for the toupees and the length

and number of curls it makes it appear greatly less thick than in reality it is. Such are the gifts that nature has bestowed upon him and which the world says she has bestowed on him with a generous hand.'

He stopped to laugh at himself. This *was* amusing. He was beginning to see himself very clearly indeed. But to look in a mirror and write of what one saw was one thing; to assess the character quite another.

He took up his pen.

'I now come to the qualities of his mind and his heart.'

He paused, put his head on one side and began to write rapidly:

'His sentiments and thoughts are open and generous. He is above doing anything that is mean (too susceptible even to believing people his friends and placing too much confidence in them, from not yet having obtained a sufficient knowledge of the world or of its practices), grateful and friendly when he finds a *real friend*. His heart is good and tender if it is allowed to show its emotions. He has a strict sense of honour, is rather too familiar with his inferiors, but will not suffer himself to be browbeaten or treated with haughtiness by his superiors.'

He sighed. What a lot of virtues he seemed to possess. If she believed this Mary would surely find him irresistible. But he would not have her think he was boasting or wished to influence her unfairly. Indeed he would perhaps more likely win her esteem by giving her an account of his faults.

'Now for his vices,' he went on. He hesitated. It was a strong word.

'Rather let us call them weaknesses. He is too subject to give vent to his passions of every kind, too subject to be in a passion, but he never bears malice or rancour in his heart. As for swearing, he has nearly cured himself of that vile habit. He is rather too fond of wine and women, to both which young men are apt to deliver themselves too much, but which he endeavours to check to the utmost of his power. But upon the whole, his character is open, free and generous, susceptible of good impressions, ready to follow good advice, especially when he receives it from so affectionate and friendly a sister as you are.'

He stopped again; the vices had somehow turned themselves into virtues. But that was exactly how they seemed to him. He was a good young man–or he would be to those of whom he was as fond as he was of Mary.

Mary, adorable Mary, who had inspired him with such a noble passion. No wonder he felt good when he wrote to her.

'Adieu for the present. I will finish this in my next. I have been too favourable I fear for my manifold faults, my dearest, dearest Friend; I shall try to correct them, for you shall ever find me ready to lend an attentive ear to your advice. Great imperfections and faults I have, but ingratitude towards you shall never be reckoned among them. My attachment to you shall never cease with my life.'

It was very pleasant to ride in Hyde Park in the company of Frederick. The people recognized him at once and cheered him as he passed. He always ackowledged their acclaim with a bow that was not only gracious but friendly. He wanted them to know that it was his desire to be liked by them. There was nothing of the German about him; he was entirely English. His father was the first of the Georges to speak fluent English, but he had somehow remained a German. There was nothing Teutonic about the Prince of Wales; he had all the gaiety and charm of the Stuart side of the family; and the people recognized this in him.

As for Frederick, he was happy as usual to see his brother's popularity and to take second place, which was one of his most endearing traits and was one of the reasons why they were the closest friends.

Now, to ride through the park side by side, made him feel free. They might have equerries in front and attendants behind but they could forget them and chat together like two young men out to take the air, unencumbered.

The Prince was talking of the perfections of Mary Hamilton, but Frederick was aware that his brother was not insensible to the charms of some of the ladies who passed by. There were some beauties. Very different from the young women who made up the household at Kew–with one or two exceptions of course like Harriot Vernon and Mary Hamilton. Beautiful ladies in hoops and feathers, with tight bodices cut low to disclose exquisite necks and bosoms, brocade and silk gowns open in front or looped as a polonaise to show an ornamental petticoat. They were rouged and patched and made a brilliant picture in their big straw hats decorated with flowers and ribbons. And all eyes were on the elegant Prince who sat his horse so skilfully and those eyes were so languishly and, yes . . . inviting . . . that he found his attention straying from his pure love and an excitement possessed him.

'Riding here like this, I feel free, Fred. By God, what the devil are we doing allowing ourselves to live like children in the nursery?'

And just at that moment a carriage came bowling towards them, a very ornate coach bearing the royal arms, and seated in it was their uncle the Duke of Cumberland who, perceiving them, immediately called to his coachman to stop.

He alighted and approached the Prince with tears in his eyes.

'Your Highness, my dear, *dear* nephew. Forgive the intrusion, but I cannot pass you by without the greeting due to your rank when I long to give you a warmer one. When all is said and done I am your uncle.'

Cumberland! thought the Prince. The rebel. The uncle who was concerned in the Grosvenor scandal and had such a fascinating wife!

Cumberland had taken the Prince's hand and was kissing it with emotion.

'And . . . Your Highness Prince Frederick. This is a happy day for me.'

'We are pleased to have an opportunity of speaking with you, Uncle,' said the Prince warmly.

'I knew you would be. I trust this will be no isolated meeting. The Duchess and I have talked of you often . . . with tears in our eyes. We feel for you so much . . . my dear, *dear* nephew.'

Uncle Cumberland was determined to be friendly and the Prince had been right when he had said he was susceptible and ready to accept friendship when offered. Uncle Cumberland had quarrelled with the King and the Prince could well understand that, for his uncle represented the great exciting world outside the royal nurseries. He was implying by his words, his looks and his manner that he felt the Princes were badly treated by the King; they were shut away from the world, treated like children. What could be more humiliating to young men of seventeen and sixteen.

'We hope you will do us the great honour of allowing us to entertain you sometime. There are men . . . and women . . .' Just a little avuncular leer suggesting the delight this could be. '. . . charming men, beautiful women . . . witty, worldly . . . who long to make your royal acquaintance. They have caught glimpses of you now and then . . . in public places, and been enchanted. But it is not enough, nephews, it is not enough. Why at Drury Lane . . . where Sheridan's *School for Scandal* has been playing to packed houses . . . there is the most beautiful little play actress I ever set eyes on. Mrs Robinson is the most beautiful woman in London and London abounds with beautiful women. You should be meeting the world. It's a shame to keep such charm . . . such elegance shut away at Kew. What a coat! What cut! What shoe buckles! I swear I never saw the like . . . Why Your Highness is the leader of the *ton* . . . and shut away at Kew. I have said too much. Why, nephews, I fear I am the most indiscreet man you ever met. But I let my concern for you run away with my tongue . . . and my pleasure too . . . my deep, deep pleasure in this encounter.'

The Duke of Cumberland touched his eye with the corner of his lace kerchief and the Prince of Wales was a little affected too.

'Well, I must not delay you. We are being watched. This will mayhap be reported. I shall be in even greater disgrace. But it's a sad world when a loving uncle cannot have a word with his two handsome nephews. Adieu, my dear, dear boys.'

'Let us rather say *au revoir*,' replied the Prince.

Cumberland kissed first George's hand, then Frederick's; and went back to his coach.

The Prince's eyes were shining as they rode on.

'Why,' he demanded, 'should we be kept shut away? Our uncle is right. We should be out in the world. We should not be living like children. I tell you this, Fred, I'll not endure it much longer. The day is fast approaching when I shall *demand* my freedom. And when I have my rights I shall visit our uncle. It was most affecting, was it not? Why should he be kept from us merely because he fell in love with a woman.'

'Lady Grosvenor was a married woman.'

'Ah, love!' sighed the Prince. 'How can we be sure where it will appear. Is one supposed to wait for it to come *suitably* . . . as our father did with our mother. I hear our uncle's wife is a most fascinating woman, Fred. I should like to meet her.'

'It will never be permitted.'

The Prince pressed his horse into a canter.

'All that, Fred,' he prophesied, 'will shortly be changed. You will see.'

Command Performance at Drury Lane

Richard Brinsley Sheridan, twenty-eight years old, witty, brilliant and the most successful playwright in London and manager of the Drury Theatre, was on his way to Buckingham House for an audience with the King. He knew what this meant: a royal command performance, always good for business. He was well aware that it was no use offering *The School for Scandal*. He laughed inwardly, thinking of some of the epigrammatical gems of that piece, of the screen scene, of his adorable but rather naughty Lady Teazle, and imagining the reception this would get from humourless George and Charlotte.

He was going to offer them *The Winter's Tale*. It would have to be Shakespeare although he knew full well that the King found the great playwright dull. Still, his subjects expected him to see Shakespeare. Shakespeare was respectable, which seemed a little odd to Sheridan as some of the lines came into his mind–but Shakespeare had his place in the literature of the land and his poetry made up for his bawdiness. Any of the Restoration plays with their cynical approach to marriage would be definitely unsuitable for the King.

Arrived at Buckingham House Sheridan was conducted to the King's apartments and in a very short time was granted an audience.

'Mr Sheridan, it is good of you to come.' The King was always considerate to his subjects, and behaved with an absence of arrogance. The epithet homely was apt.

'At Your Majesty's pleasure,' replied Sheridan with a courtly bow.

'You will have guessed why I asked you to come, Mr Sheridan, eh, what?' Sheridan was about to speak for one did not realize when first in the King's company that the queries were merely rhetorical. The King went on without a pause: 'We are thinking of coming to the theatre . . . the Queen and myself in the company of the Prince of Wales.'

In the company of the Prince of Wales! Sheridan felt excited. This would indeed be an occasion.

'Drury Lane will be honoured, Sir.'

The King looked pleased. He enjoyed doing good turns and he knew how these theatre people liked a command performance. They were rare. He preferred the opera and a good concert; but it was his duty to see a play now and then.

'The point is,' said the King, 'what will be played for us? It should be something in . . . er . . . good taste, eh, what?'

'The utmost good taste, Sir.'

The King looked quizzically at Mr Sheridan. He had heard that this young man was a little wild in his habits. There had been some elopement, he believed; though why he should have heard these bits of gossip about a theatre manager he could not imagine. Except of course that Mr Sheridan had taken the town by storm with that play of his. It was his wife of course. One of the finest singers in the country. Mrs Sheridan made Mr Sheridan more respectable in the royal eyes.

'Well,' said the King, 'what would you suggest, Mr Sheridan?'

'Has your Majesty decided on Shakespeare?'

The King looked scornful. 'Sad stuff . . . most of it,' he said. 'Eh? What?' Mr Sheridan was pleased not to answer. The King went on: 'But the people of this country seem to have made a god of the fellow. Mustn't say a word against him. He's perfect, so they tell me. I don't see it, Mr Sheridan. I don't see it.'

'Then, sir . . .' Sheridan's eyes were alight with hope. Why not? Mrs Abington would have to play Lady Teazle of course. And what a player! And Mary Robinson . . . dear, exquisite Mary Robinson would be Maria . . . as they were before. Mary would want to play Lady Teazle . . . but she wasn't up to the part really . . . lovely as she was to look at; and for all her cruderies Abington was an actress to her fingertips whereas Mary owed her success to that incomparable beauty. Incomparable but not quite. His own Elizabeth, the wife with whom he had eloped . . . had perhaps a greater beauty than Mary Robinson's, but more ethereal. Elizabeth? Mary? Elizabeth would always be first but Mary was so alluring; and a man whose career necessarily brought him into the company of so many desirable women could not be expected to remain faithful to his wife even though she were delightful, understanding, virtuous . . . in fact all that a wife should be. Elizabeth would understand his weaknesses. But his thoughts were straying. A royal command performance for *The School*. It would be the crowning triumph and what fun to watch the royal disapproval of the wit . . . though would they grasp it? What would prim George and dull Charlotte make of the wittiest play in London? How amusing to discover.

The King had interrupted: 'Yes it must be Shakespeare, Mr Sheridan. The people expect it of us.'

Sheridan sighed. 'I believe Your Majesty does not greatly care for tragedy, so I will not suggest *Macbeth*.'

'Can't stand the stuff. People killing each other all over the stage, eh, what? I call that even worse than the rest of the fellow's plays, Mr Sheridan.'

'Then Your Majesty would perhaps care to see *The Winter's Tale*. A charming story of virtue rewarded, Sir. And we have a very good production of this play. It is a favourite of mine, if Your Majesty would allow me to express my opinion. It is a play for the family, Sir. One could take one's children and not be dismayed.'

'Ah,' said the King. '*The Winter's Tale*. I remember it. A silly story, but as you say nothing to offend.'

'I have an excellent actress in the part of Perdita, Your Majesty. She has been delighting my audiences for some little time and I am sure will please you.'

The King grunted, implying that he was not interested in actresses. But the voices in his head were telling him that he would enjoy seeing this beauty perform.

'She made quite a name for herself as Juliet, Your Majesty; and since then has been a favourite of the public.'

'Good. Then let it be *The Winter's Tale*, Mr Sheridan.'

'Sir, the players will be enchanted . . . and a little nervous, I dareswear. I shall take the first opportunity of letting them know the honour that awaits them.'

The King smiled, in a good humour. He liked giving pleasure and discussing the visit of the family to the play was more comforting than those interviews with his ministers.

Sheridan went back to his house in Great Queen Street . . . that house which was far more expensive than he could afford. But he was by nature reckless and extravagant.

He went straight to the drawing room, for he knew that he would find Elizabeth there at the harpsichord. She invariably was because it was essential for her to do a great many hours practice a day. She was reckoned by the musical world to have one of the most enchanting voices of all time.

He was right. She was there; and she rose at once to greet him, coming forward her arms outstretched. Even now, her beauty struck him afresh and he had to stifle a feeling of shame for the infidelities he had practised since their marriage. Not that she would not understand. Not that she would ever withdraw the comfort of her serene presence. Elizabeth was a saint–and how could a man like Richard Sheridan live up to the high ideals of a saint?

'Elizabeth my love.' He kissed her hands; he did not have to feign affection; it was there, rising up, swamping all other emotions temporarily whenever he saw her. 'What do you think? I have just come from the presence of His Majesty, King George III.'

'A royal command performance?'

'You have guessed rightly, my dear.'

She drew him on to the sofa and said: 'Come, tell me all about it.' Her lovely face was framed by soft dark hair, the sweet mouth and the lovely long-lashed eyes under delicate but beautifully arched brows, glowed with interest.

Sheridan then gave an imitation of his interview with the King, exaggerating it, mocking both himself and the monarch so that Elizabeth laughed immoderately and begged him to stop.

'The outcome of this historic interview, my love, is that we are to play *The Winter's Tale* for the royal family. And the Prince of Wales himself will be present.'

'This is a sign that the Prince will be seen more frequently in public.'

'Papa holds the knife that will cut the apron strings. It is poised, but the cut has not yet been made.'

'I am sorry for His Majesty. He is so good, really, Richard.'

'Alas for the good! They suffer so much. Unfair of fate is it not? It's the wicked who should suffer.'

He looked at her wistfully and she understood; but she smiled brightly. She would not show him that she often wondered where he was when not at home; that she trembled when she saw the accounts which came too frequently to Great Queen Street. She did not reproach him for those gambling debts which sucked up most of the profits from Drury Lane. But she was constantly worried about money.

'Well, my love,' he said, 'this should bring in the cash. You know what a help these performances are. Everyone will want to see *The Winter's Tale* because the royal family did. And, by God, we need the money.'

She knew it. She helped with the accounts at Drury Lane; and she knew too that they could have lived in comfort–indeed, luxury–but for her husband's wild extravagances.

There could be a way out of their difficulties. She herself could earn money. Her voice could have been her fortune and was on the way to becoming so before her marriage. She had been offered twelve hundred guineas to sing for twelve nights at the Pantheon, but her husband's pride would not allow her to do this.

It was something Elizabeth could not understand. How much more dishonourable to run up bills which one could not pay than to allow one's wife to sing for money. But Richard had his pride. Pride indeed. One of the seven deadly sins. Pride insisted that he must consort with rich men, that he must gamble with them, that he must do all that they did, though they were rich and he must needs earn his living.

But she could not understand Sheridan; she could only love him.

She did not remind him that the theatre was doing well, that he himself had a brilliant future before him. She would have been happy to live as they had in those ecstatic days of their honeymoon in the tiny cottage at East Burnham; but that of course was not what Richard wanted. He needed the gay life of London–the theatrical world, the literary world, the wits, the men and woman of brilliance to set off the sparks which lighted his talents.

'It will have to be a superb performance,' he said; and she was astonished at the manner in which he could throw aside all financial anxieties at the thought of the production. 'We must go into rehearsal right away. Nothing but the best, Elizabeth.'

'And will Mrs Robinson perform?'

He did not meet her eye. He wondered how much she knew of his relationship with the beautiful play actress. He felt angry suddenly. He was a man of genius, wasn't he? She could not expect to apply ordinary standards to him. She should know that however much he strayed he always came back to her. He would never cease to love her; he knew there was not a woman in the world like her. Wasn't that enough? Mary Robinson was beautiful . . . in a different way from Elizabeth. Elizabeth's beauty was of the heavenly variety–'as beautiful as an angel', they had said that of her. But a man of genius must experience the world. He cannot spend his life among angels.

He spoke irritably. 'Of course. Of course. Why not? She's our biggest draw.'

'Of course,' said Elizabeth calmly. 'I merely wondered whether she was experienced enough.'

'Experienced? She's been playing for more than three years. Her Juliet was an immediate success.'

'I see. So she will play Perdita.'

'Perdita it shall be.' He looked at his watch. 'I can't delay. I must tell them of this great honour. We must begin our preparations at once.' He stood up uneasily. Was she wondering whether his affair with the actress was still going on? Did she know it had ever existed?

That was the trouble with these good women. One could never be sure how much they knew because they met all calamity, all disaster and the deceits of others, with a calm tolerance which, although it smoothed out the difficulties of life, could be damnably exasperating.

He embraced her with fervour and her response was immediate. She had sworn to love him and naturally she kept her vows.

'I had to come home to tell my Elizabeth first of all,' he said.

Then he was out of the house and as he called for his chair his anxieties fell from him. It was only when he entered the house that he remembered what it had cost and that a great deal of the furniture was not yet paid for. It was only when he was in the company of his wife that he remembered his sins.

Now to Mary Robinson. He imagined himself telling her the news.

When he had gone Elizabeth returned to the harpsichord, but instead of singing sat silent, thinking of her romantic elopement, of the transcending joy of those days when she had believed that when she and Richard were married they would live happily ever after. At least, she could console herself, she would never be happy without him.

Yet before he had come into her life, she had lived serenely in her father's house where everything was subservient to music. All day long the sounds of music had filled the house. Bath was such a gracious city; often here in London she dreamed of Bath. But Richard must be in London naturally for London was necessary to him. Here he had his theatre and he was in the centre of the gay life; here were the gaming houses, the clubs which he could not resist; here were the brilliant men like Charles James

Fox whose company he so enjoyed.

But the old days had been sweet. She smiled to remember singing with her sister Mary; and her brother Tom's playing of the violin when he was in the nursery had been declared nothing short of genius.

And how proud her father had been of his brilliant children–perhaps particularly of her! His 'song bird', he had called her, and she remembered well the day when he had said to her: 'Elizabeth, I believe there never has been a sweeter voice than yours.' How happy that had made her! And she had become famous–or almost–when she had sung in an oratorio before the King. Everyone had been talking of her voice then. And her sister Mary who had a beautiful voice of her own had said it was only a pale echo of Elizabeth's.

Those were happy days when they had all been together in the big house in Bath and their father had taught singing. Then had come that fateful day when Mrs Sheridan, wife of a teacher of elocution, had come to the house for singing lessons; the friendship between the two families had begun and Richard was a constant visitor to the singing master's house.

She had often thought of going into a convent and when the odious Major Matthews had pursued her and would not be repulsed she had felt the need for the sequestered life more than ever. She had a beauty which almost rivalled her musical talents and she knew that she would be pursued by men. Some in high places had their eyes on her. Horace Walpole had written in one of those letters which so many people seemed to read that the King had been unable to take his eyes from her when she had sung in the oratorio and had ogled her as much as he dared in so holy a place.

A convent promised a blissful retreat in which she could sing holy music for the comfort of its inmates. But Richard was there–the good friend, the gay young man with ambitions of which he talked to her and to whom she was able to confide her desire for the retired life. He was entirely sympathetic and she had wondered how this was possible since his ambitions lay in such a different direction.

When Sir Joshua Reynolds painted her as St Cecilia she was famous. None of the angels among whom he had placed her, so it was said, had a sweeter and more angelic face than hers. She was fragile, unworldly; and the desire to go into a convent was greater than ever; and then the doubts had come. Who had planted them in her mind but the young and virile companion of her childhood? What was the attraction between her and Richard? Why should one so worldly find such delight in the company of a woman whose ideal was a convent life?

Major Matthews had come into her life, and even now she shuddered to recall him. How she loathed that man! He was coarse; he was sensuous; and her very remoteness from all that he was made him desire her the more. He was a man of means and persistent and she feared her father would want to make a match for her.

'I must go into a convent,' she told Richard. She knew of a convent in France, and if she could reach it, she was certain she would be given sanctuary there.

Dear Richard. How chivalrous he was! She knew now that he was fighting against his own emotions. He realized the incongruity of a match between themselves; how would such a delicate creature fit in with his ambitions? But he could not allow her heart to be broken, her spirit quenched by the hateful Major Matthews. He must save her from that so he had conceived the plan for conducting her to her convent and with only her maid for company and as chaperone they had fled from Bath. It was a mad adventure; and before they had reached London Richard had declared his love for her. At that time it had seemed more important than ambition. And herself? She had made a discovery too. It was not life in a convent she wanted but life with Richard.

'We must marry,' said Richard, 'for even if we did not wish to, now that we have eloped together there is no other course open to us.'

She smiled recalling it; that hasty marriage; the solemn words said before the priest, and no sooner was the ceremony over and they returned to the lodgings Richard had found for them than her father arrived in a great state of agitation, threatened to horsewhip Richard and carried his daughter back to Bath.

'But we are married,' she had insisted.

'Doubtless a mock marriage,' growled her father. 'I know these scoundrels.'

But this was not a scoundrel. This was Richard, the friend of her childhood. Her father must realize this. He did and was somewhat mollified to recall it. He cared so much for me, she thought tenderly. He wanted my happiness above all things. He would never have forced me into marriage with Major Matthews. If she had not been so young and impetuous she would have known that. But perhaps she had deceived herself then. Perhaps at heart she had wanted to elope with Richard, had wanted to marry him all along. Could it be that she had always seen the prospect of life in a convent as an impossible dream?

Richard would always be surrounded by drama. She caught her breath with horror even now as she remembered hearing the news that Major Matthews had challenged him to a duel, that Richard had accepted the challenge and had been wounded. She had wanted to go to him at once but her father had restrained her and Richard had written to her–impassioned letters with that touch of brilliance which playgoers were finding so much to their taste.

And her father . . . her dear father had relented. 'Since you feel as you do, there'd better be a proper ceremony and you can set up house together.'

And so they were married in a manner fitting her father's position in Bath; and they went to live in the little cottage at East Burnham.

How many times during the years that followed had she thought of that little cottage and the happiness she had had there! Far more so than in this luxurious house in Great Queen Street. There had been no debts then, no knowledge of what the future with a brilliant man could be like. Romantically innocent she had believed that life would be one long round of bliss.

But he had soon begun to talk of London–wistfully at first. It was his Mecca; it was the centre of the literary world. There was no intellectual life at East Burnham. One *must* be in London.

'And, Elizabeth my love, there is money. It has to be earned you know.' London where the streets are paved with gold, the great city which was waiting to acclaim Richard Brinsley Sheridan, the only place where he could give free play to his talents.

And so . . . goodbye to the cottage where she had been so happy, and to Orchard Street where she learned about debts and witty men who took her husband from his own fireside to clubs where they gambled. To chocolate and coffee houses where men congregated to talk of the events of the day, to read the lampoons which were handed round about the famous and notorious, to laugh at the cartoons. 'To *live*,' said Richard.

It was to her that he read *The Rivals*. She was the first to sit entranced, her hands clasped together, and to call him a genius.

He accepted her verdict. He knew he had genius.

And the people accepted him. They saw *The Rivals* and decided they wanted more of Sheridan. Success came quickly, for he was only in his twenties, and the most talked of playwright and soon . . . manager of Drury Lane.

But oh the debts! The eternal demands for money! Why was it that as he grew more successful his debts increased and the more money he earned the more he needed?

'The company we keep is too grand for us, Richard,' she expostulated.

'Too grand for the Sheridans!'

'We cannot afford to entertain them, Richard. If they need such entertainment shouldn't we tell them it is beyond our means.'

He had laughed at her, lifted her and held her above his head.

'Now you look like an angel . . . looking down on a poor weak mortal. An avenging angel! My dearest St Cecilia, we cannot reach our rightful place in society unless we mingle with the *ton*. If we did not mingle with the rich and the noble we should soon be relegated to a back seat.'

'It is your plays surely that have made you famous–not your acquaintances.'

But he had laughed at her and said she was his angel; she lived in the rarefied atmosphere far, far above him, so far that she could not see what life was like among ordinary mortals.

And the bills continued to come in and her dowry of three thousand pounds which had once seemed so considerable was quickly swallowed up; and she had asked her father to help them out of their pecuniary embarrassments so many times that she could not bring herself to ask again. She was ashamed to ask, for Richard earned far more money than her father ever had and it seemed so wrong to take his money. When she told Richard this he laughed at her. 'But it is not what one earns that is important, my love. It's what one spends.'

How true . . . how sadly true!

And they could have been so comfortable. She had never wanted luxury . . . luxury that was unpaid for and a reproach to her every time she was aware of it. If she told him that she had been happier in the little cottage in East Burnham he would have laughed that mocking laugh of his. St Cecilia! he called her. His angel who was too good for ordinary mortal man.

If he would be reasonable . . . if he would give up the worldly life . . . if he would be content to live simply and write his plays . . .

But that was to hope for the impossible. Why had they fallen in love? Why had they not seen that they were so different, that each had their eyes fixed on a different ideal? He was gay, handsome, witty and brilliant–a man of the world. And she asked for nothing from life but her music and his love.

She sighed and turned to the harpsichord.

Yet I would not change him, she told herself. As if I could! For if I changed him he would not be Richard Sheridan–and it is Richard Sheridan whom I love.

Sheridan did not go to the theatre. None of the players would be there at this hour. Instead he directed the chairman to the house of Mrs Mary Robinson, where the lady's maid, Mrs Armistead, received him, for Mary Robinson's hired footman had not yet appeared for duty.

His eyes followed Mrs Armistead as she took him to a small drawing room where he could wait while she went to tell her mistress of his arrival. Mrs Armistead was so quiet, so discreet, yet one could not help but be aware of her. She was handsome, but in a way which was by no means flamboyant; neatly dressed in her maid's uniform, yet she did not look like a maid. Sheridan had noticed more than once that she walked with unusual grace; and it suddenly struck him that it was her dignity which drew attention to her.

In a short time Mrs Armistead returned to tell Mr Sheridan that her mistress would be with him very soon.

'Thank you,' said Sheridan. He was at the point of detaining the woman, but she seemed to sense this and with unhurried dignity left him.

No nonsense, thought Sheridan with a smirk. No flirting with the lady's maid behind the lady's back.

Then he forgot the maid because Mary had come in. He had to admit that every time he saw her she took his breath away. Her beauty burst upon the eye as the sunlight would after coming out of the dark. Mary was a dazzling beauty. Different from the handsome maid–whose looks were of a more subtle nature and had to be discovered gradually; Mary's were so brilliantly obvious that their impact was immediate.

Conscious of the effect she had on people Mary always dressed for the part. Today she wore a pink satin gown, fashionably hooped and ornamented by a silver pattern. Her hair was dressed in loose curls and lightly powdered, her exquisite neck and bosom rather freely exposed.

Sheridan opened his eyes to express the wonder she expected to see in the eyes of any man; then taking her hand humbly kissed it.

Mary smiled; she was satisfied.

'Sherry, my dear, *dear* friend.'

'My angel!'

He would have embraced her, but she lifted a hand. Mary gave herself airs now that she was a well-known actress.

'What an unexpected pleasure to see you at this hour! What will you take? Coffee? Chocolate? Tea? Wine?'

He would take nothing, he told her; it was enough for him to drink in her charms.

She laughed–a little refined laugh. Mary was always anxious that she should be treated as a lady. She liked to think that she had brought refinement to the stage and as a good business manager he was ready to humour an actress who had the gift of bringing in the people. It was enough for them to look at Mary Robinson, irrespective of the play. And there was no doubt that she had brought in the nobility too. The Duke of Cumberland was an admirer, though Mary–wisely perhaps–had resisted all his offers.

'What brings you, truly? You are not going to tell me that you could not wait for a glimpse of me at the theatre today?'

'If I told you that it would be true too.'

'Oh, come, come.'

Yes, she was a little imperious. Well, with beauty such as hers perhaps it was forgivable. Her dark hair was luxuriantly abundant; her brow was a little high and the deeply set eyes under the level brows, the straight nose, the perfectly formed lips, were touched with an air of haunting melancholy which made her face unforgettable. This was no mere pretty girl. This was beauty. The contours of her face were perfect; her body was beautifully proportioned; she moved with the utmost grace; she was conscious, Sheridan was sure, every minute of the day, of her beauty.

'Well, my beautiful Mary, there is something else. I was determined to tell you first.'

'A new play?'

He shook his head. A faint irritation had passed across her face. She had not really forgiven him for not giving her the part of Lady Teazle. 'Mrs Abington is so . . . vulgar,' she had declared. Always eager that her refinement should be acknowledged, she invariably called attention to the vulgarity of others. 'Precisely so,' he had retorted. 'That's why it's Abington's part. Don't forget Lady Teazle was not of the *ton*. You, my dearest Mary, have only to walk on a stage and everyone knows you are a lady. And, bless you, you are not a good enough actress to hide it.' Careful, he had thought. A backhanded compliment. But one thing he had been determined on: Abington was going to play Lady Teazle–and not even for beautiful Mary would he allow his play to have anything but the best. She had not been reconciled and continued to believe that she had been slighted.

Now he said quickly: 'No, no. Guess again.'

'You are deliberately keeping me in suspense.' She moved to a sofa and holding out her hand bade him sit beside her.

'Then I will do so no longer. His Majesty sent for me to tell me that there is to be a command performance.'

'I see.' She was pleased, and tapped lightly with long tapering fingers. A habit, he had noticed, to call attention to them. They were as perfectly formed as the rest of her. 'And I am to play before the King and Queen?'

'Of course. How could it be otherwise? And there is something else. The Prince will accompany them.'

There was no sign of melancholy in her face now. Her eyes sparkled. 'What play?' A terrible fear showed itself. It would be *The School*. Trust Sheridan to put on his own play. And Abington would have the better part!

'Shakespeare, of course. His Majesty thinks the "fellow" wrote "sad stuff" but the people seem to think it's all that's suitable for royal consumption.'

'*Romeo and Juliet*?' Juliet had been her first part. He remembered how beautiful she had looked.

'*The Winter's Tale*. You will be Perdita.'

'Perdita!' She was not displeased, but she was apt to think Juliet would have been better.

Sheridan disillusioned her. 'Young love in defiance of parental authority is a sore point with H.M. at the moment. You know the Prince is apt to give Papa anxious moments on that account.'

She laughed. Perdita. Innocent, wistful, beautiful Perdita. She was growing more and more excited every moment.

'I have seen him now and then,' she said. 'He's a pretty boy.'

'I feel sure he will be delighted to see *you*.'

Her mind immediately went to costumes. She saw herself in pink . . . her favourite colour because it became her most. But blue, perhaps. Satin? Velvet?

'We should go into rehearsal immediately,' said Sheridan.

He was looking at her appraisingly. She was even lovelier animated than melancholy, and the most susceptible young man in the country was the Prince of Wales. Surely he would not be able to look on all this beauty unmoved?

Was that what Mary was thinking? She had refused the protection of many rich and notorious men. Suppose . . . But that was looking too far ahead.

He leaned towards her and kissed her lightly.

'Well, think about it, and be at the theatre early. We'll go into rehearsal right away. I want perfection. You must please their Majesties . . . and the Prince . . . Perdita.'

He rose to go and Mrs Armistead, who had been listening at the door, walked out of sight unhurriedly and with dignity just as he came out of the room.

'Armistead,' said Mrs Robinson, 'Come here. I'm to play Perdita in *The Winter's Tale*.'

'Is that so, Madam?'

'It's not a bad part.'

'No, Madam.'

'There's something special about this performance though. The King and Queen will be there with the Prince of Wales.'

'That will be a triumph, Madam.'

Mrs Robinson sighed and looked at herself in the mirror on the wall. She always seated herself so that she could comfortably see into it.

'I am not sure, Armistead.'

'No, Madam?' The cool raising of very well marked brows matched the voice. Armistead was merely respectfully polite to a mistress who wished to confide in her.

'I should never have been a play actress. It is hardly becoming to a lady.'

'No, Madam.'

Mrs Robinson looked surprised. She had expected contradiction.

'Somewhat higher than a lady's maid,' said Mrs Robinson, a little tartly.

'Certainly, Madam.'

'And several of my friends have noticed you, Armistead. They say you look too good for a lady's maid.'

'Then, Madam, that makes two of us.'

Mrs Robinson was a little startled. But then Armistead did startle her now and then. But what an excellent servant she was! Always so discreet! Besides, she could not concern herself with Armistead now. She had Perdita to think of.

The Prince's servants had prepared him for his visit to the theatre and very handsome he looked in blue velvet trimmed with gold embroidery. He was particularly delighted by the diamond buckles on his shoes. All the same he must go with his parents and this in itself was an indication of his position. His father had commanded that there should be a royal visit to the theatre, had chosen the play and selected the date.

What fun it would have been to have strolled into the theatre with his chosen companions: to have gone to see a witty comedy such as *The School for Scandal*. Instead it was to be *The Winter's Tale*. He did not share his father's opinion of Shakespeare, but he would have liked to see a racy comedy of manners all the same, and the fact that his father had chosen the play immediately made him long for something else.

He turned to his equerry Colonel Lake and said: 'I am ready. Let's go.'

Together they went to the King's apartments where his mother received him. Her eyes lit up at the sight of him. This gorgeous glittering creature, her son! She could never see him without recalling the wax image at which she had gazed so often and so fondly. Dear handsome George! In spite of his wildness and all the trouble he caused them he would always be her favourite.

'You look . . . splendid,' she whispered.

'Thank you, Madam.' He wished he could have said the same for her. Pregnant as usual, she resembled a barrel; her face was sallow and she looked old. He thought of Mary Hamilton's rosy face.

Ah, Mary, Mary, I would rather be in my room at the Dower House writing to you than going to the theatre. In one of his pockets he carried the lock of her hair. '*Toujours aimée*,' he thought. Yes, Mary forever. A pure love. If he could have married her that would have been wonderful, but since they could not marry she was right of course to keep their love pure.

The King was ready to leave.

'Ah.' His anxious eyes were on his son. Not so many scandals now, he thought. Settling down, aware of his responsibilities. He could even look with approval on the Prince. He was a handsome fellow, all said and done; and the people liked a handsome fellow. If he would behave reasonably, he would do very well.

People cheered the royal cavalcade as it passed through the streets to Drury Lane. The news that there was to be a command performance at the Lane had been circulating for days and since the Prince was to be present, this won public approval.

At the theatre Mr Sheridan greeted them. The Prince was interested in Mr Sheridan. He had heard talk of what an amusing fellow he was–one of the most witty in London; and he certainly liked the look of him, and subtly Mr Sheridan managed to show that, honoured as he was to receive a royal visit, it was the presence of the Prince of Wales which gave him particular pleasure.

He conducted the King and Queen to their box and the Prince to his.

The theatre was crowded and every eye it seemed was turned not on the royal box but on that one which jutted out over the stage and in which sat the glittering handsome Prince of Wales with his two attendants, Colonel Lake and Mr Legge.

The curtain went up and the play began.

The Prince was startled. He could not believe his eyes. There on the stage was the most enchanting creature he had ever set eyes on. He could scarcely believe that she was real. He could not take his eyes from her. What a figure! It was perfection! Those eyes. Had there ever been such eyes? That dark hair . . . those beautiful teeth, the softly smiling mouth. This was not a woman. This was a goddess.

'Gad,' murmured the Prince. 'The most perfect creature I ever saw in my life. This is perfection. This is beauty. She is a goddess. What charm! What grace! What acting! Stab me–but I would not have missed this for the world.'

He was leaning over the side of the box and Perdita was close to him. She could not help but be aware of him. Beside her was Prince Florizel–but she was far more conscious of the Prince in the box than the one on the stage.

It was as though she spoke to him and not to Florizel. It was as though he were down there on that stage . . . She was his Perdita; he was her Florizel.

He was in a daze of delight. He knew now that he had never been in love before. He would never be in love like this again . . . except of course that he would be in love with Perdita until he died.

When her presence on the stage was not needed, the play had no interest for him, but actresses waited in the wings for their cue and they often contrived to stand where they could be seen by those who had boxes overhanging the stage. So even when she was not playing, he did not lose sight of her, for she stood opposite his box where he might have a full view of her.

It was the custom in the theatre for young men to step up on to the stage while the play was in progress, and make comments on the performance or slip into the wings to exchange a little conversation and perhaps make assignations with the actresses. It was unlikely that anyone would criticize the play while the King was present, but Lord Malden, who greatly admired Mrs Robinson, could not resist the temptation to mount the stage and slip into the wings.

Malden, a handsome twenty-two–one year older than Mary Robinson–magnificently attired in pink satin and silver, with pink heels on his shoes to match the colour of his coat–was completely visible to the Prince as he chatted with the actress and young George could scarcely bear to sit in his box and see the young viscount in that place where he, above all others, longed to be.

Malden, bewildered by her beauty, was unaware of the jealousy he was arousing, but Mary was fully aware of it and delighted by it. One of the actors had said to her in the Green Room before the performance had started: 'By Jove, Mrs Robinson, you look more handsome than ever. You will surely make a conquest of the Prince tonight.' And when he had spoken those words and she had caught a glimpse of her reflection, when she realized that it was true, that never before had she looked so beautiful, she had begun to consider what a conquest of the Prince of Wales might mean and the prospect seemed very alluring.

And sure enough there he was, beside himself with jealousy, leaning over the side of the box, paying no attention to the players on the stage, his eyes on her and Malden in the wings while he muttered to his equerries about Malden's great good fortune.

As all eyes were on the Prince, most members of the audience were well aware of what was happening. The King and Queen, however, could not see their son and they were unconscious of his behaviour; what they did realize was the pleasant mood of the audience and the King was congratulating himself that it was a very loyal company.

Perdita came on to play her scene with Florizel and the audience broke into frantic applause, in which the Prince joined, and when she raised her eyes to his box and smiled he was in transports of delight.

'What a night, what a play, what a goddess!' he murmured. 'What beauty! What Art!' This was said so that she could hear and she blushed becomingly, which delighted him still further.

He could scarcely restrain himself. He wanted to leap on to the stage, to thrust Florizel aside, to cry: 'I am your Florizel from now on–as long as I live.'

When the play was over and the players assembled for the applause, the Prince leaned forward. Perdita lifted her eyes to his and smiled; he inclined his head twice and everything he felt for her was in his eyes.

But it was time to leave the theatre. He was in an agony of despair. What was happening back stage? He imagined amorous gallants likew Malden storming her dressing room, daring to approach her, talking to her, paying compliments. It was unendurable.

His equerries were waiting. The King was growing impatient. He scowled. He–the Prince of Wales–was not free. He must go home with Papa and Mamma like some schoolboy.

He *must* have his independence. It was never so important as now that he had found Perdita, sweet Perdita!

But wait, he thought. I may not see her tonight, but there is tomorrow. And I shall never forget this night.

He spent a restless night. He dreamed of her; he longed for her.

It was no use trying to think of Mary Hamilton. What a child he had been to have imagined that was love. A *pure* love. He laughed. He had grown up tonight, when he had fallen in love with Mary Robinson. He was going to waste no time in letting her know of his devotion.

He was still fond of Mary Hamilton, but this was different; this was real love such as he had never known before.

He would not completely neglect poor Mary. He would still write to her because writing to Mary had become a habit with him. She was after all his dear sister and he her brother.

He could see nothing but Perdita . . . talking in the wings with Malden–pink satin jacket and pink heels! he thought disparagingly, but the rogue had looked handsome and *he* was not treated like a schoolboy–Perdita acting a love scene with the actor who had played Florizel.

Oh, beautiful Mrs Robinson, I am a *real* prince. I am your Florizel.

It was impossible to sleep, obsessed as he was by such emotion. So he did what he had done frequently when he needed to be soothed; he wrote to Mary Hamilton. He told her of his visit to the theatre and all that had happened there, that on this night he had discovered a goddess. What a comfort for a brother to write to his dear sister.

'*Adieu, adieu, toujours chère*,' he wrote. And added for the sheer thrill of writing that name: 'Oh, Mrs Robinson.'

Such a tumultuous success must be celebrated and, anticipating it, Mary Robinson had invited a few friends to supper at her house near Covent Garden.

Lord Malden, who was at her side as soon as the curtain had fallen and the royal party had left, begged to be allowed to be her escort, and knowing of his close association with the Prince of Wales graciously she accepted this.

Sheridan was of the party. He was flushed with triumph. The evening had been as successful as the first night of *The School for Scandal*, and he had to acknowledge the part Mrs Robinson had played in that success.

It was a gay company which assembled in her drawing room. Mrs Armistead, hovering in the background, never obtruding, noticed a new face among the guests.

We are rising in the world, she thought. Not only Lord Malden but Mr Charles James Fox himself. Who knows where this might end.

And she was elated, seeing in her mistress's success her own; for Mrs Armistead knew that she was too handsome, and more important still, too clever, to remain a lady's maid all her life.

Lord Malden whispered to Mrs Robinson: 'I never saw His Highness so enchanted before, Mistress Perdita.'

And Mrs Robinson flushed and said he was very young, the dear Prince, and so handsome that she could scarcely believe it was possible.

Everyone was talking of the Prince, how different he was from his father; how elegant, how graceful, how gracious. An Englishman, nothing of the dull German about him.

He was no longer a boy either. They could not keep him in leading strings much longer. And when he attained his majority he would be the most powerful young man in the country.

Mr Fox was determined to ingratiate himself with the beautiful actress and she was wary of him. She was deeply conscious of his reputation with women; and had no intention of offering him any encouragement–particularly now the Prince had made his interest so clear. It was a pleasant compliment, of course, that the great statesman should visit her house; it meant that everyone of importance would be clamouring for an invitation; especially now that the Prince had noticed her.

Mrs Robinson felt intoxicated with success and the excitement of the prospect before her.

'You have won on all sides,' whispered Mr Fox. 'The Queen thought your performance very fine. As for the Prince . . .' He laughed aloud. 'He gave the whole house no doubt of *his* feelings. He could not take his eyes from you. I congratulate you on making the greatest conquest in the world.'

'You are flattering me, Mr Fox. I daresay he was merely carried away by the play.'

'Carried away by so much beauty, Madam. And it would not be possible to flatter you, for whatever hyperbole one employed one could not praise you more than you deserve. I shall now give a toast to the whole company.'

Mr Fox had risen and raised his glass. All were silent, listening.

'I give you the Prince–and the beauty and genius he has tonight had the wit to admire. Ladies and Gentlemen: the Prince and the fair Perdita.'

The Reflections of Perdita

When the guests had gone and Mrs Armistead was helping Perdita to bed she lingered over the night toilette longer than was necessary and Perdita did not deter her. It was pleasant to talk with someone–even a lady's maid.

'Madam's success was complete,' said Mrs Armistead, helping her mistress into her nightgown. 'That much I gathered from the remarks I could not help overhearing from the noble company.'

'Yes, Armistead, the Prince quite clearly enjoyed the play.'

'And admired Madam.'

Perdita laughed lightly. 'He is a very young man.'

'And a prince, Madam.'

'As you say, Armistead, a prince.'

'And the company tonight, Madam . . . it was more brilliant than we usually entertain.'

'It was a special occasion.'

'Madam will no doubt wish to hire a butler if er . . . if we are frequently to have such noble guests.'

Perdita drew her brows together. She had her commitments. A mother, a child and the ever demanding Mr Robinson who had to be paid to be kept in the background. Her clothes were a vast expense, but necessary, of course, to her profession. A woman with her reputation for beauty must never be seen in public except in the most becoming garments–and these were apt to be the most expensive. But Armistead was right. She would need to hire a butler as well as the footman. If one mingled in high society one must follow their customs. It would never do for them to regard her merely as a play actress. Every moment she must be on her guard that no one should forget she was a lady.

'I will consider this, Armistead. I think you may be right.'

Mrs Armistead lowered her eyes and smiled discreetly. She was looking into the future no less than her mistress.

'Thank you, Armistead.' It was dismissal. And Mrs Armistead went to her own room where she looked at her face in her mirror, compared it with that of her mistress, and remembered the glance that Mr Fox had sent her way. He was a very discerning man. It might be possible that he recognized a clever woman when he saw one, even if she was dressed as a lady's maid.

How could one sleep on such a night? Perdita asked herself. From now on she would think of herself as Perdita because Perdita was a princess–of the rank to match that of a prince.

This was surely the most significant night of her life and all sorts of glittering prospects were presenting themselves to her.

The Prince was undoubtedly more than ordinarily enamoured. He was young and impressionable and very romantic. That was what made him so enchanting and the situation so alluring.

She had heard rumours of palace scandals. Quite clearly he was interested in women, but from now on he must be interested in one woman only and to such an extent that he was ready to go to any lengths for her sake.

Delicious thoughts came into her mind. Impossible, she cried. But why? Suppose she insisted on marriage. Hadn't the Duke of Cumberland married the Luttrell woman without the King's consent? But she was of noble family. And so am I, cried Perdita angrily. But what was the use of proclaiming it. She had become convinced that she was the daughter of Lord Northington. Otherwise why should she have been taken to visit him when she was a child? But of course it was the wrong side of the blanket and she had had to own Mr Darby as her father. Well, Cumberland had married without the King's consent–and although the lady was not received at Court she was married to the Duke and was a royal Duchess. The Duke of Gloucester had also married without the King's consent–and Lady Waldegrave was illegitimate . . . and, it was whispered, a milliner's daughter–yet that had not prevented her from becoming a royal Duchess either.

So . . . what of Mary Robinson? What of Perdita?

There was the Royal Marriage Bill which had been brought in not so long ago. And this was the Prince of Wales, the future King. Even Perdita did not believe she could become the Queen of England. Perhaps a morganatic marriage was the answer. She would be the Princess in the beautiful house he would provide for her and to it would come all the most noble and the most brilliant members of London society. And the Prince would adore her; they would have three butlers and six footmen and none of them would be hired!

It was a wonderful dream. It would not be the first time an actress had enslaved a monarch. The Prince was not that yet, but it would come. There had been Nell Gwyn who had enchanted Charles II and had kept her place in his affections from the moment he saw her until he died. Well, if she could not be the wife of the Prince–apart from his station there was also Mr Robinson, whom she had temporarily forgotten–she would be his cherished and respected mistress, for everyone knew that to be the mistress of a Prince or a King was no disgrace. It was an honour. It would bring the *ton* flocking to her doors; it would mean that the utmost respect was paid to her wherever she went. And her case would be different from that of Nell Gwyn, whom everyone knew was not a lady.

Luxurious thoughts. Was she wise to indulge in them after such a short meeting? Yes, she was certain of it. What a meeting! And everyone had declared that they had never seen the Prince so enamoured. Yes, this was certainly a beginning–from here she would go forward; she would forget everything that had happened to her before this night–all the doubts and fears, the horrors of existence with Mr Robinson, the great struggle which had brought her to where she was. Mary Robinson was finished; from her ashes had risen the fair Perdita.

But having started to think of the past she could not stop, and scenes which she would rather have forgotten kept coming into her mind, and she saw herself little Mary Darby going daily to school in Bristol and waiting for the return from the whaler on which he was employed, of the man who accepted her as his daughter.

From the first she had given herself airs. Perhaps she had been taught to. Her mother had been very proud of her, very anxious that she should be 'a lady'.

Echoes of the over-refined voice: 'Mary, sit up straight. Don't slouch in your chair. Is that the way a *lady* would sit?' 'Now, Mary, go and wash your hands. Ladies *always* have clean hands.'

That had presented no difficulties. She had been very ready to sit up straight, wash her hands, do anything that a lady would do; for as long as she could remember Mary Darby had been determined to *be* a lady. She had known instinctively whether a dress required a blue or a red sash; she moved with grace; she dreamed fantastic dreams in which her father, some noble lord, came and claimed her and carried her away to his mansion and perhaps to Court. She had heard stories of the royal family, and it was all vitally interesting to her; she had longed to go to London and perhaps catch a glimpse of royalty and the great.

She was a romantic dreamer. She would build up legends about herself; it was inconceivable that she could be the fruit of a union between a Bristol whaler and his wife. Her mother was inclined to foster this belief and now and then gave out dark hints, and when Mary was taken to visit Lord

Northington who showed a great interest in her, she was certain that he was her father.

Her mother she accepted, and although she had three brothers–obviously the whaler's children–it was to Mary that Mrs Darby gave her attention. And small wonder, for Mary was very young when it became obvious that she was going to be a beauty and Mrs Darby was proud of her daughter.

The boys were of small account. Mrs Darby spent a great deal of her money on dresses for Mary; and when she visited friends Mary would sing or dance for the company, for she had a sweet singing voice and a natural grace, and if these were not up to professional standards, even as a child Mary had that quality which made people enjoy looking at her.

'You'll have a great future, Mary,' prophesied Mrs Darby; and Mary would sit and daydream about Lord Northington who, alas, made no effort to claim her.

The family fell on hard times. The whaler went off with another woman and they heard that he had gone to America; he left his family unprovided for, but Mrs Darby was resourceful; she was connected with the philosopher Locke and she was very proud of this, and from her family came a little financial help without which they could not have managed.

But they could not go on living on their relatives indefinitely and one day when Mary came home from school Mrs Darby told her that something would have to be done.

Mary was downcast. She smoothed the muslin of her dress–so beautifully white and laundered. She had a picture of them begging in the streets. One could not beg in a muslin dress; one would have to wear something ragged and dirty. She would rather be dead, she decided. She would never suffer the humiliation.

'I could run a school as well as the Mores,' went on Mrs Darby, for Mary's teachers were the sisters of Hannah More. 'Why not? I'm as well educated. And you could help me and learn at the same time.'

To teach children was not Mary's idea of a career. It was preferable to begging in the streets it was true, but she could feel no enthusiasm for it.

Then her mother said: 'Not in Bristol, of course, where we are known. People would never come to us. We should have to start afresh somewhere.'

'Where?' asked Mary.

The reply enchanted her. 'London, I think.'

London! Chelsea in fact. She could see the school clearly now. There were never enough pupils, but they had not made a bad job of it. Her mother proved to be an excellent teacher–as for herself . . . no one would have guessed she was only thirteen years of age. She looked sixteen . . . possibly seventeen; she already had a well-developed figure and her face was growing more beautiful with every day.

Then her father came home. He had tired of his mistress and thought he would spend a little time with his family. With him came a captain in the navy who promptly did what men were to do from then onwards, fell in love with Mary. She shuddered to remember her innocence. What had she been taught of life and what time had she had to learn! She was thirteen and a half. She had perhaps been a little attracted by the captain. She could not remember very clearly now; and all her memories were rose tinted so she saw rather as she would like it to have happened than as it had.

His embraces! His compliments! So rare then, so commonplace now. His talk of marriage and the grand life they would have. He had known how to tempt Mary, and he had almost succeeded in seducing her. Not quite, she insisted, and shut her eyes tightly so that she could not remember too clearly. Then it had been discovered that he was already married, that he had told her lies, had no intention of marrying her as he promised to do, and his one goal was the seduction of this tender maiden.

'A fortunate escape,' murmured Perdita. 'Oh, what a fortunate escape!'

Mr Darby, after having left his wife and family to fend for themselves, suddenly decided to be righteously indignant because they had done so. He would not have his wife and daughter working, so the school, which had begun to be fairly prosperous, was closed and Mary was sent to a school in Chelsea which was run by a Mrs Lorrington. This lady was fond of the bottle, but when she was not under its influence was a very good teacher and she took an immediate interest in the strikingly lovely young girl who was so eager to learn.

At Mrs Lorrington's Mary worked hard, received encouragement and learned fast; not only did she work at her lessons, but in deportment and elocution, for both of which she had a natural flair.

Her mother watched her development with pride and the utmost interest. Mr Darby, too, was interested in his daughter and, with a little prompting from his wife, agreed that she should go to Mrs Hervey's Finishing Academy at Oxford House in Marylebone. And there she had met . . . what was the name of the man? He in himself was of little importance to her, except for the fact that he was the ballet master at Covent Garden and had introduced her to David Garrick. Hussey! That was his name. He had taught dancing at Mrs Hervey's school and had immediately singled her out as his most promising pupil.

She remembered the day he had brought in Mr Garrick. A somewhat irascible old man he had seemed to her, although she had been overawed by his fame. Very sombrely dressed in brown he did not look in the least like any of the great romantic roles he had played in the past. He had been running Drury Lane then, for it was just before Sheridan had bought his share in it. He had grunted at her and made her recite and sing and dance and then he had walked away as though disgusted with her. She had felt so depressed that she had gone home and wept and her mother had been very angry that Mr Garrick should have failed to appreciate her daughter.

But the next day Mr Hussey had called her aside from the other pupils and told her she could be a very fortunate girl if she was prepared to work hard because Mr Garrick–although he found her raw and in great need of tuition–thought that there might be a small talent in her and he was prepared to give her a chance.

What a different story she had to take home on that day. But Mrs Darby was immediately thrown into a fluster. The theatre! But was it the profession for a lady? She was not at all sure. She was in a terrible dilemma. Mr Darby had disappeared again, having gone to America, and before he had gone, so impressed was he by the beauty of Mary which was growing more and more obvious every day that he had threatened Mrs Darby with dire punishment if any ill should befall her.

'I do not think ladies become play actresses,' she reiterated.

'But what should I become, Mother? What *can* I become? Should I teach in school?'

'No, that is no good either. Oh dear. With looks such as yours . . .'

'Mamma,' implored Mary, 'we must be practical. Some actresses have done very well. If one is clever . . .'

'You are not yet sixteen. I should die of fear every time you went to the theatre. You are too young.'

'One must begin. It is really a great stroke of good fortune. Mr Hussey tells me that Mr Garrick said I might be trained to play Cordelia to his Lear.'

'How I wish I knew what to do.'

And then Thomas Robinson appeared. Perdita did not wish to think of Thomas Robinson. How much happier she would have been if she had never heard his name. But at the time her mother had rejoiced in that young man because he seemed to provide the soothing answer to her fears.

Marriage was the answer–marriage to a man with good prospects, a man who would provide for Mary, give her a good establishment, servants and keep her in comfort for the rest of her life. Then this dream of theatrical fame could be thrust aside without regret.

And Thomas Robinson would provide these.

Her mother had heard of Thomas Robinson through an attorney whom she had once consulted, a Mr Wayman. He assured her that Thomas Robinson was a man with prospects. Although he worked in a solicitor's office, he was no ordinary clerk, and had excellent prospects. His father, Mrs Darby was assured, was a Welsh nobleman who had sent his son to London because he believed it would be good for him to have something to do. In due course he would inherit a vast estate in Wales and maintain a large establishment in London.

Mrs Darby's eyes glowed at the thought. It was exactly what she would have chosen for her daughter. As the wife of rich Mr Robinson there would be no need for her to show off her beauty every night on a stage and have people make all sorts of proposals to her.

The first thing was to arrange a meeting with Mr Robinson, which the obliging attorney was prepared to do.

And Perdita? How had she felt? She liked to think now that she had viewed the prospect with horror, that she had flung herself on to her knees and implored her mother to allow her to take the more honourable line and play for Mr Garrick. She liked to picture herself weeping stormily, declaring dramatically that she preferred to sell her talents rather than herself.

And over the span of years . . . it was not really so many yet . . . she had forgotten so much; she had coloured here, tinted there, and even she was not quite sure how it happened. Yet even she could not sketch in pretty pictures of what followed.

She saw the meeting at the Star and Garter at Greenwich. She remembered the dress so well. That was the one aspect which remained clear to her in every detail. It was more pleasant to think of the dress–an evening dress, long and flowing, of pale blue lustring; and a big chip straw hat swathed with the same material as her dress.

Thomas Robinson had taken one look at her and was in no doubt. He was conscious of the many eyes turned in their direction–all in homage to the young girl's beauty. Endless possibilities, thought Thomas Robinson, whose greatest ambition was, she had quickly discovered, to live in luxury with the smallest possible personal effort. Through the rich clients who came to his office and a knowledge of the difficulties in which they became entangled he saw a way in which this way of life might be accomplished through a wife of such extraordinary beauty.

So he was eager for the marriage. He was chivalrous and attentive, not only to Mary but to her mother. He visited their home; he made casual references to the family estate in Wales; he talked of running an establishment in London and the names of certain well-known noblemen were scattered lightly throughout his conversation until Mrs Darby was all impatience for the wedding, and when Mr Robinson suggested it should take place immediately, she agreed with alacrity.

It was an April day–five years ago. Was it only five years? Perdita asked herself. Could one live through a lifetime of misery, despair and horrific adventure in such a short time? It was a wonder that she had come through with her beauty unscathed–and in fact more dazzling than ever.

St Martin's Church–and Mr Robinson looking elegant in clothes for which she later discovered he had not paid–a presentable bridegroom, she had thought then; and knowing little of the obligations of marriage she had not been unduly downcast.

And so she had become Mrs Robinson.

Before the wedding he had explained that his father would have to be *prepared* for his marriage. 'Of course once he *sees* Mary he will be reconciled . . . enchanted as everyone must be. But just at first we had better not set up house together.'

How gullible they had been. It had all seemed so plausible. After all, the heirs of vast estate did not marry penniless girls without some obstacles being raised by their parents. So Mary would continue to live for a while in her mother's house in Great Queen Street and he would spend his nights there, keeping on his lodgings a few streets away. These humble lodgings were explained by the story that his father wished him to be independent for a short period, and he was proving that he could stand on his own feet and as soon as possible he proposed to go to Wales to inform his father of what had happened.

So during those weeks Mary had merely to receive him in her own bed in her mother's house each night, which was no great pleasure to her. She was by no means sexually avid, preferring–now as then–romantic dalliance to consummation, and she quickly discovered that Mr Robinson's habits in the bedchamber were far from romantic.

Perhaps she had begun to doubt him before her mother had. Perhaps some instinct warned her that this was not the way in which a gentleman behaved. Disillusionment, however, quickly set in. There was the discovery that Mr Robinson's prospects were non-existent. He was soon proved to be a liar, being but the bastard son of a Welsh farmer who had no intention of leaving him even his small farm; all Mr Robinson possessed was his salary as a clerk and it was for this reason that he had been unable to set up an establishment for Mary; and until he could raise money through moneylenders to begin his projects, it suited him that she should continue to live with her mother.

The truth gradually dawned on mother and daughter, but when they realized the trap into which they had fallen they were, after the first shock, philosophical.

They had blundered terribly, but they must now make the best of it.

Perdita closed her eyes now as though by so doing she could shut out the memories of the next two years–the shameful memories! She put her hands over her face. 'I was so young,' she kept repeating to herself. Better to forget those years before she became an actress. She had hated the life. It was . . .

she shivered, besmirching. Even so she could not shut out memories of the joy with which she had contemplated a certain new velvet gown, the pleasure in an exquisitely quilted petticoat, or a hat trimmed with feathers or ribbons. It had given her great pleasure to study the reflection of herself in these garments–which would never have come her way but for the life they led. Whenever she went out people looked at her–so many men showed admiration, so many women envy. This was the tribute to her beauty and it was the knowledge of her beauty which maintained her through all her disasters.

Mr Robinson had rented a house in Hatton Garden and there had 'entertained'. This meant bringing gentlemen to the place and introducing them to his wife. For this privilege he was able to mix in a noble but extremely rakish society, and because of these friendships was given credit by various tradesmen. Mrs Darby was allowed to come and live with them to save employing more than one servant and running two establishments. Mr Robinson had no need now to act so he appeared in his true character–a lecherous man without principles, aping the nobility to which like his wife, he longed to belong.

And for a year or so they lived on the edge of this society. Men like the libertine Lord Lyttelton–something of a politician, artist and poet, was a constant visitor, his object being the seduction of Mrs Robinson. Another visitor was the notorious rake George Robert Fitzgerald, known as Fighting Fitzgerald, whose object had naturally been the same as that of Lord Lyttelton.

Because of his beautiful wife these men were ready to treat Mr Robinson as an equal which meant that they allowed him to accompany them to gaming clubs and brothels. Mr Robinson had very soon betrayed himself as an unfaithful husband–a fact which had not altogether dismayed his wife since it prevented his pressing his attentions on her too frequently, although she deplored the fact that he slept with their slut of a maid.

That had been a curious year or so . . . when they had lived on the edge of society and Mr Robinson had tried to make a high class prostitute of her. She would never forget the occasion when George Robert Fitzgerald had tried to abduct her in Vauxhall Gardens. She had resisted him and Mr Robinson had appeared which put an end to the adventure because the last thing Mr Robinson wanted was to lose his wife.

Such a life could not go on. Her husband must have realized that. But he seemed not to be able to think beyond each day. Everything began to go wrong; she became pregnant; the creditors began to threaten; Thomas Robinson's luck at the tables ran out.

No, she would not think of it. She had found a way out of trouble. By her own efforts she had provided for herself, her mother, her child . . . and the means of shutting Thomas Robinson out of her life. She was not to blame. She liked to see herself as virtuous, noble, unscathed by these humiliating adventures. And it was so . . . if she shut her eyes to certain moments . . . and she had shut her eyes; she had quickly learned the necessary art of doing so.

Then . . . the end of the gay life, waiting for the birth of her child, the fear every time the bills arrived. So many of them . . . and the child on the way. What could they do? The birth of little Maria was some comfort; the child was enchanting and although Mary had discovered that being a mother could never be her whole life, she loved the child. But the inevitable result of such riotous living had caught up with them and Thomas Robinson was sent to the King's Bench Prison for debt.

She accompanied him there with her child and there was no doubt that he was a chastened man, although she guessed that if he ever were released he would act in the same way as he had before. He was weak and unprincipled; and it was the unhappiest day in her life when she had married him.

When she heard of the success of Richard Sheridan's *The Rivals* she thought of the chance she had had to become an actress for which many ambitious young women would have given a great deal–and which she had foolishly thrown away. For what? Marriage with a rogue who had attempted to thrust her into a life of sin–and finally a debtors' prison.

The misery around her filled her with horror; it was no use now pining for fine clothes, but there was one comfort left to her: her pen. She discovered then that in times of stress it could give her a great deal. She cared for her child and grew closer to it, and she wrote poetry.

It suddenly occurred to her that if she could publish this poetry, if people would buy it this might be a source of income. It would not provide the means to live the grand life which she had once believed Mr Robinson would provide for her, but it would at least be dignified. She immediately built up a picture of the salon she would have. She would be the beautiful poetess. With this in mind she wrote feverishly and very soon she had enough poems to make a book. Now she needed a patron; she would not go to a man–she had had enough of men for a while–and she did not want it said that she was patronized for her beauty. She had heard of Georgiana, Duchess of Devonshire, leader of fashion, lover of the arts.

Was it possible to obtain an introduction?

This presented some difficulties, but not insuperable ones. There were some admirers from that fantastic year who would not be averse to helping her now that she had fallen on hard times. She saw the way out of her troubles. When the introduction was made the Duchess was not only impressed by the poems but by the beauty of the poetess, and when the noble lady heard that she was living with her husband in a debtors' prison and had one young daughter she determined to help such a deserving young woman out of her predicament. So the Duchess not only found a publisher for the poems but brought about the release of the Robinsons.

Free! She remembered the first day when she came out of the prison to find her mother, who had managed to keep the home going, was waiting for her.

There was no need now to placate Mr Robinson, and both women showed their contempt for him. He had her permission, his wife told him, to sleep with any servant girl he cared for; his visits to brothels were no concern of hers; all she asked was that he made no demands upon her, and that was something she would insist upon.

Mr Robinson replied that he was not at all sure of that; but he had to remember that his wife had brought about his release from prison and that she was not the pretty puppet he had imagined her to be.

She and her mother ignored him, although he inhabited the house. He had gone back to his clerking, but it was not easy to live on his salary.

'I want independence from him,' said Mary to her mother. 'I should like to walk out of this house and never have to see him again.'

That, Mrs Darby had to admit, would be a desirable state of affairs. But how could it be achieved?

'I shall never make enough money from writing poetry,' said Mary. 'What a fool I was to reject the offer Mr Garrick made to me.'

'You'll never have another like it,' sighed her mother sadly; the guilt was hers, she admitted freely. She should have known better. One could not expect a fourteen-year-old girl to recognize a rogue . . . but she was a woman and a mother! What would her husband think when he came home. She remembered his threats before his departure! But he did not come home and Mary was right. The need to find money was urgent, for if they did not they would be back in that prison which they had so recently left and they could not expect such opportune deliverance again.

'Why should I not?' demanded Mary suddenly.

'But . . . Mr Garrick would never give you another chance. He'd think you were a fool to have rejected him before.'

'I heard that Mr Sheridan is going to buy him out of Drury Lane and take over Mr Garrick's share in the theatre and that Mr Garrick, now that he is getting old, will retire.'

'But you don't know Mr Sheridan.'

'Not yet,' admitted Mary. 'But why shouldn't I?'

Her success with the Duchess of Devonshire had given her confidence. Why should she not offer her services to Drury Lane? It was a way of life–an exciting way of life; she who was so startlingly beautiful, could dance and sing tolerably well, had had elocution lessons and could recite well–and above all had a strong sense of the dramatic. Surely she was a born actress. She was immediately beginning to believe she was and was already preparing herself to convince Mr Sheridan, and Mr Garrick if need be, of this.

'I see no reason why I should not have another chance,' she told her mother. 'I will seek an introduction to Mr Sheridan.'

'But how?'

'Well, Mr Hussey introduced me to Mr Garrick, did he not? I think Mr Hussey would be inclined to help me.'

And he had been. The ballet master was a little startled when she called on him, but, in the manner of everyone else, completely enslaved by so much beauty.

'A stage career. Why, with looks such as yours you could not fail.'

'If you would do me the favour of introducing me to Mr Sheridan . . .'

'It is Mr Sheridan who will be favoured.'

And so to the meeting which was to change her life and to bring her to this night when she could dream of dazzling possibilities which did not seem absurdly out of her grasp.

The Green Room at the theatre. She could see it so clearly. Was she not familiar with every aspect of it? But then it had been new to her and there was the handsome Mr Sheridan taking her hand, kissing it and being so charming because she was so beautiful.

So she wanted to be an actress?

Mr Garrick himself, she told him, had once offered her a chance.

'And you didn't take it?'

'I married instead.'

'The old man will never forgive you that. In offering you a chance to act with him he thought he was giving you the keys to heaven. And you chose . . . marriage.'

'Unhappily.'

Mr Sheridan was alert. She knew now, because he had told her, that all the time he was weighing her up, and that almost at once he made up his mind that he wanted her . . . for Drury Lane and himself.

No need now to hasten over her memories, to close her eyes and glide over the thin ice which could break suddenly and plunge her into horrid memory. From now on it was success.

At the theatre Mr Sheridan presented her to Mr Garrick. He had aged since she had last seen him but he remembered her well.

'I offered you a chance in the theatre and you refused it,' he accused.

'It was madness,' she admitted meekly.

'Madness, folly, stupidity. None of these is a quality that makes a good actress.'

'I know.' She was meek and forlorn; but she knew that he would not have bothered to come and see her if he had not thought her worth a little effort.

'Do you know, young woman, that there are thousands of would-be-actresses who would give twenty years of their lives for the chance you had . . . and threw away.'

'I know it well,' she said. 'It was the biggest mistake of my life.'

He turned away from her as though in disgust and said to Sheridan: 'And you want this young woman to play Juliet.'

'At least she'll look the part,' answered Sheridan.

Without glancing at her Garrick muttered: 'Let's hear you. Begin here.

"O Romeo, Romeo! wherefore art thou Romeo?
Deny thy father and refuse they name . . ."'

She knew it well. How many times since Sheridan had suggested she might play Juliet had she enacted the balcony scene before her mirror, seeing herself in some diaphanous garment leaning over the balustrade in moonlight, picturing the gasp of admiration from the audience when she appeared.

And as she began to say the words she was on that stage; she was the young girl in love for the first time.

' "Or, if thy wilt not, be but sworn my love,
And I'll no longer be a Capulet."'

And the old man beside her was suddenly transformed. The most beautiful voice that had been heard in the theatre for years–perhaps the most beautiful ever–was answering her:

' "Shall I hear more, or shall I speak at this?"'

She went on:

' "Tis but thy name that is my enemy . . ."'

Perhaps she was not word perfect, but she was over-dramatic; she would need a great deal of coaching, but the fire was there. He carried her through the scene and then she heard him murmur in that glorious voice of his:

' " . . . all this is but a dream,
Too flattering-sweet to be substantial." '

She knew that she must succeed; that she wanted more than anything to play Juliet and to play her as she had never been played before.

Romeo, as if by magic, had become Mr Garrick–no longer the passionate and romantic lover, but a carping old man.

He said nothing and had started to walk away.

Sheridan walked after him while Mary stood trembling.

'Well?' said Sheridan.

Mr Garrick stood still and seemed to consider. Mary thought he was not going to answer.

She ran to him. 'If you will give me a chance I will work, I will study . . . I will learn . . .'

'You'll need to,' said Mr Garrick; and walked out of the room.

But that was Mr Garrick's way. He was not unimpressed; and although she was a mere novice he had discovered that sense of drama in her character without which he would not have considered her. But to Sheridan's delight and her unbounded joy Mr Garrick said he would coach her himself and this meant that she would make her debut at Drury Lane in the exciting and all important role of Juliet.

Juliet! She would remember that night in every detail. It was worth remembering–even her stage fright just before the curtain rose. She had worn pale pink satin trimmed with crêpe and ornamented with silver and spangles; white feathers were in her hair; and for the tomb scene she had appeared in satin with a veil of transparent gauze; there had been beads about her waist on which a cross hung. She did not have to be told that there had never been a lovelier Juliet. This knowledge had carried her through; she was never unaware of her beautiful image and the very thought of it gave her courage.

She had been eighteen–a few years older than Juliet, but she looked like a child in the early scenes; later in the play when she was in love and loved she matured slightly. Garrick had said this miracle must be subtly conveyed; he had made her *live* Juliet, *be* Juliet, the innocent child and the girl who became a woman overnight. And because the genius of Mr Garrick was such that made all those whom he honoured with his advice determined to please him and win a word of praise for him, she, knowing he was in the audience that night, made up her mind that she would force the old man to admire her.

Oh, the glory of that never-to-be-forgotten night when she faced an audience for the first time! There had been a moment of silence and then an audible gasp from the audience. It was the expected homage to her beauty; and what better foil could there have been than the ageing figure of the old nurse!

'How now, who calls?'

She had been afraid her voice would fail her but there it was high and clear–the voice of Juliet.

She was launched. This was her métier.

What an evening, with the excitement rising higher with every moment. An audience that would not have missed a word she said, that could not take its eyes from her. It was Juliet's night. It was an enchanted night. It was her night of triumph. She could not but be conscious of this. Mr Sheridan had caught her coming off the stage and taking her in his arms had kissed her with reckless passion.

'You're wonderful, Juliet. You're all that I knew you would be.'

And she had laughed and been happy. 'The Happiest night of my life,' she had cried; and he had said: 'It's but a beginning. You will see . . . Juliet.'

And back to play and to sense the excitement in the audience . . . on to the last scene in the tomb . . .

> *'. . . oh happy dagger!*
> *This is thy sheath. There rest and let me die.'*

The great sigh as she fell beside Romeo's body and lay there.

The play went on . . . and she was thinking: This is the end of our troubles. I shall make my fortune. I shall be a great actress. And I owe all this to Mr Garrick and Mr Sheridan . . . and to my own resolution.

> *'For never was a story of more woe*
> *Than this of Juliet and her Romeo.'*

The curtain had come down and the applause was instantaneous.

Up it went and there they all were with herself in the centre smiling, taking the bow.

Flowers were thrown at her feet, exquisitely dressed men were crowding to the front of the stage. Down went the curtains, to howls of protest and up again . . . and there she was alone and the whole of the theatre going wild with joy.

And in the Green Room, later, they had crowded about her. Names she had heard Mr Robinson mention with awe. There had been Lord Malden, friend and equerry of the Prince of Wales, in black velvet trimmed with gold. 'Mrs Robinson, it's an honour to kiss your hand . . .'

His Grace of Cumberland had eyed her with appreciation. The King's own brother! What society she was climbing into! And being paid for it–not falling deeper and deeper into debt.

'His Grace of Cumberland desires to be presented.'

Lecherous eyes examined her. His Grace had never seen a Juliet he so admired. He trusted she would grant him the pleasure of seeing more of her.

Oh no, my lord, she had thought; I must tread warily. You and others will have to learn that even though I am a play actress I am a lady.

Sheridan was watchful of her. He looked upon her as his creation. He had seen her possibilities; he had persuaded Garrick to coach her; she was going to add to his fortune and his personal happiness.

'Mrs Robinson is fatigued, gentlemen. I know you will wish her to have the rest she so well deserves.'

And so home to the house in Great Queen Street where she had sat with her mother talking of that night and the triumphs to come.

They *had* come, so quickly and in such number, but she would never again know the excitement of that first night. The theatre became her life. Her mother took charge of little Maria; Mr Robinson lived in the house but he had no say in the running of it now. He had to be quiet; he had better keep out of his wife's life or he might ruin her chances which would be of little use to him, for with her salary she was able to pay his card debts and make him a small allowance which she told him scornfully, added to his salary, would have to suffice for him and his mistresses.

Mr Robinson was a subdued man. He had been wise to marry Mary; he had always known it; and now he was proving how right he had been. It was disconcerting to be pushed into the background, but at least she provided him with money and he preferred the kitchen sluts to his lady-like beauty.

'The bad days are behind us,' Mary told her mother.

And so it seemed. With each role she played she improved her acting ability and she grew more and more beautiful. The costumes she wore on the stage delighted her and she gave a great deal of thought to them, and whenever a new play was to be put on playgoers would ask themselves what Mrs Robinson would wear this time. Of one thing they could be certain; it would be unusual and becoming.

She appeared in public places–the Pantheon and the Rotunda, Vauxhall and Ranelagh, always exquisitely gowned, gaped at, stared at, quizzed–the famous Mrs Robinson, dressed as no one had ever dressed before.

Sheridan delighted in her and she in him. She had found him irresistible and she could never forget that he had given her her chance. To him she confided her troubles; he knew how she was plagued by Mr Robinson and the fear of what debts he would accumulate; to him she confided of the horrors she had suffered in the debtors' prison. He knew that that memory would never entirely leave her and being the brilliant playwright that he was, he understood Mary better than she understood herself.

She was a born actress; in fact she acted all the time off stage as well as on. Her life story was one big part in which she was always the wronged or admired but always honest and virtuous heroine. Her motives were always what they should have been, not always what they were. He knew his Mary and she fascinated him. Besides, her beauty was unique. He could not compare it with his own Elizabeth's. Elizabeth's was of the soul. Ah, his saintly Elizabeth! He loved Elizabeth, but he was in love with Mary Robinson and, as he would say, he was not a man to pamper himself with noble sacrifice. She became his mistress. She was coy, feigning reluctance. She felt uneasy about this relationship, she told him, because he had a wife.

And she a husband, he reminded her. 'Which makes us eligible.'

'You jest about a sacred matter.' Dear Mary had little appreciation of humour. But he was enchanted with her faults as well as her virtues.

She had met Elizabeth and that, she had declared, filled her with dismay.

He wondered whether Elizabeth knew. He could not be sure. But Elizabeth had become disillusioned long ago. He would have explained that what he felt for Mary Robinson was a transient emotion. His life was bound up with Elizabeth; he was sure he could have explained it to her had she asked. But she did not. At this time she was obsessed by their baby son, young Thomas; that, her singing, reading plays for him which came into the Lane in hundreds from would-be playwrights, and helping with the accounts. What time had Elizabeth for suspicions?

But perhaps her family would tell her. Her brother Thomas was musical director of Drury Lane and worked closely with its manager. Thomas was a brilliant musician like all the Linley family and had composed the songs for *The Duenna*. Then there was sister Mary, wife of Richard Tickell, who knew almost everything that was going on and was constantly with her sister.

But Elizabeth gave no sign and the affair went on while Mary Robinson rapidly climbed to fame. She and Elizabeth Farren were the leading actresses of the day; when they played people flocked to see them; they were favourites both of the young bucks and the more sober-minded. To the former they were the loveliest girls in Town; to the latter they were ladies. It was the pleasure of both these *ladies* to bring a new refinement to the stage and to show that the theatre could be entertaining without vulgarity.

What days! What triumphs! She remembered her part of Statira in *Alexander the Great* when she had enchanted the house with her Persian draperies of white and blue, her dark hair unpowdered; and she had played Fanny Sterling in *The Clandestine Marriage*, and Lady Anne in *Richard III*. All successes, every one. What a triumph she had scored in *The Relapse* and *All for Love!* and then Viola in *Twelfth Night*. Only one failure and that was not hers. Sheridan had been at his wits' end for a new play and to deceive the playgoers had put on *The Relapse* under the title of *A Trip to Scarborough*. The audience had quickly detected the deception and had immediately expressed their indignation by catcalls and hissing. What a horrible moment–standing there on the stage and for the first time realizing that the audience no longer loved her.

But even that had turned into triumph, for the Duke of Cumberland, who came often to the theatre to ogle her from his box and to see her in the Green Room afterwards, leaned over and shouted to her: 'Don't worry, Mrs Robinson. It's not you they're hissing. It's the play.' Then Sheridan had come to the front and told the audience they would get their money back and a riot was so averted.

Yes, she could look back on three years of success; and now . . . Perdita. In future, she told herself, I shall always think of myself as Perdita.

Incident at Covent Garden

Perdita gazed anxiously at herself in the mirror, but lack of sleep had had no effect on her appearance. Her eyes looked brighter and there was the faintest flush in her usually pale cheeks. Well, although she had not slept she had not been tossing and turning with worry. She had been lying still and relaxed in a haze of contentment and excitement–certain that something miraculous was going to happen while she went over the events which had led up to this day.

Mrs Armistead would soon arrive to help her dress. How wise she had been to set up this separate establishment with her mother and her child not far off so that she could see them frequently, without having them living under the same roof. Of course the pay of an actress was not so great that she could afford many luxuries. Luxury could have been hers had she been prepared to pay for it. The Duke of Rutland had offered her six hundred pounds a year and a smart town house if she would become his mistress. The Duke of Cumberland had promised even greater remuneration. But she had refused them all, explaining to Sheridan: 'What do they think I am? A superior kind of prostitute . . . because I'm an actress?'

Sheridan had helped her write the letters to these noblemen. 'We won't be too severe,' he had told her. 'The theatre can't afford indignant virtue. We'll be a little coy–perhaps hold out hope . . . but not yet . . . not yet . . . This should ensure their regular attendance at the theatre.'

Sherry was a charming rogue. She was ashamed really that she had succumbed to him; but during those early days in the theatre she had needed support. But when she had known Elizabeth . . . Yes, that was how she saw it. It was nothing to do with his refusing her the part of Lady Teazle. It was because of her refinement of feeling over Elizabeth.

The point was that they remained great friends although they were no longer lovers.

Mrs Armistead was at the door–neat and discreet as ever.

'Madam has rested well, I trust?'

'I slept very little, Armistead.'

'It is understandable. What will Madam wear today?'

Perdita was thoughtful. What might happen today? Who could say? She must be prepared. Pink satin. Blue silk?

Mrs Armistead had taken out a white muslin dress trimmed with blue ribbons. It was one of her simplest.

She held it up so that above the dress her own face appeared and it was as thought she were wearing it. What a handsome creature she would be . . . *dressed*! thought Perdita.

'One of Madam's simplest but most becoming,' said Mrs Armistead.

A simple dress for a special occasion. How did she know it would be a special occasion? It was a feeling in her bones perhaps.

'I will wear it, Armistead.'

And strangely enough Mrs Armistead seemed satisfied. As though my triumph were hers, thought Perdita, which in a way, of course, it was. For if I fell on hard times how should I be able to employ her, and if rich people come to my house she might ingratiate herself with some and find herself serving a lady in a very great household. It would be a blow to lose Armistead.

'Armistead, you looked very well when you held the muslin up . . . as though you were wearing it. It would become you.'

'Thank you, Madam.'

'There is that other muslin . . . the one with the lavender coloured buttons. I caught it . . . and there is a little tear in the skirt.'

'I saw it and mended it, Madam.'

Oh, excellent, Armistead! It would be a great loss if she went.

'With a little alteration it could be made to fit you. You may have it.'

'Thank you, Madam.' No show of pleasure. Just a cool thank you. One could never be sure what Armistead was thinking; all one knew was that she was the perfect lady's maid.

As soon as Perdita slipped on the white dress she knew it was right for the occasion. *If* there was a visitor she could play the lady surprised in this dress to perfection. A simple morning gown–and in its simplicity as becoming–perhaps more so in the cold light of morning–than satin and feathers.

She waited for Armistead to put on her powdering wrap, but Armistead said: 'Madam's hair worn loosely about her shoulders *unpowdered* is so becoming.'

Of course; she sat at her dressing table and Armistead dressed her hair. A curl over the left shoulders. How right she was.

Armistead stood back to admire her handiwork and Perdita said: 'Thank you, Armistead. Now pray bring me a dish of chocolate.'

Mrs Armistead scratched lightly on the door. Perdita knew it was a visitor because she had seen the chair arrive.

'A gentleman to see you, Madam.'

'A gentleman, Armistead.' Her heart had begun to beat rapidly. She must calm herself. Could it be . . . Did royalty arrive in a sedan chair? Did it ask humbly to be admitted? She looked down at her hands and went on: 'Is it someone I know, Armistead?'

'Yes, Madam. The gentleman was here last night.'

She hoped she did not betray her disappointment to the watchful Armistead.

'It is my lord Malden, Madam.'

Malden! The young nobleman with whom she had talked in the wings and who had so obviously expressed his admiration for her. He was at least a *friend* of the Prince of Wales.

'Show him in, Armistead.'

Mrs Armistead bowed her head and retired to return in a few minutes and announce: 'My lord Malden, Madam.'

Lord Malden entered the room and it immediately seemed the smaller for his presence–so elegantly was he dressed. His ornamented coat was frogged with gold braid, his wig curled and perfectly powdered, his heels were lavender coloured to match his breeches. He was indeed a dandy.

His eyes were alight with admiration.

'Your humble servant,' he said, and kissed her hand.

'Lord Malden, it is good of you to call on me.'

'Madam, it is angelic of you to receive me.' He coughed a little as though slightly embarrassed. 'I trust, Madam, that you will forgive . . . the intrusion. My er . . . my mission is one . . .'

He looked at her as though he were at a loss for words and she prompted coolly: 'Pray proceed, my lord.'

'It is a mission which I must needs accept . . . having no alternative, as I trust you will believe, Madam.'

'But of course I believe you.'

'And pardon me, Madam.'

'For what, pray?'

'That is what I have to explain.'

'You are intriguing me mightily, my lord. I shall begin to suspect you of I know not what if you do not tell me what *mission* has brought you here.'

He fumbled in the pocket of his coat and brought out a letter.

'I was requested, Madam, to see that this was put into none but your own fair hands.'

She took it. 'Then now, my lord, your mission is completed.'

He was still looking at her rather fearfully and glancing down she saw that 'To Perdita' was written on it.

She opened it; it was brief. Just a few words to Perdita telling of admiration and a desire to see her again and it was signed Florizel.

'Florizel,' she said. 'And who is Florizel?'

'Madam, can you not guess?'

'No,' she retorted. 'Any young gallant might sign himself so. It is not you, I hope, my lord. Did you write this letter?'

'No, I did not.'

'I am surprised that a noble lord should play the part of messenger.'

'Madam, I beg of you do not despise me for doing so.'

'Well, is it not a little undignified to run errands? Why could not the writer of this letter bring it himself? Why should he *send* you.'

'I dared not refuse, Madam. It was a commission from His Royal Highness, the Prince of Wales. He is Florizel.'

She was silent. She was unsure. This was not the manner in which she had expected to be approached. As she had pointed out, Florizel could be anyone. If the Prince of Wales wished to be her friend he could not do so under a cloak of anonymity. Prince Florizel would not do. It must be Prince George.

She handed the letter back to Lord Malden. 'I do not believe it,' she said.

'Madam, I assure you. His Highness brought the letter to me himself. He commanded me to bring it to you.'

'My Lord Malden, there are men in the world who believe that because one is an actress one cannot be a lady. They stoop to all kinds of tricks to entrap an actress. I wish to know the truth. Who wrote this letter?'

'I *am* speaking the truth, Madam. I would not dare tell you that His Royal Highness had written this letter if it were not so. You should not feel insulted. There is no insult intended. His Royal Highness merely expressed the wish that you will give him an opportunity of making your acquaintance. He was greatly affected not only by your beauty but by your acting. He admires acting, the arts, literature. He is besides being a prince a very cultivated gentleman.'

'To meet the Prince of Wales is an honour, I am sure, but . . .'

'You hesitate, Madam? It is indeed an honour that the Prince should seek acquaintance. Will you write a note in reply? It is what His Highness hopes for.'

She hesitated.

'But surely, Madam. You cannot still be suspicious.'

She looked at him sadly. 'My life has made me so, I fear. If this letter was truly written by His Highness pray tell him that I am overwhelmed by the honour he does me. I can say no more than that.'

Lord Malden considered. Such a message delivered as he would deliver it could imply success. He bowed low and left her.

In his apartments at Kew the Prince was eagerly awaiting the return of Malden. With him was Frederick, to whom he was confiding his new passion.

'You have never seen beauty until you have seen her, Fred.'

Frederick replied that he had heard of Mrs Robinson's beauty, for rumour did seep into their quarters in spite of their parents' efforts to keep them unsullied by the world. 'I know she is one of the finest actresses in the theatre and one of the most beautiful women in England.'

'It's true,' cried the Prince ecstatically. 'I cannot wait to embrace her.'

'Will she receive you at her house, do you think? You had better be careful this does not come to our father's ears.'

'You can trust me, Fred.'

'It is a little difficult to get away. What if you were wanted when you were visiting? Remember Harriot Vernon.'

'This is quite different.'

'I know it,' replied Frederick, 'but you *were* wanted when you were meeting her, and it *did* become known and she was dismissed because of it.'

'He could not touch her, Frederick. She is not a member of his Court.'

'But you are, George. You could be *forbidden* to see her.'

George's face flushed with fury. 'It's true,' he cried. 'I'm treated like a child. It will have to stop soon.'

'It will stop soon. When you're eighteen, and that's only a few months away.'

'Yes, then I shall have an establishment of my own. Then I shall be my own master. God speed the day.'

Frederick looked out of the window. 'Malden has just arrived,' he said.

The Prince was beside his brother and was in time to see Malden entering the Palace.

'Now,' cried George, all his ill humour vanishing, 'I shall have her answer.'

'You have no doubt what it will be?'

George tried to look serious, but he could not manage it. Of course she would be ready to fall into his arms. He was the Prince of Wales, young, handsome, popular, the most desirable lover in the country. Mary Hamilton had refused to become his mistress purely on moral grounds. He was well aware that she had difficulty at times in holding out against him.

How different it would be with Perdita.

He was thinking of Florizel on the stage.

> '*. . . but come; our dance, I pray:*
> *Your hand, my Perdita; so turtles pair*
> *That never meant to part . . .*'

But it was her voice that he kept hearing:

> '*. . . like a bank for love to lie and play on . . .*'

How beautiful those words on her lips; what pictures they had conjured up in his mind.

Oh, Perdita, why waste time in love scenes on a stage!

And here was Malden. He strode to him holding out his hand.

'Her letter! Her letter! Where is it?'

'She did not write, Your Highness.'

'Did not write! But you took my letter to her?'

'Yes, Your Highness.'

'And what said she? What said she?'

'She was a little inclined to disbelieve.'

'Disbelieve?'

'That Your Highness had written it.'

'But you told her. . .'

'I told her, but as it was signed Florizel she said she could not be sure.'

'Florizel to Perdita. You assured her?'

'Yes, Your Highness, to the best of my power.'

'And she did not answer the letter?'

'She is no ordinary actress, Your Highness, to come quickly when beckoned.' The Prince's face had grown scarlet and Malden hurried on: 'I think she would wish to be wooed. She is modest, Your Highness, and could not believe she was so honoured. She thought it was some gallant playing a trick.'

'So she wrote no answer.'

'She would not do so.'

The Prince was baffled. Malden said: 'I think if Your Highness wrote again . . . wooed the lady a little, assured her that it was indeed yourself . . .'

'So you think then . . .'

Malden was silent.

He himself had had hopes of the lady, being half in love with her himself. It was a little hard to have to plead another man's cause, even if that man were the Prince of Wales.

Malden went on: 'I think, Your Highness, that Mrs Robinson wishes to imply that she is a lady of high moral character and does not indulge lightly in love affairs.'

The Prince was momentarily exasperated. He had had enough virtue from Mary Hamilton. But almost immediately he was laughing. Why of course. He would not have wished her to give in immediately. She wanted to be wooed. Well, he was capable of doing the wooing. She had had his letter; she had expressed herself honoured . . . if the letter had in truth come from him.

Very well, he would begin the pursuit and in time she would be his.

He was smiling, thinking of future bliss.

Oh, Mrs Robinson!

The King had come to Kew for a little respite. How much simpler life seemed at Kew. He woke early, looked at the clock and, getting out of bed, lighted the fire which had been laid the night before by his servants.

How cold it was! 'Good for the health,' he muttered, for he talked to himself when he was alone. 'Nothing like fresh air, eh?'

He lighted the fire and went back to bed to watch it blaze. Soon the room would be warm enough for him to sit in . . . comfortably.

Lying in bed, he started to worry. Even at Kew he worried. Yet when he was with his ministers he felt capable of controlling them and the affairs of the country; sometimes when he was in the council chamber at St James's he would hear his mother's voice admonishing him: 'George, be a king.'

Yes, he would be a king. He would control them all. Nobody was going to forget who was ruling this country. He would like to see that man Fox banished from the House. There he was . . . popping up . . . always ready to make trouble. His father had been a sly one and so was his son. Sarah's nephew, he thought. And there was Sarah mocking him, laughing at him, as clear in his mind's eye as she had been that summer's morning when he had seen her making hay in the gardens of Holland House as he rode by.

His mind went to Charlotte, perpetually pregnant Charlotte. He would lecture her about her health. Not that she needed the lecture, but he wanted her to know that he was concerned for her. And Octavius, the baby; he was fretful. His nurses said that he cried in the night and wouldn't take his food. He would have to work out a new routine for Octavius.

It was more pleasant thinking of the nursery than state affairs, even though all was not well there. There will always be worries with children, eh, what?

But he must remember that he was the King and he was the last man to shirk his responsibilities. This American affair. If only it could be satisfactorily ended. North wanted to resign, but he would not let North resign. If the Government would stand firm he was sure their troubles would be over. But when had a government made up of ambitious men ever been in unison? Men like Fox . . . 'I hate Fox,' he said aloud. He imagined the fellow–apart from all his political fireworks–was remembering the King's folly over his aunt Sarah. Perhaps Sarah had confided in the fellow. After all, although she was his aunt there was not so much difference in their ages and Sarah had lived at Holland House with her sister, who was Fox's mother. Fox was there . . . to put his mischievous finger in every pie; to laugh and sneer and scatter his wit about so that all wanted to know what Fox's latest quip was.

He remembered Fox at the time of the Royal Marriage Bill which he had felt it urgent to bring in after the disastrous marriages of his brothers Gloucester and Cumberland. Fox had been one of those who had opposed it. 'The Bill to propagate immorality in the descendants of George I,' they had called it. Fox had resigned because of it. 'Good riddance, eh, what?' As if the Bill was not necessary–with the Prince of Wales and young Frederick showing themselves as a couple of young fools with their minds always on women. There'd be disaster from that direction if steps weren't taken. Why even he . . . as a young man . . .

There was Hannah coming out of the past to regard him with mournful and reproachful eyes. But Hannah had never been reproachful. She had been too fond of him. Mournful, yes. She blamed herself. He was but a child, she said, when he had first seen her sitting in the window of her uncle's linen-draper's shop. The follies of youth! And yet at the time they seemed inevitable. But he had lived *respectably* with Hannah . . . as respectably as an irregular union could be. And then for her sake and for the sake of his conscience he had committed that act which had haunted him for the rest of his life. The marriage ceremony . . . that was no true ceremony of course . . . and yet . . .

This was dangerous thinking; this could set the voices chattering in his head even more insistently than thoughts of rebellious colonists, the slyness of Mr Fox, the pleading of Lord North to be released from office.

He guided his thoughts to North–a safer subject. He had always been fond of him; they had played together in the nursery when they were both young children, acted in plays together–for George's father, Frederick Prince of Wales, had been fond of amateur theatricals–and he and North had been so much alike that his father had remarked to North's father that one of their wives must have deceived them and either he or Lord North must be the father of both of them. Now of course they were not so much alike–or George hoped not; North was fat as the King knew he himself would be–for it was a family failing–if he did not take exercise and watch his diet; North had bulging short-sighted eyes which he appeared to be unable to control so that they rolled about aimlessly; he had a tiny nose, but a mouth too small for his tongue, and when he spoke his speech was slurred and he spat unbecomingly. His appearance was almost ridiculous, yet he was a likable man and because they had been friends for so long the King was fond of him. Poor North, he was extravagant and could never live within his means. As Prime Minister, of course, he had great expenses and it had been necessary for the King to help him out of financial difficulties now and then. North on the other hand would come to the King's assistance when he needed money and would prod the Treasury into supplying it. That unfortunate matter of the Grosvenor case . . . Thirteen thousand pounds for those letters Cumberland had written to the woman . . . And now there he was sporting with a different one; the woman with the eyelashes. Mr Fox, who had raged against the Royal Marriage Act; Hannah and Sarah; Elizabeth Pembroke, who did not belong to the past but who was at Court now; she was a woman to whom his attention kept straying; American Colonies; little Octavius who wasn't strong; the Prince of Wales. All these subjects raced round and round in the King's mind like trapped animals in a cage.

'Careful,' said the King aloud, 'Eh, what?'

But how could he stop his thoughts?

Now his mind had switched to the riots which had broken out in Scotland and had been going on all during the year. A protest against the Catholic Relief Bill to which he had given his assent the year before. He had been glad to do it; he felt that people should be free to worship in the way they wished–as long as they worshipped; he had little patience with those atheists and agnostics or whatever they called themselves. People should go to church; they should obey the commandments; but high church, low church . . . that was a matter for individual conscience. But up in Scotland the low church didn't like it at all. 'No Popery,' they shouted. Troublemakers. Mob mostly. Seriously minded people *discussed* their differences. They didn't go about burning people's houses because they thought differently on certain matters. Ever since he was a young man he had believed in religious tolerance. He had been lenient to all denominations. Quakers, for instance. And there he was back to Hannah.

No, no, go away, Hannah. I must not think of you . . . dare not, eh, what?

'Pray God the riots don't spread below the Border,' he said.

Time to get up. Yes, the room was warm now . . . or warmer. He would devote himself to going through the state papers and then he would go to the Queen's apartment to take breakfast with her.

When he arrived there he found the Queen already seated at the table with Madam von Schwellenburg in attendance. The King did not like that woman. He remembered how his mother, when she was alive, had tried to get her dismissed because she felt she had too great an influence on the Queen; but Charlotte had showed herself remarkably stubborn and refused to let the woman go. It was not that she wanted her; it was simply that she clung to the right to choose her own servants. He had decided then that although Charlotte might have some sway over her own household she should have none in political affairs. No, said George. I have seen what havoc women can play in politics. Look at the late King of France, how he had allowed his women to rule him. Madame de Pompadour. Madame du Barry. And look at the state of that country! 'Not very happy,' murmured the King. 'Not very happy. Would not like to see my country like that. Women ruin a country. They shall never lead me by the nose.'

Charlotte dismissed Schwellenburg. The arrogant German woman was quite capable of remaining if she had not done so.

'Your Majesty looks a little tired,' said the Queen solicitously.

'Eh? What? Not a good night.'

'You have been worrying about something?'

He did not answer that question. She was not going to worm state matters out of him that way.

'Your Majesty should take more than a dish of tea.'

'A dish of tea is all I want.'

'But . . .'

'A dish of tea is all I want,' he repeated. 'People eat too much. They get fat. All the family have a tendency to fat. Young George is too fat, eh, what?'

Charlotte's doting look illuminated her plain face. 'Oh, I wouldn't say that. He is well formed and because he is so handsome and fairly tall he can carry a little weight gracefully.'

'No one can carry too much weight with grace,' declared the King. 'I shall have to make sure that he is not eating too much fat on his meat. Pie crust, I'll swear . . . in spite of my orders that they were not to have it.'

'George is nearly eighteen now . . .' began the Queen timorously.

'Not yet. Not yet. He's a minor. He'll have to remember that, eh, what?'

'But of course, of course,' said the Queen hastily.

'Seems to have settled down, eh? Not so much chasing the maids of honour. There hasn't been one to take the place of that Harriot Vernon, has there?'

'Schwellenburg told me that he was very friendly with Mary Hamilton, but I discovered that it was a very *good* friendship. Mary is a good girl and he regarded her as his sister.'

'Sister. He's got sisters . . . five of them. What's he want with another sister?'

'It was a pleasant friendship, that was all. Mary Hamilton is one of the girls' attendants and he saw her when he visited them. It meant he was visiting his sisters quite frequently and I'm sure Your Majesty will agree that is a good thing.'

'Should have gone to see his own sisters . . . not this young woman.'

'They were just friends.'

'You're keeping your eye on him?'

'I wish I saw more of him.' The Queen sighed.

'Send for him then. Send for him.'

'I would like him to come of his own accord. But when he does come, all the time he seems to be thinking of getting away.' The King frowned and the Queen went on hastily: 'Of course he is so young and full of high spirits. I hear that he only has to appear to set the people cheering. In Hyde Park the people nearly went wild with joy when your brother stopped his coach to speak to them. They were cheering George . . . not Cumberland.'

'Cumberland had no right. . .' The King's eyes bulged. 'I've forbidden him to the Court.'

'This wasn't the Court. It was the Park. After all they are uncle and nephew. They could scarcely pass by.'

'Family quarrels,' said the King. 'I hate them. They've always been. I thought we'd avoid them. But I never could get along with Cumberland. It was different with Gloucester. I'm sorry he had to make a fool of himself. But Cumberland . . . I don't want the fellow at Court, brother of mine though he may be.'

'I must say he lives . . . scandalous . . .'

The King spoke bitterly: 'So even eyelashes a yard long can't satisfy him.'

'I've heard some of the women talking about the house he keeps . . . the people who go there. Fox is a frequent visitor. Do you think because you won't have him at Court he's trying to build up a little court of his own?'

The King looked at his wife sharply. This sounded remarkably like interference. Any conversation which brought in Mr Fox could be highly political. He was not going to have Charlotte interfering. He'd tell her so;

he'd make it plain to her. But for a few moments he gave himself up to imagining the sort of 'court' there would be at the Cumberlands. Men like Fox . . . Fox was a lecher . . . Fox had all the vices and none of the virtues; but he was a brilliant politician, and if he was a habitué of Cumberland's court that could be very dangerous. For where Fox was other men of affairs gathered.

The King looked distastefully at the Queen. She was not really an old woman . . . thirty-five or so . . . but having spent some nineteen years in almost continuous child-bearing this had naturally aged her. Compared with women like Elizabeth Pembroke she was old and ugly. And she was the woman with whom he was expected to be content while his brother sported on sofas with Grosvenor's wife and before that matter was settled was doing the same with a timber merchant's wife and before very long marrying the woman he had made his Duchess. Not that he was faithful to her. He was living dissolutely . . . frequenting gaming clubs, hanging about the theatres in the hope of seducing every little actress that took his fancy. Disgusting! The King could not bear to think about it . . . yet he could not stop himself thinking about it . . . and when he looked at Charlotte . . . plain, fertile Charlotte sitting there, smug and so obviously with child . . . he felt bitter against a fate which had made him a king with a high moral standard who had forced himself to be a faithful husband all these years to a woman who did not attract him at all.

'I will deal with this affair of Cumberland,' he said sternly.

'Do you mean you will summon him to an audience?'

'I will deal with him,' said the King finally.

Charlotte looked disappointed. It was humiliating never to be able to voice an opinion. She would not have believed all those years ago when she had come here from Mecklenburg-Strelitz that she could have been relegated to such a position. She had been quite a spirited young woman when she arrived. But of course she came from a very humble state to be the queen of a great country and that had overawed her a little, and just as she was growing accustomed to that she had become pregnant–and she had been pregnant ever since.

So she accepted the snub as she had so many others, and, sighing, thought: It is no use trying to change it now. If she attempted to it would anger the King; it would upset him; and the most important thing to her now was not to upset the King. At the back of her mind was a terrible fear concerning him. At times he was a little strange. That quick method of speech, the continual 'eh's' and 'what's'. He had not been like that before his illness . . . that vague mysterious illness, the truth of which his mother and Lord Bute had tried to keep from her. But she had known. During it George's mind had become affected. It had passed, but he had never been the same again; and always she was conscious of the shadow hanging over him. Sometimes . . . and this worried her most . . . she thought he was haunted by it too.

So the last thing she wanted to do was disturb the King.

The King changed the subject to the Prince of Wales.

'I think the people liked to see the Prince with us at the theatre.'

'I am sure they did,' replied the Queen, glad to see him more easy in his mind. 'It was a splendid evening. I thought the players very good. That actress who played Perdita was very pretty.'

'H'm,' said the King. Very pretty, he thought. Too pretty for comfort. He had seen a young man flirting with her in the wings when she was waiting to go on stage and he believed the fellow was attached to the Prince's entourage. He didn't want young profligates who flirted in public with actresses about his son.

He went on: 'The Prince should be seen more often in public with us.'

'I am sure that is so.'

'But I am not sure that I like to see those play actresses parading themselves before young men. I would prefer something more serious. Some good music.'

'I am sure,' said the Queen, 'that would be an excellent idea and far more suitable than a play.'

Now the King was happier. He could settle down cosily to arrange an occasion when it would be most suitable for the King, Queen and Prince of Wales to appear in public.

The Queen smiled contentedly. After all, she had accepted the subservient role all these years, why complain about it now?

She folded her hands in her lap; she would never complain, she vowed if only all the children remained in good health, her firstborn did nothing to offend his father and the King remained . . . himself.

The King had sent for the Prince of Wales and when young George faced his father, the latter thought: He is handsome. Looks healthy too. A little arrogant. But perhaps we all are when we know that one day we will wear a crown.

The King cleared his throat. 'Well, well,' he said. 'I hear you've been meeting your uncle Cumberland in the park.'

'We passed while taking the air, Sir.'

'H'm. And your uncle stopped and behaved very affectionately, I hear.'

'He behaved as one would expect an uncle to.' Just faintly insolent . . . as insolent as he dared be. Resentful too. No doubt imagined he was a man already. Well, he was not. His eighteenth birthday was months away–and even then he was not fully of age. The King started to wonder as he often did in his eldest son's presence why there was always this tension between them, as though they were enemies rather than father and son. When had he ceased to regard the Prince as one of the greatest blessings in his life and seen him as one of his greatest burdens? He kept thinking of the pink chubby baby who, everyone declared, was a bold young rascal. Spoilt from his birth, thought the King. The lord of the nursery, charming everyone with his good looks and his laughter and his arrogance . . . yes arrogance even in those days. But how they had doted on him–he as well as Charlotte. This Prince who, he thought then, had made marriage to Charlotte worth while. He had been almost as foolish about the child as Charlotte, gloating over that wax image she had had made of him and which she still kept under a glass case on her dressing table. In the Park people had crowded round to look at him, to adore him; and he had accepted all this with a cool disdainful gaze of those blue eyes as the homage due to him but of which he had such a surfeit that it bored him.

And then the others had come along and they had begun to realize that the Prince of Wales was headstrong, liked his own way, screamed for it, cajoled for it–and, the King thought grimly, invariably got it.

The result: the handsome dandy who now stood before him, seeking to discountenance him because he was young and handsome and George was old and looked his age . . . because he was a prince who would one day be

King and perhaps resented the fact that he was not already.

There he was working up a hatred of the boy before he had done anything to aggravate him, except to stand there with insolence in every line of his–the King noted–slightly too fat body.

'Your Uncle Cumberland is not received at my Court,' said the King. 'Therefore I find it unfitting that he should stop to speak to you in the Park.'

'The people seemed pleased that he did.'

'I have refused to receive him at Court.'

'Yes,' repeated the Prince, 'the people were pleased. They are not fond of family quarrels.'

'Your uncle Cumberland has shocked the whole country by his behaviour.'

'I don't think they hold it against him. Perhaps they were amused.'

How dared he stand there and say such a thing! He was trying to behave as a man of the world. Why, he was not out of the nursery yet!

'You should take more exercise,' said the King. 'You've put on weight.'

The insolent eyes swept the King's figure and the King was unable to prevent himself straightening up, holding in his stomach. In spite of all his efforts he did have too much flesh there.

'I would not wish the people to think I was starved as well as treated like a child,' murmured the Prince.

'Eh? What?' demanded the King.

'I said, Sir that I should not wish people to think I was starved.'

'H'm.' The King changed the subject. 'The people were pleased to see us at the theatre together. It was a pleasant evening.'

A dreamy look came into the Prince's eyes. 'A very pleasant evening, Sir. One of the pleasantest I have ever spent.'

'The play was well done, though it was Shakespeare and not as good as some.'

'They do other plays, Sir,' said the Prince eagerly. 'There is Sheridan's *School for Scandal*, and er . . .'

'I don't much like what I hear of that fellow Sheridan.'

'Sir, he's a brilliant playwright.'

'A bit of a profligate, I fear. He has a beautiful wife and I'm sorry to see her married to such a man.' It was the King's turn to look sentimental. Elizabeth Linley with the golden voice. He had heard her sing several times in one of those concerts her father arranged. A beautiful voice . . . the best he had ever heard; and she looked like an angel herself. One of the most beautiful women I ever saw, he thought. I'd set her side by side with Hannah . . . or Sarah.

'He's a friend of Mr Fox and I've heard it said they are the most brilliant pair in the whole of London–and act as a foil to each other.'

'Any friend of Mr Fox is no friend of mine,' said the King shortly. 'I am very sorry to know that Miss Linley has married that fellow. Nor do I wish to go to his theatre. I was thinking of something more suitable.'

The Prince looked scornful. What a fool the old man was! he was thinking. He deliberately turned his back on the people who would be most well worth knowing. No wonder his Court was the dullest the country had ever known. He was not surprised that his Uncle Cumberland tried to set up a rival court. It was time somebody did.

His own turn must come soon. Was that what the old man was afraid of? The Prince's eyes glistened. He thought of the people he would gather round him when the time came. Mrs Robinson would be there. What joy!

what bliss! Mrs Robinson in pink satin with feathers in her hair–or simply gowned as she had been in some scenes of the play with her dark hair about her shoulders. He was not sure whether he did not prefer her like that than more grandly attired. Oh, no, he preferred Mrs Robinson any way. It would not matter how she were dressed. Everything she wore . . . everything she did was perfect.

That was why he felt so frustrated. Here he was unable to behave like a Prince . . . and a Prince of Wales at that . . . forced to present himself to his father whenever he was summoned, to stand before him and listen to his drivel about Mr Fox and Mr Sheridan. They were the sort of men he would have at *his* Court. Wait . . . just wait until he had his own establishment. It will be when I'm eighteen. I swear I'll not allow them to treat me as a child any longer.

'More suitable,' went on the King, 'and I have sent for you to tell you what I have chosen.'

Sent for you! What *I* have chosen! Oh, it was humiliating!

'I have ordered a performance at Covent Garden–an Oratorio. Handel's setting of *Alexander's Feast*. You will accompany the Queen and myself there.'

'Oh?' said the Prince of Wales and the King thought he detected a trace of insolence in his voice.

'And now I give you leave to go and visit the Queen.'

'Your Majesty is gracious.'

The King studied his son intently; he always felt the young fellow had the advantage because he was quicker with words than he was himself. That was the pity of it, he had turned all his good points to disadvantage–his good looks, his ready tongue, his scholastic accomplishments which far surpassed those of most young men . . . all these were now turned into weapons to use against his father.

'And don't show her how anxious you are to run away, eh, what?'

The Prince bowed. 'I shall, as ever, obey Your Majesty's commands.'

He retired; and the King said of his son what his grandfather George II had said of his: 'Insolent young puppy.'

When the Prince of Wales returned to his apartments he sent for Lord Malden.

'I cannot understand,' he said, 'why Mrs Robinson will not agree to a meeting.'

'Sir, Mrs Robinson is a lady of great sensibility. She is not even sure that Your Highness is the author of the notes she has received.'

'But you have told her.'

Lord Malden lifted his eyes to the ceiling. 'She cannot believe it. She still fears that someone may be signing himself Florizel. What if she agreed to meet you in some place and then found it was not Your Highness after all? I think that is what she fears.'

'Then we must put an end to her fears. I will make her sure. I have it. I am to go to Covent Garden to the Oratorio. She must go, too.'

'Your Highness, the King and the Queen . . .'

The Prince laughed. 'My box is opposite theirs at Covent Garden. See that Mrs Robinson is in the box above the King's and Queen's. There they will not see her, and I can spend the whole evening gazing at her.'

'Your Highness, what if you betray yourself?'

'Malden, I think the King is not the only one who forgets I am the Prince of Wales. I pray you make these arrangements without delay. Go to Mrs Robinson. Tell her that I beg her to come to Covent Garden and there I will give her reason to doubt no longer that those notes have come from me.'

'Lord Malden to see you, Madam.' It was the discreet voice of Mrs Armistead.

'Show him in at once, Armistead.'

Lord Malden appeared, elegant as ever. What a handsome man he was and his eyes told her how much he admired her, and for a moment disappointment swept over her because she feared he might have come on his own account.

He soon reassured her.

'I come direct from His Highness, the Prince of Wales.'

She forced herself to look sceptical.

'Mrs Robinson, I assure you this is so. His Highness is most unhappy because he fears that by approaching you he has offended you. He wishes to assure you that this is not the case. He would die rather than offend you.'

'I would not wish to be responsible for the death of the heir to the throne.'

'So I thought, Madam. Therefore I hope you will listen sympathetically.'

'If the Prince wishes to write to me why does he not do so in a manner which could leave me in no doubt that he is the writer of the letters?'

'His Highness is romantic. He thinks of you as Perdita and himself as Florizel.'

'So could a hundred other gallants.'

'His Highness is determined that you shall cast away your doubts. That is why he suggests a meeting.'

She was alarmed. She had heard rumours of the Prince's light love affairs. If she met him clandestinely he would doubtless seek a quick consummation; and in a short time she would be known as Mary Robinson, one of the Prince's light-o'-loves for a week or so. Oh, no. She had too strong a sense of her own worth, too much dignity. Nothing like that was going to happen to her, no matter if the Prince of Wales did desire it.

'I could not agree to a secret meeting,' she said firmly. 'I have my reputation to consider. This happens to be rather dear to me, Lord Malden.'

'Quite rightly so,' said the young man fervently. 'But hear what His Highness wishes. You could, I am sure, have no objection to being in a public place where he might see you . . . and give you some sign of his devotion. I am referring to Covent Garden. There is to be a royal occasion. The King and Queen will be there and the Prince begs . . . implores . . . that you will grace the evening with your presence. All he wishes is to assure you by a look and gesture that he is your fervent admirer and the writer of these letters.'

Her first thought was: What shall I wear? She thought of pink satin and discarded that. Blue! Lavender perhaps. She would have a new gown for the occasion. Because of course she was going.

'Did you say the King and Queen will be present?'

'Yes. The King, the Queen and the Prince of Wales.'

'And before the King and Queen . . .'

'Have no fear. Leave all arrangements to me. I will see that all is as it should be.'

'I have not yet made up my mind whether it would be wise for me to come.'

'Madam, I beg of you. The Prince will be desolate: he is beside himself with anxiety because he receives no reply from you. All you have to do is sit in the box I shall choose for you. He will do the rest.'

'You plead his cause with fervour, Lord Malden. If it were your own you could not do so more earnestly.'

'Ah, madam. Would it *were* my own.'

She laughed lightly. It pleased her to be so admired.

'Well, I do not wish to disappoint . . . er, Florizel.'

Malden kissed her hand. 'Madam, this will make the Prince of Wales a very happy man. I must go to him at once and acquaint him with his good fortune.'

Mrs Armistead, listening, heard that her mistress was going to the Oratorio. A step forward indeed, she thought. The Prince will not rest until she is his mistress. He himself will come here.

There would be opportunities; and when Mrs Robinson was at the height of her ambitions–loved by the Prince of Wales–there would be a chance for a woman who was both handsome and clever to climb a little too. Perhaps not to such dizzy heights as her mistress, but . . . perhaps so. For all her dazzling beauty Mrs Robinson was scarcely wise; whereas her lady's maid made up for in wisdom what she might lack in looks–only compared with Mrs Robinson, of course, because Mrs Armistead, by ordinary standards, was a very handsome woman indeed.

Her mistress was calling for her. She must show Lord Malden to the door. He scarcely glanced at Mrs Armistead so bemused was he by the more flamboyant charms of Mrs Robinson. But it would not be so with all of them.

As soon as he had gone Mrs Robinson was calling for her.

'Armistead. Armistead. I have agreed to go to the Oratorio at Covent Garden. The King, Queen and Prince of Wales are to be present.'

'Madam will wish to look her best.'

'I thought of lavender satin.'

'Madam will need a new gown for the occasion. Something which she has not worn before.'

'Exactly, Armistead.'

'I think madam . . . white.'

'White, Armistead!'

'White satin and silver tissue, Madam.'

'But so pale. I shall pass unnoticed.'

'Madam could never be unnoticed. I was thinking that the simplicity of your gown would be great contrast to the brilliance of your beauty.'

Armistead stood there, eyes lowered–very neat and quite elegant herself in her black gown over which she wore a white apron.

'The touch of colour could come from the feathers in your headdress.'

Mrs Robinson nodded. 'What colours, Armistead?'

'Well, Madam, that is a matter to which we should give a little thought. This will be a very important occasion and we must make sure that all is just as it should be.'

Mrs Robinson nodded. Oh, excellent Armistead.

For us both, thought Mrs Armistead, who was visualizing not so much the scene at Covent Garden but what would follow . . . the great men who would come to this house, among whom would surely be some who would realize the quite considerable charm of Mrs Armistead.

Covent Garden! A blaze of Glory. Crowds had gathered in the streets to see the royal cavalcade. The Prince of Wales looked magnificent with the glittering diamond star on his blue satin coat. How different from his poor old father and plain pregnant mother!

'God bless the Prince!' the cheers rang out.

The King was pleased. It was good for any member of the royal family to be popular. Good for the monarchy. As for the Queen, she was proud when she heard them calling for her son. 'He is so handsome,' she murmured.

It was a glittering company. Red plush and gold braid and the finest musicians in the country; and the most notable people in the land were present.

There was an atmosphere of anticipation engendered by the implication that now the Prince was growing up there would be more of this kind of thing, and there was no doubt that it was what the public liked to see.

'It was a good idea, eh, what?' murmured the King to the Queen. 'The family . . . in public . . . together . . . in harmony.'

The Queen thought it was a very good idea.

In her box sat Mrs Robinson, attracting a great deal of attention, for she had rarely looked so beautiful. Between them she and Armistead had decided what she would wear. The white satin and silver tissue had been a brilliant idea, particularly as her feathers were of the most delicate shade of pink and green.

How much more elegant she looked than some of the women in their bright colours. She felt the utmost confidence as she reclined in her box which was immediately above that occupied by the King and Queen.

And then . . . the excitement. The royal family were in the theatre. She could not see the King and Queen, but when the house stood to attention she knew they were there. And almost immediately *he* appeared in the box opposite her. The handsome glittering Prince of Wales and for companion, his brother Frederick.

Perdita's heart began to beat very fast for no sooner had the Prince of Wales acknowledged the cheers of the people than he sat down and leaning on the edge of the box gazed with passionate adoration at Mrs Robinson.

It was true, she thought. But of course she had never doubted it. She had pretended to give herself time to decide how best she could handle this enthralling but very delicate situation. Now she could no longer plead suspicion that the letters were written by someone other than the Prince. He was giving her no doubt of his feelings.

The music had started but the Prince's gaze remained fixed on the box opposite and many members of the audience quickly became aware of this. Whispers! Titters! Who is this at whom the Prince of Wales is casting sheep's eyes? Mrs Robinson, of course, the actress from Drury Lane. The woman who had had such an effect upon him when he went to see *The Winter's Tale*.

The audience were far more interested in this byplay between the two boxes than they were in the music. They were a very striking pair for the Prince of Wales in his most elegant clothes with the glitter of royalty was the most handsome young man in Covent Garden and Mrs Robinson was undoubtedly the most beautiful woman. And the point which was so amusing was that all this was going on right under the noses–literally speaking, one might say–of the King and Queen, whom everyone knew kept the Prince so guarded that he found the utmost difficulty in following his inclinations.

The King noticed nothing; he was absorbed by the music. Handel's setting was perfect, he thought. Not a musician in the world to touch him . . . now or at any time.

The Queen, however, was less interested in the music although she thought it was fine. She had an opportunity of gazing in uninterrupted admiration at her adored first-born. How handsome he looked! How proud she was! Frederick was a good looking boy too, but he could not really be compared with George. She thought of his odd little sayings when he was very young. Old-fashioned he had been, never at a loss for a word. And how proud she had been of his ability to master his lessons! He was really brilliant. He had been a little wayward. What child was not? She had been upset when he had been beaten and the King had told her she must not be foolish, for to spare the rod was to spoil the child. The King would now say that even applications of the rod had not achieved that purpose and none was more aware than herself of the growing animosity between father and son.

She tried to catch his eye to send him an affectionate motherly smile but he would not look her way. His eyes were fixed above their box. She wondered why.

He was smiling now; he was making strange gestures. What did it mean? Now he was holding the programme up to his face; he was drawing his hand across his forehead as though in utter despair. Extraordinary! And all this was directed somewhere over their heads.

He had lowered the play bill and cast off his mournful expression; now he was smiling in a manner which might be described as pleading. He was leaning forward and with his right hand was actually pretending to write on the edge of the box in which he sat. What *was* he doing?

The Queen had now lost all interest in the music; like most people's all her attention was centred on the Prince of Wales who continued behaving in this odd manner, pretending to write; looking as though he were the most miserable of young men one moment and the most joyous the next.

I believe, thought the Queen, he is making signs to someone.

Every now and then the Prince spoke to his brother and Frederick too was gazing as if spellbound somewhere above the royal box.

Then she understood.

The first part of the Oratorio had come to an end. The King turned to the Queen. 'Magnificent!' he said. 'Handel's setting is perfect. Everything he has written has shown his genius. I find this excellent.'

'I have been wondering about the Prince . . .'

'The Prince, eh, what?' The King shot a glance across the theatre. 'He's there. Glad he likes good music. One point in his favour, eh, what?'

'Oh, he likes good music,' said the Queen, 'but he seems to be very much attracted by something above our box. I have been wondering what it can be.'

The King frowned. Then he summoned one of his equerries who had been at the back of the box.

'Who is in the box above ours, eh?' he demanded.

The equerry who had not been unaware of the excitement in the theatre–and its cause–was able to answer immediately: 'It's a Mrs

Robinson, Your Majesty. An actress from the Drury Lane Theatre.'

The King was silent for a few seconds and the Queen watched him fearfully, heartily wishing that she had not called the King's attention to what was going on.

The King was thinking: An actress from Drury Lane! It would be one of those young women he had seen perform not very long ago. And here she was at Covent Garden and the young fool was ogling her so that people were noticing.

The King again summoned his equerry. 'Tell the actress who is occupying the box above this one that her presence is no longer required in this theatre. She is to leave at once.'

The music was resumed and the King's equerry went to tell Perdita that she must leave at once, for this was the order of the King.

Mrs Armistead was surprised to see her mistress's chair so early. Could she have left before the performance was over? As soon as she opened the door to receive her she had no doubt that something was wrong . . . very wrong indeed.

Mrs Robinson said nothing but went straight to her bedroom and there tore off the feathers and flung them on to her bed. She stood looking at her angry reflection, her usually pale face under her rouge was scarlet.

Mrs Armistead was at the door.

'Madam sent for me?'

Mrs Robinson was too angry to deny it. Moreover, it was a relief to talk to someone.

'Madam is ill. Allow me to help you to bed. The evening was not a success?'

Mrs Robinson looked at her maid in sudden suspicion. Was the woman too forward? Did she feel that because her mistress was a play actress she could treat her differently from the way in which she could a noble lady? She was ready to suspect everyone of insulting her.

Mrs Armistead arranged her features into a look of deep concern, which was not difficult since she believed her mistress's success at this stage was her own.

Mrs Robinson softened towards her. Armistead was a good servant, good enough to be a confidante too.

'I have been insulted tonight,' she said. 'I have been sent out of Covent Garden. Dismissed. Told to leave. As though . . . as though . . .' Her lips trembled. 'I wish to God I had never gone.'

'But, Madam, surely the Prince . . .'

'The Prince could do nothing. In fact I doubt he was aware of it until it was over.'

'Madam!'

'You may well look startled, Armistead. I have never felt so humiliated.'

'But who would dare, Madam?'

'The King's orders. Very simple. His equerry came to my box. "His Majesty's command, Madam. But he has no longer need of your presence here. I have orders to take you to your chair." And he did.'

'Then . . .'

Her face softened. 'The Prince showed too clearly his devotion to me. I admit it was rather obvious. The King must have noticed. Hence my dismissal. I am deeply sorry that I laid myself open to this insult.'

'Madam, I doubt not that this will but increase the Prince's affection for you.'

'I cannot say. But of one thing I am certain. I shall never put myself in such a position again.'

'Tomorrow it will seem less humiliating. Allow me to help you to bed and bring a dish of warm chocolate. It will soothe you.'

Mrs Robinson sat at her mirror and Mrs Armistead let down the dark hair and helped her into her bedgown.

'There, madam. I will have your chocolate ready in a few moments.'

Preparing the chocolate she was thinking: What airs these play actresses give themselves! Does she think the Prince should marry her and make her Queen of England? Did she think the King would give his consent to that! And what of Mr Robinson? How dispose of him? But I believe our dear lady feels this is not impossible.

She sipped the chocolate. Delicious. Then she took it to her mistress's room.

Mrs Robinson was sitting up in bed, the angry flush still on her cheeks.

'There, Madam. Drink this.'

She handed her the cup and picked up the dress and feathers which had been flung aside.

'Take those away,' said Mrs Robinson. 'I never want to see them again.'

In her own room Mrs Armistead held the white and silver dress against her and studied her reflection. A little alteration would be necessary. She tried the feathers against her own dark hair. Very becoming. Perhaps at some future date . . .

Lord Malden arrived next day. He brought a letter and a package from the Prince.

'His Highness was most distressed by what happened at Covent Garden,' Malden told her. 'The whole company was aware of his anger. When you disappeared from your box he was quite distraught.'

Mrs Robinson bowed her head, her eyes on the letter which she was longing to read.

Lord Malden handed it to her. It was addressed to 'Dearest and Most Beautiful Perdita' and begged her to meet him. It was signed as usual Florizel.

Lord Malden watched her while she read it and then handed her the packet. She gasped with pleasure when its contents were revealed. There was an exquisite miniature of the Prince of Wales painted by Meyer, delicately coloured, accentuating his good looks. The Prince had cut a piece of paper into the shape of a heart and on one side had written '*Je ne change qu'en mourant*', and on the other: 'Unalterable to my Perdita through life.'

'Now, Madam,' said Lord Malden, 'have you any doubt of His Highness's devotion?'

She admitted that she had not; but at the same time she did not think it was wise for them to meet.

'His Highness will never accept such a verdict.'

'And if our meeting should come to the ears of the King?'

'Madam, the Prince will be eighteen in August. Then he will have an establishment of his own. He cannot be kept at the Dower House at Kew after his eighteenth birthday.'

'August!' sighed Mrs Robinson. 'That is a long way off!'

'There is no need to wait until August.'

'You were at Covent Garden, my lord. You saw me ignobly dismissed.'

'Madam, the Prince will never allow you to be banished from his life.'

'I think that until he is of age he will have to obey his father. You should tell him that much as I admire him, greatly as I appreciate his gift, which I shall treasure until the day I die, I must advise caution.'

'Advise caution to a lover, Madam! And such a lover!'

She sighed and turned away. Then gazing at the miniature she smiled tenderly.

And Lord Malden went back to report to his master.

'A Triumph of Chastity!'

Letters and poems were arriving frequently from Florizel and the theme of these letters was: 'When shall we meet?' But Perdita's answers always showed the same evasiveness. The Prince must be cautious; he must remember his rank; he must not offend his father.

'My fate is in the hands of my Perdita,' he wrote. 'My life is yours to save or ruin. Your Florizel.'

Carefully she preserved the letters, reading them over and over again, soothing her hurt vanity through them; dreaming that this chaste romantic idyll would go on all their lives and be a lesson for the whole world to admire. Lovers parted by two insuperable obstacles–his crown and her husband.

Florizel had different ideas. He raved to Malden. There must be a meeting. She could not go on like this.

The romance was no longer a secret. It was hinted at in the more scurrilous papers. 'A certain illustrious Personage and a famous actress have become aware of each other's undoubted charms . . .' 'A new Florizel for Perdita . . .' And such allusions.

The theatre was doing business such as it had rarely done before, for people wanted to see the actress who had enchanted the Prince. They were more pleased with him than ever. What a change from his dull old father!

Sheridan was delighted with his audiences, but a little apprehensive of the future. Perdita was a very lovely woman but he did not think for one moment that she would be wise enough to hold the Prince of Wales for long.

If she became the Prince's mistress she would continue to bring in packed houses. He would not be able to accommodate all the people who would be clamouring to get into the theatre to see her; but of course the Prince would never allow his mistress to appear on the stage–and that would be the end of good business for Drury Lane. And if the Prince discarded her? A royal mistress could not return to the stage. The public would come to see her once . . . twice and then lose interest in her.

He decided to speak to her and called at her house to do so, for they could enjoy more privacy there than at the theatre. In her muslin and ribbons she was very appealing. One of the prettiest women he had ever known. If she would not take herself and her virtue and her ladylike ways so seriously, she would be very attractive indeed. Being frank with himself he admitted that he had quickly tired of her. Beauty alone was not enough. Would the Prince tire as quickly? He was young, and at the moment inexperienced, the prisoner in that Puritan Palace set up by Papa; but when he had his establishment, that would be different. We shall see a change in H.R.H. when that happens, mused Sheridan. And I doubt that our dear ladylike Mrs R. will then seem to him the ideal of perfection that she does seen through prison bars. Now his–Sheridan's–dearest Amoret (Mrs Crewe), that sparkling witty creature whom he adored and to whom he had dedicated *The School for Scandal*, would hold any man. If she had been in Perdita's shoes . . . But God forbid. Amoret was too enchanting to be thrown away on a callow prince; only the most brilliant playwright in England was worthy of her.

Fleetingly he thought of Elizabeth. He was sorry Elizabeth had to know of these things. But Elizabeth was a saint and a man of flesh and blood cannot live with a saint.

But here was Mrs Armistead–that most discreet of women–to usher him in.

'My dear Sherry!' Perdita rose to greet him, so pretty with the faint flush in her cheeks. He knew what that meant. A letter from Florizel. What a correspondent the Prince was! And so was Perdita! She had always been one to pour out her heart and soul on paper, which was probably fanning the flame of H.R.H.'s ardour. Those poems she had written from her debtors' prison! No merit in them but lots of feeling–and that was a commodity the public were often more ready to pay for than genius.

'My blessed Perdita!' He kissed her hands ardently. It was always wise to feign regrets for a love affair that was over in the presence of the one who had shared it. It was advisable to blame circumstances–'coming to one's senses', 'it is better for you, my dear, and I am thinking of you', 'my own inclinations are of no account'–than to speak of satiety, boredom a new and more exciting mistress.

'But how enchanting you look.'

She would never grow accustomed to compliments. He wondered lightly what proportion of her life was spent studying her reflection in the mirror and deciding what clothes she would wear.

She sparkled at once–and now she showed some vitality which was more attractive than that look of melancholy which was her usual expression.

'The simplicity of the gown throws up the contrast of your dazzling beauty.'

'This morning gown . . .' she said disparagingly, and he could see that she was wondering whether to order a new muslin to be made . . . one in which she could appear in public, and startle the world of Ranelagh, the Rotunda, the Pantheon by appearing in muslin and ribbon among all the satin and feathers.

'. . . is most becoming,' he finished for her. 'But, my dear, I have not come to talk to you of gowns. I am concerned for you . . . greatly concerned.'

'Sherry?'

'I am thinking of Prince Charming's very public passion.'

'Alas, people in our position cannot live secret lives.'

'That is indeed true and is why you should consider your situation from all aspects before taking any step.'

'I am sure you are right. And that is what I am doing.'

'So far you and the Prince have not met . . . alone.'

'Certainly we have not.'

'But how long do you think he will be content with this state of affairs?'

'The Prince is content that he loves me and I . . .'

'And you, Perdita, adore him. Naturally, all ladies adore Royalty.'

'I don't understand.'

'A simple fact, my dearest.'

'I hope you are not suggesting that I love the Prince because of his rank. You have forgotten how his uncle the Duke of Cumberland plagued me. But you should remember how I repulsed his advances.'

An ageing roué of a duke. A young and charming prince with a crown in view. The one was a much more glittering prize than the other. Moreover, the Duke's character was well known. He had had several mistresses and had merely invited Perdita to join the group. He had not written the sentimental love letters which she had just been reading and which she would tie up with blue ribbons–or possibly pink–and gloat over in her old age . . . that was if she did not use them to financial advantage at some earlier stage. The very fact that Florizel *wrote* to his loved one pointed to his inexperience. The Duke was no scholar; he could not have compiled those flowing phrases had he wished to; but although the Prince might chatter in French, Italian and German like a native, although he was familiar with Horace and Virgil and was reputed to have some taste for Tacitus, he was clearly not aware of the ways of the world or he would never have so guilelessly handed over to an actress those letters which, Sheridan had no doubt, the young fool would in a year's time curse himself for having written. In this Perdita had shown herself wise. She repulsed the roué and encouraged the innocent boy; for much as she might protest, her coy reluctance to become his mistress was the best method of luring him on.

'I remember well,' said Sheridan. 'And that was wise. It would have done your reputation no good at all to be concerned with my lord Duke.'

Perdita shuddered piously.

'And the Prince . . .' mused Sheridan. 'Oh, my dear, dear lady, you must tread very cautiously. What do you think will be the outcome of all this?'

'The outcome? Why, I think we shall learn to content ourselves with our fate.'

Clichés! thought Sheridan. Could she really see a lusty young man being content with letters.

'I think His Highness will become more and more insistent in his request for a meeting.'

'I have advised him to consider his position.'

'And I have come here to advise you to consider yours.'

'That I am doing.'

'I know you well. I shall never forget the day we met. I recognized your ability the moment I saw you and so did Garrick. God rest his soul.'

'Poor Mr Garrick! Dear Mr Garrick! What I owe him! It is very sad to think he will never again coach ladies for the stage.'

A short pause to pay respects to Garrick who had died a few months before.

Garrick had said: 'With looks like that, she'll bring in the audiences. If we can teach her to act a little that could be a help.'

How right he was! How right he had always been! He was greatly missed.

'But even now,' went on Sheridan, 'that you have your place in your profession, it could be easy to throw it away.'

'Throw it away? How?'

'By becoming the Prince's mistress.'

She drew back at what she considered an unpleasant word. She would never see herself as the Prince's mistress no matter if he set her up in a house and openly visited her. His friend? wondered Sheridan. The lady whom he favours with his confidences? His wife in name only? Never mistress!

No, he would not give her a long hold on the fickle favour of a young Prince avid for experience, avid for life.

'My dearest, let us face the facts. That is what is in the Prince's mind.'

'I appreciate your anxiety for me, dear Sherry, but I do not think you know the Prince.'

A little better than you do, he thought, for you my dear have not yet spoken to him face to face.

'Listen to me,' he said. 'You know I speak for your good. If you become the Prince's mistress you will lose your place on the stage. You have too much sensibility to become the mistress of a king or a prince. You are too romantic. It would be necessary for you to consider all sorts of propositions which would be distasteful to you.'

'What do you mean?'

'Before entering into such an arrangement you should make sure that some provision was made for the days when it would be over. Tell me this, what would you do if you could no longer act? Don't forget you have a child, a mother . . . and a husband to support.'

She turned away; he was forcing her to see the ugly truth; he was spoiling her romance. And she wanted to go on in her dream.

'My dear Sherry,' she said, 'I know you speak out of your concern for me. But rest assured I shall never do anything which would make you ashamed of me.'

'I should tremble less for you if I thought you would,' he said.

'You must have your quips.' She swept away the unpleasant discussion with a wave of the hand. 'Now, would you take a dish of tea, a dish of chocolate?'

He declined. Business at the theatre, he pleaded. He had no desire to drink tea or chocolate with a mistress of whom he had tired.

Mistress? he chided himself. No, lady friend . . . the lady whom I favoured with my confidences . . . once.

He took his leave, kissing her hand fervently to assure her that it was her good for which he was concerned and that she should consider very carefully before throwing away a career which had been built up to fame since that night when her Juliet had first enchanted his audiences.

Mr Fox chose a time when Mrs Robinson was out to call on her. He had his reasons for this. He had not been unaware of the lady's maid. An extremely handsome woman, he had noted, and he had a liking for handsome women; moreover, there was an air about this one which had specially intrigued him. Not only was she handsome, but intelligent.

It was a matter of some importance to follow the course of Perdita's romance with Florizel, because if the lady in fact became the Prince's mistress and remained in that position when the Prince became a man of independence, Perdita could be a very significant person indeed.

Mr Fox had been present at the Oratorio and had witnessed the strange behaviour of the Prince; he had read the papers with those hints of the romance; he had heard rumours in Brooks' and other clubs; and he had listened attentively.

But he wished to follow the affair more intimately and believed that if he had a friend inside Perdita's establishment he could be completely in the picture and would not have to rely on hearsay.

A small matter in all his concerns? Not exactly. Because the Prince was destined to be in a position with relation to the Whigs that his father was with the Tories–and Mr Fox, being an ardent Whig and with nothing to hope for from the King or the Tory Party, was eager to bring back the Whigs to power–and who could be more helpful in this than the Prince of Wales?

The young man could not take his place in the Lords until he attained his real majority, that would be in 1783–more than three years from now; but at eighteen he would gain his freedom and his own establishment and he must be drawn into the right circle before the time came for him to enter the Lords. Three years was not too long; and if Mr Fox was not ready, others would seize the advantage. So therefore the affair between the actress and the Prince was politics.

'Madam is not at home.' The young woman spoke coolly and none would have guessed that the sight of the famous politician had set her heart racing and her hopes soaring because she had a very strong notion that Mr Fox had been well aware that her mistress was not at home and that was why he had called.

Mr Fox had already entered.

'Perhaps I could wait a while?'

'I am sure that is what Madam would wish.'

'And she would wish you to stay and have a civil word with me, I don't doubt.'

'It is my duty, sir, to be civil to all Madam's friends.'

'And mighty civil I am sure you are.'

Mrs Armistead curtsied and turned away, but he said: 'Now, you promised to chat.'

'I cannot imagine, sir, that a gentleman of your position would want to chat with a woman in mine.'

He smiled at her. 'And I had imagined you to be a woman of . . . imagination.'

'What would you wish of me, sir?'

'To ask you first perhaps how a woman of your undoubted ability should be content to find herself a lady's maid to an actress.'

'I did not say I was content, sir.'

'Ah.' He smiled at her. He was a strangely fascinating man. She had thought him the most exciting of all those gentlemen who called on her mistress. Mr Charles James Fox who could make the King uneasy, who was said to be the most brilliant politician in Parliament, a rival to young Mr Pitt, to the Prime Minister, Lord North. He was scarcely attractive to the eye, for in this age of elegance he was noticeably slovenly. Now she could see the grease spots on his coat; he was too fat; he had a double chin and his paunch was obvious; he had not bothered to shave himself. She had heard that he thought nothing of losing twenty thousand guineas in a night's gambling at

Brooks'. But he was the great Charles James Fox and it excited her that he had noticed her.

'Then I'll swear that from your present post you are looking for a better one.'

'Should not one always keep one's eyes open for advantage, sir?'

'Wise as well as beautiful.' He moved closer to her and although she did not retreat she conveyed by her expression that she did not expect familiarities and for a moment her spirits sank, for she feared that he had come in merely for a quick physical encounter with the handsome lady's maid who would be ready to serve Mr Fox in whatever capacity he thought fit for half an hour and then be forgotten. But that was not the intention of Mrs Armistead; nor must Mr Fox–famous as he might be–be deluded into thinking this could be.

He understood.

He said: 'Shall we sit down?'

She led the way into the drawing room and with the utmost dignity seated herself some distance from the chair which he had selected.

'I see that you are too clever for me to pretend my mission is other than it is.'

She inclined her head.

'Mrs Robinson is on the way to becoming the mistress of the Prince of Wales,' he went on. 'I am sure you realize the significance of this.'

'I do.'

'The Prince is young and impressionable. And a mistress could hold considerable sway over such a romantically minded young man. It is very necessary for the heir to the throne to be guided by those who can do him most good.'

'Such as Mr Charles James Fox?' she asked.

'Exactly. Exactly. The affair is hanging fire, is it not?'

'It is many weeks since His Highness first saw Mrs Robinson in *The Winter's Tale* and they have not yet met.'

'Why?'

'Mrs Robinson is a lady of much refinement.' In some way Mrs Armistead managed to speak exactly as Perdita did in her most refined moments. 'She wishes to be the Prince's mistress but cannot bear to admit even to herself that this is so. She writes long letters telling him of his duty and urging him to consider his position.'

'If she goes on in this way he will soon be considering some other fair charmer.'

'Yes, sir.'

'It would be better if this matter were brought to a logical conclusion.'

'Better for whom, sir? The Prince, Mrs Robinson or Mr Fox?'

He looked at her with admiration. 'For all three,' he said. 'And possibly . . . for Mrs Armistead.'

'Why should this last person be concerned, sir?'

'Because her advancement could well depend on it.'

She nodded slowly.

'Mrs Armistead, I should be glad to call you my friend.'

'A simple lady's maid is undeserving of the friendship of the greatest of statesmen.'

'Not so simple, if I have guessed aright and it is ability at the guessing game which makes a great statesman.'

'What is your wish?'

'That you persuade your mistress to make the Prince a happy man and that you keep me informed of the lovers' progress.'

'Why should I serve you, sir, instead of the mistress who pays me?'

He felt in his pocket and she recoiled in haste.

'I am not asking for money. I should not take it.'

He nodded. 'Then,' he said, 'I would answer your question. You would serve me because you have no intention of remaining in a humble position for the rest of your days. It is you, my dear, who should have a lady's maid. And I am sure that if you are as clever as I believe you to be, one day this will be so.'

She stood up, here eyes were bright, but she lost none of her serenity.

'I know,' he said, 'I can rely on you.'

'It will be an honour to serve Mr Fox,' she said.

He moved towards her. She thought he was going to embrace her; but again she held him off with her eyes.

He accepted her decision, and when she showed him to the door, he bowed to her as he would have bowed to her mistress.

After his chair had carried him away she went to her room; she held the white and silver tissue dress against her.

Folly! she thought. I am being as foolish as our play actress. But from the way he looked, the way he spoke, it was obvious that he respected me.

On the evening of that day Fox made his way to Cumberland's Mansion in Pall Mall where the Duchess received him with pleasure; and he was genuinely delighted to be in the company of this fascinating woman who had snared a royal duke and had kept her place in his affections because she was twenty times cleverer than he was. One of the most beautiful women in London–and she would have been so without the famous eyelashes–she was also one of the most witty; her wit was spiced with malice, it was true, and often expressed in the coarsest terms, but Fox admired and respected her.

'A game of faro is what you want,' she said.

Of course he wanted a game of faro. He could not see a gaming table without wanting to try his luck. A born gambler always hoping for the success which never came, he had already lost a fortune. It was his sublime indifference to money which had helped to set him in his peculiar position, for it was not only money, but honours which he did not seek. It was enough to be Mr Charles James Fox–the man recognized as the most brilliant statesman of his country, and not only by his country but by all the courts of Europe. He was bold and independent, aloof from all blandishments, even of the King himself–for George had at one time known that if he could have had Mr Fox as an ally he could have left the Government in more capable hands than those which guarded it at present. For all his affection for North, the King was well aware of his deficiencies. But Fox had set himself up in opposition to Tory doctrines; Fox was a Whig; and he opposed every Tory measure with the most cutting scorn. Fox declared he was for the people and he was going to maintain their privileges in the face of all opposition.

Such a man could have been an irresistible power in the land but for the fact that he possessed a dual personality. The statesman of integrity was a voluptuary of the most blatant kind. Drink, women and the gaming table were his recreations; and as he was a man of unbounded energy he gave to these activities the same indefatigable enthusiasm that he did to politics. He took a new mistress more frequently than he took a bath; his debts ran into five figures; and it was only because through long practice he could drink most men insensible that he was rarely drunk.

Yet he was sought by all the greatest hostesses in London and now the Duchess of Cumberland had caught the Duke's eye and he, seeing that Mr Fox was with her, hastened to greet his guest.

'A game of faro?' said the Duke, his eyes glistening.

Fox replied that nothing would give him greater pleasure later; there was a little matter he wished to discuss with the Duke and if it were possible for him and the Duchess to leave their guests for a while, he would like a little serious conversation with them.

The Duchess replied that it should be arranged and if Mr Fox would slip into the ante-room near her bedroom they could be quite undisturbed there.

It was not easy for such flamboyant characters as Mr Fox and the Duke and Duchess to slip away unnoticed, but in due course they met in the ante-room and Mr Fox came straight to the point.

'The Prince of Wales is making slow progress with his inamorata,' he said.

'A prude!' retorted the Duke spitefully.

'Dearest Henry must be forgiven a little sourness towards the lady, but he'll make up for it in sympathy towards our nephew,' explained the Duchess. 'He once had a fancy for her. Poor Henry, it was such a waste of valuable time. I told you, Henry, did I not, that many other ladies would have been far more likely to provide a satisfactory end to the chase. Do you know of anything more frustrating, Mr Fox, than a hunt when the victim gets clean away.'

'None,' said Mr Fox. 'But the victim must not be allowed to elude the hunter this time.'

Cumberland shrugged his shoulders. But Fox was not going to let personal resentment interfere with his plans.

'He'll soon be eighteen. We should not imagine that we are the only people who are aware of that. We have to get him on our side. If we don't the Tories will have him.'

'He'd be a Whig just because the King is a Tory.'

'I am not so sure. You can be certain that your brother Gloucester will step in if you don't, and don't forget he has the advantage. In spite of his marriage and the fact that his wife is not received at Court His Majesty is quite fond of him.'

'More than he is of me,' grimaced Cumberland.

'So Your Highness will see that it is necessary for us to act promptly.'

'Our little encounter in the Park didn't do much good.'

'I am forced to disagree with your Highness. I believe that the Prince was most touched and thought his uncle a charming fellow. He was more resentful against his father than ever for denying him the company of such fascinating relations. When he is free–and that may well be in a few months' time–he will want to show his affection, I am sure of it. That is why we must be ready for him.'

'Mr Fox is right,' said the Duchess. 'This must be the house which he must feel is a home to him.'

Fox threw her a grateful glance. Trust Madam Horton to see the advantage. She would deal with her less perceptive Duke.

'Well?' said Cumberland, deferring to the Duchess as always.

'Mrs Robinson should be your guest.'

'If I asked her she would suspect an attack on her precious virtue.'

'Her Highness the Duchess would be her hostess.'

'The lady shall come,' promised the Duchess. 'Why not with Sheridan?'

'That is no hardship I do assure you.'

'An entertaining fellow. He'll bring a new shine to Cumberland House.'

'And the lady should be persuaded to stop teasing the Prince.'

'Why?' demanded Cumberland.

'Because, my lord Duke, if she does not, our Prince will grow so impatient that he will look elsewhere. We cannot expect a full blooded young man as your nephew undoubtedly is to live on sighs. What if he chose a mistress in the Tory camp? It could be fatal to our hopes. No, it shall be Perdita. But she has to be persuaded that there is more glory to be found in the arms of a Prince of Wales than in prudery.'

'Her prudery could be overcome,' grumbled the Duke.

'How so?' demanded his Duchess. 'How was it that you who are skilled in the arts of overcoming that horrid vice could not overcome it in her case?'

'Every woman has her price.' He looked hard at his Duchess.

That she conceded. 'Even if it's marriage.' She fluttered her lashes, as though calling attention to her big bargaining counter. 'But Perdita could not be such a fool as to imagine she could marry the Prince of Wales. And since she is answering his letters and writing to him as passionately and as yearningly as he is writing to her, somewhere underneath all that display of virtue there must be some small idea of what she would accept.'

'That's it,' said the Duke. 'After all if they're going to make the affair so public–and his behaviour at the Oratorio suggests he will–she would have to give up the stage; and if he tires of her in a month or so, which is not inconceivable, the lady should naturally look for some security.'

'The Prince should offer her bond of some sort,' said the Duchess. 'He should do so in the most delicate terms. The lady will refuse indignantly; then it will be offered again and she will refuse hesitantly; and at the third time she will accept reluctantly. Would you care to take a bet on it, Mr Fox. A thousand guineas.'

'Done,' said Mr Fox, 'Although I think you have the better chance. But I'd be so pleased if it happened that I wouldn't mind paying up. But how is the Prince to be made to realize how he should act?'

The Duke and Duchess were silent for a while then the Duchess said: 'Lord Malden is the messenger. Part of his duty as H.R.H.'s equerry is to carry his master's love letters to the ladies of his choice. Malden has been our guest. He shall be so again. Never fear the Duke shall drop a word of advice into Malden's ear. Poor Malden, I fancy he is in love with the lady himself. He will be glad to please his master and at the same time release himself from a mission which, in the circumstances, must be somewhat odious.'

'But if he is in love with the woman will he want to pass her over to the Prince?'

The Duchess looked mockingly at her husband. 'Sometimes the dogs enjoy the crumbs which fall from their master's table. Malden will be waiting, chops slavering, tail wagging ever faithful for the day when Florizel takes on a new role. After all, we must have a change of show sometimes. And when *The Winter's Tale* becomes *The Lady Dishonoured*, Malden will stėp in with a show of his own, *Patience Rewarded.*'

Mr Fox said: 'The Duchess as usual has found the solution. Now we will see if this lady–like so many others–has her price. I have no doubt that she has, but it may be marriage, which in her case would be impossible for her lover, however enamoured, to meet. But if she will set her sights a little lower . . .'

'Then,' said the Duchess, 'the Prince shall have his Perdita and Mr Fox would lose a thousand guineas.'

'In the circumstances,' said Mr Fox, ''tis a consummation devoutly to be wished!'

Perdita was thrown into a state of excitement by the invitation from the Duchess of Cumberland. She called to Mrs Armistead, for the woman was growing more and more useful and more and more Perdita was taking her into her confidence.

'An invitation from a very illustrious quarter. I confess I should refuse it immediately if it had come from the Duke.'

'The Duke admired you greatly, Madam.'

'He was in the theatre night after night and I remember when we were playing Vanburgh's *Relapse* under the title of *A Day in Scarborough* and the audience showed their annoyance, how he publicly defended me.'

'Madam was wise to spurn the gentleman. He has not a good reputation with the ladies.'

'But since it is his Duchess who invites me . . .'

'Madam will not refuse to grace their company with her presence.'

'I am of a half mind to refuse, Armistead. Perhaps the Prince would not like me to go.'

'But this is his uncle!'

'A well-known seducer.'

'His Highness was pleased to act most affectionately with him in the Park and I cannot help feeling that it would give him a great deal of pleasure if he knew you visited his uncle's house.'

'I am not sure, Armistead.'

Mrs Armistead, knowing that it was Mr Fox's wish that Perdita should visit Cumberland House, was determined to persuade her mistress to do so; and Perdita was so bemused with the daily letters from her lover that she allowed herself to be persuaded.

It was with a sense of a good piece of work completed that Mrs Armistead put on her becoming cloak with its concealing hood–a gift from Perdita and therefore of excellent cut and material–and hurried to Mr Fox's lodgings in St James's to tell him that the first step in his mission was accomplished.

Such pleasant company at Cumberland House! And how they had acclaimed Perdita! The Duchess was quite charming to her, and although Perdita was a little uneasy in the presence of such a woman and was a little afraid that such dazzling good looks might draw attention from her own, she could remind herself that the Duchess was considerably older than she was and that she, Perdita, had youth on her side.

There she met old friends. Sheridan was present, enchanting the company with his witty sayings; and with him his Amoret, so he had little time to spare for Perdita. She had no cause to complain. Mr Fox was charming to her; Lord Malden of course could always be relied upon to play the faithful swain; and the Duc de Chartres paid marked attention.

She was not of course interested. She did not wish it to reach Florizel's ears that she had encouraged the attentions of that notorious roué from across the Channel.

'How pleased I should be,' the Duchess whispered to her, 'if our beloved Prince could be here.'

Perdita blushed becomingly; and the Duchess continued in the most friendly manner: 'Perhaps in the future I shall have the pleasure of being hostess to you both . . . together.'

If that was not an indication that she would be accepted in some of the family circles, Perdita was not sure what was.

She went home flushed with triumph and confided in Mrs Armistead during her disrobing.

The Prince's impatience was increasing. When, oh when, was he going to see her, to hold her in his arms, to tell her by word of mouth of his devotion. He could not live on letters for ever.

'Patience,' she replied. She would not have him act rashly. He must never forget that he was heir to the Crown.

To which he replied impetuously that he was ready to forget–and forgo–everything if he might but be the lover of Mrs Robinson. It was now May, nearly six months since he had seen her in *The Winter's Tale* and he had not yet kissed her lips. Something must be done.

She was kept busy at the theatre. She played Mrs Brady in *The Irish Widow* and went on to a stupendous success in the part of Eliza Camply in *The Miniature Picture*. People crowded to the theatre to see her in this part because during it she masqueraded as Sir Harry Revel, which meant that she appeared on the stage in breeches. These set off her fine figure to perfection, revealing her shapely limbs, and the people went mad with joy over her, and demanded Mrs Robinson in more breeches parts.

When she appeared at Ranelagh or the Rotunda and the Pantheon, she was surrounded by people who came to look at her. She was becoming notorious, for many people believed that she was in fact the mistress of the Prince of Wales.

And then Lord Malden came with a very special gift for her.

'Madam,' he said, 'it is imperative that you give His Highness some satisfaction or I fear for his health. He is pining away. He has sent you this gift as a sign of his devotion and good faith. I beg of you accept it and help to restore His Highness to his former robust health.'

'He is ill?' She was all concern.

'Pining for you, Madam.'

She opened the package and turned pale and then red as she glanced at it. It was a bond for twenty thousand pounds which His Highness would honour at his coming of age. This was sealed by the royal arms.

Twenty thousand pounds! How long would it take her to earn so much in the theatre with Mr Sheridan always hinting at cuts in salaries because in spite of full houses he could not make ends meet.

Twenty thousand pounds! It sounded almost as joyous as wedding bells in her ears.

There was a letter from Florizel. He implored her to take this gift because it would show her confidence in him. He hoped he had not offended her by offering it but it was given from the depth of his heart. He would like to lay all he had at the feet of his fair Perdita.

Her eyes filled with tears, but she did not let them fall; they were so disastrous to the complexion and she never for one moment forgot what an ardent admirer Lord Malden was.

'The Prince is the most generous of men, but I could not accept such a gift.'

'But Madam, it will break His Highness's heart if you don't.'

'Wrong constructions could be placed on such a gift.'

'His Highness would be desolate if you placed any but the right ones.'

'I know . . . I know . . . I never for one moment doubted *his* intentions. But if it were known . . .'

'Why should it be known?'

'You must take it away. Tell him the whole notion is repugnant to me.'

'I dare not, Madam. You cannot believe how deeply upset the Prince can be on your account.'

'How I wish he could have all he deserves.'

'It is in your power to give it to him, Madam. I fear he will become ill if he does not see you soon.'

'Take this away!' She picked up the bond. Malden laid his hand lightly on it but did not take it–nor did she release it.

'At least do not make a hasty decision, Madam. Think of the Prince.'

'I am thinking of him . . . constantly. Not what would be best for me but for him.'

'Hold the bond here for a while, I beg of you. To return it now would be such a blow to him.'

'Very well, I will do that. But I have no intention of taking it.'

Lord Malden left and Mrs Armistead learned from her mistress that she had received the bond. She even was allowed to study it. 'You are so clever at that sort of thing, Armistead.'

A bond sealed with the royal seal, for £20,000 to be paid when the Prince came of age. There was no doubt about it. There it was in black and white.

At the earliest opportunity she reported to Mr Fox.

'She says she will not take it but she will. She studies it even more constantly than she does his letters . . . and more lovingly. She will accept it.'

'And once she has,' mused Mr Fox, for he was finding Mrs Armistead worth a confidence or two, 'the meeting will take place. The Prince will gain a mistress and I shall lose a thousand guineas.'

He kissed Mrs Armistead lightly on the forehead as though to say Well done, thou good and faithful servant.

Their relationship was changing. Attraction was springing up between them which might have seemed incongruous. She was so neat, fastidious in her cleanliness; he so slovenly; she a servant in the house of an actress and he a welcome guest in high society.

They were both aware of the incongruity of this attraction because it was of the mind as well as the body; but it was none the less irresistible because of this.

She would keep the bond, she explained to Lord Malden, because she feared that to return it would hurt the Prince's susceptibilities.

'It is true,' replied Malden.

'I fear it to be a little indelicate to take it . . . but I see no alternative.'

There was no alternative, Malden assured her.

And she bowed her head.

And each day she looked at it, at those magic words Twenty thousand pounds, and the royal seal. It is after all, she told herself, a measure of his devotion to me. I must try to see it in the spirit in which it is meant.

And after accepting the bond it was a short step to a meeting.

When? the Prince was constantly demanding, and Perdita knew that she could hold out no longer.

She explained to Lord Malden.

'The Prince is asking me to give up my career, my husband . . . my reputation for his sake. Oh, do not mistake me. I would gladly give my life for him. I fear, though, the anger of the King and Queen. And what if he should change towards me? I should have no wish to live.'

Lord Malden reminded her of the paper heart which had come with the miniature. 'Unalterable to my Perdita through Life.'

'Madam, all this time when you have refused to meet him he has been faithful. How much more so will he be when you are his.'

'Do you believe that, Lord Malden?'

'With all my heart,' said Malden.

'And when the world knows what I have done . . .'

'Yours is a triumph of chastity,' he told her.

A triumph of chastity! The expression appealed to her. Yes, she could see it that way. For nearly six months the Prince had sighed for her, implored her to meet him; and always she had replied that he must consider his position, that she must not think of her own desires but what was best for him.

And now at last she was capitulating; and it was a triumph of chastity.

The Meeting at Kew

The Prince was delighted, impatient and angry. The meeting must take place, but where? Never before had he raged so fiercely against the way he was treated. Here he was almost eighteen and a Prince of Wales and he could not freely arrange a meeting with the lady of his choice! Their meeting must be a secret in case it reached the ears of his parents.

He paced up and down his apartments, raging to Frederick and Lord Malden.

'You remember where you used to meet Harriot Vernon,' suggested Frederick.

'I could never meet Perdita there.'

'My house in Dean Street is at Your Highness's service,' said Malden.

The Prince looked hopeful. 'That's a better idea.'

'But,' said Frederick, 'you could never go to Dean Street and it not be known. People recognize you passing through the streets. Moreover, it is too far. You would be away too long. There would be enquiries. What if the King decided to send for you as he did for that game of chess?'

The Prince looked in dismay at his brother. Frederick was right.

'There is only one answer,' he said. 'She must come to Kew.'

'To Kew, sir!' cried Malden, aghast.

Frederick's eyes were alight with excitement. 'We shall smuggle her into the Dower House. She should come in breeches–her Sir Harry Revel costume. . . and no one would know who she was.'

'It's the answer,' said the Prince. 'Fred, you have talent.'

'In breeches!' cried Perdita, aghast. 'That would be quite out of the question. I should feel so . . . indelicate.'

'It would mean,' Lord Malden explained, 'that you would not be easily recognized.'

'And if I were? Imagine! The scandal! Oh no, no. I could not do it.'

'It was the best plan we could think of.'

'I could never do it,' said Perdita firmly.

Finally, it was decided that there was something in Frederick's first idea. The meeting must be highly secret and the only safe spot would be out of doors. The Prince would at least have an opportunity of talking to his love, of clasping her in his arms and making plans for the future; and all he had to remember was that in three months' time he would be eighteen, have his own establishment and then be free to come and go as he wished.

'Your Highness has waited six months,' pointed out Lord Malden. 'In another three all will be settled to your satisfaction.'

The Prince retorted that he had no intention of waiting three more months for Perdita, but they would have a meeting in any case. Lord Malden was to go ahead and make plans without delay.

He came to see Perdita and looking at her with yearning eyes told her of the arrangements.

'I will take you to Brentford and from there row you out to Eel Pie Island. There we will dine and after that I will row you to Kew Gardens where the Prince will be waiting for you.'

'I am glad,' she told him, 'that you will be accompanying me. You will make me feel . . . secure.'

At this Lord Malden dropped to his knees and taking her hand covered it with kisses.

'Madam, all these months when I have been pleading another's cause I have been filled with a mad desire to plead my own.'

'I know, my lord.'

'It has been a well-nigh irresistible temptation to me. If it had been any man but the Prince . . .'

'I know. I know. You have been both loyal and faithful. It is something I shall never forget.'

Her eyes filled with tears; she dashed them away dramatically. She could almost hear the applause of the audience, the murmurs of 'None can play a scene like this to compare with Mrs Robinson'. In fact she had an audience. Mrs Armistead had her eye to the keyhole and knew that her lady was to dine with Lord Malden on Eel Pie Island and then be rowed by that self-sacrificing lover to the Prince.

'I have decided that there shall be a meeting between me and the Prince.'

Mrs Armistead feigned surprise.

'Oh, yes, Armistead. He has pleaded with me so earnestly that I can no longer refuse him.'

'I understand, Madam.'

'And we are going to Brentford tomorrow.'

'*We*, Madam?'

'The coach will call for me and take me to Lord Malden's house in Dean Street where he will join me and together we shall ride to Brentford.'

'You will go alone, Madam, to Brentford with my lord Malden?'

'Why, Armistead . . .'

Mrs Armistead's features had formed themselves into an expression of horror. Then almost immediately they returned to their familiar respectful state. 'Forgive me, Madam. I forget my place.'

'No . . . no, pray go on.'

'Well, Madam, begging your pardon, I should have thought it unwise for you to go . . . alone with Lord Malden on such a journey. If you were seen and recognized . . . Madam must forgive me. I think of your reputation.'

'But, I have . . .'

'Madam, when ladies travel their maids accompany them . . . not only for reasons of propriety but in case their toilettes should need some attention.'

Perdita was smiling, and yet again asking herself what she would do without Armistead.

In the coach that rattled along to Dean Street Mrs Armistead sat very upright, her hands folded in her lap. She was not thinking of the excited young woman opposite her, who was deep in her own thoughts.

Could it possibly be, Mrs Armistead was asking herself. Mr Fox himself! Many people of humble circumstances had probably been his mistresses . . . briefly. She had no doubt that in the first instance he had decided that she herself was worthy of a brief dalliance. But surely this was something deeper? She could not contemplate it with her usual good sense. She had always been clever, and when the late Mr Armistead had left her unprovided for she had chosen this profession–for a purpose. As a lady's maid to an actress she would have opportunities. She had briefly before coming to Mrs Robinson served Mrs Abington. The possibilities were there; but she had not visualized anything like the present situation. Nor could it have come about if she had not had the great good luck to serve a mistress who had attracted the Prince of Wales. This could bring her into the most exalted circles. She could work so well for Mr Fox because the outcome of the affair was of equal importance to them both.

Mr Fox. Oddly enough for all his greatness she saw him as a man in need of care. It was his weakness which appealed to her as much as his strength. She had learned a great deal about him, that some years earlier, his father Lord Holland had paid £140,000 to settle his debts. Lord Holland was dead now and had left Charles James Kingsgate Castle which had had to be sold. There was a jingle sung in the streets about the great man.

'If he touches a card, if he rattles a box,
Away fly the guineas of this Mr Fox.'

She did not glorify him as Perdita glorified her Prince. She did not wish to clothe him with virtues he did not possess. She would not deny that he was short and fat and rather gross, but there was a look of his ancestor, Charles

II, in his face, and his slovenly cravat, his none too clean coat, were forgotten when he talked. One could not be in the company of Mr Fox without recognizing his greatness and his charm–but it was his weakness that touched the cool serene heart of Mrs Armistead deeply.

Perdita would have been astonished if she could have read the thoughts of her lady's maid. She would not have been able to imagine that the woman's affairs could be thought of–even by herself–when they were on the brink of this stupendous adventure.

Was her gown suitable? Indian muslin and not too decorated with ribbons.

'So becoming, Madam,' had soothed Armistead. 'I have never seen you look so beautiful.'

And what would *he* say when he saw her?

She was rehearsing what she would say to him over and over again. A woodland scene in Kew Gardens. There was a moon and the weather was fine. It would be like a Shakespearian scene. She would play it with the utmost emphasis on romance.

And the Prince . . . what was he doing at this moment? She pictured his impatience. She could already hear his impassioned words. How handsome he would look and the diamonds flashing on his coat would be real, not paste as worn by mock princes on the stage.

This was romance.

The coach had come to a stop at Lord Malden's door. He was waiting. He seated himself beside Mrs Armistead so that he could gaze in rapture at Perdita throughout the journey. Very little was said. Mrs Armistead's presence was a restraining factor; but Perdita saw that although Lord Malden was disappointed that there should be a third member of the party he applauded the wisdom of it.

Silence prevailed for most of the journey; each occupant busy with his and her own thoughts. Mrs Armistead continued to think of Mr Fox, Perdita of her Prince and Lord Malden of Perdita; and at length they arrived at Brentford where the boat was waiting to take them over to Eel Pie Island.

At the island inn a room had been prepared that Perdita might use before taking dinner, and to this she repaired with Armistead, 'to rest,' she told Lord Malden, 'for indeed I fear my heart may fail me.'

In the room she gave what Mrs Armistead later reported to Mr Fox a study of the doubts and apprehensions of a woman on the brink of taking a mighty decision which she had long since made up her mind to take for the adequate reward.

'Armistead, I cannot do it. Am I right? Don't forget who he is. If the King learned of this night, what would he do? I have to remember that the Prince will one day be the King of this country. It could happen at any moment, Armistead.'

'I don't think Madam should disturb herself too much on that score, Madam. His Majesty is a comparatively young man, some forty-two years old. He should have many years left to him.'

'I did not mean to be disloyal to His Majesty, but consider my position, Armistead.'

'Madam, I have considered it and it is one which most women would envy you.'

That pleased her, although she struck a tragedienne's role, putting her hand to her brow. 'The responsibility, Armistead. The responsibility!'

'Madam, I should think only of pleasing the Prince and leave the responsibility of everything else to others. I fear you will crumple your dress. And I think your hair needs a little attention.'

She was ready to listen to such sound advice. She was at the mirror. 'Yes, my hair, Armistead, my hair. Oh how right I was to bring you with me.'

'There!' Mrs Armistead had arranged the beautiful dark curls in what she considered their most becoming fashion. 'But you look a little melancholy, Madam, as though you are going to a burial rather than to meet a Prince who adores you.'

'It is a solemn moment, Armistead.'

'The Prince will be so happy that he may well consider it a gay one.'

'No, no, he will feel solemn too.'

'I have heard that he loves people about him to be gay. He has lived so long under the eyes of his solemn parents. He will look for laughter, not for tears.'

Perdita had become suddenly aloof. Who was this woman to tell her of the Prince's feelings?

'I am sure the Prince will be ready to fit into *my* mood.'

Mrs Armistead was alarmed. How long could it last if she were going to weep for her responsibilities and remind him constantly of what *she* was giving up. Oh, what a fool the woman was! Her folly might mean that very soon Mrs Armistead would be serving a woman who was nothing but an actress.

She hesitated; she had always adapted herself to her mistress's moods.

'He is a great Prince, Madam. The people adore him. He is the most popular young man in the country.'

This was better. Perdita was smiling.

'All his life people will have been fitting themselves in with *his* moods,' ventured Mrs Armistead. 'Everyone has fallen victim to his charm. The only one who has not is perhaps the King. But the King is important and the Prince has doubtless spent many hours in his father's company; he will be weary of melancholy. I would like to see Madam smiling and gay . . . for so she looks most beautiful.'

Perdita looked at her reflection. There was something in what Armistead said. She would be the woman who laughed and was merry for the sake of her lover and kept her melancholy locked away in her heart.

And so downstairs to dine and afterwards out to the boat which would row them over to Kew Gardens where the impatient lover would be waiting.

The boat was pushed out from Eel Pie Island. Perdita sat back listening to the sound of the oars skimming the water. Lord Malden's eyes were fixed on the approaching bank. Mrs Armistead sat, the picture of discretion, back straight, arms folded in her lap.

Suddenly Lord Malden said: 'They're here.'

And they all looked and saw a white handkerchief waving in the dusk.

The boat touched earth. Lord Malden leaped out of the boat and helped Perdita to land. Mrs Armistead remained seated.

Two young men had appeared on the bank, one stood a little behind the other. Mrs Armistead, watching closely, saw the glittering diamond on the coat of the former and her heart leaped with excitement. The Prince of Wales in person; and behind him his brother Prince Frederick.

Then Malden was saying, 'Your Royal Highness, I have the honour to present Mrs Robinson.'

The Prince gave a cry of joy and gathered Mrs Robinson in his arms. Lord Malden turned back to the boat and got in. Prince Frederick stepped back a few paces; and the lovers remained locked in a fond embrace.

'Let us walk among the trees,' said the Prince. 'Oh Perdita . . . my beautiful Perdita, how I have waited for this moment.'

Perdita was too overcome by her emotions to play her part.

'But . . . my Prince . . . at last . . . we are together.'

'Never to part,' declared the Prince, quite unconscious of the figures in the boat or Frederick close by. 'This is the happiest moment of my life. But it is only the beginning, my precious Perdita.'

'Only the beginning,' she agreed.

'We must find a way of meeting. I will come to you. In a very short time . . .'

'Oh, my love,' she cried, 'you will soon be of age and then . . . and then . . . there will be no barriers.'

'You will never regret it, I swear. I shall adore you as long as I have breath in my body. No one in the world was ever loved as Florizel loves his Perdita.'

'George!' It was Frederick's voice, eager, alarmed. 'There are people coming this way.'

'The devil take them.'

'This is the only path. For God's sake, George . . .'

Perdita cried, 'I must go. There will be other times . . . This is only a beginning.'

Lord Malden too had heard the voices. He had jumped out of the boat and was approaching them.

'Your Royal Highness it would never do . . . if this were discovered . . .'

'He is right,' cried Perdita. 'Adieu, my Prince.'

The Prince seemed as though he was going to ignore the intruders and refuse to part with Perdita. But Frederick was pulling at his arm and Perdita was releasing herself.

'We shall meet soon . . .' she whispered.

'When, when?' demanded the Prince.

'It shall be when you wish,' she told him; and with that fled towards Lord Malden and the boat.

Perdita was in transports of delight while Mrs Armistead helped her disrobe.

'What a day, Armistead! What a day!'

'What a day indeed, madam. And the forerunner of many others like it, I daresay.'

'He is so impatient,' sighed Perdita fondly.

'He is an ardent lover, Madam.'

'Armistead, did you see him?'

'Not clearly, Madam.'

'He is very handsome. I never saw a man so handsome.'

'I rejoice for you, Madam.'

'Yes, Armistead, what have I done to deserve such devotion?'

Act on a stage, thought Armistead. Possess undoubted beauty. Hold him off for six months talking of virtue while all the time hinting at surrender. Well played, Madam. Yes, you do deserve a small success with His Highness.

'Madam is so beautiful–and I never saw you more so than tonight.'

'Do you think he was satisfied with me, Armistead?'

'There could have been no doubt of it.'

'Ah . . . Armistead. The grace of his person, the irresistible sweetness of his smile, the tenderness of his melodious yet manly voice will remain with me till every vision of this changing scene shall be forgotten.'

'I am sure he would be delighted to hear you say that, Madam.'

'Perhaps he will. I shall write it down so that I don't forget it. But I mean it, Armistead. I mean it from the bottom of my heart.'

'Madame is a poet as well as an actress and great beauty.'

Perdita smiled in a congratulatory manner at her reflection.

And so, said Mrs Armistead, reporting to Mr Fox, did she continue to applaud the good looks and accomplishment of her Prince on that night. It was indeed a step forward. Even Perdita knew now that there could be no holding back and she was prepared to become the mistress of the Prince of Wales.

Mr Fox calls on Mr Sheridan

That was the first of many meetings. The Prince declared that never had he been so happy in his life. He lived for the excitement of these encounters; and the knowledge that at any moment during them he could run into disaster only made them the more exciting.

Kew Gardens. Eel Pie Island. For ever more, he declared, these will be paradise to me.

Each encounter was an adventure in itself. Donning a dark coat he would slip out of the Dower Lodge and make his way to the appointed spot; there had been one occasion when it had been necessary to disguise himself–and Frederick–as watchmen. How they had laughed as they had planned climbing the walls and slipping away.

While this provided the romantic adventure it stirred up all the resentment in the Prince's mind. Why should it be necessary? he constantly demanded of Frederick. That they enjoyed it was beside the point. He was the Prince of Wales and he had to leave the Palace like a thief. And why–because of their father–that spoilsport of a king who thought the height of happiness was to go farming and make buttons and plans for the nursery, drink lemonade and play backgammon and who had never been unfaithful to his wife. Not that the Prince believed in infidelity. He would be faithful to Perdita until death, but at the same time Fred had to agree that their father was a dull dog and it would have been more natural–their mother being as she was–if he had a mistress or two.

Frederick agreed as he always did with his brother; and threw himself into the nocturnal adventures as though they were his own.

And then the meetings with Perdita–herself wrapped in a dark cloak–to walk under the trees, arms entwined, talking of the future, stopping every now and then to embrace while Frederick kept watch on one side and Malden and the lady's maid on the other.

This was wonderful at first but it could not satisfy an ardent lover to wander about the leafy glades of Kew, more often than not having to take a hasty farewell because of intruders.

There must be a better arrangement, and between them George, Frederick and Malden decided that they should make use of Eel Pie Island.

'It would be so much easier if Your Highness rowed over to the Island and Mrs Robinson was there to meet you.'

Frederick said: 'The inn people wouldn't dare. What if it reached my father's ears?'

There were ways and means, Malden pointed out. For instance, need the innkeeper and his servants know. They could be told it was a gentleman of high rank who visited them and if the Prince was sombrely clad and kept his face in shadow as much as possible, need they guess? He, Malden, would make all the arrangements; and it was surprising what a little persuasion could do if it was backed up by the right sort of 'appreciation'.

The Prince said it was an excellent idea. Malden must arrange it right away.

So Malden dropped a few bribes here and there, and a new trysting place was found for the lovers.

In the finest room the inn could provide they met while Prince Frederick sat outside the inn keeping a lookout and Malden, with him, thought enviously of the Prince's pleasure; and Mrs Armistead took careful note of every little incident so that she might not fail in her report to Mr Fox.

While the Prince was sporting with his mistress an alarming situation had sprung up. Lord George Gordon who had become President of the Protestant Association of England was stirring the capital to riot. Lord George–brother of Sarah Lennox's lover, the man by whom she had had an illegitimate child–was an insignificant fellow who determined to draw attention to himself by some means, and as he could not do so by his brilliance chose this way. He led his followers with shouts of 'No Popery' and the King was horrified to discover how quickly a crowd of ordinary people defending what they believe to be right can be turned into a mob bent on destruction.

During the hot days of June, the trouble increased. The homes of Catholics were burned to the ground; so were their places of worship; those members of Parliament who had supported the Catholic Relief Bill were similarly treated and many of them lost their homes; then the mob began attacking prisons. It was shocking to discover how quickly a great city could be in the grip of terror. The Palace of St James's itself and Buckingham House were in danger, and the guard had to be doubled.

The King remained in London; he was not going to leave the soldiers to protect his palaces while he remained at Kew. North suggested that the Prince should be in London. He was popular and his presence might have some effect on the people. The implication being, thought the King sadly, that he himself was not popular. What a sad state of affairs when a man who tried to live honourably and virtuously earned the dislike of his subjects while a young rip who thought of nothing but his own pleasure should have their regard!

But he would not have the Prince in London.

'What, heir to the throne placed in danger? You'd have that, eh, what?'

'What of Your Majesty?'

'My responsibility! Let the Prince stay with his tutor at Kew. Only a boy yet.'

Little did he guess that the boy was at that moment stealing out of the Dower Lodge to row over to Eel Pie Island and his mistress.

The King felt ill. A crisis always set his head zooming with hundreds of thoughts and ideas which he could not always comprehend. And such a crisis! Bloodshed. The stupid destruction that a mob of blood-crazy illiterate men and women could bring about, people who scarcely knew what they were fighting against–for it was not the members of the Protestant Association who were causing this trouble; it was the mob–that rag-taggle in any big city–beggars, thieves, prostitutes whose mean and sordid lives were brightened by a disaster such as this. He knew this and he had to stop it. But he would not allow the Prince of Wales to risk his life in London.

The King knew too when he went among the soldiers who were guarding the Palace that at any moment someone might kill him. It was by no means a wild impossibility. He thought of an occasion little over a year ago when, on alighting from his chair at the back stairs of St James's a woman had run up to him and seized him. He had not been afraid. He was never alarmed at such times. He felt no fear when he showed himself among the soldiers. It was not physical courage he lacked; there *were* things of which he was afraid–the loss of the Colonies, financial difficulties, government dissensions, the vices of his brothers and his sons, the voices in his head–but never of sudden death which could come perhaps to a king more likely than to one of his subjects. And this woman? He had spoken to her gently. He was always gentle with his poorer subjects, looking upon them as children to be cared for. 'What do you want, my good woman?' he had asked her. He would never forget the wildness of her eyes, the blankness in them. 'I am Queen Beck,' she told him. 'Get off the throne. It's mine.' Poor, poor creature! 'Do not harm her,' he had ordered. 'She is mad, poor soul.' He had a passionate desire to protect the mad from those who might be harsh with them. It was like his desire to protect the Quakers. Perhaps that was why he had been so ready to give his consent to the Catholic Reform Bill. Religious tolerance! Hannah had always wanted it for her own Society of Friends.

But this was not the time for brooding on the past. Action was needed. The riots must be stopped. If they were not, this could be the prelude to civil war. A war between Catholics and Protestants. It must never be. He wanted his country to be known as one where religious tolerance prevailed.

He sent for North and told him that the disturbances must be stopped without delay.

'We must get the better of these rebels before further damage is done,' he declared.

Lord North agreed on this, but was nervous.

George himself was undecided because he knew that only by calling out the military and proclaiming martial law could the rioting be stopped. It was a great decision to make and he was the only one who could make it. He alone could order his army to fire on his own subjects.

A sleepless night. Pacing up and down. The voices in his head were silent. There was only one problem with which to grapple. He forgot his anxiety about the Prince of Wales. He forgot everything but the need to stop the Gordon Riots.

The rioters were marching on the Bank of England. They must not be allowed to destroy this as they had Newgate Jail.

The King gave the order. The troops went into action. Several hundred people were killed but the Gordon Riots had been brought to an end.

The riots over, the King was surprised to find that his subjects were ready to give him back a little of that affection which over the years he had somehow lost. His action in giving the order to fire on the mob was approved of because it had been successful in dispersing the mob and ending the riots.

George felt strong. He was indeed that King which his mother had constantly urged him to be. There was no strong man to guide him. William Pitt was dead; he had a son who had yet to prove himself. Grenville was no longer in power, nor was Grafton. Lord Bute had when he first came to the throne stood beside him and he had never felt safe without him; his mother had advised him on every action he took. Now there was only Lord North and, firm friends that they were, the King did not expect great brilliance from North–only loyal friendship.

So he would govern alone, make his own decisions as he had over the Gordon Riots so satisfactorily. He was glad. He would work better on his own.

'Could never abide a lot of magpies chattering round me,' he said aloud. 'I'll stand alone. I'll show them I am their king, eh.'

In such a mood he went down to Kew for a breath of country air and a little peace and quiet.

Charlotte was glad to see him–very obviously pregnant now. He told her about the riots, for now that they were over she could offer no interference.

He sat with the children and told them what had happened. He had played such a decisive part, and it was good for them to learn how affairs were conducted.

He took young Mary on his knee and looking round at the pink faces, the big eyes, the heavy chins–they all looked so much alike and so like himself–he explained how he came to his decision, through prayer and meditation, which was how they should all solve their problems.

The Queen said that Lord George Gordon was clearly mad and in her opinion mad people could not be blamed for their actions.

'Your Majesty will remember when we were driving through Richmond in an open chaise . . . now it would be just after the birth of William . . .' Fifteen-year-old William looked very pleased with himself. 'And Charlotte . . .' The Queen smiled at her fourteen-year-old daughter . . . 'was on the way and had not yet put in her appearance.' She remembered all her dates through the births of her children. 'Yes, we were riding through Richmond, your Papa and myself, when a man and woman began to shout at us. And then . . . the woman threw something at me. It landed right in my lap. What do you think it was?'

'A knife!' shouted William.

'Flowers,' cried ten-year-old Elizabeth.

Augustus, the seven-year-old, began to gasp and tried to hide the fact. He did not want to get a beating for not being able to breathe because the King believed the cane was a cure for asthma.

'Both wrong,' cried the Queen. 'It was her shoe. She had taken it off to throw it at me.'

'Wasn't that wicked?' asked William.

'It was wrong, but your Papa was kind and said there was to be no punishment. She could in fact have been put to death.'

William whistled.

'Pray do not do that,' said the Queen. 'It sounds like a stable boy.'

The King frowned and William immediately tried to efface himself. He did not want to be sentenced to a caning. Nor did the Queen wish him to be, so she immediately began telling another story which she knew would please the King.

'I remember once when a basket was left at one of the gates. I wonder whether His Majesty remembers . . .' Queen Charlotte looked at her husband and went on quickly: 'But of course your Papa has so much to remember . . . affairs of state . . . he can not be expected to remember these little things.'

'What was in the basket, Mamma?' asked William.

'Can you guess?'

The children all had a guess each but none of them was right.

'A little baby,' cried the Queen triumphantly. 'It was about two months old.'

'Was it a present for Papa?' asked Elizabeth.

'Oh . . . no . . . not for Papa specially. But your Papa found a home for it.'

'And did it live happily ever after?'

'If it was good,' said the Queen piously. 'And what do you think it was called?'

The children guessed again, several of them suggesting their own names.

'It was a boy,' the Queen told them. 'George . . . George was the name. The same as your Papa's.'

'And our brother's,' William reminded her.

There was silence. The King looked round the family circle as though he had not before noticed the absence of his eldest son.

'It's a pity that our eldest son does not see fit to honour a *family* occasion with his presence.'

'Frederick is not here either,' the Queen reminded him, as though excusing the Prince.

'Where George is, Frederick will be,' William told them.

The Queen silenced her son with a look.

'Would Your Majesty care for a little music?'

'I want to know why the Prince of Wales and his brother behave as though they are apart from the rest of us.'

'They are growing up,' sighed the Queen.

'They should have been here.' The King looked round him and one of his pages immediately came to him.

'Go to the Dower Lodge at once,' he said. 'Tell the Prince of Wales and Prince Frederick that I command their attendance without delay. Did you hear that? Without delay, eh, what?'

'Yes, Your Majesty.' The page disappeared and the King glowered into space, and neither the Queen's attempts to amuse him nor the chatter of his children could divert him from his irritation with his eldest son.

Nor was his mood improved when shortly afterwards the page returned to report that neither the Prince nor his brother could be found in the Dower Lodge.

The King looked at his watch. 'Is this not the time when they should be doing their private study?'

'On a fine afternoon like this they might decide to do it in the gardens,' suggested the Queen.

The King replied: 'If they are shirking their lessons . . .' And he immediately felt frustrated, for if he attempted to question his sons, George would in a few minutes show him that he was so much more educated than his father and would immediately have the advantage. He had that way with him–which was growing more and more obvious–of mocking his father without saying anything that could be complained of. Young George was clever. He had been able to learn his lesson with the utmost ease; he had actually liked Greek and Latin and languages and literature and poetry; he could talk about pictures and artists in a way his father could not understand. Yet he never seemed to try as his father had. The King's mind went back to those hours in the schoolroom when he had worked so hard and assimilated so little; and there was George, his son, even outstripping some of his tutors as though that was something he did without effort while he went on with the serious business of plaguing his father.

'The Prince is a natural scholar,' said the Queen quietly. 'I don't think he ever shirks his lessons. He likes them. Perhaps having completed their work they have taken a stroll. That is it.'

'There is a time for strolling,' muttered the King. 'I'll speak to the young puppy tomorrow.'

The Queen was relieved. Tomorrow. Yes, tomorrow.

Mrs Papendiek, the wife of one of the flautists who was in attendance on the Queen, wondered whether she ought to tell Her Majesty that something very strange was going on in the Dower House. She had actually seen the young Princes scaling the wall; and they went off regularly somewhere along the river.

Should I? Mrs Papendiek asked herself.

The Prince would be annoyed with her. She had mentioned the affair to her husband; he had said: 'Don't do anything to upset the Prince. Once he's of age there'll be no holding him. The King won't have the power to either. See and say nothing. It's safer.'

Yes, thought Mrs Papendiek, seeing the increased colour in the King's face and noting that he was speaking more quickly than normally, better to hold one's tongue.

The Queen said: 'I am sure Your Majesty would like a little music.'

The King agreed that he would, so the Queen soothed him by her skilful performance on the harpsichord.

It was July.

'Next month,' declared the Prince, 'I shall be eighteen years old. Even the King cannot deny me my privileges then.'

'Ah!' sighed Perdita. 'How I look forward to the day when we no longer have to meet in this clandestine way.'

'You shall have a fine establishment. The best house we can find.'

Perdita sighed and the Prince hurried on: 'You will be so happy in it and I shall be there all the time. The whole world shall know that it is the place where I most long to be.'

Perdita he knew felt her position deeply. She was a good woman and believed that a union could only be perfect if it were legal. The Prince hated legality. Already he was hedged in by rules, and to him no relationship could be as perfect as that which existed between himself and Perdita.

She could become melancholy easily, wondering if, in being with him in this way, she was sinful. The Prince did not wish to consider sin. He was interested only in pleasure. He would do everything in the world to please her, he assured her, but he thought that when they were together they should be happy.

For fear that she would brood on the loss of her reputation, for as soon as she was set up in that establishment which the Prince would provide for her, the whole of the Court–the whole of London–would know of their relationship, the Prince brought in a grievance of his own.

'I could not allow you to continue on the stage.'

She was silent.

'Oh, no, no,' he went on. 'I do not wish you to be paraded for other men to look at, to comment on.'

'But . . . it is my living.'

The Prince laughed. She was not going to *think* about money again. When he was eighteen he would have an income, an establishment. By God, his Perdita forgot that the man who adored her, worshipped her, who would be faithful to the end of his days, was the Prince of Wales. No sordid considerations of money! No talk of working for a living! He would not *allow* her to continue on the stage. She was for him . . . for him alone.

She was not displeased at this display of authority. When the whole of London knew the position it would have been a little humiliating to appear at the theatre, to be gazed at while everyone pictured her with the Prince. No, she was not displeased at all.

But she performed a touching renunciation scene. She told him of how Mr Garrick himself had prophesied a great future for her; of the days when he himself tutored her; and would Mr Garrick have concerned himself with anything short of genius? The Prince should have seen her Juliet. 'Pale pink satin. Spangles of silver. White feathers. But the most becoming scene was the last. My transparent gauze veil fell from the back of my head to my feet.'

'Yes, and you looked like an angel. But no more stage. Do you think I will allow anyone to gaze at you in breeches!'

'Ah, those breeches parts! Some thought them my best. But all this I will give up . . . for you.'

More lovemaking. More professions of eternal devotion.

When she was home in her bedroom she told Mrs Armistead: 'I am looking forward to the adjusting of His Royal Highness's establishment for the public avowal of our mutual attachment.'

It was mid-morning when Mrs Armistead, after having given her mistress a dish of chocolate in bed, said she must go out as there were several items she needed such as ribbons, rouge and patches.

She might be gone for a couple of hours but in view of Madam's being so late the previous night, she was sure the rest in bed would do her the world of good and she would of course wish to be fresh for the trip to Eel Pie Island.

Wrapping her cloak about her and pulling its hood well over her head she left the house and, instead of making her way to the market, went straight to St James's Street where Mr Fox had his lodgings. His servant, knowing that his master always received her whatever the hour, ushered her in and went to tell Mr Fox that she had arrived.

'Bring the lady in,' cried Mr Fox; and Mrs Armistead was a little astonished to be taken into his bedroom.

'I rarely rise before eleven,' he told her; and indeed he was wearing a linen nightgown which was none too clean. Mrs Armistead wondered angrily why his servants did not take the soiled nightgown away and put out a new one. His hair, which was black and thick, was dishevelled.

He laughed at her dismay for although she had believed she was hiding it, she had for a second betrayed it.

'Yes,' he said, 'If I were female you might with reason call me a slut.'

'Sir!'

He laughed at her and putting his hands on her shoulders studied her face.

'Do you know, Mrs Armistead, at one time I, my friend Richard Fitzpatrick and my cousin the Earl of Carlisle were regarded as the three best dressed men in London? Times change and we change with them, eh. Look at me now. You could not, in reason, call me the best dressed man in London.'

'I would not call you dressed at all, sir.'

'Stop calling me sir,' he said. 'And I refuse to call you Mrs Armistead.'

'My name was Elizabeth Bridget Cane before I married Mr Armistead.'

'Well Lizzie, now you have formally introduced yourself and I am very pleased that we have become good friends.'

'I came to tell you that Mrs Robinson is going to give up the stage.'

He grimaced. 'Sheridan won't like that. He's playing to excellent business. Everyone wants to see Mrs Robinson. It's rumoured, but the audience is not certain, that she is the mistress of the Prince of Wales.'

'When the Prince has his establishment he is going to set her up in a house.'

Fox nodded.

'Their little affair goes according to plan. There are other matters.'

He was looking at her intently. She had known it must come to this; and when it did of course this would not be the end. There was more between them than a passing desire for a handsome lady's maid on his side and the need not to offend an important man on hers.

As he came nearer she did not draw back. He took her hand and she let it rest in his.

Sheridan sat in his office at the theatre surrounded by playbills, plays which had been sent in for reading, and bills which he chose to ignore because he knew he could not settle them.

He was surprised when Mr Charles James Fox was announced. They were acquainted and had an admiration for each other; but as yet their interests had been divergent. Sheridan followed political affairs with a mild interest; Fox was an occasional visitor to the theatre; but Sheridan, himself a Whig, had been impressed by Fox's adroit manoeuvres and Fox by *The School for Scandal* and *The Rivals*.

But why, wondered Sheridan, had the important gentleman seen fit to call upon him?

'Mr Fox, sir, at your service,' he said.

'At yours, sir. I trust this is not an inconvenient hour to call?'

'Any hour would be convenient to receive a visit from Mr Fox.'

Fox laughed to imply they could dispense with trite formalities.

'Business is booming, I see,' said Mr Fox. He was well aware that although business boomed so did Sheridan's debts. Sheridan was a gambler and a gay liver; moreover, he was of an intellectual calibre to match Fox's. Such kindred spirits were rare.

Sheridan, knowing that Fox would be well aware of his financial difficulties, shrugged his shoulders and nodded in the direction of the pile of bills. No need to excuse himself to a man who had been–was constantly–in a similar position.

'So tiresome,' said Mr Fox, 'to have to pay for one's pleasures!'

'But if one did not make a pretence of doing so we should have every Tom, Dick and Harry scrambling for them. Would there be enough to go round?'

'I do not think it would be beyond the powers of our invention to create new ones, Mr Sheridan.'

Sheridan opened a cupboard and brought out two glasses.

Without speaking he filled them and handed one to Fox.

'Your very good health, sir, and good fortune to the project you have come here to discuss with me this day.'

Fox laughed. 'Mr Sheridan, your talents are considerable. Words are your forte. The same thing applies to me. To be brief I have come to suggest that you stand for Parliament.'

'Did I hear you aright, sir?'

'As a Whig. You are a Whig, sir. No doubt of that.'

Sheridan lifted his glass. 'To wine, women and Whigs, sir.'

Mr Fox drank and said: 'So, Mr Sheridan?'

'Mr Fox, sir. I am sitting here among my accounts, doing my theatre business with no thought of taking on the office of Lord of the Treasury.'

'You will not be hurried into that position quite yet, Mr Sheridan.'

'But no one enters politics surely without dreaming of the Great Seal. It is the Field Marshal's baton . . . it is the Admiral's . . . Forgive me, sir, but what is the insignia of our sea lords? Is it the holy grail?'

'Dream of it then, Mr Sheridan! Dream of it! You are too clever a man to concentrate all your efforts into one undertaking. Your plays . . . your theatre . . . yes, excellent for an ordinary man. But you are not an ordinary man, Mr Sheridan. You have a touch of genius. Give it to your country.'

'Are there not too many at this moment offering their genius to the country? See what such genius has done. Lost us the American Colonies, for one thing.'

'Alas, politicians are legion; genius is rare. North is the biggest blundering idiot that ever held the Great Seal. And H.M. clings to him. Why? Because he sees himself as a Supreme Ruler. In that addled head of his he's thinking of Divine Rights. North and the King. By God, what a pair. I have to put the King and his Tories out of office, Mr Sheridan; and I can only do that by putting the Whigs in.'

'Surely the people are behind the Government.'

'Mr Sheridan, you will have to learn your politics. The people will be Tory one day and Whig the next and it is our task to see that they are Whig the day after and the week after and the year after. How do we do it? By teaching them, educating them, by making them realize what a holy mess we're in, what the loss of the colonies mean to us.'

'We?'

'Those of us who have the power to do so. Men who are on familiar and caressing terms with the English language.'

'Like Mr Fox for instance.'

'Mr Fox, sir, and Mr Sheridan.'

'A place in politics . . . a Member of Parliament,' mused Sheridan.

Fox leaned forward. 'If the right party were in power it could be a high place in the Government. It would be a different life from this . . .' Fox waved his hand with a faintly disparaging gesture. 'You would be the friend of anyone you chose to meet. I personally would see that you were a member of Brooks' . . . or any club you fancied. You would be welcome in the most noble houses. Oh, I know these are the outward trappings of power . . . of no importance in themselves. But they are a measure of success.'

'You speak as though Power is the ultimate goal of all men.'

'Men such as you and myself, Mr Sheridan. We were sent in the world with our talents. Is it not incumbent upon us to use them?'

'I am using mine. I think I have written plays which will be performed a hundred years hence. If the Playmaker Sheridan is not forgotten after he's dead is that not enough?'

'It depends on what talents you arrived with, Mr Sheridan. A brilliant playwright . . . yes. And the theatre will rejoice in that talent for years. Generations will rise up and call you blessed. But this country is rushing ahead to disaster. Pitt saw it, but he was defeated by the gout and changing his title from The Great Commoner to Chatham. Politicians can't afford to make mistakes. By God, Mr Sheridan, it's the most exciting game on earth. Loo, Faro, Macao, Hazard! You haven't gambled until you've played politics.'

Sheridan's eyes were shining and Fox knew that he would achieve his purpose.

He leaned forward. 'This, Mr Sheridan, sir, is a turning point in British politics. Our monarchs carry a certain power. True they cannot act without the backing of their governments but the power is there. The King–between men of good sense–is far from clever. I won't say he's a fool . . . not for fear of committing lese-majesty but because it is not entirely true. George is a simpleton. He should have been a farmer. A good man let us say . . . who has never known the pleasures of life, and who feels it his duty to see that these are kept from others. A failing of the virtuous, Mr Sheridan, as I'm sure you will agree. But what H.M. fails to see is that the pleasures a man indulges in are not his whole life. A man can be a brilliant politician in the House, a lecher in the bedchamber and a gambler at the clubs. A politician can set the country's economy to rights while he's at his wits' end to know how to placate his own creditors. Mr Pitt happened to be a model husband and a great politician at the same time. That in itself provided his downfall. He didn't become Lord Chatham for his own sake . . . but that of Lady Chatham. And that, one might say, was the end of his career. So you see, Mr Sheridan, this is the greatest gamble and I know that your fingers are itching to have a throw of the dice.'

Sheridan was silent, turning over the possibilities in his mind. It seemed a glittering prospect because this was not merely going into Parliament–it was going in arm in arm with Mr Fox.

Mr Fox continued: 'As I was saying, the King has a certain power and the King is my enemy, and that of the Whigs. But a new star is rising and to this star shall we hitch our wagon. The Prince of Wales will be eighteen in August. He will be to us what the King is to the Tories.'

'The Prince! A young man bent on pleasure!'

'Don't underestimate him. Bent on pleasure certainly. Young, lusty and so far kept under the stern eye of their Majesties. "Eat this. Don't eat that". "Get up at this hour. Go to bed at that." Now what effect is this going to have on a young fellow whose high spirits are higher than average? There is one answer: Rebellion. Believe me, Mr Sheridan, the Prince has a very good reason to support the Whigs. His father is a Tory. That is the only reason he needs at this stage. Later he will find others. Don't make old George's mistake of thinking that because young George frolics with the ladies, selects his shoe buckles with care, has a passion for gold frogged coats and exquisitely cut breeches, that he's a fool. He has been educated and significantly has made no effort to elude that education. He has the power to make his father feel a dunce in his presence. He is a boy . . . not yet eighteen . . . but time does not stand still. In three years time he will be the most powerful man in the country and . . . our friend.'

'*Our* friend, Mr Fox?'

'Yours and mine.'

'But I have not yet made up my mind to go into politics.'

'You will.'

Mr Fox drained his glass and rose.

'So Turtles Pair'

While Sheridan was thinking of Fox's proposition he received another visitor.

Very different this one–a vision of beauty in muslin and ribbons and a dark silk coat.

'Perdita!' Like everyone else he called her by that name nowadays. The Prince had given it to her and it was an indication that everyone was aware of the relationship between them.

He kissed her hands with a fervour which she was too distraught to see was absentminded.

'Oh, Sherry, I have something to say to you, and I fear you may be a little angry with me.'

'Never,' he declared gallantly.

'I scarcely know how to begin.' A faint smile curled Sheridan's lips. Of course she would have been rehearsing the scene for hours before she came. He knew his Perdita.

'My dearest, you look distrait. Is all well between you and the Prince?'

She threw back her head and a smile illuminated her face. By God, he thought, how beautiful she is when she smiles. She should smile constantly. What a fool she is to cultivate this melancholy aspect! He won't like it. She won't last if she is not careful.

'The Prince is magnificent. The grace of his person . . . the sweetness of his smile . . .'

'Yes,' said Sheridan. He had heard that before.

'He is quite . . . irresistible.' That was the excuse clause, he thought. She was his mistress–but only because he was irresistible.

'But you have not come to tell me of his perfections, I am sure, because, as you know, I am well aware of them. Come, Perdita, what is on your mind?'

'The Prince can be very masterful.'

'Naturally. He is a Prince and in spite of Papa's restrictions I've no doubt he gets his way with everyone else.'

'Believe me, Sherry, this distresses me. Not on my own account . . . oh, no,

I am ready to make any sacrifices . . . but I do wonder how you will receive this news. Oh, my dear, what are you going to say?'

'I will tell you when I hear what it is.'

She lowered her eyes and stood before him in a pose of abject distress.

'The Prince insists that I leave the stage.'

Sheridan was silent. He pictured it; the falling off of business. There was Abington and Farran. Perhaps he could revive *The School*; but although it was a favourite the people were crying out for new plays–though while Mrs Robinson paraded the boards, particularly in breeches, they did not so much care what the play was.

He could not pretend that this was not a disaster.

'Oh, Sherry, Sherry, what could I do? I remonstrated but he was most emphatic. "No." he said, "I cannot have other men's eyes feasting on the charms of my loved one." You must confess, Sherry, that he has a point.'

'So,' said Sheridan, 'you are leaving the stage.'

'Oh, Sherry, Sherry, you know I don't want to. You know that I fought against it. But the Prince was adamant . . . and in the circumstances you must admit that I could not . . . with decency . . . remain.'

Oh, God, he thought, what a woman! She decided on the angle from which she would view life and made everything fit into her cosy pictures. What was she dreaming of now? One would think from her attitude that the Prince was proposing to marry her. Was she thinking that he would behave as his uncles Gloucester and Cumberland had? Did she realize that their Duchesses were very different women from herself? He could imagine her drawing herself up to her full height and declaiming that she hoped she did not resemble the Duchess of Cumberland whose morals and bawdy wit were the talk of the town. In one thing only, misguided Perdita. She is beautiful . . . and so are you. You lack her mental agility, her wit, her brilliance, her knowledge of the world . . . everything that has put her where she is. And dear Perdita, have you ever heard of the Royal Marriage Bill? No descendant of George I is allowed to marry without the consent of the sovereign. And do you think His Most Holy Majesty will agree to his son's marriage with a play actress? Silly little Perdita . . . moth dancing round the candle. How many months . . . weeks . . . before your pretty wings are singed and you fall to the ground? And then . . . what will you have? A career that is over. Do you think the theatre will allow you to throw her aside and then meekly take you back?

He should warn her, of course. He had been quite fond of her once. Not that it would be of any use. Her mind was made up. She, with all her reluctance, with all her mock propriety, wanted to be set up in that establishment, wanted the whole world to know that the most eligible bachelor in Europe had chosen her. Briefly, Perdita, briefly! But that thought of course must not be allowed to disturb her golden dream.

Sheridan sighed. 'I could almost thank God that Mr Garrick is not here to see this day.'

'Mr Garrick? What has he to do with this?'

'What indeed! Did he not teach you what you most needed to know when you most needed it? Mr Garrick would never have understood your throwing away a great career.'

'Mr Garrick understood the theatre so well, but did not understand love.'

'I'll warrant he did. Could he have been the greatest actor otherwise? So you will leave us.' He looked at her. He must warn her. He would not forgive himself otherwise.

'Perdita, this is a big step you are taking.'

She nodded dramatically.

'Princes are perhaps more fickle than most men.'

'What are you suggesting?'

'What if this love should not last?'

'He has sworn to be faithful till death.'

'By the moon, the inconstant moon, Juliet?'

'He swore by all he holds most sacred.'

'What a man holds sacred one day he finds profane the next. I am an old friend, Perdita. Take care. Consider before you throw away a certain future for an uncertain one.'

'I cannot grasp your meaning.'

'Because you will not. Has it not occurred to you that the Prince might desire another woman?'

'I see you make the common mistake of presuming this is an ordinary light affair.'

'I hope I am making that mistake, Perdita.'

'But I know you are. And I know you, Sherry. You are angry with me . . . that is why you say these things. I am not ungrateful. I know what you have done for me. Mistake that not. But this is my future. I must obey the Prince.'

'For if you did not he would cast you aside?'

She flushed. 'Never. But I must think of him . . . first. I owe it to him.'

'You mean the Prince's mistress should not appear on the boards.'

'Sherry!'

He laughed inwardly. What a woman. She could not bear the use of that word which was commonly used to describe what she was. He felt an affection for poor Perdita. She was such a fool. And this was particularly noticeable after one had so recently been in the company of Mr Fox.

Mr Fox! His mind was alert. This very day Mr Fox had called to offer a dazzling prospect . . . this day when Perdita had come to offer her resignation.

Could there be any significance in this? Could Mr Fox have known she would come? But how could he? He was only just acquainted with Perdita. And she would never have confided in him. And yet . . . here was this new proposition side by side with the certainty that theatrical business must suffer a setback.

Suppose Mr Fox wished no obstacle to be put in the way of this love affair between the Prince and Perdita–suppose it was Mr Fox's desire that the Prince should set up his mistress in a fine house and the whole world know of the relationship between them? Then he would not wish Mr Sheridan to persuade Perdita of the follies of leaving the stage, of the inconstancy of princes. He had not *said* so, but politics was a game of innuendoes. And surely it was a strange coincidence that Mr Fox had called on this very day when Perdita was handing in her resignation?

Had the subtle game of intrigue already begun? It excited him to think so. Rarely, he supposed, had he been so flattered in his life.

Mr Fox planned to use the Prince . . . and perhaps Perdita.

She was looking at him earnestly. 'If, as you so unkindly suggest . . . But Sherry I know you do not do it from unkind motives for you have always been my friend . . . If the Prince should . . . If the Prince and I should no longer be together . . . why then, Sherry dear, I should most certainly come back to the stage.'

He did not explain to her once more that he doubted she would be able to do that. He was concerned with his own affairs which seemed to him of far greater importance than the amours of a Prince and an actress.

'Thank you, Sherry, for taking it so . . . magnificently.'

She held out her hand for him to kiss, a pretty, wistful expression in her beautiful dark eyes.

Then she returned home to report to Mrs Armistead: 'Mr Sheridan was certainly distressed, but he took it better than I thought he would. I have always known that he was my very good friend.'

The Duke of Gloucester drove out to Kew to see his brother. When he asked for an audience the King received him immediately. He had always been fond of Gloucester. Cumberland was the brother he detested. But there had certainly been a breach between them over his brother's marriage. The King had been hurt to have been kept out of his brother's confidence, yet he had to admit that had Gloucester asked his permission to marry Lady Waldegrave he would have refused it. He would have told Gloucester that a Prince of the Blood Royal could not marry a woman who was not only illegitimate but was said to be the daughter of a milliner.

So Gloucester had married without his sovereign's consent and kept the matter a secret until the passing of the Royal Marriage Act had forced him to reveal it.

And then . . . George had refused to receive him officially and Charlotte had said she would never make a milliner's daughter welcome at her Court. But the King was a sentimental man, a family man, and although the Duchess was not received, the King was always pleased to see his brother.

'Well, well, William,' said George. 'Be seated, be seated.'

William sat and thought poor old George looked older than when he had last seen him. That affair of the Gordon Riots must have upset him. What a decision to make and fancy old George having the guts to make it. Firing on his own subjects, eh? Right, absolutely right in the circumstances and George had earned the approval of his grateful Capital–which was something rare for the poor old fellow.

William–content with his life and his Duchess–felt sorry for George's hard lot. Not much fun in being the King, particularly for a man like George who took himself seriously. It would be different when the Prince took over. Not for many years yet, he trusted. Couldn't help being fond of good old George although he was a pompous, self-righteous old devil now and then.

'I've come to talk with you, George, about the Prince.'

An expression of anxiety crossed the King's face.

'What? Eh? What's he been at now, eh? You've heard something. Rumours . . . rumours . . . there are always rumours. Some of them true too . . . about that young puppy . . .'

'He's been up to nothing that I know of, George. Only pleasing the people. I hear nothing but praise for him wherever I go. He's won the people's approval without doubt.'

'Because he's got a handsome face . . . not yet marked with evil living. Because he's been well looked after all these years . . . diet, exercise, discipline. All very necessary, eh what?'

'He certainly does his upbringing credit. The point is, he'll be eighteen in August.'

'A fact I'm not allowed to forget.'

'With his own establishment . . .'

The King grunted.

'I should like to have an opportunity of seeing him, George. It's a long time since I have.'

'People who act rashly take the consequences. Why, your marriage has given offence to all the royal families in Europe. Marrying a woman who . . .'

'I am happy in my marriage, George, and regret nothing.'

The King's eyes were momentarily clouded with emotion. 'Wouldn't have wanted to hear you say aught else,' he said gruffly. 'Still, you must understand. I can't have the Duchess at Court. The Queen wouldn't hear of it.'

'Don't expect me to believe that if the King gave the order, the Queen would not obey.'

'There are some matters she must be the judge of, eh, what?'

Gloucester said: 'I came to ask your permission for an interview with my nephew. Don't you think that we should have a chance to know each other? Should members of families be kept apart?'

'I never wanted to part families. But if people will make reckless marriages there's no help for it.'

'I hear that Cumberland has met the Prince.'

'What, eh?'

'In the Park. They met by chance and there was a touching scene. The people looked on and cheered the avuncular embrace.'

'The fellow's a rogue,' muttered the King, 'for all that he's my own brother. And more so because of it. Ingratiating himself with the Prince. I'll put a stop to that.'

'It still remains that he has spoken with Cumberland and not with me. Don't you think that I should have a chance of congratulating my nephew.'

'There's nothing to congratulate him about, I do assure you.'

'On his approaching birthday. A milestone in the life of a young prince. Eighteen. The age when he ceases to be a boy and realizes he's only three years off his manhood.'

'He has not only just realized it, I can assure you. He's been thinking of it for months.'

'Perfectly natural, George.'

'You seem determined to defend the puppy. Well, you shall see him. I don't see why not. Cumberland waylaid him in the Park. If you come to Kew next Friday, you can call on him and stay for half an hour.'

Gloucester was well pleased.

The Queen sent for Colonel Hotham, one of the members of the Prince's household. She was disturbed because the Duke of Gloucester was going to spend half an hour with her son. The Prince's visits to her were growing less and less: he never came until commanded to do so. It was very sad. When he was in her presence she longed for him to show a little affection. He never did; all he showed was his longing to get away.

And his uncle was going to see him. She would not have allowed it; but the King was weak where his brother was concerned. She imagined how Gloucester would put his case to the Prince; his version of the reason why he had been banished from Court would sound very romantic to young ears. She could imagine the Prince's sympathy; and he would not feel very kindly towards his mother, she knew, if Gloucester should tell him that she had said she would not receive a milliner's daughter at her Court.

Oh, dear, her darling son's growing up did create problems. And just now she was feeling the heat very much, for in a very short time now her child would be born.

'Colonel Hotham,' she said. 'His Majesty has given the Duke of Gloucester permission to see the Prince of Wales. I want you to be in the room during the interview. I want you to tell me *everything* that is said.'

'Yes, Your Majesty.'

'I feel sure that your presence will prevent the Prince's uncle from saying anything that it would not be good for His Highness to hear. But if he should . . . I wish to know.'

Colonel Hotham assured the Queen that she could trust him to be her very good servant . . . now as always.

When the Queen dismissed him Colonel Hotham went back to the Dower Lodge, but on his way there he reflected that if he insisted on remaining in the room where the Prince would meet the Duke he would have some explaining to do. The Prince was on the whole good tempered, but he could fly into rages–particularly if he felt his dignity was impaired. And surely by appointing an onlooker at this interview it could be said that the Queen was treating him as a child.

What a quandary! It was, in fact, a choice between pleasing the Queen or the Prince. The Queen had no power whatsoever. Indeed the King himself might be displeased by the presence of a third party at the interview, and as it would be only on the Queen's orders that he would be there, was he not placing himself in an invidious position?

Family dissensions would make a great deal of trouble–not only for the family but for those who served them. Wise men remained outside them, particularly when a dangerous situation was arising–a powerful king and very soon to be an equally powerful prince.

Yes, he must drop a hint to the Prince *before* the meeting took place.

'What!' cried the Prince. 'You will stay in the room when my uncle calls. But on whose orders, pray?'

'On those of the Queen, sir.'

'So the Queen sees fit to meddle now. And His Majesty?'

'I have no orders from him, Your Highness.'

The Prince smiled slowly. 'I do not think you will be present, Colonel Hotham.'

'Do you not, sir?'

'No, because I will write to the King and ask that you may not.'

'Very well, sir. As you know I shall await orders.'

'Thank you,' said the Prince.

He sat down at once and wrote a letter to his father. The Queen had ordered that one of his servants should be present at the interview between himself and his uncle, and as he was certain that this would give displeasure to his uncle, he was humbly entreating His Majesty to rescind the order.

He had correctly calculated the effect this would have on the King, who heartily disliked the Queen to interfere in any matter, and would think it was presumptuous of her to take it upon herself to give this order to Colonel Hotham. Charlotte had still not learned her lesson; then she must be taught it. No interference. Get on with the task of bearing the royal children at which she was extremely efficient. But certainly she was not when she meddled in matters of state and diplomacy.

The King wrote back to the Prince who for once had remembered *his* manners and written in the respectful way a son should write to his father. Certainly Colonel Hotham should not be present.

Gleefully the Prince acquainted the Colonel with this fact and the Colonel congratulated himself that he had had the good sense to inform the Prince of the matter and so not incur his displeasure.

There was no doubt that the Prince was becoming more important every day. It seemed to the Colonel that today he was only second to the King. And tomorrow? Who could say? But it was as well to be prepared.

The Duke of Gloucester embraced his nephew warmly. There were tears in his eyes which the Pirince was quick to notice, and he himself took a perfumed lace-edged kerchief from his pocket and wiped his eyes.

'So long . . .' sighed Gloucester. 'And you have become a man.'

'I am glad you recognize it, Uncle. It is more than some do.'

'You'll shortly be eighteen. You'll notice the difference then.'

'But still three years from twenty-one. I never knew time could pass so slowly.'

'Ha, there'll come a time when you'll remember those words.'

'So I am constantly told, but I find the passage of time so slow that it infuriates me. You can guess how I long to be of age . . . with my own establishment . . . my *independence.*'

'I can understand it well.'

'I wish my father did.'

'Oh, there is always this difficulty with fathers and sons.'

'You think uncles understand nephews better?'

'I am certain of it.'

They were laughing together. Why isn't the King more like his brothers? the Prince asked himself in exasperation. When have I ever been able to speak lightly about anything, to have a little joke with him. Never! He has no humour. What a bore the old man is!

'Well, perhaps now you are permitted to come to Court you will be able to drive a little understanding into my father's head.'

'It'll come. He'll realize you are grown up all of a sudden.'

'I intend him to,' said the Prince. 'For one thing, I think it quite absurd that I have not been able to meet my uncles before this simply because my father did not like their Duchesses.'

'We married without his consent.'

'And why should you not? Why should one grown man have to ask the consent of another?'

'Well, his Marriage Bill was fortunately too late to affect us.'

The Prince laughed. 'I'd like you and my Uncle Cumberland to know that I admire you for what you did.'

'I must thank Your Highness for those kind words. But you won't attempt to follow our example will you?'

The Prince was on the verge on confiding his devotion to Mrs Robinson but decided against it. In any case his uncle probably knew about it. Most people did; the only ears it had not reached were those of the King and the Queen.

'If I did,' joked the Prince, 'I would first come to you to ask your advice as to how to set about it.'

Both uncles were so easy to get on with. He enjoyed chatting with them. He asked after the Duchess, for he was not going to follow his father's stupid example. And his uncle was very pleased to speak of her, for there was no doubt that his marriage had been a success.

When the half hour was over, and the Prince took leave of his uncle, he said: 'I cannot see you now without the King's leave, but in three years I shall be of age, and then I may act for myself. I declare I will visit you.'

The King sent for his son. As the rumours and gossip concerning Perdita Robinson and the Prince had so far been kept from him and the Queen, he believed that young George had been behaving during the last months with unusual propriety and had told the Queen that he believed that he was settling down at last. Charlotte was only too happy to agree.

Therefore when the Prince arrived the King greeted him without the usual irritation. The Prince's manner seemed subdued. He was in fact wondering whether the King had sent for him because he had discovered about Perdita; and when he found that this was not the case he was distinctly relieved.

'Your eighteenth birthday will soon be with us,' said the King. 'A milestone, eh, what?'

'A milestone,' repeated the Prince, his hopes soaring. Now he was going to hear of the allowance he would get, the house which would be his. The gates of freedom were slowly opening.

'No longer a boy! Responsibilities, eh? Well, it is fitting that you should have an apartment of your own.'

Apartment, thought the Prince; and visualized the fine house which would be his. If he did not like it he would have it altered to his design. He had a distinct flair for architecture and had told Perdita that when his father gave him some noble house it should be a love nest for them both.

'You are not yet fully of age. Another three years before that. But eighteen . . . yes, an apartment certainly. I have decided that part of Buckingham House shall be assigned to you and your staff.'

Part of Buckingham House! How could he and Perdita make their love nest in his father's palace! The Prince was aghast.

The King went on: 'You'll have an allowance that'll be adequate and you shall have your own horses. You'll not be under the same restraint . . .'

The Prince was not listening. A red haze seemed to swim before his eyes. Was this what he had been waiting for?

Rooms . . . rooms in Buckingham House!

He could not speak what was in his mind. He dared not. He was a minor still. Three long weary years stretched out before him. He had expected to gain so much and had gained so little.

One prison door had been opened, but he was not to be allowed his full freedom.

'Rooms in Buckingham House!' he told Frederick. 'Think of it! Under Papa's constant eye. I thought I was going to have my own establishment. I thought I was going to invite my friends.'

'You'll choose your friends now,' Frederick pointed out. 'For instance, you won't have to scale walls when you go and meet them. You won't have to hire rooms in inns surely. You have gained something.'

'By God,' cried the Prince. 'I mean to show them. His and Her Sainted

Majesties! I will make them wish they had never tried to put their fetters on me. I shall live as I like . . . do as I like . . . even though it is only in a part of Buckingham House.'

He determined to show the Court that he would not tolerate restraint. Even the apartments in Buckingham House were not to be occupied until January. But at least he had more freedom and he intended to exploit it to the full. No longer was it necessary to disguise himself as a night watchman and go clandestinely to Eel Pie Island. The Countess of Derby wanted to sell her house in Cork Street and it seemed to him ideal for Perdita. The money to buy it? Who would deny credit to the Prince of Wales?

So the house in Cork Street was his and he met Perdita there and together they went over it planning how it should be decorated. Perdita was all for discreet pastel shades; but the Prince wanted scarlet and gold. It was to be a royal residence; he himself intended to spend much of his time here. He would furnish it as a surprise for her.

And so he did . . . sparing no expense. On the command of the Prince of Wales, was enough to make any tradesman rush to execute the order. Most expensive materials must be used, everything of the finest–and no questions asked about the price.

The Prince, inhaling the air of freedom, was happier than ever before, he told Frederick; and his ecstasy was reflected in the lover's knots which appeared on the furnishing, the entwined initials G and P, the gilded mirrors, the velvet curtains of the bed.

The Prince's orders were that the work must be completed at express speed. He could not wait to have his Perdita installed in Cork Street.

There came the day when he was waiting there to greet her. There he stood in the hall to embrace her and like an excited child to conduct her from room to room to show her how an ordinary house could be made into a royal residence.

Perdita was delighted with the entwined initials. A kingly custom. She did not recall, if she ever knew, that so had Henry VIII entwined his initials with those of Anne Boleyn in Hampton Court, but that poor Anne had lost her head before the work was completed.

Why should such thoughts occur to her? The Prince was as devoted as ever. He had bought this charming house for her and it was their home; and if it was the grandest she had ever lived in, well then, by his devotion he had lifted her to an eminence which some years before she would not have dreamed of attaining. She had come a long way from the rooms in Hatton Garden which she had shared with Mr Robinson when they were first married. But she would not think of Mr Robinson who was an uneasy subject at the best of times.

To the bedroom–with its velvet bed curtains caught up in a coronet under which they could make love.

'Different from that inn room, eh?' laughed the Prince.

'So different. How can I ever thank you, my Prince.'

'If you go on loving me, it is enough,' he answered.

She must be painted, he said. Of course he must have a portrait of her. He would arrange for one of the great painters of the day to come to Cork Street. His very own picture of his very own Perdita.

And so he sent the artist Stroehling to her; and she was painted reclining on a velvet-covered couch–a flimsy gown cut low to give a glimpse of a charming bosom, sloping shoulders and rounded arms. About her lower limbs was wrapped a cloak lined with ermine; and the artist had painted a fountain in the background.

The Prince came to watch the work in progress and was delighted with it.

'I shall keep it for ever,' he declared. 'It will remind me of the day I first saw you, when you came on to the stage and changed my whole life. I remember how jealous I was when Florizel came on and you took his hand. How I longed to play Florizel!

"So turtles pair,
Who never mean to part . . ."'

he quoted.

Then he had an inspiration. The artist should paint two turtle doves into the picture.

This was done and when it was completed he was delighted.

As soon as he had his own apartments he would have it hung in his cabinet–a constant symbol of two lovers who were never meant to part.

Cumberland House

Elizabeth Sheridan was apprehensive. She rarely saw her husband now. The East Burnham days seemed so far off that they might never have existed. She feared the future.

The School for Scandal alone could have made Richard a rich man; the theatre brought in a good income; but what happened? The gaming tables claimed a large share of it; and women? She often wondered about women.

How different it was from those days when they had run away together. Richard was not the same man. She had known he had great talent, and had rejoiced in it; but to what had it brought him?

If only he would have allowed her to earn money by her singing, her name could have brought an audience to rival those of Perdita Robinson. But he was too proud, he said. Vanity perhaps would be a more apt term.

But she never showed her fears. She knew that that would have alienated him more quickly than ever. In his way he had an affection for her which went deep and none of his light amours could shake. She must accept him as he was. She must never attempt to change him, for to do so would be to lose him altogether.

Sometimes she thought longingly of the old days in Bath–the happy home, the musical family . . . the carefree days. She had visualized life going on in the same serene way when she had married Richard. She wanted to help him succeed as a playwright and she had thought that would have been the most important thing in the world to them both.

But it was not. He would start a play and tire of it. He did not want to work; he wanted to live in gay society; he was famous for his wit which came to him spontaneously; she had heard him scatter conversational gems to the right and left–to the delight of his listeners–they came and carelessly were lost when they should have been stored for posterity's delight.

He was indifferent to such suggestions; he only lived for pleasure. He caroused half the night and rose late in the mornings; sometimes he did not come home at all and she would lie in her bed wondering where and with whom he was sleeping that night.

And now he had become friendly with Mr Fox, and she was afraid of where this friendship would lead. Fox was brilliant; Fox was influential; she had no doubt of that. He was also a gambler and a lecher. And . . . she had to admit it . . . so was Richard.

The friendship had begun suddenly and since then had ripened; and it was going to change Richard's career, she knew.

If he had a seat in Parliament he would become the close ally of Fox. She had tried to reason with him when he had come home so excited on that day to tell her that Fox had been to see him. 'You would be drawn into a circle, Richard, where living is high. We could not afford it. We are in debt now.'

'You look at life through your Bath eyes, my darling. You see life provincially. This will be the making of our fortunes if I am clever. And do you doubt that I am?'

'No, no, Richard, but there are your plays . . . the theatre . . .'

And he had laughed at her and said: 'St Cecilia, go back to your angels.'

And if he were successful . . . if he won this seat. She could see it so clearly. He would be reaching for power, he would move among men who had no need to consider money–or if they had, did not–men like Fox who had been bankrupt several times. But Fox was the son of a noble house. His father had been rich Lord Holland; he was connected with the Duke of Richmond. Sheridan could not afford to move in such circles. But he would do so all the same. The mound of bills would become a mountain. The nights away from home would be more numerous; and her anxieties would increase a hundredfold. But there was nothing she could do.

Sheridan himself came in to interrupt her brooding.

'Elizabeth, where are you?'

She ran to him; he swung her up in his arms.

'Now, my girl,' he said, 'show proper respect to the Member of Parliament for Stafford.'

Prince Frederick was dismayed, and he went at once to his brother to tell him the reason for his concern.

'They are sending me away, George.'

The Prince stared at him in horror. Sending Fred away! Why they had been together all their lives, shared a thousand adventures; George constantly confided in Fred; they were inseparable.

'What are you talking about, Fred?'

'I have just had an audience with the King. He says that before the year's out I am going to go to Germany.'

'Whatever for?'

'To start learning how to be a soldier. Colonel Greville is going with me.'

'You could learn that here in England.'

'I know. But they're sending me to Germany.'

'By God,' cried the Prince. 'Can't he forget his ancestors were Germans!'

'I suppose not. There's too much German in the family for that.'

The Prince looked at his brother in amazement, trying to imagine what it would be like without him. He sensed that it would be the end of their close relationship. They would remain friends, but their lives would be so different.

'I believe he does it just to irritate *me*,' cried the Prince pettishly.

'No, because he thinks it's good for discipline.'

'You could have a commission in the army here. We could both have one.'

The Prince saw himself in a dazzling uniform of his own designing. He pictured himself parading before Perdita's admiring eyes in Cork Street.

'That would suit me very well,' he went on. 'And why not?'

Frederick shook his head. He was as desolate as George at the prospect of parting.

The Prince stood before the King.

'I have come to ask you, sir, for a commission in the army.'

'Eh? What?'

'A commission, sir. In the army.'

The King was not altogether displeased by what he considered a show of seriousness.

'Not possible,' he said. 'Government . . . and people . . . would never allow the Prince of Wales to go out of the country.'

'A commission *here*, sir. Germany hasn't the only army in the world.'

How the young dog could anger him merely by a word and a look. The manner in which he said Germany–as though it were some inferior state!

'That's so,' said the King. 'But you will not have a commission in any army. Have you understood that, eh, what?'

'And why not, pray?'

'Are you addressing me?'

The Prince looked round the small chamber with an air of surprise. 'I was not aware that anyone else was present, and as I am not in the habit of talking to myself . . .'

'You insolent young dog!'

The Prince realized that he had spoken to his father in person as he often addressed him in his own private thoughts.

He murmured an apology.

'I should think so, eh, what? And let me tell you this, sir. You have to learn to be a king, not a soldier. You will need all your time and talents to achieve that. And you'll find there isn't time to go chasing young maids of honour round gardens, eh?'

Oh, God, thought the Prince, is he still thinking of Harriot er . . . What was her name?

He said placatingly: 'I had thought, sir, as Frederick is going into the army and we have always been together, we might have both had commissions and as I may not leave the country we might both do our training over here.'

'You think too much, sir,' said the King, 'of matters that are not your concern. You have enough to concern yourself with, eh, what? Now go and do it, and understand once and for all. Frederick goes to Germany; and you stay here and there is no commission for you, understand, eh, what?'

The Prince retired; as he came out into the King's drawing room he kicked a stool across the floor to relieve his feeling.

Bumbling old idiot! he thought. How much longer shall I have to listen humbly to his drivelling nonsense?

Such changes, sighed the Queen, lying in her bed awaiting the birth of her child. Frederick to leave the family circle–and young William too! Frederick for the army and William for the navy. William was very young, but the King had said a little experience of the sea would do him no harm.

And George–dearest and best beloved–to have his own establishment.

How I wish he would come and see me *without* being asked to. He never did, of course. Perhaps he felt it would not be in accordance with the dignity due to the Queen. Oh, but I am his mother!

It would not be long now before the child was born. She was so accustomed to giving birth that it held few alarms for her. How different that first occasion–that hot August day eighteen years ago when she had prepared herself for her first confinement and prayed for a boy.

And her prayers had been answered–and what a boy she had produced . . . what a marvel of a boy, although a little wayward! But so handsome! She wished she could show them at home what a wonderful Prince she had given to the nation. They would hear of his exploits of course. The whole world talked of the Prince of Wales. She would never forget the welcome sentence: 'It's a boy!' Nor would she forget how Lord Cantelupe had been so eager to tell the King that the child was safely delivered that he had not waited to ascertain its sex and had told him that it was a girl. Cake and caudle for all visitors to the Palace. And what that had cost–because the visitors had been numerous! No cake and caudle for this one. That was a blessing. After all, this was not the Prince of Wales.

Eighteen years ago; and now he was to have his own establishment. She believed he was very happy about that. Oh dear, she did hope he would not be too wild and quarrel with his father. She was terrified of those occasions when the King was displeased with his children. As she listened to his talk growing faster and faster and sometimes a little incoherent because he did not finish his sentences, that terrible fear came to her. Then she would say: It is because there is still much I have to learn about the English language that I cannot catch what he says.

She could hear Schwellenburg's guttural accents not far off.

'*Nein, nein.* Give to me. Selfs will do it.'

The pains were coming frequently. It would be soon now.

'I think,' she said, calmly, 'the time has come.'

Very shortly afterwards she was delivered of a son.

The baby was christened Alfred by the Archbishop of Canterbury and his sponsors were the Prince of Wales, Prince Frederick and their sister Charlotte, the Princess Royal.

This caused some comment in ecclesiastical circles and the Bishop of Salisbury came to see the King on account of it.

'Your Majesty,' he said, 'the ceremony of the baptism of Prince Alfred has given grave cause for alarm throughout the Church.'

'What's that?' asked the King.

'Sir, the sponsors of an infant take on a solemn responsibility.'

'I am well aware of that, my lord Bishop.'

'And this has been undertaken by people who are scarcely of an age to recognize this. The Prince of Wales himself is but eighteen years of age. His brother and sister younger. I would like Your Majesty to consider authorizing another baptism. Your Majesty could then select persons of a more responsible age.'

The King prided himself on his reasonableness.

'I understand, my lord Bishop, your point of view. But by the time Prince Alfred is of an age to need the guidance of his sponsors, they themselves will have reached an age to give it.'

'Sir, I believe you should reconsider this matter.'

'Thank you, my lord. I believe I have considered it and answered your fears. You have understood, eh, what?'

No one would have dared argue with George I or George II. It was different with George III; although once he had made a decision he could rarely be shifted from it, he was always ready to treat anyone who doubted his wisdom with courtesy.

'The Prince of Wales,' he explained, 'in view of his peculiar position as heir to the throne, is not to be judged by ordinary standards. When in due course he is King of this country he will be the best possible guardian for a brother who is eighteen years his junior. Thank you, my lord Bishop, for raising this point. Now it is explained, eh, what? And you have business to attend to . . . and so have I.'

With that the Bishop had to be content.

But when the Prince heard an account of the Bishop's criticism he was annoyed.

'This is what happens,' he said. 'It is because I am treated like a child that people regard me as a child. I, the Prince of Wales, am not considered worthy to be my young brother's sponsor.'

He could not forget the insult to his dignity; and some days after he had heard of the incident, coming face to face with the Bishop of Salisbury, he stopped him and demanded in a voice which could be heard by all around: 'Have you heard the news, my lord Bishop?'

'What news, may it please Your Highness?' replied the Bishop.

'My father,' the Prince told him, 'has sent to the sponsors of the Bishop of Salisbury to know how they could so egregiously have neglected their duty, as not to have taught their godchild to hold his tongue when it becomes him.'

The Bishop was too disconcerted to reply and the Prince swept on haughtily.

Soon everyone was discussing–and laughing at –the incident.

The Prince of Wales was indeed feeling his independence.

The Prince was biding his time until he could move into his new apartments in Buckingham House. So were others. Meanwhile he had to brace himself for the parting with Frederick and not spend too much time in Cork Street because until he was free of the Dower Lodge he was so close to his parents at Kew that his actions would not pass unnoticed by them; it would be different once he was in his own apartments.

After Christmas the time had come for the brothers to say goodbye.

The whole family assembled; the King wept openly and kept murmuring rather incoherent instructions to Frederick as to how he should behave.

The Prince of Wales felt numb. He was surprised that he could shed no tears, for never had he felt such sadness.

So close was the bond between them that Frederick understood; in fact he himself felt similarly and could shed no tears.

The brothers gripped each other's hands and stared wordlessly at each other. There was in any case no need for words.

Then Frederick left for Germany and the Prince of Wales moved to Buckingham House. Only a round of gaiety could help him to overcome his desolation at the loss of his brother.

Riding in the Park he met his uncle, the Duke of Cumberland. As on another occasion Cumberland called to his coachman to stop, alighted and kissed the hand of his nephew.

'Well met, Your Highness. This is a wonderful moment for me. And now you are indeed a man!'

'I am glad to see you, Uncle.'

'By God, what a fine coat that is you are wearing. I like the frogging.'

'I had it made to my orders.'

'Have I your Highness's permission to copy it?'

'As it is in the family . . . yes.'

'Your Highness, my wife, the Duchess, was speaking of you but yesterday. She had had a glimpse of you and I'll not tell you what she had to say of your charms. By God, I said, Come! come! You can't expect me to compete with the youth of my handsome nephew.'

'I did not see the Duchess or I should have had a word with her.'

'I'll tell her that. By God, it will make the day for her.'

'Pray do,' said the Prince.

'Your Highness's kindness makes me very bold. Dare I? I wonder.'

'You have a reputation for daring, Uncle.'

'So I have. Well, I shall live up to that reputation and say this: If Your Highness should ever see fit to honour us at Cumberland House . . . if by your great good sense . . . which I see exceeds that of some others . . . but my tongue runs away with me . . . If Your Highness should ever be in Pall Mall and have the fancy to be treated like a king, well, nephew, you would make a certain duke and duchess the happiest people in the world.'

'But of course I shall come,' said the Prince. 'If I had had my will I should long since have put an end to these stupid family quarrels.'

'Your Highness! You will indeed!'

'I will. Tell the Duchess that I am curious to discover if she is as beautiful as rumour paints her.'

'She will be overcome with joy.'

The Prince was delighted. After that old fool the Bishop of Salisbury this was the sort of thing he liked to hear.

'And so,' he said gallantly, 'shall I be to meet her.'

'May I tell her this, Your Highness?'

'Pray do.'

'And when . . .'

'I will call on her this evening . . . if that would please her.'

'Please her. She will swoon at the thought.'

'I would not wish to put her to any discomfort.'

'She would swoon with *joy*, Your Highness. I will return to her at once. This is the happiest day since our wedding day. I know she will agree with me. I will tell her of the great honour which awaits her.'

Cumberland returned to his coach and the Prince rode on.

Cumberland House! The forbidden territory. What would his father say if he knew he had accepted an invitation to visit it?

He broke into a gallop. To hell with his father's rules and regulations!

It was with a feeling of great excitement that the Prince set out for the home of his uncle. The King and Queen were enjoying a period of domesticity at Kew and were well out of the way. No one could stop him now. If he wanted to visit his uncle he would.

Stepping into Cumberland House was like stepping over the threshold of a new life. All were waiting for him; there was no doubt that he was the most important man in the country.

The Duke was on the threshold to receive him; he bowed formally and then with tears in his eyes embraced him. And there was his Duchess waiting to give a profound curtsey to lift the most famous eyes in England to his face in a look of such adoration that his heart was immediately touched and had he not already been deeply in love with Perdita he would have fallen in love with his newly discovered aunt without fail.

She was tall and slender–like a flower, he thought; her hair was thick and gold coloured and she wore it unpowdered, dressed very high on her head with little curls and tendrils escaping here and there; her face was small, fairylike, almost fragile; she looked angelic but for her eyes which brimmed over with mischief; they were huge and green at the moment because she was wearing a green dress and emeralds sparkling about her person; and fringing them were the magnificent eyelashes–black as night, sweeping her delicately coloured cheek at one moment, lifted up like black feathery fans the next.

The Prince said: 'They are indeed the most fantastic eyelashes in the world.'

'I trust they please Your Highness,' she said. 'If they do not they shall be cut off this instant.'

'Pray do no such thing. I could not be responsible for destroying one of the wonders of the world.'

'How gracious, how charming of Your Highness! And how happy you make me. But we are being selfish. Some of our guests are aware of the great honour that awaits them . . . but not all. We have kept our little secrets . . . and we trust in doing so we have not incurred Your Highness's displeasure, because from now on it shall be *my* pleasure to maintain yours.'

What delightful company! How free and easy! And to think he had been deprived of it all these years. He thought of Kew. Backgammon! Lectures! The only dissipation–chamber music in the family circle.

Oh, life was going to be different from now on!

His bewitching aunt–and he was overcome with amusement to consider her as such–begged for the honour of slipping her arm through his ('for I am your aunt, you know') and conducted him to her guests. And willingly he offered his arm and happily he talked to her, for to tell the truth he was completely fascinated by those eyelashes.

And so, the Duchess on his arm, the Duke on the other side of him, he was led to the company.

This was, of course, how it would be from now on. People–interesting, important and amusing people–would be jostling each other to have a word with him. Beautiful women swept deep curtsies as he passed and lifted their eyes admiringly to him; men bowed low.

It was a glittering assembly at Cumberland House. All the most famous Whigs had been gathered together for the occasion and they all wished to be presented to him.

There was Mr Fox and Mr Burke and Mr Sheridan, and their

lighthearted, witty conversation had an immense appeal for him.

And then the surprise of the evening.

The Duchess said: 'There is a lady to whom I feel sure Your Highness would like to be presented. Have I your permission?'

It was granted at once–and the Duchess took him to an alcove and there to his great joy and gratification was Perdita herself.

He took her hand; he kissed it; and she lifted her eyes brimming over with love for him to his face.

'This,' he whispered, 'is the most wonderful moment of our lives.'

It meant that they were at last together in public, that his uncle Cumberland accepted Perdita. Never again need they meet in secret.

This was indeed independence!

What an evening that was! For the first time since Frederick had gone he ceased to miss him.

He was astonished at the company–the free and easy manners, the talk which could be bawdy and at the same time witty and brilliant. Politics were discussed; so was art and literature. Everyone listened respectfully when he spoke but he had no need to feel ashamed of ignorance, for if he were not as yet fully versed in politics he could compete successfully in discussions on art and literature. There was dancing and gambling. The stakes were high but that seemed to him right in such distinguished company. He played at Faro and watched Loo and Macoa; the men who most fascinated him were Fox and the playwright Sheridan. They were the sort of men he would have liked to have had for his tutors. Well, now he might have them for his friends. Might have them? He would if he wished. This night had taught him that what he asked would be readily given, and he was intoxicated with the joy of being the Prince of Wales.

He would come again and again to Cumberland House. There would, said the fascinating Duchess, always be a welcome for her handsome nephew at any hour of the day or night–and for Perdita.

She fluttered her lashes at Perdita who was perhaps a little jealous. She need not have been. He was her faithful lover; but he had to admit that his aunt was a damned attractive woman.

He would, he declared, come again and often.

Cumberland House, he was told, was his home whenever he cared to make it so.

And when he left with Perdita the Duke and Duchess savoured their victory; because it was now quite clear that it was the Cumberlands who were going to launch the Prince of Wales.

The Prince and Perdita went back to Cork Street. He was flushed not only with triumph for he had drunk more than usual.

Perdita had drunk very little and was sober in both senses.

'What an evening! By God, what a house! I declare ours looks like a cottage in comparison.'

He looked round it disparagingly.

'I would rather be happy in a cottage than unhappy in the finest mansion.'

The Prince laughed: 'Well, so would everyone else.'

She stood there, arms folded across her breasts, very pretty but too dramatic, and the Prince was in no mood for histrionics. He had caught the mood of the people he had been with and they would have been very quick to ridicule sentiment–particularly if it were false.

'Come here and stop acting, Perdita. You are not on the stage now. Come and be my turtle dove.'

She came and sat beside him–all grace and willowy draperies.

He kissed her with passion, but his thoughts were still with the company.

'Fox is one of the best talkers I ever heard,' he said. 'And Sheridan's another. By God, they are men I would be happy to call my friends.'

She shivered. 'You promised me once that you would not use bad language.'

'Did I, by God.' He laughed aloud. 'What did you think of Fox?'

'I thought his linen was . . . unclean.'

The Prince laughed again. 'You met the most brilliant man in London and the first thing you have to say about him is that his linen is unclean.'

'I cannot see why his brilliance should prevent his putting on a clean shirt.'

'How severe you are. And Sheridan?'

'You forget I know him well.'

'A damned fine fellow. Words! He has a way with them.'

'They're his trade.'

'Perdita, one would think you did not greatly like the company tonight. I trust you did because *I* found it most diverting.'

'There were some ill reputations among that company,' she said, pursing her lips.

'Ill reputations are often the most interesting.'

She drew away from him. 'I do not like to hear you talk like that.'

He was startled. After all the approval he had had tonight this sounded like criticism. Perdita seemed to have forgotten that although he loved her he was still the Prince of Wales.

'That,' he said coolly, 'will not prevent my saying what I mean.'

She was alarmed; she saw the angry lights in his eyes. They were a warning. He had of course drunk more than was good for him. She must be careful, but she would do her utmost to prevent visits to Cumberland House. She did not trust the Duchess–nor the Duke for that matter. Ah, the Duke! How did he feel about *her* now? Did he remember the time when he had done all in his power to seduce her?

If she told the Prince that, perhaps he would not think so much of his uncle. But not now. This was not the moment, when he was a little peevish.

'No one could prevent the Prince of Wales doing what he wished,' she told him soothingly. 'And as he is a man of great good sense, none but fools would wish to.'

She was on her feet, making a sweeping bow which was somehow reminiscent of a plump lady who had been at Cumberland House that evening. The Prince laughed–his good humour restored. Perdita laughed with him. She was so pretty when she laughed.

'Come,' he cried. 'Let us have a song.'

She sat at the harpsichord and he leaned over her. He had an excellent voice of which he was very proud; she sang well, for when she had decided to go on the stage Elizabeth Sheridan had given her lessons. Their voices mingled perfectly. She wanted to sing a sentimental song of love; but the Prince was not in the mood for sentimentality.

With Sheridan in mind he began to sing the song from *The School of Scandal*:

'Here's to the maiden of bashful fifteen;
Here's to the widow of fifty;
Here's the flaunting extravagant quean,
And here's to the housewife that's thrifty.
Let the toast pass
Drink to the lass
I'll warrant she'll prove an excuse for the glass.'

A little primness had returned to Perdita's mouth; she did not want to be reminded of drink, for she had always known that the Prince was too fond of it.

However, the Prince was in good spirits; and when he had enough of singing, he declared that there was no better way to end a perfect evening than by spending the night with Perdita.

In the Duchess of Cumberland's bedchamber she discussed the evening with the Duke.

She curved her little white hands to make them look like claws and murmured: 'We have him. He is ours.'

The Duke nodded with satisfaction. 'Wait!' he cried. 'Just wait until this gets to old George's ears!'

'He may forbid it to continue. Then I suppose we should have to obey?'

'For a time.'

'For three years. God knows what will happen to our little Prince in that time.'

'You fascinated him. By God, he could scarcely take his eyes off you.'

'Don't play the jealous husband. It's too difficult a role for you.'

'I'll tell you this if you'd like to hear it. I've never seen a woman to come near you for looks.'

'What about Propriety Prue?'

'Who in God's name is she?'

'She goes under the name of Mrs Perdita Robinson and I can tell you that she was not as pleased with our little entertainment as His Highness was.'

'What! That little play actress.'

The Duchess regarded him sardonically; she knew all about those visits to the theatre which had not been crowned with success as far as the Duke was concerned.

'You will I know agree that she is a beautiful one.'

'I don't doubt she's pretty enough.'

'Pretty enough for a prince . . . if not for a duke?'

'That was long ago. I thought she looked well in breeches.'

'So did many others. But this is beside the point. P.P. does not like us, I fear; and she undoubtedly will have influence with H.H.'

'Propriety Prue! And openly living in sin!'

'With a prince. You must admit that makes it a very *venial* sin.'

'Don't mock, Anne.'

'I'm deadly serious. In fact so serious that I am reminding you of something you may have forgotten.'

'What's that?'

'That women can beg and plead very prettily; they can also very slowly poison a man's mind against those who would be his friends. All these little tricks performed at dead of night in a velvet curtained bed . . . and the curtains, so I have heard, are held together overhead by a coronet, if you please . . . these tricks can be very effective. And I repeat, you should know.'

'Since it was in such circumstances that you forced me to marry you . . .'

'Not forced. I never use force. Only persuasion.'

He laughed. She never bored him in spite of his infidelities. He had given her what she wanted–marriage into the royal family, and she was content with that. He was a conceited little man–by no means the most attractive of the King's brothers, but he had married her and she must be thankful for that. She was not of course of lowly birth like her sister-in-law the Duchess of Gloucester, whose origins were very questionable. They did not meet often; they had so little in common, except that they were married to brothers and had both made marriages which were unacceptable to the King. The Duchess of Gloucester, Lady Waldegrave that was, was dignified, and in spite of her birth played the part of Duchess to perfection. The daughter of a milliner some said and of Sir Edward Walpole–the elder brother of that gossip and writer Horace–her father had supervised her education and in due course married her to Lord Waldegrave; and when Lord Waldegrave had died, Maria, the pretty creature, had taken a fancy to the Duke of Gloucester, and he to her it seemed, for he had impetuously, without consulting his family, rushed into marriage with her.

As for the Duchess of Cumberland–there was no question of her birth. She was the daughter of Lord Irnham and one of the Luttrells; she had married a country squire, Christopher Horton, who had died leaving her very young and ready for adventure. In London she had found it–in marriage with the dissolute Cumberland soon after he had brought scandal on the family through the notorious Grosvenor case.

He didn't regret it. She was the most amusing woman in London besides being one of the most beautiful. She was capable of acting hostess in Cumberland House and attracting all the most brilliant Whigs there–in opposition to the Tory friends of the King. For she agreed with her husband that since the King had refused to receive them at Court they must do everything they could to discomfit him. They would, if they could, have set up a rival court; but this was not possible, for Cumberland lacked the intelligence and his Duchess while not suffering from this lack, while being extremely witty in a malicious way, was so coarse in her conversations that it had been said that one was forced to wash out one's ears after visiting her. Nevertheless they did attract the Whigs to Cumberland House; and if they could only gather the Prince of Wales into their fold they could at once set up that rival court. The fact that the Prince had no establishment of his own but only an apartment in his father's palace at Buckingham House was in their favour. They would strive to lure him to Cumberland House and keep him there so that until he had a house of his own, this might be his home. Then they could form the rival court, 'The Prince's Court', 'The Cumberland's Court'–what mattered what it was called as long as it was set up as a rival to the King's Court and would distress that self-righteous old fool the King, who had banished them from *his* Court.

'But to get back to Propriety Prue,' went on the Duchess. 'We must watch that young lady or she will persuade our little Prince that Cumberland House is not for him.'

'You think she could?'

The Duchess lowered her eyes and then lifted them–a trick she had long practised to call attention to her eyelashes. If she had persuaded a dissolute

Duke to marry her in the face of tremendous opposition, surely a beautiful actress could persuade a susceptible young man to discontinue visiting his uncle.

'He was impressed with Fox . . . no doubt about that,' said the Duke.

'There are other places where he could meet the people he met here tonight.'

'But . . . I am his uncle.'

'That old mollycoddle up at the Palace of Piety is his father, but I don't fancy he is yearning to spend his evenings there.'

'By God, you're right. That woman could spoil our chances.'

She leaned towards him. 'And you know, my dear ducal lord, that we can only have one answer to that.'

He waited for it. He accepted her as the leading spirit.

'Spoil hers,' she spat out venomously, and her green eyes scintillated with malice.

Mrs Armistead had overheard the conversation between the Prince and Perdita.

What a fool that woman is, she thought. How long can it last? Didn't she understand the Prince at all? He had an eye for a pretty woman. She had even caught his gaze on herself. Of course, thought Mrs Armistead, if I had gowns of silk and satin and velvet, even muslin and lawn, I could be a fair rival to Perdita.

But who is going to look at the lady's maid? Some would, was the answer, providing the maid was good looking enough. And she was. There was no doubt of it.

And if the Prince was going to tire of Perdita, if they no longer mixed in the highest society, what of Mrs Armistead?

There was Mr Fox. She smiled, rather fondly, and she told herself foolishly. It would not serve to be foolish. She had a good example of folly before her now. She would never be guilty of that. Mr Fox would always have a special place in her life; she knew that. He had wanted to reward her but she would not accept money. Was that foolish? Did she not need money more than most. What would become of her when she was no longer young enough to work, when she had lost her handsome looks? No, she could take nothing from Mr Fox. What she gave him she gave freely.

She would tell him of course every detail of tonight's conversation and that she believed that the Prince was beginning to tire a little of Perdita–although he was too sentimental to realize this and she too vain and stupid. And when he had tried to give her money she had always refused it. She believed he understood and in a way applauded this. She was his mistress . . . in a casual way. What a strange relationship, yet she would not be without it. It made her in some way long for independence. And how could a woman in her position achieve that? She must either serve a stupid woman, concern herself with rouge and powder, ribbons and patches–or seek to please some gentleman. Was one more degrading than another? It was the end which counted perhaps not the means. She was too young for a celibate existence. Mr Fox had taught her that–and of course Mr Fox was the last man to expect fidelity.

Her opportunity to win independence was now. How could she say how long it would last?

Here in Cork Street the richest men in England would be congregating. A clever woman who kept her dignity, could have a chance to win independence and a gracious middle age. All she must do was stifle a few scruples and handle the situations which arose with tact and care.

There was a young gentleman whom she had noticed and who had noticed her. He was Lord Dorset; and she did not think she could demean herself if she allowed the attraction to ripen . . . providing she did so gradually and above all with dignity.

Mrs Armistead had made a decision.

Now before she retired she would go over the report she would take to Mr Fox in the morning. Then to bed. But first to take out of her cupboard the white satin gown with the silver tissue and one or two other dresses which had come her way.

She held them against her. Yes, a woman was a fool who did not use the gifts a munificent nature had bestowed upon her.

Visits to Cumberland House had whetted the Prince's appetite for gaiety. A circle was quickly forming round him. It was a wide circle, for he was ready to welcome into it men who were talented in any direction. He had quickly become on intimate terms of friendship with Charles James Fox, Edmund Burke and Richard Sheridan; but men like Lord Petersham and Lord Barrymore were also his close friends. Petersham was the best dressed man in London who would discuss for hours the right cut of a coat or what trimming should be used. He applauded the Prince's taste and assured him that the shoe buckle he had designed was in his opinion the most elegant he had ever seen. Barrymore was a great practical joker and the Prince found this form of releasing his high spirits to his taste. But he had discernment and would not try his practical jokes on Fox any more than he would talk politics or literature with Petersham. The world was opening out for him and with his great gift for falling violently in love, he was in love with his new life. He often said that one should go to the French for fashion and the English for sport; he enjoyed both. He took lessons in boxing and fencing and excelled in them. He rode well and would drive himself in his phaeton at a startling speed. He even drove his Tilbury through the Park with his groom sitting beside him. He was beginning now to be seen not only in various houses but in public, and the people greeted him with affection wherever he went; he was always gorgeously attired and spent a great deal of time planning his toilette, very often with the help of Petersham. He could dance well, sing well, talk well; and he was undeniably handsome. He was, it was said, the finest gentleman in Europe, and the English were proud to own him as their prince.

He kept a mistress, it was true, but very few held that against him. It all added to the gaiety of life and after years of old George–who was not so old but had always seemed so–with his virtuous but oh so dull Queen who did nothing but bear children for the state to support . . . after these two, young George was a source of great amusement and delight.

He was imbibing Whig politics at a great rate from Fox and Sheridan; they had become his closest friends, with Burke a good third. Elizabeth Sheridan was growing more and more anxious at the turn in her husband's fortune. They had been in debt before, but how could they afford to entertain the Prince of Wales? For the Prince insisted on visiting his amusing friend and was enchanted by the beauty of his wife and her singing in which he joined her for many a musical hour. A simple evening at the Sheridans the Prince might call it; but Elizabeth was aghast to realize what it cost to give such an evening to a prince. And there was Mr Fox with his careless attitude towards debts. Money was something neither of the three ever gave a thought to. It was merely a word . . . a magic sesame to give them what they wanted. One bought and forgot that it was necessary to pay.

The Prince had become a frequent visitor to Cumberland House. Perdita did not care for Cumberland House so she was not often asked, but that was not going to prevent the Prince visiting his own uncle. Fox took him along to Devonshire House where he met the beautiful Georgiana, Duchess of Devonshire, another of whom the King would call 'those damned Whigs'.

The Prince was delighted with the Duchess as he had been with his aunt; she was gay, she was witty and there was the same sort of welcome for him at Devonshire House as there was at Cumberland.

Hostesses were vying for his company. He was half in love with Georgiana, half in love with his aunt; and it seemed to him that he was surrounded by beautiful women. If it were not for Perdita . . .

Perdita herself was drawn into the gay world. It was no use thinking she could hide her position. Everyone knew that she was the Prince's mistress and the interest in her was at fever pitch. The papers mentioned her every day. Stories were told of her which at worst had little truth in them and at best were grossly exaggerated.

Tradesmen were constantly at the door with beautiful materials to be made into clothes for her; she bought lavishly. She had always had a passion for clothes, and now recklessly unleashed it, for she believed there was no need to consider the expense. Several seamstresses were working for her night and day; newspapermen called to ask Mrs Armistead what her mistress would be wearing that day. Descriptions of her dresses were given to journalists and according to their accounts she was always decked out in diamonds, rubies, sapphires and emeralds. 'Gifts', the public avid for news of the Prince and his affairs were told, 'of his Royal Highness.'

Cartoons were in circulation depicting her with the Prince; they were often ribald, often bawdy. Mr Robinson was not forgotten either; he was known to the public through the horns without which he was never depicted. Every time she went out it was to find a crowd waiting outside the house; women came forward to touch her gowns, feel the material, comment on its cost; some would make jocular remarks about the Prince's prowess as a lover. These she ignored and she would return to the house crying: 'Armistead. I am exhausted! Oh, how vulgar the people are!'

And Armistead would say: 'Yes, Madam.' And despise her mistress more than ever. She was so false, thought Mrs Armistead. No one could have loved this interest she aroused more than herself. As she did, why not admit it, for this pretence of finding it tiresome was so stupid. In fact the more Mrs Armistead felt her independence, the more she despised her mistress. Lord Dorset had been very kind and considerate. At length he had prevailed upon her to accept a little present. A *little* present indeed! She was mixing in the right society, for what was little to such a gentleman was a great deal to Mrs Armistead. She reckoned she had enough to invest in a little house. Why not? A roof over her head. What could be wiser? And she would furnish it with simple good taste–and it should be as different from this gilded mock palace in Cork Street as a house could be.

It was inevitable that the King should hear not only of his son's visits to Cumberland House but that he was keeping a young actress in Cork Street.

'Small wonder,' he said to the Queen, 'that I can't sleep at night. I have had ten nights without sleep thinking of that young rake. No good, eh? What?'

'Your Majesty will speak to him?' suggested the Queen timidly.

'No good,' said the King sadly. 'Too late. My eldest son . . . the Prince of Wales, is a . . . profligate, a rake . . . he keeps a play actress. You see, he's gone over to my enemies . . . eh, what? Took the first opportunity. Always knew we'd have trouble with him. Keeping a play actress! Gambling! Going to see Cumberland when he knows that I . . .' The King was too distressed to continue. He could only look at the Queen and whisper, 'Eh? What?' again and again so that she wanted to stop her ears and shout to him to stop, because she was so frightened to see him in that mood.

Perdita was faintly uneasy. Was the Prince changing towards her? Did he treat her with more familiarity? Was he using the bad language which she so deplored more frequently?

He was constantly at Cumberland House and she was not invited. Sometimes he talked of his aunt in a manner which disturbed her.

'By God, what a woman! I'm not surprised my uncle flouted my father for her.'

It was as though he were comparing them. Surely he could not compare her with that coarse-spoken woman!

But she was at least a Luttrell . . . a noble family. 'How strange,' she had said, 'that a woman of noble birth should be so coarse.'

'She's damned amusing,' retorted the Prince.

'For those who like vulgarity, yes.'

Had she seen the look he gave her she might have been warned, but she did not; she had a glimpse of herself in a distant mirror and was admiring the blue satin bows on her white dress.

'I personally could never endure it.'

The Prince did not answer; he was studying the buckles on his shoes with a sullen expression.

He left early although she had expected him to stay the night. And he gave no excuse for going.

So she was anxious; but the next time he saw her he was all devotion. Gently she reminded him of all she had given up for his sake. She did not want him to take her for granted. Her husband . . . well he was not much to relinquish, but she had loved her child and although the little girl lived not far away with her grandmother and she could see her now and then, the devotion she gave to the Prince left her very little time.

The Prince would suggest they sing together or perhaps take the air. He liked to ride with her through the Park and the crowds came to watch them, for she must be exquisitely dressed on these occasions; and they made a colourful picture.

Even she was cheered on occasions like that.

Sometimes he would stay away from Cork Street for several days; and then he would come in a mood of such gaiety that she could not doubt that he was happy to be with her. He would stay for several days and nights and declare that all he wanted in the world was to be with his Perdita.

She loved to ride in the Park, St James's or Pall Mall, in her newest creation–always a different ensemble for she could never appear twice in the same; she would be most exquisitely powdered and patched; her face flower-like with its contrast of rouge and white lead. Sometimes she was in frills and ribbons, at others she would wear a flowing cravat and a tailored coat, the very masculinity of which only accentuated her femininity. In satin and brocade, in muslin and linen, dressed simply in a hat resembling a sun bonnet or in a fashionable hat spilling feathers down her back and round her face, she always provided excitement for the spectators and there were crowds to see Perdita Robinson as they called her on parade. As she passed some called after her coarse enquiries but members of the Prince's circle doffed their hats and bowed low as they went past on foot or rattled by in their carriages; and members of the King's circle looked through her as though she did not exist.

She would return home as she said 'exhausted' and walked up and down her bedroom declaiming: 'Am I a peepshow for people to peer at? How I long for the quiet and peace of obscurity.' And, as Mrs Armistead reported to Mr Fox, savouring it all with relish.

She had ordered a new carriage and when it arrived she was delighted with it. No one could fail to notice it and to realize that its owner must be a very important person indeed. It was scarlet and silver; and the seat cloth was decorated with silver stars. It was lined with white silk and scarlet fringe. On the door had been painted a basket of flowers beneath which was a wreath and her initials M.R. in silver. The wreath had all the appearance, particularly from a distance, of a coronet, which was exactly what Perdita had intended.

She was delighted with her carriage and went everywhere in it. When it was seen outside shops people would gather round it, recognizing it, so that they might have a glimpse of her when she came out.

If the Prince was in love with his life so was Perdita with hers; but whereas he was all gaiety and high spirits, her method of enjoying life was to dramatize it. She would talk to Mrs Armistead of her child for whom she said she longed; and indeed Mrs Armistead believed she did miss little Maria; for she was fond of her. But it was absurd, commented that practical lady in her private thoughts, to choose a way of life and then complain because one had not chosen another.

It cannot last, thought Mrs Armistead. Most certainly it cannot last. And then what? Where shall we be? The debts which were accumulating were alarming, but Perdita was becoming like her lover and gave no thought to them. She was the mistress of the Prince of Wales and no one denied her credit.

Mrs Armistead often thought how differently she would have behaved had she been in Perdita's position. There would have been no debts. Quite the contrary. Mrs Armistead would have had a nice little fortune tucked away by now. In her own small way she was not doing badly. Lord Derby had shown interest and the Duke of Dorset had not lost his; so she had her little house in Chertsey very pleasantly and safely waiting for her.

A refuge! How unusual it was for a lady's maid to compare her position so favourably with that of her mistress.

But this was, of course, no ordinary lady's maid.

Blackmail

The Prince had sent word that he would be visiting Cork Street that evening. A quiet evening, he said, merely a few friends, Fox and Sheridan among them.

Mrs Armistead would arrange the evening; they no longer had to hire their footman, but Mrs Armistead thought they should have more servants for this occasion. Because of the excellent qualities Perdita was constantly discovering in her lady's maid she was delighted when she had suggested she should take over the arrangement of dinner parties; and Mrs Armistead performed these duties with distinction. Now she set herself to plan the meal and order the wine . . . plenty of it. What drinkers Mr Fox and Mr Sheridan were . . . and the Prince was beginning to rival them.

'Madam,' declared Mrs Armistead, 'you must rest during the afternoon so as not to be too tired.'

Perdita agreed that this was so.

'The Prince is so full of high spirits,' she said fondly.

'And expects Madam to be the same.'

'Ah yes, indeed. Sometimes I long for a quiet retreat, Armistead. A little house in the country . . .'

'It would not suit His Highness, Madam. He has just escaped from a little house in the country. Kew, to be precise.'

Perdita looked coldly at her maid. There were times when she thought that the woman was inclined to forget her place.

There was no time to reprimand her, for there was loud knocking on the door.

Perdita gazed at Mrs Armistead. 'Who can it be?'

'The footman will discover, Madam.'

They were soon in no doubt, for the visitor did not wait to be announced but strode straight into Perdita's bedroom. It was Thomas Robinson, his face flushed, his eyes bloodshot.

The creature is drunk, thought Mrs Armistead.

'Where is my wife, eh? Where is my lady wife?'

Perdita lay back on her pillows looking as though she were about to faint.

'Why have you come here?'

'Why should I not? I have a right.' He looked at the coronet into which the curtains were gathered above the bed and sneered at it. 'So this is the bed where you frolic with His Highness? You don't think of your husband then, I'll warrant.'

'I prefer never to think of him.'

'I daresay, I daresay. So do most whores.'

Perdita flinched and blushed scarlet. 'How dare you! How dare you! Go away.'

'Why? This is where I belong. It's my wife's house . . . and what's hers is mine.'

'No,' cried Perdita, too upset to act. 'Go away, Thomas. Go away, I beg of you.'

'Would you make it worth my while if I did?'

'Yes . . . yes . . . yes . . .'

'Now you're talking. I'm in debt. I want some money. I want it now.'

'Armistead! Armistead!'

That excellent lady was at the door listening, and appeared immediately.

'Bring . . . bring . . .'

'That's right,' said Mr Robinson, 'bring all you have . . . and that won't be enough. Why should I be jeered at? Why should I see my picture all over the place? And not a good likeness either. Me in horns!'

'We all have to suffer from these scandal sheets . . . I more than most!'

'Well, you deserve to. I don't.'

'When I think of all the serving girls . . . the dirty sluts . . .'

'Compensation, Mrs Robinson. So you've still got that lady's maid. She's a sly piece . . . and not all that unbedworthy either.'

'Thomas. For God's sake be silent.'

Mrs Armistead had overheard. So even he had noticed. She was not displeased. She had brought a few pounds for the man and she told him that this was all there was in the house. Perdita shot a grateful glance and once more asked herself what she would do without Armistead.

When the lady's maid had left the room, Perdita said: 'You have what you have come for . . . now go.'

'I don't intend to go. I like this little place. Why should I live in my little hovel while the wife of my bosom has a snug place like this?'

'Please, *please* go at once.'

But Mr Robinson sprawled in a chair and regarded the tips of his boots, a sly look of determination on his face.

'I want some compensation for losing my wife,' he said in a whining voice.

'You have . . . as you said. Your kitchen sluts.'

'Even they have to be kept and living's costly.'

'So it's money you want. Well, you've had it.'

'I want it regularly. I want to know where I stand. I want an allowance from you. Why shouldn't I? I've a right.'

'If you will go away you shall have it.'

He nodded slowly, and began to haggle over the amount.

She lay back on her pillows thinking: Go away. Leave me. If he were here when the guests arrived what would happen? The Prince would be annoyed. But Thomas Robinson would never dare. He was a coward. He was a braggart. He would go before they came. But he was in a truculent mood. He had clearly been drinking. And she needed to rest. Late nights with the Prince were beginning to leave their mark–very slightly it was true–but she had noticed faint shadows under her eyes this morning.

Go! she wanted to scream. Leave me in peace.

But the more she showed her agitation the more advantage that gave him. She was ready to promise anything if only he would go.

'Then that's settled,' he said. 'And I want it regularly remember.'

'You shall have it. I must rest now. I am very tired.'

'Yours is an exhausting profession.'

She did not answer that and he continued to sit there leering at her.

At length she said: 'Well, you have what you want.'

'Partly, but not entirely.'

'Pray, what do you mean?'

'I like this place. There's plenty of room here.'

'Are you mad?'

'No, only a husband with rights.'

'Do you think your presence here would be tolerated?'

'Not welcomed probably, but that wouldn't worry me.'

'Thomas, I beg of you to go. If you stay here . . . you will ruin *everything*.'

He still continued to leer at her.

She closed her eyes; she had a horrible vision of her guests arriving to find this unkept drunken sot sprawling in her house. Mr Robinson of the cartoons, husband of Perdita.

She was distracted. What could she do? The more she showed her terror the more determined he would be to plague her. She thought of some of the people who were coming tonight–outwardly her friends, but a woman in her position had to face a great deal of envy. It was everywhere–in the lampoons, the wicked verses, the eyes of women who called lewd names after her. Everything she did was noticed. They would say Mr Robinson has moved in with his wife. *Ménage à trois*. And the Prince would never tolerate it.

And what can I do? she asked herself.

Mrs Armistead came into the room. She was a little flushed and breathless and looked as though she had been hurrying.

'Madam,' she said, 'Lord Malden is here.'

Perdita looked alarmed and glanced in horror at Mr Robinson, but Mrs Armistead said firmly: 'I will show him in.'

Mr Robinson said: 'So you receive men in your bedroom, do you?'

'Don't be a fool. I am not alone here.'

'No, your husband is here to protect you. Ha! ha!'

Mrs Armistead appeared with Lord Malden exquisitely dressed as usual in a light brown velvet coat with gold frogging. He kissed Perdita's hand and turned to Mr Robinson.

However truculent the latter had felt before the entrance of Lord Malden, he could not prevent himself being overawed by the elegance of dress and manners, and as Lord Malden treated him with the utmost courtesy–and interest–his mood changed completely. He was ingratiating and pleased to be noticed.

While Perdita lay back on her pillows exhausted, the men talked and after a while Lord Malden suggested Mr Robinson come with him to a club he knew that they might continue their interesting conversation.

Mr Robinson was delighted and both men took their leave of Perdita.

When they had gone, she cried: 'Oh, what a stroke of good fortune. I shall never be able to thank Malden enough. And the manner in which that creature went . . . as meek as a lamb.'

Mrs Armistead said demurely: 'It was certainly a stroke of good fortune that I found Lord Malden at his residence.'

'You?'

'Yes, Madam. When I saw that Mr Robinson intended to stay I slipped out of the house and went to Dean Street. As I say it was fortunate that his lordship was at home. I told him that Mr Robinson was here and in what mood and begged him to come at once and dislodge him. This he did. He will take him to some club or tavern and there ply him with drink. So I do not think we need worry ourselves this evening with Mr Robinson.'

Perdita sighed. She must endure Armistead's familiarities now and then; she really was a most excellent servant.

The incident had unnerved her. She could not help thinking that but for the prompt action of Armistead Mr Robinson might be at this moment in the house. The Prince noticed her lack of spirits and chided her affectionately.

'You look tired, my angel,' he whispered.

Oh God, she thought, and looked for the nearest mirror.

'Smile,' urged the Prince. 'You're more beautiful when you smile.'

And she fixed her features into a false smile which could not deceive any.

Perdita was melancholy by nature, thought the Prince, faintly critical. He was comparing her with his aunt Cumberland and the very thought of her made him smile. She could always amuse him. She was so full of gaiety *always* and never failing to come up with a quip which brought tears of mirth to the eyes. And Georgiana, the lovely Duchess of Devonshire–there was another. His eyes grew soft at the thought of her. She was a beauty and no mistake. Of course Perdita was the queen of beauty–but so damned melancholy. Then that lady's maid–Mrs Armistead–he had asked her her name the other day and she had curtsied so prettily. . . . Well, elegantly, he would have said. It was a curtsey that would have become a duchess and she was a handsome woman too. Not perhaps his ideal of beauty; he liked dazzlers like Georgiana, Anne Luttrell . . . and Perdita; but that waiting woman had something.

It was a good evening. The usual practical jokes which he so enjoyed and at which Sheridan was beginning to shine. Sheridan was a great fellow–he loved the man. He had yet to find a friend who compared with Fox or Sheridan. When he was with them he could talk and talk and as they talked they drank and he was beginning to be able to drink as much as they could, which was a good deal. They never bored him; they never wearied him; they were never melancholy, whatever the subject they made it amusing. Cynics both of them–and yet both capable of affection and devotion and they made it clear that they had this for the Prince of Wales. There were sycophants and he was not such a fool as not to recognize them; but these two were his genuine friends. He had never understood the American situation until it was explained to him by Fox, Burke and Sheridan. Fox railed against North's conduct of the affair–and that included the King's because the King and North were together in everything that was done. The more he learned of affairs, the more the Prince deplored his father's attitude. He himself was firmly against the Government and that meant North and his father; the Prince was determined to take his stand with Mr Fox and the Whigs.

This was the life! He regretted that Fred was not with him to enjoy it. Poor Fred learning army tactics! The use of arms! By God, one thing Mr Fox had taught him was that words were the finest weapons in the world.

Gambling, prizefighting, horse-racing and loving a beautiful mistress–these were some of the greatest pleasures life had to offer; but he was not sure that he did not enjoy most being in the company of Fox and Sheridan, listening to their erudite conversation, joining with it, growing more and more mellow as the evening wore on. Sometimes of course he was a little hazy after these sessions; sometimes they had to take him back to Cork Street and help him in. This they never failed to do with the utmost care and tact and they would recall similar incidents in their own youth in case he should feel he had not yet learned to take his liquor like a man. He was not a fool. He knew they were wise men of vast experience in all the ways of life which were most exciting to him. He was willing to be tutored. And Perdita would be waiting for him . . . reproachful. Oh yes, she was reproachful even though she might not put her reproaches into words. There he was back at Perdita's melancholy. He'd be ready to swear that that was one thing his lively aunt at Cumberland House never felt–melancholy. Nor would she ever be reproachful. Why she would have to be continually so when one considered the exploits of that wicked old reprobate his Uncle Cumberland.

There was some music and he became proud of Perdita as she sat at the harpsichord in her becoming pink draperies; and a pretty voice she had too. Not as good as Sheridan's wife. Poor creature! There was another. No gaiety, no spirit. Poor Sherry. But he managed to enjoy life in spite of her. She never appeared at these parties. He would never have thought of her being at them–except at moments like this when she might have sung for them. But he liked a gay song–the sort Sherry put in his plays. Elizabeth Sheridan was all for serious music. The King admired her. That spoke for itself.

The Prince must sing, the company declared.

Nothing loth he obliged. He sang by himself and he sang with Perdita. In perfect harmony, he thought, as we shall be all our lives, forgetting that he had only such a short time ago deplored her melancholy and compared her unfavourably with other women.

And afterwards a game of faro, with Perdita's lips slightly pursed, not approving. The stakes were very high. Mr Fox always played for high stakes and the Prince had lost a thousand guineas in a very short time.

A thousand guineas. What was that added to all he owed? And a Prince of Wales should not concern himself with money. It was so easy to scribble an I.O.U. Mr Fox did it constantly and with the same abandon as the Prince.

And after that . . . talk, political because after all this, with Cumberland House and Devonshire House, was the centre of Whiggery, and any hostess who could get Mr Fox to talk was sure of a successful party.

So Mr Fox talked and of course he talked of America which was the great controversy of the moment. The King, he said, would accept no man who disagreed with him. This was no way to govern. Were the King the most brilliant administrator in the world–which Mr Fox very respectfully wished to point out that he was not–still this would be wrong. It was through discussion and debate that conclusions should be reached.

'We are going to lose America,' declared Mr Fox, 'and I say this: Serve us right. There should never have been this conflict with our brothers. Fools . . . fools . . . fools . . . have governed us, have decided on our policies and they are destroying the greatness of this land. This government must go before it is too late. There is a country to be saved.'

The Prince listened entranced. He knew that they were looking to him to be the saviour. When he was in control he would summon men like Fox, Burke and Sheridan to form his government and he would not presume to think that because he had inherited a crown he was some supreme being. And to think that the King was that bumbling old gentleman the farmer, the button maker, the home lover, the man who was only capable of begetting children and making their childhood unbearable with his discipline which was absurd and old fashioned . . . and should never have been in fashion in any case.

But never mind. The day would come. In three years time he would take his place in the House of Lords–and during that time he would learn his politics and Mr Fox would be his most excellent tutor.

Across the room he caught sight of Perdita and Malden. What a handsome fellow Malden was and that coat of his was of the latest cut and fashion. He admired the new style of button. He had not seen them before. In a second he had crossed to them, but so absorbed were they in their conversation that they had not heard him approach.

Perdita was saying: 'I shall never be able to show you how grateful I am to you . . .'

The feeling in her voice was astonishing.

Why? He wondered what Malden had done that she should be so grateful; and Malden was looking at her with such a look of devotion that the Prince felt a wave of indignation.

They were aware of him. Perdita's face was transformed by the most loving smile.

'I trust Your Highness is enjoying the company tonight.' He was immediately delighted with her. She was so pretty; and what love for him shone in her eyes. She was merely being gracious to Malden. Hadn't he been an excellent emissary during their courtship?

He replied that it was an excellent gathering and that there must be more like them. He had particularly enjoyed her singing and would like to hear her again.

And she sang once more and they sang together, in harmony.

Mrs Armistead called at St James's Street to tell Mr Fox that Mr Robinson had called and was making a nuisance of himself.

'I brought Lord Malden to come and take him away. The drunken fellow had no notion that it was a plot to get rid of him. He went with the utmost alacrity to drink with a noble lord.'

'Excellent, my dear Lizzie. You'll make a fine politician.'

She was pleased to please him. His approval was the only reward she asked. She would have liked to serve him–to see that his linen was washed and a clean shirt laid out for him each day; she would have liked to have sponged the grease spots from his coat.

'And how is it between our lovers? I thought Mrs Robinson looked less blooming than usual.'

'I think we are moving into the last phase.'

'Is that so?'

'You are displeased?'

'No, no. I had thought in the beginning that she might have carried some influence, but I see she carries none.'

'So it is of no interest to you whether the affair continues or not?'

He shook his head and was thoughtful. Perdita was a most desirable woman, but doubtless he himself would be interested in her for no more than a very short time–but for that short time he would be definitely intrigued. He was rather amused by the manner in which she acted her way through life and would have liked to discover a little of the real woman beneath; but it would probably not be worth the trouble. No, it was not very important that the affair should continue, except of course that if the Prince gave Perdita her congé, there would be another–and perhaps someone who might influence him.

He answered: 'Perhaps on the whole it is better that it should continue a little longer.'

Mrs Armistead nodded. She would do her best to keep it going. Mr Fox would understand that but for her prompt action this afternoon there could have been disaster.

He did understand. He could trust her. It was interesting how they could work together.

She told him about the house in Chertsey. He knew, of course, how she had earned the money which had brought it. He advised her about her affairs which he was well able to do in spite of the fact that his own were in disorder.

'Why, Lizzie, you are a woman of property.' And he did not speak slightingly but with admiration.

He talked of the American situation with her for it was very much in his thoughts. He believed that if the Colonies were lost it could bring down the Government.

She listened, made intelligent comment, and later spent an affectionate hour in his company.

The Queen Plots

News of the life the Prince was leading came in time to the King's ears. He could not sleep at night for thinking of it. George . . . young George . . . little more than a boy and keeping a play actress! The King's mind went back to the days when he himself was eighteen. He thought of that establishment in which he had set up Hannah, where their children were born. But it was discreet. No one knew. It was wrong, it was foolish, and he deeply repented it; but it was *discreet*. That was the first quality a prince who would be king must acquire. It was not generally known about his affair with Hannah, although it had been rumoured and whispered of here and there. This was different. This was blatant. Going out together . . . her in her carriage . . . painted like a harlot–although the women in the Prince's set all did the same. Rouge and white lead, bah! Didn't they know it stopped up the pores and caused consumption?

And the company he kept. That was the real source of trouble! He was a frequent visitor at Cumberland House. Nothing he could have done could have been more designed to flout his father. To go . . . as soon as a little freedom was granted him . . . to that hotbed of Whiggery which was in complete opposition to everything his father stood for. To choose *them* as his friends. If it had been the Gloucesters it would have been different. But it was not. It was Cumberland, that lecher who had made a scandal with Grosvenor's wife–Cumberland and that woman with her eyelashes. George must have set out deliberately to defy his father.

He summoned Gloucester to Kew and told him of his anxieties.

'You've heard, of course,' he said.

'The whole town is talking of it,' replied Gloucester. 'He's there every other night. Sometimes with his play actress, sometimes without her. He's constantly in the company of Fox and Sheridan.'

'Rogues, both of them. Fox would do anything to plague me. As for Sheridan, he's a drunkard and a lecher and I think it the greatest shame that he should have married that charming Miss Linley.' The King's eyes clouded momentarily with sentiment. 'I shall never forget hearing her sing in an oratorio. Never heard singing like it. Sang like an angel, looked like an angel. I'm sorry to see her married to a fellow like that.'

'They say he's talented. I heard it said that on the first night of his *School for Scandal* a journalist passing the theatre ran for his life because he thought the thunder of applause would bring the roof down.'

'Bah! Pandering to the senses! Low taste. The man's a drunkard and a gambler and he and Fox are teaching George to be the same.'

'What are you going to do about it?'

'What can I do? The young dog's eighteen. They say that's the time for a little independence. Fox, Sheridan, Cumberland . . . Cumberland most of all.'

'I wonder you allow them to meet.'

'I don't care to part relations.'

Gloucester looked surprised considering the manner in which he–as well as Cumberland–had been kept from their nephews and nieces for so many years, but old George was behaving oddly nowadays; one could never be sure of him.

The King began to pace up and down, his face growing scarlet.

'What would you have me do in my present distress?' he demanded. 'Eh, what? If I attempt to put a stop to this I shall drive my son further and further into the arms of the opposition. And that would increase my distress.'

Gloucester agreed that taking into account the Prince's age and the freedom he had already had it would be difficult to intervene now. Perhaps if he had not been so rigorously controlled beforehand he would not have rushed so madly into freedom. But he did not distress his brother still further by telling him this.

'He comes to see you, I suppose?' said the King.

'Not often.'

'But he is fond of you?'

'Yes, I think so. But when I have tried to remonstrate with him he has hinted that he does not care to be preached at.'

'You see. You see. What can you do with such a young dog? Tell me that, eh, what?'

'It may be that after a while he will grow less wild.'

'Less wild! Less wild! I hear that he is beginning to talk like that woman . . . that coarse creature with the eyelashes. I hear that he drinks to excess . . . that he has actually been carried home to that place where he lives with the actress. A pleasant story to be set about the Prince of Wales.'

'Many princes have behaved in similar fashion,' soothed Gloucester.

'I won't have my sons doing it. I won't, I say. But how can I stop it? Tell me that, eh, what?'

The Duke of Gloucester could give no answer. 'I fear Cumberland may be attempting to blackmail me into receiving that woman of his,' went on the King.

'Well,' retorted the Duke of Gloucester speaking for his own Duchess, 'she is after all a member of the family.'

'Eyelashes, bah!' said the King.

When Gloucester left he went to see the Queen. She was a little worried about the health of the baby, for young Alfred had not picked up as her older children had and as little Octavius had never really been strong there were new anxieties in the nurseries.

She was sitting in her drawing room at her embroidery, her snuff box beside her, some of her women with her, contented apart from her anxiety about her family, to be staying at 'dear little Kew'.

She gave the order for dismissal because she saw at once from the King's expression that he was upset and she knew that if he talked too quickly or incoherently some of these women would gossip about it, so she took every opportunity of keeping them out of the King's way.

She did not have to ask what was wrong. She guessed the American Colonies might have something to do with it, but he would not of course come here to discuss those with her. She was supposed to be unaware that any conflict was taking place. If she had offered an opinion it would have been received with cold surprise. She had grown accustomed to this, and only resented it now and then.

But the family was a different matter. So it was family affairs of which he had come to speak.

'The baby?' he asked.

'As well as we can expect. He grows a little stronger each day, I think.'

'I'm glad of that. And Octavius? Eh! What?'

'He has had a little cold but it is better,' soothed the Queen.

Now to the subject which had brought him here; George, Prince of Wales.

'It's young George,' he said.

The Queen put her hand involuntarily to her heart.

'Up to his tricks,' went on the King. 'Gambling, drinking and keeping a play actress.'

'No!' cried the Queen.

'But I say it is so and something will have to be done about it. He'll have to be taught his duties to the state, to his family . . . eh? what?'

'There are always people to gossip . . . to lie . . . about us.'

'These are not lies. I've heard from too many sources. He's wild. He's set this woman up in a house . . . He lives there with her. His friends are my enemies. Fox is always with him. He goes to Cumberland and that woman of his. He's with the Whigs . . . he's with the Opposition. His bosom friends are the people I most dislike. He does it to spite me, eh, what?'

'A play actress,' murmured the Queen. 'George with a play actress.'

'I'm afraid our son is too fond of women.'

The Queen was silent.

'If that were all . . . I'd understand.' The King seemed as though he were talking to himself. 'Young man . . . hot blood. It happens now and then. They grow out of it . . . become sober . . .' He looked at Charlotte with her big mouth and her lack of eyelashes. 'They do their duty, are faithful to the wives that are chosen for them . . . But he has deliberately gone to Cumberland. My brother is teaching him to despise everything that I wish him to respect. That's what is happening to the Prince of Wales and what am I going to do about it, eh, what?'

The Queen did not know. She wanted to soothe him, to stop him talking too rapidly. She knew her son well enough to realize that if his father tried to direct his actions he would be more rebellious than ever.

And as the King walked up and down murmuring half sentences to himself she was more concerned for him than for her son. Loving young George she believed that there was nothing really wrong with him. He was a little wild, it was true. But he would grow out of that. The fact was that he was so attractive that he could not help being the centre of attraction, but he would settle down.

She was a little worried about the play actress, though. That was the woman who had made a scene at the Oratorio when George had attracted so much attention by staring at her.

She sighed. But young men would be young men and until they found a wife for him he must she supposed have a mistress.

She wished though that he would choose some good quiet young woman–someone at Kew so that he could call and see his mother often–and perhaps confide in her.

She had to prevent the King becoming too excited and she said something of this to him.

'Young men will be young men. They must not be judged too harshly.'

And oddly enough this did seem to soothe. Then she suggested a little walk or a drive in the carriage round 'dear little Kew which I know Your Majesty loves as much as I do.'

This was indeed a success, for he agreed to go. It was so pleasant riding in Kew, for the place was like a little village with the houses round the Green which were occupied by the children's governesses and tutors, the ladies in waiting, doctors and gardeners. '*Dear* little Kew,' murmured the Queen; and the King echoed her sentiments, for to him this little world seemed far from the ceremonies of St James's or Buckingham House; and here George was the Squire–the benevolent landlord, beloved of his tenants. Farmer George, in fact, who delighted in the people who came out of their cottages to curtsey and pull a forelock as he and the Queen rode by.

The river flowed peacefully by and there on Strand-on-the-Green the Queen saw Mrs Papendiek about to go into the painter Zoffany's house where she had lodgings, but when she heard the royal carriage she turned and curtsied; the King raised his hat and inclined his head. He liked Mrs Papendiek and Charlotte could see that he was forgetting his troubles momentarily, as she had intended he should.

The Queen thought a great deal about the play actress, trying to remember what she looked like. She recalled the performance of *The Winter's Tale* in which the woman had played Perdita. What a pity they had ever gone to see that play! But then they would have seen something else and it would probably have been another play actress.

If only he could have found a *nice* lady–not an actress. There had been Mary Hamilton to whom he had been devoted and had written charming letters and looked upon as a sister. And that had taken him often to his sister's apartments and no one could say that wasn't a good thing! But a play actress! Suppose he had fallen in love with someone in the Queen's household and it was all very discreet. The Prince would visit his mother often–and that could do nothing but good.

How pleasant if he would break this association with the play actress and find a kind, clever and above all *discreet* lady in his mother's household.

At the Queen's robing Madam von Schwellenburg was ordering the women to do this and that in her hectoring manner.

Charlotte had been helped on with her gown and her powdering robe was being put about her. While her hair was being dressed she read the newspapers and looked for references to the Prince and Mrs Perdita Robinson. She always tried to keep these from the King.

She was well aware that her women discussed this matter; in fact she believed that the whole Court was discussing it.

Perhaps she should ask Schwellenburg. Not that she wanted to talk of it, but at least Schwellenburg was German and she would be honest. She never chose her words with much care and would be as outspoken to the Queen as to anyone else.

While her hair was curled and crimped she was thinking of the women of her household. It would have to be someone young and there was no one young. It would have to be someone beautiful and there was no one really beautiful . . . at least not that a young boy of eighteen would think so; and most important of all *discreet*. The trouble was that people who possessed youth rarely had discretion and vice versa.

Should she speak of the matter to the King? She imagined his dismay at the thought of providing a mistress for his son. She wondered at herself. But she was desperate; and she proved in the past that, docile as she might seem, when she was determined she could act boldly.

She wanted to save the Prince from folly and the King from anxiety; and surely it was worth while stepping outside one's usual moral code to do that?

The thought of intrigue was exciting. This was one of the rare times in her married life when she was not pregnant. And the King had agreed with her that in view of the fact that Alfred was their fourteenth and that neither he nor Octavius were as strong as the others, perhaps the time had come to call a halt to child-bearing.

Just suppose she were successful in finding the right sort of woman who would lead the Prince away from his wicked uncle and bring him back into the family circle? What ever means were necessary, the result would justify them.

She decided that she would choose an opportunity to speak to Schwellenburg to discover what was being said among the women; and she might even find out through her if there were any women of the household who combined enough beauty to please the Prince and enough discretion to satisfy his mother.

Madam von Schwellenburg was in her room surrounded by her caged toads when Madam Haggerdorn came to tell her that the Queen requested her presence.

Before obeying the summons she insisted on Madam Haggerdorn's witnessing the cleverness of her favourite toad by tapping on his cage with her snuff box.

'He know. He know,' she cried animatedly. 'Listen . . . see, he croak. You hear?'

Madam Haggerdorn said it was a wonderful performance, for like everyone else in the Queen's household she was afraid of offending Schwellenburg. The woman was heartily disliked; the King had made two mild attempts to have her sent back to Germany; but for some reason the Queen–although she herself did not greatly care for the woman–had insisted that she stay; and because the King was determined to keep his wife out of important affairs he conceded her complete sway in her own household. Consequently Schwellenburg remained, growing more objectionable and arrogant every week.

Schwellenburg's repulsive face was softened by her affection for the animals–the only living creatures who could soften her; and Haggerdorn reminded her that the Queen was waiting.

'Go when want,' said Schwellenburg and deliberately went on tapping the cages and listening ecstatically to the croaking of her pets.

When Haggerdorn had left, with a studied leisureliness, Schwellenburg made her way to the Queen's apartments.

Charlotte was alone and invited her Mistress of the Robes to be seated.

'I want you to talk to me about the Prince of Wales,' said the Queen.

Schwellenburg's features formed themselves into the sort of smile she bestowed on her pets. She liked to think she was the confidante of the Queen.

'Is vild,' she said. 'Very vild. Drink too much; too much gamble; too much vimen.'

'I fear so,' mused the Queen. 'And the King is most distressed.'

Schwellenburg nodded, well pleased; she was glad the King was distressed. He had tried to send her back to Germany.

'What have you heard? That he keeps a play actress?'

'Everyvon talk. Everyvon know. Is dronk . . . has house in Cork Street. Herr Prince very vild.'

'I fear there is truth in the rumours. Do the women talk much about it?'

'All the time. Everyvon talk.'

'Do any of the women er . . . envy this play actress?' Schwellenburg opened her eyes in surprise. And the Queen went on: 'Perhaps some of the younger and prettier ones . . . perhaps they feel that they would . . . like to be in her place.'

'There vos von. Harriot Vernon . . .'

'I know about her. She was dismissed from Court.'

'He like very much Mary Hamilton . . . but no more. Never see now.'

Mary Hamilton! thought the Queen. Oh, no, that was no use. One could not expect to revive an old attraction. He had given up Mary Hamilton when the play actress came along; he could not go back to her.

'I do not like his friends. I think this play actress is having a bad effect on him, taking him to his uncle. If there was someone here at Court . . . at Kew . . . I am not condoning immorality, of course, but young men are such that they need a . . . a friend, a female friend. You may know what I mean, Schwellenburg.'

Schwellenburg knew. She muttered: 'These girls . . . they are vild. Like Herr Prince. All they think is . . . dance . . . and patch and rouge and white lead . . . That is English girls. German fräuleins do as told. Much better.'

The Queen was suddenly excited. A German mistress for the Prince. What an excellent idea. But where? The King had dismissed all the German women who came over with her–except Schwellenburg and Haggerdorn. There might be one or two others, but they were old, old as herself. No, what they wanted was a young, buxom German girl who was disciplined and discreet and would do as she was told.

'Thank you, Schwellenburg.'

She was indeed grateful. Schwellenburg had given her an idea.

When the Mistress of the Robes had retired she sat down and wrote home to Mecklenburg-Strelitz. In that poor little province there were always people who were longing to get to England and enjoy the patronage of Queen Charlotte.

In Cumberland House the Duke and Duchess were discussing the Prince on similar lines.

'Do you fancy,' asked the Duchess of her husband, 'that he is quite so happy in our company as he was?'

'He comes here.'

'But not so often. And he is always in a corner with Fox or Sheridan. They often leave early together to go off to Devonshire House I believe.'

'I'm sure we have entertained him lavishly.'

'He's certainly lost a lot of money at our tables.'

'It's at his wish.'

'But he is drifting. I sense it. And I think that Propriety Prue is at the bottom of it. She doesn't like us.'

'She fears you outshine her.'

'And she remembers that you once chased her. She may still think you have designs on her virtue. Have you?'

'Pah!' cried the Duke. 'Does she think she's so irresistible?'

'I'm sure she does. Otherwise she might be a little more careful with H.R.H. Because I think that we are not the only people who have had the misfortune to weary him now and then.'

'You mean Prue is on the way out.'

The Duchess nodded slowly. 'I have seen the writing on the wall. She won't last more than a few more months.'

'And then?'

'That is what we have to be prepared for.'

'And knowing you, my love, I am prepared to stake a thousand guineas that you are already prepared.'

'Dally the Tall,' she said.

'What?'

'Why so surprised? Have I not seen your lustful eyes studying this tall one appraisingly? You must admit your tastes are not dissimilar to those of your amorous nephew.'

'Well, Dally's a charmer.'

'I know you think so; and I am sure the Prince will too.'

'What do you propose to do?'

'See that they have the opportunity they desire.'

'You mean that *you* desire.'

'Dally has a reputation for er . . . pleasing men.'

'So has Perdita.'

'And I'll tell you something else. I am not the only one who has noticed a falling off in His Highness's devotion. The jackals are gathering round . . . hopefully. Malden is ready to leap in as soon as H.R.H. retires. Poor Malden. His faithful service should be rewarded. And Fox is biding his time. Malden should take care. He is rather lamblike and what chance has a lamb against a fox?'

'And such a fox! So he is waiting to drag Perdita into his lair, is he?'

'And I hope you, my lord, will have enough respect for your Ducal rank not to join the patient throng.'

'What are you going to do about Dally?'

'From now on she should be treated with respect. Mrs Grace Elliott, one of the most amusing and beautiful young women in London! She is perfect in every way. Three years his senior–as Propriety Prue is. Have you noticed how His Highness likes his women to be older than himself? And she will be a complete change from Prue because there is no propriety about Grace Elliott.'

'When does the battle start?'

'Tonight, my love. We dare, not delay. Don't imagine because you are blind to what is happening about you others are. Depend upon it, many people are noticing that the chains of love are slackening. But she could do harm to us before she goes. And others will be bringing forward their candidates for his approval. It is always best to be the first, my love. Leave this to me.'

This the Duke was very happy to do.

Perdita was far from tranquil. Mr Robinson was constantly threatening and he demanded his payments promptly. She wished that she could have had her mother and daughter to live in Cork Street. What a comfort that would be! The little girl adored her and Mrs Darby was so proud of her beautiful daughter and on her visits to them, taking costly presents, Perdita was really happy.

Then she would come back to Cork Street and rest for a while and submit herself to the ministrations of Mrs Armistead to be prepared for the night's company. There were times when she would have given a great deal to go to bed and stay there. But the Prince's energies were unflagging.

She had returned from a visit to her mother and daughter and had rested and been powdered and rouged and dressed in a gown of rose coloured velvet when the Prince arrived.

He kissed her absentmindedly and made no comment on her appearance, but sprawling in a chair said he had only come to stay an hour or so.

She was disappointed, although a short while before she had been longing for a restful evening. What she had meant was a quiet evening with the Prince.

She said: 'I had hoped we could have been together . . . just the two of us . . . for one evening. I have a new song I want to sing to you. We can sing it together, too.'

'Another time,' he said.

She looked mournfully up at the ceiling and pressed her lips slightly together to imply resignation and restraint. This annoyed the Prince. He would rather she had openly protested. He was becoming a little exasperated now and then with this martyr's role which was such a favourite one of hers. There was a pause. The Prince was thinking it was a mighty long hour.

She said: 'I saw little Maria today.'

'I trust she is well.'

'And so delighted to see me. She wept when I left. Sometimes I wonder . . .'

The Prince said nothing.

'It was a great sacrifice to make,' she went on. 'Perhaps I was wrong to give her up. After all, I am her mother. I think sometimes she wonders . . . One day I shall tell her of how I suffered because I could not give her the time which most mothers give their children. I hope she will understand.'

The Prince yawned. It should have been a warning.

'Yes.' She was warming to her role now. She had risen, and putting her hand to her throat gazed before her. There were tears in her eyes. 'It was a great decision to make . . . this renunciation. Husband, child . . . and virtue . . . all I abandoned.'

'I did not know,' said the Prince coldly, 'that you so regretted leaving your husband.'

'He was not good to me but at least he was my husband.'

'Then perhaps Madam you feel you should return to him?'

Danger signals. She changed her tactics. 'I would never return to him. You must know that better than anyone.'

'Yet you sounded as though you regretted his loss.'

She went to him and put her arms about his neck. 'You . . . you are handsome . . . all that a Prince could be. How could any woman be blamed for not being able to resist you?'

This was more like it.

'My angel,' said the Prince, but he was still a little absentminded.

'Pray come and sing a little.'

'Not now. There is not the time. I but called in to see you for an hour.'

'You used not to be so eager to get away.'

'Eager? I'm not eager. Or if I am it's because of all this damned melancholy.'

'And you promised me not to use bad language.'

'I only do so in your presence when goaded.'

'Goaded!'

'Oh, Perdita, stop being the tragedy queen. You came here because you wanted to. And there's an end to it.'

She was silent, and going over to the harpsichord played a melody. Even her tunes were melancholy, thought the Prince. Why be melancholy when there was so much in the world to be gay about?

She looked over her shoulder. 'And where are you going to in such haste? Or would you rather not tell me?'

'I have no reason to hide my actions. I am going to Cumberland House.'

Cumberland House! And they had not invited her. She knew they called her Propriety Prue and mocked her behind her back. And when she thought that the Duke had once pursued her so relentlessly and had admired her so! Of course it was the Duchess. The woman was jealous.

'My dear George, do you think you should go to Cumberland House?'

'In God's name, what do you mean?'

'I do not think the Duchess behaves in a manner which could be called ladylike.'

'She doesn't have to ape ladies. She's a duchess . . . and a royal one at that.'

'I still think she is a little coarse. And I do not like to hear you talking as she does.'

'Madam,' said the Prince, incensed now, 'I have been treated like a child by my father for eighteen years. I have no intention of allowing my mistress to do the same.'

Mistress! That dreadful word which always unnerved her. She felt the tears brimming over on to her cheeks. They were splashing on to the red velvet. She hoped they would not mark it. It was too good and too new to be given to Armistead just yet. But she could not hold back the tears.

The Prince saw the tears and said in a shamefaced way: 'Well, you should not attempt to dictate to me, you know.'

She could never stop play acting; she wanted all the best lines. So she said:

'I have angered you, but I cannot let that influence me when I speak for your own good. The King and Queen do not wish you to go to Cumberland House. This distresses them.'

'So you are in Their Majesties' confidence?'

'Everyone knows it.'

A suspicion came into his mind. 'They have not given you some command to stop my going to Cumberland House, have they?'

'Do you think they would notice me! They despise me as so many do . . . because I gave up my home, my husband, my daughter . . . everything . . . for you.'

Because the Prince had known his fancy was straying, because he realized the inconstancy of the vows of constant devotion, he was ashamed of himself and sought to shift the blame to her.

'I believe,' he said, 'that you wish to be rid of me.'

'Oh, no . . . no!' That at least was genuine.

'I have seen men here . . . with you. Malden for instance. You are so grateful to him. I overhead you telling him so.'

'That was because he had helped us to come together. Why should I be grateful to him for anything else?'

'So you are grateful for that, are you?'

'More than I can say. Oh, if you but knew . . .' She was smiling through her tears; and now she was very appealing. He wanted to be the faithful lover; he did not wish to break the vows he had made. If only she would not be so melancholy, if only she would not talk so much about her sacrifices.

He kissed her.

'Please don't quarrel with me. It breaks my heart.'

He quarrel with *her*? But she was the one who made the quarrels. Still, she was loving and sweet now, declaring that it was only her anxiety for him that made her so sad.

So they embraced and when she said: 'Is everything as it was,' he answered: 'Nothing has changed. Constant unto death, my Perdita.'

So she was relieved and not sorry too that she had voiced her disapproval of his going to Cumberland House. Lord Malden had told her that that was what had upset the King more than anything and that if the King and Queen believed that she kept him from Cumberland House they might begin to take a much kindlier view of her relationship with the Prince.

But in spite of the reconciliation the Prince would not linger. He went, as he had said he would, when the hour was up.

Saucy Grace Elliot was delighted at the prospect of taking Perdita's place. The Duchess of Cumberland had explained the position quite frankly for Grace Elliott and Anne Luttrell were of a kind and understood each other perfectly.

Grace was very tall but slender and willowy; her hair was of a delightful gold colour, fine and abundant; she had large grey eyes; the manner in which she walked, gesticulated and talked betrayed her sensuality. A glance from Grace was an invitation and a promise, and as she kept her promises she was constantly surrounded by would-be lovers.

Perhaps her father, Hew Dalrymple, a Scottish Advocate, recognized this, for at a very early age she was married off to a Dr Elliott, who at forty looked fifty, and in any case in years was quite old enough to be her father.

In her mid-teens she was already a lusty creature and marriage with Dr

Elliott was not her idea of bliss and as shortly after the marriage she made the acquaintance of Lord Valentia, she became his mistress and eloped with him.

This caused a great scandal because Dr Elliott decided to divorce Grace and at the same time demand damages from Lord Valentia, which he was granted. The escapade with Grace cost Lord Valentia £12,000 and the case was compared with that of the Grosvenors and the Duke of Cumberland. Lord Valentia's expensive escapade proved to be impermanent, and when he left Grace, unprotected and ostracized by society, there seemed only one course for her to take. She announced her intention of going into that French convent where she had received her education and left the country.

Grace's character was not exactly suited to convent life and very soon she left this refuge and, living on the fringe of the Court of France, met Lord Cholmondeley who was on a visit from England.

Lord Cholmondeley was gallant, and Grace was homesick, so they comforted each other and Cholmondeley brought her back to England . . . and to Cumberland House.

Grace was gay and unscathed by her adventures. She knew herself well enough to realize that though men were necessary to her full enjoyment of life, she would never remain faithful to one for any length of time. She would flit from one to another, enjoying each encounter to the full because she knew that when it was over there would be no regrets, no looking back and sighing over the past; Grace could only live life in the present; it was this quality which many found so attractive and Golden Dally the Tall was welcomed into society such as that at Cumberland House.

She had seen the Prince of course and could imagine nothing more desirable than to be his mistress for a while. She was growing a little tired of Cholmondeley in any case.

So she listened to the Duchess's plans and agreed at once that if she did not win His Royal Highness from Perdita it would not be her fault.

Cumberland House looked gayer than usual after the scene with Perdita.

There was dancing and gaming as usual, as well as good talk. The Duchess had a word in private with the Prince when he arrived, asking if all was well. 'Your fond aunt fancies you look less contented than usual and she is concerned for you.'

'I'm not discontented.'

'But it is not enough that you should merely be not discontented. I must see you basking in complete contentment.'

'My dearest aunt!'

'So tell me what I must do for your delight.'

'What more could you do?'

She fluttered her eyelashes at him. 'Anything in the world you asked of me, dear nephew. And I will tell you this: I certainly feel very angry towards any who disturb you.'

It was a reference to Perdita, he knew, for she suspected that Perdita was playing the injured woman who had given her 'all'. She had told him an amusing story about a woman who had left her husband for a lover and who comically dramatized the situation. He had laughed with the rest of the company and it was not until later that he had realized how those time-worn clichés she had put into the woman's mouth were the very ones Perdita would have chosen.

She was frowning, which was rare with her. 'I am a little disturbed, dear nephew. So disturbed because I know it is my duty to speak and wondering whether it will make you angry with me.' Again one of those coquettish looks. 'Could you imagine circumstances in which you would be angry with me?'

'Impossible because none exist.'

'Not only the most elegant, the most handsome, but the most gallant of princes!' She was laughing again. 'I have found my courage and I will speak. You should take care. I believe your father has set a spy very close to you.'

'To report on my actions! The newspapers do that very well.'

'More than that. He wants to guide your actions. He is trying to stop your visits here.'

'He'll never do that.'

'Poison works slowly sometimes, but it can kill in the end. I know that your father deplores the fact that you come here. He hates Cumberland because he married me. He's never forgiven him. And that you should choose to visit us infuriates him. He wants to stop it.'

'He has not commanded me to stay away.'

'No, because he realizes he could not do that. If you refused, the people would be on your side. There is Fox or Sheridan to mention it in Parliament. It is not the wish of the people, dearest nephew, that you should be treated like an infant in arms.'

'That I will resist at all costs.'

'The King wishes you to live as he does. Early to bed, early to rise. Lemonade your drink; a little backgammon your sole dissipation. Lucky nephew, to have two Holy fathers–one in Heaven and one on Earth.'

'He knows it's hopeless to force me to live the kind of life he does.'

'Does Propriety . . . Does Perdita ever mention your coming here?'

The Prince hesitated.

'Oh, you are too honourable to tell, but of course she does. This is why it is so difficult. She wishes you to stay away because the King wants it. He would be even ready to accept the fact that you keep a mistress if he could stop your coming here and break up your friendship with your uncle and myself and Fox and Sheridan.'

'Nothing would induce me to break up the friendships I most treasure. You cannot mean that the King has approached Perdita . . .'

'I do not mean that His Majesty has been visiting Cork Street nor that your mistress has been summoned to St James's or Kew. But there are ways of communicating messages, and I know for certain that the Queen believes that although it is deplorable that you keep a mistress it is not the first time an heir to the throne has done so. The King is more concerned with your politics and the fact that you have made a friend of the brother he refuses to receive than your association with a mistress.'

'Is this so?'

She laid a hand appealingly on his arm. 'Do not believe me until you have proved this for yourself.'

'I will prove this. I will ask her if she is doing the King's work for him.'

'She would deny it. Imagine her. "Do you think I would allow myself to be the King's spy!"' The Duchess had put her hand to her throat and was staring before her in a perfect imitation of Perdita. '"Do you think I would work in the dark against the man for whom I gave up husband, home and child?"' It was cruelly similar and he felt ashamed and yet not as angry as he should have done. There was almost a feeling of relief. Once again he felt that the door of a cage in which he was locked–and this time he himself had turned the key–was slowly opening for him to escape if he wanted to.

The Duchess was quick to sense his mood. 'Don't blame her too much. She would naturally wish to please the King, and if it meant that her liaison was not frowned on in those circles, imagine how relieved that would make her.'

'It is certainly a disturbing thought,' he said. 'But I believe your zeal for my comfort has perhaps led you to the wrong conclusion.'

She was smiling happily. 'Oh, I do hope so, for your happiness is the most important thing to me. I do want all to be well. The King may banish *us* from Court if he wishes. Who wants to visit the Palace of Piety? But if you should withdraw *your* presence . . . well, then Cumberland House would hang out the mourning.'

He laughed. 'You'd look very well in purple and black.'

'But better wrapped in smiles.'

'Dear aunt!'

'And I have not offended? I have not been too outspoken?'

'As if you could ever offend.'

'Then I am happy. But, Prince of Princes, you will be watchful.'

He promised that he would.

He was thoughtful when Grace Elliott was presented to him. He could not help assessing her charms though. She was exciting. But he kept thinking of Perdita, perhaps receiving a message from the Court. Could it be Malden? No, Malden had been a good friend. Yet if the King commanded Malden to tell Perdita his pleasure, who could blame Malden?

An uneasy thought. Spies in the very house which was to have been his refuge!

He danced with Grace. He complimented her on her dancing and her beauty.

She conveyed as she could so well that she had other attributes which she would be pleased to put at the Prince's service. He was aware of this but his attitude was vague; and Grace knew that she was not going to step into his bed immediately.

The next day the Prince called at Cork Street, his mind full of the accusations he had heard on the previous night.

Perdita had had a sleepless night; when he had left her she had gone over everything that had been said and she remembered those early days when he had contrived to be with her every possible moment and had never left her side until he was forced to. Nowadays he merely announced that he was going to Cumberland House or Devonshire House, to neither of which households was she invited.

She had thought the Duchess of Devonshire might be her friend since when Perdita had been in the debtors' prison the Duchess had helped her. But while the Duchess was ready to help a poor woman of talent, she was not prepared to receive a play actress in to her house. Perdita had been very angry and instead of making it tactfully known to the Prince that she longed to go to Devonshire House–for had he asked that she should go his request would have been immediately granted–she had tried to outshine the Duchess in public at such places as the Rotunda, the Pantheon and Ranelagh. She had dressed herself in magnificent gowns, colourful and dazzling, certain to attract the eye and wherever the Duchess was there was Perdita–always calling attention to herself, determined to oust the Duchess from her position as the leader of fashion.

And when she had, coming face to face with the Duchess, bowed, the Duchess had looked through her as though she did not exist and the crowds had seen the snub.

That had sent her home in tears, railing against her position and all she had given up for the Prince; and she continued with the theme when the Prince called to see her.

So, after that near quarrel Perdita was uneasy. She lay in bed thinking not so much of her child as of the changing attitude of the Prince. There was one other subject of which she refused to think. Every time it came into her mind she pushed it away. This was Debts. She did not know how much she owed but she knew the amount must be considerable. The cost of entertaining at Cork Street was enormous; her dresses cost a fortune; her wine bill she dared not think of–the Prince and his friends were heavy drinkers. No, she dared not think of money. And while she had the Prince's affection it was unimportant.

She must keep that affection; so when he arrived that day she was all charm and sweetness and he was obviously deeply affected by her beauty.

During his visit he mentioned Cumberland House.

'Why,' he said, 'do you dislike the place so?'

'Because I think it is not a worthy setting for you.'

'My uncle's house!'

'But an uncle who, in the King's eyes, has brought disgrace on your royal family.'

'So you would side with the King against me?'

'I would never side with anyone against you. They could torture me . . . they could do anything they would with me . . . but I would always stand by you.'

It was the answer he wanted. In fact when he thought of his father's approaching Perdita he saw how improbable that was. Dear Aunt Cumberland! It was her concern for him, of course . . . and her fear of losing him. She need not have feared. He would remain faithful to her *and* to Perdita. As for the King, he could go to the devil.

It reminded him that the King's Birthday Ball would soon be taking place. He told Perdita of this and said: 'You shall come.'

She clasped her hands in ecstasy. Pink satin? White perhaps as she had worn at the Oratorio. Lavender? Blue?

'Why not?' cried the Prince. 'You cannot join the dancers, but you will be watching in a box of course . . . and you will be there.'

The Prince specially noticed Mrs Armistead that evening. A strange woman who while she did not immediately catch the eye remained in the mind. How gracefully she moved! And there was an air of assurance about her. He had often wondered why a woman who had such an air of breeding should be a lady's maid. A disloyal thought occurred to him. One would have thought she was the lady of the house rather than Perdita, but for Perdita's fine clothes.

And then a thought suddenly struck him.

He called at Cumberland House to see the Duchess, who received him with arms outstretched.

'Prince of Princes!'

'Most enchanting and incongruous of Aunts.'

They embraced.

'I have come to speak to you about our recent conversation.'

The black feathery fans shot up to disclose the glitter of the green eyes.

'There may well be a spy in Cork Street.'

'So you have discovered . . .'

'The lady's maid. Her name is Mrs Armistead.'

The Duchess threw back her head and laughed. 'Now there is a woman.'

'You know of her?'

'She is becoming rather well known.'

'For what reason?'

'The usual reasons.'

'Dear Aunt, pray explain.'

'Dear Nephew, certainly. She is a very unusual and attractive lady's maid, is she not? You think so. So do other gentlemen . . . Mr Fox, Dorset, Derby . . . so I've heard.'

'By God, but why does she continue to serve Perdita?'

'She is no ordinary woman. She wishes to preserve her independence.'

'In being a lady's maid!'

'In rather special circumstances. I . . . who make it my pleasurable duty to keep a close watch on all that concerns my Prince. . . .'

'At least a very charming spy.'

She curtsied. 'But I love you as a mother, as an aunt . . . as anything you care to name. And so I learn these things. No, you must look elsewhere for your spy. It's not the lady's maid. She is a Whig . . . a good Whig. A friend of Mr Fox. She would never spy for the King.'

The Prince was laughing. 'I had always thought there was something unusual about her.'

'So you must look elsewhere, dear one.'

She was thinking: Armistead. Not a bad idea. If Grace cannot do, why not Armistead?

It was a scene of splendour at the Haymarket theatre where the King's birthday ball was being held, and although as many members of the royal family who were of an age to attend were present, it was the Prince of Wales who attracted all the attention. As usual he was dressed in the height of fashion, augmented by inventions of his own which would be copied immediately to become the very pinnacle of good taste and elegance.

Watching him from her box Perdita's feelings were mixed. Pride, pleasure, gratification, apprehension and humiliation. She herself came in for a good share of the attention; in fact it was divided between her and the Prince and whenever he gazed up at her box, which he did frequently, many were aware of it.

It had been most galling to arrive to find that she was to share a box with Mrs Denton who was the mistress of Lord Lyttleton. It was, she felt, a humiliation–as though she were judged to be of the same calibre. Why, when she had been at the theatre Lord Lyttleton had pursued her and offered her a luxurious house and a good income if she would become his mistress, and she had refused him. Mrs Denton had accepted–and here they were in a public place–grouped together as it were.

Mrs Denton was leaning forward in the box pointing out this person and that, excited and *honoured* to be present. How difficult life was! sighed Perdita. She wished she had not come.

'There is the Duchess of Devonshire,' whispered Mrs Denton. As if I did not know the creature, thought Perdita. 'Is she not beautiful? And her gown! No wonder she is the leader of fashion.' Is she! thought Perdita. Indeed she is not. I can outshine her any day. And I will. The arrogant woman snubbed me in Pall Mall. I shall not forget it.

And the Prince was talking to the Duchess and showing so clearly that he admired her and was delighted with her company.

'Of course she is very clever and her house is the meeting place for the Whig opposition. His Majesty won't be too pleased to have her here, but it's clear the Prince is delighted. And look . . . Oh, is she not beautiful! The tall one with the golden hair. I know who she is. Mrs Grace Elliott. There was a big scandal about her. I wonder the Queen allows her to come to Court.'

'She is too tall,' said Perdita.

'Do you think so? They call her Dally the Tall. It's because her name was Dalrymple before she married Mr Elliott . . . who divorced her, I might say.'

Perdita pursed her lips. Such a woman could mingle with guests while virtuous people must be seated in boxes!

'Oh . . . look.'

Mrs Denton had no need to direct Perdita's attention for she had already seen. The tall Mrs Elliott had selected two rosebuds from her corsage and had approached the Prince, curtsied and offered them to him.

'What . . . blatant impudence!'

'They say she is very free in her manners, but . . . at a public ball . . . !'

'It is quite shocking.'

'He's taking them.'

'He's too chivalrous to do anything else.'

The Prince was standing smelling the rosebuds while Grace Elliott remained before him, smiling complacently. Then the Prince looked up at the box and caught Perdita's eye.

He called to one of the members of his suite and handed the rosebuds to him.

'What does it mean?' twittered Mrs Denton.

Perdita was silent. It was a direct insult to her. This tall woman with the golden hair was telling her, and the Court, that she was ready to be–or already was–the *friend* of the Prince of Wales; and the fact that he had taken the flowers was almost an acknowledgement of this.

There was scratching on the door of the box.

Perdita did not look round; she felt too mortified.

Then a voice said: 'Er . . . Mrs Robinson . . .' And she saw the gentleman of the Prince's suite to whom he had handed the flowers standing there in the box and holding in his hands the rosebuds.

'With the compliments of His Royal Highness, Madam.'

Perdita felt almost hysterical with joy. She took the roses. She was well aware of the watching eyes. Dramatically, as though acting for an audience, she put the rosebuds into her corsage making sure that they were very prominent.

She sparkled. It was a successful ball. No matter that she must sit in a box while others danced with her lover. He had shown his regard for her publicly.

She was happier than she had been for some time.

The King and Queen were at Windsor–not so homely and comfortable as 'dear little Kew' but preferable to St James's.

The Queen was pleasantly excited and the King was pleased to humour her.

She explained to him: 'It is always pleasant to see people from one's native land even though it has ceased to be one's home.'

The King could see this point.

'Herr von Hardenburg and his wife are charming people. I trust you will honour them with an audience.'

'Pleased to, pleased to,' said the King.

'They have with them a young woman . . . about eighteen years of age. She is very pretty and of good family. I wish them to be comfortable during their stay here.'

Any such problem pleased the King. There was nothing he enjoyed more than planning domestic details. So he threw himself wholeheartedly into the matter and questioned and cross-questioned the Queen about the arrangements which had been made for the Hardenburgs.

She had asked that a house be found for them in Windsor; and she believed that they were very happy there. They had several small children and Fräulein von Busch, the young lady whom they had brought with them was such a pleasant creature . . . very handsome but modest; the Queen was sure that His Majesty would find her a pleasant change from some of these garish women who seemed to be considered so fashionable nowadays . . . women like the Duchess of Cumberland and Devonshire . . .

'Dabbling in politics,' grumbled the King. 'Never should be allowed. Women . . . in politics, eh! what?'

The Queen did not answer, but her resentment on that score was appeased a little. There were ways in which women could play their part in state affairs–for the amours of a Prince of Wales could be state affairs, witness the way he had fallen into the hands of Mr Fox–subtle ways; and because she was not pregnant she now had the time and energy to exert herself in her own particular brand of statescraft. And the King knew nothing about it. Comforting thought.

She suggested that they go for a drive and ordered the coachman which way to go. This took them past the house occupied by the Hardenburgs and as Frau von Hardenburg was in the garden with her children and swept a most demure and becoming curtsey, the Queen ordered the coachman to stop.

'Would Your Majesty allow me to present these pleasant people to you?'

The King was happy that this should be so. Beaming with goodwill he even condescended to dismount and go into the house.

It was pleasant to talk in German again. Even the King spoke in it as though it were his native language. The Hardenburgs were delighted and honoured. The wife, the King noticed, was a very pretty woman indeed, and as for the children they were quite enchanting. The King sat down and took several of them on his knee, questioning them and smiling at their bright answers.

'Charming, charming,' he muttered.

And there was Fräulein von Busch. What a pleasant creature! Plump, pink and white, golden haired and so modest.

When the visit was over and they rode off the Queen was smiling complacently. As for the King he declared himself to have been enchanted.

'Must make friends from Germany welcome. Very nice people. Homely

. . . pleasant . . . eh, what?'

The Queen agreed that the Hardenburgs–and Fräulein von Busch–were indeed homely and pleasant and she could wish that there were more like them.

The Prince came down to Windsor. This was what the Queen had been waiting for. The King had gone to London on government matters, and she had taken advantage of his absence to summon the Prince.

Windsor; thought the Prince. What was there to do in Windsor? There was only one place to be and that was London.

He was bored; he could not think why his mother had sent for him.

Did she want to chatter to him of what a bonny baby he had been while she did her tatting or sewed for the poor (Pious Person in the Palace of Purity). If so he would return to London at the earliest possible moment. He would do that in any case.

'You should drive with me,' said the Queen.

'For what purpose?'

'Because the people would like to see us together.'

So he rode with her and the carriage stopped at the Hardenburgs' house and there was Frau von Hardenburg in the garden making a pretty domestic scene with her children which would have delighted the King, but the Queen feared it would not make the same impression on the Prince of Wales.

'I should like to present you to these visitors from Germany.' She spoke quickly knowing that the Prince did not care to be reminded of his German ancestry.

The Prince was however extremely affable–and how charming he could be when he wished to!

He stepped down from the carriage and went into the house; and there was the enchanting Fräulein von Busch, flushing with her realization of the honour and looking so pretty and modest.

The Prince was clearly impressed. On the drive back he asked a great many questions about the Hardenburg *ménage*.

The Prince stayed at Windsor to make arrangements, was his excuse, for his birthday ball in August. He would be nineteen–only two years off his majority. In the last year he had changed considerably; in the next two years there would be more changes.

In the meantime he was happy–yes, really happy to stay at Windsor, and the Queen was so pleased with the success of her little bit of diplomacy that she was looking forward to telling the King about it when the Prince had given up that play-acting woman and his Whig friends and settled quietly down with that young German girl who would do as she was told and help to guide the Prince to a better life. How amazed his Majesty would be! Perhaps he would realize then that women were not such fools. After all it was the Duchess of Cumberland who was the leading light in Cumberland House. But one did not have to be a bad woman to be clever.

She knew that the Prince was calling frequently on the Hardenburgs, and about two weeks after she had introduced the Prince to them, Schwellenburg came bustling into her room in a state of some excitement.

'Haf news. Said vill tell Her Majesty selfs. Herr and Frau von Hardenburg left . . . is gone.'

'Gone?'

'To Germany. The childs are there. He come back for them.'

'You mean that Herr von Hardenburg and his wife have gone away and left their children behind?'

'Come back for them. Fräulein von Busch stay and look after them.'

'So Fräulein von Busch is here. But how strange. Why have they gone?'

Schwellenburg looked sly.

'Herr Prince,' she said.

'What do you mean?'

'He likes too much vimen.'

'But . . . Fräulein von Busch . . .'

'It is Frau von Hardenburg he likes . . . so her husbint say. There is von I can do . . . I take her vay from Herr Prince. So he go in night . . . and come back for the childs.'

The Queen could not believe it. She called for her carriage; she went to the house. There she found, as Schwellenburg had said, Fräulein von Busch looking after the children.

She explained in German that Herr von Hardenburg had thought it wiser to leave at once for he feared that their Majesties would be as displeased as he was by the Prince's too fervent attentions to his wife.

The Queen was dumbfounded. Frau von Hardenburg! When there was this fresh young girl brought over for one special reason.

She could not understand it. Her little effort at diplomacy had failed. And that day the Prince, bored with a Windsor that did not contain Frau von Hardenburg, returned to London.

Danger on Hounslow Heath

One thing he was sure of, he was tired of Perdita. Her continual hints of sacrifice, her frequent tears, the theatrical tones in which she talked of her position and her wrongs, the turgid sentimental poems she was fond of writing–and they were all addressed to him–these were more frequent than the gay times. He was beginning to make excuses for not calling at Cork Street. And when he did call, his visits were enlivened by the brief chats he indulged in with Mrs Armistead.

He was discovering how handsome she was, and she always seemed so sensible when compared with Perdita. When he kissed her hand in an excess of gallantry she did not protest or show any surprise but accepted his attentions as natural. Even when he went so far as to kiss her lips she returned the kiss in a sensible way.

He was greatly intrigued; and one thing the Hardenburg affair had taught him was that he no longer had any intention of remaining faithful to Perdita.

He had already accepted Grace Elliott's invitation to be her lover. She was amusing–just what he needed as an antidote to Perdita. A little cynical, extremely worldly; and a woman to whom one did not have to swear eternal fidelity every few minutes. He knew what his affair with Grace meant. It was good while it lasted and when it was over there would be no recriminations on either side. He knew that Grace had several lovers. He believed Cholmondeley was still one. There was St Leger, Selwyn, Windham . . .

Safety in numbers. He could be gay with Grace.

But he was tremendously intrigued with Mrs Armistead. In fact it was an unusual situation. He visited the mistress and desired the maid. Opportunities would have to be made for they could not very well make love under Perdita's nose.

She would be different from everyone else, he was sure.

His Aunt Cumberland knew that Grace had become his mistress and was delighted.

He talked of Mrs Armistead.

'Intriguing creature,' agreed the Duchess; and thought how amusing it was that under her very roof Perdita was housing a rival. If she but knew! And she would, in due course. Silly little Perdita had some shocks coming to her. 'A meeting with Mrs Armistead could easily be arranged.'

'It's a devilishly ticklish situation.'

'You will not have to consider it so much longer, I gather.'

The Prince looked startled. Of course he would not! How much longer was he going on with this farce of being Perdita's devoted lover? Why should he not meet the interesting Mrs Armistead if he wished?

'Why not invite her to Windsor. You could meet at an inn there. That would be discreet. I am sure the good woman would wish for discretion.'

'An inn at Windsor. Why not?'

'You will have to go there for your birthday celebrations.'

He was thoughtful. He could not help remembering the inn on Eel Pie Island to which he had gone in such a state of ecstasy.

His uncle appeared.

'Ha, so we have the pleasure of His Highness's company. Looking well and debonair. Better to be the lover of women in the plural than in the singular.'

'He speaks from experience,' said the Duchess coolly.

'Am I right or wrong, eh, Taffy?'

Taffy? thought the Prince. Oh, Wales, of course. It struck a discordant note. *Taffy*.

It occurred to him for the first time that his uncle was a very crude man and that he did not really like him very much.

Perdita was not at home. Gorgeously painted and patched she had gone out for one of her morning drives. She had not felt in the mood for such an outing, she told Mrs Armistead; the Prince's attitude lately had worried her. But she did not want people to notice that she was less happy than she had been. The Prince was young and gay and he had fallen into bad company; and as she naturally had tried to make him understand this, it had caused a little lovers' quarrel.

Mrs Armistead, who had overheard the lovers' quarrel, thought it far from little. She had already decided that Perdita had not very many weeks left to her in which to bask in the glory of the Prince's favour. Let her dress in her silks and muslins, her fantastic hats. Poor creature, she would very soon be dislodged from her position.

So she had driven out in the ostentatious coach with the wreath of flowers which looked like a coronet and she would be gone for at least another hour.

Mrs Armistead, reviewing her mistress's position, was in fact thinking of her own. Things will change mightily when we have lost His Highness, she thought. Would that be the time to retire to Chertsey? She had not only her house but enough money to live on in modest dignity. Mr Fox was her friend. He would visit her there and they would talk politics together; he had paid her the compliment of actually letting her share in a discussion with him and although perhaps she could not go so far as to say he had taken her advice, he had listened to it.

The footman came to her room to announce that a Mr Meynel had called from the Prince of Wales.

'Mrs Robinson is not at home, but perhaps I should see him. Bring him in,' she ordered.

Mr Meynel appeared and bowing asked if he had the pleasure of meeting Mrs Armistead.

'I am Mrs Armistead. But I'm afraid I have to tell you that Mrs Robinson is not at home. Any message you care to leave . . .'

'I have not come to see Mrs Robinson, Madam, but yourself.'

'Indeed?'

'Yes, Madam. His Highness the Prince of Wales asks that you take supper with him.'

Mrs Armistead flushed a faint pink. 'Is this really so?'

'Yes, Madam. His Highness is shortly leaving for Windsor; he wishes you to take supper in an inn near that town, and wishes to know whether you accept this invitation.'

'His Highness does not issue invitations but commands.'

Mr Meynel inclined his head in acknowledgement of the truth of this statement.

'Then, Madam, I am to understand you accept His Highness's command?'

'Being fully conscious of the honour, indeed I do.'

'I will tell His Highness, who I am sure will be delighted.'

'And when . . . ?'

'Madam, you may leave these arrangements to me. A carriage will pick you up and take you to the inn. All you must do is hold yourself in readiness. You will have notice.'

'Thank you, sir. I shall await His Highness's instructions.'

Mr Meynel departed and Mrs Armistead sat down, for once without her usual serenity. So it had come! Fox, Derby, Dorset and now the Prince of Wales.

Oh, indeed Perdita's day was done.

In the days which followed, Mrs Armistead was busy. During one of Perdita's absences she moved many of her belongings to the house of a friend. They should be taken to Chertsey at the first opportunity.

It would not be possible for her to stay with Perdita after taking supper with the Prince. At least she would not deceive her and remain under her roof. There should be a complete break. A friend of the Prince of Wales could not remain the lady's maid of his ex-mistress.

It was a very extraordinary situation, but she would be able to handle it.

The message would come any day now for she knew that the Prince would most certainly be going to Windsor soon to celebrate his nineteenth birthday there.

She had no illusions. This would be no grande passion. She was not the sort of woman to inspire that; nor did she wish to be. Perdita was a sad warning to any woman who might have such dreams. No, she and the Prince would have a quiet discreet friendship which would go as far as he wished and be terminated at his desire–which was the best in the long run. Only a fool would expect fidelity from such a young man; she did not even expect it from Mr Fox and her feelings towards him were different from any she felt towards anyone else.

She was excited. She knew now that she was an extremely attractive woman. She guessed she would last as long as Dally the Tall; and she had no objections to running simultaneously with that notorious lady.

Perhaps she should warn Perdita. She imagined the effect that would have because the vain creature was beginning to learn how much she owed to her maid, and the more she considered the matter the more certain she was that once she had supped with the Prince she could not come back to Perdita. It would be undignified to do so; and her dignity had been her most characteristic trait; it had helped to bring her to the position in which she now found herself.

Meanwhile Perdita was growing more and more melancholy.

There were hints everywhere about the Prince's friendship with Mrs Grace Elliott.

'Friendship!' cried Perdita. 'That creature is so impertinent that she would presume on any friendship.'

'She is certainly a very bold lady,' agreed Mrs Armistead.

'How do you know, Armistead?'

'I have seen her, Madam. She is constantly showing herself in her carriage.'

'And doubtless you have heard rumours?'

'Yes, Madam, there are rumours.'

Perdita went into a mood of morbidity; and Mrs Armistead chose this moment to hint that she might be leaving.

'Personal affairs are beginning to intrude a little, Madam. I may find it necessary in the near future to give up my post and attend to them.'

'Personal affairs,' murmured Perdita vaguely.

'Yes . . . my own affairs, Madam.'

Perdita looked at Mrs Armistead. How strange! One had never expected her to have *personal* affairs. They sounded very vague. Perdita could not pay much attention to Mrs Armistead's personal affairs; she had so many of her own. Then it suddenly struck her. Armistead wanted more money. This was her way of asking for it. Of course she should have it.

She offered it and it was gratefully accepted. Mrs Armistead had done her duty, she considered; she had warned Perdita.

Perdita was in her room; she was weeping undramatically. She was too unhappy for drama. It was true; he had a mistress. She was this woman who had been divorced by her husband for eloping with Lord Valentia. Mrs Grace Elliott–Dally the Tall–the golden haired beauty who had dared to give him rosebuds while she, Perdita, had looked on.

Of course she had opportunities of seeing him which were denied to Perdita. But they need not have been. He could have been constantly at Cork Street if he had wished. But he did not wish; he came less frequently and when he did come he stayed for such a short time. Why? So that he could hurry away and be with Grace Elliott at Cumberland House. For she had no doubt of this. Her enemies were the Duke and Duchess of Cumberland. The Duke hated her because he had wanted her for his mistress and the Duchess hated her for the same reason. They had been against her from the first. It was they who had brought this Grace Elliott to his notice. But he had been ready enough to be unfaithful to her.

And she had given up everything for him!

She had shut herself in her room; she could not bear to see anyone. She had not even sent for Armistead to dress her. She could only lie in bed and contemplate her misery.

What would this mean? Humiliation. The whole world would know. One could not hope that it would be a secret. The papers would be filled with cartoons and lampoons; when she rode out people would laugh at her. There would be no more of those rides along the Mall when people stopped to stare at her, and gallant gentlemen doffed their hats and almost swept the ground with them to do her the utmost homage.

And the Prince would flaunt another mistress. And . . . hideous thought and one which she tried to shut out altogether . . . the creditors would demand their money. They would not humbly request payment as they had in the past; they would make ugly demands. And what would she do? Where would she find the money to pay?

She thought of the cold stone walls of the debtors' prison . . . the hopelessness, the despair of those within.

No! she thought. Never, never! Anything is better than that.

The Prince was going to Windsor for his birthday celebrations. There would be beautiful women there . . . women of the Court. But she was shut out. She was not received. At one time he would have deplored this. He would have said: 'I will go to Windsor for the birthday ball because I needs must and then I will fly back to my Perdita.'

But now he was going to Windsor days before the ball; he was going to make the arrangements himself. He had no desire to be where Perdita was.

Oh it was so different; it was all that the moralists would have told her that she must expect.

So she lay in bed all day, too limp to get up, to care, and it was a measure of her misery that she did not care what she looked like.

There was a scratching at the door.

'Is that you, Armistead?'

Mrs Armistead entered. 'A letter, Madam.'

Eagerly she took it because she saw that it came from the Prince.

Her fingers were trembling as she opened it. She could not believe those words. They could not be true. He was telling her that their idyll was over and that they should not meet again.

She lay back on her pillows, her eyes closed. Mrs Armistead picking up the letter, took the opportunity to read it.

She understood. The moment had come.

'Madam has had bad news?' she asked soothingly.

Perdita nodded vaguely.

'I will make you some chocolate.'

'Chocolate!' cried Perdita bitterly.

'Then, Madam, a dish of tea.'

'Leave me, Armistead. Leave me alone.'

Mrs Armistead quietly shut the door, leaving Perdita to her misery.

The Prince she guessed was on his way to Windsor. Soon now, if it were coming at all, the summons would come.

She went to her room–bare of all her private possessions. The beautiful gowns which Perdita had given her were all safely stored in Chertsey.

All day long Perdita stayed in her room, wanting nothing but to be left alone with her misery.

What a fool she is, thought Mrs Armistead. She will ruin her looks with weeping–and there is Lord Malden, and a host of others who will cherish her. She could discover that it is not such a bad thing to have been the mistress of the Prince of Wales.

Mrs Armistead looked at her own reflection in the mirror and smiled secretly.

There was an air of waiting about the house in Cork Street. The servants knew. Perhaps like Mrs Armistead they had seen it coming; they knew how infrequent were the Prince's visits, they had heard his voice and that of their mistress raised in anger against each other. Doubtless, thought Mrs Armistead, they imitated those in higher circles and wagered how long it would last. They would know that their mistress had shut herself in her room and that she refused to eat or see anyone.

Mrs Armistead stayed close to the window. Every time she heard carriage wheels she was intent.

And at length a carriage stopped at the door of the house and glancing out of the window she saw Mr Meynel step from it.

She was at the door and herself let him in.

'The time has come, Madam,' said Mr Meynel.

'Now . . . this minute?' she asked and her serenity amazed Mr Meynel.

'The carriage is waiting, Madam. We should leave in ten minutes. It's a long journey to Windsor.'

'Pray go to the carriage, Mr Meynel, and wait for me there. I will be with you in ten minutes.'

Mr Meynel bowed his head. He could see that she was a woman of her word.

Mrs Armistead scratched lightly on the door. Perdita did not answer, so she opened it and looked in. Perdita lay in her bed, her lovely hair in wild disorder, her face devoid of rouge, powder and patches looking strangely childlike. She did not glance at Mrs Armistead, but stared before her as though she were in a dream.

'Mrs Robinson, Madam.'

Perdita shook her head. Her lips framed the words Go away, but no sound came from them.

'It distresses me to disturb you with my affairs at such a time, Madam. But I have to leave.'

Perdita did not speak.

Very well, thought Mrs Armistead, if she did not wish to hear there was no need to force an explanation upon her. She had done her duty. She had told her that she was leaving. This was an easy way out.

Mrs Armistead shut the door and, putting on her cloak, quietly left the house.

The following day Perdita roused herself and saw ruin staring her in the face. The Prince had deserted her; he no longer wished to see her. She picked up the note he had written and read it again and again.

The fashionable world would know by now: Perdita's day is over. Now he would be flaunting that woman–riding with her, dancing with her in Cumberland House and even perhaps at his own birthday ball.

He was at Windsor now. And he would not be thinking of her; but would he not? He had cared for her so deeply and that was not so long ago.

She had done everything to please him. Where had she failed? When she thought of what she had spent in this house to entertain him in the manner to which he was accustomed . . . !

Oh God, she thought, bills! Those outstanding accounts which she had thrust away so impatiently because there had been no time to consider the cost. All her energies had had to go into keeping her Prince happy. There had been no time for anything else. But when the dressmakers, the wine merchants, the butchers, the pastrycooks . . . when they all knew that the Prince had deserted her, they would lose their patience.

She was a frightened woman.

She got up from her bed. She could not allow him to treat her like this. Where was her confidence? She thought of how not so long ago she had been able to change his mood to one of peevish dissatisfaction to one of adoring contentment.

She was being foolish. All she had to do was see him, to tell him she adored him, that she could not live without him. That was all he needed. After all he was such a boy, a spoilt boy. Of course he was a spoilt boy. There were so many people around him showing him how important he was. Would he not one day be king?

Then she must see him. But he was at Windsor. Well, what was to prevent *her* going to Windsor?

She felt better now that she had decided on some action.

She leaped off her bed, looked at herself in the mirror and gasping with horror covered her face with her hands. What a fool she was! What if he had repented and called and seen her like this? The damage must be repaired without delay; and she would go to Windsor. She would take Armistead with her and it would be rather like the old days on Eel Pie Island.

She pulled the bell rope for Armistead and went to her wardrobe. Now what should she wear? A becoming gown and a cloak in a contrasting colour. Her hair dressed simply as he had liked it best, perhaps with a curl over the shoulder.

Why did Armistead not answer her summons? It was unlike Armistead.

She frowned and brought a blue silk dress from her wardrobe. She was feeling better already. Once Armistead had done her work she would have transformed this pale and sad creature into the most beautiful woman in London.

Hurry Armistead! What has happened to you.

It was five minutes since she had rung.

She opened her door and called: 'Armistead.'

She went along to Armistead's room. The footman was on the stairs. He looked flushed and it occurred to her later that he must have been at the wine.

'Where is Armistead?' she asked.

'She left, Madam. Yesterday.'

'Left!'

'Yes, Madam. She went away. She said she was leaving and had told you.'

'Leaving . . . But . . .'

The footman shrugged his shoulders . . . insolently, she thought. What had happened? Armistead . . . gone!

Then she remembered that the woman had come to her yesterday and said something. What had she said? She, Perdita, had been too unhappy with her own affairs to listen to Armistead's account of hers.

The footman was watching her covertly. Of course he was seeing her as he never had before . . . unkempt, carelessly dressed, her face unpainted.

He knows, she thought. He will tell the servants that the Prince has deserted me.

So she *must* see her lover. She must go to Windsor without delay.

She went back to her room. It was mid-afternoon. Why had she not realized before what she must do. If it had been morning she could have reached Windsor in daylight.

But first she must make herself beautiful. Oh, how she missed Armistead! And where had Armistead gone? Some family matter . . . was that what she had said? Why hadn't she listened? Why hadn't she insisted on retaining Armistead's services at all costs?

Because she was taking some action she felt better. After all, she was capable of choosing the most becoming and suitable of her dresses, capable of applying the patch close to her eyes to call attention to their brilliance.

Dressing took a long time and she could not arrange her hair as effectively as Armistead could, but at length she was ready. Perhaps she should start tomorrow morning. No, she could not endure another night of suspense. She must see the Prince–and the sooner the better.

She sent for her young postilion–he was only nine years old–and told him that she wished to drive her small pony phaeton to Windsor, so he was to saddle the ponies and bring it to the door.

The boy looked astonished, but when she told him to be quick he went away to do her bidding.

How long it seemed while she waited there! The time seemed to have flown by since she had made her decision; again and again she looked at her reflection and thought of how much better a job Armistead would have made of her toilette.

At length the phaeton was waiting and she climbed into it while her youthful postilion took his place and they set off. Preparations had taken so long that it was getting dark when they reached Hyde Park Corner.

As the coach rattled on she was rehearsing what she would say to the Prince when she saw him; but first she must make sure that he would see her. This thought made her shiver with sudden anxiety. What if he refused? He had sounded so insistent in his letter. 'We must not meet again.' But he could not really have meant that. He had written it in a sudden passion. Perhaps inspired by Grace Elliott or her enemies at Cumberland House.

They had reached Hounslow and pulled up at an inn.

The innkeeper came out to welcome her and usher such an obvious lady of quality into the inn parlour.

She declared that she could take nothing. She was only eager to continue her journey as soon as possible.

'Whither are you bound, Madam?' asked the innkeeper.

'To Windsor.'

'Madam, you cannot cross the Heath at this hour. Stay here until morning.'

'I must press on.'

'I must tell you, Madam, that every carriage which has crossed the Heath these last ten nights has been attacked and rifled.'

'I must take that chance.'

'But you . . . a lady and no one to protect you but that young boy!'

She smiled. 'I am not afraid,' she said.

'There are some dangerous men about.'

She was immediately dramatic. She threw back her head and smiled. Let me be murdered, she thought; and then he will be filled with remorse. For the rest of his life he will remember that my death was due to his treatment of me.

'I do not fear dangerous men,' she said.

'You will be risking your life.'

'Perhaps I have no great desire to save it.'

The innkeeper looked at her oddly. Her face was vaguely familiar to him. It could not be. Not *the* Mrs Robinson! But of course, and she was going to Windsor because His Highness had lately arrived there.

All the same, if she were to encounter a highwayman he wouldn't care if she was the Prince's mistress; and now he knew who she was, the innkeeper believed that that was a diamond she was wearing at her throat. She was asking for trouble, she was, but he could do no more than warn her.

As she rode off into the darkness he stood at the door of the inn scratching his head and watching until the phaeton was out of sight.

Perdita rode on. Hounslow Heath! Notorious as the haunt of the most desperate highwaymen. Her little postilion was frightened; she could sense his fear. The Heath stretched out before them–ghostly in starlight. At any moment from behind one of those bushes a dark figure might rise up, flourish a pistol and call 'Stand and deliver.'

She herself caught the boy's fear. All very well to act a part before the innkeeper, to pretend that she did not care whether she was murdered or not. That was a part she played. But this was reality. Deep emotions, such as fear and misery penetrated the mask. She suddenly knew as they crossed the Heath that she did not want to die at the hands of some rough murderer.

She heard something like a sob from the little postilion; and then she saw the masked figure on the road.

Providence was with her, she was sure, for just as he was about to grasp the reins, the phaeton bounded over a hump in the road which threw the man backwards and gave her the chance she needed. She whipped up the horses and before the highwayman had a chance to recover his balance she had a start. He was running behind them, calling them to stand and deliver, shouting that he wanted their money or their lives.

Perdita did not heed him; the ponies seemed to sense the danger and galloped as never before, and after some moments of intense anxiety with great relief she saw the lights of an inn. She decided that if she reached it safely she would spend the night there for in any case it would be too late to get a message to the Prince at Windsor now.

The poor little postilion was white with fear and a little resentful, wondering why they had had to risk their lives by crossing the Heath only to pull up at the Magpie.

The landlord received them with pleasure and when she recounted the adventure assured her that she was a very brave lady and lucky to escape not only being robbed but with her life.

She was exhausted she said, and would have food sent up to her room. Her young positilion needed food too; he had acted with courage in an alarming situation and she wished him to know that she was pleased with him.

When the food was brought to her room she found she was very hungry and remembered that it was long since she had last eaten. She ate and lay down on her bed and was soon fast asleep.

She was awakened after a while by the sounds of commotion in the inn yard, where there was a great deal of running to and fro; visitors she supposed, and slept again to be awakened some hours later by more noises. This time it sounded like departures.

The busy life of an inn, she supposed, and slept again.

She was awake early and immediately became anxious to continue the journey to Windsor. She was washed and dressed, put on her rouge and patches to the best of her ability, sighing for Mrs Armistead who would have done so much better than she could.

Then she went down to take a little refreshment before leaving.

This was brought to her and when she had eaten and had made her way out of the dining room, she saw a woman descending the staircase. At first she thought she was dreaming.

Mrs Armistead!

But what could her lady's maid be doing here at the Magpie Inn at this hour of morning?

It was a mistake. It could not be Mrs Armistead. It was her double.

For a few seconds they stood perfectly still looking at each other. Surely that calm handsome face could belong to no one else.

Then the woman turned and unhurriedly, and with the utmost dignity, made her way back the way she had come.

Perdita cried suddenly and imperiously: 'Armistead.' But the woman did not look back as she disappeared round a turn in the staircase.

Impossible, thought Perdita. I must be dreaming.

The innkeeper was at the door rubbing his hands, trusting she had spent a good night and had had a good breakfast.

She assured him she had and he told her that the phaeton was ready to leave when she was.

And then she received her second surprise. A man sauntered across the yard. She knew that man. He was a servant of the Prince's. His name was Meynel. He had on one or two occasions brought messages to her from the Prince.

How strange. It was like a dream. First she imagined she had seen Armistead–but she *had* seen Armistead–and then the Prince's servant.

The innkeeper was beside her.

'Is that man attached to the household of the Prince of Wales?' she asked.

The innkeeper looked sly. 'Oh, Madam, we entertain the quality here. I could tell you . . .'

She did not answer. She went out to the phaeton. Mrs Armistead! Meynel! How very strange.

All the way to Windsor she was thinking of the strangeness of this encounter. A suspicion had come into her mind. The Prince had shown an interest in Armistead. She had caught him watching her now and then. There had been an occasion when she had seen his arrival and he had been a long time coming into her room. And Armistead had left her . . . after all those years . . . so oddly.

Armistead! An assignation with the Prince!

'Oh no, no,' she murmured.

But in her heart she believed it was true; and something told her that if it was, this was indeed the end.

The next day she arrived in Windsor. She gazed wistfully at the castle and thought of how happy she could have been had she been a princess who might have married him. Everything would have been so different then. There would have been none of the anxieties which had led to friction between them.

She saw herself as a princess arriving from a foreign country, startling him with her beauty.

But encroaching reality was so alarming that it robbed her dreams of any substance; at such a time even she was forced to recognize them for the fancies they were.

She would be brisk and practical; so she pulled up at an inn where she wrote a letter and sent the postilion to the castle with it instructing him to find Lord Malden who, she was sure, was with the Prince, and when he had found him to tell him from whom the note came and beg him to deliver it into no hands but those of the Prince of Wales.

The boy was away for a fretful hour and a half before he returned and said that he had at length been taken to Lord Malden and given the note to him.

'You did well,' she told the boy.

The waiting was almost unbearable. At one moment she was assuring herself that the note would bring the Prince to the inn full of remorse; at another she pictured his becoming angry with her for following him to Windsor, but soon to be placated by her soft words and beauty. One thing she would not visualize and that was that he would not come at all.

It was Lord Malden who came, looking melancholy and anxious. Dear Lord Malden, who had always been such a good friend!

She greeted him eagerly. 'The Prince . . .'

Lord Malden shook his head.

'You gave him my note?'

'I did.'

'And you have a reply for me. Why did he not come himself when I begged him to?'

'The Prince is determined not to see you.'

'But why . . . why . . . what have I done to deserve this? Did he read my note?'

'Yes and . . .'

'What? Pray do not hide anything.'

'He tore it into pieces and said he had no wish to see you again.'

'But . . .'

Lord Malden took her hand and looked into her face. 'You should return to Cork Street. You will find you have many friends . . . many friends . . .'

He was regarding her with that hungry expression which she knew so well.

She withdrew her hands impatiently.

'I must see the Prince.'

Malden shook his head. 'He is determined.'

'And so am I.'

'But . . .'

She seized his hand suddenly. 'Promise me this, that you will do your best to persuade him . . .'

Lord Malden replied tenderly: 'You know that if there is anything on earth I can do to add to your happiness it shall be done. You have lost the Prince of Wales but you have friends left.'

She felt so sickened with anxiety that she turned peevishly away. She had never known Malden not to plead his own cause! She knew what he was hinting. Don't mourn because you are no longer the mistress of the Prince of Wales. There are many other men who are ready to take you on.

The shame of it! she thought. That was what they would be saying and thinking now.

'I will go back to Cork Street now,' she said. 'There is nothing more to be done here.'

Malden bowed his head.

And Perdita, sick at heart and defeated, climbed into her phaeton. How much better if she had never come.

She rode back to London, bruised and wounded – yet thinking not so much of the Prince of Wales as the bills which would be coming in as soon as the news leaked out that the Prince had finished with her.

How would she meet them? It seemed to her that as she rode across the Heath–in daylight this time–a shadow loomed over her. Not a highwayman, but the debtors' prison.

Birthday Celebrations at Windsor

In the great drawing room the Prince stood beside his father receiving congratulations on attaining his nineteenth birthday. He looked magnificent in his elegant coat, on which flashed the diamond star as brilliant as the buckles on his shoes.

Handsome enough, thought the King. But getting fat. Have to speak to him about it. If he shows signs at nineteen what will he be at my age?

The King felt that he was an old man although only in his early forties. The weight of state affairs, the trials of a family . . .

The Queen looked on almost complacently for having produced such a handsome son; she was pleased, too, because although her little scheme to provide him with a nice comfortable German mistress had failed, there were rumours that he was not nearly so friendly with that dreadful play actress.

He'll settle down, thought the Queen.

The Prince was thinking of women. He was free. Dally was amusing and how experienced! He was enjoying his encounters with Dally; and as for the rather sedate Mrs Armistead, she was a treasure. It was amusing to ride out to the Magpie when he felt in the mood and there she would be, never reproaching him, always pleased to see him, so different from Perdita that she reminded him of her–most pleasantly. Reminded him of what he had escaped, of course. That virago-saint! How had he endured her for so long?

There were going to be changes when he returned to London. He was not going to Cumberland House so frequently. He did not like his uncle and he was not going to pretend he did. The fellow was an ignoramus. The more friendly he became with Fox and Sheridan the more he realized this. Insolent too! *Taffy!* He would have his friends remember that although he liked to be on terms of intimacy with them he was still the Prince of Wales. No one was going to call him by familiar epithets without his permission. Taffy indeed!

Yes, there would be changes.

The celebrations were to last several days, and it was enjoyable to be the centre of them. He was behaving with such propriety that even the King had nothing of which to complain.

When they met they talked of politics, which at the moment meant the affair of the American Colonies which occupied the King's mind almost exclusively. The Prince did not set forward his views which, having been acquired through Charles James Fox, were in exact opposition to those of the King.

The King was a little optimistic.

'The French,' he told the Prince, 'are not so ready now to help our rebels. And I'll tell you why. They have troubles of their own, big troubles. I would not care to see the finances of this country in the same condition as those of France.'

The Prince nodded.

'You should take an interest in these affairs. They concern the country. More important than gambling or running after maids of honour, eh?'

Oh dear, the old fool hadn't advanced since Harriot Vernon–and he himself had almost forgotten her name and certainly could not recall what she looked like.

'I do take an interest,' said the Prince coolly. What if the old man knew about those long discussions he enjoyed with Fox and Sheridan over innumerable glasses of wine! That would startle His Majesty. But of course Mr Fox could bring a lucid and brilliant mind to the subject; not like poor old muddled Papa.

'Glad to hear it, glad to hear it. Don't forget you'll be taking your place in the House of Lords in two years' time.'

'Two years,' said the Prince ironically.

'Seems far ahead. Not so. Not so. I know what it's like at your age. I was young once myself, you know.'

Indeed, thought the Prince sarcastically. Your Majesty surprises me. But he merely smiled sycophantishly. There was no point in antagonizing the old man further at this stage. That would come when he did take his part in politics and ranged himself beside Fox against his father.

'Well, well, this has all the appearance of a long contest that will end as it ought by the colonies returning to the mother country and I tell you this: I will never put my hand to any other conclusion of this business.'

No point in telling him that Mr Fox thought differently, that Mr Fox believed that there would never have been any conflict between the mother country and her colonies if it had not been for the stupidity of the King and certain of his ministers.

It was irksome indeed to be still under the jurisdiction of such a bumbling old fool. Two more years before he could hope for complete freedom! In the meantime he had to be content with a little more than he was allowed as a boy. His cage was opened now and then; he was allowed to fly out provided he made sure of returning.

The King, thought the Prince–and he believed this because Fox had told him it was so–was a monarch who believed he should have supreme power in the country. He treated his Prime Minister, Lord North, as the man who should carry out the royal orders. This, according to Fox, was the reason why the best men in the country–Fox implied men like himself–would not serve the King. That was why they must put up with the mistakes of a second-rate politician like North. The troubles of the country were largely due to this attitude of the King's and it was one which no government worthy of its name would allow. A government headed by Fox would never allow itself to be dictated to. Pitt's had been such a government and it was under Pitt that England had gained an Empire; it was during North's ministry that England was losing one.

Oh wait, thought the Prince. Wait until I am of age. Wait till I take my place in the House of Lords. Wait till I show my hand. Then it will be Fox and the Prince. Men of intelligence at the head of affairs, not two old idiots like North and the King.

The King had now started on a lecture about the evils of gambling, drink and women. The Prince must remember his position. Never gamble. It meant heavy debts. (The Prince mildly wondered what he owed.) Drink ruined any man–physically and mentally. As for the company of light women that meant scandal; and that was something of which the royal family had to beware more than anything.

'That play actress . . .' said the King gruffly. 'It's over now, is it?'

The Prince could say truthfully that it was.

'Good thing. Hope you realize now . . . those women can be dangerous. Grosvenor's wife and your uncle Cumberland. Shouldn't go there, you know. They're not received and it looks bad.'

'I don't intend to go there so much in future.'

'That's good . . . that's good.'

'And that fellow Fox. He's sharp. I don't trust him. Hear you see something of him. And Sheridan. They say he's a clever fellow. Can't see it. Writes a few plays . . . just words . . . words . . . and married that good woman and treats her badly. These people are no good to you. Understand, eh, what?'

The Prince changed the subject. 'Several people have invited me to their houses. I thought I would do a tour of the country. It might be interesting and the people like to see us in other parts of the country besides the south.'

He was thinking: It would be an excellent idea. He would get right away from Perdita in case she became importunate. She had dared come to Windsor to see him. Impertinence. But Perdita could be persistent and she was not going to be easily cast off. He remembered the protestations he had made of fidelity. Well, it was the usual lovers' talk. And how was he to have known that she would be so melancholy and write those dreadful poems about how she had suffered and all she had given up. It had become unendurable. No one could have endured it–few would as long as he had.

'Oh,' said the King. 'where have these invitations come from, eh what?'

The Prince told him, enumerating some of the most well-known families in the country.

The King grunted. They would entertain him lavishly. There would be drinking and gambling and women. He did not think that this was the time for his son to go gallivanting all over the country. Not until he was a little more mature . . . and the King was a little more sure of what was going on in his mind. He seemed to have improved a little but he could not be sure.

'When did they wish you to go, eh, what?'

'Almost immediately. Before the summer is over. Travelling up to the north would present difficulties later.'

'H'm. Have to think about this. After all, Prince of Wales has his duties. Have to be careful. Go to one, and another wouldn't like it. Understand, eh, what?'

'No,' said the Prince. 'I hope to visit frequently and if I don't take in some this visit I'll do another later. I think it is wrong for us to stay in the south all the time as though we hadn't a country outside this area.'

'Oh, you do, do you? Well, we'll see. I'll look into this and let you know my decision.'

The Prince's face was pink. He could not keep on friendly terms with the old man for long. He was impossible. How much longer must he be treated like a child. He knew the answer to that. Two years. Not until he was twenty-one could he escape.

But the visit to Windsor had its compensations.

At the dinner which preceded the birthday ball he found himself seated next to the lovely Lady Augusta Campbell.

The banquet was held in St George's Hall and to accommodate the eighty members of the nobility who were the guests of the royal family three long tables had been set up. At the head of one of these sat the King and Queen and at another the Prince of Wales.

Lady Augusta was young and charming and she talked gaily of the review in the Park which had taken place that afternoon as part of the birthday celebrations. The Prince talked to no one else and this was noticed–and not without some dismay by Lady Augusta's mother, the Duchess of Argyll.

As soon as the banquet was over and the ball began the Prince danced with Lady Augusta and it was clear that he was reluctant to partner anyone else.

There were whispers and sly glances. He has finished with Perdita Robinson. Will Lady Augusta be the next? And what of Dally the Tall? Was she going to stand aside and see the prize snatched from her by this young inexperienced girl.

Lady Augusta was certainly a lovely creature. She lacked the art of beautifying herself which a woman like Perdita Robinson possessed; but beside the actress she would seem young and pure.

During the evening the Prince persuaded her to leave the ballroom and walk in the moonlit park, but when he attempted to kiss her she was a little reluctant.

'Why?' he demanded. 'Don't you know I have fallen in love with you?'

'Oh yes,' she answered. 'I know that–or you have for me what passes for love. But where could it lead? My parents will never allow me to be your mistress and yours would never allow you to be my husband.'

'Ah, my dearest angel, I am not so easily defeated.'

But she was firm, and although she was undoubtedly attracted by him she was not so much so that she would forget discretion.

The Prince was not going to lose heart because he had failed after one banquet and ball. He had a new excitement in his life.

He had amusing Dally; intriguing Mrs Armistead; and now he sought to add Lady Augusta to his reason for finding life enjoyable.

The Prince sat in his apartments at Windsor writing a poem to Lady Augusta Campbell.

'Oh! Campbell, the scene of tonight
Has opened the wound of my heart;
It has shown me how great the delight
Which charms of thy converse impart.
I've known what it is to be gay,
I've revelled in joy's fleeting hour,
I've wished for the close of the day,
To meet in a thick-woven bower.'

He laid down his pen and thought of Perdita whom he had met not exactly in a thick-woven bower; but an inn room on Eel Pie Island could be as romantic.

When Lady Augusta succumbed to his pleading would it be the beginning of a great love affair, such as he had once believed there would be with Perdita?

He forced himself to believe it would be so. He was at heart romantic. Fox might imply that he would be much more content if he did not allow himself to become deeply involved with one woman; but he knew that it was something more than a passing appeasement that he desired. He enjoyed being in love, being ready to die–or at least renounce a great deal–for love.

So he would continue to write letters and poems to Lady Augusta and if she returned his passion he might insist on marrying her. The Argylls were a great family; but his father, he knew, would never consent to a marriage; it would be some plain German frau for him.

He shivered at the prospect and picked up his pen.

''Twas there that the soft-stolen kiss,
'Twas there that the throb of our hearts,
Betrayed that we wished for the bliss
Which love, and love only imparts . . .'

He sighed, thinking of her beauty.

He did hope she was not going to remain aloof, insisting on preserving her virtue as Mary Hamilton had. In any case she with Grace Elliott and Mrs Armistead were helping him to forget Perdita; and that was what he wanted almost as much as Lady Augusta's surrender–to forget Perdita completely, to forget her reproaches, her sacrificial sermons; he wanted to wash all memory of Perdita from his mind for he was heartily tired of her.

But as the days passed it became clear that Lady Augusta would cling to her virtue.

'There could be no future for us,' she said. 'Your Highness cannot imagine that my parents would allow me to become another Perdita Robinson.'

By such words she irritated him. The very thing he did not want was to be reminded of Perdita.

So he decided to give up the pursuit of Lady Augusta and devote himself to those ladies who appreciated his attentions. There was no doubt that Grace did–gay abandoned creature. Though she was not entirely satisfactory because she kept on her old lovers at the same time.

Mrs Armistead was perhaps the more comforting of the two. She was always so delighted with some small diamond trinket that he found pleasure in making her little gifts.

Perhaps Charles James Fox was right. It was better not to become too involved.

The King sent for his son to tell him that he had come to a decision.

'I cannot give my consent to these proposed trips of yours.'

'But why not?' The King looked surprised that the Prince should address him so curtly. 'I can see nothing wrong in visiting some of Your Majesty's most highly respected subjects.'

'I have a treat for you,' said the King. 'Something you will enjoy more than these rounds of draughty country houses.'

'A treat.'

The King nodded smiling. 'You'll see, eh? Patience . . . a virtue, eh, what?'

The Prince was disgusted. Treats? As though he were a boy.

His frustration was strengthened when he reminded himself that he could not disobey the King and accept invitations which His Majesty did not wish him to.

It was maddening. Let him wait, thought the Prince, until I'm twenty-one.

The 'treat' which the King was offering his son as a compensation for refusing his permission for the country visits was a trip to the Nore.

When the Prince heard of this he was disgusted. This in place of those country visits where he would have been fêted and treated according to his rank, entertained lavishly and enjoyed good conversation and the company of pretty women.

But such was his position that it was useless to protest. The King had decreed that he should go and go he must.

The King and the Prince rode in their separate yachts down the river and were saluted by the ships they passed. Through Woolwich, Tilbury and Gravesend they went accompanied by numerous small craft and cheered along the way until they anchored in Sea Reach for the night. They set off again at five in the morning for Blackstakes; and here the King and Prince left their yachts and toured the dockyards, then proceeded to the Nore where they went on board Admiral Parker's flagship.

There officers and men were presented to the King and the Prince and after these ceremonies, which were somewhat tedious in the Prince's opinion, he and his father returned to their yachts. This, fumed the Prince, was his treat for being denied the ability to accept invitations when he wished. It was too humiliating. Particularly as before long what had happened was the talk of the town. A verse was circulated to commemorate the occasion.

'The King and the Prince went to the Nore,
They saw the ships and main;
The Prince and King they went on shore
And then came back again.'

The people were laughing at the King. Couldn't he see it? And until the Prince was considered of an age to make his own decisions and cut himself free of his father's control he would be laughed at too.

Returning to Windsor he went to the Magpie for the solace of Mrs

Armistead's company. She might lack the obvious beauty of Lady Augusta Campbell but she never irritated and she always knew how to soothe him.

No *grande passion* this–but eminently satisfactory.

Humiliation in Hyde Park

Bills! Every day they were coming.

'Madame Duvernay regrets she must call Mrs Robinson's attention to this long overdue account.'

Perdita frowned and read the long list of articles. That pelisse which she could well have done without. The muff. The cloaks. The gowns . . . numerous gowns. They had all seemed so essential at the time. And Armistead had been so good at planning them.

Armistead! She did not wish to think of that woman. Traitor. Spy in her own house. Going off for *personal reasons* . . . which meant to the bed of the Prince of Wales!

Bills for wine. How could they have consumed so much? The poulterers, the butchers, the bakers . . . There was no end to it.

She started to attempt to add up the amounts but she was no good at it and it was so depressing in any case. And what good would it do to know how much she owed? There was one fact which she knew well enough now. She had not the money to pay them.

Oh, God, she thought. What shall I do?

There was Malden, dear faithful Malden; he would be the Earl of Essex one day but he had no money now. He could not help her.

Cumberland?

'Oh, no, never, never,' she cried dramatically. 'I would rather die.'

And then suddenly she was aware of the desperate position she was in and broke down and wept.

Lord Malden called. He looked very anxious.

'Have you any news?' she implored.

He could only shake his head.

'You have seen him?'

'I have.'

'And has he spoken of me?'

'I'm afraid not.'

'But that does not mean he does not *think* of me.'

Lady Augusta Campbell the elusive one; Dally the Tall the gay one; Mrs Armistead the cosy one . . . How could he tell Perdita that the Prince no longer needed her? And that all he asked of her now was that she should cease to bother him and forget him as quickly as he was forgetting her.

'If I could but *see* him,' sighed Perdita.

'He will not see you. He was annoyed that you came to Windsor.'

'I risked my life in doing it.' Dramatically and with some embellishments she told the story of how she had crossed Hounslow Heath and had by a miracle escaped.

'Surely if he knew I did that for him . . .'

Lord Malden sighed. How could he tell her that all the Prince wanted was that she should go out of his life and stay out.

'My dear lord,' she said, 'if I could only *see* him. You are close to him. You could do so much . . . if you would.'

'You know there is nothing in my power I would not do for you.'

'I know it. And you will arrange a meeting. If I could but see him *once* . . .'

She might be right, thought Malden. She was very beautiful. Dally and the Armistead women were nothing compared with her. Nor was Lady Augusta. Surely he must be moved if he could see her looking as appealing as she did now?

And if he could bring them together again . . . if they could be happy together. And surely Perdita would have learned her lesson. Then they would both be very grateful to him.

'Rest assured that I will do everything . . . everything.'

'But you will speak with him?'

'I will take the first opportunity, and if it is at all possible I will bring about that meeting.'

When he had gone Perdita felt greatly relieved. She thrust all the bills into a drawer out of sight and gave herself up to the contemplation of what she would wear for the meeting and rehearsed what she would say. She would not reproach him; she would be humble, pleading, assuring him of her complete submission and devotion.

She was sure then that he would find her irresistible.

A few days later Lord Malden called again.

'I have good news for you. The Prince will see you.'

'My dear friend, how can I thank you!'

What should she wear? Lilac satin . . . pale green silk . . . one of the many dresses which had not yet been paid for? No need to worry herself on that score. All would soon be well. No one would worry her for money when they knew she was back with the Prince of Wales.

'When is he coming?' she cried. 'I must have time.'

'He will not come here.'

'But why not?'

'Er . . . I think it better if you were to come to my house in Clarges Street. The Prince could see you there.'

She took his hand and kissed it. 'Oh, how can I thank you.'

His ardent gaze was enough to tell her how. But he could say nothing as yet, of course.

Surely she was as beautiful as ever. Hope had restored the beauty she feared she had lost. Her carriage rattled through the streets and she was happy for the first time since she had quarrelled with the Prince and been aware that she was losing him.

That should never happen again. She would be so careful. She would never reproach him again; she would be sweet and loving and ever grateful for being given a second chance.

Lord Malden received her with the admiring looks which he had never failed to bestow upon her. What a good faithful creature he was! Especially as by being her friend he incurred the displeasure of the King–and perhaps would risk losing the Prince's favour if all did not go well between him and her. Dear, good faithful Malden, who would even now have paid her debts for her had he been able!

'His Highness is here,' he whispered.

And he took her into his drawing room where, his back to the door, stood the Prince.

She stood waiting and he being aware of her slowly turned.

'My . . . Prince . . . !' she cried and went towards him, her hands outstretched.

As he took them and kissed them, great floods of relief swept over her.

'I . . . I feel as though I am alive again,' she said.

'I am happy to see you,' he told her. And taking her hand drew her to a couch where they sat side by side.

'I have been so unhappy,' she told him.

'My dear Perdita!'

'I thought you would never forgive me. I thought you hated me.'

'Do you think I could ever hate Perdita?'

'But you went away . . .' Careful, she thought. No reproaches.

'It was a state affair in fact,' he said easily. 'My birthday had to be celebrated in the heart of the family at Windsor.'

'Of course.'

He began to chat of the festivities at Windsor, describing the public celebrations and the review in the Park; the banquet and the ball; but he made no mention of Lady Augusta.

She was longing to ask him questions about Mrs Armistead but she dared not. She had learned one lesson at least.

They talked of mutual friends and it was a most pleasant hour. Then the Prince said he must go; he had an engagement. She suppressed the desire to ask if it was at Cumberland House; and he said an affectionate goodbye to her in which she was certain that he meant to imply they would meet again soon.

Lord Malden conducted the Prince to his coach and came back to Perdita.

'I can only tell you how grateful I am.'

'His Highness was friendly.'

'Extremely so.'

'That I can see, for you are radiant.'

'It was just a little misunderstanding. I shall see that it does not happen in the future.'

Poor Perdita! thought Malden. She did not know how difficult it had been. The Prince had most certainly not wished to see her and Malden was sure had no intention of renewing the acquaintance.

Still let Perdita be happy for a little longer.

She returned to Cork Street, played a little on the harpsichord and sang softly. She retired to bed and lay listening, wondering whether he might call.

The next morning she dressed with the greatest care. She wore one of her fantastic hats, all ribbons and feathers; and a lavender silk gown which was exquisite. And taking her carriage with the coronet-like wreath went into the Park.

She felt intoxicated by the sunshine. It was a beautiful morning; the grass had never seemed so green, the flowers so beautiful. People gazed at her, nudged each other and whispered together. Perdita was about again.

And suddenly she saw him. He was walking with a crowd of his friends about him laughing and chatting; and as usual he was the centre of attraction. Now the moment was at hand. He would come to her carriage, take her hand, kiss it, perhaps ride with her. They would be together again.

She stopped the carriage. The Prince and his group were approaching. She smiled. He looked at her blankly as though he did not know her; and then turning his head began to talk animatedly to one of his companions.

She was stunned. It was a deliberate cut, a deliberate insult.

He had seen her and pretended he did not know her. He had shown her publicly that he had finished with her.

But after their meeting yesterday . . .

She could see it all now. He had been persuaded to it; it had meant nothing. He did not wish to resume their relationship. More than that he did not wish to know her.

No one could have been told more clearly.

She was aware of curious eyes on her; she could hear the sounds of laughter floating back to her. His laughter! And she wanted to die.

Love Letters of a Prince

Back to Cork Street.

This is the end, she said. He will never come back now.

She took the bills from the drawer and looked at them. It was better to do something than nothing.

How can I pay all these debts? she asked herself. They were all incurred for him. But for him I should be a famous actress, earning a good living from the theatre. I gave up everything for him. Everything.

She forced herself to add up the amounts she owed. No, it was impossible. Seven thousand pounds. They could not be so much. She had been extravagant . . . for him, she repeated bitterly. But surely not as extravagant as that.

'Where can I find seven thousand pounds?' she asked herself.

Where indeed?

And then she remembered. She took a key from the drawer and opened a box which she kept in her bedroom.

From this she took out a piece of parchment. It was the Prince's bond for £20,000, and it was sealed with the royal seal.

She remembered his giving it to her, and how she had declared she would not have it and he had had to persuade her to accept it.

It was the answer, of course. It would be the only way in which she could pay her debts.

And yet she shuddered to think of asking him to honour it.

Yet . . . £7,000! How could she produce that sum of money unless he did.

If it were possible I would work, I would do anything, she told herself. I would not take a penny of his . . . if I could help it.

Work. There was a possibility.

In feverish haste she put on her cloak. She could not bear to sit down and think quietly. The only way in which she could endure to live through this terrible day was by taking action.

She sent for her carriage and drove to Bruton Street.

The Sheridans had moved to Bruton Street when Richard had become a Member of Parliament and so frequently entertained the Prince of Wales.

Perdita asked if Mr Sheridan was at home, for she wished to see him urgently. She was taken into an elaborately furnished room and while she waited there the door opened and Elizabeth Sheridan came in.

Perdita had not seen her since she had become the Prince's mistress and was shocked by the change in her appearance. Her beautiful eyes looked enormous, her face thinner which did not detract from its beauty, but in fact accentuated the exquisite bone structure; and the flush on her cheeks.

Perdita rose and held out her hand uncertainly.

Elizabeth Sheridan took it and said gently: 'Are you well?'

'I am . . . distraught,' replied Perdita.

'I am so sorry.' She said it as though she meant it and there was a world of understanding in the musical tones.

Poor Elizabeth Sheridan, who had suffered no less than Perdita herself, and there in that room Perdita–which was rare for her–ceased to think of her own tragic situation in contemplating that of this woman. Elizabeth, fragile and clearly not long for this world, for the change in her appearance could only mean that she was consumptive, had suffered even more at the hands of her husband than Perdita had at those of her lover.

I might have expected it; I broke the rules; I loved a feckless boy and expected fidelity; I was extravagant and vain. But this woman was a saint . . . and she had married a man of genius and had looked forward to a life with him which could have been perfect.

But Sheridan was ambitious. Not only did he wish to write immortal plays, he must be a statesman, friend of the Prince of Wales, lover of many women . . . And because he believed these glittering prizes to be more valuable than the love of his wife he had thrust her aside to reach them.

Ambition, thought Perdita. By that sin fell the angels.

'I must see Richard,' said Perdita.

Elizabeth nodded. 'He will shortly be with you. I am so glad that you have found him at home. He is rarely here now.'

'You have a magnificent home,' said Perdita.

Elizabeth looked about the room sadly.

Perdita understood. Debts, she thought. Living beyond their means. But then he always had. And Elizabeth was not the woman to thrust the bills into a drawer and forget them. She imagined her brooding over them. I am not the only one to suffer.

And then Richard Sheridan came into the room.

How he had changed from the handsome man who she had known when she first went into the theatre! It was not such a long time ago. Four years . . . five years. He had coarsened, grown fat, and his face was an unhealthy red. Too much drink; too many late nights. Would the Prince grow like this in time?

She could see at once that he knew why she had come. He had been a good friend to her even after they had ceased to be lovers, and she felt an uneasy twinge of conscience. How much did Elizabeth know of that episode which she, Perdita, would rather forget?

'I will leave you together,' said Elizabeth. 'You will have business to discuss.'

She took Perdita's hand and pressed it. 'May God go with you,' she whispered.

Perdita faced Sheridan; was she right and did she detect a faint impatience in his expression?

'Sherry,' she said, 'I had to come and see you. You know what has happened?'

'The whole of London knows,' he said. 'The whole of the Court.'

'Does the news travel so fast?'

'It is some time since he left you. He has other mistresses now.'

She winced and he smiled a little sardonically. So after all her adventures she still could not bear to hear the word spoken. It was ironical to him that an act should be less repulsive than the words which described it. He thought there was an idea there for a *bon mot*. He should make a note of it and use it some time . . . but like all his ideas they came to nothing and he lost them because he would never put himself out to record them.

But the theatre took second place now. The future stretched out brilliantly before him as the politician, friend of Fox and the Prince of Wales.

'I have debts, Sherry.'

'You are–as always–in the fashion, Perdita.'

'But I cannot pay them.'

'Still in the fashion.'

'Because of all this . . . they will not wait. I must earn money quickly. My creditors must be made to understand that although I cannot pay them immediately I intend to do so . . . in due course.'

'And how will you convince them of these noble intentions?'

'By going back to work. I want to come back to the theatre.'

He looked at her blankly. 'You couldn't do it, Perdita.'

'Why not?' she demanded shrilly.

'They would never let you.'

'Who . . . Who? Do you mean *you* would not?'

'I have to consider my audiences. They would jeer you off the stage.'

'Why, why?'

'Because of the past. They would crowd the theatre for the first night and like as not there would be a riot. I could not risk it.'

'How can you be sure if you will not give me a chance?'

'I tell you I *know* it. It is not the way. I warned you. Remember? Do you remember?'

She nodded sombrely.

'Did I not tell you that you should never have become his mistress?'

She was too shaken to wince now. Poor Perdita, denuded of her mask. She was herself now, and that was a desperate and frightened woman.

She nodded. 'Yes, you warned me.'

'And I told you then that afterwards you could never return to the theatre.'

'You mean you won't have me?'

'Willingly would I, if it were possible. But it is not possible. You must find some other way.'

'How? How can I pay my debts?'

'I wish I could answer that one. Most willingly would I use the information.'

'I owe seven thousand pounds.'

'I wish I owed as little.'

'But *I* have no means of paying it.'

'I too am living beyond my means.'

Did she imagine it or was he bored? Oh, God, she thought, this is how people will be towards me in future. I am no longer of any consequence.

Then she said: 'There is no help for it. I have his bond.'

'What bond is this?'

'The Prince's bond for twenty thousand pounds. He gave it to me and I have kept it. I shall need this money . . . badly. I had hoped not to touch it.'

Sheridan was silent. A bond for £20,000! The Prince would never honour it. He happened to know that His Highness had a mound of debts of his own which would make his, Sheridan's, let alone Perdita's, seem paltry.

'It has his signature and seal,' she said. 'He would have to honour it.'

'You mean . . . you would insist?'

'Please tell me how else I can pay my debts.'

Sheridan was silent.

Then she said wearily: 'I will go. I see that you cannot help me.'

'If I could . . .'

'Yes, if you could you would. But you cannot give me this chance in the theatre.'

'Perdita, if it were possible . . .'

'It is not possible to give it a test?'

'No,' he said firmly. 'No.'

She hesitated. 'You are the Prince's friend. Perhaps you could make him aware of my plight. I did not wish to ask him for money, but in the circumstances, what else can I do?'

Sheridan was alarmed. He did not wish to be the man who conveyed to the Prince the information that his discarded mistress was demanding the money he had promised her. That was not the sort of entertainment the Prince looked for from Sheridan. He wanted to be amused, not disturbed.

She laid her hand on his arm. 'You will do this for me?'

What could he say but: 'You may rely on me to do what I consider best for your welfare.'

'For old times' sake,' she said with a return of her old manner.

And Sheridan nodded and conducted her to her carriage.

He called on Fox in St James's, and without preamble came straight to the point.

'Perdita Robinson has been to see me.'

Fox nodded. He knew how the affair had ended. His good friend Mrs Armistead visited him now and then and let him know the Prince's attitude to various matters not excluding that towards his old mistress. He was well aware of the meeting between the two women in the Magpie and how the Prince's own relationship with Mrs Armistead progressed.

'She is in a desperate situation. Her debts amount to some seven thousand pounds and the creditors are making a nuisance of themselves.'

'They've heard of course that she is now discarded.'

'She is a desperate woman.'

'And came to ask you to allow her to resume her career as an actress, I'll swear.'

'Which I have most definitely refused.'

'Naturally, naturally. The poor improvident creature!'

'Well, Charles, we are two fine ones to talk of improvidence.'

'We are not the Prince's mistresses, my good fellow. Perdita should have made herself very comfortable on the gifts she received.'

He thought of his friend Mrs Armistead who was fast becoming a woman of some substance, with a house of her own most tastefully furnished, and she was now building up a pleasant little fortune. But Perdita was of course no Mrs Armistead. Such excellent creatures were rarely met with. All Perdita had accumulated were debts.

'He gave her a bond for twenty thousand pounds and she is talking of claiming it.'

Fox was alert at once.

'She will never get it.'

'No, I daresay it's completely invalid.'

'She'll put herself into an unfortunate position if there is a scandal over this. Does she realize this?'

'The poor woman is too frantic to realize anything but that she has debts of seven thousand pounds and it seems her only possession is this bond for twenty thousand pounds. She has asked me to convey to H.H. that she intends to claim the money as her due.'

'And what was your answer?'

'I prevaricated. I was vague. I should certainly not like to be the one to pass such an item of news to the Prince.'

'It would scarcely make him jump for joy. Imagine the news reaching the Hall of Purity. It would be as bad as the Grosvenor affair. Worse! This is not a mere duke but the Prince of Wales.'

'That is why I came to see you immediately.'

'I think,' said Fox, 'that I must, immediately, go and see Mrs Perdita.'

Sheridan was relieved. If anyone could handle this situation it was Fox; and Fox's great attraction for his most ardent admirers–among them the Prince of Wales–was that he never sought to curry favour with anyone. He stated his views frankly. The Prince had accepted this and had the intelligence to know its worth. Other men might fit their words to suit a royal mood. Fox never did. It was strength and his dignity.

Frantic with grief Perdita was going through the latest bills to arrive accompanied by demanding letters–insolent letters–when Mr Fox was announced.

She thrust the bills out of sight, hurried to a mirror and hastened to compose herself when he came in.

How gross he was! He was growing more so each week; his swarthiness was not attractive and his chins rested on his soiled cravat. One would never have thought that he was the great Mr Fox, who was received with delight in all the noblest Whig houses, until he bowed and began to speak. Then the regality and charm which he had no doubt inherited from his ancestor King Charles II was obvious.

'My *dear* Mrs Robinson.'

What a comfort to be treated so respectfully by Mr Fox after the veiled insolence of servants and the truculent manners of creditors.

'Mr Fox, welcome.'

He was holding her hand and seemed reluctant to let it go. She flushed a little. Everyone knew Mr Fox's manners with women. He was as fond of them as he was of wine and gambling. And in spite of her misfortunes she was a very beautiful woman. 'Pray be seated,' she said.

He sat down heavily, legs apart, surveying her.

'It is good of you to call, Mr Fox. People do not call so frequently now.' Her lips trembled.

He said: 'Had you asked me to call, Madam, I should have been here at once.'

'How kind you are, sir.'

'Who would not be kind to a beautiful woman? But let us speak frankly. I do not care to see beauty in distress. Sheridan has talked to me.'

She flushed. 'If he could be persuaded to give me another chance . . .'

'If those beautiful eyes could not entreat him, the case is hopeless.'

'Mr Fox, I am desperate. I owe a great deal of money.'

Fox nodded lugubriously. 'A situation with which I can heartily sympathize. I am in such a one myself at this time . . . in fact I have rarely been out of it. But you spoke of a bond.'

She hesitated and Fox went on: 'Madam, I have come here to help you. I can only do this if you trust me.' He rose and coming to her chair laid his hands on the arms and brought his face close to hers. 'Shall I tell you this. I have long admired your beauty.' He kissed her on the lips. She gasped and drew back and he thought: Not called Propriety Prue for nothing! He laughed. 'Forgive the impertinence, Mrs Robinson, I wished to show you that admiring you as I do, I am ready to do what is within my power to help you. The kiss was a bond. Perhaps as significant as that of His Royal Highness. Would you let me see this bond so that I can assess its value.'

'I cannot understand, Mr Fox, why you who are His Highness's friend should wish to help me.'

'Madam, I am the friend of you both. And I see this: I may best serve you both by helping to bring this little matter to a satisfactory conclusion. If you will show me the bond I promise you . . . on this new understanding which is between us two . . . that I will do all in my power to help you.'

Perdita said: 'I will get it. I will be back with it shortly.'

In her bedroom she went first to her mirror. Her eyes were brilliant and there was a faint colour in her cheeks. She had not had time to paint her face but perhaps it looked more attractive without rouge and white lead. It certainly did with that faint rose-like flush. And the gown she was wearing . . . it was not one of her best but quite becoming. And Mr Fox? He was repulsive. How different from the Prince. And yet he was so clever. If anyone could help her he could. And what had he meant by that kiss? Was it a suggestion? She knew of his reputation. She was trembling as she opened the box and took out the bond.

When she returned Mr Fox was sitting back in his chair as though deep in thought. He took the bond from her without a word and studied it.

'He won't honour it,' he said.

She cried in horror, 'But what can I do? I must have money. All these debts . . . Do you think I should have incurred them but for entertaining him and his friends?'

'My dear lady, creditors alas are never interested in why debts are incurred . . . only that they are.'

'But, Mr Fox . . . what am I to do?'

Mr Fox said nothing for a few moments; Perdita began to pace up and down the room wringing her hands like a tragedienne on a stage. Fox watched her and thought: She acts naturally without knowing she is doing it. Poor creature, she will be demented if she goes on like this. And so pretty.

He thought of all the jackals who would be waiting to step into the Prince's place. There would be many of them. That old reprobate Cumberland was one. He only had to set her up and the creditors would be ready to wait. The jackals could wait. Meanwhile the Fox would step in. He had always thought that it would be rather amusing to share her with the Prince of Wales. Such beauty was rare and he never liked to miss anything. But although as the mistress of Mr Fox she would be able to hold her head up again in some circles–for he flattered himself that it was in fact no step down from the Prince to Mr Fox, her creditors would view the move with disfavour. Whereas Cumberland–royal Duke that he was–would not displease them.

A piquant situation.

'Madam,' he said, 'I pray you do not distress yourself. We will put our heads together . . .' He smiled at her. He was giving her hints enough. Did she grasp them? She must. However innocent she was of financial matters she was well versed in dealing with the advances of men.

'But Mr Fox, I am a desperate woman. I did not wish to take this bond, but the Prince insisted. I gave up a lucrative career for his sake. He insisted that I accept this recompense. I must pay my debts. Mr Fox, I have lived in a debtors' prison. I will never go back to such a place. I will die first . . . I will do anything. Why should he not honour his bond? Everyone knows of the relationship which existed between us. Everyone knows what I gave up for him. If they do not . . . I have his letters to prove it. I would publish those letters. I would . . .'

Mr Fox sat up very straight. 'Letters, you say, Madam? Letters? Ah, now that might be a very different matter. You have these letters . . . here?'

'Indeed I have them and I must pay these debts. I will never again . . .'

Mr Fox interrupted. 'Madam, show me these letters.'

She was not a fool. She had noticed the change in the atmosphere, the change in Mr Fox. The letters made all the difference. The letters were more important than the bond.

She hesitated. Fox was after all the friend of the Prince. What if the Prince had sent him to get the letters?

'I cannot help you,' said Mr Fox gently, 'if you will not show me the letters.'

She went to her bedroom. She unlocked the box and took out the letters tied up with lavender coloured ribbon. How many times had she read them and treasured them . . . and wept over them. She hesitated. What if he took them away. What if he took them to the Prince. She could no longer trust the Prince.

No, she would not give Fox the letters. She would select one and that would be a good sample.

She untied the ribbon. There was one in which he had referred to his father in the most disparaging terms, also of his great devotion to herself. She glanced through it, remembering every word. Oh, he would regret he had ever humiliated her in the Park!

She was elated. These letters were the answer. Let him throw the bond in her face. There were still these most valuable letters.

Mr Fox read the letter she gave him and even he could not hide the fact that he was deeply impressed.

'Only one letter, dear Mrs Robinson?'

'There are many more.'

'And all in this strain?'

'Yes, Mr Fox.'

He smiled at her. 'And you do not propose to let them out of your hands. I rejoice in your wisdom, Mrs Robinson, which in this matter almost equals your beauty. You should keep those letters under lock and key. They are very valuable.'

'And what shall I do, Mr Fox?'

He rose and still holding the letter in his hand approached her.

'Will you trust me, Mrs Robinson?'

She hesitated, and he laughed. 'Again you show your wisdom. But in view of our growing er . . . friendship . . . I think you might trust me . . . a little. Not too much as yet. But remember that such is my position that I am one of the few people who could approach His Highness personally and believe me, Mrs Robinson, this is not a matter which should be handled with anything but the utmost tact.'

'I am certain of it.'

'Then allow me to take this one letter. For what is one among so many? If you will allow me to do as I think fit, I believe we shall together drive those braying dogs of creditors from your door.'

'Oh, Mr Fox, if that could happen I could never be grateful enough.'

'And I should be a very happy man to earn that gratitude.'

He took his leave of her; and she felt better than she had for some time.

Fox! she thought and shuddered. In a way he was so repulsive and yet not without attraction. And if he could only extricate her from this frightening situation she would indeed do anything to show her gratitude.

Sitting in the chair which took him to Buckingham House Fox read the letter again. By God, he thought, how could he have been such a fool!

He was not thinking so much of the Prince's dilemma, nor of Mrs Robinson's gratitude to come–although both these matters were in his mind–but the effect the publication of those letters would have on the Party. The Prince was to be the leader–in name only of course. It would be Fox's party. But if these letters were published there would be a Grosvenor scandal all over again and it was clear that the Duke of Cumberland had lost much prestige through that affair. But he had not spoken in derogatory terms of the sovereign as this foolish young man had done. What would ministers think of a prince, a leader of a Party, who could be so indiscreet to a play actress who was his temporary mistress? Those letters would spoil the plans Fox had been making for that time when the Prince attained his majority and took his seat in the Lords. It was not the Prince's morals which would destroy his prestige as a leader, but his indiscretion.

Putting the letter carefully into a pocket of his waistcoat Fox alighted from his chair and went to the Prince's apartments where he was immediately received and with the utmost pleasure.

'Apologies for disturbing Your Highness at such short notice.'

'No need to apologize for giving me pleasure, Charles.'

'I fear this visit will not give Your Highness much pleasure.'

'Oh, Charles, what have you on your mind?'

'Perdita Robinson.'

'Oh, no. That's all over.'

'I fear not, sir. I wish to God it were. I have been to see her.'

'You, Charles? Good God, don't tell me you and she . . .'

'Your Highness! How could such a lady step so quickly from a handsome

Prince to a seedy politician.'

'Well, if the politician were Charles James Fox . . .'

'But the Prince was His Royal Highness the Prince of Wales. However, allow me to get to business. She is in dire distress. Her creditors are bothering her.'

'Charles, have you any idea of the size of my own debts?'

'A rough idea, sir, and it appals me.'

The Prince laughed. 'I fear I cannot give her money.'

'She has a bond.'

The Prince turned pale.

'Your Highness should not be distressed on that account. I have seen the bond and I think it is useless. It's not to come into effect until you are of age and that's two years off, in any case. I don't think we need concern ourselves with the bond.'

The Prince's relief was obvious. 'Charles, how glad I am that she showed this to *you*.'

'Yes, well I heard of it and thought I should see it without delay. But there is another matter which gives me cause for great disquiet.'

'What is this?'

'The letters you wrote to her.'

'Letters . . . I wrote?'

'Your Highness has a ready, fluent and eloquent pen. With such a gift it often seems a sin not to use it. I could have wished Your Highness less gifted in this direction.'

'But these letters . . .' The Prince wrinkled his brow, trying to remember.

'I have one here,' said Fox, and took it from his waistcoat pocket. He handed it to the Prince who read it, flushing.

'It is not so much the tender and explanatory terms used as the references to His Majesty. I fear this would be judged a most damaging letter to the sovereign.'

The Prince flushed and was about to tear it in two.

'Stop . . . please. I beg Your Highness's pardon, but that would be unwise. Mrs Robinson would never part with the others . . . moreover she would realize even more than she does now their value.'

'So she has been hoarding these letters . . . keeping them until she could use them. The cheat. The blackmailer!'

'Your Highness . . . forgiveness again . . . but this will not solve our problems. We have on one side this frail lady who is–let us be fair–in a desperate position. I do not believe she would wish to sell those letters if this were not the case. I feel she would prefer to keep them tied up with ribbons to read to her grandchildren in the years to come and so recall those days of romance and passion. But she is in debt. She lives in terror of the debtors' prison of which she has had a taste. Let us see Mrs Robinson as she is. It will help us. A blackmailer? Well, perhaps. But she is in a corner and she has to fight her way out.'

'Well, Charles, you make a good advocate for the woman. I thought you were on my side.'

'On your side in the past, now and for ever. But my plan is to settle this matter as speedily as possible. To have those letters where they belong–and that is consigned to the flames . . . before they have done irreparable damage.'

'What damage could they do?'

'They could hold you up to ridicule, they could place a strong weapon in the hands of your enemies; they could rob you of the popularity you now have and which is so important to you and our plans. Your Uncle Cumberland is an instance. He is not greatly loved by the people. They have heard passages from those letters he wrote to Lady Grosvenor and they will never forget them. Moreover, there is your father to face. He is after all the King. What have you said of him in those letters? You cannot even remember, but in this one you have been damaging enough. Even those with whom he is not popular recognize him as the King. This criticism of him, to a light woman . . . I know of course how deep your feelings towards Mrs Robinson were when you wrote those words and that you did not see her in this way, but that is how she will be looked upon . . . will be frowned on, not only by his friends but yours. Discretion is the first quality men look for in a leader and, my Prince, you are soon to be our leader. I know you understand.'

'Yes,' said the Prince heavily. 'I understand that I have been a fool.'

'Well, so are we all in our times. And Your Highness could turn this affair into valuable experience. But first we have to deal with this situation. We have to buy these letters from Mrs Robinson. We have to see that they and the bond are safe in our hands.'

'Do you mean pay her twenty thousand pounds *and* buy the letters?'

'I think she can be persuaded to hand over the bond; but the letters are what concern me. Any young man in love might give a woman a bond he finds it difficult to honour; but the letters are our concern.'

'Charles, I know you are right. But I cannot raise the money. You know how short my father keeps me. It is easy enough to run up debts. People are only glad to serve me. But I cannot raise this money.'

'I have thought of this. There is only one thing to do.'

'Yes, Charles, yes?'

'You must go to the King, confess your folly and ask him to buy the letters.'

'What! It's the last thing I could do.'

'Maybe, sir, but as I see it it's the only thing you can do.'

'I never will.'

Fox shook his head sadly and said: 'Then, Your Highness, I must leave you to settle this matter your own way.'

'Charles . . . how can I? You *must* help me.'

'Everything I have is at Your Highness's service. Unfortunately I have no money or it should be yours. I am in the same position as Your Highness. I can run up debts but raise no cash. I have nothing to offer you but my advice.'

'Which is the best in the world, I know.'

'It is disinterested, that much I can tell you. I have thought of this problem as though it were my own–and indeed it is my own, for apart from my affection and friendship for Your Highness my future plans are concerned in it. I dream of that day when Your Highness takes his place in the affairs of the nation and I want nothing to spoil that. But I can see only one way out. These letters must be bought back from Mrs Robinson and the only way this money can be raised is through the King. Your Uncle Cumberland was in a similar position. I pray this affair will not be so public. Nor need it be if we act with care and speed. But there is no time to lose. Let Mrs Robinson go to a lawyer . . . and she is desperate . . . and we are lost. We have to find that money quickly and settle this matter once and for all.'

'Charles, you must help me.'

'I am asking Your Highness to place this matter in my hands; but if I am to be your adviser you must perforce follow my advice.'

'To go to my father . . .'

'To confess the whole affair, your folly, the realization of what you have done, your growing responsibility to your position. The King is not an ogre.'

'You don't know him as I do.'

'He is a sentimental man . . . and I'll swear at heart he is fond of you. Be tactful. He must supply the money. It is important to him that there should be no more family scandals. Do as I say and in a short while when this unfortunate matter is over you will see that it was the only way in which you could have acted.'

'And Charles . . . you will be my ambassador with Perdita?'

'I will. And I'll swear that if you will face up to this interview, painful as I know it is going to be, you will very soon be able to put this matter behind you–and little harm will have been done.'

'Charles, I rely on you.'

'In which,' said Mr Fox with a bow, 'Your Highness shows your wisdom.'

The Prince humbly requested an audience with his father, which the King willingly granted. The terms in which the request was written pleased him. His son showed a proper–and unusual–respect.

He's growing up, thought the King. He was wayward at first . . . but so are most young men.

He was in a mellow mood as he greeted the Prince who, he noticed, had what might be called a hangdog expression.

'You have something to say to me, eh?'

'Yes, Father, and I am going to ask Your Majesty's indulgence for the follies of youth.'

'What's this, eh, what?' The King shot a suspicious glance at his son. Such humility was a little disturbing. 'Go on, go on,' he commanded. 'What are these follies, eh?'

'I have to confess that I have formed an . . . an association with an actress.'

'I know. I know.'

'A Mrs Robinson who played at Drury Lane with Sheridan's company.'

'Can't abide the fellow,' said the King. 'Drinks, gambles . . . leads that nice woman a life. Pity she married him. He's not faithful to her. Rackets about the town. Don't like the fellow. Friend of Fox.'

The Prince saw it was a mistake to have mentioned Sheridan.

'Well, Father, this woman is no longer . . . my friend.'

'Come to your senses, eh? Perhaps time you were married. Bit young. I was young myself . . . but perhaps it's best.'

The interview was going badly. The outcome might be that his father would discover some plump German princess for him. That he would stand out against with all his strength. If his father would wait until he was twenty-one he would have some say in the matter . . . but if he should produce the woman now . . . But he was straying from the unpleasant point and the sooner this was reached the better.

'I wrote her letters . . . foolish letters.'

The effect on the King of that word letters was great. His mouth slightly open, he stared at his son.

'It was foolish,' admitted the Prince. 'I know that now. I've learned my lesson.'

'Letters?' breathed the King. 'It's like that fool Cumberland all over again. What possessed you, eh? Letters! Don't you know better than that, eh, what?'

'I do now,' said the Prince.

'Letters,' murmured the King. He looked at his son and thought of the folly of youth; and Hannah Lightfoot's image rose up before him. Remember your own youth, George. Were you so wise? 'Not letters,' he mumbled.

'Yes, Father, I fear so. She has them and she is threatening to publish them.'

The King closed his eyes.

'There is only one thing to do. We must buy those letters from her.'

'This woman . . . she has a husband?' The King could not get the thought of Lord Grosvenor out of his mind.

'Yes . . . a low fellow . . . a clerk of some sort.'

'Shocking! Disgusting! You realize that, eh, what?'

'I realize it fully but I know something has to be done.'

'What sort of letters, eh? Love letters? That sort?'

'That sort,' admitted the Prince; 'and I fear that I was a little indiscreet about . . . family matters.'

'Family matters! You mean you discussed your family . . . the royal family . . . with this . . . this . . . woman. Eh! What?'

'I fear so.'

'And she wrote you letters?'

'Yes.'

'And where are they?'

'I destroyed them.'

'So you destroyed hers and she kept yours, eh?'

'It seems so.'

'It seems so! How do you know she has these letters?'

'I have been shown one . . . and that itself is enough to . . . er . . .'

'I know, I know. Letters!'

'I gave her a bond.'

'What?'

'A bond for twenty thousand pounds.'

'You are mad.'

'I fear I was at the time, sir. But the stipulation was that I could not honour it until I was twenty-one.'

'I doubt it's valid. And you've another two years to go. I trust you learn a little sense by then.'

'I trust so, sir.'

'Letters,' mused the King. 'Damning, humiliating letters! What have I done to be cursed with a family like this?'

'We are not so bad, sir,' said the Prince soothingly. 'It is only when compared with Your Majesty's high code of morals and blameless existence that we appear so.'

The King looked sharply at his son. The young dog was too free with words–always had been. One never could be sure what he was driving at.

'Go away,' he said. 'I'll think of this.'

'Sir, we must get those letters.'

'Do you think I don't understand the trouble this sort of folly can bring to the family?'

'I did not think that for one moment, sir, that was why I plucked up my courage to bring the matter to your attention.'

'You'd do better to consult me more often.'

'I know that now, sir.'

'Then go and I will consider this in due course. But I'd have you know that I am preoccupied with weighty matters of State which one day perhaps you will know something about. And you have to disturb me with your follies. I tell you this, sir, I am displeased. I am disgusted and this sort of thing will have to stop. You understand that, eh, what?'

'I understand it well, sir; I admit my folly. We all have to learn by the mistakes of youth, sir.'

For one moment the King could almost have believed that this son of his, who knew so much, was aware of that period of his father's life which all this time the King had been striving to forget.

It was on occasions like this that one remembered and the past came up to mock. It had the effect though of making a man more lenient than he might have been.

He said in a milder tone: 'If it's taught you a valuable lesson then perhaps it is not such a disaster as it appears. Go now. You will hear more of this from me.'

The Prince knelt and kissed his father's hand. There were tears of real gratitude in his eyes–but tears came easily to the whole family. Yet, this had changed the young dog. He was worried, and there was no doubt that it had brought him to heel.

Charles James Fox was a constant visitor to Cork Street. Perdita had also received a visit from Lieutenant-Colonel Hotham who had told her that he came on the King's business.

Perdita was thrown into a state of great anxiety by the visit of this gentleman who pointed out to her that in attempting to blackmail the Prince she was placing herself in a very dangerous position. The Prince had confessed to the King the fact that he had written indiscreet letters to her and the King was most distressed, first that his son should have written the letters and secondly that he should have so far forgotten the dignity due to his position as to become involved with a woman who could offer to treat them as merchandise.

So terrified had Perdita been that she had almost agreed to hand over the letters; but the thought of her debts and her interview with Mr Fox sustained her; and she had told the Lieutenant-Colonel that she could do nothing without consulting her friends.

Thank God for Mr Fox!

He listened gravely to all that Hotham had said and had told her that she must act with the utmost caution and not allow herself to be bullied. He would tell her exactly what she must do.

She was very ready to lean on him. He was so clever. She had never known such a clever person. Of course his appearance was a little repulsive–particularly if one were as fastidious as Perdita undoubtedly was–but even that was a little piquant. On each visit he became a little more familiar; and she could see, of course, to what he was leading. No, she told herself. Never. Yet what would she do without him? He only had to appear and she could forget those hideous bills. Moreover, it was known that Mr Fox was visiting her and this meant that the tradespeople were not so insolent. They were holding off a little. Mr Fox was making some arrangements for her, therefore they would be patient for a little longer.

Mr Fox persuaded the Prince of Wales to allow her to remain in the house in Cork Street until some other arrangement could be made. That was a great comfort.

And now there was this terrifying man, Hotham, who wanted to know the extent of her debts and how many of the letters there were and to see some of them (but not to let them out of the house, said Mr Fox) and with whom she could never have bargained, if Mr Fox had not been in the background telling her exactly what to do.

There came a day when Hotham arrived, stern and disapproving and not even glancing at her as though she were some ordinary woman and not one of the most beautiful in London.

'I have an ultimatum from His Majesty, Mrs Robinson,' he told her. 'You will be paid five thousand pounds and on accepting this you will hand to me the bond given to you by His Royal Highness the Prince of Wales in addition to the letters he wrote to you and this will be an end to the matter.'

'My debts alone amount to seven thousand pounds,' she told him.

'This, Madam, is no concern of His Majesty nor the Prince of Wales.'

'But indeed it is. The debts were incurred for the Prince's pleasure; and for this also I gave up a lucrative career.'

'The King's last words are five thousand pounds or, Madam, I fear you may publish the letters and take the consequences.'

'I will take the consequences.'

'They will hardly bring credit to you, Madam, I assure you. If you are wise you will take this money, sign these papers and hand me the bond and the letters.'

'I will consider this,' said Perdita. 'Call back tomorrow.'

Mr Fox came to Cork Street. He embraced her with passion. The consummation could not be long delayed. Mr Fox very clearly showed that he had worked indefatigably on her behalf and that her gratitude was the natural course of events.

She told him of Hotham's ultimatum.

'Five thousand pounds,' he said. 'Not a bad figure.'

'But he promised twenty thousand pounds.'

'I told you to put the thought of the bond out of your beautiful head. It's practically worthless. The five thousand pounds is for the letters. I think we shall have to consider this very closely.'

He gave the impression that if he stayed the night they could discuss it at greater length. He would have more time for working out a satisfactory conclusion, for although they must not say no to the £5,000, they should make it a bargaining point towards a solution.

'What solution?' Perdita wanted to know.

Mr Fox said he had no doubt he could work that out.

They had a pleasant supper. Perdita was excited, for she reminded herself that he was an unusual man, and there was nothing to be lost by being his friend. Perhaps if they became more and more friendly she would give him a hint about changing his linen more frequently and bathing now and then.

'You're thoughtful,' he said.

'I was thinking of the future . . . when this terrible anxiety is no more.'

'Our future?' asked Mr Fox.

And then he began to talk of what he envisaged as his future. England was going to lose America and this would bring down the Government. Then those who had deplored the way affairs had been conducted would come into their own. Mr Fox would doubtless lead a new ministry.

Perdita saw herself queening it in a salon in which she would receive all the most important people in the country. It was a wonderful dream. She saw herself in velvet and feathers. Society's leading hostess. The Prime Minister's dearest friend and adviser. Had she really stepped down when she lost the favour of the Prince?

She toasted the future with Fox. For the first time since the Prince had deserted her she was really happy.

And everything depended on this man who was clearly going to be her lover.

In the morning a gratified Mr Fox had the solution. She would surrender the bond and letters on these terms: Her debts were to be added to those of the Prince (which were so enormous that hers would not make much difference in any case) and paid by the Treasury; instead of the £5,000 she would accept a pension of £500 a year for the rest of her life and on her death her daughter was to receive £250 per annum until the end of her life. To these terms and these only would she agree.

Mr Fox was a wonderful man.

She was not surprised that he was so universally admired.

The King wrote to Lord North:

> 'I am sorry to be obliged to open a subject to Lord North that has long given me much pain, but I can rather do it on paper than in conversation; it is a subject to which I know he is not quite ignorant. My eldest son got last year into a very improper connection with an actress and woman of indifferent character through the assistance of Lord Malden and a multitude of letters passed which she has threatened to publish unless he, in short, bought them off her. He has made very foolish promises which undoubtedly by her conduct to him she entirely cancelled. I have thought it right to authorize the getting them from her and have employed Lieutenant-Colonel Hotham on whose discretion I could depend to manage this business. He has now brought it to a conclusion and has her consent to get these letters on her receiving £5,000, undoubtedly an enormous sum. But I wish to get my son out of this shameful scrape.'

The King sat back and put his hand over his eyes. Memories came to him. Hannah would never have attempted to blackmail him. Hannah had been a good woman. Why should he be reminded by this 'scrape' of his son's of that episode in his life?

But he was and the last few days Hannah had begun to haunt him as she had years ago.

He was weary. This continual conflict among the ministers; Fox standing threateningly with the opposition; the family–Frederick in Germany, William at sea. Were they going to confront him with similar episodes like this?

There was no peace . . .

'Uneasy lies the head that wears a crown . . .'

Didn't that fellow Shakespeare say something like that? Not that he admired the poet. Too much fuss made of him and he had always said so; but now and then he would say something which was true–and by God, he had when he said that.

What sort of a king would young George make when his time came? It was years away. He himself was not old. It was the Prince who made him feel old. He was in his early forties. That was not old.

And yet somewhere at the back of his mind there was an uneasy feeling, a foreboding of disaster.

There had been a time when a mysterious illness had overcome him, changing him while he was in its grip. It had terrified the Queen so much that she never spoke of it. But he had seen her looking at him oddly sometimes when he became too excited.

It was nothing. It would pass. It was just at times like this . . . times of great anxiety when his head started to buzz with strange voices and ideas darted in and out of his mind and escaped before he could catch them.

How dared his son add to his troubles! As if he had not enough.

But George was young yet. He had to learn his lessons, and what of himself? Had he lived so blamelessly?

He picked up his pen and added to the letter he had just written to Lord North:

> 'I am happy at being able to say that I never was personally engaged in such a transaction which perhaps makes me feel this the stronger.'

Mr Fox's arguments carried weight and Perdita's terms were accepted.

She was happy. She was no longer bothered by her creditors. The Prince would take on her debts. She could live in Cork Street until other plans could be made; she had an unusual lover, and the whole world knew it. She could still ride out in her carriage and people stopped to stare at her.

'Mrs Robinson has quickly found a new protector in Charles James Fox,' they said.

When the Prince heard that his old love was Fox's mistress he was very amused.

'Why, Charles,' he cried, 'if you have done me the honour of taking on my mistress, I have done the same by you, for I believe you were once on very friendly terms with Mrs Armistead.'

It was amusing, said Mr Fox; and more than that, most convenient.

But when he returned to his lodgings in St James's he thought of Mrs Armistead and he was surprised that he had not enjoyed hearing the Prince discuss her as though she were a woman of the town, lightly to be exchanged from one man's bed to another.

Yet he had felt no such resentment at the mention of Perdita in the same connection.

He had known from the start that he was quickly going to tire of Perdita. She had little to offer him but her beauty. She was undoubtedly a pretty creature and she had a certain slender talent both for acting and writing. She liked to read her poems to him–sentimental stuff, but a pleasant enough jingle.

Thinking that the day would come when his sojourns at Cork Street would be less frequent he had taken some of her poetry along to various newspapers with whose proprietors he was on excellent terms.

As a result poems were appearing now and then under the name of

Tabitha Bramble and the little money they earned was greatly appreciated by Mrs Mary Robinson.

Poor Perdita, thought Fox. So soon to be deserted again. Well, at least I arranged that she should have five hundred a year and see her poems profitably in print.

Not poor Perdita. Lucky Perdita. There were many who would be eager to supplant the Prince and Mr Fox.

Mr Fox and the Government

Perdita was sad to lose the companionship of Mr Fox, but he eluded her so skilfully and so gradually that she scarcely realized he had gone.

Even when their relationship was at its closest, there were so many matters to which he must give his attention and Perdita had made up her mind that she would make no demands on him. Therefore she never reproached him when he did not appear. He had done so much that she must be grateful to him for ever. She would never forget the horror of the debtors' prison from which with a few deft arrangements he had delivered her. He had brought interesting people to her house; and he had allowed her to play the hostess as she had dreamed of doing.

Among the guests had come one of the most interesting men she had ever met. This was General Banastre Tarleton who had just returned from the most exciting adventures in America. He entertained the company with accounts of his exploits and at that time everyone was talking about the Colonies.

In fact it was because of them that Charles absented himself so often; great disasters meant great opportunities; and perhaps she had always known that Charles would rather lose a mistress than an opportunity.

Banastre Tarleton was so gallant. He told her that she was the most beautiful woman he had ever met; and it was perfectly clear that he was only waiting for Charles to move out before he moved in. It seemed a delicate touch which she would have expected of Banastre. He understood that she was not the sort of loose woman who would have more than one lover at a time.

So although she had not been able to have the political salon of which she had dreamed, there was something comforting about a soldier's return from the wars. And when Charles was no longer her lover she slipped gracefully and happily into the protective arms of her soldier lover.

Fox often rode out to Chertsey to Mrs Armistead's comfortable little residence. He found it very pleasant to sit in her garden or at her fireside whichever the season warranted, and talk to her. She had kept herself informed of politics and he was astonished at her insight. Not that she was inclined to put forward an opinion unless asked. She preferred to listen.

He could talk to her about the worsening situation which he saw developing.

The King and North he said would be remembered by future generations with contempt. It was their policies and nothing else which had lost the

American Colonies–for lost they were whatever these two blind dodderers might think.

'He thinks Cornwallis will beat Lafayette and that he'll link up with Clinton and together they'll fight the main force under Washington. My dear Lizzie, it is easy to win battles in an armchair.'

'How can they be so foolish as not to beg you to take charge of affairs.'

'But it is precisely because they are foolish that we are in our present dilemma. If we had had wise men in the Government we should never have allowed this quarrel to reach this point. Poor old George! He means well, you know. But how many well-meaning people have fallen into disaster. He babbles about our troops being excellent fellows and he talks of the justice of our cause and he is quite certain that God is on our side.'

'Do you think he is seriously worried and that is why he talks like this?'

'I think there is a great deal in what you say. Our gracious King while decrying the deceit of the French is guilty of the most damning deceit of all–self deceit. Where is this policy leading us? Holland declares war on us. The French have blockaded Gibraltar; and France and Spain have captured fifty of our ships in the West Indies. This Empire which Pitt built up is disintegrating.'

'And when we have lost the Colonies will the Government fall?'

'Undoubtedly the Government will fall.' Mr Fox looked as sly as his name, and Mrs Armistead knew that he was thinking that that would be the time for Mr Fox to realize his dream.

Meanwhile Mrs Armistead could enjoy the realization of her own. She would never again serve other ladies; she would have her own lady's maid. The Prince was her friend; this passion was less intense than it had been, but she was prepared for that. He had been a generous lover and she was growing if not rich extremely comfortable.

The most interesting days were those when Mr Fox called to talk politics; and she was very happy on those occasions to be able to entertain him not as a mistress entertains a lover, but as a friend in whom he could confide his ambitions, and the extent to which he did this was a measure of his trust.

The King could no longer deceive himself and was forced to admit the loss of the Colonies. He shut himself into his bedroom and buried his face in his hands.

'What will become of me?' he asked himself; for in times of crisis he felt the old sickness returning to him and he was afraid.

All these months he had been deceiving himself. He had defied those men who had cautioned him, who had suggested a conciliatory policy; he had believed he knew; he had forced poor North to follow his line . . . and he had lost.

Mary Tudor had said that when she died Calais would be found written across her heart; and what was Calais compared with the loss of America!

Future generations would say: 'George III! He was the King who lost us America.'

He was the most unfortunate of men. No ruler could have tried harder to do what was right. No man could have tried to lead a better life.

And there was his son who cared for nothing but frivolity, adored by the public, smiled at indulgently in spite of the fact that he had got into difficulties with a play actress–which little scrape had cost his father a small fortune.

The Colonies gone; the voices back in his head, and the future spread out before him . . . dark and unpredictable.

The Government had fallen. Rockingham had formed a new ministry and in it were men whom he personally disliked. The Duke of Richmond, Master General of Ordnance; Grafton, Lord Privy Seal; and the two Secretaries of State were Lord Shelburne and . . . most bitter blow of all . . . Charles James Fox. The only friend of the King's in the cabinet was the Lord Chancellor Thurlow.

A King of England must bow to his parliament. There was plenty to remind him of that. So there was nothing he could do but take up the reins, of course, and try to forget that he was surrounded by men whom he regarded as his enemies.

The Prince longed to play a part in politics.

'The time will come,' Fox told him. 'Wait . . . just wait until you take your place in the House of Lords.'

'There is more than a year to wait,' the Prince reminded him.

'Nothing sir. It will soon be with us.'

'An establishment of my own!' sighed the Prince. 'Freedom.'

'Let us drink to it,' said Fox. 'The Prince's Party.'

'Whiggery and women,' echoed the Prince. 'How is Perdita?'

'The answer to that question will best come from General Tarleton. He is a very great friend of the lady.'

'It is well that she is comfortably settled.'

'Most comfortably, I believe.'

'A pretty creature but a dull one. And to think that I once thought her all that I desired on earth.'

'Your Highness has found the world to be full of desirable projects.'

'True, Charles, true . . . but until I am out of the cage how can I pursue them?'

'Patience. A year or so . . . and all that Your Highness desires will be yours.'

'An establishment of my own . . . an income worthy of my rank . . . a place in politics . . .'

Fox laughed. 'And all you have to cultivate now is . . . patience.'

There was no sense in not enjoying life during the waiting period. He had his mistresses. Dally was pregnant and swore he was the father but everyone said it could as well have been Cholmondeley. The Prince shrugged his shoulders; the idea of being a father rather appealed to him and when the child was born she was christened Georgiana. There were several light affairs which pleased him; he dared not become deeply involved as he had been with Perdita. His visits to Mrs Armistead were growing less and less frequent. He would always remember her with gratitude and he really believed that she was one of his few mistresses with whom he could remain friends, but he needed change; he needed variety. He sighed for the surrender of his dearest Duchess Georgiana of Devonshire, but while she remained one of his best friends she declined to become his mistress.

Life was full of excitement and passing as quickly as could be hoped. Politics with Burke, Fox and Sheridan; visiting tailors with Petersham; studying the arts of fencing and boxing with Angelo; going about the town by day and night–often incognito.

Those were the exciting times.

One night he with several of his friends attended a masquerade in the costume of a Spanish Grandee. Heavily disguised he always enjoyed luring people on to talk of the Prince or the King and sometimes he would reveal his identity but not at others.

On this particular occasion he saw a tall willowy girl in the costume of a nun and decided that she should be his partner. As he went to claim her a masked sailor stood in his way and told him to move off for the lady was not for him.

'That,' said the Prince, 'is where you are wrong, my dear fellow.'

'It is you who are wrong, fellow,' was the reply. 'Now you will leave us if you are wise.'

'It is you who need to be wise. Come.'

The Prince seized the nun about the waist, but the sailor had pushed him aside, and put his arm about her.

'Is that the manner in which you treat a nun?' asked the Prince.

'Your opinion was not asked!' was the retort.

The nun moved closer to the sailor and this annoyed the Prince. He believed that even disguised as he was all ladies should prefer him.

'And you, Madam,' he said, 'does your character fit the robes you wear as well as your charming shape does? I doubt it . . . I doubt it . . . indeed.'

'Sir, you are insulting a lady.'

'Sir, you are insulting me.'

The sailor let out a burst of laughter, which angered the Prince.

'Where did you find her?' asked the Prince. 'On Portsmouth Point?' As this was the notorious spot where prostitutes waited for the sailors the lady uttered a shrill protest and several other sailors came up to ask who this fellow was who was daring to insult the navy and their ladies.

One of the sailors moved menacingly towards the Prince, his attendants immediately closed round him, but the sailor escort of the nun came forward and struck the Prince in the chest. The Prince, well versed in fisticuffs by Angelo's expert tuition, immediately retaliated and a crowd gathered to see the fight.

There was a general uproar and constables were called. Everyone began talking at once and the ringleaders–the Spanish Grandee and the sailor–were seized and marched off to the watch house, much to the consternation of the Prince's attending squires.

But the Prince was in fact enjoying the adventure.

In the watch house he and the sailor were ordered to take off their masks.

The Prince did so with a flourish and the gasp of dismay which followed delighted him. It was the turn of the sailor; and there standing before the Prince was his brother William.

They stared at each other and burst out laughing.

'So, William, it is you!' cried the Prince.

'So, George, it is you!' echoed William.

They fell into each other's arms and embraced and laughed until the tears ran down their cheeks while the constables looked on, not knowing what to do.

'You young rip,' cried the Prince, 'what were you doing at a masquerade?'

'Exactly the same as you were.'

'And what were your intentions regarding that nun?'

'The same as yours, brother.'

This seemed so funny to the brothers that they could not stop laughing; and when the Prince's attendants arrived breathless and anxious at the watch house, the Prince cried out that he wished all the people concerned in this adventure to receive a guinea a piece to compensate them for their trouble.

The brothers went off arm in arm; but of course it was impossible to keep such an adventure secret; and since the King had commanded that nothing regarding the Prince's conduct should be held back from him, he eventually had an account of it.

He talked to the Queen about it. What was the world coming to? America lost; and the Prince appearing in brawls with his young brother. If the others went the way of the Prince of Wales, he did not know what would become of them all.

'I have not slept for ten nights, thinking of them. Not ten nights. You understand that, eh, what?'

The Queen nodded sadly. She understood too well.

There was no end to trouble, it seemed to the King that year.

Just as he had become resigned to the new ministry, Rockingham died and it was necessary to appoint a new Prime Minister. Fox–recognized to be the ablest man in the Government–naturally expected to be appointed. But the King would not have it and sent for Lord Shelburne. Those Whig supporters of Fox known as the Foxhounds showed their indignation by resigning, Fox at their head, and Burke and Sheridan–who had a minor post in the Government–among them. Fox, however, still held control over a considerable number of votes in the House of Commons and was in the strong position of holding the balance between North's opposition and the Government. The King knew that his wily enemy would not rest until he had ousted Shelburne from his place.

The wrangling went on as to how the ignoble peace with America should be settled; and that August a great family tragedy occurred. Little Alfred, who had been ailing since birth, died.

The King was desolate; so was the Queen; and the fact that little Octavius was so delicate added to their anxieties.

The Prince followed these political events with the utmost interest. And all during the trying times when the King was in conflict with Fox, the Prince was seen with him in public places–arm in arm with Fox, gambling with Fox, drinking with Fox.

As soon as he was of age he would openly side with Fox–and that meant, of course, against his father.

And so the King grew more and more melancholy; and the Queen wondered where it would all end; and she often said that she wished the Prince would come and talk to her as any son might be expected to visit his mother.

And the months of his minority were passing; and at last it was the year 1783 when, in August, he would be twenty-one.

Carlton House

'I have not slept for ten nights,' said the King. 'Ten nights. Twenty nights. Thirty nights. I doubt I shall ever sleep peacefully again. I wish I were eighty, or ninety, or dead.'

The Queen tried to comfort him. It was alarming when he talked in this way. But he had never allowed her to share his burdens so how could she do so now? She could only talk to him about the family–and God knew that was a depressing enough subject. Little Alfred gone; Octavius ailing; the Princes indulging in brawls . . . and the approaching majority of the Prince of Wales.

'Thirty-nine thousand pounds owing to tradesmen!' wailed the King. 'And a good proportion of it for wine . . . When I think of the way I ordered their diet . . . Why did my son become a drunkard?'

'It is because he is young.'

The King ignored her. 'I was young, Madam. But I was never a drunkard. Tailors, trivialities, jewellers . . . Wine and women . . . He thinks of nothing else. Can you make excuses for that, Madam, eh, what?'

The Queen looked sad. It was no use blaming her for the Prince's wildness.

'It is his companions, I doubt not.'

His companions! The King nodded. Fox–that man who haunted his dreams, who mocked him in his secret thoughts, the nephew of Sarah Lennox, the man with Stuart blood in his veins, who was a distant connection of his from the gay feckless charming side of the family. And the Prince had chosen this man for his companion. No, it was Fox who had chosen the Prince. The King knew why. To turn him against his father; to make a rake of him, a drunkard, a womanizer, a politician in direct opposition to his own father. And Sheridan was another as bad as Fox. The King could imagine their witty conversation, the barbs which would be directed against the Palace of Piety. Oh he knew what they called his Court; he knew how they jeered at him and the Queen. And the Prince with them!

It was intolerable. But what did he do when he wanted to buy his indiscreet letters from a play actress? Come to his father! What did he do when he wanted an allowance, his own establishment? Come to the King.

He was asking for £100,000 a year–and Fox would try to help him get it.

'He'll not have it,' said the King, his eyes protruding.

'What's that?' asked the Queen fearfully.

'One hundred thousand pounds a year he wants. To spend on wine and women.'

The Queen looked shocked.

'He'll not get it. He'll not get it. You understand me, eh, what?'

The Queen nodded sadly and the King was a little mollified. At least she caused him no anxiety.

He almost confided his worries to her over the Government. He had felt stricken since North had formed a coalition with Fox. The idea of his trusted 'good Lord North' going over to the enemy. A coalition with Fox! He had thought North loathed the man as he did. But North for all his good qualities was a weak man. But to side with that man whom he knew the King hated, whom he knew was working with the Prince!

He felt so angry about this sometimes that he told himself it would be better if he abdicated and let his son rule in his place. Then 'they' would see what would happen to the country.

'A strange thing,' said the King sadly, 'when a man's son is against him, eh, what?'

'It is not that he is against Your Majesty. He is in the hands of bad companions . . .'

She trailed off ineffectively. How could she comfort him? And when she saw him lashing himself into a state of anger her one thought was to do so.

'An establishment, he wants. He wants his own house. You know what that means, don't you, eh, what? It means that he'll set up in rivalry to St James's. There'll be two Courts before we know where we are! People are already likening this to the quarrel between my father and grandfather. They are saying it's a royal custom for fathers and sons to quarrel.'

'I suppose there are little upsets in all families.'

'This is the royal family. This is politics. Something of which you know nothing.'

No, thought the Queen, and whose fault is that? I wanted to know. I wanted to help you, but I have been kept in the background. I have been allowed to hold no position but be the mother of your children.

She was resentful, and yet in a way sorry for him. She did not love him. How could she when he had never taken her into his confidence, when she had always known he had married her under sufferance. Her compensation in life had come through her children, not through him.

But she was alarmed when she saw him working himself into a state of tension because she was terrified that one day he would lose his reason.

The King said: 'He wants his own establishment. Buckingham House is not good enough for him. I have decided he shall have Carlton House.'

'Carlton House! But no one has lived in it since your mother died. It's almost a ruin.'

'It's good enough for my lord Prince,' said the King vindictively.

Carlton House. A house of his own.

The Prince could not wait to take possession.

He went in with a group of friends; they ran up the staircases and in and out of the rooms. Cobwebs clung to the Prince's fine velvet coat, and rats hurried out of the way. Beetles scuttled across the floor. There were patches of damp on the walls and the banging of a door brought down a ceiling.

The Prince stood in the garden among the battered statues and folded his arms.

'It's a ruin,' he said, 'but I never saw a house with greater possibilities. Carlton House will in a few months be the most elegant residence in town.'

He brought Georgiana, Duchess of Devonshire, to look at the place. She caught his enthusiasm. She went from room to room and decided what furniture should be needed.

'Henry Holland is the architect we need,' said the Prince, 'and I'll have that Frenchman Gaubert for the inside decorations. And of one thing I am certain: there shall be no delay.'

Nor was there. The Prince was kept informed of how the work progressed–and it did so at a great pace.

No expense was spared. Why should it be? This was for the Prince of Wales and Parliament had voted a sum of £39,000 to pay his debts.

The Prince was happy and excited.

He had visited his Uncle Cumberland who had a house by the sea and he found the place enchanting. Brighthelmstone–Brighton for short. He spent his time supervising the alterations to Carlton House, designing his clothes, dancing, drinking with men like Fox and Sheridan, making love with his mistresses, gambling, horse-racing, attending prize fights and driving down to Brighton. He had designed his own phaeton with which he always used three horses one before the other like a team–a postilion mounted on the first and himself driving the other two. It was the speediest vehicle on the road.

Artists, mercers, tailors, furriers, shoemakers, waited on him daily. He discussed with Gaubert the pillars of porphyry he would have erected in the hall; he chose yellow Chinese silk to line the walls of his drawing room; he even had a bathroom installed and this was to lead from his bedchamber.

All the alterations he planned could not be completed before his twenty-first birthday, but the house must be made ready for his occupation by that time. And this would be done.

He was contented. Even when it was decided he should receive only £62,000 a year instead of the hoped for £100,000, he was not unduly dismayed. He would go on making plans for Carlton House for a long time to come–but in the meantime he would live there. At last his dream had come true. He had his own establishment. He was independent. Now he would do as he liked. Not even the King should curb the Prince of Wales.

In November 1783 three months after his twenty-first birthday, the Prince took his seat in the House of Lords.

It seemed as though the whole of London had come out to see him ride through the streets on his way from Carlton House.

And it was well worth it. The Prince was a dazzling spectacle dressed in black velvet embroidered with gold and sprinkled with pink spangles; the heels of his shoes were the same pink as the spangles; and his hair was frizzed and curled.

The people cheered him wildly. They were greatly interested in the work going on at Carlton House. The Prince was extravagant, but this gave work to thousands and the builders and mercers, the tailors and hairdressers could not speak too highly of him. He was setting new fashions, and fashions were good for trade.

The Lords–in the traditional scarlet and ermine–were astounded by the unconventional but spectacular appearance of their Prince.

His maiden speech was greeted with loyal cheers. All forward looking men, he believed, had their eyes fixed on him.

He existed, he announced, by the love, the friendship and the benevolence of the people. He would never forsake their cause as long as he lived.

When he left the House of Lords he went to the Commons where his friend Fox was speaking in defence of the East India Bill, the object of which was to put the Company under the jurisdiction of directors who should be selected by the Government.

Fox–whose Bill this was–spoke passionately in its favour, but he had a strong opponent in young William Pitt, a boy of about twenty-four who had all the fire and shrewdness of his father, the Great Commoner. The Prince knew that young Pitt had to be watched for the King was taking him into favour–largely because he was an opponent of Fox's.

When the Prince entered the Commons and took his place in the gallery all eyes were on him–and not only because of his black velvet and pink spangles; but because this was a gesture. He had come to hear Mr Fox, to applaud Mr Fox and to show parliament that he stood with Mr Fox against his enemies even though the chief of these was the King.

Mr Fox looked ruefully about his lodgings at St James's. He would have to sell every piece of furniture that was left if he was going to fight this election. He could no longer stave off his creditors; his gambling debts were enormous. If he were going to fight this Westminster election he must have the money to do so.

And there was no question of his fighting. He *must* fight.

This was one of the rare moments when he forced himself to think about money. Lucky Prince of Wales, he thought ruefully, with a parliament to take care of his debts.

But there was nothing he enjoyed like a fight–so he must call in the dealers and sell his home–and after that? He would trust to luck which had never really deserted him so far.

The Coalition had fallen on his East India Bill which although it had passed through the Commons was thrown out of the Lords. Fox knew how this had happened. The King had written to Lord Temple telling him to make it known that he would consider as his enemy any man who voted for the Bill. Although not all the lords were intimidated by this threat, the Bill was defeated by a narrow margin; and this had brought down the Government. With what joy had the King commanded Fox and North to return their seals of office!

The King had then summoned young William Pitt and appointed him Prime Minister.

'We have a schoolboy to rule us,' was the comment, for Pitt was twenty-four years of age.

But he was the son of the great Pitt and had already shown signs of having inherited his father's powers.

And then . . . Pitt demanded a dissolution of Parliament–and the result was this election which Fox could ill afford to fight.

While he sat wondering where he would go when he had sold up his home, his manservant announced a visitor.

He rose to greet Mrs Armistead.

She looked very elegant. There was no sign now of the lady's maid.

'My dear Lizzie,' said Fox, taking her hand and kissing it.

'I hope I have not called at an inconvenient time?'

'It is in fact most convenient. Had you called a few days later that would have been another matter. Then I might not have had a chair to offer you.'

'Ah, yes, this election. You have to fight it.'

He nodded. 'And to provide the means I shall sell all my possessions.'

'And then?'

'I shall win.'

'Of a certainty, but I was thinking of your home.'

Fox shrugged his shoulders.

'You will need somewhere to live.'

'I have friends.'

'Devonshire House?' she asked. 'But your stay there would be temporary. You must have a home, Mr Fox. There is one waiting for you at Chertsey.'

He rose and took her by the shoulders. He was visibly moved, which was touching in a man such as he was.

She looked at him steadily. 'I think,' she said slowly, 'that when I bought my home, when I accumulated my little fortune, I had something like this in mind. You are a brilliant man, Mr Fox, but a somewhat feckless one.'

He raised those bushy eyebrows which added to his unkempt appearance and said: 'My dear dear Lizzie, are you sure that you are not at this moment being guilty of the one feckless action of a hitherto sensible career?'

'I am quite sure, Mr Fox, because if you decide to come to Chertsey the purpose of my sensible career will have been achieved.'

He was silent for a moment and then he said: 'I cannot understand why this good fortune should be mine, for even if I lost the Westminster election I should still be one of the most fortunate men on earth.'

'But you will not lose, Mr Fox.'

'No, I shall win the Westminster election–and I hope I shall be worthy of my electorate . . . and my sweet Liz.'

There had never been such excitement. The whole of Westminster seemed to be in the streets and taking sides over the election. Georgiana, Duchess of Devonshire, canvassed for Fox wearing a cape of fox fur and carrying a fox muff, giving kisses in exchange for promised votes. The Prince of Wales toured the streets dressed in a blue frock coat and a buff waistcoat–dull for him but an exact replica of the clothes Fox wore for the House of Commons; and great was the excitement when Fox was returned.

The Prince determined to celebrate. It was to be a special occasion in Carlton House. Six hundred guests were invited–all Foxites. Nine marquees were erected in the grounds and four bands played constantly.

The Prince himself was a brilliant figure in pearl grey silk decorated with silver, and crowds gathered in the Mall to listen to the sounds of joy.

The King rode down the Mall on his way to open Parliament.

'What's the fuss at Carlton House?' he wanted to know.

'It is the Prince, Your Majesty. He is celebrating the victory of Mr Fox at Westminster.'

The young dog! The traitor to his father!

'He never loses a chance to plague me,' muttered the King. 'And Fox is still in the House. Thank God for good Mr Pitt. He'll be a match for him, eh, what? But why did I have a son like this? Who would have thought he would turn out to plague me.' The people scarcely glanced at him. They were all for the Prince. They liked the rip-roaring, hard-drinking, gambling lecher. They could not appreciate a good man. These people were a feckless crowd. 'I don't belong here,' thought the King. 'We ought never to have come.'

He fell to wondering what life would have been like if the English had never driven the Catholic Stuart away, or if they had decided to take him and send the Germans back to Germany. It could have happened in 1715 or more likely in 1745. But the Germans had won and they had stayed . . . and as a result he was the King of England and one day that reckless young fool, that gambling, that deep-in-debt pursuer of women would be their king.

'Serve them right,' said the King aloud. 'By God, serve them right.'

And the sounds of revelry from Carlton House kept echoing in his ears as he rode on to Parliament.

Epilogue

In the year 1800 Perdita Robinson lay in her bed and because she knew she was soon to leave it for ever, thought over the events which had made up her life.

Crippled after rheumatic fever, she had yet made a place for herself in society with her poems and novels and for a time had reigned over that salon in which she received distinguished guests who came attracted by her fame.

But this was the end; and she was not sorry. She was forty-two years old and still beautiful; but she felt she had lived long enough and she could never endure the prospect of old age.

Sometimes she thought of those days of glory when she had appeared in the Pantheon or the Rotunda in some fantastic concoction of ribbons and feathers for all to gaze at. The Prince's beloved mistress, the famous Perdita.

It was so long ago and she had ceased to regret, ceased to reproach. There had been a time when she had railed against a lover who had so quickly tired of her and gone to other women, who had given her but a mere pittance (for £500 a year seemed a pittance when her carriage alone had cost £200 to maintain). But all that was over.

Banastre Tarleton had been a good friend and had remained faithful all these years. It was for his sake that she had gone to France in winter and suffered so acutely from the dreadful cold at sea that she had contracted rheumatic fever which had left her paralysed.

Since then she had never walked again. Oddly enough–and this surprised her–she had borne her misfortune with fortitude. Looking back she wondered how she had endeavoured to be so calm, so philosophical. When she remembered all the men who had sought her favours she would tell herself she was a most remarkable woman.

Malden–dear Malden–who had loved her from the first; Cumberland who longed to add her to his retinue of mistresses; Mr Fox, to whom she had surrendered and, she would confess it, been a little piqued at the short duration of a relationship from which she had hoped for much; the Duc d'Orléans had sought her, had implored her to become his mistress; and she had refused him. Queen Marie Antoinette had sent her a purse which she herself had netted because she had refused Orléans. And that was long ago. The Revolution had come to France and Marie Antoinette had gone to the guillotine and Orléans had become known as Philippe Egalité . . . That was long ago.

She had seen a great deal happen about her, but now she remembered most the personal incidents. She had been fortunate. Maria, her daughter, had come to live with her when Mrs Darby had died and bore no resentment to her mother for deserting her when she was a child.

They had grown closer with the years and it was to Maria whom she read her verses and the chapters of her novels as they were written; and Maria herself had displayed a talent for literature.

As Tabitha Bramble, called by some the English Sappho, Perdita had had her salon; she had received her guests; and she had felt no bitterness–not even when she heard that Mr Fox had married Mrs Armistead and that they lived together afterwards as before in harmony.

Sometimes she wondered whether the Prince ever thought of her. She liked to imagine his recalling that gilded nest in Cork Street, those meetings on Eel Pie Island.

She would let herself dream that he came to her salon and knelt before her.

'I have come back, Perdita,' she imagined his saying. 'There has never been anyone to compare with you.'

And she found pleasure in acting scenes of reconciliation which she knew would never take place.

But there was Maria, dear Maria, who was happy to wait on her and she herself was not strong. Maria would not live long after her she was sure, and she was glad that she would get her £250 a year which had been a part of the settlement Mr Fox had arranged for her.

Mr Fox, dearest Banastre, they had been good friends to her. The Prince too.

Ah, the Prince! He was never far from the surface of her mind. How could he be? She constantly heard news of him. It was inevitable. His exploits were on everyone's lips. He must soon be the King of England.

She wished that she had been able to keep those letters he had written her. How she would have enjoyed reading them again! But they had been sold for the pension she now enjoyed and which would continue after her death to be paid to Maria. At least she need not worry about Maria–her dear daughter who had nursed her and loved her over the years of her affliction.

And to think that Maria had come from her union with the hated Mr Robinson who had long since through death ceased to trouble them.

Such, she thought, was life.

But it was death which was now her concern.

She called Maria to her, for she knew there was not much time left.

'Maria, my dearest daughter,' she said, 'I should like to be buried in the churchyard at old Windsor . . . close to the river. I have always loved the river.'

'Do not speak of death, Mamma,' begged Maria.

'My dearest, we cannot ignore it. It is coming soon, I know.'

She could not bear to see Maria's tears yet she could not prevent herself playing the part of the dying woman. It was natural for her to act. She knew this was so and wanted to explain to Maria. Her mind was wandering a little. She talked of Mr Garrick who had been so brusque but who had promised to teach her; she talked of Mr Fox and the Prince.

'Is that someone at the door, Maria? He's come. I knew he would come at the last.'

Maria shook her head, but Perdita was already seeing him–not as he was now but as a charming prince, eager and loving.

'Maria love, give me the paper heart . . . "Unalterable to my Perdita through life." He meant it then . . . He will remember . . .'

'No, Mamma,' whispered Maria gently.

But she did not hear.

She was quoting to herself the poem she had written and which Maria had always known referred to the Prince of Wales.

'Thou art no more my bosom friend,
Here must the sweet delusion end,
That charmed my senses many a year
Through smiling summers, winters drear.'

Ah, yes, thought Maria, here must the delusion end. The Prince of Wales deeply immersed in his own tempestuous life could scarcely be expected to be aware of the passing of one who had amused him briefly twenty years before.

Perdita was smiling. Perhaps, thought Maria, she believes he has come to her. Perhaps the sweet delusion is still with her.

Maria put her arms about her mother and Perdita lay in them, smiling as life passed away.

Cubase SX/SL
The Reference

Cubase SX/SL
The Reference

Windows Version

Order No. WZ00738
International Standard Book Number: 0-8256-2719-2

Exclusive Distributors:

Music Sales Corporation
257 Park Avenue South, New York, NY 10010 USA

Music Sales Limited
8/9 Frith Street, London W1D 3JB England

Music Sales Pty. Limited
120 Rothschild Street, Rosebery, Sydney, NSW 2018, Australia

Printed in the United States of America byVicks Lithograph and Printing Corporation

Authors: Steinberg Media Technologies AG and Mark Wherry
Publisher: Peter Gorges
Cover art: Schmidtdesign, Hamburg
Project editor: Reinhard Schmitz

Table of Contents

Introduction 15

1 Preface 17
1.1 Foreword 17
1.2 About this Book 19
1.3 How to Get in Touch with Steinberg 20

2 Cubase SX/SL Tutorial 21
2.1 A Better Way to Start the Day 22
2.2 Creating a New Project 24
2.3 Adding Tracks 26
2.4 Importing an Audio File 30
2.5 Getting the Tempo Right 32
2.6 Moving Events and Parts 35
2.7 Copying Events and Parts 35
2.8 Diving into Your Audio 37
2.9 Getting the Tempo Right (Again) 39
2.10 Making Twelve Bars Blue (or Orange) 41
2.11 Mix and Match 44
2.12 Adding an Insert Effect 52
2.13 Working with VST Instruments and MIDI Tracks 56
2.14 Adding Reverb as a Send Effect 62
2.15 Having Fun with MIDI Effects 64

Cubase SX/SL in Detail 69

3 Playback and the Transport Panel 71
3.1 Background 71
3.2 Operations 73
3.3 Options and Settings 76

4 Recording 79
4.1 Background 79
4.2 Basic Recording Methods 79
4.3 Audio Recording Specifics 82
4.4 MIDI Recording Specifics 93
4.5 Options and Settings 102

5	**The Project Window**	**107**
5.1	Background	107
5.2	Window Overview	109
5.3	Operations	117
5.4	Options	149
6	**Folder Tracks**	**153**
6.1	About Folder Tracks	153
6.2	Using Folders	153
7	**Using Markers**	**159**
7.1	About Markers	159
7.2	The Marker Window	160
7.3	Using the Marker Track	163
8	**Fades and Crossfades**	**169**
8.1	Creating Fades	169
8.2	The Fade Dialogs	172
8.3	Creating Crossfades	174
8.4	The Crossfade Dialog	177
8.5	Auto Fades and Crossfades	179
9	**The Mixer**	**183**
9.1	About this Chapter	183
9.2	Overview	184
9.3	The Audio Channel Strips	189
9.4	The MIDI Channel Strips	190
9.5	The Common Panel	191
9.6	The Master Section	192
9.7	The VST Outputs Window	193
9.8	Basic Mixing Procedures	194
9.9	Audio Specific Procedures	198
9.10	MIDI Specific Procedures	210
9.11	Utilities	212
10	**Audio Effects**	**219**
10.1	Background	219
10.2	Using Effects	221
10.3	The Included Effects	234
10.4	Installing and Managing Effect Plug-ins	236

11	**VST Instruments**	**241**
11.1	Introduction	241
11.2	Activating and Using Instruments in Cubase SX/SL	242
11.3	A1 Synthesizer	245
11.4	VB-1 Bass Synth	256
11.5	LM-7 Drum Machine	257
11.6	JX16 Synthesizer	260
11.7	CS40 Synthesizer	269
11.8	The Neon Synthesizer	271
11.9	LM-9 Drum Machine	273
12	**Surround Sound (Cubase SX only)**	**277**
12.1	Background	277
12.2	Window Overview	279
12.3	Operations	281
13	**Automation**	**291**
13.1	Background	291
13.2	Automation Subtrack Operations	294
13.3	Using Write/Read Automation	299
13.4	Working with Automation Curves	302
13.5	Tips and Common Methods	309
13.6	Options and Settings	309
14	**Remote Controlling the Mixer**	**311**
14.1	Background	311
14.2	Operations	311
14.3	Remote Control Device Specifics	314
15	**Audio Processing and Functions**	**329**
15.1	Background	329
15.2	Audio Processing	330
15.3	Applying Plug-ins (Cubase SX only)	347
15.4	The Offline Process History Dialog	349
15.5	Detect Silence	352
15.6	The Spectrum Analyzer (Cubase SX only)	355
15.7	Statistics (Cubase SX only)	357
16	**The Sample Editor**	**359**
16.1	Background	359
16.2	Opening the Sample Editor	359
16.3	Window Overview	359
16.4	Operations	363

16.5 Options and Settings 374

17 The Audio Part Editor 377

17.1 Background 377
17.2 Opening the Audio Part Editor 377
17.3 Window Overview 378
17.4 Operations 381
17.5 Common Methods 382
17.6 Options and Settings 384

18 Working with Hitpoints and Slices 385

18.1 Background 385
18.2 Using Hitpoints 385
18.3 Editing Hitpoints 388
18.4 Creating Slices 394
18.5 Creating Groove Quantize Maps 395
18.6 Divide Audio Events 395
18.7 Using the Close Gaps Function 396

19 The Pool 397

19.1 Background 397
19.2 Window Overview 399
19.3 Operations 402
19.4 Options and Settings 418

20 MIDI Devices and Patches 419

20.1 About Program Change and Bank Select 419
20.2 Opening the MIDI Device Manager 420
20.3 Installing a MIDI Device 421
20.4 Selecting a Patch for an Installed Device 423
20.5 Renaming Patches in a Device 424
20.6 Defining a New Device 424
20.7 Exporting and Importing Device Setups 428

21 MIDI Realtime Parameters and Effects 429

21.1 Introduction 429
21.2 The Inspector—General Handling 429
21.3 Basic Track Settings 430
21.4 Track Parameters 432
21.5 MIDI Effects 436
21.6 The Available Effects 439
21.7 Managing Plug-ins 462
21.8 The Channel Section 463
21.9 Merge MIDI in Loop 464

22	**MIDI Processing and Quantizing**	**467**
22.1	Introduction	467
22.2	Quantizing	468
22.3	Other MIDI Menu Functions	476
22.4	Dissolve Part	481
23	**The MIDI Editors**	**485**
23.1	About Editing MIDI	485
23.2	Opening a MIDI Editor	486
23.3	The Key Editor—Overview	487
23.4	Key Editor Operations	491
23.5	The Drum Editor—Overview	509
23.6	Drum Editor Operations	512
23.7	Working with Drum Maps	514
23.8	Using Drum Name Lists	522
23.9	The List Editor—Overview	522
23.10	List Editor Operations	524
23.11	The Score Editor—Overview (Cubase SL only)	529
23.12	Score Editor Operations (Cubase SL only)	531
23.13	Common MIDI Editor Options and Settings	546
24	**The Logical Editor, Transformer and Input Transformer**	**549**
24.1	Introduction	549
24.2	Opening the Logical Editor	550
24.3	Window Overview	551
24.4	Selecting a Preset	551
24.5	Setting Up Filter Conditions	552
24.6	Selecting a Function	561
24.7	Specifying Actions	563
24.8	Performing the Logical Editing	567
24.9	Working with Presets	567
24.10	The Input Transformer	568
25	**The Tempo Track Editor**	**571**
25.1	Background	571
25.2	Opening the Tempo Track Editor	571
25.3	Window Overview	572
25.4	Operations	574
25.5	Options and Settings	579
25.6	The Beat Calculator	580

26	**The Project Browser**	**583**
26.1	Background	583
26.2	Opening the Project Browser	583
26.3	Window Overview	583
26.4	Navigating in the Browser	584
26.5	Customizing the View	585
26.6	About the Sync Selection Option	586
26.7	Editing Audio Tracks	586
26.8	Editing MIDI Tracks	588
26.9	Editing Automation Tracks	591
26.10	Editing the Video Track	592
26.11	Editing the Marker Track	592
26.12	Editing the Tempo Track	593
26.13	Editing Time Signatures	594
27	**Working with System Exclusive Messages**	**595**
27.1	Introduction	595
27.2	Bulk Dumps	595
27.3	Recording System Exclusive Parameter Changes	598
27.4	Editing System Exclusive Messages	598
28	**Export Audio Mixdown**	**601**
28.1	Background	601
28.2	Mixing Down to an Audio File	601
28.3	File Format Specifics	603
29	**Synchronization**	**613**
29.1	Background	613
29.2	Window Overview	619
29.3	Operations	619
29.4	Options	625
30	**VST System Link**	**629**
30.1	Introduction	629
30.2	Preparations	629
30.3	Activating VST System Link	635
30.4	Application Examples	641
31	**Video**	**645**
31.1	Background	645
31.2	Operations	645
31.3	Options	648

32 ReWire 649
32.1 Introduction 649
32.2 Launching and Quitting 650
32.3 Activating ReWire Channels 651
32.4 Using the Transport and Tempo Controls 652
32.5 How the ReWire Channels Are Handled in Cubase SX/SL 652
32.6 Routing MIDI via ReWire2 653
32.7 Considerations and Limitations 654

33 File Handling 655
33.1 File Operations 655
33.2 Options and Settings 668

34 Key Commands 671
34.1 Background 671
34.2 The Key Commands Dialog 672
34.3 Setting Up Tool Modifier Keys 678

Appendix 679

A Menu Reference 681
A.1 About this Chapter 681
A.2 File Menu 681
A.3 Edit Menu 685
A.4 Project Menu 691
A.5 Audio Menu 693
A.6 MIDI Menu 698
A.7 Scores Menu (Cubase SX only) 703
A.8 Pool Menu 703
A.9 Transport Menu 707
A.10 Devices Menu 709
A.11 Window Menu 711
A.12 Help Menu 712

B Parameters of the Included Effect Plug-ins 713
B.1 DoubleDelay 713
B.2 ModDelay 714
B.3 DaTube 716
B.4 Overdrive 717
B.5 QuadraFuzz 718
B.6 SPL DeEsser (Cubase SX only) 722
B.7 Dynamics 724

B.8 VST Dynamics 729
B.9 MIDI Gate 731
B.10 StepFilter 734
B.11 Chorus 737
B.12 Flanger 738
B.13 Metalizer 739
B.14 Phaser 741
B.15 Ringmodulator 742
B.16 Rotary 744
B.17 Symphonic 746
B.18 Tranceformer 748
B.19 Bitcrusher 750
B.20 Chopper 751
B.21 Grungelizer 752
B.22 Vocoder 753
B.23 SMPTE Generator (Cubase SX only) 758
B.24 Reverb A 760
B.25 Reverb B 761
B.26 Mix6To2 (Cubase SX only) 762

C Parameters of Cubase 5 Effect Plug-ins 763

C.1 Introduction 763
C.2 Autopole 763
C.3 MIDI Comb 767
C.4 Mysterizer 770
C.5 Phatsync 773
C.6 Ring Modulator 776
C.7 subBASS 778
C.8 Distortion 779
C.9 Chopper2 780
C.10 Reverb 782
C.11 Reverb 32 783
C.12 Metalizer2 784
C.13 Tranceformer2 785
C.14 Karlette 787

D Parameters of Earlier VST Effect Plug-ins 789

D.1 Introduction 789
D.2 Auto Panner 789
D.3 Choirus and Choirus 2 790
D.4 ESpacial! 790
D.5 Electro Fuzz 791
D.6 Scopion 792
D.7 Stereo Echo 792

D.8 StereoWizard 793
D.9 WunderVerb 3 794

E Frequently Asked Questions **795**

Index **797**

Introduction

1 Preface

1.1 Foreword

Allow me to start off this foreword with a quote that I discovered on the Cubase.net forum on May 27, 2002, just two weeks after the release of Cubase SX:

"The Mixer setup ... totally easy to set up ANY way you want. The Project window ... same ... Everything so logical and easy to find out! Now I'm not working under-cover for Steinberg or anything, but I've waited a long time for a sequencer like this. This is the sequencer of 2002. Thank you Steinberg!"

"I've waited a long time for a sequencer like this." The gracious author of these lines wasn't the only one to have awaited the arrival of Cubase SX. Here in Hamburg, the Steinberg crew was no less eager in its anticipation.

The story of Cubase began in 1989 on Atari ST. Though with MIDI only, b&w visuals, 8 MHZ processor clock, and 4 RAM MB, Cubase's appointments were few, it nonetheless ushered in a revolution in computer-assisted music making.

Cubase evolved at a hypersonic pace. We soon ported it to the Macintosh and, in 1992, to the personal computer. Then we endowed it with audio—at first just two tracks to be followed later by the sensational number of four tracks courtesy of ProTools.

VST Cubase first saw the light of day at the 1996 Frankfurt music fair. Then came VST effects plug-ins, followed by virtual instruments such as synthesizers, pianos and guitars. Offering a complete studio with a mixing console, instruments and effects, all in real time and in professional audio quality, VST was a dream come true for many musicians.

I like to compare software with urban development. A group of founding fathers spot an inviting meadow and put up a few houses here, a few bridges there. Soon the village confines become too cramped and narrow. Civil engineers add a thoroughfare, a tunnel, a railway station. The village grows, the town becomes a city. Thousands of cars motor down teeming streets originally designed for a few horse-drawn carriages. Seeing this urban sprawl makes one want to wipe the slate clean and start over again, factoring in all past experiences and foreseeable future problems.

That's the point we had arrived at in 1998. VST Cubase's excellent functionality had made it the tool of choice for a huge community of musicians. However, it carried with it the burdens of its past—a decade's worth of too many concepts and compromises.

When we set out to develop Cubase SX/SL, we were certainly keen to apply our experiences. But we were equally eager to implement our customers' experiences, suggestions and wishes. The Internet affords us the opportunity to keep in touch with hundreds of users and learn their opinions on what's good and what's not.

And we pledge to take customers' wishes to heart in the further development of Cubase SX/SL, doing everything in our power to satisfy them. For this reason, I urge you to take part in Cubase.net forums at Steinberg.net. Tell us what you like about Cubase SX/SL and what we can do to make it even better.

This book is your ticket to the world of Cubase SX/SL. Explore it with an inquisitive mindset. Experiment freely, even if your attempts culminate in unusual or even bizarre sounds. After all, a new program is a new world and this book will help you chart your voyage of discovery.

Here's wishing you lots of fun and success in your musical endeavors; I hope that for you too, Cubase SX/SL will prove to be the sequencer that you've been waiting for.

Manfred Rürup

CEO Steinberg Media Technologies AG

1.2 About this Book

This book is based on the original documentation of Cubase SX/SL and consists of the following parts:

Introduction

The majority of this section comprises a hands-on tutorial by Wizoo author Mark Wherry; it grants you insight into many areas of Cubase SX/SL. As you follow along and create an example song, you will learn how to handle key features and functions with ease. The author also lets you in on an advanced trick or two.

Cubase SX/SL in Detail

This is the main section offering extensive explanations of Cubase SX/SL parameters, functions and techniques.

Appendix

In this section you'll find a chapter's worth of answers to frequently asked questions and detailed documentation on the following topics:

- Cubase SX/SL menus
- The parameters of effects plug-ins that ship with Cubase SX/SL
- The parameters of effects plug-ins that ship with Cubase VST 5.x
- The parameters of effects plug-ins that shipped with earlier versions of VST Cubase

1.3 How to Get in Touch with Steinberg

A list of key Steinberg Internet links pops up when you open the submenu "Steinberg on the Web" from the Help menu. When you select one of the options, your Web browser launches and the given Web site appears in its window.

You have the following options if you choose to use one of the direct links or select the commands "Steinberg Home Page" or "Users Forum":

- You can access the "Knowledge Base" to get information on technical support, answers to frequently asked questions, and so forth.
- You can send emails to the Steinberg support team.
- You can view product news and the latest info on product updates.
- The menu option "Users Forum" takes you directly to the www.cubase.net Web site. This is where you can get touch with users of Steinberg products all over the whole world and swap info, insights and opinions.

2 Cubase SX/SL Tutorial

Cubase is one of the most advanced music production packages available, yet it's surprisingly intuitive and rarely gets in the way of actually making music. Having a reference manual is a great help, especially for all those 'what does that do again?' moments. But to make it even better, we've added a hands-on tutorial to help you get the most from Cubase.

If you want a tutorial to guide you through a few basics, the process of recording a song and some bouncing, be sure to check out Wizoo's Cubase SX Quick Start. However, in the tutorial you're about to read, we'll cover topics such as Key Commands, Hitpoints, MIDI plug-ins, and share some interesting tips and tricks along the way.

You don't need to be a Cubase guru in order to follow this introduction—it's written with both beginners and intermediate users in mind. The only thing assumed is that you have Cubase set up and working properly with your MIDI and audio hardware. Don't worry if you haven't got this far, though, since the Getting Started manual that came in your Cubase box, or the later chapters of this very book, will be able to help you out.

I hope you have as much fun with Cubase as I do, and also that this introduction helps you learn a few interesting things along the way.

Mark Wherry

2.1 A Better Way to Start the Day

Before we get started, let's consider an aspect of Cubase you'll be confronted with all the time: What happens when the application first loads. By default, you're presented with a blank screen, and while there might not seem anything wrong with this, there are so many other options available.

1. **Run Cubase as normal.**
2. **Select "File > Preferences."**
3. **Display the User Interface panel by selecting User Interface in the left-hand list.**

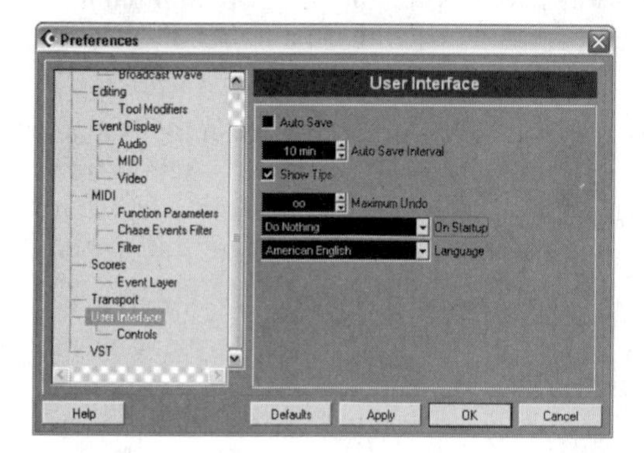

4. **You can choose from a variety of start-up behaviours by clicking on the On Startup pop-up menu.**

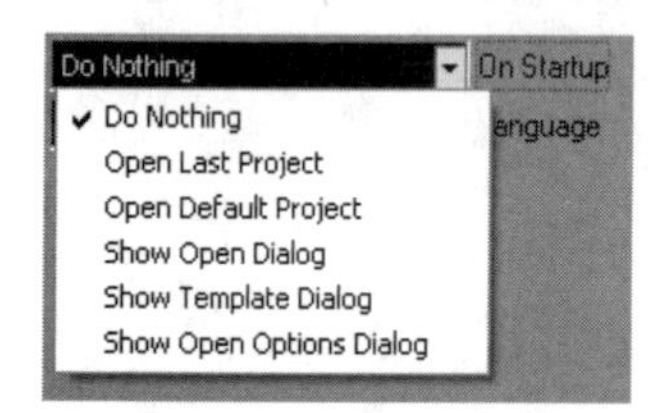

As you can see, the default option really is Do Nothing, but fortunately Cubase also provides five other possibilities, including Open Last Project, which automatically opens the last Project you were working on when you next run Cubase.

If you've ever used the older Cubase VST, the Open Default Project option will be very familiar to you: Every time Cubase SX/SL starts it will load a Project File named "default.cpr," which should be saved in the same folder as the Cubase application. (For most users, this will be "C:\Program Files\Steinberg\Cubase SX/SL.")

Show Open Dialog displays a file selector for you to load a Project from disk (just like selecting "File > Open") and Show Template Dialog starts the process for creating a new Project (as if you'd selected "File > New").

The four options described so far are all perfectly useful, but my personal favourite is the fifth option, Show Open Options Dialog. The Open Document Options window provides access to every function you'd need when you run Cubase at the start of a session. Creating a new Project, opening an existing file, or choosing a recent Project are presented right in front of you every time you run the application—what more could you ask for?

- It's worth noting that you can only see the Open Document Options window when you first run the program.

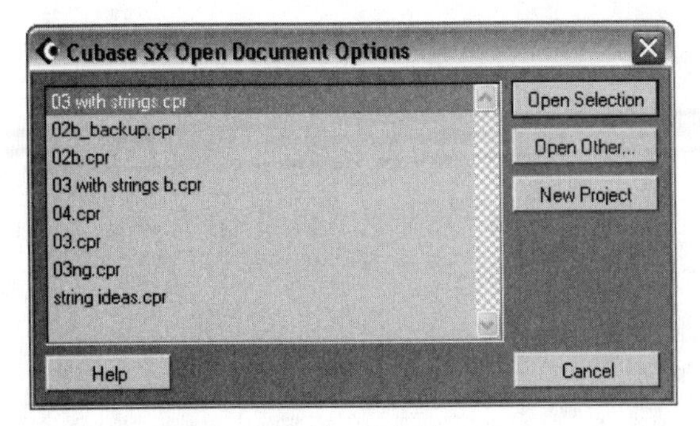

The Open Document Options window

Once you've chosen a start-up behaviour:

1. **Click OK.**
2. **Close and restart Cubase so you can experience the new behaviour for yourself.**

- When you make changes in the Preferences window, the new settings apply globally to Cubase and are totally Project independent—note that we didn't even have a Project open when changing the start-up behaviour. This means that settings from the Preference window don't get saved with the Project, and apply automatically to any Project you open in Cubase.

2.2 Creating a New Project

Having configured Cubase to start up exactly the way we want, let's go ahead and create a new Project. Depending on which start-up behaviour you picked, the new Project procedure may start automatically (if you chose Open Template Dialog) or you might need to click New Project in the Open Document Options window. Otherwise, select "File > New" or press [Control]+[N] to create a new Project.

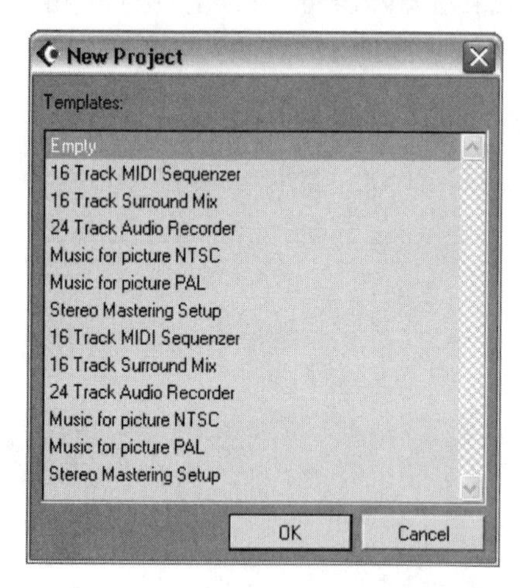

In the New Project window, Cubase offers a range of templates that can be used as starting points when creating a new Project.

I don't want to dismiss templates altogether because they can be extremely useful. For example, a common starting point for my own musical endeavours involves simply playing The Grand (a grand piano VST Instrument from Steinberg) via my MIDI keyboard and trying out ideas through improvisation. If I had to start from scratch every time, it would involve creating a MIDI Track, opening the VST Instruments window, loading The Grand and routing the MIDI Track to play through The Grand. None of this is particularly difficult, of course, but it means a good minute or two of time is wasted on technology rather than creativity.

Instead, I do this once, select "File > Save As Template" and call it something like "Mark's Grand Opening." Now, every time I want this for my starting point, I simply choose "Mark's Grand Opening" as my template from the New Project window and I'm ready to become the next Liberache. But I digress.

However, for this tutorial select Empty and click OK, which will provide a completely blank canvas to add Tracks and configure the set-up specifically for this particular Project.

After this, the Select directory window will appear asking you to set the Project Folder for the new Project.

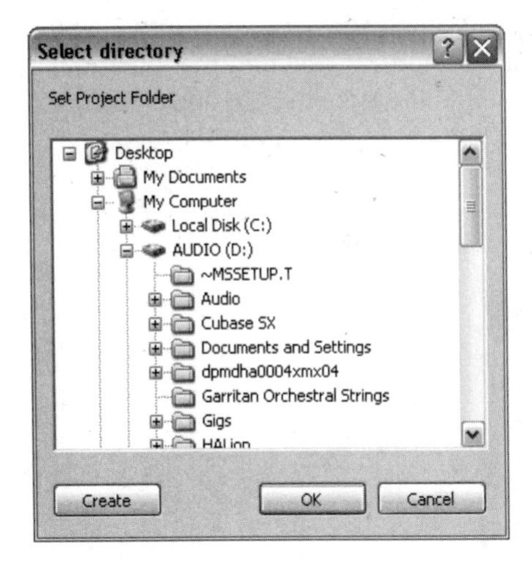

1. **Highlight the directory or drive where you want a new Project Folder to be created.**

   Although it's possible for Projects to share the same folder, this really isn't a good idea since it could easily cause confusion. As a general rule, always create a new Project folder for every Project.

2. **Click the Create button.**
3. **In the Select/Create New Directory window, type in a suitable name and click OK or press [Return].**

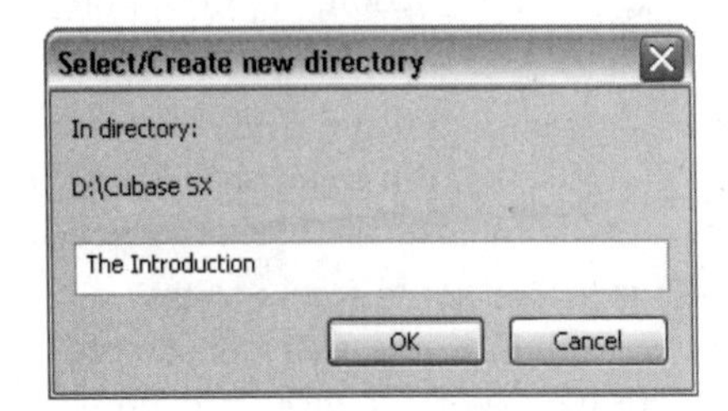

4. **Make sure the folder you just created is highlighted and click OK.**

Cubase should now present you with an empty Project window to start making music in.

At this point, it's worth 'interrupting the broadcast' for a few words about Project Files and Folders. When you create a new Project, Cubase guides you through the process of creating and assigning a new folder for the Project. This folder is known as the Project Folder and contains a number of subfolders (which are created automatically) for storing any audio files we import or record, along with various other Project-specific information.

However, the one thing that doesn't get created automatically when you start a new Project is a Project file, which is the file that actually stores all the information about a Project we create in Cubase. For this reason, saving a Project file right after creating a new Project is a good habit to get into.

1. **Select "File > Save" or press [Control]+[S].**
2. **In the file selector, navigate to your new Project Folder.**

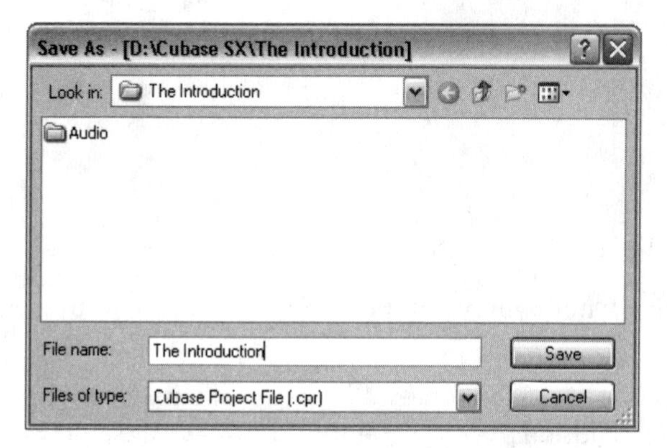

3. **Type in a suitable filename and click OK or press [Return].**

- It makes sense to keep all the files relating to a Project in the Project Folder. Not only does this keep the organisation of your Projects neat and tidy, but it makes backup much easier and reduces the chances of accidentally losing important files.

2.3 Adding Tracks

The first thing you need to do with an empty Project is to add some Tracks to the Project window for recording and importing music onto. It turns out that Cubase provides many methods of adding new Tracks, allowing us to choose the most convenient to suit our way of working. While we won't be looking at all the possible ways of accessing every feature we explore in this tutorial, I'm going to make an exception with adding Tracks to demonstrate some other, more interesting features along the way.

The first method of adding a Track to a Project is to select from the "Project > Add Track" submenu on the Cubase menu bar.

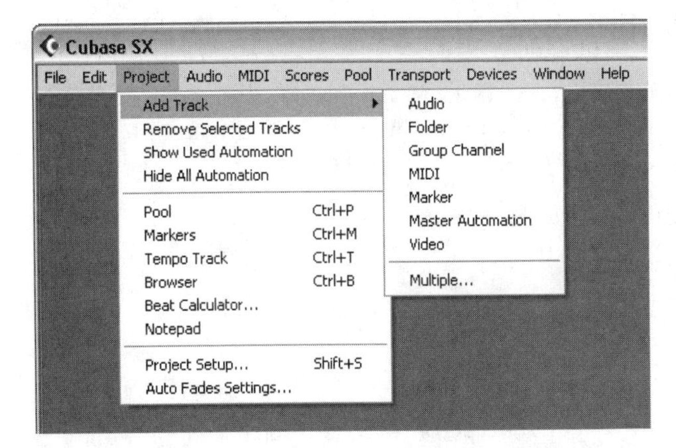

Notice that Cubase supports many different types of Tracks for handling various types of music and video data. For this tutorial we need to create a new Audio Track, so choose "Project > Add Track > Audio" to add a new Audio Track to the Project.

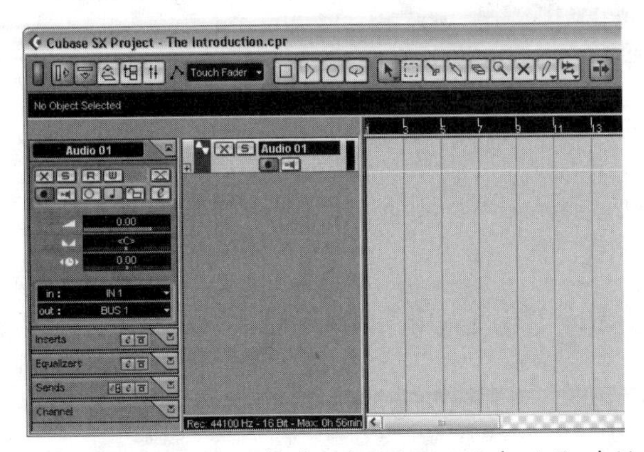

A new Audio Track is added to the Project window's Track List

The column to the left of the Track List is known as the Inspector and provides various controls and parameters specific to the currently selected Track.

Since we're going to be looking at other ways of adding Tracks to the Project window, delete the Track we just added by making sure it's selected (a selected Track will be highlighted in a very light blue) and chose "Project > Remove Selected Tracks".

2.3.1 Adding Multiple Tracks

Quite often you'll want to add more than one Track to the Project, and the Add Multiple Tracks command can be a real timesaver in these situations. To add multiple Tracks to the Project window select "Project > Add Track > Multiple."

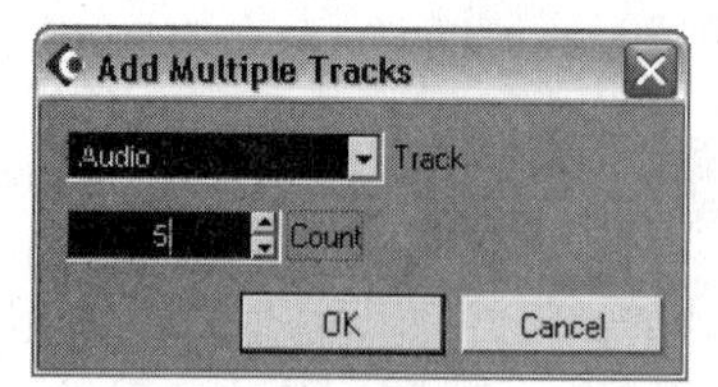

In the Add Multiple Tracks window, select the type of Track you want to add to the Project (in this case, Audio), enter the number of Tracks you want to add in the Count field (let's say five), and click OK.

With several Tracks on the Project window, it's worth noting that selecting multiple Tracks on the Track List works in exactly the same way as selecting multiple files on your computer's Desktop. For example, you can [Control]-click Tracks to select them one by one, or [Shift]-click a Track to select from the currently selected Track to the Track you [Shift]-clicked on.

Using whichever method of selecting Tracks suits you best, select all the Tracks on the Project window and delete them in the same way as before ("Project > Remove Selected Tracks").

2.3.2 Adding Tracks Using the Quick Menu

When you click the right mouse button in Cubase, the Quick Menu is displayed. The Quick Menu is a neat pop-up menu that offers a range of options relevant to the current position of the mouse. For example, try right-clicking in the Event Display (the large grey area of the Project window) and keep a mental picture of the menu you see. Click outside of the Quick Menu to close it and now right-click in the Track List instead—notice how you see a completely different menu.

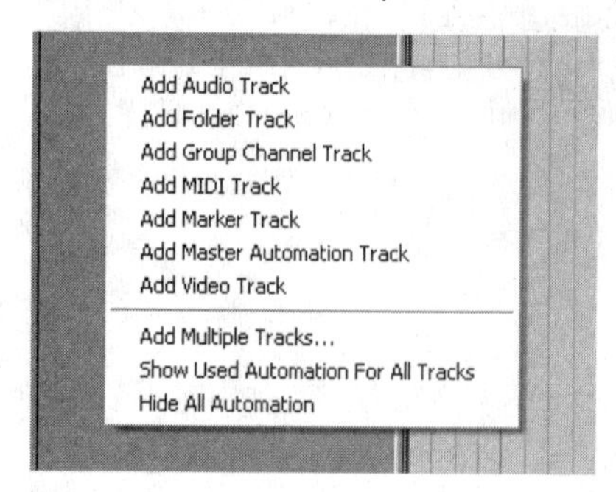

Since Cubase recognises that you're right-clicking in the Track List, it senses you might want to create a Track and therefore provides all the commands from the "Project > Add Track" submenu, which behave in exactly the same way—which is to say that they create Tracks.

2.3.3 Adding Tracks Using the Double-Click Trick

A quick way to create a single Track is to double-click in an empty space in the Track List—try it now. When there are no Tracks in the Track List, Cubase will always create a MIDI Track first, which is very useful, except in cases where you don't want a MIDI Track. Hit the [Backspace] key to delete the Track.

However, the double-click trick isn't a lost cause. When you have Tracks of different types in the Track List, double-clicking in an empty area of the Track List will create a Track of the same type as the one currently selected in the list. So if an Audio Track is currently selected, double-clicking in an empty space will add a new Audio Track to the bottom of the Track List—one to remember.

2.3.4 Adding Tracks Using Key Commands

The final way of creating a New Track is by assigning Key Commands to the Add Track commands. Key Commands basically enable you to trigger features in Cubase with user-defined keyboard shortcuts.

1. Select "File > Key Commands" to open the Key Commands window.

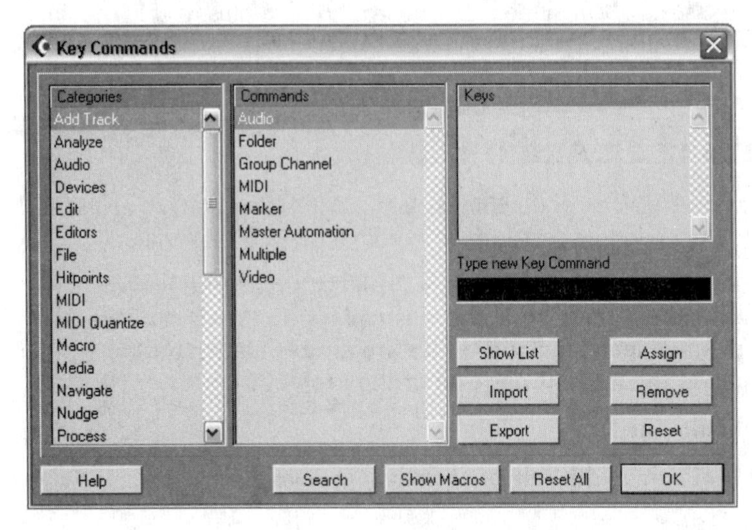

2. The Add Track category should be selected by default. If it isn't, simply click Add Track in the Categories list to highlight it.

3. **Select the command in the Commands column that you want to assign a keyboard shortcut to—in this case, Audio.**
4. **Click in the black box underneath the "Type new Key Command" label.**
5. **Press the keyboard shortcut you want to assign to the command—I use [Alt]+[A].**
6. **Click the Assign button.**
7. **If the keyboard shortcut you've entered is already assigned to a command, you'll see an alert asking if you want to reassign the Key Command. Click Cancel, try another keyboard shortcut and click Assign again until you don't see this alert.**

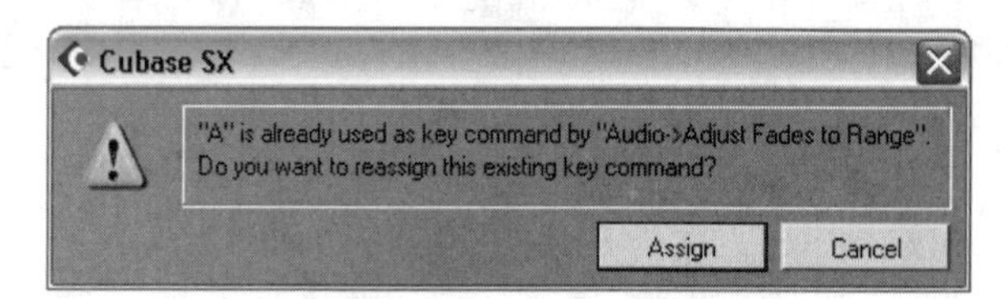

8. **Click OK when you've finished to close the Key Commands window.**
9. **Now, press [Alt]+[A] (or the keyboard shortcut you assigned) to add an Audio Track to the Project window.**

Key commands can be a great way of making Cubase more convenient for the tasks you carry out regularly. If you explore the Key Commands window, you'll notice practically ever action in Cubase can be assigned a keyboard shortcut; plus, you'll also find some 'hidden' commands that only exist as Key Commands.

2.4 Importing an Audio File

The starting point for a new musical production is often a drum loop; so with an Audio Track created on the Project window, let's import a drum loop into the Project.

1. **Press [.] on the numeric keypad. This sets the Project Cursor (the horizontal line that moves across the screen while the music plays) to the start of the first bar, which is useful since imported audio files are always placed on the selected Audio Track at the current position of the Project Cursor.**
2. **Select "Import > Audio File."**
3. **Put the CD-ROM that came with this book into your computer.**

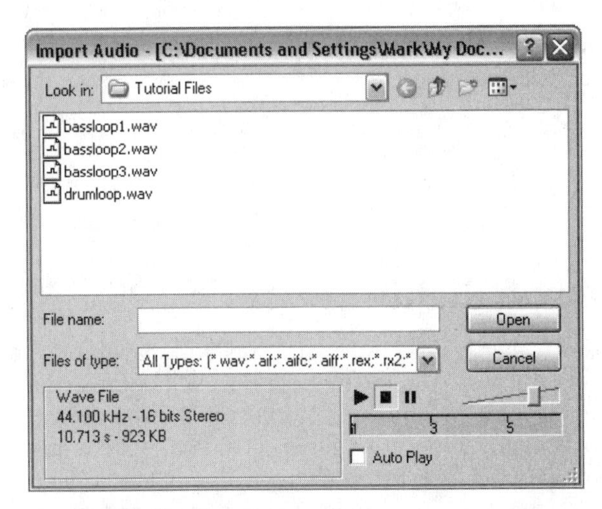

4. **In the file selector, locate the "Tutorial Files" folder on the CD-ROM and open the "drumloop.wav" file.**

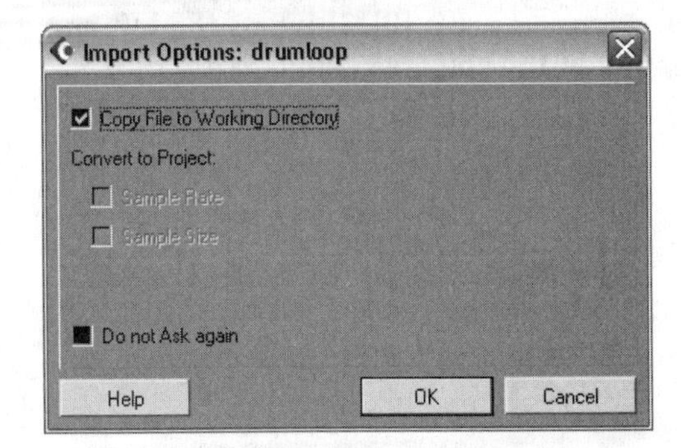

5. **In the Import Options window, make sure that "Copy File to Working Directory" is activated and click OK. Cubase will now transfer the file from the CD-ROM to the Project Folder. It's always a good idea to do this so a Project Folder always contains every file needed to open that particular Project.**

The imported audio file should now appear as an Audio Event at the first bar of the Audio Track on the Project window.

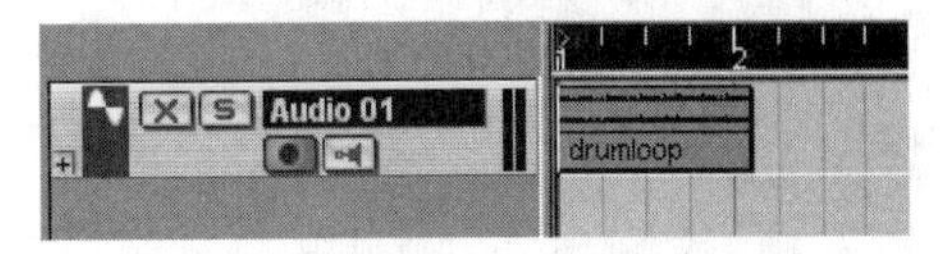

You might want to adjust the horizontal and vertical zoom sliders, which are located at the bottom right of the Project window, if the audio event appears too small for comfortable viewing.

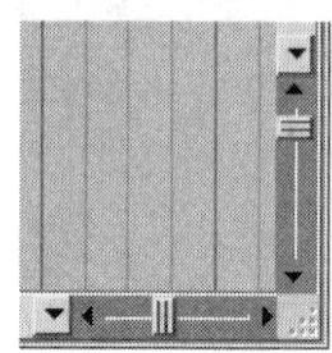

2.5 Getting the Tempo Right

If you make sure the Click button is activated on the Transport Panel and play the Project, you'll notice that the loop is out of time with the metronome click because the Project's current tempo is different to the tempo of the loop. To overcome this problem, what we need to do is find out the tempo of the loop and either set the Project's tempo to the same value, or change the tempo of the loop to match the tempo of the Project. While this sounds potentially complicated, Cubase actually makes it very easy for us.

1. **Select the imported Audio Event on the Project window.**
2. **Choose "Transport > Locators to Selection" or press [P]. This sets the left and right locators to the start and end points of the selected Audio Event.**

The left and right locators are two markers that have many uses in Cubase, including setting the boundaries for Cycle Playback mode, or, in this case, specifying the length of an Audio Event before manipulating its tempo in Cubase.

3. **Double-click the selected Audio Event to open the Sample Editor.**

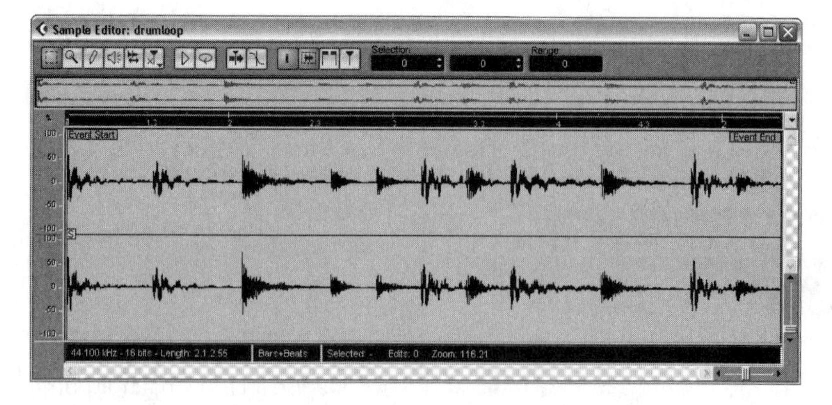

4. **Click the Hitpoint Mode button on the Sample Editor's toolbar to activate Hitpoint Mode.**

5. **Notice how hitpoints are created where beats are detected in the audio event. If you've ever used Propellerhead's ReCycle application, this should look very familiar.**

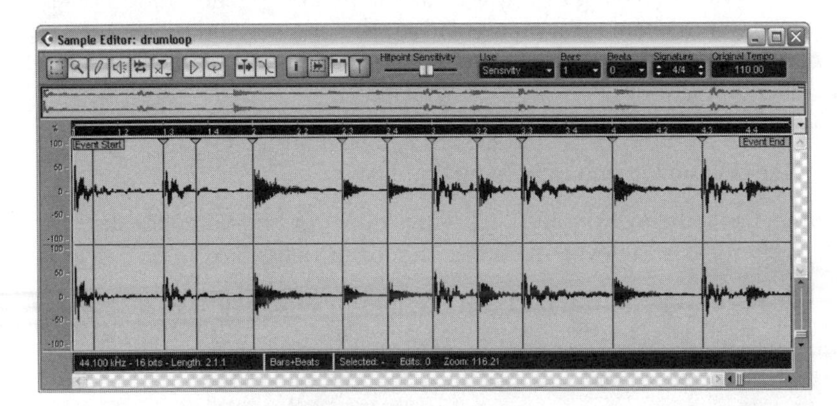

6. **If Cubase doesn't appear to have identified all the beats correctly, make sure that Use is set to Sensitivity and drag the Hitpoint Sensitivity slider to adjust the threshold at which beats are detected. Dragging this slider to the left creates fewer hitpoints, while dragging it to the right creates more hitpoints. In this case, the default setting should be fine, but when dealing with other material, you basically want to make sure every beat has a hitpoint without filling the screen with them.**

7. **Alongside the Hitpoint Sensitivity slider, make sure Bars is set to 1 (as this is a one-bar drum loop), Beats is set to 0 (since it's a full one-bar drum loop) and Signature is set to 4/4 (as the loop is clearly in 4/4 time). With everything set correctly, Cubase should identify that the Original Tempo of the loop is 110.00 bpm (beats per minute).**

8. **At this point, you could simply set the tempo of the Project to 110 and the loop would play in time with the Project's tempo. However, if we wanted to make the tempo of the loop flexible, so it could theoretically playback at any tempo, this requires just one extra click of the mouse.**

9. **Select "Audio > Hitpoints > Create Audio Slices."**

Cubase will now close the Sample Editor and slice the Audio Event into smaller Audio Events, according to the Hitpoints we just created. This gives the loop a degree of tempo independence, without having to play the loop at different pitches, time-stretching, or any other forms of mathematical manipulation. The original Audio Event is replaced by an Audio Part on the Project window, which contains all the newly created Audio Events making up the loop.

The start and end points of Audio Parts (and Events) can be adjusted by dragging the square handles at the bottom left and right-hand corners.

If you play the Project with the metronome click active now, you should notice that the two are perfectly in time. This is clever, of course, but it gets better.

1. **Disable the Master button on the Transport Panel if it's highlighted.**

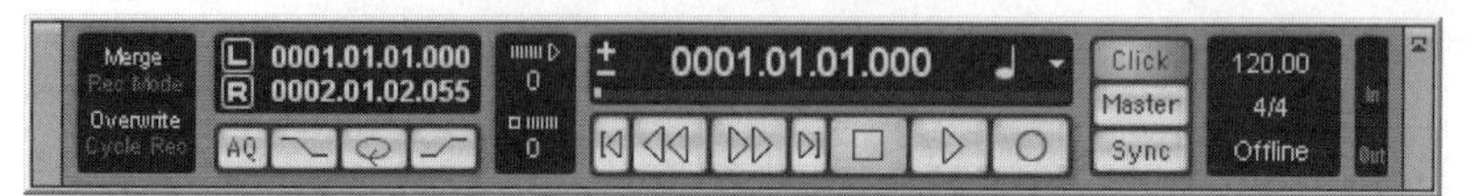

When the Master button is active on the Transport Panel, Cubase uses a tempo set by the Tempo Track instead of the tempo you type directly into the Transport Panel by clicking the current value, typing a new tempo and pressing [Return]. The Tempo Track is a hidden Track that can be edited in the Tempo Track window and allows you specify tempo and time signature changes.

When the Master button is disabled on the Transport Panel, Cubase ignores the Tempo Track and uses what's known as the Rehearsal tempo instead. If your Project isn't going to contain any tempo or time signature changes, it can often be easier just to use the Rehearsal tempo, which is what we're going to do here.

2. **Click the current tempo on the Transport Panel to select it, type 130 as the new tempo and press [Return].**

3. **Try playing the Project again and notice how the tempo of the loop changes to match the new tempo of the Project—pretty neat. While you can't stray too far from the original tempo, this potential does at least offer more flexibility when working with audio loops.**

4. **Change the tempo back to 120.**

2.6 Moving Events and Parts

Moving events and parts around the Project window is easy: simply drag them with the mouse. Try this for yourself with the Audio Part we now have on the Project window. One thing you might notice, however, is that when you're dragging the part around, it seems to automatically 'snap' to certain locations. This mode is, unsurprisingly, known as Snap mode and can be toggled with the Snap button on the Project window's toolbar.

Next to the Snap button on the Project window's toolbar are three pop-up menus to configure the way Parts and Events 'snap' when you're dragging them around: Snap, Grid and Quantize.

The Snap pop-up menu defines the behaviour for Snap mode, and if you've ever used a graphics package with a snap function, where objects might snap to a 10-pixel grid, for example, the default Grid option in the Snap menu isn't all that different. Instead of a 10-pixel grid, Cubase uses a more musical resolution for the grid, which is specified in the Grid pop-up menu. With Grid set to Bar, Parts and Events will automatically snap to whole-bar positions—try it for yourself.

The Grid can also be set to Beat, where Parts and Events will snap to quarter-note positions in a 4/4 time signature, for example, or Use Quantize, which allows Parts and Events to snap to the musical resolution set by the Quantize menu.

Generally speaking, I usually leave Snap set to Grid, and Grid set to Bar, other than when I need to make slightly more precise adjustments.

2.7 Copying Events and Parts

The procedure for copying Parts and Events is just like moving them, except you need to hold the [Alt] key while you drag. Assuming the first drum loop event is back at bar one, make a copy of the Audio Event at bar two—this will be easy if Snap is set to a one-bar grid.

While this isn't too difficult, the Alt-'n'-drag method of copying Parts and Events can quickly become tedious if you have more than a couple of copies to make. A quick way of making a couple of copies is to select the "Edit > Duplicate" command or press [Control]+[D].

1. **Select the Part or Event you want to copy, which in this case is the drum loop Event at bar two.**
2. **Press [Control]+[D].**
3. **Press [Control]+[D] a couple more times until you have six drum loop Events on the Project window.**

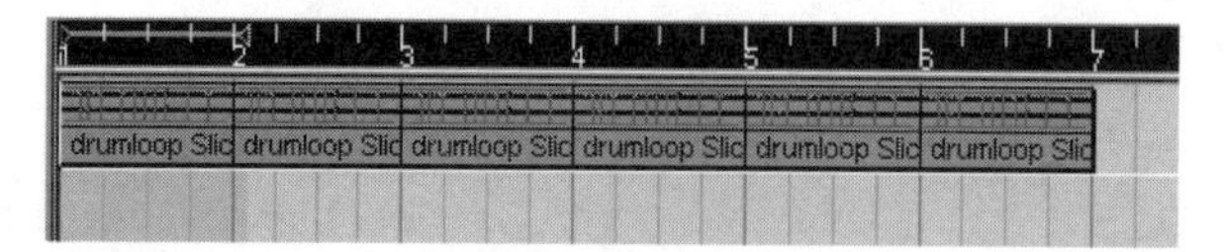

When using the Duplicate command, you have to select the last Part or Event before the empty space, since the object is always duplicated after the position of the selected object. This could easily result in overlapping objects, which is why the duplicated object always becomes selected on the Project window, allowing you to use the duplicate command several times without creating overlaps.

As we discovered earlier when creating Tracks, there are always many ways of achieving the same results in Cubase, and since we need to make six more copies of the drum loop, giving us 12 in total, here's another way of making multiple copies.

1. **Select the Part or Event you want to copy—the last drum loop event at bar six.**
2. **Choose "Edit > Repeat" or press [Control]+[K].**

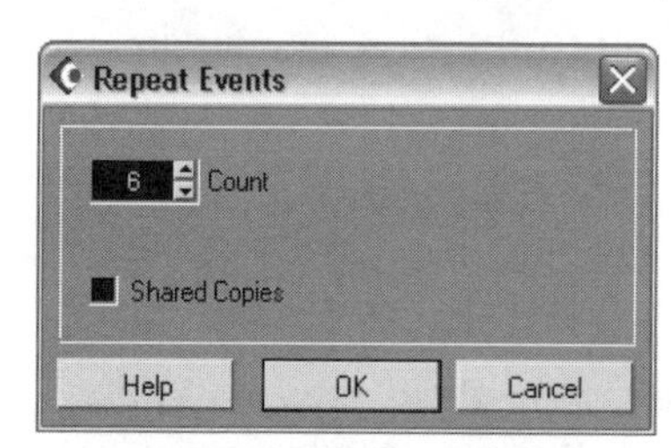

3. **In the Repeat Events window, set the Count parameter to the number of copies you want to make, which in this case is 6.**
4. **Click OK.**

You should now have twelve copies of the drum loop on the Project window, and at this point, we should really give the Audio Track a more meaningful name.

1. **Double-click the Audio Track's name in the Track list.**
2. **Type in a unique and original name, like "Drums", for example, and press [Return].**

2.8 Diving into Your Audio

When you record and import audio into Cubase, a library of every Audio Clip being used is kept in a window known as the Pool. Select "Project > Pool" or press [Control]+[P] to open the Pool.

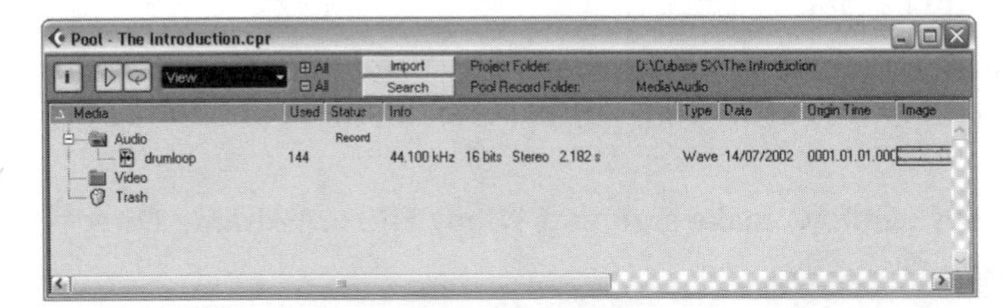

An Audio Clip is the way an audio file is referenced in Cubase—however, an Audio Clip is not the same as an audio file. For example, if we processed the second half of an Audio Clip in Cubase, the original audio file would not be changed. Instead, a new audio file is created with the processing, and the Clip in Cubase is updated to automatically play the first half of the original file before, transparently to the user, switching to the processed file to play the end of the Clip. The best way to think of an Audio Clip is like a play list.

The Pool is divided into three groups for Audio, Video and Trash. The latter works in much the same way as the Recycle Bin on your desktop. For example, clips can be dragged to the Trash group manually, or are automatically placed in the Trash group by Cubase when they're no longer used on the Project window. The user can later select "Pool > Empty Trash" to remove them from the Pool or delete the files permanently from the hard disk, and this provides a safe way to delete files that are no longer used in your Project.

Getting back to the germane issue, we're now going to import some more audio files; but this time, instead of importing directly to the Project window, we're going to import the files into the Pool.

1. **Click the Import button on the Pool's toolbar.**
2. **In the file selector, locate the "Tutorial Files" folder on the CD-ROM, select the file "bassloop1.wav" and click Open.**
3. **In the Import Options window, make sure that "Copy File to Working Directory" is activated and click OK.**

4. **A Clip is created for "bassloop1" in the Pool.**

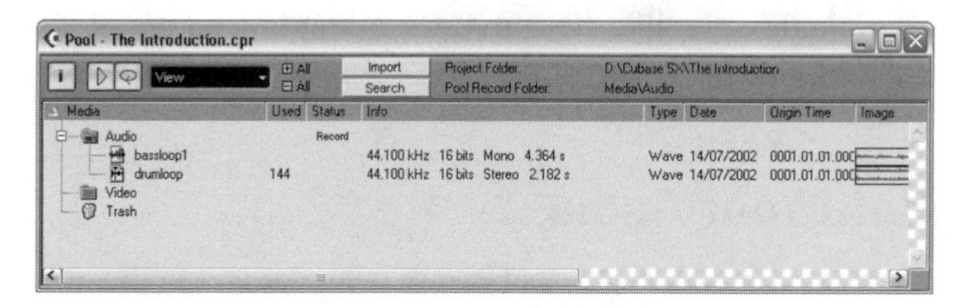

We can also import multiple audio files in one go.

1. **Click the Import button again.**
2. **Select the files "bassloop2.wav" and "bassloop3.wav" and click Open. Note that you have to hold down the [Control] key to select multiple files in the file selector.**
3. **In the Import Options window, make sure that "Copy File to Working Directory" is activated and click OK.**
4. **Two more Clips are created in the Pool for "bassloop2" and "bassloop3."**

You can create Audio Events to play Audio Clips from the Pool on the Project window by simply dragging a Clip from the Pool onto the Project window.

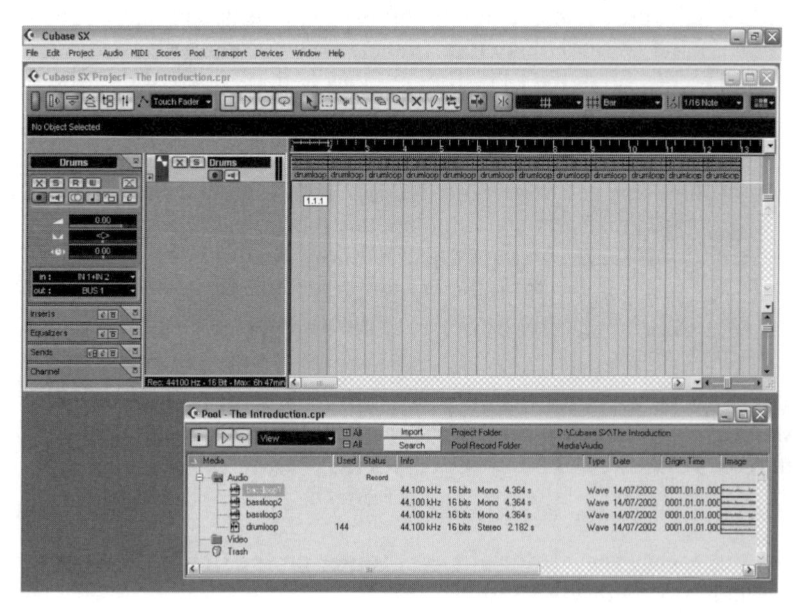

1. **Arrange your screen so both the Project window and Pool are visible.**
2. **Drag the bassloop1 clip from the Pool to the start of bar one in the empty space just below the drum loop Track on the Project window. Notice how a blue line and a time label appear to help you place the Audio Event.**
3. **A new Audio Track will be created to accommodate the bass loop. (Yes, that's yet another way to create a Track on the Project window.)**
4. **Double-click the Track's name to give it a slightly more meaningful name, such as "Bass."**

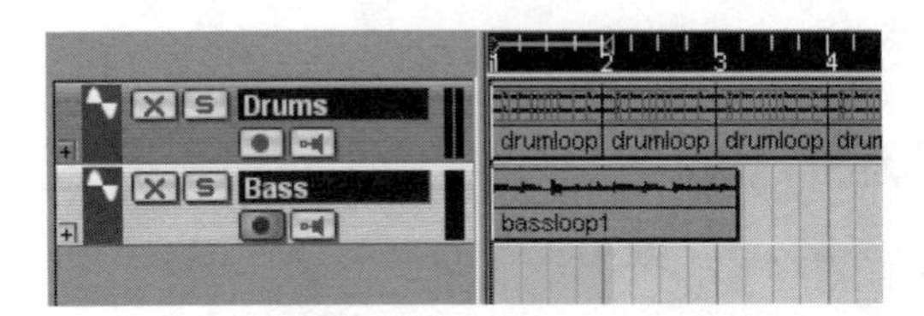

2.9 Getting the Tempo Right (Again)

If you play the Project, you'll notice that the bass loop is out of time with the drum loop, and again, this is because the bass loop is a different tempo to the Project. However, you should be able to solve this problem by following the same procedure as before.

1. **Select the bass loop Audio Event on the Project window.**
2. **Choose "Transport > Locators to Selection" or press [P].**
3. **Double-click the selected bass loop Audio Event to open the Sample Editor.**
4. **Click the Hitpoint Mode button on the Sample Editor's toolbar to activate Hitpoint Mode.**
5. **Make sure Cubase has identified all the beats correctly, and adjust the Hitpoint as required, although, again, the default setting should be fine.**
6. **With the Hitpoint parameters, this time make sure Bars is set to 2 (as this is a two-bar bass loop), Beats is again set to 0 (since it's a full two-bar drum loop) and Signature to 4/4. With everything set correctly, Cubase should identify that the Original Tempo of the loop is 110.00 bpm (beats per minute).**

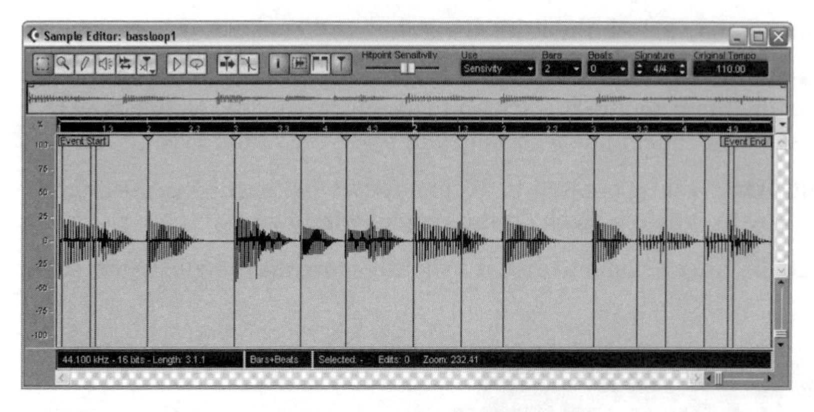

7. Select "Audio > Hitpoints > Create Audio Slices."

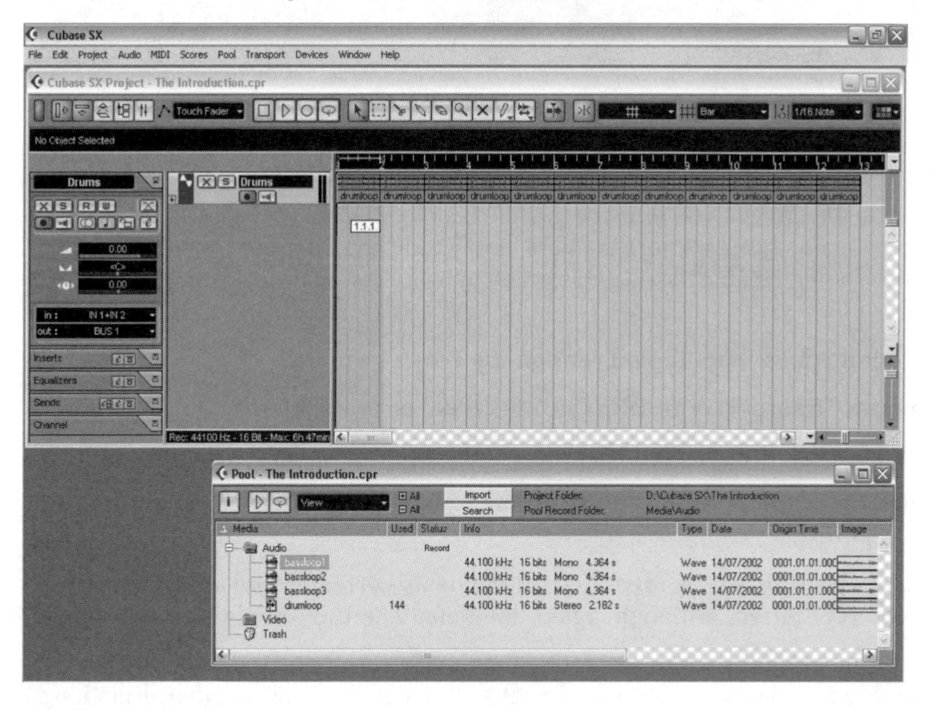

As before, Cubase will close the Sample Editor and create a two-bar bass loop Part on the Project window—if this isn't what you see, drag the lower right-hand handle to change the length of the Part. The bass and drum loops now play in time with each other, and they'll still play in time even if you change the tempo. Again, straying too far from the original tempo will have mixed results, but at least you get a bit of flexibility.

To finish the basic framework of our Project:

1. **Set the tempo to 110.**
2. **Make a copy of the bass loop at bars three, seven and eleven.**
3. **Drag bassloop2 from the Pool to bar five on the Bass Track.**
4. **Drag bassloop3 from the Pool to bar nine on the Bass Track.**

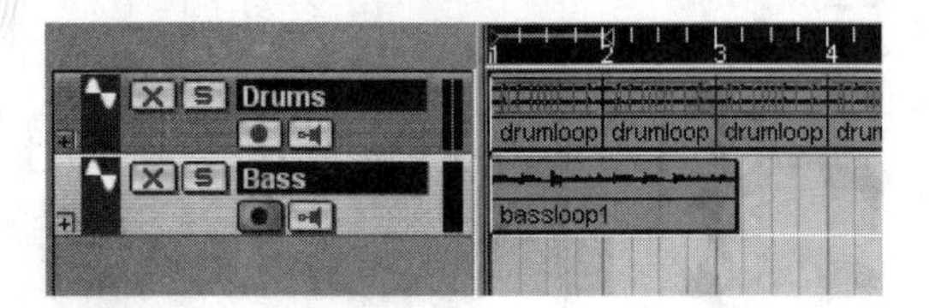

2.10 Making Twelve Bars Blue (or Orange)

At this point, you might notice that the Event Display, which is the main arranging area of the Project window where both Events and Parts are displayed, isn't looking particularly colorful. Aside from pure aesthetics, the fact that everything's the same color can make it hard to distinguish the Events and Parts belonging to the different Tracks at a casual glance. While this isn't too bad when you only have a couple of Tracks on the Project window, it can become more confusing when you have Projects with a large number of Tracks.

In order to make our Project window look a little prettier, not to mention more usable, it's possible to assign colors to every Part and Event on a Track, or to individual Events and Parts.

1. **Select the first Part (at bar 1) on the Bass Track.**
2. **Click the Color pop-up menu and select a Color, say Orange.**

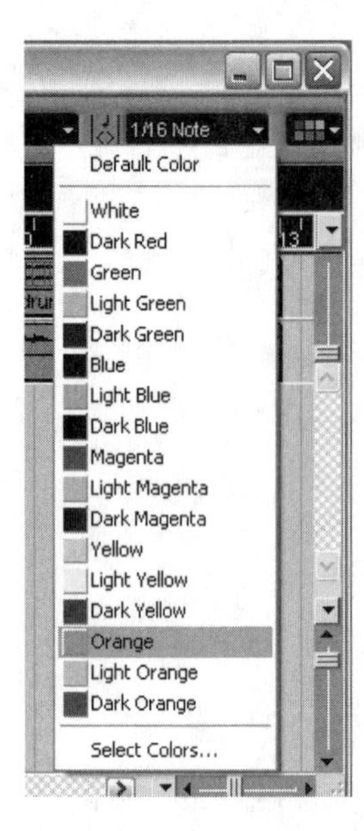

3. **Notice how the Part's Color changes from grey to orange.**
4. **To select multiple Parts (or Events) on the Event Display, simply [Shift]-click each Part (or Event) in turn. Using this technique, [Shift]-click the other bassloop1 Parts at bars 3, 7 and 11 so they're all selected.**
5. **Click the Color pop-up menu and select the color Orange again.**
6. **Select the bassloop2 Event on the Bass Track (at bar 5), click the Color pop-up and choose Light Orange.**
7. **Select the bassloop3 Event on the Bass Track (at bar 9), click the Color pop-up and choose Dark Orange.**

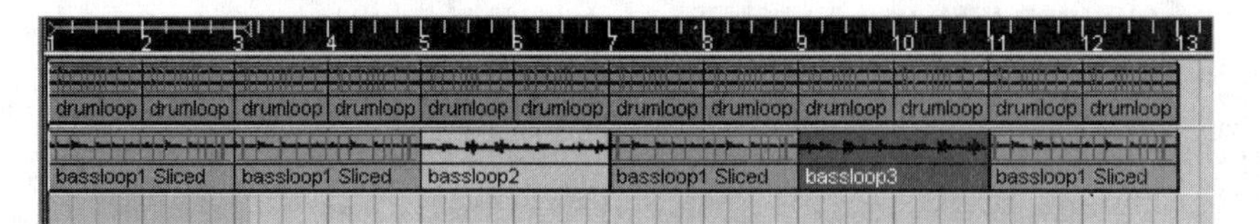

The Bass Track now looks much more colorful than before, but, more importantly, we've actually color-coded the structure of the music. This is one technique I use quite frequently: keeping the same basic color for a Track, in this case orange, and using different shades to highlight different 'building blocks' where the structure of the music is concerned.

Sometimes, you might not want to color code individual objects; for example, there would be no need to do this on the Drums Track in its current state. So to color all the Parts on the Drums Track:

1. **Make sure that no objects are selected on the Event Display. Simply click in an empty area of the Event Display to deselect everything.**
2. **Select the Track where you want to color all the Parts and Events, which in this example is the Drums Track.**
3. **Click the Color pop-up menu and choose the color, say Yellow.**

All the Events on the Drums Track are automatically turned yellow, but best of all is the fact that Cubase remembers the Drums Track is now set to yellow, meaning that a new Part or Event added to the Drums Track will be automatically displayed yellow. In fact, Parts and Events will always take on the color of the Track they're currently assigned to, unless you've specifically assigned a color to an individual object, as we did with the Parts and Events on the Bass Track.

2.10.1 Color Me Bad

Obviously there are no strict rules when it comes to assigning colors for Tracks, Parts and Events—different users will have their own preferences for color coding. However, setting up every Track for a different color before you start work on a Project is probably a good starting point for most users.

If you find the choice of colors limiting, it's possible to configure the color swatches available in the Color pop-up menu.

1. **Choose Select Colors from the Color pop-up menu.**

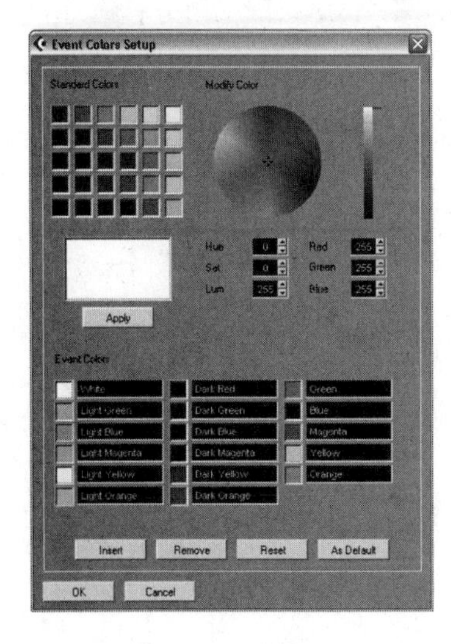

2. **Use the color controls in the upper part of the Event Colors Setup window to select either the color you want to replace an existing color swatch with, or the color to add as a new color swatch in the Color pop-up menu.**
3. **If you want to replace an existing color swatch, select the swatch to be replaced once you have a color you're happy with and click the Apply button.**
4. **If you want to create a new swatch, simply click Insert.**
5. **Click OK to keep the changes and close the window.**

- Color swatches can also be removed by selecting them and clicking Remove, and you can revert to the original set of color swatches by clicking Reset. The text labels for the color swatches can be renamed by clicking them and typing in a new label, which can be useful if you want to name them after Tracks, structures, or anything else that might be helpful.

2.11 Mix and Match

One of factors that makes Cubase an effective environment for making music is its ability to let you work on different aspects of a production simultaneously. In older hardware-based studios, you might have recorded all the elements of your Project before working on the arrangement, followed by any extra editing, mixing, and so on. However, with Cubase you can be trying out ideas in any of these areas right from the beginning.

Now we have a basic Project forming in the Project window, you could start to think about ways to make the sounds more interesting through mixing—by adding effects and balancing levels, for example. Cubase has a built in Mixer that provides plenty of mixing power, which you can open by selecting "Device > Track Mixer" or by pressing [F3].

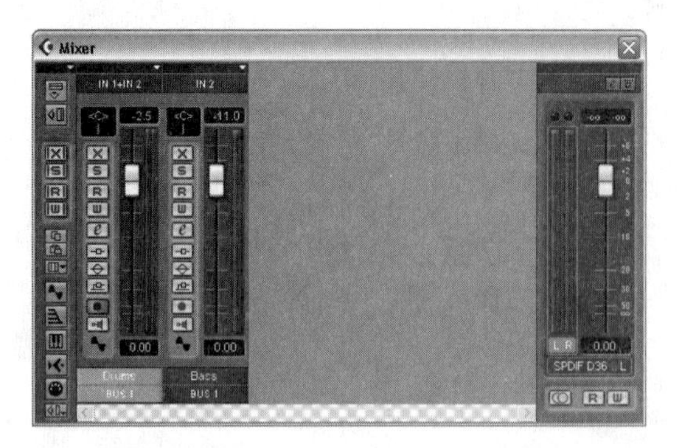

You'll notice that in the picture of the Mixer, the Master stereo channel is also shown. If you can't see this, click the Show Master Channel in the Common Panel, which is the strip on the left-hand side of the window.

One of the most convenient aspects about the Mixer is that the Tracks are arranged from left to right in the same order as they're displayed from top to bottom on the Project window. If you play the Project, you should be able to see the level meters responding on both the Drums and Bass channels. However, if you can only see the level meter responding on one channel, in the words of the Hitchhiker's Guide to the Galaxy: don't panic!

When a level meter doesn't light up as expected, it's usually because the Record Enable button is activated for that Channel. If this is the case, it's fairly easy to spot as the button will be highlighted in red on that particular Channel in the Mixer, and can be disabled by simply clicking it.

- When the Record Enable button is active on a channel, the level meter for that Channel displays the level of the incoming signal, whether you've got one plugged in or not, rather than the level of the Track's playback.

If you can't remember activating the Record Enable button in the first place, don't worry, you're not going mad. By default, Cubase always activates Record Enable on the Track currently selected in the Project window, which is also the currently selected channel on the Mixer. This behaviour is great when you're doing a great deal of recording, but can get quite annoying when you're mixing, especially if you constantly have to disable it. To prevent Record Enable from being activated automatically on the currently selected Track or Channel:

1. **Select "File > Preferences."**
2. **In the Preferences window, display the Editing panel by selecting Editing from the list on the left.**

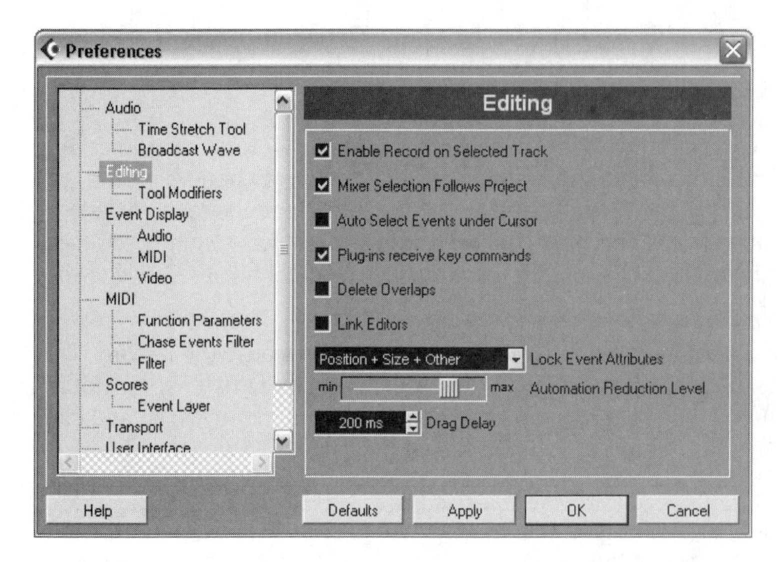

3. **Notice that the first option, Enable Record on Selected Track, is activated.**
4. **Click the checkbox to disable it.**
5. **Click OK to close the Preferences window.**

- It's worth noting that the Record Enable button must be active for MIDI Thru to work on a selected Track. MIDI Thru is the term given to the feature that sends MIDI notes you play on your keyboard to the output of the selected MIDI Track. For this reason, you might want to activate the Enable Record on Selected Track option again when you start working with MIDI Tracks.

2.11.1 Getting Familiar with the Mixer Windows

The Mixer provides basic controls for each Channel, and each Channel strip contains volume and pan faders, Mute, Solo, automation, Bypass, Record Enable and monitoring buttons. Have a play with the volume and pan faders, which allow you to adjust the volume (no surprises there) of a channel and its position within the stereo field.

The default position for volume faders is 0dB (meaning that nothing is added or taken away), and the default position for pan controls is center. Rather than fumbling around dragging a control when you want to reset it to the default position, you can simply [Control]-click the fader instead.

There are a couple of other tricks worth remembering when adjusting the mixer controls, and not just for volume and pan faders. You can [Shift]-click a control to drag it with a much finer resolution, and if you have a mouse with a compatible scroll wheel, you can use the scroll wheel while the mouse is hovering over a control to adjust that control rather than dragging.

If you want a full set of controls for a particular channel on the Mixer, click that channel's Edit VST Channel ('curly e') button. Try clicking the Drums Channel strip's Edit VST Channel button now.

The VST Channel Settings window displays the settings for individual Channels, and you'll notice that, in addition to having a duplicate Channel strip from the Mixer, there are insert and send effects panels, plus a four-band parametric equalizer. We'll come back to this window again in a moment, but close it for now and keep it in the back of your mind.

If you're using Cubase SX, you can also access the insert, send and EQ controls for each Channel on the Mixer itself as SX's Mixer offers two views, known as Normal and Extended. Cubase SL users only get the Normal Mixer View, which is what we've been looking at up until now.

To display the Extended Mixer View, click the Show Extended Mixer button on the Common Panel, and notice how the Mixer window is extended upwards, although you may need to reposition the window so its full contents are visible.

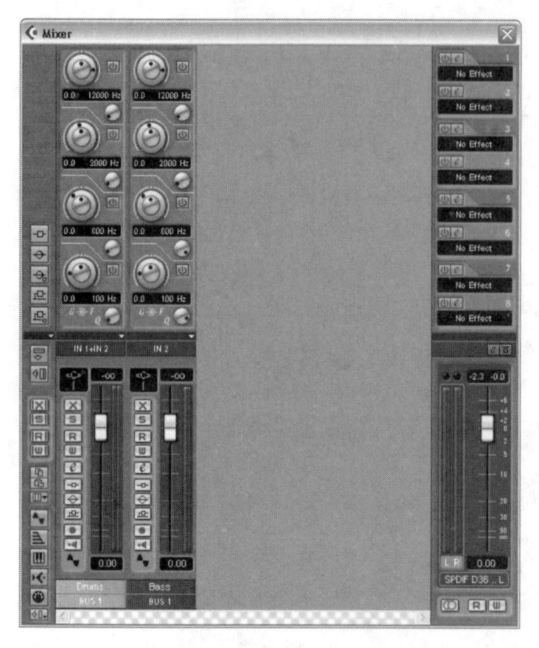

Just above the Input Routing selector for each channel is a slim dark blue strip with a small white arrow, which you can click to display the Channel View pop-up menu for that particular channel. This allows you to set a different Extended View for each channel, but if you want every channel to display the same Extended View, you can click the Global View pop-up menu in the Common Panel.

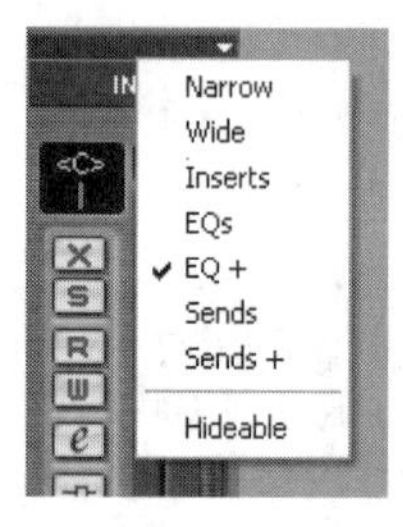

Take a moment to familiarize yourself with how these menus work and what the different extended views look like. You'll notice there are two views available for Sends and EQ controls—the "+" sign indicates that rotary controls are displayed instead of sliders.

2.11.2 Mixing From the Project Window

Even if you can't use the Extended Mixer View, there's another brilliant way of accessing the full set of mixer controls for both Cubase SX and SL users, this time on the Project window. That's right, you could in fact mix an entire Track without ever leaving the Project window!

If you can't see the Inspector, click the Show Inspector button on the Project window's toolbar.

The Inspector provides various settings for each Track and is split into several Sections, depending on the type of Track selected—for now, select the Drums Track. The General Parameters Section is usually shown by default, and this shows the name of the currently selected Track at the top. You'll notice there are a full set of Track controls, which can also be displayed on the Track List, plus an alternative volume and pan controls, with Input and Output Routing selectors just below.

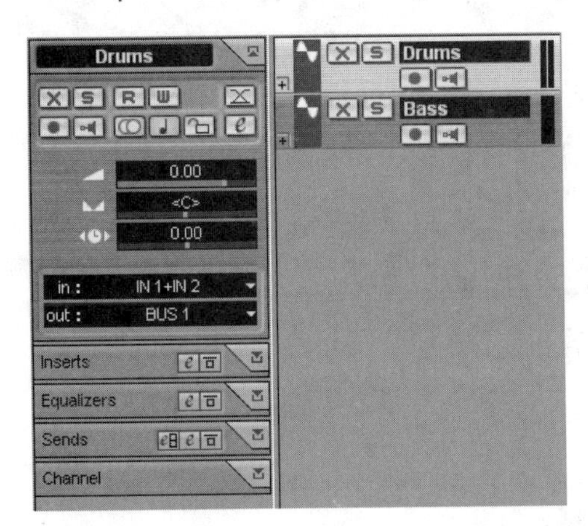

You can, of course, use the controls in the General Parameters Section for basic mixing, but there are many other Sections in the Inspector that are 'collapsed' by default: Inserts, Equalizers, Sends and Channel. If you can't see these other Sections, you may need to enlarge the Project window and, at this point, it would be good idea to resize the Project window to fill the screen.

- One thing you'll notice about Cubase is that it needs a minimum monitor resolution of 1024 × 768—larger resolutions and multiple-display configurations can make your life more pleasurable if you spend a great deal of time with Cubase.

To display a different Section in the Inspector, click the Show Section buttons to the right of each Section's name.

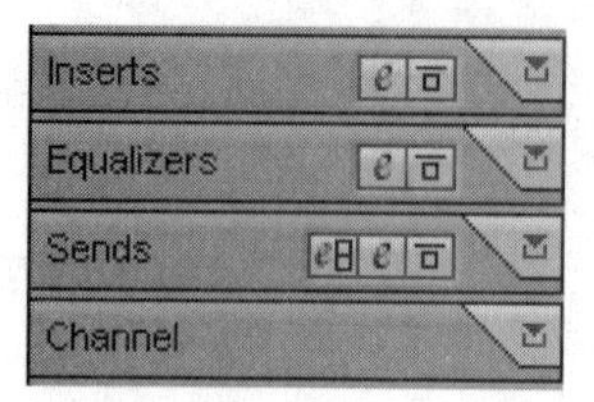

As you select the different Sections, you'll notice that the Inserts and Sends Sections look exactly like the Inserts and Sends panels in the VST Channel Settings window. In fact, clicking the "e" button by the name of the Inserts, Equalizers and Sends Sections opens the VST Channel Settings window for that Channel. The Equalizer Section is a little more compact, and Cubase SX users will recognize this from the EQ Extended Mixer View.

The Channel Section displays a complete Channel strip for the selected Track, just like the one we looked at in the Mixer, which is why I said you could mix a track without ever leaving the Project window. If you select the Bass Track on the Project window now, you'll notice that the Inspector remembers the Channel Section is open and displays the Channel strip for the Bass Track instead.

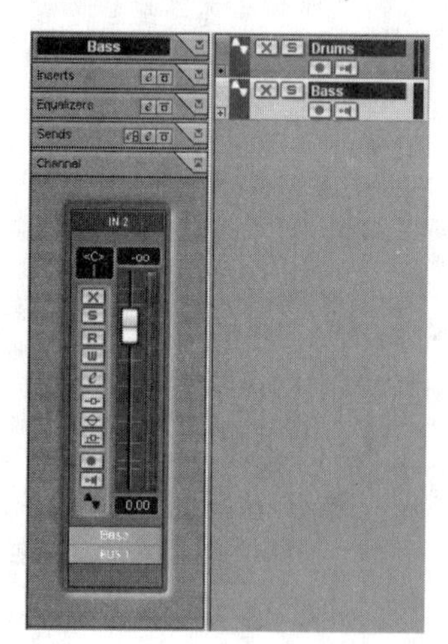

If you have a large monitor, you might think it's a shame that the current Section closes when you click on a different Section in the Inspector, meaning you can only display one Section at a time. However, fortunately this isn't the case:

1. **Set the Inspector so the General Parameters Section is displayed.**
2. **[Control]-click the Insert's Show Section button, and notice how the General Parameters Section doesn't close.**

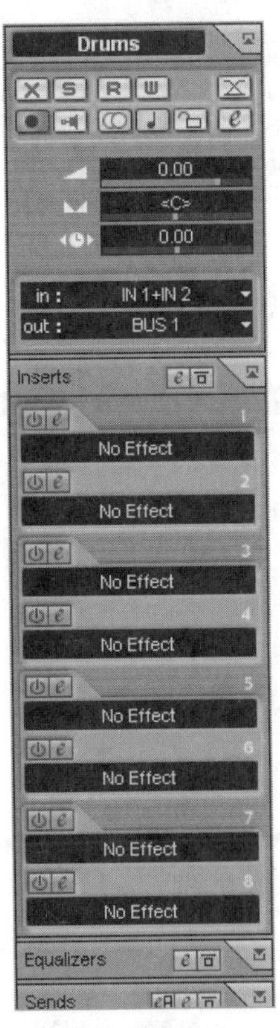

3. **Click the General Parameters Section's Show button—this Section closes, leaving the Insert Section visible, as you'd expect.**

   Rule of thumb: Once a Section is open, you can click it as normal to close the Section. You only need to [Control]-click to display a Section without closing the currently open Section.

4. **You can also [Alt]-click any Section's Show button to open every Section for a display in the Inspector, although you'd need a rather large monitor in order to see them all.**

2.12 Adding an Insert Effect

Now you know where to find Cubase's various mixing options, let's look at ways of making sounds more interesting, starting by adding an insert effect to the drum loop.

For these examples, I'm going to use the Project window's Inspector since most people prefer to adopt a working method that requires the minimum number of windows open at any one time. However, if you prefer to use the VST Channel Settings Window or the Extended Mixer View on the Track Mixer, you'll find the procedure is pretty much the same.

When adding effects, it's very handy to have the Project playing so you can hear exactly what you're doing. So, before we start, let's activate Cycle Playback mode in Cubase, meaning that Cubase will keep looping between the left and right locators until you press Stop.

1. **Select every object on the Project window by pressing [Control]+[A] or choosing "Edit > Select > All."**
2. **Press [P] to position the left and right locators at the start and end of the selection, or select "Transport > Locators to Selection."**
3. **Activate Cycle mode by clicking the Loop button on either the Transport Panel, the Project window's toolbar, or by pressing [/] on the numeric keypad.**

4. **Press Play.**

   It's important to note that the Project Cursor has to be within the locators for Cycle Playback mode to work. You can press [1] on the numeric keypad to set the Project Cursor to the position of the left locator.

With the Project playing, let's add some insert effects:

1. **Select the Drums Track on the Project window.**
2. **Select the Inserts Section of the Inspector.**
3. **Click the No Effect label in the first insert effects slot and choose "Dynamics > Dynamics."**

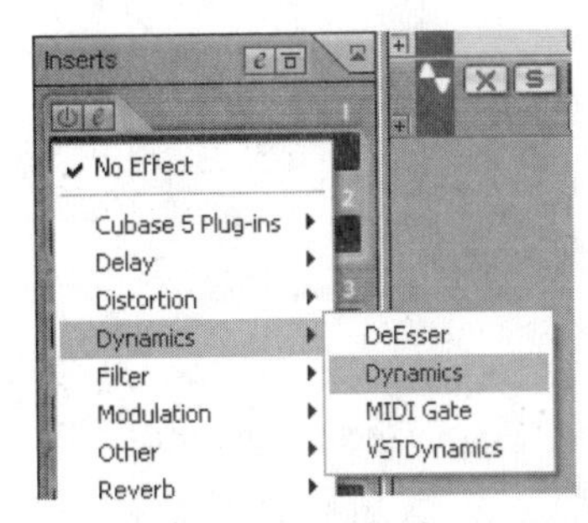

4. The editor window for the plug-in opens automatically and the Dynamics effect becomes immediately active. The Dynamics plug-in is named literally and offers a variety of dynamics processors, including a compressor, a noise gate and a limiter.

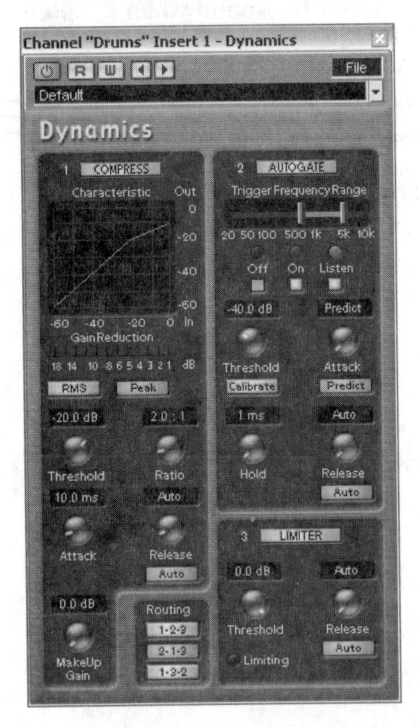

5. Click the arrow button to the right of the long black bar labelled Default to display a pop-up menu of preset configurations for this plug-in and choose Compressor.

6. **You'll hear that the drums suddenly sound a bit more aggressive than before, and you can bypass the effect by clicking the power button in the top left-hand corner of the toolbar on the plug-in's editor window.**
7. **Toggle the power button so you can compare the difference in sound when the plug-in is enabled and disabled—I think you'll prefer the sound when the plug-in is active.**
8. **Close the Dynamics plug-in's editor window.**

Notice there's a duplicate power button for each insert slot in the Insert Section, allowing you to bypass an effect without having to open the editor window first. However, if you do want to open the editor window again, click the 'e' button just above the insert's effect slot.

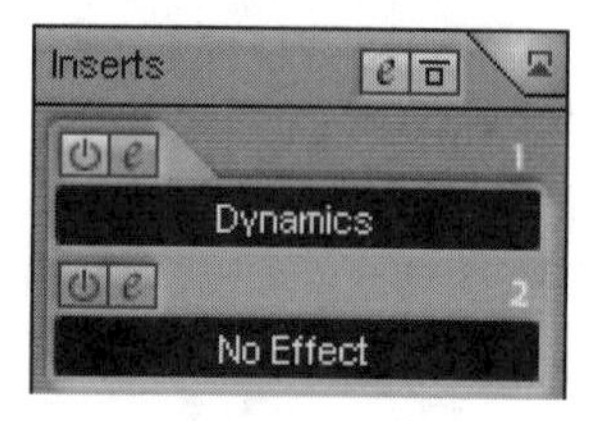

Using the same approach, add the "Distortion > QuadraFuzz" plug-in as an insert effect on the Bass Track:

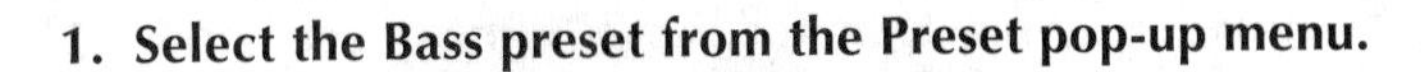

1. **Select the Bass preset from the Preset pop-up menu.**

2. **Experiment with QuadraFuzz's own internal Presets slider at the bottom of the plug-in to find a sound you like—there are plenty of great presets, but Bright Notes is perhaps an appropriate choice.**

2.12.1 Are You Seeing Red?

While it is possible to mix from the Project window, the Mixer is still useful when you want to see the level meters of all the channels simultaneously, along with the master stereo channel.

1. **Open the Mixer. (Press [F3] or select "Devices > Track Mixer.")**
2. **With the master stereo channel visible (click Show Master Channel in the Common Panel if it isn't), notice that the two red lights are lighting up at the top of the level meter.**

When you get red lights on any Channel, it means the signal is too loud and is overloading that Channel. You can often hear this because the sound will become distorted, but since Cubase's mixer operates at such a high resolution, it's possible to overload it without necessarily hearing any nasty artefacts. Once a red overload light comes on, it stays active until you click on it to reset.

3. **You could pull the master fader down, but it's better practice to adjust the individual levels of Tracks and keep the master fader at 0dB.**

4. **Try adjusting the faders until you stop getting red lights (remembering to click the red lights to reset them once they light up) and notice that the numerical value of the volume fader is displayed just below the fader strip—adjusting both Drums and Bass volume faders to -4.24dB should solve the problem.**

2.13 Working with VST Instruments and MIDI Tracks

Until now, we've been exploring the audio facilities of Cubase, and while many of the features we've discussed are also relevant to MIDI Tracks and Parts, let's turn our attention to some of Cubase's particularly interesting MIDI features.

- This tutorial uses virtual instruments, although there's nothing to stop you using any external hardware MIDI synths you have connected instead. Rather than setting a MIDI Track to play through a virtual instrument, which we're about to look at, simply set it to the output of one of your other MIDI devices.

1. **Select "Devices > VST Instruments" or press [F11] to open the VST Instruments window.**

2. **Click the "No VST Instrument" label and choose "Synths > a1" from the pop-up menu of installed VST Instruments.**

   The A1 is a virtual analogue synth designed by Waldorf and, in addition to sounding fantastic, it's capable of producing a wide range of sounds.

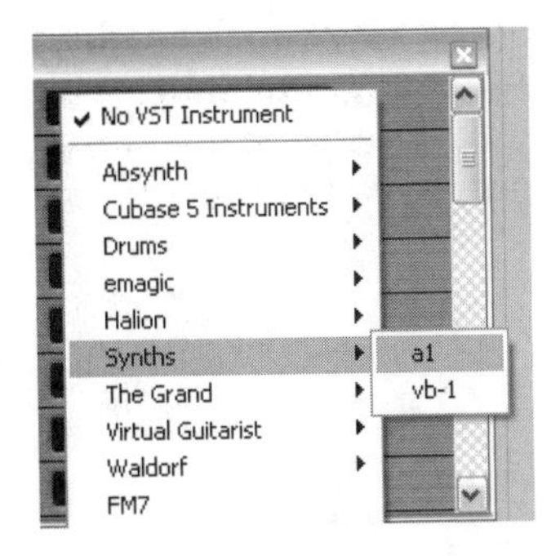

3. **Notice that the synth turns itself on automatically (the power button is highlighted blue).**
4. **Click the "e" button on the first slot of the VST Instruments window to open the instrument's editor window and see what the synthesizer actually looks like.**

5. **If you click with the mouse on the A1's virtual keyboard, you should be able to hear a sound if everything's set-up correctly. Consult the later chapters of this reference manual if you run into difficulties.**
6. **Close the A1's editor window.**

With the A1 synth ready to go, we need to create a MIDI Track and set its output to play through the VST Instrument.

1. **Create a new MIDI Track on the Project window. You can do this using one of the methods we explored earlier, except this time you'll need to choose the Add MIDI Track command.**
2. **Make sure the newly created MIDI Track is selected on the Project window.**

3. **In the Inspector, click the "out:" pop-up menu and choose "a1" from the list of MIDI outputs available. VST Instruments are always listed in the second group of the MIDI output pop-up menu.**

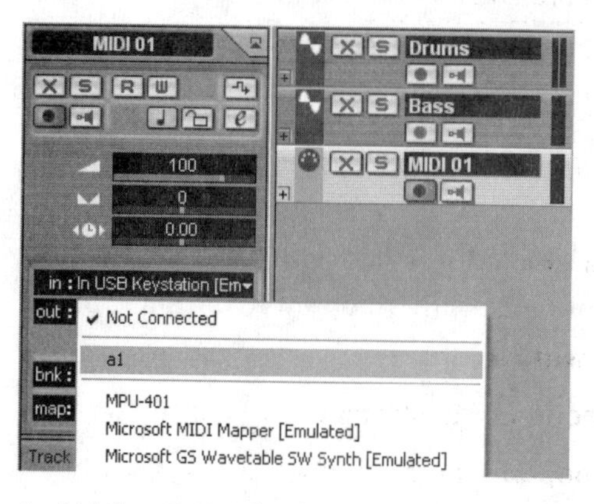

4. **With a MIDI keyboard connected to your computer, you should be able to play some notes and hear the sound coming from the A1 synth. Remember that you need to have the Record Enable button activated on a MIDI Track for this to work.**

5. **Open the Mixer. Notice that there are two additional channels: one for the MIDI Track we created on the Project window, and one for the audio output of the A1 synth we installed in the VST Instruments window.**

6. **If you play some notes on your keyboard, you'll notice both the MIDI and VST Instrument Channels' level meters respond.**

- Notice that different Channel types appear with a different colored background behind the fader: Audio Channels have a dark-blue background, MIDI Channels are beige, and VST Instrument Channels are green-ish.

7. Close the Mixer.

2.13.1 Choosing Sounds

We're going to use the A1 synth to record a simple chord track using a pad sound, but first we need to choose a suitable sound.

1. **Select the MIDI Track on the Project window.**
2. **Make sure the General Parameters Section is displayed in the Inspector.**
3. **Click the "Prg:" pop-up menu and a pop-up patch selection window will appear to let you choose a sound.**

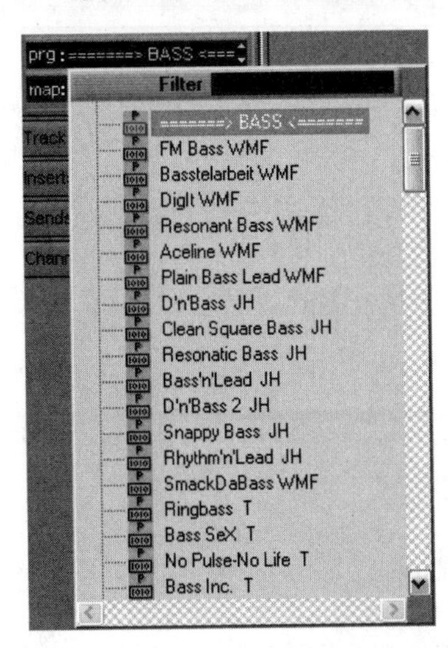

This pop-up window is one of the features that makes Cubase a joy to use, particularly because it stays open until you double-click a patch, or click outside the pop-up window area to close it. While it's open you can do several things:

1. **Use the [Up] and [Down] cursor keys to scroll through the list of sounds, while still playing notes on your MIDI keyboard to audition the currently selected sound.**

2. **Press the keyboard shortcuts for the transport controls without closing the pop-up patch selection window.**

   If you're not sure of these shortcuts, on the numeric keypad [0] stops the Project, [Enter] plays the Project, [+] and [-] moves the Project Cursor forward and backward respectively, and [.] resets the Project Cursor to the beginning of the Project.

3. **Type in a search string into the Filter field at the top of the window and press [Return]. The patch selection window will now show only the patch names containing the search string you entered, which makes finding the patch you want in a long list a piece of cake.**

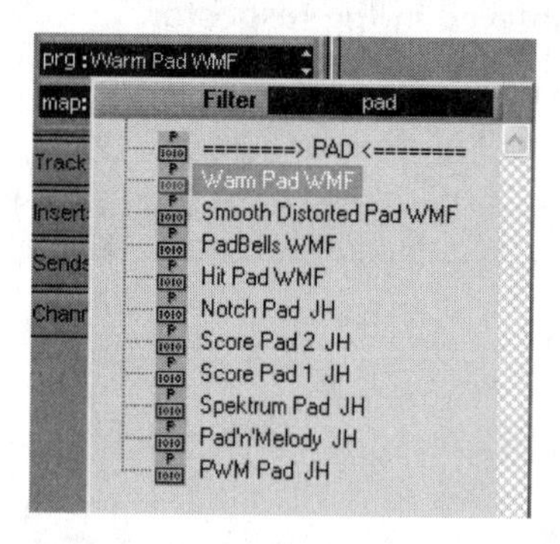

Having mastered the patch selection window, choose a suitable pad sound — for the sake of this tutorial, "Warm Pad WMF" is a good choice.

2.13.2 Programming a MIDI Part

You could now record a chord part via your MIDI keyboard, or program the notes manually using one of Cubase's MIDI editors. Both the Getting Started manual and the Wizoo Cubase SX Quick Start contain tutorials for recording MIDI Tracks, and later chapters in the book also explain how to do this, so have a look at any one of these sources if you fancy recording your own pad track. Instead, let's look at how you could program the track manually, which could be especially useful for times when you don't have a MIDI keyboard handy.

1. **First we need to create an empty MIDI Part on the MIDI Track in the Project window.**
2. **Select the Draw tool from the Project window's toolbar.**

   You can also switch to the Draw tool by pressing [8] on the main part of your keyboard. In fact, the first eight tools on the Project window's toolbar correspond to the keys [1] to [8] on your keyboard, though not on the numeric keypad.

3. **Drag the Draw tool from the beginning of the first bar to the start of bar 13, which will create an empty 12-bar MIDI Part on the MIDI Track.**

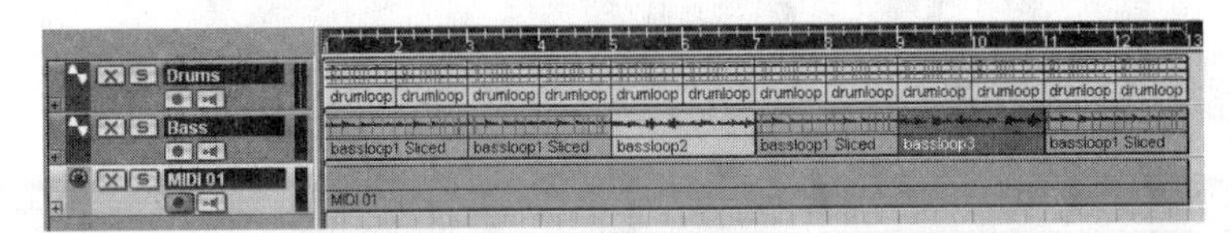

4. **Select the Object Selection (arrow) tool again from the Project window's toolbar, or press [1] on the main part of your keyboard.**
5. **Double-click the empty MIDI Part, which should open Cubase's default MIDI editor, the Key editor.**

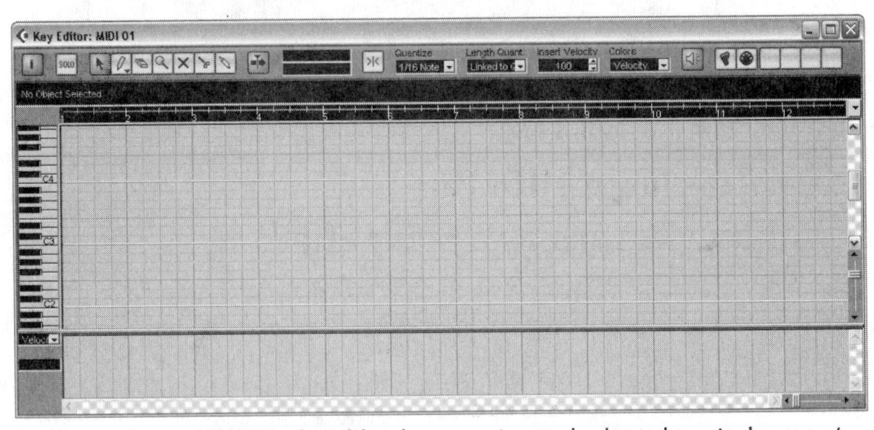

   If you don't see a window like the one pictured, close the window you've opened, make sure the empty MIDI part is selected on the Project window and choose "MIDI > Open Key Editor."

6. **Adding MIDI notes to the Key editor is just like adding MIDI parts to the Project window—you need to use the Draw tool. So select the Draw tool either by clicking it on the Key editor's toolbar or pressing 8 on the main part of your keyboard.**

   Even though the Draw tool is in the second position in the Key editor, next to the arrow, you always select the tools on the keyboard based on their arrangement on the Project window.

7. **Make sure you activate Snap on the Key editor's toolbar and you can set Quantize to 1/1 for making it really easy to enter the notes accurately.**

8. **Using the Draw tool, drag out notes as pictured below.**

9. **Select the Object Selection (arrow) tool again when you've finished, close the Key editor (you can also do this by pressing [Return]), and play the Project.**

2.14 Adding Reverb as a Send Effect

One thing you'll notice when you play the Project is that the pad sound we've just added drowns out the sound of our original drum and bass loops. Pad sounds generally work better when they're further back in the overall mix, which can be achieved by turning the volume down slightly and adding some reverb to give a sense of depth.

1. **Open the VST Send Effects window by selecting "Devices > VST Send Effects" or pressing [F6].**

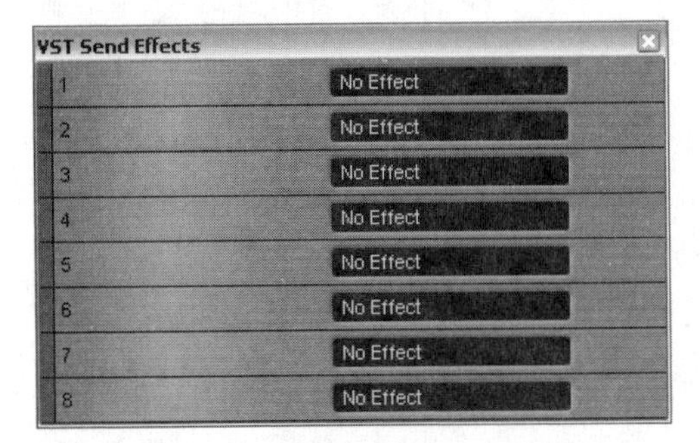

2. **In the first empty rack slot, click the "No Effect" label and choose "Reverb > Reverb A" from the pop-up menu of effects installed on your computer.**

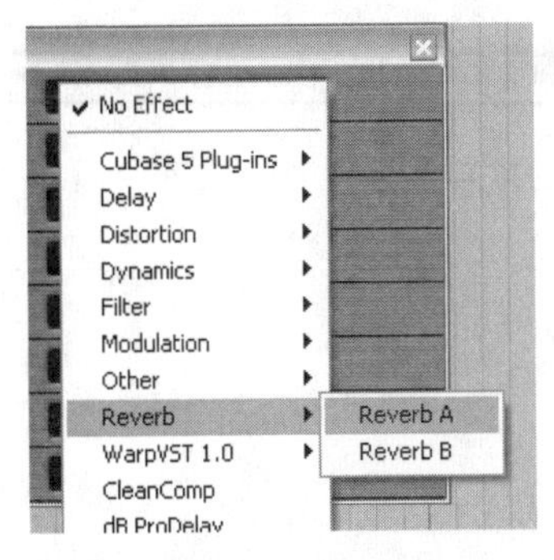

3. **The plug-in is automatically activated and the editor window is opened.**

4. **Select Large from the Preset menu. (Notice how using VST send effects is almost the same as using VST Instruments.)**

5. **Since the audio output of VST Instruments isn't represented on the Project window, we have to use the Mixer to send the pad sound to the reverb.**
6. **Open the Mixer.**
7. **Cubase SX users can use the Sends Extended View on the Mixer, but Cubase SL users will need to open the VST Channel Settings window for the A1.**
8. **Click the power button on the first send effect to activate it. The first send effect should automatically be labelled (and routed to) Reverb A.**
9. **Drag the slider underneath the "Reverb A" label about half way along to send a proportion of the signal to the reverb effect.**

10. **Turn the volume fader down to around -9.85dB.**

Before we leave the pad sound alone, adjusting the Cutoff control in the synth itself would also make it sit better in the overall mix.

1. **Open the A1's editor window.**
2. **Set the Cutoff value to 1551Hz, or thereabouts.**

2.15 Having Fun with MIDI Effects

The insert and send effects we've looked at so far have been audio plug-in effects, which is to say they process audio data from an Audio Track, or the audio output of a VST Instrument. Cubase also includes MIDI plug-in effects, which allow you to process the output of a MIDI Track in much the same way. So first of all, let's look at MIDI insert effects:

1. **Select the MIDI Track on the Project window.**
2. **Display the Inserts Section in the Inspector, and notice how it looks virtually the same as the Inserts Section for an Audio Track.**

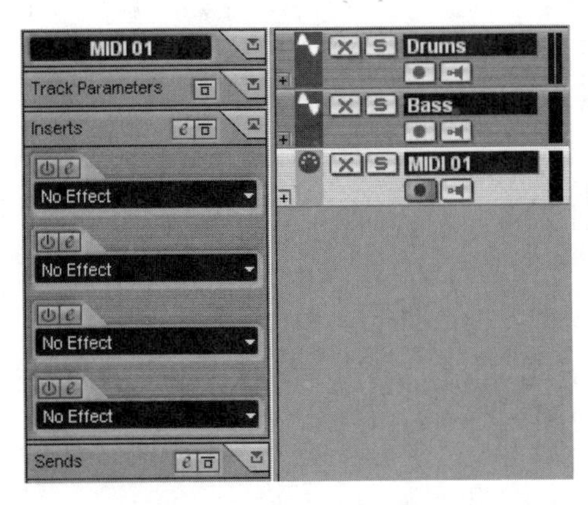

3. **In the first insert slot, click the "No Effects" label and select "Track FX" from the list of available MIDI effects.**

4. **While some MIDI effects have their own editor window, like the audio effects we've already seen, certain MIDI effects, like Track FX, display their editor in the Inspector.**

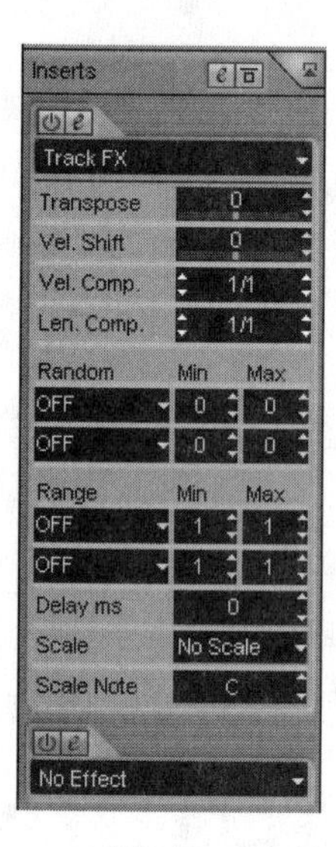

5. **With the Project playing, try changing the Transpose value to 12, either by clicking the number, typing a new one, and pressing (Enter], by clicking the small up and down arrows, or by dragging the slider. The pad sound will now play an octave higher than before.**
6. **Bypass the MIDI insert effect for now by clicking its power button.**

MIDI send effects work in a slightly different way to audio send effects, but they can be extremely useful.

1. **Install another A1 synth in the second slot of the VST Instruments window.**

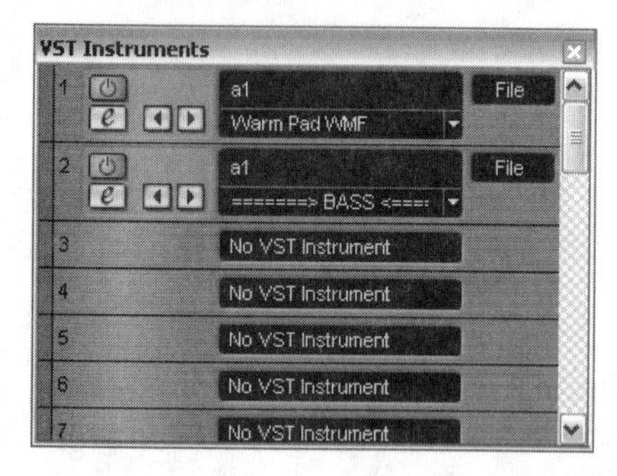

2. **Select the "Sounds Synk'd WMF" patch from the Preset menu. Unfortunately, this works like a traditional Windows pop-up menu, not the more preferable Cubase patch selection pop-up we looked at before.**

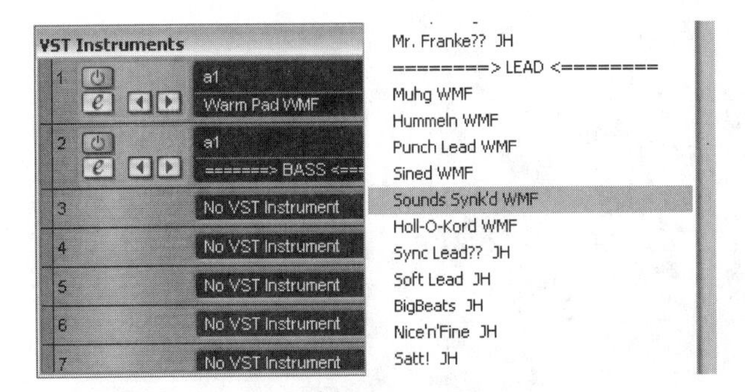

3. Close the second A1's editor and the VST Instruments windows.
4. Make sure the MIDI Track is selected.
5. Display the Sends Section on the Inspector.

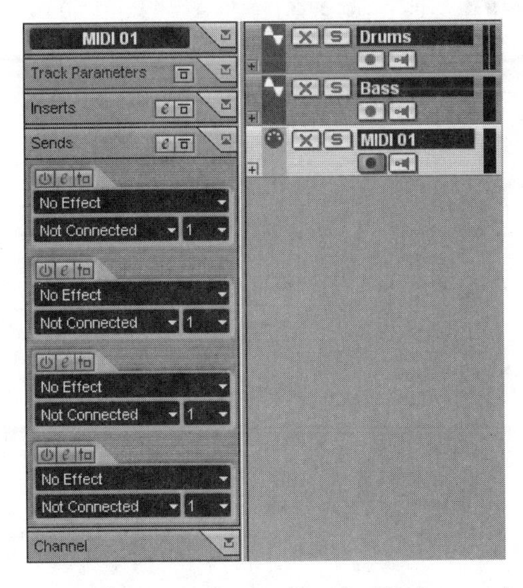

6. Make sure the Project is playing and click the first send's power button to activate it.
7. Click the "Not Connected" label and choose "a1 2" from the list of available MIDI outputs. Notice how the second A1 now mirrors what the first A1 is playing.
8. This sounds a little boring, so let's spice it up with an arpeggiator by clicking the first send's "No Effect" label and choosing "Arpache 5" from the list of installed MIDI effects.

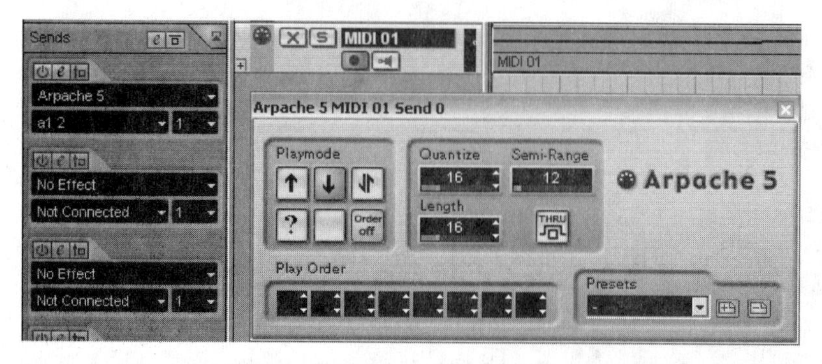

9. Arpache 5's editor window opens and the effect becomes active as soon as new notes are sent through it. You should now hear quite a different sound!

If you open the Mixer now, you should see two VST Instrument output channels for our two A1 synths, and, as with the pad sound, you might want to turn down the volume of the second synth and add a little reverb. To take things further, try adding "Delay > Double Delay" as a second audio send effect, use the "Ghost Tales" preset and send some of the second A1's audio output to it.

And that's it—we've reach the end of the tutorial! I hope you've picked up some useful tips and tricks along the way, and feel much more comfortable about producing music with Cubase. The secret, as with any creative endeavour, is to have fun and experiment constantly; so never be afraid to try out something crazy, especially when it comes to using plug-ins and layering effects.

The final result from the tutorial is also included on the CD-ROM that accompanies this book so you can check your Project against mine.

Cubase SX/SL
in Detail

3 Playback and the Transport Panel

3.1 Background

This chapter describes the various methods available for controlling Playback and Transport functions in Cubase SX/SL.

3.1.1 The Transport Panel

Below you can find a brief description of each item on the Transport panel.

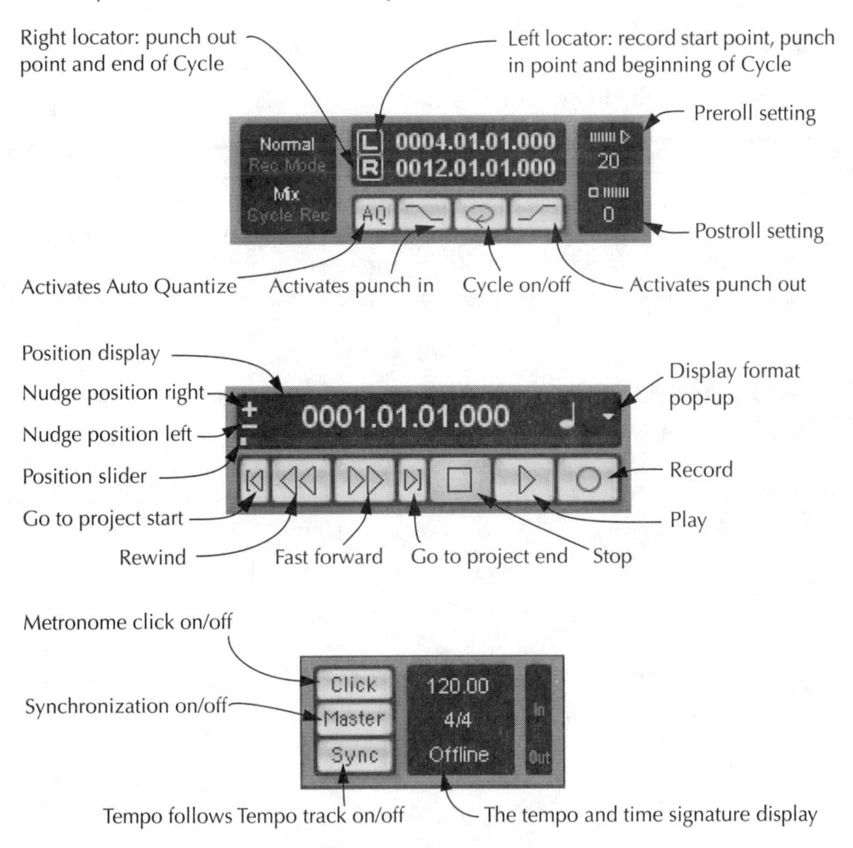

- **The main Transport functions (Play/Stop/Cycle/Record) are also available on the toolbar.**

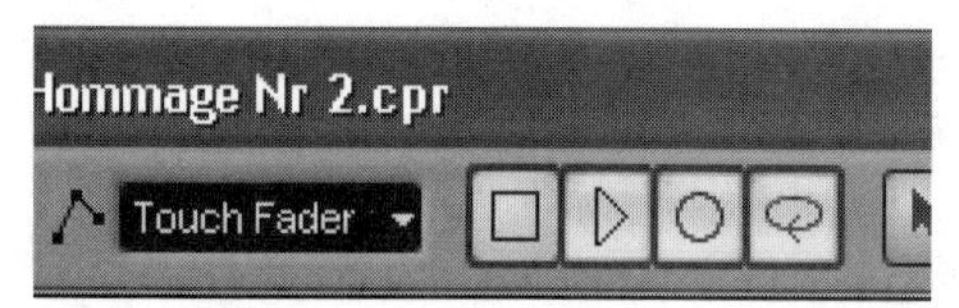

In addition, various play options are available on the Transport menu.

Hiding and Showing

The Transport panel is shown by default when you launch a new project. To hide or show it, select the "Transport Panel" item from the Transport menu (or use the corresponding key command, by default [F2]).

About Preroll and Postroll

These items are described in the Recording chapter—see page 102.

Resizing

You can change the size of the Transport panel by deciding which parts of it you wish to be visible. If you right-click anywhere within the Transport panel area, a pop-up menu will appear. On this menu, you can check or uncheck elements of the Transport panel as desired.

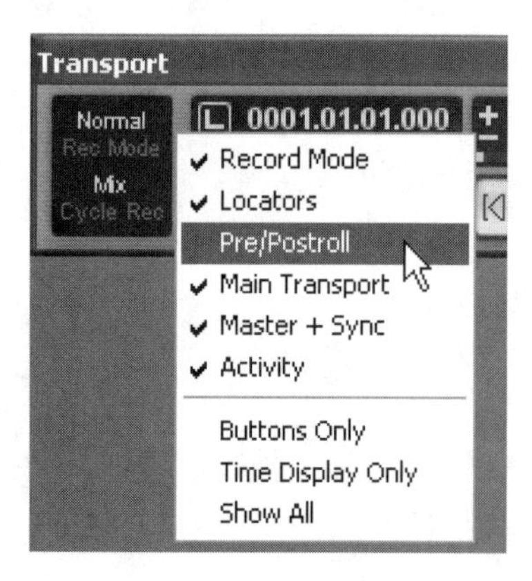

3.1.2 The Numeric Keypad

In the default Key Command settings, the numeric keypad on the computer keyboard is assigned various Transport panel operations:

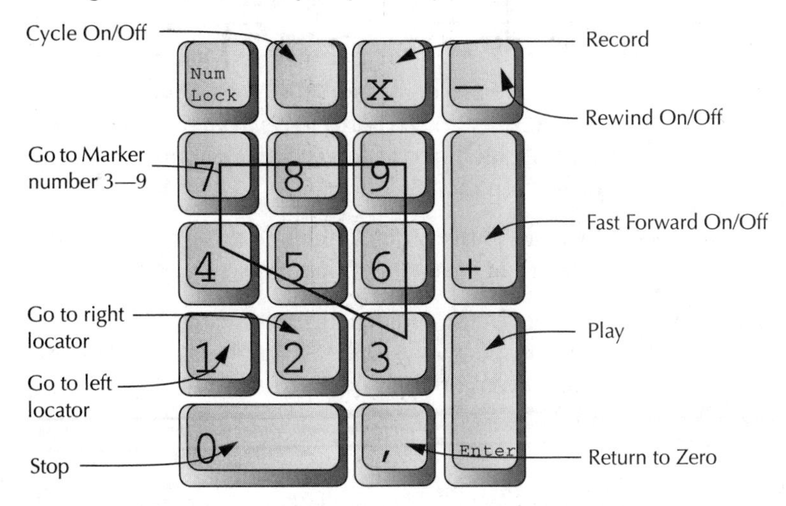

3.2 Operations

3.2.1 Setting the Project Cursor Position

There are several methods you can use to move the project cursor position:

- By using Fast Forward and Rewind.
- By dragging the project cursor.
- By clicking in the ruler.
  Double clicking in the ruler will start or stop playback, moving the cursor at the same time.
- If the option "Locate When Clicked in Empty Space" is activated in the Preferences (Transport page) you can click anywhere in an empty section of the Project window to move the cursor position.
- By changing the value in the position display.
- By using the position slider.
  The range of the slider relates to the Length setting in the Project Setup dialog. Hence, moving the slider all the way to the right will take you to the end of the project.
- By using the nudge position buttons (see page 75).

- By using markers (see page 159).
- By using playback options (see page 77).
- By using functions on the Transport menu.
  The following functions are available:

Function	Description
Locate Selection	Moves the project cursor to the beginning of the current selection. For this to be available, you must have selected one or more events or parts, or made a selection range.
Locate Next/Previous Marker	This moves the project cursor to the closest marker to the right or left (see page 159).
Locate Next/Previous Event	This moves the project cursor forwards or backwards respectively, to the closest beginning or end of any event on the selected track(s).

● If Snap is activated when dragging the project cursor, the Snap value is taken into account. This can be helpful for finding exact positions quickly.

About the Transport Panel Display Format

The time unit shown in the ruler can be independent from the time unit shown in the Transport panel. This means that you can display timecode in the transport position display and bars and beats in the ruler, for example. The following rules apply:

- **If you change the display format from the Transport panel, this will apply "globally" in the project.**

  This is the same as changing the display format in the Project Setup. Thus, to have different display formats in the ruler and the Transport panel, you should change the format in the ruler.

- **The Transport panel display format is set on the pop-up menu to the right in the position display.**

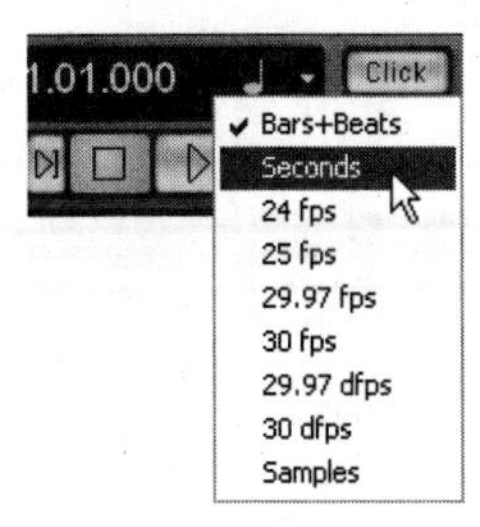

- **The setting here also determines the time format displayed for the left and right locators.**

Using the Nudge Position Buttons

The + and—buttons to the left of the Position slider allows you to nudge the project cursor position to the right or left, respectively. The increments depend on the display format selected on the Transport panel:

- If the Seconds format is selected, the position will be nudged by whole seconds.
- If any frame-based format is selected, the position will be nudged by frames.
- If Bars+Beats is selected, the position will be nudged by ticks. There are 480 ticks per beat.
- If the Samples format is selected, the position will be nudged by samples.

3.3 Options and Settings

3.3.1 The "Return to Start Position on Stop" Preference

You have the option to set the behavior of the project cursor when you press Stop. This is done in the Preferences dialog on the Transport page:

1. **Open the Preferences dialog from the File menu and select the Transport page.**
2. **Activate or deactivate the "Return to Start Position on Stop" item.**

- **If activated (ticked), the project cursor will automatically return to the position where recording or playback last was activated from, when you press Stop.**
- **If deactivated, the project cursor will remain at the position where you hit Stop.**

  Pressing Stop *again* will return the project cursor to the position where recording or playback last was activated from.

3. **Click OK to close the Preferences dialog and apply the changes.**

3.3.2 About Track Disable/Enable

For audio tracks, the track context menu contains an item named "Disable Track". This shuts down all disk activity for the track, as opposed to using Mute, which merely turns down the output volume for a track. If you often record "alternative takes", you can easily build up a large number of takes that are actually still "playing back" from the hard disk during playback, although the tracks may be muted. This puts an unnecessary load on your disk system, so using "Disable Track" is recommended for such situations.

- **Select "Disable Track" when you have recorded many alternative takes of a performance on separate tracks, that you want to keep for later evaluation and/or editing.**

  Select "Enable Track" from the track context menu to re-enable disabled tracks.

3.3.3 Playback Functions

Apart from the standard transport controls on the Transport panel, you can also find a number of functions that can be used to control playback on the Transport menu. The items have the following functionality:

Option	Description
Play from Selection Start	This activates playback from the beginning of the currently selected range.
Play from Selection End	This activates playback from the end of the currently selected range.
Play until Selection Start	This activates playback two seconds before the start of the currently selected range and stops at the selection start.
Play until Selection End	This activates playback two seconds before the end of the selected range and stops at the selection end.
Play until Next Marker	This activates playback from the project cursor and stops at the next marker.
Play Selection Range	This activates playback from the start of the selected range and stops at the selection end.
Loop Selection	This activates playback from the start of the selected range and continuously starts over again upon reaching the selection end.

- The functions listed above (except "Play to Next Marker") are only available if you have selected one or more events or made a selection range.

3.3.4 About Chase

Chase is basically a function that makes sure your MIDI instruments sound as they should when you locate to a new position and start playback. This is accomplished by having the program transmitting a number of MIDI messages to your instruments each time you move to a new position in the project, making sure all MIDI devices are set up correctly with regard to Program Change, controller messages (such as MIDI Volume) etc.

For example, let's say you have a MIDI track with a Program Change event inserted at the beginning. This event makes a synth switch to a piano sound.

In the beginning of the first chorus you have another Program Change event which makes the same synth switch to a string sound.

You now play back the song. It begins with the piano sound and then switches to the string sound. In the middle of the chorus you stop and rewind to some point between the beginning and the second Program Change. The synth will now still play the string sound although in this section it really should be a piano!

The Chase function takes care of that. If Program Change events are set to be chased, Cubase SX/SL will track the music back to the beginning, find the first Program Change and send this out, so that the synth is set to the right sound.

The same thing can apply to other event types as well. The Chase Events Filter settings in the Preferences dialog (MIDI-Chase Events Filter page) determine which event types will be chased when you locate to a new position and start playback.

- Event types for which the checkbox is activated in this dialog will not be chased.

4 Recording

4.1 Background

This chapter describes the various recording methods that you can use in Cubase SX/SL. As it is possible to record both audio and MIDI tracks in Cubase SX/SL, both of these recording methods are covered in this chapter.

4.1.1 Before You Start

This chapter assumes that you are reasonably familiar with certain basic recording concepts, and that the following initial preparations have been made:

- **You have properly set up, connected and calibrated your audio hardware.**

  This is described in the Getting Started book.

- **You have opened a project and set the project setup parameters to your specifications.**

  Project Setup parameters determine the record format, sample rate, project length etc. that affect the resulting audio recordings you make during the course of the project. See page 117.

- **If you plan to record MIDI, your MIDI equipment should be set up and connected correctly.**

  See the Getting Started book.

4.2 Basic Recording Methods

This section describes the general methods used for recording. However, there are additional preparations and procedures that are specific to audio and MIDI recording respectively. Make sure to read these sections before you start recording (see page 82 and page 93).

4.2.1 Record Enabling a Track

Cubase SX/SL can record on a single track or on several tracks (audio and/or MIDI) simultaneously. To make a track ready for recording, click the Record Enable button for the track in the Track list, in the Inspector or in the Mixer. When activated, the button(s) turn red, indicating record ready mode.

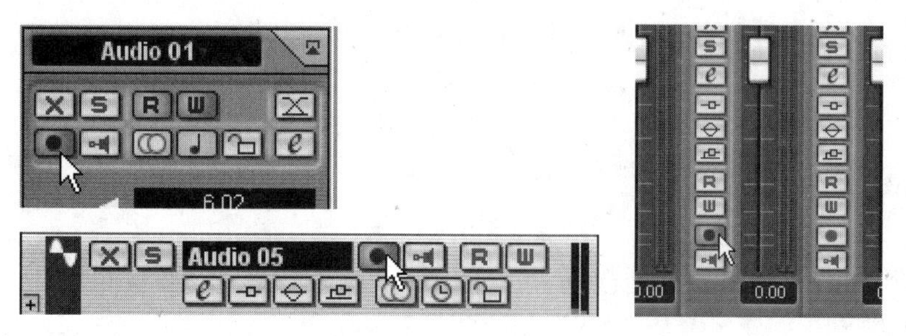

Record Enable in the Inspector, Track list and Mixer.

- If the option "Enable Record on Selected Track" is activated in the Preferences dialog (Editing page), tracks are automatically record enabled when you select them in the Track list.
- The exact number of audio tracks you can record simultaneously depends on your computer CPU and hard disk performance.
  Furthermore, it would be pointless to record more audio tracks than you have audio inputs, since this would only result in duplicate tracks and audio files (see page 82).

4.2.2 Manually Activating Recording

You activate recording by clicking the Record button on the Transport panel or toolbar, or by using the corresponding key command (by default [*] on the numeric keypad).

Recording can be activated from Stop mode (from the current cursor position or from the left locator) or during playback:

- If you activate recording from Stop mode, and the option "Start Record at Left Locator" is activated on the Transport menu, recording will start from the left locator. The preroll setting or the metronome count-in will be applied (see page 102).
- If you activate recording from Stop mode, and the "Start Record at Left Locator" is deactivated, recording will start from the current project cursor position.
- If you activate recording during playback, Cubase SX/SL will immediately enter Record mode and start recording at the current project cursor position.
  This is known as "manual punch in".

4.2.3 Automatically Activating Recording

Cubase SX/SL can automatically switch from playback to recording at a given position. This is known as "automatic punch in". A typical use for this would be if you need to replace a section of a recording, and want to listen to the previously recorded audio up to the recording start position.

1. **Set the left locator to the position at which you want recording to start.**
2. **Activate the Punch In button on the Transport panel.**

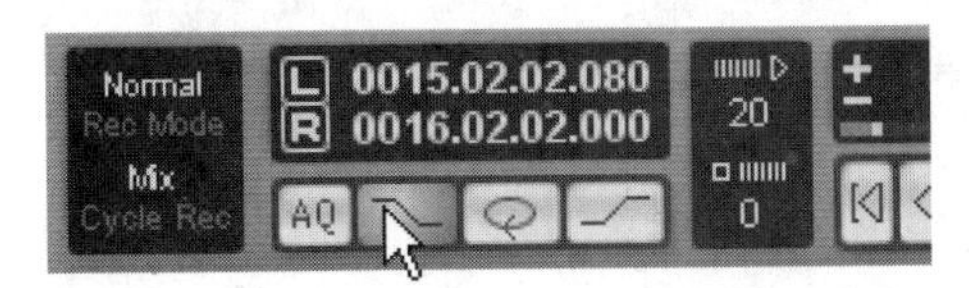

Punch In activated.

3. **Activate playback from some position before the left locator.**

When the project cursor reaches the left locator, recording is automatically activated.

4.2.4 Stopping Recording

Again, this can be done automatically or manually:

- **If you click the Stop button on the Transport panel (or use the corresponding key command, by default [0] on the numeric keypad), recording is deactivated and Cubase SX/SL goes to Stop mode.**
- **If you click the Record button or use the key command for recording, by default [*], recording is deactivated but playback continues.**

  This is known as "manual punch out".
- **If the Punch Out button is activated on the Transport panel, recording will be deactivated when the project cursor reaches the right locator.**

  This is known as "automatic punch out". By combining this with automatic punch in, you can set up a specific section to record—again very useful if you want to replace a certain part of a recording. See also page 102.

Punch In and Out activated.

4.2.5 Cycle Recording

Cubase SX/SL can record and play back in a cycle—a loop. You specify where the cycle starts and ends by setting the left and right locators. When cycle is active, the selected section is seamlessly repeated until you hit Stop or deactivate cycle mode.

- **To activate cycle mode, click the cycle button on the Transport panel.**

  If you now activate Play, the section between the left and right locator is repeated indefinitely until you stop.

Cycle activated.

- **To record in Cycle mode, you can start recording from the left locator, from before the locators or from within the cycle, from Stop mode or during playback.**

  As soon as the project cursor reaches the right locator, it will jump back to the left locator and continue recording a new lap.

- **The results of cycle recording are different for audio (see page 90) and MIDI (see page 98).**

4.3 Audio Recording Specifics

4.3.1 Activating and Selecting VST Inputs

Cubase SX/SL allows you to use audio hardware with multiple inputs and route different inputs to different audio channels. To activate inputs, first open the VST Inputs window on the Devices menu.

- Note that active inputs use processing power! Make it a habit to only activate audio inputs that you actually intend to use.

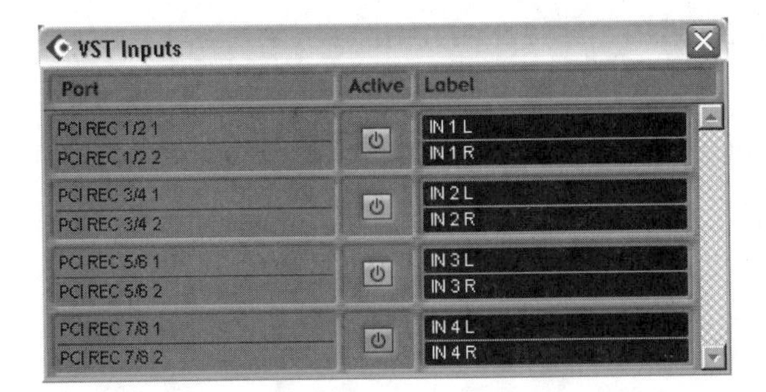

The VST Inputs window is divided into three columns:

- The left column contains the available physical input ports on the audio hardware.
- The middle column indicates which input pairs are activated. You turn input pairs on or off by clicking the buttons in this column.
- The right column shows the names that will be used for each input throughout the program. You can rename an input by clicking in this column and typing a new name.

● If you deactivate an input pair that is currently used (selected as input source for one or several audio channels), you will be asked whether you want Cubase SX/SL to remap these inputs (change the input source selection for the channels in question).

Routing Activated VST Inputs to a Channel

Selecting an input source for a track's corresponding channel is done in the Mixer. Proceed as follows:

1. **Open the Mixer from the Devices menu.**
2. **Locate the mixer channel strip for the audio track on which you plan to record.**
3. **Pull down the input pop-up for the channel strip and select the input to which the signal source you want to record is connected.**

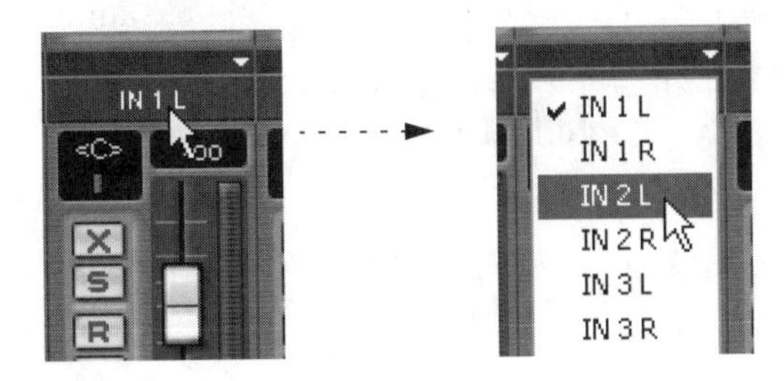

4.3.2 Selecting a Recording File Format

The format of recorded files is set in the Project Setup dialog on the Project menu. There are three settings: sample rate, record format (bit depth) and record file type. While the sample rate is set once and for all when you start working on a new project, the bit depth and file type can be changed at any time.

Record Format (Bit Depth)

● The record format setting is disregarded if you activate the TrueTape recording mode (see page 85).

The available options are 16 bit, 24 bit and 32 bit float. Use the following guidelines:

- Normally, select record format according to the bit depth delivered by your audio hardware.
  For example, if your audio hardware has 20 bit A/D converters (inputs), you may want to record at 24 bit resolution, to capture the full bit depth. On the other hand, if your hardware has 16 bit inputs, it's pointless to record with a higher bit depth—this will only make the audio files larger, with no difference in audio quality. The exception to this is the TrueTape recording mode, which produces 32 bit float files but is fully usable with 16 or 24 bit audio hardware—see below.
- The higher the bit depth, the larger the files and the more strain is put on the disk system.
  If this is an issue, you may want to lower the record format setting.

Record File Type

The Record File Type setting determines which type of files will be created when you record:

File Type	Description
Wave File	Wave files have the extension ".wav" and are the most common file format on the PC platform.
Broadcast Wave File	In terms of audio content, the same as regular Wave files, but with embedded text strings for supplying additional information about the file (see below).
AIFF File	Audio Interchange File Format, a standard defined by Apple Computer Inc. AIFF files have the extension ".aif" and are used on most computer platforms.

- **If you select Broadcast Wave File, you can specify Author, Description and Reference text strings that will be embedded in the recorded file.**

  This is done on the Audio—Broadcast Wave page in the Preferences dialog.

4.3.3 Activating TrueTape™ (Cubase SX only)

TrueTape is a unique Steinberg technology that emulates the behavior of a professional analog tape recorder. While digital audio recording has a number of benefits, some may perceive digital sound to be somewhat "sterile" and "cold" compared to high quality analog recordings. The TrueTape feature remedies this problem by recreating the sound of analog tape saturation at the recording stage.

Note:

- TrueTape produces 32 bit float files.
  The hard disk and processor speed considerations of the regular 32 bit format apply here as well.
- Unlike the regular 32 bit float record format, you can use the TrueTape mode even if your audio hardware only supports 16 bit resolution.
  This is because the TrueTape feature converts the signal to 32 bit float format, and adds audio information in the floating point domain.

You activate and set up TrueTape in the following way:

1. **Pull down the Devices menu and select TrueTape.**

   The TrueTape panel appears.

2. **Click the power button in the top left corner to activate TrueTape.**
3. **Use the Drive control to adjust the amount of tape saturation effect to your liking.**

   If you are monitoring through Cubase SX/SL, you will hear how the changes color the sound of the monitored signal. This allows you to try out the settings before actually recording.

- **The pop-up menu above the TrueTape panel allows you to select one of four Drive presets, for quick changes.**

  These contain no "hidden parameters"—selecting the "24dB Super Saturation" preset is the same as moving the Drive control all the way to the right. Note that any adjustments you make to the Drive control are automatically applied to the selected preset. You can also rename a preset by clicking and typing in a new name.

- Raising the Drive level will also raise the level in the audio file, and you can easily reach 0.0 (clipping) on the input level meters.
  Unlike when recording in 16 bit format, this is nothing to worry about—it is virtually impossible to get digital distortion in a 32 Bit float file. However, you may want to check your input levels with TrueTape turned off to make sure the clipping doesn't occur in the audio hardware.

4.3.4 Setting Up Tracks for Mono or Stereo Recording

One of the initial decisions you have to make before you start recording audio is whether the recording should be stereo or mono. This is determined by the stereo/mono status of the audio track selected for recording:

- **To set a track to mono or stereo, click the Stereo/Mono button in the Track list or in the Inspector.**

  A lit stereo button indicates a stereo track, while a dark mono button indicates a mono track.

The Stereo/Mono button.

- For more details about mono/stereo track compatibility, see page 130.

4.3.5 Monitoring

In this context, "monitoring" means listening to the input signal during recording. There are three fundamentally different ways to do this: via Cubase SX/SL, externally (by listening to the signal before it reaches Cubase SX/SL) or by using ASIO Direct Monitoring (which is a combination of both of the other methods—see page 88).

Monitoring via Cubase SX/SL

If you monitor via Cubase SX/SL, the input signal is mixed in with the audio playback. The advantage of this is that you can adjust the monitoring level and panning in the Mixer, and add effects and EQ to the monitor signal just as during playback. The disadvantage of monitoring via Cubase SX/SL is that the monitored signal will be delayed according to the latency value (which depends on your audio hardware and drivers). Therefore, monitoring via Cubase SX/SL requires an audio hardware configuration with a low latency value (see the Getting Started book).

When monitoring via Cubase SX/SL, you can select one of four modes in the Preferences dialog (VST page):

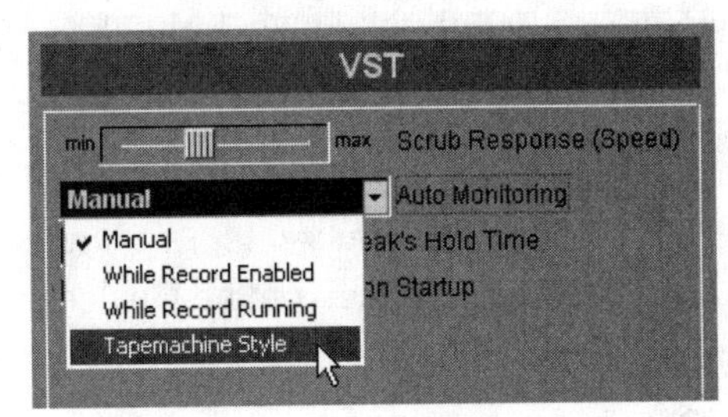

- Manual.
  This option allows you to turn input monitoring on or off by clicking the Monitor button in the Inspector, the Track list or in the Mixer.
- While Record Enabled.
  With this option you will hear the audio source connected to the channel input whenever the track is record enabled.
- While Record Running.
  This option switches to input monitoring only during recording.
- Tapemachine Style.
  This option emulates standard tapemachine behavior: input monitoring in stop mode and during recording, but not during playback.

External Monitoring

External monitoring (listening to the input signal before it goes into Cubase SX/SL) requires some sort of external mixer for mixing the audio playback with the input signal. This can be a stand-alone physical mixer or a mixer application for your audio hardware, if this has a mode in which the input audio is sent back out again (usually called "Thru", "Direct Thru" or similar).

When using external monitoring, you cannot control the level of the monitor signal from within Cubase SX/SL, or add VST effects or EQ to the monitor signal. The latency value of the audio hardware configuration does not affect the monitor signal in this mode.

- If you want to use external monitoring, you need to make sure that monitoring via Cubase SX/SL isn't activated as well.
  Select the "Manual" monitoring mode in the Preferences dialog (VST page) and simply don't activate the Monitor buttons.

ASIO Direct Monitoring

If your audio hardware is ASIO 2.0 compatible, it may support ASIO Direct Monitoring. In this mode, the actual monitoring is done in the audio hardware, by sending the input signal back out again. However, monitoring is *controlled* from Cubase SX/SL. This means that the audio hardware's direct monitoring feature can be turned on or off automatically by Cubase SX/SL, just as when using internal monitoring.

- To activate ASIO Direct Monitoring, open the Device Setup dialog on the Devices menu and use the Direct Monitoring checkbox on the Setup tab for the VST Multitrack device.
  If the checkbox is greyed out, this means that your audio hardware (or its current driver) doesn't support ASIO Direct Monitoring. Consult the audio hardware manufacturer for details.

- When ASIO Direct Monitoring is activated, you can select a monitoring mode in the Preferences dialog (VST page), as when monitoring via Cubase SX/SL (see page 87).
- Depending on the audio hardware, it may also be possible to adjust monitoring level and panning from the Mixer.
  Consult the documentation of the audio hardware if in doubt.

- VST effects and EQ cannot be applied to the monitor signal in this mode, since the monitor signal doesn't pass through Cubase SX/SL.
- Depending on the audio hardware, there may be special restrictions as to which audio outputs can be used for direct monitoring.
  For details on the routing of the audio hardware, see its documentation.

- The latency value of the audio hardware configuration does not affect the monitor signal when using ASIO Direct Monitoring.

4.3.6 Setting Input Levels

When monitoring a channel signal source in stop mode, the meters show the level at the input selected for the audio channel. So if the connected signal source is sounding you should see activity in both the Track list meter and in the mixer strip for that channel.

- Note that it is not possible to set input gain with the mixer fader!

Check the levels coming in to Cubase SX/SL, and if necessary, adjust the input level in one of the following ways:

- **Adjust the output level of the sound source or external mixer.**
- **Use the audio hardware's own application program to set the input levels, if this possibility is provided.**

  See the documentation of the audio hardware.
- **If your audio hardware supports the ASIO Control Panel function, it may be possible to make input level settings.**

  To open the ASIO Control Panel, open the Device Setup dialog on the Devices menu and click the Control Panel button on the Setup tab for the VST Multitrack device.

- Input levels should be as high as possible, without exceeding 0dB.

4.3.7 Recording

Recording is done using any of the general recording methods (see page 79). After you finish recording, an audio file has been created in the Audio folder within the projects folder. In the Pool, an audio clip is then created for the audio file, and an audio event that plays the whole clip appears on the recording track. Finally, a waveform image is calculated for the audio event. If the recording was very long, this may take a while.

- If the option "Create Images During Record" is activated in the Preferences dialog (Audio page), the waveform image will be calculated and displayed during the actual recording process.
  This should only be activated if you have a fairly powerful computer system, since the real-time calculation uses some extra processing power.

Undoing Recording

If you decide that you don't like what you just recorded, you can delete it by selecting Undo from the Edit menu. The following will happen:

- The event(s) you just created will be removed from the Project window.
- The audio clip(s) in the Pool will be moved to the Trash folder.
- The recorded audio file(s) will not be removed from the hard disk.
  However, since their corresponding clips are moved to the Trash folder, you can delete the files by opening the Pool and selecting "Empty Trash" from the Pool menu.

About Overlap and Audio Tracks

If you record again where something has already been recorded, you get a new event that overlaps the previous one(s). When you play back, only the events that are actually visible are played back.

- One audio track can only play back one audio event at a time.

The functions "Move to Front" and "Move to Back" on the Edit menu (see page 135) are useful for managing overlapping events, as is the "To Front" function (see below).

4.3.8 Recording Audio in Cycle Mode

If you are recording audio in Cycle mode, the result depends on the "Cycle Record Mode" setting in the Preferences dialog (Audio page):

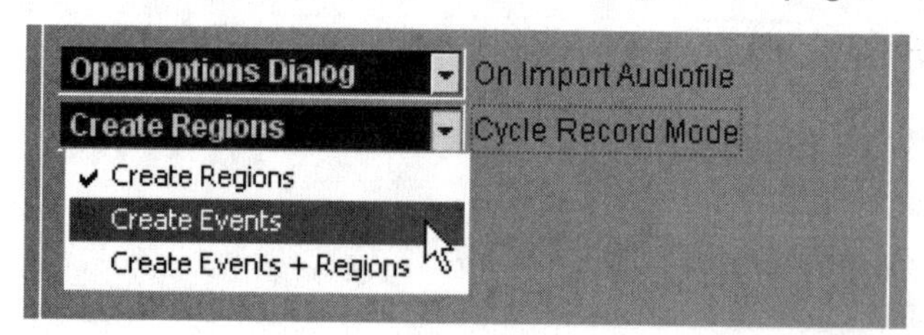

Create Events

When Cycle Record Mode is set to "Create Events", the following will happen when you record audio in Cycle mode:

- One continuous audio file is created during the entire recording process.

- For each recorded lap of the Cycle, one audio event is created.
  The events will have the name of the audio file plus the text "Take *", where "*" indicates the number of the take.
- The last take (the last recorded lap) will be on top (and will thus be the one you hear when you activate playback).

To select another take for playback, proceed a follows:

1. **Right-click the event and select "To Front" from the pop-up menu that appears.**

   A submenu appears, listing all the other (obscured) events.

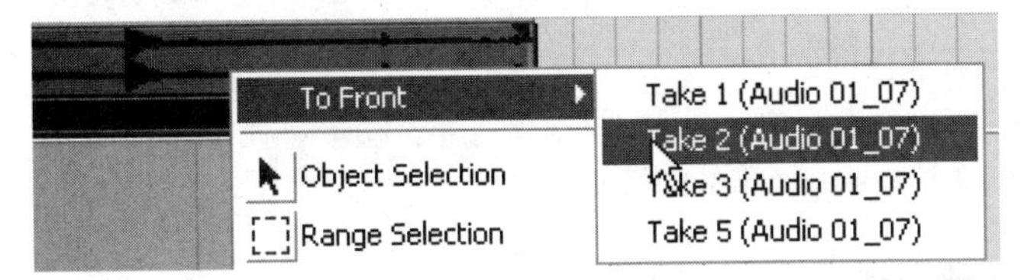

2. **Select the desired take.**

   The corresponding event is brought to front.

This method allows you to quickly combine the best parts of each take, in the following way:

1. **Use the Scissors tool to split the events in several sections, one for each part of the take.**

   For example, if you recorded four lines of vocals (in each take), you can split the events so that each line gets a separate event.

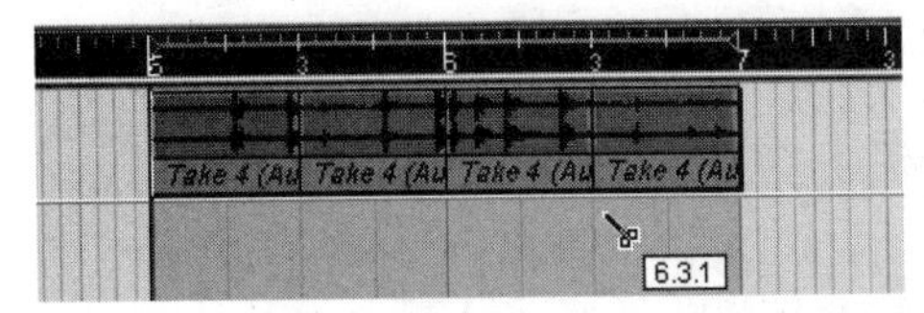

The events after splitting. Note that since the original take events overlap each other, clicking with the Scissors tool will split all takes at the same position.

2. **For each section of the take, use the "To Front" function to bring the best take to the front.**

   This way, you can quickly combine the best sections of each take, using the first vocal line from one take, the second line from another take and so on.

You can also compile a "perfect" take in the Audio Part Editor, as described on page 382.

Create Regions

When Cycle Record Mode is set to "Create Regions", the following will happen when you record audio in Cycle mode:

- One continuous audio file is created during the entire recording process.
- The audio event in the Project window displays the name of the audio file plus the text "Take *" (with "*" indicating the number of the last completed Cycle lap).
- If you play back the recorded event, you will only hear what was recorded during the last lap of the Cycle recording.
  The previous "takes" recorded in the Cycle are still available, however.
- The audio clip is divided into regions (called takes), one for each lap of the Cycle that was recorded.
  If you locate the audio file you just recorded in the Pool, and click on the plus sign beside it, you can see the regions that have been created, one for each lap of the Cycle that was completed during recording.

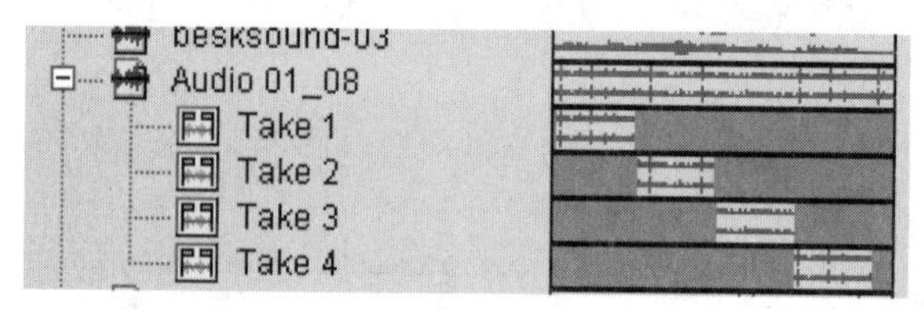

"Take" regions in the Pool window.

To play back the different "takes", proceed as follows:

1. **In the Project window, right-click the event that was created during Cycle recording.**

   The Quick menu appears.

2. **Select the "Set To Region" menu item.**

   A submenu appears with the takes you recorded during Cycle record.

3. **Now you can freely select any of the takes from the submenu and it will replace the previous take event in the Project window.**

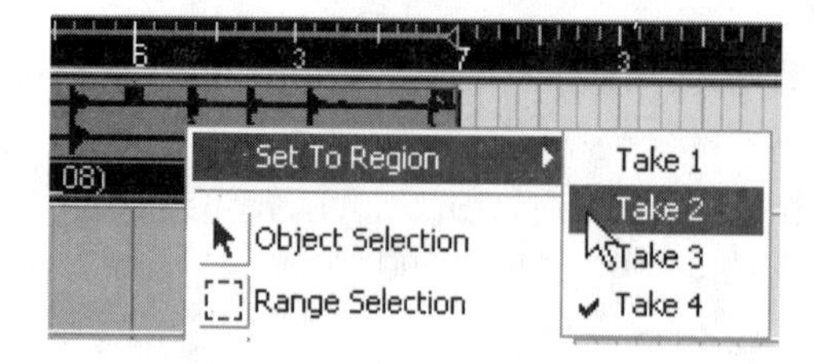

Use this method to listen through the various takes. Select the best single take, or compile a "perfect" take by cutting out the best bits from each take and putting them together (see page 382).

Create Events + Regions

In this mode, both events and regions are created. If you work with the takes as events in this mode, you can edit the events freely (e.g. splitting them as described on page 90). However, in case you want to go back to the original takes, they are still available as regions (on the "Set To Region" submenu, in the Pool or in the Sample Editor).

4.4 MIDI Recording Specifics

4.4.1 Activating MIDI Thru

As described in the Getting Started book, the normal way to work with MIDI is to have MIDI Thru activated in Cubase SX/SL, and Local Off selected in your MIDI Instrument(s). In this mode, everything you play during recording will be "echoed" back out again on the MIDI output and channel selected for the recording track.

1. **Make sure the option "MIDI Thru Active" is activated in the Preferences dialog (MIDI page).**
2. **Record Enable the track(s) on which you want to record.**

   Now, incoming MIDI is "echoed" back out again, for all Record Enabled MIDI tracks.

Record Enable button. Monitor button.

- If you just want to use the thru function for a MIDI track without recording, activate the monitor button for the track instead.
  This is useful e.g. if you want to try out different sounds or play a VST instrument in real time without recording your playing.

4.4.2 Setting MIDI Channel, Input and Output

Setting the MIDI channel in the instrument

Most MIDI synthesizers can play several sounds at the same time, each on a different MIDI channel. This is the key to playing back several sounds (bass, piano etc.) from the same instrument. Some devices (such as General MIDI compatible sound modules) always receive on all 16 MIDI channels. If you have such an instrument, there's no specific setting you need to make in the instrument. On other instruments you will have to use the front panel controls to set up a number of "Parts", "Timbres" or similar so that they receive on one MIDI channel each. See the manual that came with your instrument for more information.

Naming MIDI Ports in Cubase SX/SL

MIDI inputs and outputs can often be shown with unnecessarily long and complicated names. If you wish, you can rename your MIDI ports to more descriptive names:

1. **Open the Device Setup dialog from the Devices menu.**
2. **Select the Windows MIDI device in the Device list.**

   The available MIDI inputs and outputs are listed under the Setup tab.
3. **To change the name of a MIDI port, click in the Device column and type in a new name.**

   After closing the dialog, the new names will appear on the MIDI "in:" and "out:" pop-ups.

Setting the MIDI Input in the Inspector

You select MIDI inputs for tracks in the Inspector—the area to the left of the track list in the Project window:

1. **If the Inspector is hidden, click the Show Inspector button on the toolbar.**

2. **Select the track by clicking in the Track list.**

   The Inspector shows the settings for the selected track (for details, see page 111).

3. **Click the tab in the upper right corner of the Inspector to make sure the top-most section is shown.**

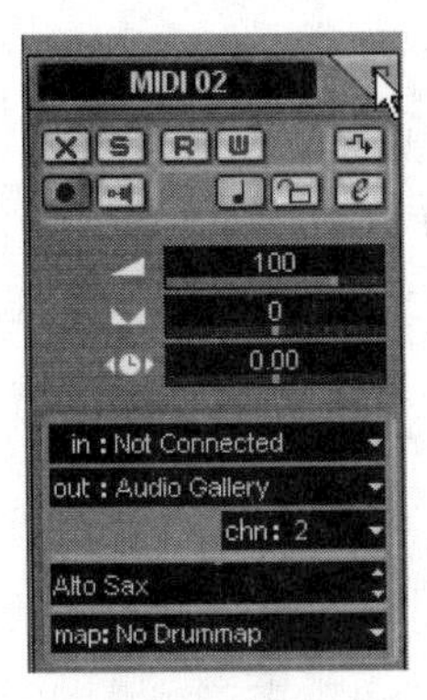

4. **Pull down the "in" pop-up and select an input.**

   The available MIDI inputs are shown. The items on the menu depend on the type of MIDI interface you are using etc.

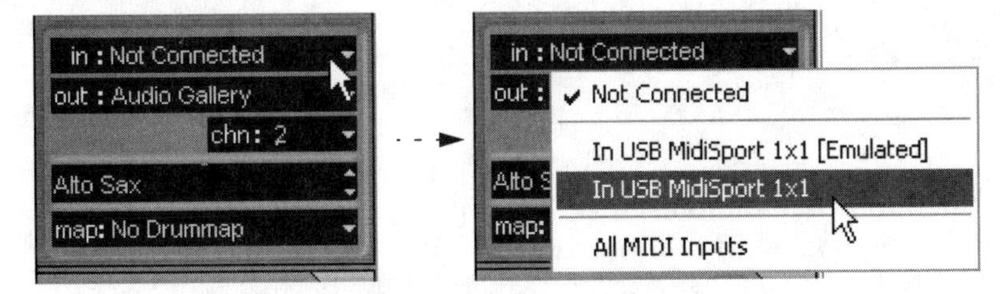

- **If you select the "All MIDI Inputs" option, the track will receive MIDI data from all available MIDI inputs.**
- **If you hold down [Ctrl] and select a MIDI input, this is selected for all MIDI tracks.**

Setting the MIDI Channel and Output

The MIDI channel and output settings determine where the recorded MIDI is routed during playback, but are also relevant for MIDI Thru in Cubase SX/SL. Channel and output can be selected in the Track list or in the Inspector.

1. **To show the settings in the Inspector, proceed as when selecting a MIDI input (see above).**
2. **Pull down the "out:" pop-up and select an output.**

   The available MIDI outputs are shown. The items on the menu depend on what type of MIDI interface you are using etc.

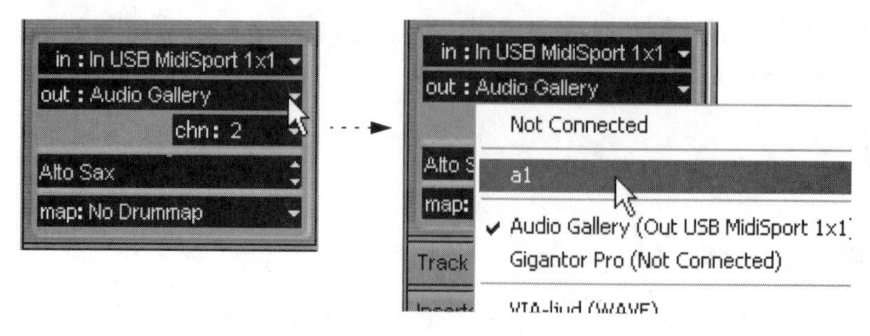

- **If you hold down [Ctrl] and select a MIDI output, this is selected for all MIDI tracks.**

3. **Use the "chn" pop-up menu to select a MIDI channel for the track.**

- **If you set the track to MIDI channel "Any", each MIDI event on the track will be sent out on the channel stored in the event itself.**

  In other words, the MIDI will be played back on the channel(s) used by the MIDI input device (the MIDI instrument you play during recording).

4.4.3 Selecting a Sound

You can select sounds from within Cubase SX/SL, by instructing the program to send Program Change and Bank Select messages to your MIDI device. This is done using the "prg" and "bnk" value fields in the Inspector or Track list.

However, it is also possible to select sounds by name. For descriptions of how to set this up, see page 419.

4.4.4 Recording

Recording MIDI is done according to the basic recording methods (see page 79). When you finish recording, a part containing MIDI events is created in the Project window.

About Overlap and the Rec Mode Setting

MIDI tracks are different from audio tracks when it comes to overlapping parts:

- All events in overlapping parts are always played back.
  If you record several parts at the same locations (or move parts so that they overlap), you will hear the events in all parts on playback, even though some of the parts are obscured in the Project window.

When recording overlapping parts, the result depends on the Rec Mode setting on the Transport bar:

- **If Rec Mode is set to "Normal", overdub recording works as with audio tracks, i.e. if you record again where something has already been recorded, you get a new part that overlaps the previous one(s).**
- **If Rec Mode is set to "Merge", the overdubbed events are added to the existing part.**

About Punch In and Out on MIDI Tracks

Performing and setting up manual and automatic punch in/out recording for MIDI tracks is done in exactly the same way as for audio tracks. There is one thing to note, however:

- **Punching in and out on recordings with Pitch Bend or controller data (modulation wheel, sustain pedal, volume etc.), may lead to strange effects (apparently hanging notes, constant vibrato etc.).**

  If this happens, you may need to use the Reset command on the MIDI menu (see page 99).

About the Auto Quantize Function

If Auto Quantize is activated on the Transport panel (the "AQ" button), the notes you record are automatically quantized according to the current Quantize settings. For more information about quantizing, see page 468.

4.4.5 Recording MIDI in Cycle Mode

When you record MIDI in Cycle mode, the result depends on which Cycle Rec mode is selected on the Transport panel:

Cycle Rec Mode: Mix

For each completed lap, everything you record is added to what was previously recorded, in the same part. This is useful for building up rhythm patterns, for example. Record a hi-hat part on the first lap, the bass drum part on the second lap etc.

Cycle Rec Mode: Overwrite

For each completed lap, everything you record replaces what was previously recorded in the same part.

4.4.6 Recording Different Types of MIDI Messages

- You can decide exactly which event types should be recorded by using the MIDI filters—see page 101.

Notes

With MIDI, when you press and release a key on your synth or other MIDI keyboard, a Note On (key down) and a Note Off (key up) message are sent out. The MIDI note message also contains the information which MIDI channel was used. Normally, this information is overridden by the MIDI channel setting for the track, but if you set the track to MIDI channel "Any", the notes will be played back on their original channels.

Continuous Messages

Pitch bend, aftertouch and controllers (like modulation wheel, sustain pedal, volume etc.) are considered as MIDI Continuous events (as opposed to the momentary key down and key up messages). If you move the Pitch bend wheel on your synthesizer while recording, this movement is recorded together with the key (Note On and Note Off messages), just as you'd expect. But the continuous messages can also be recorded after the notes have been recorded (or even before). They can also be recorded on their own tracks, separately from the notes to which they belong.

Say for instance that you record one or several bass parts on track 2. If you now set another track, like track 55, to the same output and MIDI channel as track 2 you can make a separate recording of just pitch bends for the bass parts. This means that you activate recording as usual and only move the pitch bend wheel during the take. As long as the two tracks are set to the same output and MIDI channel it will appear to the MIDI instrument as if the two recordings were made at the same time.

Program Change Messages

Normally, when you switch from one program to another on your keyboard (or whatever you use to record), a number corresponding to that program is sent out via MIDI as a Program Change message. These can be recorded on the fly with the music, recorded afterwards on a separate track, or manually entered in the MIDI or List Editors.

System Exclusive Messages

System Exclusive (SysEx) is a special type of MIDI message used to send things that only make sense to a unit of a certain make and type. Every major MIDI manufacturer has its own SysEx identity code and these are part of practically all SysEx messages. SysEx can be used to transmit a list of the numbers that make up the settings of one or more sounds in a synth. For more about viewing and editing SysEx messages, see page 595.

4.4.7 The Reset Function

The Reset function on the MIDI menu sends out note-off messages and resets controllers on all MIDI channels. This is sometimes necessary if you experience hanging notes, constant vibrato, etc.

- **Cubase SX/SL can also automatically perform a MIDI Reset after recording, during playback (after each part) and/or on stop.**

  You turn these functions on or off in the Preferences dialog (MIDI page).

4.4.8 MIDI Preferences

The following options and settings in the Preferences dialog (MIDI page) affect MIDI recording and playback:

"Note On" Priority

When this is activated, MIDI Note On messages are given priority over other types of MIDI messages, ensuring tight timing even if you use a lot of continuous MIDI data.

Length Correction

Adjusts the length of notes so that there always is a short time between the end of one note and the start of another (of the same pitch and on the same MIDI channel).

Snap Record Parts to Bars

When this is activated, recorded MIDI parts will automatically be lengthened to start and end at whole bar positions. If you are working in a Bars+Beats-based context, this can make editing (Moving, Duplicating, Repeating, etc.) easier.

Solo Record in Editors

If this is activated and you open a part for editing in a MIDI editor, its track is automatically Record Enabled. Furthermore, Record Enable is deactivated for all other MIDI tracks until you close the editor again.

This makes it easier to record MIDI data when you're editing a part—you will always be sure the recorded data ends up in the edited part and not on any other track.

Record Catch Range

When you record starting at the left locator, this setting helps you make sure the very start of the recording is included. A very annoying scenario is when you have recorded a perfect MIDI take, only to find out that the very first note wasn't included—because you started playing a little bit too early! If you raise the Record Catch Range, Cubase SX/SL will catch the events played just before the recording start point, eliminating this problem.

4.4.9 Filtering MIDI

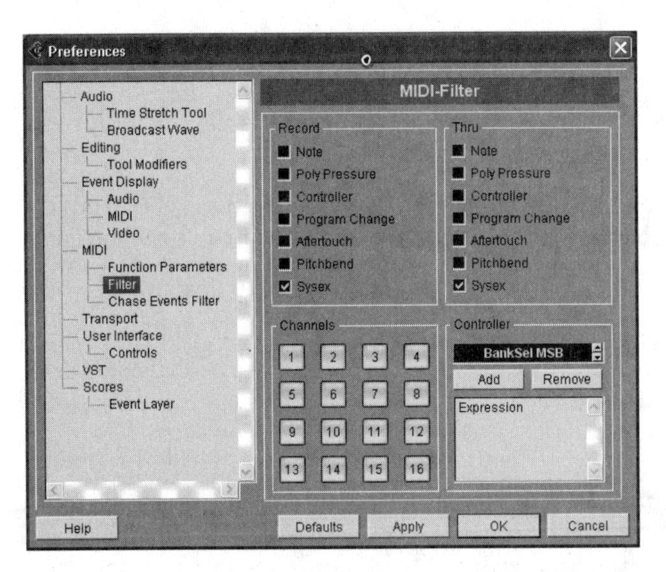

The MIDI-Filter page in the Preferences dialog allows you to prevent certain MIDI messages from being recorded and/or "thruput" (echoed by the MIDI Thru function).

The dialog is divided into four sections:

Section	Description
Record	Activating any of these options prevents that type of MIDI message from being recorded. It will, however, be thruput, and if already recorded, it will play back normally.
Thru	Activating any of these options prevents that type of MIDI message from being thruput. It will, however, be recorded and played back normally.
Channels	If you activate a channel button, no MIDI messages on that MIDI channel will be recorded or thruput. Already recorded messages will, however, be played back normally.
Controller	Allows you to prevent certain MIDI controller types from being recorded or thruput. To filter out a controller type, select it from the list at the top of the section and click "Add". It will appear on the list below. To remove a controller type from the list (allow it to be recorded and thruput), select it in the lower list and click "Remove".

4.5 Options and Settings

4.5.1 Recording-related Preferences

A couple of settings in the Preferences dialog (Transport page) are relevant for recording. Set these according to your preferred method of work:

Deactivate Punch In on Stop

If this is activated, punch in on the Transport panel is automatically deactivated whenever you enter Stop mode.

Stop after Automatic Punchout

If this is activated, playback will automatically stop after automatic punch out (when the project cursor reaches the right locator and punch out is activated on the Transport panel). If the postroll value on the Transport panel is set to a value other than zero, playback will continue for the set time before stopping (see below).

4.5.2 About Preroll and Postroll

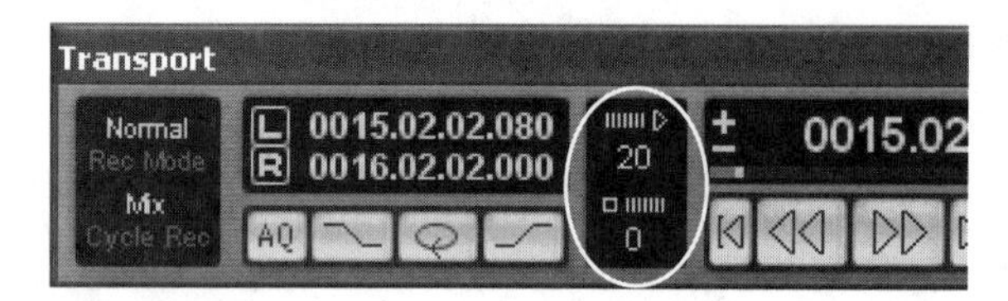

The preroll and postroll value fields on the Transport panel have the following functionality:

- By setting a preroll value, you instruct Cubase SX/SL to "roll back" a short section whenever playback is activated.
  This applies whenever you start playback, but is perhaps most relevant when recording from the left locator (punch in activated on the Transport panel) as described below.
- By setting a postroll value, you instruct Cubase SX/SL to play back a short section after automatic punch out, before stopping.
  This is only relevant when punch out is activated on the Transport panel and "Stop after Automatic Punchout" is activated in the Preferences dialog (Transport page).
- To enable or disable the pre/postroll function, select the option "Use Pre/Post-Roll" on the Transport menu.

An example:

1. **Set the locators to where you want to start and end recording.**
2. **Activate punch in and punch out on the Transport panel.**
3. **Activate the option "Stop after Automatic Punchout" in the Preferences dialog (Transport page).**
4. **Set suitable preroll and postroll times by clicking in the corresponding fields on the Transport panel and typing in time values.**
5. **Make sure Click is deactivated on the Transport panel.**

   If the Click is activated when you record from the left locator in stop mode, the pre-roll setting is disregarded and the metronome precount is used instead (see page 103).
6. **Pull down the Transport menu and tick the option "Use Pre/Post-Roll".**
7. **Activate recording.**

   The project cursor "rolls back" by the time specified in the preroll field and play-back starts. When the cursor reaches the left locator, recording is automatically activated. When the cursor reaches the right locator, recording is deactivated, but playback continues for the time set in the postroll field before stopping.

4.5.3 Using the Metronome

The metronome will output a click that can be used as a timing reference. The two parameters that govern the timing of the metronome are tempo and time signature, and these are edited in the Tempo Track window (see page 575).

- **To activate the metronome, click the Click button on the Transport panel, or use the corresponding key command (by default [C]).**

Metronome Settings

You make settings for the metronome in the Metronome Setup dialog, opened from the Transport menu.

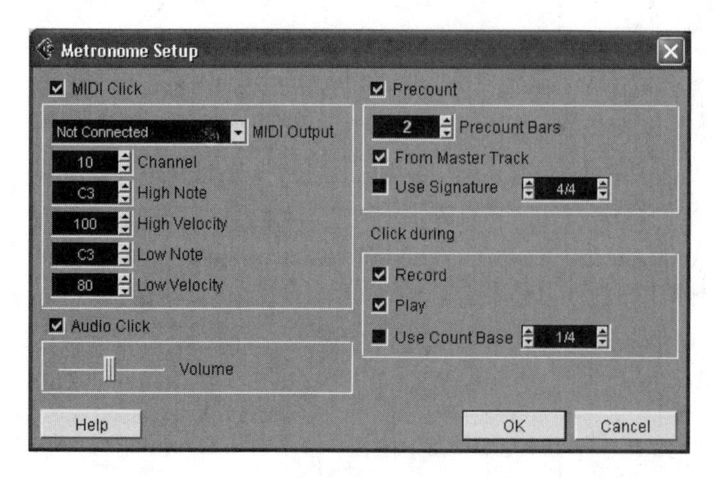

The metronome can use either an audio click played back via the audio hardware, send MIDI data to a connected device which will play back the click or do both. The following metronome parameter settings can be made in the dialog:

Parameter	Description
MIDI Click on/off	Selects whether or not the metronome will sound via MIDI.
MIDI Output	Use the pop-up to select a MIDI output for the metronome click.
Channel	Selects the MIDI channel for the metronome click.
High Note	Sets the MIDI note number for the "high note" (the first beat in a bar).
High Velocity	Sets the velocity value for the "high note" (the first beat in a bar).
Low Note	Sets the MIDI note number for the "low note" (the other beats).
Low Velocity	Sets the velocity value for the "low note" (the other beats).
Audio Click On/Off	Selects whether or not the metronome will sound via the audio hardware.
Audio Click Volume slider	Adjusts the volume for the audio click.
Precount on/off	Turns on or off the metronome count-in before recording starts (when starting recording from stop mode).

Parameter	Description
Precount Bars	Sets the number of bars the metronome will count in before it starts recording if precount is activated.
From Master Track	When this is activated, the precount will be in the time signature set in the Master Tempo track.
Use Signature	If "From Master Track" is deactivated, you can use these fields to set a time signature for the precount.
Click during	Allows you to specify whether the metronome should be heard during playback, recording or both (when Click is activated on the Transport bar).
Use Count Base	If this option is activated, you use the field to the right to specify the "rhythm" of the metronome. Normally, the metronome plays one click per beat, but setting this to e.g. "1/8" gives you eighth notes—two clicks per quarternote beat. It's also possible to create unusual metronome rhythms such as triplets etc.

5 The Project Window

5.1 Background

The Project window is the main window in Cubase SX/SL. This provides you with an overview of the project, allowing you to navigate and perform large scale editing. Each project has one Project window.

About Tracks

The Project window is divided vertically into tracks, with a time line running horizontally from left to right. The following track types are available:

Track type	Description
Audio	For recording and playing back audio events and audio parts. Each audio track has a corresponding audio channel in the Mixer. An audio track can have any number of automation "subtracks" for automating mixer channel parameters, insert effect settings etc.
Folder	Folder tracks function as containers for other tracks, allowing you to edit several tracks at the same time amongst other things. See page 153.
Group Channel	Group channels function as subgroups: by routing several audio channels to a Group channel, you can mix them with a single set of controls, apply the same effects to them, etc. (see page 206). A Group channel track contains no events as such, but displays settings and automation curves for the corresponding Group channel. Each Group channel track has a corresponding channel strip in the Mixer.
MIDI	For recording and playing back MIDI parts. Each MIDI track has a corresponding MIDI channel strip in the Mixer. A MIDI track can have a number of automation "subtracks" for automating mixer channel parameters, insert and send effect settings etc.
Marker	The Marker track displays markers, and allows you to move and rename them directly in the Project window (see page 163). There can only be one Marker track in the project.

Track type	Description
Master Automation	Contains automation curves for master volume and global effect input levels. There can only be one Master Automation track in the project, but you can expand it to display any number of automation curves.
Plug-in Automation	Each send effect, master effect or VST Instrument can have its own individual Plug-in Automation track, allowing for automation of all plug-in parameters. An automation track for a plug-in is automatically created the first time you automate any of its parameters. See page 299.
Video	For playing back video events. A project can only have one Video track.

About Parts and Events

Events are the basic building blocks in Cubase SX/SL. Different event types are handled differently in the Project window:

- Video events and automation events (curve points) are always viewed and rearranged directly in the Project window.
- MIDI events are always gathered in MIDI parts, containers for one or more MIDI events. MIDI parts are rearranged and manipulated in the Project window. To edit the individual MIDI events in a part, you have to open the part in a MIDI Editor (see page 485).
- Audio events can be displayed and edited directly in the Project window, but you can also work with audio parts containing several events. This is useful if you have a number of events which you want to treat as one unit in the project.

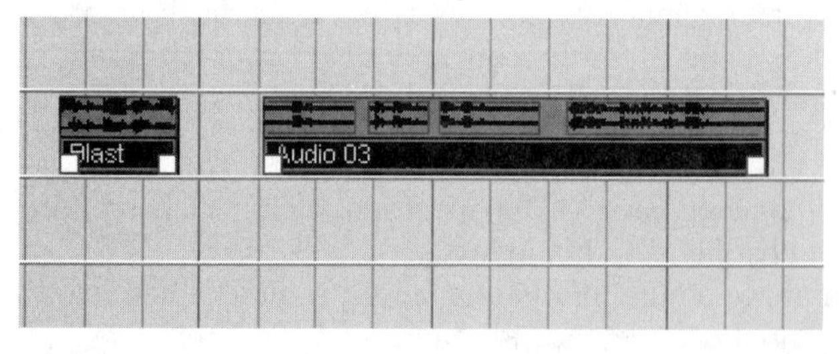

An audio event and an audio part.

5.2 Window Overview

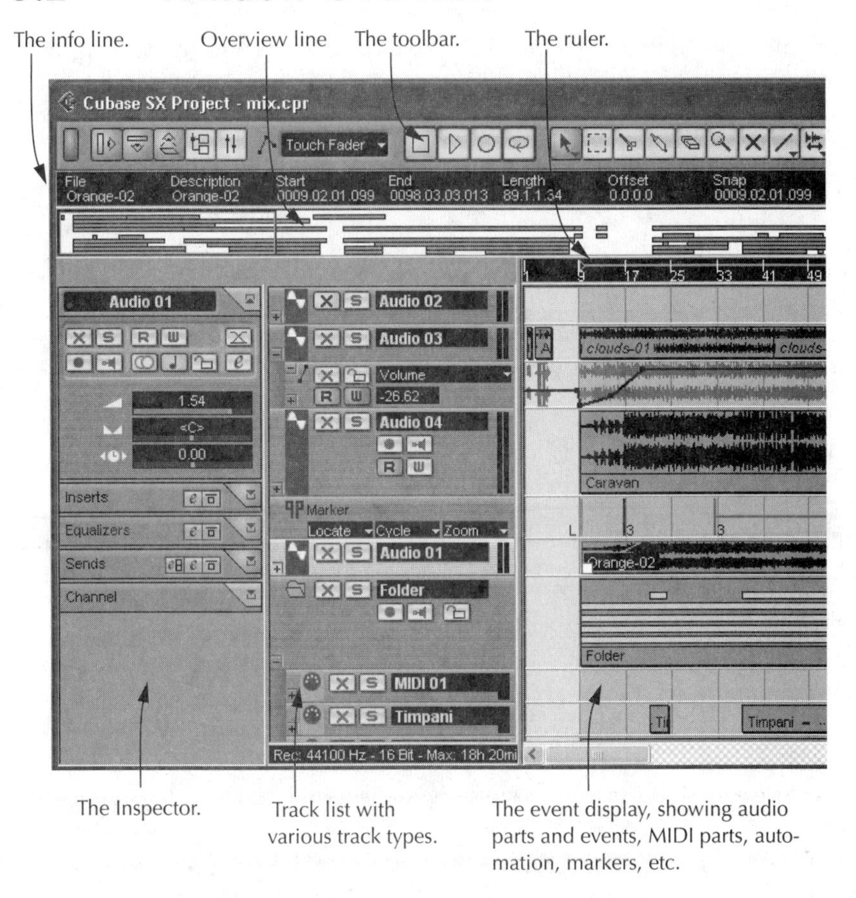

5.2.1 The Track List

The Track list is the area to the left in the Project window. It contains name fields and various settings for the tracks. Different track types have different controls in the Track list. To see all the controls you may have to resize the track in the Track list (see page 120):

- **The Track list area for an audio track:**

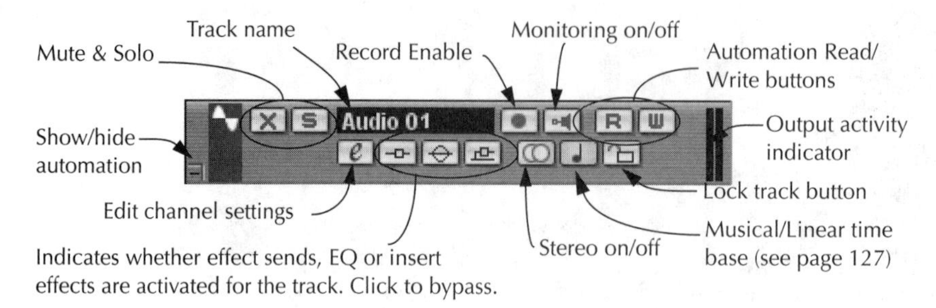

- **The Track list area for an automation subtrack (revealed by clicking the + button on a track):**

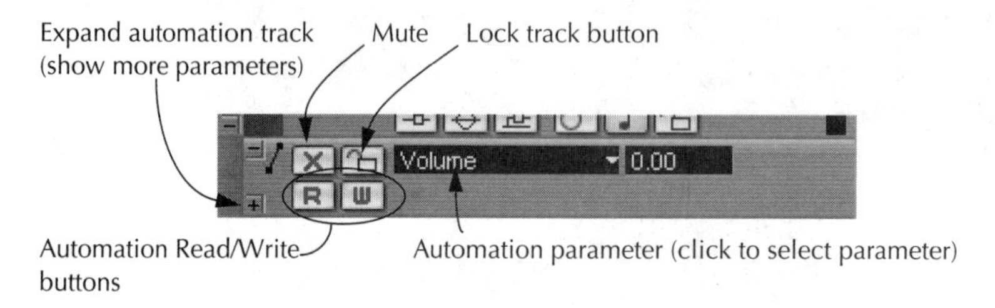

- **The Track list area for a MIDI track:**

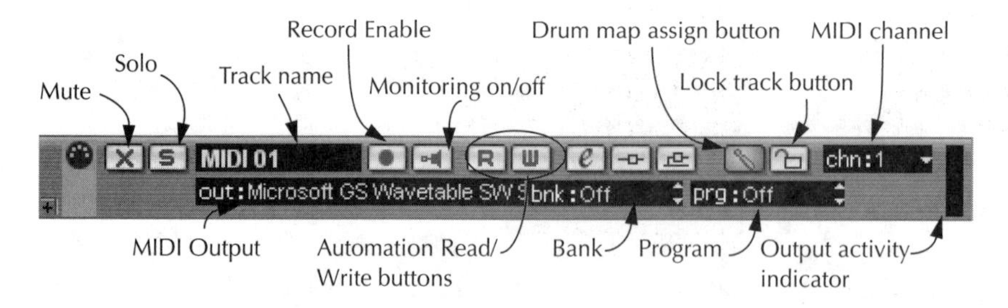

5.2.2 The Inspector

The area to the left of the Track list is called the Inspector. This can show additional controls and parameters for the track you have selected in the Track list. If several tracks are selected (see page 126), the Inspector shows the setting for the first (topmost) selected track.

To hide or show the Inspector, click the Inspector icon in the toolbar.

The Inspector icon.

The contents and usage of the Inspector depends on the selected track's class, as described below.

- **For some track classes, the Inspector is divided in sections. You can hide or show sections by clicking the tabs in their top right corner.**

  Clicking the tab for a hidden section brings it to view and hides the other sections. [Ctrl]-clicking the tab allows you to hide or show a section without affecting other sections. Finally, [Alt]-clicking a tab shows or hides all sections in the Inspector.

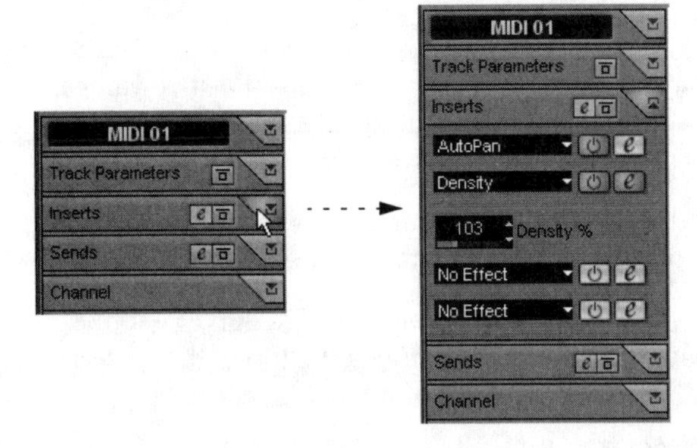

- Folding a section does not affect the functionality but merely hides the section from view.
  In other words, if you have set up a track parameter or activated an effect, your settings will still be active even if you fold the Inspector section.

Audio Tracks

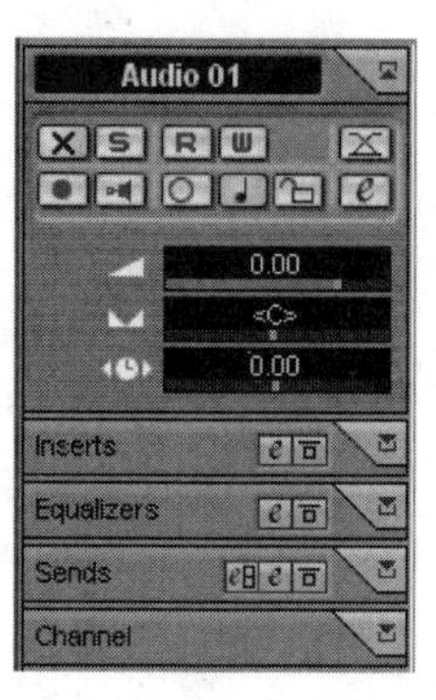

For audio tracks, the Inspector contains the same controls as the Track list, as well as some additional buttons and parameters:

Parameter	Description
Auto Fades Settings button	Opens a dialog in which you can make separate Auto Fade settings for the track. See page 181.
Edit button	Opens the Channel Settings window for the track, allowing you to view and adjust effect and EQ settings, etc. See page 200.
Volume	Use this to adjust the level for the track. Changing this setting will move the track's fader in the Mixer window, and vice versa. See page 194 to learn more about setting levels.
Delay	This adjusts the playback timing of the audio track. Positive values delay the playback while negative values cause the track to play earlier. The values are set in milliseconds.
Pan	Use this to adjust the panning of the track. As with the Volume setting, this corresponds to the Pan setting in the Mixer.
Inserts section	Allows you to add insert effects (up to eight for SX—up to 4 for SL) to the track, see page 225. The Edit button at the top of the section opens the Channel Settings window for the track.
Equalizers section	Lets you adjust the EQs for the track. You can have up to four bands of EQ for each track, see page 201. The Edit button at the top of the section opens the Channel Settings window for the track.

Parameter	Description
Sends section	Allows you to route the track to one or several send effects (up to eight), see page 221. There are two edit buttons at the top of this section—the left opens the VST Send Effects window and the right opens the Channel Settings window for the track.
Channel section	Shows a duplicate of the corresponding Mixer channel strip.

MIDI Tracks

When a MIDI track is selected, the Inspector contains a number of parameters and effects, affecting the MIDI events in real time (e.g. on playback). This is described in a separate chapter, see page 429.

Marker Tracks

When a marker track is selected, the Inspector shows the marker list. See page 160.

Folder Tracks

When a folder track is selected, the Inspector shows the folder and its underlying tracks, much like a folder structure in the Windows Explorer.

- You can click one of the tracks shown under the folder in the Inspector to have the Inspector show the settings for that track.
  This way, you don't have to "open" a folder track to access the settings for the tracks within it.

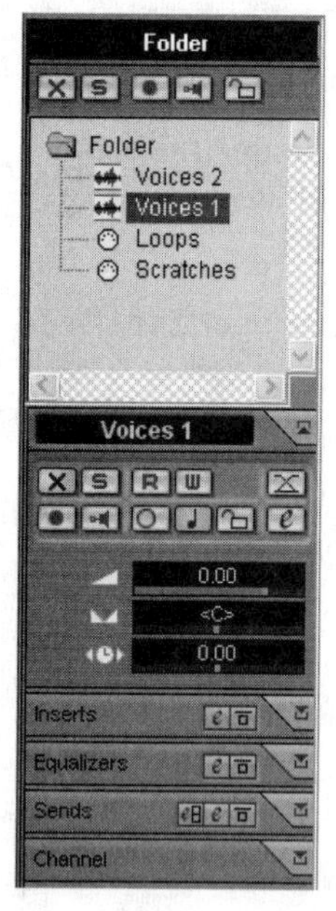

Here, an audio track within the folder is selected.

Other Tracks

For the remaining track classes, the Inspector isn't used.

5.2.3 The Toolbar

The toolbar contains tools and shortcuts for opening other windows and various project settings and functions:

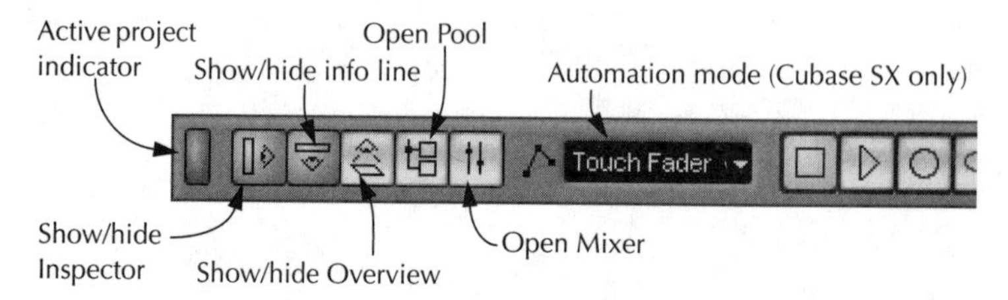

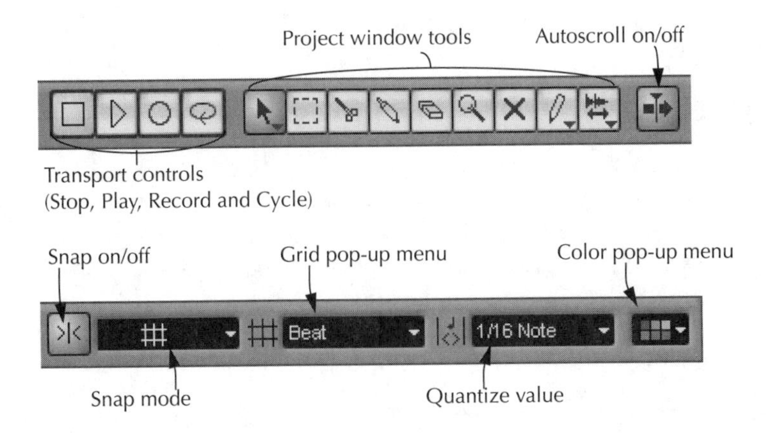

5.2.4 The Info Line

The info line shows information about the currently selected event or part in the Project window. You can edit almost all values in the info line using regular value editing. Length and position values are displayed in the format currently selected for the ruler (see page 116).

- **To hide or show the info line, click the corresponding icon on the toolbar.**

The following elements can be selected for display and editing on the info line:

- Audio events.
- Audio parts.
- MIDI parts.
- Video events.
- Markers.
- Automation Curve Points.

● Note that the info line will only display information if a single element is selected.

5.2.5 The Ruler

The ruler at the top of the event display shows the timeline. Initially, the Project window ruler uses the display format specified in the Project Setup dialog (see page 117), as do all other rulers and position displays in the project. However, you can select an independent display format for the ruler by clicking on the arrow button to the right of it and selecting an option from the pop-up menu that appears.

Option	Positions and lengths displayed as
Bars+Beats	Bars, beats, sixteenth notes and ticks, with 120 ticks per sixteenth note.
Seconds	Hours, minutes, seconds and milliseconds.
24 fps	Hours, minutes, seconds and frames, with 24 frames per second.
25 fps	Hours, minutes, seconds and frames, with 25 frames per second.
29.97 fps	Hours, minutes, seconds and frames, with 29.97 frames per second.
30 fps	Hours, minutes, seconds and frames, with 30 frames per second.
29.97 dfps	Hours, minutes, seconds and frames, "Drop frame" with 29.97 frames per second.
30 dfps	Hours, minutes, seconds and frames, "Drop frame" with 30 frames per second.
Samples	Samples.

- **The selection you make here affects the ruler, the info line and tool tip position values (appear when you drag an event in the Project window).**

  You can also select independent formats for other rulers and position displays.

- **To set the display format globally (for all windows), use the display format pop-up on the Transport panel, or hold down [Ctrl] and select a display format in any ruler.**

5.3 Operations

5.3.1 Creating a New Project

You create a new project in the following way:

1. **Select "New Project" from the File menu.**

   A dialog appears, listing a number of project templates, including any custom templates that you have created (see page 658).

2. **Select a template and click OK.**

   A file dialog appears, allowing you to specify a location for the project folder. This will contain all files related to the project.

3. **Select an existing folder or type the name of a new one. Click OK.**

   A Project window appears. The new project will be based on the selected template, and include tracks, events and settings from the template.

The Project Setup Dialog

General settings for the project are made in the Project Setup dialog. This is opened by selecting "Project Setup..." from the Project menu.

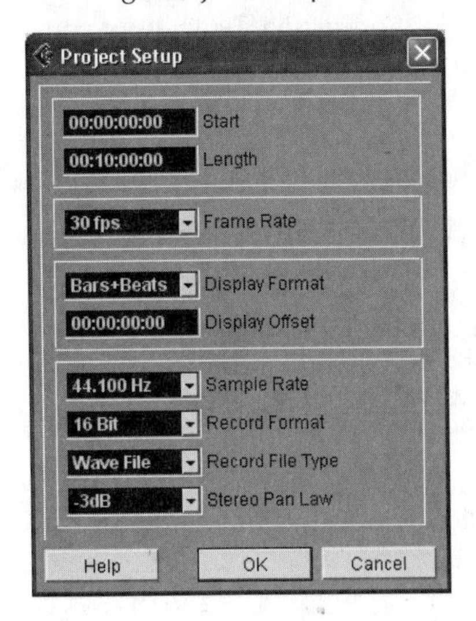

The following settings are available in the Project Setup dialog:

Setting	Description
Start	The start time of the project. Allows you to have the project start at another time than zero. Also used for setting the sync start position when synchronizing Cubase SX/SL to external devices (see page 621).
Length	The length of the project.
Frame Rate	Used if you are synchronizing Cubase SX/SL with external equipment. If Cubase SX/SL is the slave, this value is automatically set to the frame rate of the incoming sync signal. If Cubase SX/SL is master, this determines the frame rate of the sent sync signal. See page 625.
Display Format	This is the global display format used for all rulers and position displays in the program. However, you can make independent display format selections for the individual rulers and displays if you like. For descriptions of the different display format options, see page 116.
Display Offset	Offsets the time positions displayed in the ruler etc., allowing you to compensate for the Start Position setting. Typically, if you synchronize Cubase SX/SL to an external source starting at a frame other than zero, you set the Start Position to this value. However, if you still want the display in Cubase SX/SL to start at zero, set the Display Offset to the same value too.
Sample Rate	This is the sample rate by which Cubase SX/SL records and plays back audio files.
Record Format	When you record audio files in Cubase SX/SL, they are recorded with this resolution. See page 84.
Record File Type	Determines which file types should be created when you record audio. See page 84.
Stereo Pan Law	Decides whether panning should use power compensation or not. This is explained on page 197.

● While most settings in the Project Setup can be changed at any time, you should select a sample rate once and for all when starting with a new project! All audio files must be of this sample rate to play back correctly.

5.3.2 Zoom and View Options

Zooming in the Project window is done according to the standard Zoom procedures (see the Getting Started book), with the following special notes:

- **When using the vertical zoom sliders, the tracks are scaled relatively.**

  In other words, if you have made any individual track height adjustments (see below), the relative height differences are maintained.

The following options are available on the Zoom submenu on the Edit menu:

Option	Description
Zoom In	Zooms in one step, centering on the project cursor.
Zoom Out	Zooms out one step, centering on the project cursor.
Zoom Full	Zooms out so that the whole project is visible. "The whole project" means the timeline from the project start to the length set in the Project Setup dialog (see above).
Zoom to Selection	Zooms in horizontally so that the current selection fills the screen.
Zoom to Event	This option is available only in the Sample Editor (see page 364).
Zoom In Vertical	Zooms in one step vertically.
Zoom Out Vertical	Zooms out one step vertically.
Zoom In Tracks	Zooms in selected track(s) one step vertically.
Zoom Out Tracks	Zooms out selected track(s) one step vertically.
Zoom Tracks Exclusive	This zooms in vertically on the selected track(s) and minimizes the height of all other tracks.

- **You can zoom the contents of parts and events vertically, using the Waveform Zoom slider in the top right corner of the event display.**

  This can be useful to better view quiet audio passages.

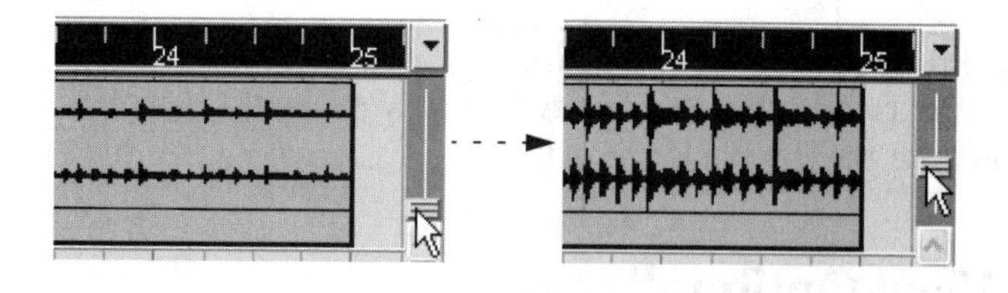

- To get an approximate reading on the level of the audio events by viewing the waveforms, make sure the slider is all the way down. Otherwise, zoomed waveforms may be mistaken for clipped audio.

- **If you activate the option Quick Zoom in the Preferences (Event Display page), the contents of parts and events will not be continuously redrawn when you zoom manually.**

  Instead, the contents are redrawn once you have stopped changing the zoom—activate this if screen redraws are slow on your system.

Resizing Tracks in the Track List

- You can change the height of an individual track by clicking on its lower border in the Track list and dragging up or down.
  To change the height of all tracks, hold down [Ctrl] and resize one of the tracks in the same way. If "Snap Track Heights" is activated on the Track scale pop-up (see below), the track height will change in larger increments when you resize it.

- You can also change the width of the Track list area, by dragging the border between the Track list and the event display.
- The controls shown for tracks in the Track list are adaptable to track size. This means that when resizing a track's height or width some of the controls will be dynamically placed where they best "fit in".
- You can use the Track scale pop-up (opened by clicking the arrow button above the vertical zoom control) to set the number of tracks to view in the current Project window.
  The track height will be adjusted to show only the number of tracks specified on the pop-up menu. By selecting "Zoom N Tracks" from the pop-up you can manually set the number of tracks to fit in the current Project window.

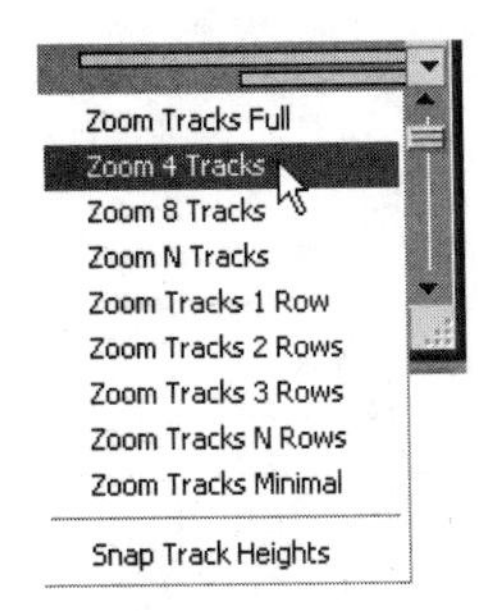

Zoom Presets and Cycle Markers

The pop-up menu to the left of the horizontal zoom control allows you to select, create and organize zoom presets. These are useful if you want to toggle between different zoom settings (e.g. one where the whole project is displayed in the project window and another with a high zoom factor for detailed editing). With this pop-up menu, you can also zoom in on the cycle markers in the project.

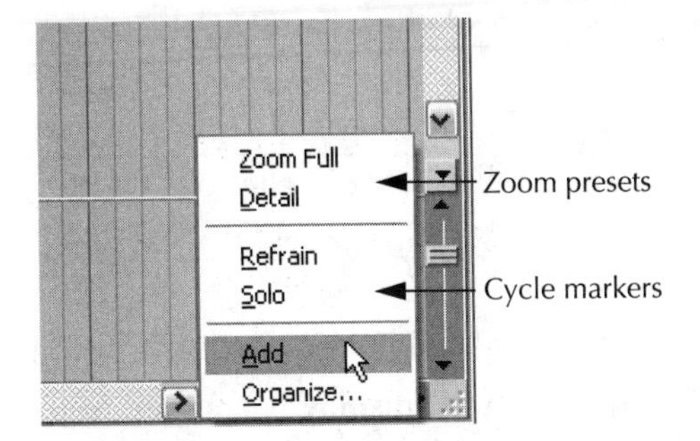

The upper part of the menu lists the zoom presets:

- **To store the current zoom setting as a preset, select Add from the pop-up menu.**

  A dialog appears, allowing you to type in a name for the preset.

- **To select and apply a preset, select it from the pop-up menu.**
- **If you want to delete a preset, select "Organize..." from the pop-up menu.**

  In the dialog that appears, select the preset in the list and click the corresponding button in order to delete the preset. The preset is removed from the list.

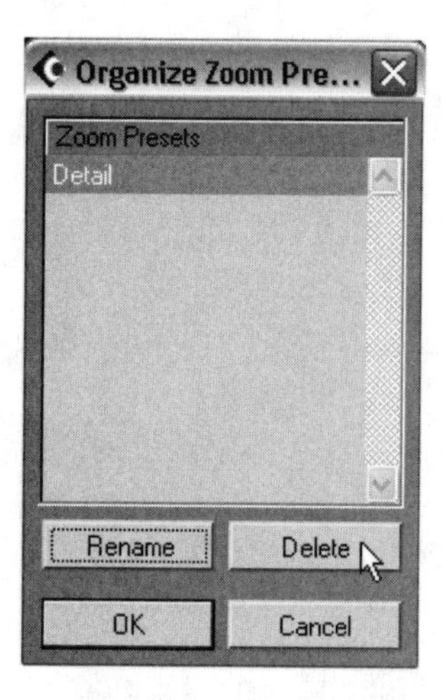

- **If you want to rename a preset, select "Organize..." from the pop-up menu.**

  In the dialog that appears, select the desired preset in the list and click the Rename button. A second dialog opens, allowing you to type in a new name for the preset. Click OK to close the dialogs.

● Zoom presets are global for all projects, i.e. they are available in all projects you open or create.

The middle part of the pop-up lists the cycle markers you created for the project:

- **If you select a cycle marker form this menu, the event display is zoomed in to encompass the marker area (see page 165).**
- **You cannot edit the cycle markers in this pop-up menu. For information on editing markers, see »Using Markers«.**

● Only the cycle markers you created in the current project are available on the menu.

Adjusting How Parts and Events Are Shown

The Preferences dialog on the File menu contains several settings for customizing the display in the Project window.

On the Event Display page you will find common settings for all track types:

Option	Description
Colorize Event Background	Determines whether the backgrounds or "contents" (wave-forms, etc.) of parts and events will be colorized. See page 127.
Quick Zoom	If this is activated, the contents of parts and events are redrawn once you have stopped changing the zoom.
Transparent Events	When this is activated, events and parts will be transparent, showing the waveforms and MIDI events only.
Show Data on Small Track Heights	If this is activated, the contents of events and parts will be shown, even if the height of a track is very small.
Show Event Names	Determines whether the names of parts and events should be shown in the Project window.

The Event Display—Audio page contains settings for audio events:

Option	Description
Interpolate Audio Images	If the option is deactivated, single sample values are drawn as "steps". If the option is activated they are interpolated to form "curves".
Wave Image Style	Determines whether audio waveforms should be displayed as solid images, frames or "inverted" images (solid+frame). This selection affects all waveform images in the Project window, Sample Editor and Audio Part Editor. Note that the "Framed" and "Solid and Framed" styles are more demanding for the computer. If the system feels slower in these modes, please switch back to "Solid" wave image style.
Show Event Volume Curves Always	If this is activated the "volume curves" created with the vol-ume and fade handles are always shown—if not, the curves are only shown for selected events.

The Event Display—MIDI page contains settings for MIDI parts:

Option	Description
Default Edit Action	Determines which editor should be opened when you double click a MIDI part or select it and press [Ctrl]-[E]: the Key, Drum, List or Score editor. Note that this setting is overridden for tracks with drum maps if the option "Edit as Drums when Drummap is assigned" is activated.
Part Data Mode	Determines how events in MIDI parts should be shown in the Project window: as lines, as score notes or as drum notes. Note that this setting is overridden for tracks with drum maps if the option "Edit as Drums when Drum Map is assigned" is activated.
Show Controllers	Governs whether non-note events (controllers, etc.) should be shown in MIDI parts in the Project window.
Edit as Drums when Drum Map is assigned	If this is activated, parts on MIDI tracks with drum maps assigned will be shown with drum note symbols in the Project window. Also, the parts will automatically open in the Drum editor when double clicked (overriding the Default Edit Action setting above).
Note Name Style	Determines how MIDI note names (pitches) should be displayed in editors, etc.

The Event Display—Video page contains settings for video events:

Option	Description
Show Video Thumbnails	When this is activated, thumbnail frames of the video contents are shown on the Video Track.
Video Cache Size	This determines how much memory is available for video thumbnails. If you have long video clips and/or work with a large zoom factor (so that a lot of frames are shown in the thumbnails), you may have to raise this value.

5.3.3 Zooming and Navigating in the Overview Line

By clicking the Show Overview button on the toolbar, an extra pane appears under the toolbar, the project overview line.

Show Overview button

In the overview line, events and parts on all tracks are displayed as boxes. You can use the overview line to zoom in or out, and for navigating to other sections of the project. This is done by moving and resizing the track view rectangle in the overview line:

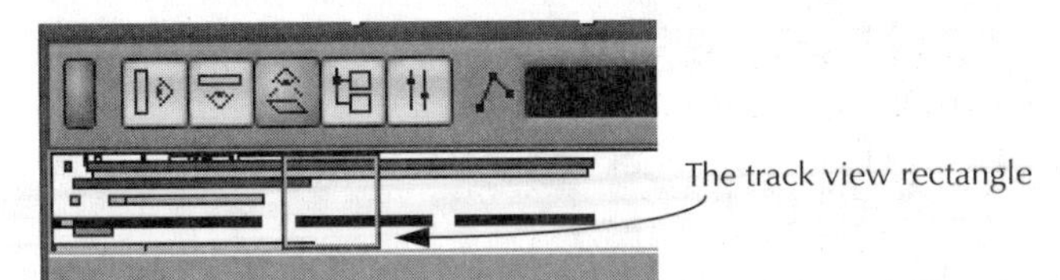

- The track view rectangle indicates the section of the project currently displayed in the event display.
- You can zoom in or out vertically by resizing the track view rectangle. Resizing is done by dragging the edges of the rectangle.

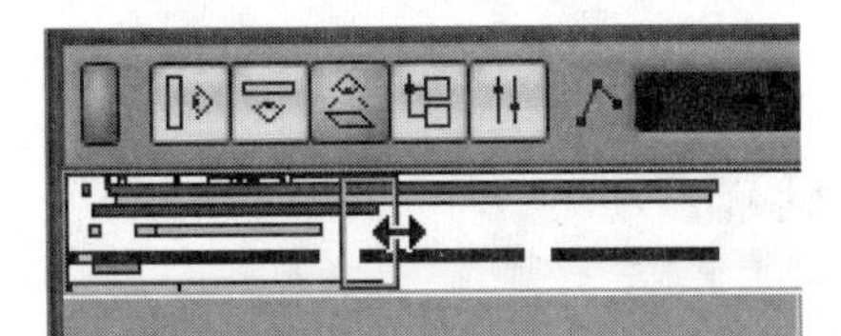

- You can drag the track view rectangle to view other sections of the project. The number of tracks shown will not change.

5.3.4 Handling Tracks

To add a track to the Project, select "Add Track" from the Project menu and select a track type from the submenu that appears. The new track is added below the currently selected track in the Track list.

- **The "Add Track" menu is also available as a separate item on the Quick Menu.**
- **There is an additional option at the bottom of the Add Track submenu, called "Multiple...". Selecting this brings up a dialog allowing you to add more than one track in one operation.**

  You can set whether audio, MIDI or group tracks should be created by selecting from the pop-up in the dialog. The number of tracks to add is entered in the "Count" value field.

Once you have created tracks, you can manipulate and rearrange them in various ways:

- **To rename an audio or MIDI track, double click in the name field and type in a new name.**

  If you hold down any modifier key when pressing [Return] to close the name field, all events on the track will get the name you entered.

- **To select a track, click on it in the Track list.**

  A selected track is indicated by a light grey color in the Track list.

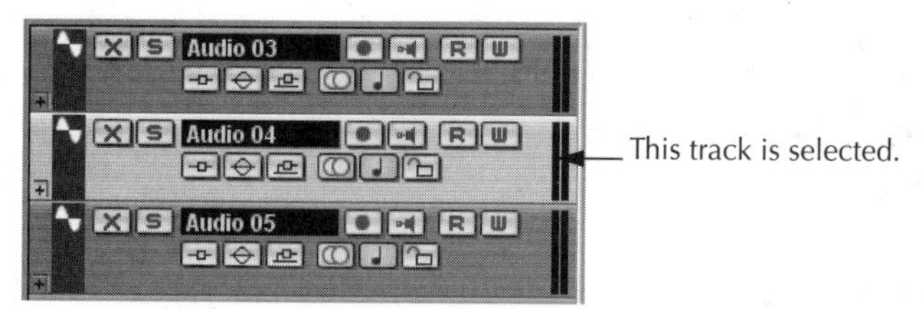

  It is possible to select several tracks, by pressing [Ctrl]. To select a continuous range of tracks, use [Shift]-clicking.

- **To move a track, click and drag it up or down in the list.**
- **To duplicate a track, complete with all contents and channel settings, right-click in the Track list and select "Duplicate track" from the context menu.**

  The duplicated track will appear above the original track.

- **You can colorize the contents of selected track(s), or selected parts and events by clicking the Color button on the toolbar and selecting a color from the pop-up menu that appears.**

  If one or several tracks are selected, all events and parts on the track(s) will get the selected color, as will any events and parts you add to the track later. If individual events or parts are selected, only these will be affected. Individually colorized events and/or parts will keep the applied color even if the track they belong to is later set to another color. The option "Colorize Event Background" in the Preferences dialog (User Interface—Event Display page) determines whether the backgrounds or waveforms of events will be colorized.

- **To remove the selected tracks, select "Remove Selected Tracks" from the Project menu.**

  You can also right-click directly on a track in the Track list and select "Remove Track" from the context menu that appears.

Switching between Musical or Linear time base

Tracks can be either "musical" (tempo) or "linear" (time) based.

- On a track using linear time base, the events will be positioned on specific time positions—changing the playback tempo will not affect the time position of events.
- On a track using musical time base, the positions of events are represented as meter values (bars, beats, 1/16th notes and ticks, with 120 ticks per 1/16th note). If you change the playback tempo, the events will play back at an earlier or later time.

Whether to use musical or linear time base depends on the type of project and recording situation. By default, audio and MIDI tracks use musical time base, while the Marker track and Video track use linear time base. However, you can change this setting individually for each audio, MIDI and marker track. This is done by clicking the musical/linear time base button in the Inspector or Track list. Musical time base is indicated by a note symbol, while linear time base is indicated by a clock symbol.

Linear time base selected. Musical time base selected.

- Note that internally, events on musical time based tracks use the same high precision for positioning (64 bit floating point values) as linear time based events. However, switching between linear and musical time base results in a very small loss of precision (introduced by the mathematical operations used for scaling values in the two different formats). Therefore you should avoid switching repeatedly between the two modes.

For more information about tempo changes, see page 571.

5.3.5 Adding Events to a Track

There are a number of ways to add events to a track:

- By recording (see page 79).
  This is possible for audio and MIDI tracks.
- By selecting "Audio File..." or "Videofile..." from the Import submenu on the File menu.
  This opens a file dialog, allowing you to locate the file you wish to import. When you import a file this way, a clip is created for the file and an event that plays the whole clip is added to the selected track, at the position of the project cursor.
  You can also import MIDI files by using the Import submenu, but this works in a slightly different way (see page 660).
- By grabbing audio CD tracks and converting these to audio files, see page 663.
- By using Copy and Paste on the Edit menu.
  This allows you to copy all kinds of events between different projects. You can also use Copy and Paste for copying events within the project, from the Audio Part Editor or Sample Editor.
- By drawing.
  Some types of events (markers and automation events) can be drawn directly into the Project window. For audio and MIDI tracks, you can draw parts (see page 131).
- By dragging files and dropping them on the track at the desired position.

You can create events by dragging and dropping from the following locations:

The Desktop.

The Pool.

The Project window of another open project.

The Audio Part Editor of any open project.

The Sample Editor of any open project—press [Ctrl] and drag to create an event of the current selection, or click in the left column of the Region List and drag to create an event from a Region.

The "Find media" dialog.

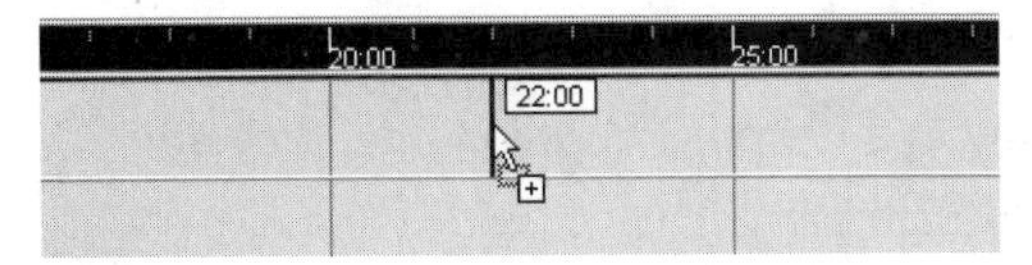

While you drag the clip in the Project window, its position will be indicated by a marker line and a numerical position box. See also page 403.

Audio File Import Options

When you are importing audio files, you can choose to copy the file into the project's audio folder and have the project make reference to the copied file instead. This helps you keep your project "self-contained". Furthermore, you may want all files in the project to have the same sample rate and sample size (resolution).

There is a setting for this in the Preferences dialog on the File menu, on the Audio page. Select one of the options on the "On Import Audiofile" pop-up:

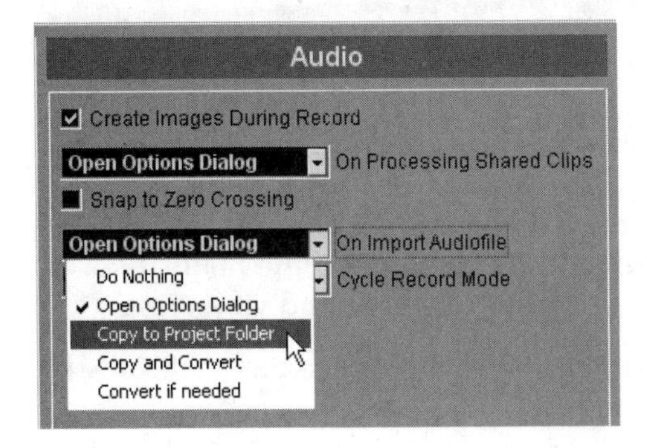

Option	Description
Do Nothing	The files are imported without being copied or converted.
Open Options Dialog	An Options dialog appears when you import, allowing you to select whether you want to copy the files to the Audio folder and/or convert them to the project settings. Note: - When importing a single file of a format other than the project settings, you can specify which properties (sample rate and/or resolution) should be changed. - When importing multiple files at the same time, you can select to have the imported files automatically converted *if necessary*, i.e. if the sample rate is different than the project's or the resolution is lower than the project setting.
Copy to Project Folder	If files are not already in the project's audio folder they are copied there before being imported.
Copy and Convert	If files are not already in the project's audio folder they are copied there before being imported. Furthermore, if the files have a different sample rate or a lower resolution than the project settings, they are automatically converted.
Convert if needed	If files have a different sample rate or a lower resolution than the project settings, they are copied to the project's Audio folder and the copies are automatically converted before being imported. Files that conform to the project settings are imported from their original location, without being copied.

About Stereo/Mono

Audio tracks can be either stereo or mono. You can change this setting manually as described below, but it can also be done automatically, according to the following rules:

- **Whenever a file is imported, copied or moved to a track, Cubase SX/SL sets the stereo/mono status of the track according to its contents: If the majority of events on the track are in stereo, the track is set to stereo and vice versa.**

  This means that if you import a file to an empty track, the track is automatically set to stereo or mono according to the imported file.

Stereo events on mono tracks (or vice versa) are indicated by the label "Mono/stereo mismatch", and will not be played back:

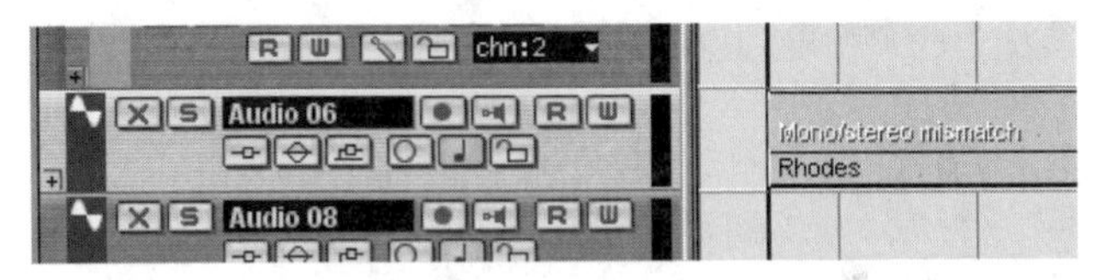

A stereo file on a mono track.

To manually change the stereo/mono status, click the stereo button in the Track list or Inspector. A lit button with double circles indicates stereo, a dark button with a single circle indicates mono.

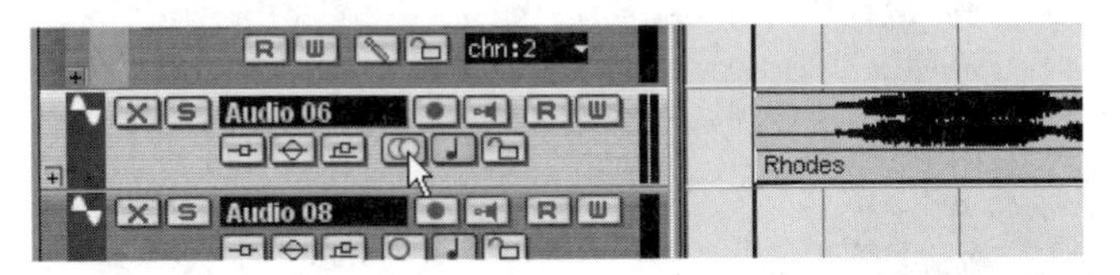

Setting the track to stereo.

Creating Parts

Parts are containers for MIDI or audio events. If you record MIDI, a MIDI part is automatically created, containing the recorded events. You can also create empty audio or MIDI parts and later add events to them. There are two ways to do this:

- **Draw a part on a MIDI or audio track with the Pencil tool.**
- **Double click with the Arrow tool on a MIDI or audio track, between the left and right locator.**

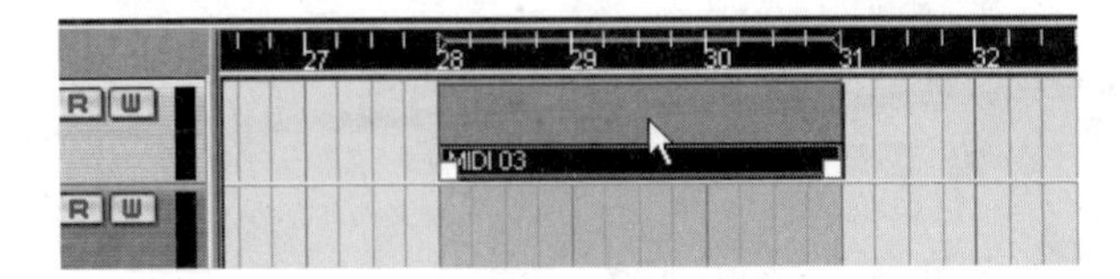

To add events to a MIDI part, you use the tools and functions in a MIDI editor (see page 487). Adding events to audio parts is done in the Audio Part Editor (see page 378) by pasting or by using drag and drop.

- **You can also gather existing audio events into a part, by using the "Events to Part" function on the Audio menu.**

  This creates an audio part containing all selected audio events on the same track. To remove the part and make the events appear as independent objects on the track again, select the part and use the "Dissolve Part" function on the Audio menu.

5.3.6 Auditioning Audio Parts and Events

Audio parts and events can be auditioned in the Project window with the Speaker tool:

- When auditioning, audio will be routed directly to Bus 1, bypassing the audio channel's settings, effects and EQs.

1. **Select the Speaker tool.**

   Note that the Speaker tool and the Scrub tool share the same icon. If the rightmost tool icon on the toolbar isn't a Speaker symbol, first click on the icon to select it, then click again and select "Play" from the pop-up menu that appears.

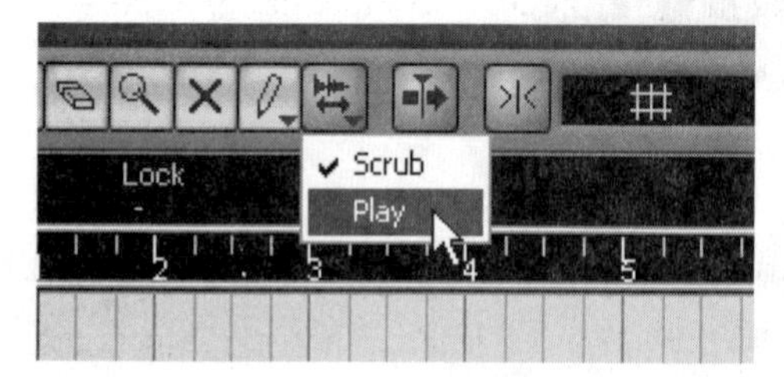

2. **Click where you want playback to start, and keep the mouse button pressed.**

   Only the track on which you click is played back, starting at the click position.

3. **Release the mouse button to stop playback.**

5.3.7 Scrubbing

The Scrub tool allows you to locate positions in the audio by playing back, forwards or backwards, at any speed:

1. **Select the Scrub tool.**

   Note that the Speaker tool and the Scrub tool share the same icon. If the rightmost tool icon on the toolbar isn't a "Scrub symbol", first click on the icon to select it, then click again and select "Scrub" from the pop-up menu that appears.

2. **Click at the desired position and keep the mouse button pressed.**

   The project cursor is moved to the position at which you click.

3. **Drag to the left or right.**

   The project cursor follows the mouse pointer and the audio is played back. The speed and pitch of the playback depends on how fast you move the pointer.

- **You can adjust the responsiveness of the Scrub function in the Preferences dialog (VST page).**

5.3.8 Editing Parts and Events

This section describes techniques for editing in the Project window. If not explicitly stated, all descriptions apply to both events and parts, even though we use the term "event" for convenience.

- When you are using the tools for editing parts and events, you can in many cases get additional functions by pressing modifier keys (e.g. pressing [Alt] and dragging with the Pencil tool creates a copy of the dragged event or part). On the following pages, the default modifier keys are described, but you can customize these if needed. This is done in the Preferences dialog on the Editing—Tool Modifiers page (see page 678).

Selecting Events

Selecting events is done using any of the following methods:

- **Use the Arrow tool.**

  The standard selection techniques apply.

- **Use the Select submenu on the Edit menu.**

  The options are:

Option	Description
All	Selects all events in the Project window.
None	Deselects all events.
In Loop	Selects all events that are partly or wholly between the left and right locator.
From Start to Cursor	Selects all events that begin to the left of the project cursor.

Option	Description
From Cursor to End	Selects all events that end to the right of the project cursor.
All on Selected Tracks	Selects all events on the selected track.
Select Event	This is available in the Sample Editor (see page 359).
Left/Right Selection Side to Cursor	These two functions are only used for range selection editing (see page 144).

● Note that these functions work differently when the Range Selection tool is selected (see page 144).

- **Select all events on a track by right-clicking in its Track list and selecting "Select All Events" from the pop-up menu that appears.**
- **You can also use the arrow keys on the computer keyboard, to select the closest event to the left, right, above or below.**

  If you press [Shift] and use the arrow keys, the current selection will be kept, allowing you to select several events.
- **If the option "Auto Select Events under Cursor" is activated in the Preferences dialog (Editing page), all events currently "touched" by the project cursor are automatically selected.**

  This can be helpful when rearranging your project, since it allows you to select whole sections (on all tracks) simply by moving the project cursor.
- **It is also possible to select ranges, regardless of the event and track boundaries.**

  This is done using the Range Selection tool (see page 144).

Moving Events

To move events in the Project window, use any of the following methods:

- **Click and drag to a new position.**

  All selected events will be moved, maintaining their relative positions. You can only drag events to tracks of the same type. If Snap is activated, this determines to which positions you can move the events (see page 149).
  Note also, that you can restrict movement to be either horizontal or vertical only, by holding down [Ctrl] while dragging.

- You will note that there is a slightly delayed response when you move an event by dragging. This helps you avoid accidentally moving events when you click on them in the Project window. You can adjust this delay with the Drag Delay setting in the Preferences dialog (Editing page).

- **Use the "Move to" functions on the Edit menu.**

  The following functions are available:

Function	Description
Move to Cursor	Moves the selected event to the project cursor position. If there are several selected events on the same track, the first event will start at the Cursor, and the following will be lined up end-to-start after the first one.
Move to Origin	Moves the selected events to their original positions, i.e. the positions at which they were originally recorded.
Move to Front, Move to Back	This function doesn't actually change the position of the events, but moves the selected events to the front or back, respectively. This is useful if you have overlapping events, and want to see one that is partially obscured. For audio events, this is an extra important feature, since only the visible sections of events will be played back. Moving an obscured audio event to front (or moving the obscuring event to back) will allow you to hear the whole event on playback. Note that it is also possible to use the "To Front" function on the event context menu for this (although this works in a different way, see page 90).

- **Select the event and edit the Start position in the info line.**

  With this method, you can only move one event at a time.

Duplicating Events

Events can be duplicated in the following ways:

- **Hold down [Alt] and drag the event to a new position.**

  If Snap is activated, this determines to which positions you can copy the events (see page 149).

- If you hold down [Ctrl] as well, movement direction is restricted to either horizontal or vertical. That means if you drag an event vertically it can not be moved horizontally at the same time.

- **Audio and MIDI parts can also be duplicated by pressing [Alt]+[Shift] and dragging.**

  This creates a *shared copy* of the part. If you edit the contents of a shared copy, all other shared copies of the same part are automatically edited in the same way.

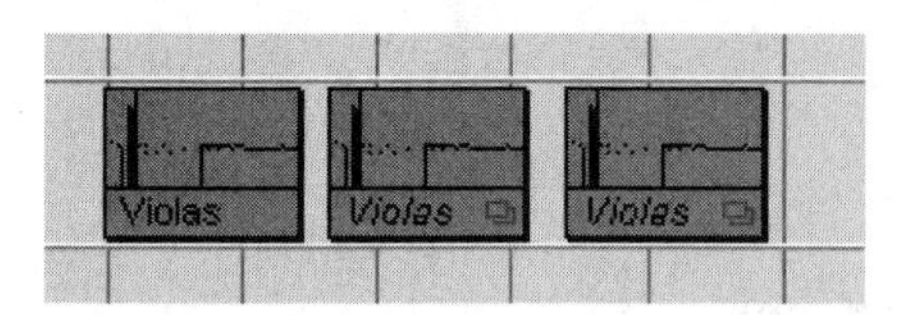

Shared copies are indicated by the part name in italics and an icon in the lower right corner of the part.

Note:

- When you duplicate audio *events*, the copies are always shared. This means that shared copies of audio events always refer to the same audio clip (see page 330).
- You can convert a shared copy to a real copy by selecting "Convert to Real Copy" from the Edit menu. This creates a new version of the clip (that can be edited independently) and adds this to the Pool. Note that no new files are created by this operation—for that you need to use the "Freeze Edits" function (see page 351).

- **Selecting "Duplicate" from the Edit menu creates a copy of the selected event and places it directly after the original.**

  If several events are selected, all of these are copied "as one unit", maintaining the relative distance between the events.

- **Selecting "Repeat..." from the Edit menu opens a dialog, allowing you to create a number of copies (regular or shared) of the selected event(s).**

  This works just like the Duplicate function, except that you can specify the number of copies.

- **Selecting "Fill Loop" from the Edit menu creates a number of copies starting at the left locator and ending at the right locator.**

  The last copy is automatically shortened to end at the right locator position.

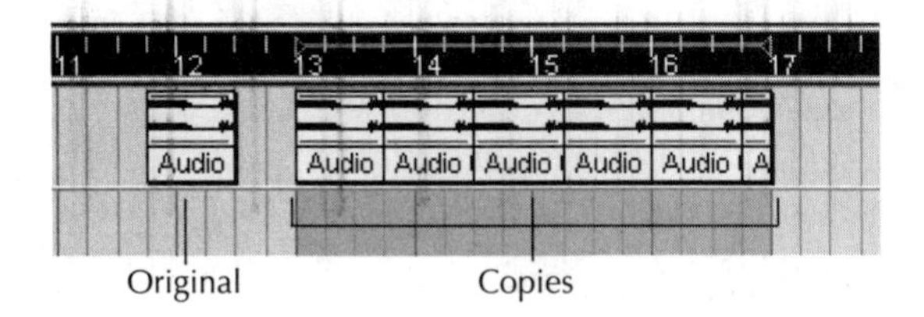

Original Copies

Using Cut, Copy and Paste

You can cut or copy selected events, and paste them in again, using the functions on the Edit menu.

- **When you paste an event it is inserted on its original track, positioned so that its Snap point is aligned with the project cursor position.**

  See page 149 for information about the Snap point.

- **If you use the "Paste at Origin" function, the event is pasted at its original position (the position from which you cut or copied it).**

Renaming Events

By default, audio events show the name of their clip, but you can enter a separate descriptive name for separate events if you like. This is done by selecting the event and typing in a new name in the "Description" field in the info line.

- **You can also give all events on a track the same name as the track by changing the track name, holding down a modifier key and pressing [Return].**

  See page 126.

Splitting Events

You can split events in the Project window in the following ways:

- **Click with the Scissors tool on the event you want to split.**

  If Snap is activated, this determines the exact split position (see page 149).

- **Select "Split at Cursor" from the Edit menu.**

  This splits the selected events at the position of the project cursor. If no events are selected, all events (on all tracks) that are intersected by the project cursor will be split.

- **Select "Split Loop" from the Edit menu.**

  This splits events on all tracks at the left and right locator positions.

- If you split a MIDI part so that the split position intersects one or several MIDI notes, the result depends on the option "Split MIDI Events" in the Preferences dialog (MIDI-Function Parameters page). If the option is activated, the intersected notes will be split (creating new notes at the beginning of the second part). If it is deactivated, the notes will remain in the first part, but "stick out" after the end of the part.

Gluing Events Together

Clicking on an event with the Glue Tube tool glues it together with the next event on the track. The result is a part containing the two events, with one exception:

- **If you first split an event and then glue the two sections together again (without moving or editing them first), they become a single event again.**

  In other words, gluing can create a single event if the two events are lined up end to start and play a continuous section of the same clip.

Resizing Events

Resizing events means to move their start or end positions individually. In Cubase SX/SL, there are three types of resizing:

Resizing type	Description
Normal Sizing	The contents of the event stay fixed, and the start or end point of the event is moved to "reveal" more or less of the contents.
Sizing Moves Contents	The contents follow the moved start or end of the event (see the figure below).
Sizing Applies Time Stretch	The contents will be time stretched to fit the new event length (see separate description on page 139).

To select one of the resizing modes, select the Arrow tool and then click again on the Arrow tool icon on the toolbar. This opens a pop-up menu from which you can select one of the resizing mode options.

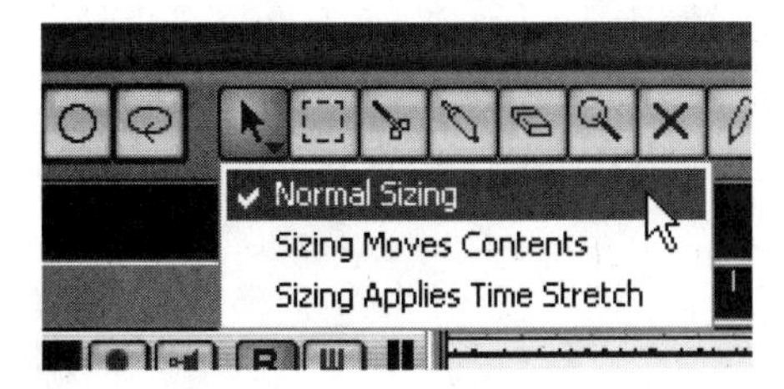

The icon on the toolbar will change shape, indicating the selected resizing mode.

The actual resizing is done by clicking and dragging the lower left or right corner of the event. If Snap is activated, the Snap value determines the resulting length (see page 149).

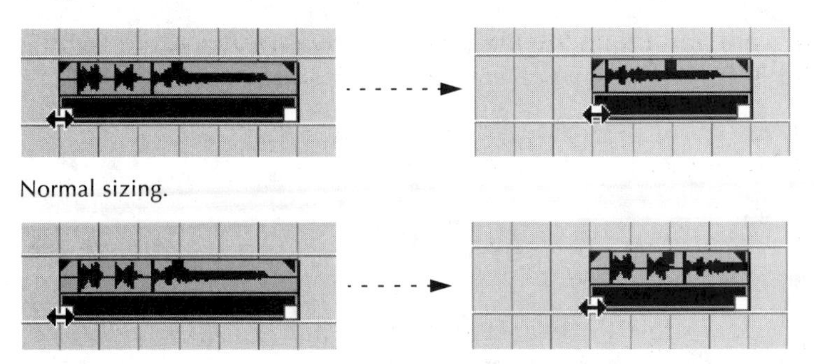

Normal sizing.

Sizing moves contents.

- If the event is selected, there will be resize handles in the lower left and right corners. However, you can resize unselected events in the same way—just click and drag one of the lower corners.

- **If several events are selected, all will be resized in the same way.**
- **You can also resize events with the Scrub tool.**

  This works just the same as when resizing with the Arrow tool, but the audio under the pointer is played back (scrubbed) while you drag.

Resizing Events Using Time Stretch

If you want to resize a part and make its contents "fit" the new size, you should use this option. Proceed as follows:

1. **Click the Arrow icon on the toolbar and select the "Sizing applies timestretch" option from the pop-up menu.**
2. **Point close to the end point of the part you want to stretch.**

3. **Click and drag left or right.**

   When you move the mouse, a tooltip information shows the current mouse position and length of the part. Note that the snap value applies, as with any part operation.

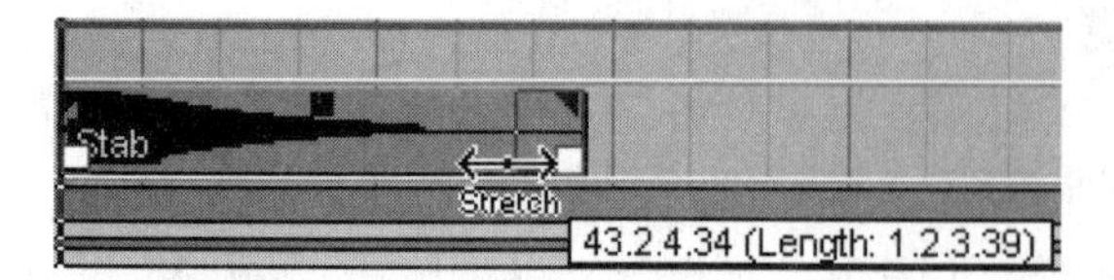

4. **Release the mouse button.**

   The part is "stretched" or "compressed" to fit the new length.

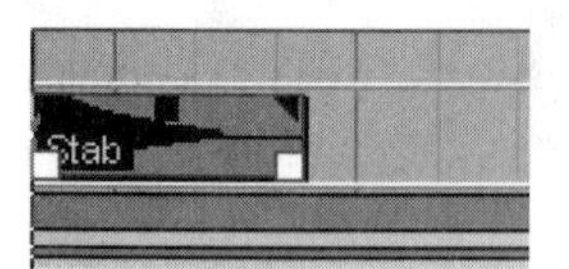

- **For MIDI parts, this means that the events are moved, so that the relative distance between events is maintained.**
- **For audio parts, this means that the events are moved, and that the referenced audio files are time stretched to fit the new length.**

  A dialog box shows the progress of the time stretch operation.
- You can adjust the quality settings for the time stretch algorithm on the Preferences page (Audio—Time Stretch Tool page).
  For more general information about time stretch, see page 344.

Sliding the Contents of an Event or Part

You can move the contents of an event or part without changing its position in the Project window. By default, this is done by pressing [Ctrl]+[Alt], clicking in the event or part and dragging to the left or right.

- When sliding the contents of an audio event, you cannot slide past the start or end of the actual audio clip. If the event plays the whole clip, you cannot slide the audio at all.

Locking Events

If you want to make sure you don't edit or move an event by accident, you can lock it. Locking can affect one (or any combination) of the following properties:

Lock Options	Description
Position	If this is locked, the event cannot be moved.
Size	If this is locked, the event cannot be resized.
Other	If this is locked, all other editing of the event is disabled. This includes adjusting the fades and event volume, processing, etc.

- **To specify which of these properties should be affected by the Lock function, use the "Lock Event Attributes" pop-up menu in the Preferences dialog (Editing page).**

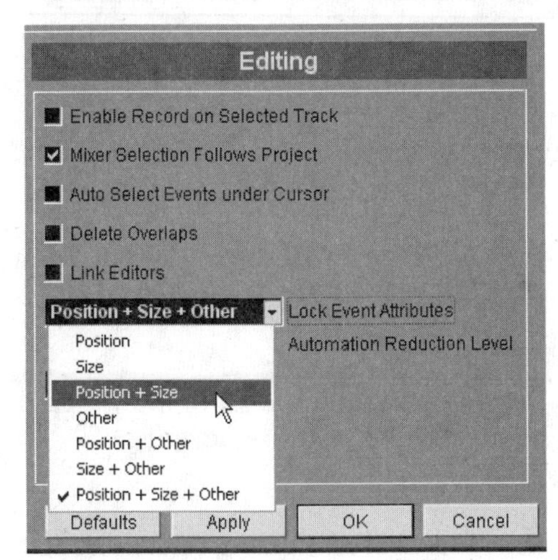

- **To lock events, select them and select "Lock..." from the Edit menu.**

  The events will be locked according to the options specified in the Preferences dialog.

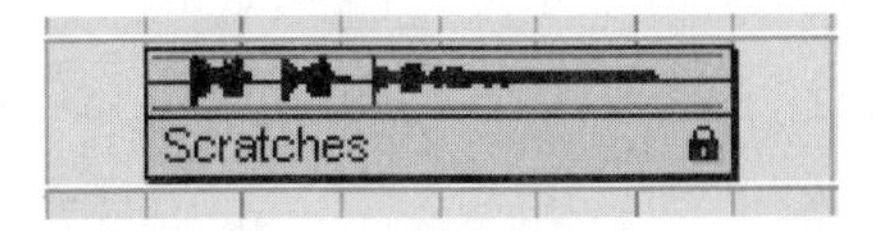

The padlock symbol indicates that one or more of the lock options are activated for the event.

- **You can adjust the lock options for a locked event by selecting it and selecting "Lock..." from the Edit menu again.**

  This opens a dialog in which you can activate or deactivate the desired lock options.

- **To unlock an event (turn off all lock options), select it and select "Unlock" from the Edit menu.**

- **It is also possible to lock a whole track, by clicking the padlock symbol in the Track list or in the Inspector.**

  This disables all editing of all events on the track.

Muting Events

You can Mute individual events in the Project window in the following way:

- **To mute or unmute a single event, click on it with the Mute tool.**

The Mute tool.

- **To mute several events, click on an unmuted event with the Mute tool, keep the mouse button pressed and drag the pointer over the desired events.**

  All events "touched" by the Mute tool will be muted.

- **To unmute several events, click on a muted event with the Mute tool, keep the mouse button pressed and drag the pointer over the desired events.**

  All events "touched" by the Mute tool will be unmuted.

- **You can click in an empty area with the Mute tool and drag a selection rectangle around the events you want to mute or unmute.**

  This changes the mute status of all events in the selection rectangle. If you hold down a modifier key when releasing the mouse button, you can force all events to be muted or unmuted, regardless of their previous status. The default modifier keys are [Shift] for mute and [Ctrl] for unmute.

- **You can mute events by selecting them and selecting "Mute" from the Edit menu.**

  Similarly, you can unmute the selected events by selecting "Unmute" from the Edit menu.

- **If a single event is selected, you can also change its Mute status in the info line.**
- **You can also Mute whole tracks by clicking the Mute ("X") button in the Track list, the Inspector or the Mixer.**

  Clicking the Solo ("S") button for a track mutes all other tracks.

Muted events can be edited as usual (with the exception of adjusting fades), but are not played back.

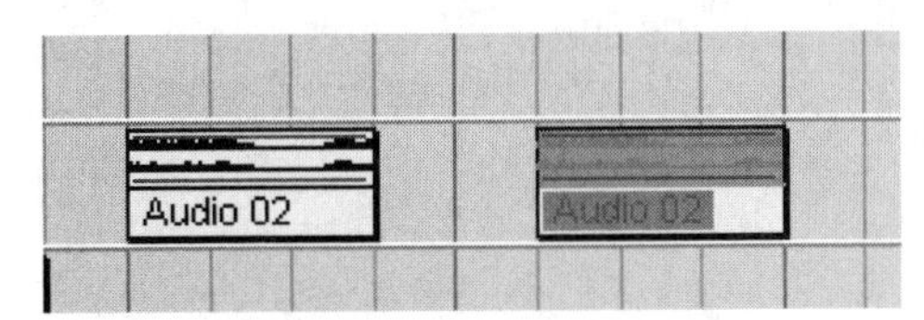

Muted events are "greyed out".

Removing Events

To remove an event from the Project window, use any of the following methods:

- **Click on the event with the Eraser tool.**

  If you press [Alt], all following events on the same track will be deleted.
- **Select the event(s) and press [Backspace], or select "Delete" from the Edit menu.**

Creating New Files from Events

As described in the Getting Started book, an audio event plays a section of an audio clip, which in turn refers to one or more audio files on the hard disk. However, in some situations you may want to create a new file that consists only of the section played by the event. This is done with the function Bounce Selection on the Audio menu:

1. **Select one or several audio events.**
2. **Set up fade in, fade out and event volume (on the info line or using the volume handle) as desired.**

   These settings will be applied to the new file. For details on fades and event volume, see page 169.
3. **Select "Bounce Selection" from the Audio menu.**

   You are asked whether you want to replace the selected event or not.

- **If you click "Replace", a new file is created, containing only the audio in the original event. A clip for the new file is added to the Pool, and the original event is replaced by a new event playing the new clip.**
- **If you click "No" a new file is created and a clip for the new file is added to the Pool.**

  The original event is not replaced.

You can also apply the Bounce Selection function to an audio part. In that case, the audio from all events in the part will be combined into a single audio file. If you choose "Replace" when asked, the part will be replaced with a single audio event playing a clip of the new file.

5.3.9 Range Editing

Editing in the Project window isn't necessarily restricted to handling whole events and parts. You can also work with selection ranges, which are independent from the event/part and track boundaries.

Creating a Selection Range

To make a selection range, drag a rectangle with the Range selection tool.

When the Range selection tool is selected, the Select submenu on the Edit menu has the following items for making selection ranges:

Option	Description
All	Makes a selection that covers all tracks, from the start of the project to the end (as defined by the Length setting in the Project Setup dialog).
None	Removes the current selection range.
In Loop	Makes a selection between the left and right locator, on all tracks.
From Start to Cursor	Makes a selection on all tracks, from the start of the project to the project cursor.
From Cursor to End	Makes a selection on all tracks, from the project cursor to the end of the project.

Option	Description
All on selected Tracks	Only used for event selection (see page 133).
Select event	This is available in the Sample Editor (see page 368).
Left Selection Side to Cursor	Moves the left side of the current selection range to the project cursor position.
Right Selection Side to Cursor	Moves the right side of the current selection range to the project cursor position.

- **Double clicking on an event with the Range Selection tool creates a selection range encompassing the event.**

  If you hold down [Shift] you can double click several events in a row, and the selection range will expand to encompass them all.

Adjusting the Size of the Selection Range

You can adjust the size of a selection range in the following ways:

- **By dragging its edges.**

  The pointer takes the shape of a double arrow when you move it over an edge of the selection range.

- **By holding down [Shift] and clicking.**

  The closest selection range edge will be moved to the position at which you clicked.

- **By adjusting the selection range start or end position numerically on the info line.**

Making Selection Ranges for Several Non-contiguous Tracks

As described above, selection ranges can cover several tracks. However, it is also possible to exclude tracks from a selection range:

1. **Create a selection range from the first to the last desired track.**
2. **Press [Ctrl] and click in the selection range on the tracks you want to exclude from the selection.**

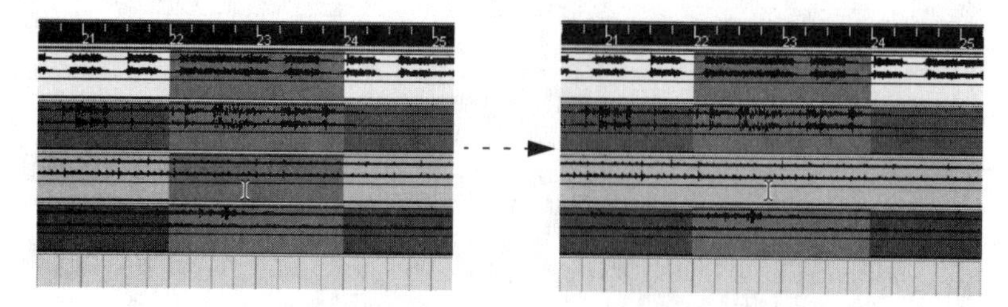

3. **In the same manner, you can add a track to the selection range by [Ctrl]-clicking in the selection range area on the track.**

Moving and Duplicating

- **To move a selection range, click and drag it to a new position.**

  This will move the contents of the selection range to the new position. If the range intersected events or parts, these will be split before moving, so that only the sections within the selection range are affected.

- **To duplicate a selection range, hold down [Alt] and drag.**

  You can also use the Duplicate, Repeat and Fill Loop functions, just as when duplicating events (see page 135).

Using Cut, Copy and Paste

When working with selection ranges, you can either use Cut, Copy and Paste on the Edit menu, or use the functions "Cut Time" and "Paste Time" on the Range submenu on the Edit menu. These work differently to their related functions on the Edit menu:

Function	Description
Cut	Cuts out the data in the selection range and moves it to the Clipboard. The selection range is replaced by empty track space in the Project window, meaning that events to the right of the range keep their positions.
Copy	Copies the data in the selection range to the clipboard.
Paste	Pastes the clipboard data at the start position and track of the current selection. Existing events are not moved to make room for the pasted data.
Paste at Origin	Pastes the clipboard data back at its original position. Existing events are not moved to make room for the pasted data.

Function	Description
Cut Time	Cuts out the selection range and moves it to the Clipboard. Events to the right of the removed range are moved to the left to fill out the gap.
Paste Time	Pastes the clipboard data at the start position and track of the current selection. Existing events are moved to make room for the pasted data.
Paste Time at Origin	Pastes the clipboard data back at its original position. Existing events are moved to make room for the pasted data.

Deleting Selection Ranges

Again, you can either use "regular" Delete or "Delete Time":

- **If you use the Delete function on the Edit menu (or press [Backspace]), the data within the selection range is replaced by empty track space.**

  Events to the right of the range keep their position.

- **If you use "Delete Time" on the Edit menu's Range submenu, the selection range is removed and events to the right are moved to the left to close up the gap.**

Other Functions

On the Range submenu on the Edit menu, you will find three more range editing functions:

Function	Description
Split	Splits any events or parts that are intersected by the selection range, at the positions of the selection range edges.
Crop	All events or parts that are partially within the selection range are cropped, that is, sections outside the selection range are removed. Events that are fully inside or outside the selection range are not affected.
Insert Silence	Inserts empty track space at the start of the selection range. The length of the inserted silence equals the length of the selection range. Events to the right of the selection range start are moved to the right to "make room". Events that are intersected by the selection range start are split, and the right section is moved to the right.

5.3.10 Region Operations

Regions are sections within a clip, with various uses. While regions are perhaps best created and edited in the Sample Editor (see page 371), the following region functions are available on the Audio menu in the Project window:

Function	Description
Event as Region	This function is available when one or several audio events are selected. It creates a region in the corresponding clip, with the start and end position of the region determined by the start and end position of the event within the clip.
Events from Regions	This function is available if you have selected an audio event whose clip contains regions within the boundaries of the event. The function will remove the original event and replace it with event(s) positioned and sized according to the Region(s).

5.4 Options

5.4.1 Snap

The Snap function helps you to find exact positions when editing in the Project window. It does this by restricting horizontal movement and positioning to certain positions. Operations affected by Snap include moving, duplicating, drawing, sizing, splitting, range selection, etc.

- **You turn Snap on or off by clicking the Snap icon in the toolbar.**

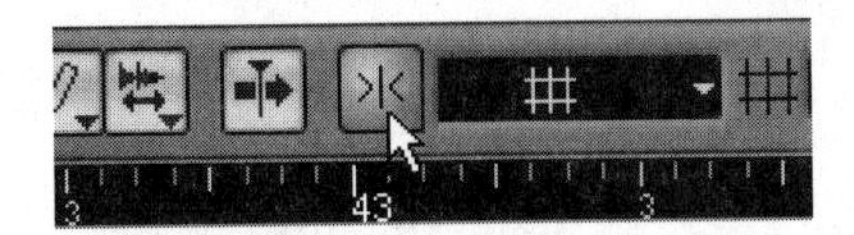

Snap activated.

- When you are moving audio events with Snap activated, it isn't necessarily the beginning of the event that is used as Snap position reference. Instead, each audio event has a Snap Point, which you can set to a relevant position in the audio (such as a downbeat, etc.).
  The Snap Point is preferably set in the Sample Editor since it will allow for a higher degree of precision (see page 366). You can however also set the Snap Point directly in the Project Window, in the following way:

1. **Select the event.**
2. **Place the project cursor at the desired position within a selected audio event.**
3. **Pull down the Audio menu and select "Snap Point To Cursor".**

   The Snap Point is set at the cursor position.

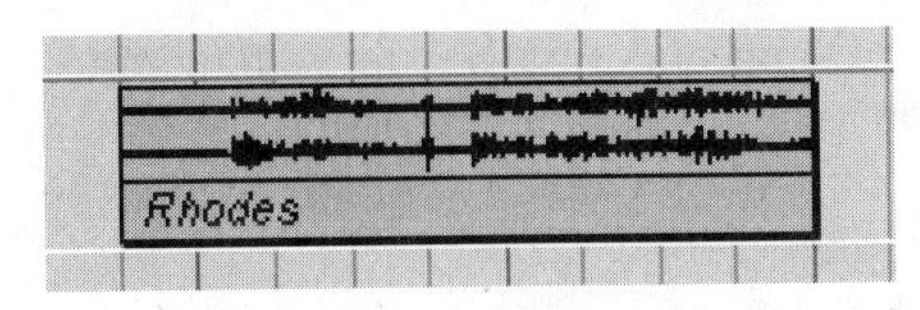

The Snap Point for an event is displayed as a blue line in the Project window.

Exactly how Snap works depends on which mode is selected on the Snap mode pop-up menu.

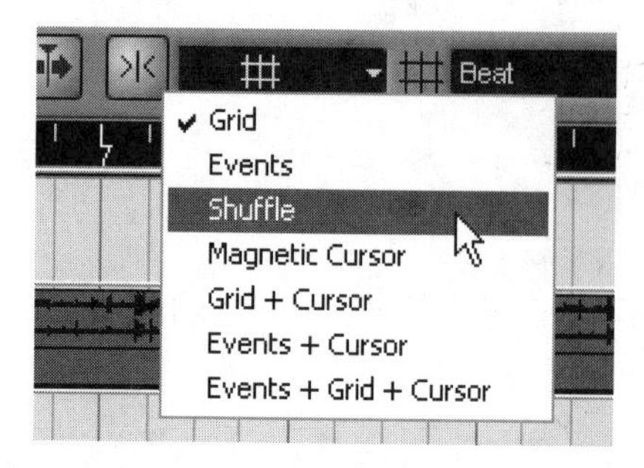

The following sections describe the different Snap modes:

Grid

In this mode, the Snap positions are set with the Grid pop-up menu to the right. The options depend on the format selected for the ruler. For example, if the ruler is set to show bars and beats, the grid can be set to bars, beats or the quantize value set with the next pop-up menu to the right. If a time- or frame-based ruler format is selected, the grid pop-up menu will contain time- or frame-based grid options, etc.

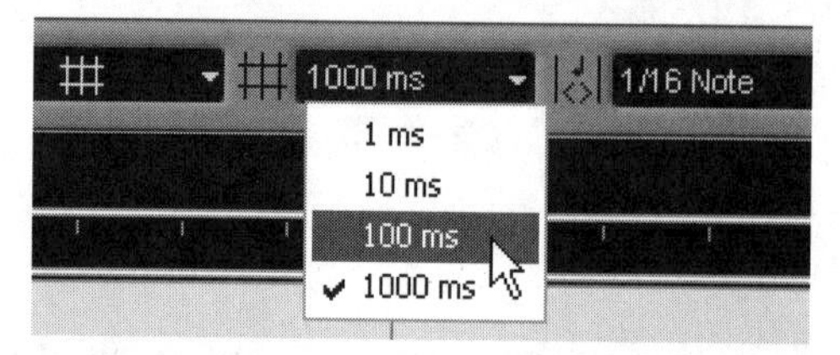

When seconds is selected as ruler format, the grid pop-up menu contains time-based grid options.

Events

In this mode, the start and end positions of other events and parts become "magnetic". This means that if you drag an event to a position near the start or end of another event, it is automatically aligned with the start or end of the other event. For audio events, the position of the Snap point is also magnetic (see page 366).

- **Note that this includes marker events on the marker track.**

  This allows you to snap events to marker positions, and vice versa.

Shuffle

Shuffle mode is useful when you want to change the order of adjacent events. If you have two adjacent events and drag the first one to the right, past the second event, the two events will change places.

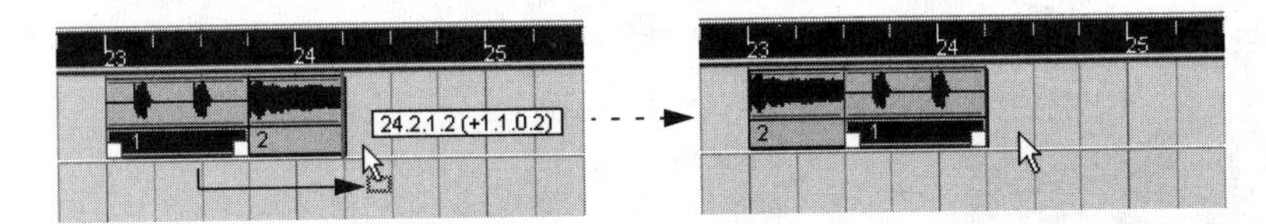

The same principle works when changing the order of more than two events:

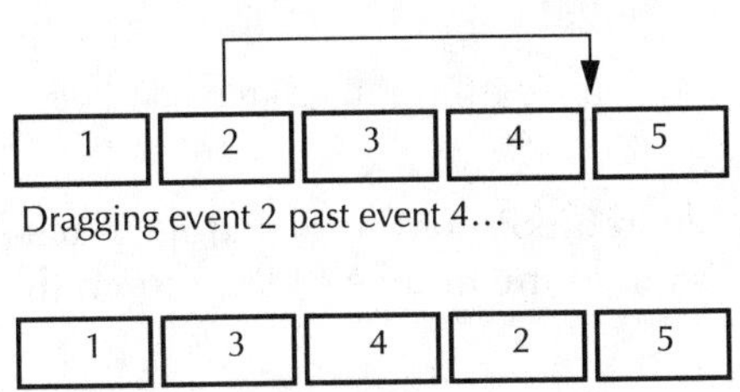

Dragging event 2 past event 4…

…changes the order of events 2, 3 and 4.

Magnetic Cursor

When this mode is selected, the project cursor becomes "magnetic". Dragging an event near the cursor causes the event to be aligned with the cursor position.

Grid + Cursor

This is a combination of the "Grid" and "Magnetic Cursor" snap modes.

Events + Cursor

This is a combination of the "Events" and "Magnetic Cursor" snap modes.

Events + Grid + Cursor

This is a combination of the "Events", "Grid" and "Magnetic Cursor" snap modes.

5.4.2 Snap to Zero Crossing

When this option is activated in the Preferences dialog (Audio page), all audio edits are done at zero crossings (positions in the audio where the amplitude is zero). This helps you to avoid pops and clicks which might otherwise be caused by sudden amplitude changes.

- This setting is global for all windows in all open projects. It is also available as an icon on the Sample Editor.

5.4.3 Auto Scroll

Auto scroll activated.

When this option is activated, the waveform display will scroll during playback, keeping the project cursor visible in the window.

- **If the option "Stationary Cursors" is activated in the Preferences dialog (Transport page), the project cursor will be positioned in the middle of the screen (if possible).**

6 Folder Tracks

6.1 About Folder Tracks

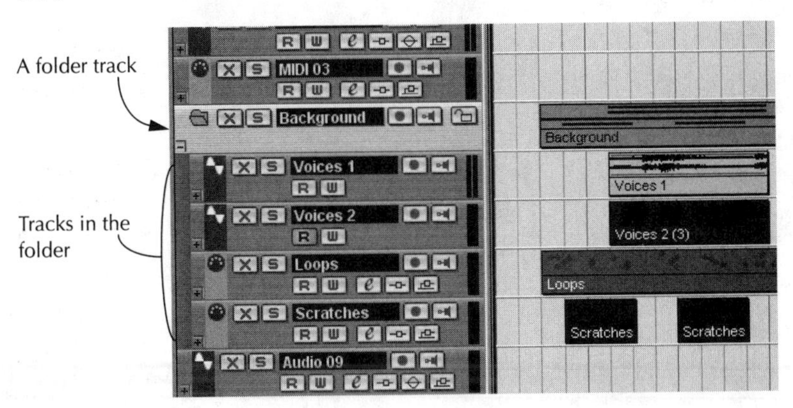

Just as the name implies, a folder track is a folder that contains other tracks. Moving tracks into a folder is a way to structure and organize tracks in the Project window. For example, grouping several tracks in a folder track makes it possible for you to "hide" tracks (thus giving you more working space on the screen). You can solo and mute several tracks in a quicker and easier way, and perform editing on several tracks as one entity. Folder tracks can contain any type of track including other folder tracks.

6.2 Using Folders

6.2.1 Creating a Folder Track

Folder tracks are created just like any other track: Select "Add Track" from the Project menu and select "Folder" from the submenu that appears.

6.2.2 Moving Tracks into a Folder

You can move any type of track into a folder by using drag and drop:

1. **In the Track List, click on a track that you want to move into a folder, and drag it onto a folder track.**

   A green arrow pointing to a folder appears when you drag the track onto the folder track in the list.

2. Release the mouse button.

The track is now placed in the folder track, and all parts and events on the track will be represented by a corresponding folder *part* (see page 155), that displays a graphical representation of all parts and events in the folder.

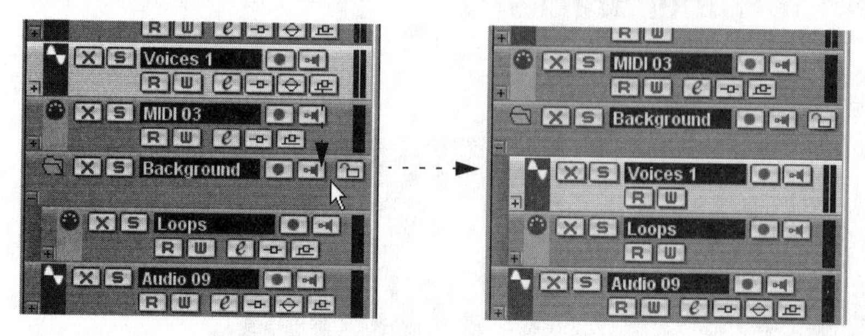

Since you can move any type of track into a folder track, it is possible to create subfolders by moving one folder track into another. This is called "nesting". For example, you could have a folder containing all the vocals in a project, and each vocal part could have a nested folder containing all the takes, in a subfolder for easier handling etc.

6.2.3 Removing Tracks from a Folder

To remove a track from a folder, simply drag it out of the folder and release it in the Track list.

6.2.4 Hiding/Showing Tracks in a Folder

You can hide or show the tracks located in a folder by clicking on the "Show/Hide" button (the plus sign) in the Track list for the folder track. Hidden tracks are still played back as usual.

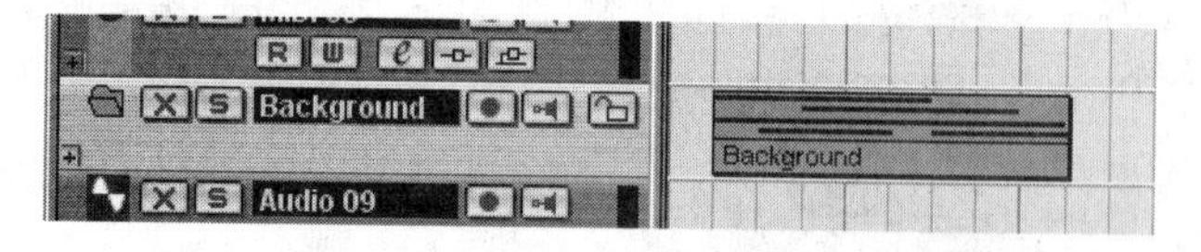

When a folder is "closed" this way, the folder part(s) still give you a graphic representation of the parts and events within the folder.

6.2.5 Muting and Soloing Folder Tracks

One of the main advantages of using folder tracks is that they provide you with a way to mute and solo several tracks as one unit. Muting and soloing a folder track affects all tracks in the folder. You can also solo or mute individual tracks in the folder.

Muting a Folder Track

You can mute a folder track (and thereby mute all tracks within it) the same way you mute other tracks by clicking in the Mute ("X") button in the Track list.

Soloing a Folder Track

You can solo a folder track (all tracks outside the folder are muted) the same way you solo other tracks, by selecting it and clicking the Solo button.

Soloing or Muting Tracks within a Folder

This can be done by showing the tracks in the folder and using the Mute and Solo buttons in the Track list as usual for any tracks inside the folder.

6.2.6 About Folder Parts

The parts contained in a folder track are shown as folder parts, a graphic representation of the contained events and parts horizontal and vertical position, as well as their respective length. If part colors are used, these are also taken into account in the folder part.

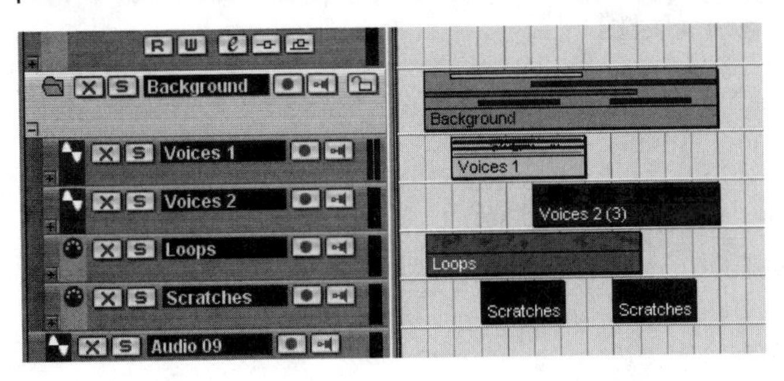

6.2.7 Handling Folder Parts

When several tracks have been put into a folder track the parts and events on the tracks may end up in several separate folder parts. A new folder part is created automatically if there is a gap between parts and events on the tracks, or in certain cirumstances if there is an overlap between the folder part and an event on a track within the folder. This works as follows:

- **When an event overlaps with a folder part more than half of its total length, it will be included in the folder part.**

  If the overlap is half its length or less it will be placed in a new folder part.

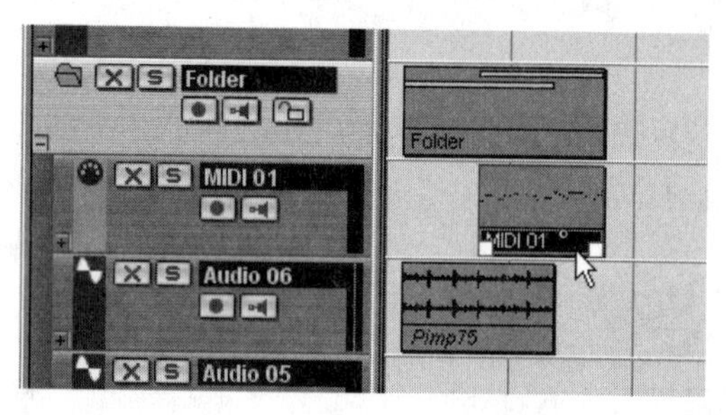

The MIDI part overlaps the folder part, by more than half its length, so it is included in the folder part.

If you move the MIDI part slightly to the right, more than half of the part is positioned outside the folder part, so a new folder part is created.

- **If a part "belongs" to a specific folder part, but is placed in a separate folder part due to the overlap, you can simply select both the folder parts if you wish to move the position of the parts together.**

6.2.8 Editing Folder Parts

Folder parts are editable. You can perform most standard editing commands like cut, copy, paste and move etc. The difference compared to normal part or event editing is that all tracks in the folder are affected. For example, in the illustration below you can see the result of splitting a folder part using the Scissor tool.

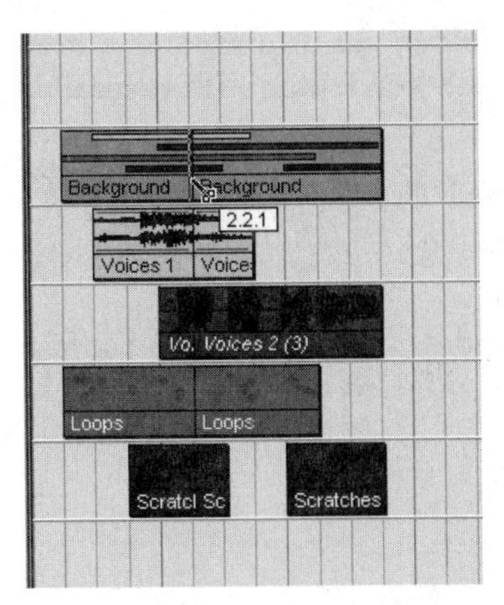

Splitting the folder part will split all contained parts or events present at that position.

In most respects a folder part can be handled just like other events or parts in the event display.

- Any editing performed on a folder part affects all tracks within the folder.

Resizing Folder Parts

If you resize a folder part, events and parts within the folder part are resized according to the currently selected type of resizing.

This is set by clicking the Arrow tool icon on the toolbar and selecting either "Normal Sizing" or "Sizing Moves Contents" from the pop-up menu—see page 138. The third option on the pop-up "Sizing Applies Time Stretch" cannot be used to resize folder parts.

6.2.9 Editing Tracks within Folder Parts

Tracks inside a folder can be edited as one entity, by performing the editing directly on the folder part containing the tracks as explained above. You can also edit individual tracks within the folder, by showing the contained tracks, selecting parts and opening an editor as usual.

Double clicking a folder part opens the editors for the corresponding track classes present in the folder. The following applies:

- **All MIDI parts located on the tracks within the folder, are displayed as if they were on the same track, just like when opening the Key Editor with several MIDI parts selected.**

  To be able to easily discern the different tracks in the Editor, give each track a different color in the Project window and use the "Part Colors" option in the Editor (see page 546).

- **If the folder contains tracks with audio events and/or audio parts, the Sample and/or Audio Part Editors are opened, with each audio event and audio part in a separate window.**

7 Using Markers

7.1 About Markers

Markers are used to quickly locate to any position. If you often find yourself jumping to a specific position, you can set up that position as a marker. There are two types of markers:

- Cycle markers, which allow you to store the start and end positions of a range.
- Standard markers which store a specific position.

Markers can be created and edited in several ways:

- By using the Marker window (see page 160).
- By using the Marker track (see page 163).
- By using the List Editor (see page 167).

About the Left and Right Locators

The first two markers are the left and right locators (indicated on the Transport panel by "L" and "R", respectively). As described on page 80, these are used for specifying punch-in and punch-out positions during recording, and as boundaries for Cycle playback and recording.

The locators can be managed in the same way as the other markers, but there are also some special functions for setting locator positions:

- **To set the left locator, press [Ctrl] and click at the desired position in the ruler.**

  Similarly, pressing [Alt] and clicking in the ruler sets the right locator.

- **Holding down [Ctrl] and pressing [1] or [2] on the numeric keypad sets the left or right locator to the current project cursor position.**

- **By creating cycle markers you can store any number of left and right locator positions, which can be recalled by simply clicking the marker, see page 165.**

- **Selecting "Locators to Selection" from the Transport menu (key command [P]) sets the locators to encompass the current selection.**

  For this to be available, you must have selected one or several events, or made a selection range.

- **You can also adjust the locator positions numerically in the Transport panel.**

7.2 The Marker Window

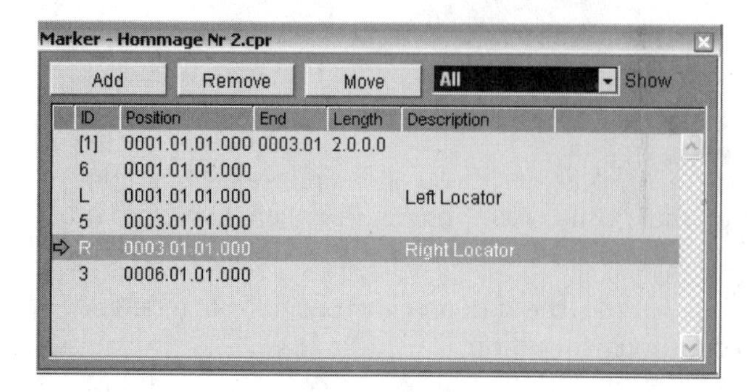

In the Marker window you can perform most editing operations concerning markers. Markers are displayed sequentially starting from the top of the window in the order that they occur in the project. Most functions in the Marker window are also available in the Inspector when the Marker track is selected.

To open the Marker window, select "Markers" from the Project menu or use the corresponding key command (by default [Ctrl]-[M]).

7.2.1 The Marker Window Columns

The Marker window is divided into six columns, which are used for performing the following operations:

- The leftmost column is the Locate column.
  Clicking in this column will move the project cursor to the corresponding Marker position. A blue arrow indicates the Marker at the project cursor position (or the closest marker before the project cursor).
- The ID column is used to edit marker ID-numbers.
  See "About Marker ID-numbers" below.
- The Position column displays the markers' time positions (or start positions for cycle markers).
  The marker positions can be edited directly in this column.
- The End and Length columns display the end positions and length of cycle markers—see page 163.
  These values can also be edited directly in the respective column.
- The Description column lets you enter names or descriptions for markers.
  The left and right locator descriptions cannot be changed.

7.2.2 Adding Markers in the Marker Window

You add position markers (in Stop mode, during playback or during recording) by clicking the Add button or by pressing [Insert] on the computer keyboard. Markers are always added at the current project cursor position.

- To add a cycle marker, select "Cycle Markers" from the Show pop-up menu and click the Add button.
  This adds a cycle marker between the left and right locator. You can also draw cycle markers on the Marker track (see page 163).

7.2.3 Removing Markers in the Marker Window

To remove a marker, select it and click the Remove button.

7.2.4 Moving Marker Positions in the Marker Window

The Move button in the Marker window can be used to "reprogram" marker positions. Proceed as follows:

1. **Set the project cursor to the position to which you want to move (or re-program) a marker.**
2. **Select the marker which you want to change in the Marker window.**

   Do not select the marker by clicking in the leftmost column, as this will move the project cursor you set up in the previous step.

- **If a cycle marker is selected, the Move operation affects the cycle marker start position.**

  The length of the range is not affected.

3. **Click the Move button.**

7.2.5 About Marker ID-numbers

Each time you add a marker it is automatically and sequentially assigned an ID-number, starting from ID 3 and onwards. Marker IDs 1 and 2 are always assigned to the left and right locators and cannot be changed, but all other ID-numbers can be changed later. The purpose of changing ID-numbers is to assign specific markers to key commands (see below).

IDs for cycle markers are shown in brackets and start from [1]. These may also be changed, but as IDs for cycle markers cannot be assigned to key commands, the numbers simply serve to identify a cycle marker. Instead you use the left and right locators to access cycle markers, see page 165.

Assigning Markers to the Numeric Keypad

As explained earlier, marker ID-numbers are assigned automatically and sequentially each time you add a marker. The (default) numeric pad key commands 3 to 9 always correspond to marker ID-numbers 3 to 9. Hence, if you have more than 6 markers in a project, markers assigned ID-numbers from 10 and onwards cannot be accessed using the numeric key pad.

If you want to keep all current markers, but want to specify which markers are assigned to the numeric key pad, the solution is to reassign the marker ID-numbers. Proceed as follows:

1. **First decide which of the current markers with an ID between 3 and 9 you want to reassign to a new ID-number, and thus remove its assignment to the numeric key pad.**

   Memorize the ID-number.

2. **Type in this ID-number in the ID column of the marker you want to assign to a numeric pad key and press enter.**

   The two marker ID-numbers are switched, and the key now locates to the marker selected in this step.

3. **Repeat as necessary for other markers.**

- **You can also simply remove a marker with an ID-number between 3 to 9 to free up a key—see "Removing markers" on page 161.**

7.3 Using the Marker Track

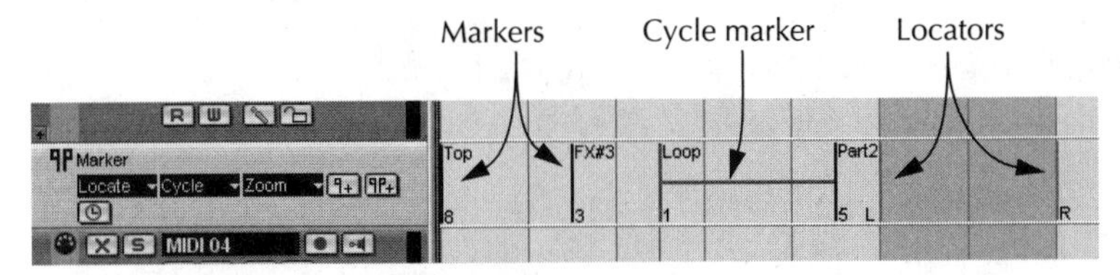

The Marker track is used to view and edit markers. Markers shown on the Marker track are exactly the same as shown in the Marker window, and any changes made on the Marker track are reflected in the Marker window and vice versa. Standard position markers in the Marker track are shown as marker events, vertical lines with the marker name (if assigned) and number beside it. If you select the Marker track, all markers are shown in the Inspector, much like in the Marker window.

About Cycle Markers

Cycle markers are shown on the Marker track as two events joined together by a horizontal line. Cycle markers are ideal for storing sections of a project. By setting cycle markers for sections of a song, for example "Intro", "Verse", "Chorus" etc., this enables you to quickly navigate to the song sections, and also to optionally repeat the section (by activating Cycle on the Transport bar).

Opening the Marker Track

To open the Marker track, select "Marker" from the Project menu—Add Track submenu. You can only have one Marker track in a project.

7.3.1 Editing Markers on the Marker Track

The following basic editing functions can be performed directly on the Marker track:

- **Add position markers "on the fly".**

  Use the [Insert] key or the "Add Marker" button in the Track list for the Marker track to add position markers at the current cursor position during playback.

Add Marker/Add Cycle Marker buttons

- **Add a cycle marker at the left and right locator positions.**

  Clicking the "Add Cycle Marker" button in the Track list for the Marker track adds a cycle marker spanning the area between the left and right locator.

- **Selecting markers.**

  You can use standard selection techniques like click dragging to make a selection rectangle or using [Shift] to select separate markers.

- **Draw position markers.**

  By clicking with the Pencil tool (or pressing [Alt] and clicking with the Arrow tool), you can create or "draw" position marker events at any position on the track. If snap is activated on the toolbar, this determines at which positions you can draw markers.

- **Draw cycle markers.**

  To draw a cycle marker range, you press [Ctrl] and use the Pencil tool or the Arrow tool. Snap settings are applied if activated.

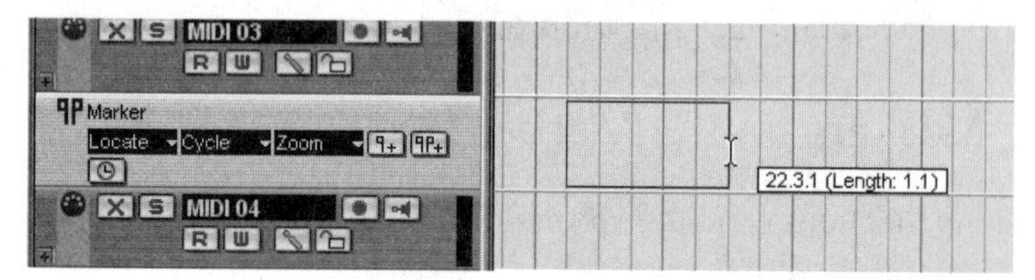

● Cycle markers can freely overlap.

- **Resize a cycle marker.**

  Select a cycle marker by clicking on it. As you can see, two handles appear at the bottom of the start and end events. If you click and hold one of the handles you can drag the event left or right to resize the cycle marker. This can also be done numerically on the info line.

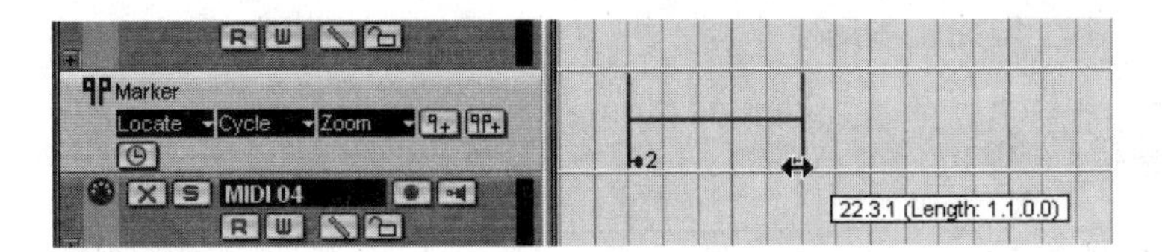

- **Move markers.**

  Use usual techniques as object selection and dragging or editing on the info line to move selected markers. As usual, snap is taken into account if activated.

- **Remove markers.**

  This is done exactly the same way as for other events, i.e selecting and pressing Backspace, using the Erase tool etc.

- **Naming markers.**

  A selected marker's name can be edited by clicking the name on the info line.

7.3.2 Navigating Using Cycle Markers

Cycle markers are not directly used to navigate the position, but represent ranges that you can move the left and right locators to by simply selecting the cycle marker.

- **If you double click on a cycle marker, or select it from the the Cycle pop-up menu in the track list, the left and right locators are moved to encompass the cycle marker.**

  You can now set the project cursor position to the start or the end of the cycle marker by selecting the left or right locator from the Locate pop-up menu, or by using the numeric pad keys [1] and [2].

Zooming to Cycle Markers

- **By selecting a cycle marker on the Zoom pop-up menu, the event display is zoomed in to encompass the selected range only.**

  This can also be done by keeping [Alt] pressed while double-clicking on the cycle marker in the event display.

Editing Cycle Markers Using Tools

Cycle markers can be edited on the Marker track using the following tools. Note that the snap value applies as with regular events:

Tool	Use
Pencil	Press [Ctrl] and use the Pencil tool to create new ranges (as described above).
Eraser	Click with the Eraser tool to delete a cycle marker. If you hold down [Alt] when you click, all consecutive markers will also be deleted.
Scissors	Click with the Scissors tool to split the cycle marker in two. If you hold down [Alt] and click, the range will be split into many ranges with the same length (the length is governed by where in the range you click).
Selection Range	This is described on page 166.

The other tools cannot be used with cycle markers.

7.3.3 Using Markers to Make Range Selections in the Project Window

Besides enabling you to quickly move the locators and the project cursor, cycle markers can be used in conjunction with the Range Selection tool to make range selections in the Project window. This is useful if you quickly want to make a selection that spans all tracks in the project.

- **Double click on a cycle marker to set the left and right locator to the start and end position of the range, then double click inside the cycle marker with the Range Selection tool.**

Or…

- **Double click with the Range Selection tool between any two position markers.**

This selects everything in the Project window located inside of the marker range (or locator positions), just as if you had used the Range Selection tool to draw a rectangle. Any functions or processing you perform will now affect the selection only.

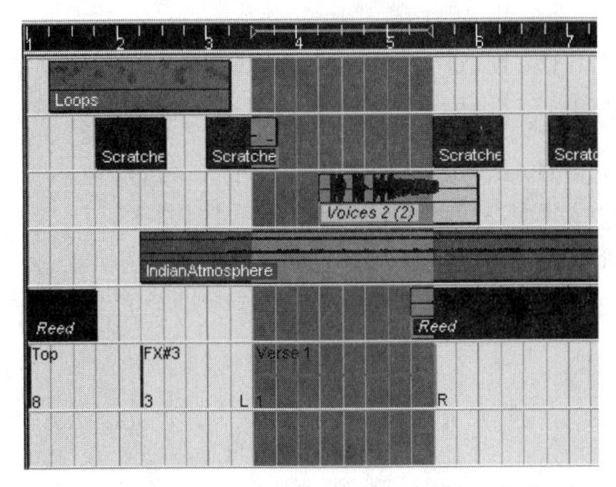

In this example, Verse 1 has been selected with the Range Selection tool.

Moving and Copying Parts

This is a quick way to move or copy complete sections of the project (on all tracks):

1. **Click on a cycle marker with the Range Selection tool.**

   Everything in the project within the cycle marker boundaries is selected.

2. **Drag the cycle marker to a new position.**

   The selection in the Project window is moved to the same position.

- **If you hold down [Alt] while you drag the cycle marker, the selection in the Project window is copied instead.**

7.3.4 Editing Markers in the Project Browser

- To view and edit markers in the Project Browser, the Marker track must be added to the Project window.

If you have a Marker track in the Project window, you can create and edit all marker parameters, including marker ID's, in the Project Browser. Proceed as follows:

1. **Open the Project Browser by selecting it on the Project menu.**
2. **Select "Marker" in the Project Structure window.**

   A list of the markers is shown in the main Browser window.

3. **Now you can edit marker names, positions and ID numbers, by selecting an item and typing in values as usual in the main Editor window.**

   For details about editing in the Project Browser see page 584.

- **You can use the Add pop-up menu and Add button to insert new markers or cycle markes when the Marker track is selected in the Project Browser.**

  This works just like the Add button in the Marker window (see page 161).

8 Fades and Crossfades

8.1 Creating Fades

There are two main types of fade-ins and fade-outs in audio events in Cubase SX/SL:

8.1.1 Fades Created by Using the Fade Handles

Selected audio events have blue handles in the upper left and right corners. These can be dragged to create a fade-in or fade-out respectively.

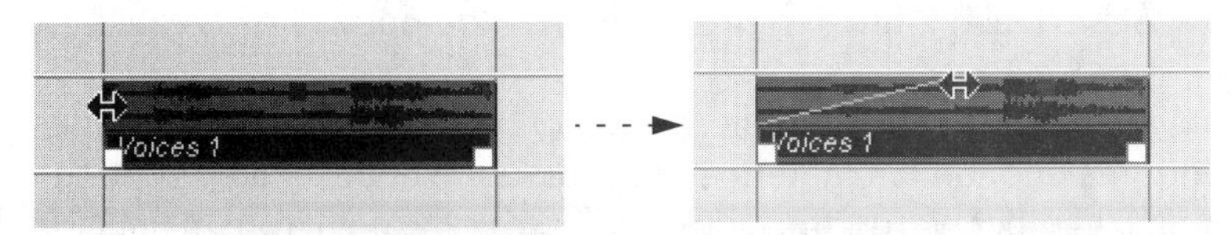

Creating a fade-in. The fade is automatically reflected in the shape of the event's waveform, giving you a visual feedback of the result when you drag the fade handle.

Fades created with the handles are not applied to the audio clip as such. Instead, Cubase SX/SL seamlessly switches between the fade sections and the actual clip on playback. This means that several events referring to the same audio clip can have different fade curves.

- Note that if you select multiple events and drag the fade handles on one of them, the same fade will be applied to all selected events.

- A fade can be edited in the Fade dialog, as described on the following pages.
  You open the dialog by double clicking on the fade, or by selecting the event and selecting "Open Fade Editor(s)" from the Audio menu (note that this will open two dialogs if the event has both fade-in and fade-out curves).
  If you adjust the shape of the fade curve in the Fade dialog, this shape will be maintained when you later adjust the length of a fade.
- You can make the fade longer or shorter at any time, by dragging the handle.
  You can actually do this even without selecting the event first, i.e. without visible handles. Just move the mouse pointer along the fade curve until the cursor turns into a bidirectional arrow, then click and drag.
- If the option "Show Event Volume Curves Always" is activated in the Preferences dialog (Event Display—Audio page), the fade curves will be shown in all events, regardless of whether they are selected or not.
  If the option is deactivated, the fade curves are shown in selected events only.

Creating and Adjusting Fades with the Range Selection Tool

"Handle-type" fades can also be created and adjusted with the Range Selection tool, in the following way:

1. **Select a section of the audio event with the Range Selection tool.**

   The result depends on your selection, in the following way:

- If you select a range from the beginning of the event, a fade-in will be created within the range.
- If you select a range that reaches the end of an event, a fade-out will be created in the range.
- If you select a range encompassing a middle section of the event, but not reaching neither the start nor the end, both a fade-in and a fade-out will be created *outside* of the selected range. In other words, the fade-in will cover the area from the beginning of the event to the beginning of the selected range, and the fade-out will cover the area from the end of the selected range to the end of the event.

2. **Pull down the Audio menu and select "Adjust Fades to Range".**

   The fade areas are adjusted according to the selection range.

- You can select multiple audio events on separate tracks with the Range Selection tool, and apply the fade to all of them simultaneously.

About the Volume Handle

A selected audio event also has a blue handle in the top middle. This is the volume handle, and it provides a quick way of changing the volume of an event, directly in the Project window. It stands in direct correlation with the volume setting in the info line, that is, dragging the volume handle also changes the value in the info line.

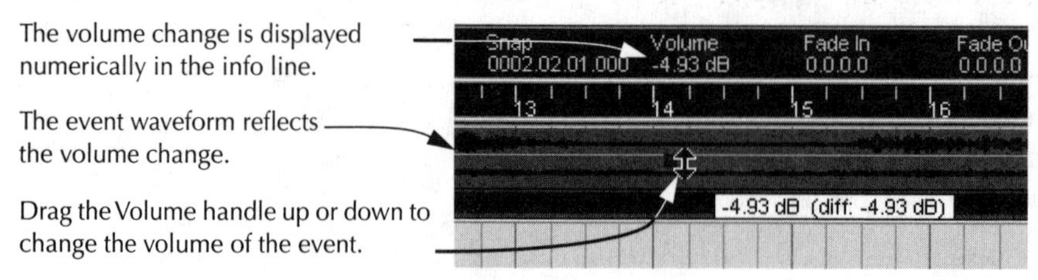

8.1.2 Fades Created by Processing

If you have selected an audio event or a section of an audio event (using the Range Selection tool), you can apply a fade-in or fade-out to the selection by using the "Fade In" or "Fade Out" functions on the Process submenu on the Audio menu. These functions open the corresponding Fade dialog, allowing you to specify a fade curve.

- Note that the length of the fade area is determined by your selection. In other words, you specify the length of the fade before you enter the Fade dialog.

- Also note that you can select multiple events and apply the same processing to all of them simultaneously.

Fades created this way are applied to the audio clip rather than to the event. This has the following consequences:

- If you later create new events that refer to the same clip, these will have the same fades.
- At any time you can remove or modify the fades using the Offline Process History (see page 349).

If other events refer to the same audio clip, you will be asked whether you want the processing to be applied to these events or not.

- Continue will apply the processing to all events that refer to the audio clip.
- New Version will create a separate, new version of the audio clip for the selected event.
- You can also choose to put a checkmark in the "Do not ask this message again" box. Regardless of whether you then choose "Continue" or "New Version", any and all further processing you do will conform to the option you select.

- You can change this setting at any time in the Preferences dialog (Audio page), under "On Processing Shared Clips".

8.1.3 Removing Fades

To remove a fade, select the event and select "Remove Fades" from the Audio menu.

You can also use the Range Selection tool to remove fades and crossfades:

1. **Drag the Range Selection tool in the Project window, so that the selection encloses all of the fades and crossfades you wish to remove.**
2. **Select "Remove Fades" from the Audio menu.**

8.2 The Fade Dialogs

The Fade dialogs appear when you edit an existing fade or use the "Fade In"/"Fade Out" functions on the Audio menu's Process submenu. The picture below shows the Fade In dialog; the Fade Out dialog has identical settings and features.

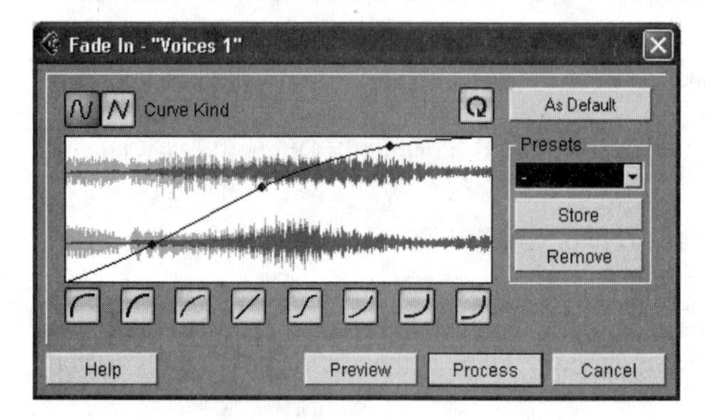

- **If you open the Fade dialog(s) with several events selected, you can adjust the fade curves for all these events at the same time.**

  This is useful if you want to apply the same type of fade-in to more than one event, etc.

Curve Kind

These buttons determine whether the fade curve should consist of spline curve segments (left button) or linear segments (right button).

Fade Display

Shows the shape of the fade curve. The resulting waveform shape is shown in dark grey, with the current waveform shape in light grey.

You can click on the curve to add points, and click and drag existing points to change the shape. To remove a point from the curve, drag it outside the display.

Restore Button

The Restore button (the button to the right above the fade display) is only available when editing fades made by dragging the fade handles. Click this to cancel any changes you have made since opening the dialog.

Curve Shape Buttons

These buttons give you quick access to some common curve shapes.

Default Button

Clicking the "As Default" button stores the current settings as the default fade. This shape will be used whenever you create new fades.

Presets

If you have set up a fade-in or fade-out curve that you may want to apply to other events or clips, you can store it as a preset by clicking the Store button.

- **To apply a stored preset, select it from the pop-up menu.**
- **To rename the selected preset, double click on the name and type a new one.**
- **To remove a stored preset, select it from the pop-up menu and click Remove.**

● Stored fade-in presets will only appear in the Fade In dialog, and fade-out presets will only appear in the Fade Out dialog.

Preview, Apply and Process

The buttons in the bottom row are different depending on whether you are editing a fade made with the fade handles or applying a fade using processing:

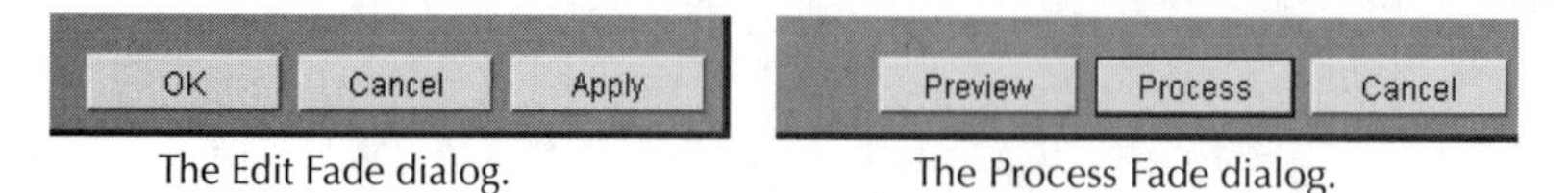

The Edit Fade dialog. The Process Fade dialog.

The Edit Fade dialogs have the following buttons:

Button	Function
OK	Applies the set fade curve to the event, and closes the dialog.
Cancel	Closes the dialog.
Apply	Applies the set fade curve to the event, without closing the dialog.

The Process Fade dialogs have the following buttons:

Button	Function
Preview	Plays back the fade area. Playback will repeat until you click the button again (the button is labeled "Stop" during playback).
Process	Applies the set fade curve to the clip, and closes the dialog.
Cancel	Closes the dialog without applying any fade.

8.3 Creating Crossfades

Overlapping audio material on the same track can be crossfaded, for smooth transitions or special effects. You create a crossfade by selecting two consecutive audio events and selecting the Crossfade command on the Audio menu (or using the corresponding key command, by default [X]). The result depends on whether the two events overlap or not:

- **If the events overlap, a crossfade is created in the overlapping area.**

  The crossfade will be of the default shape—initially a linear, symmetric crossfade, but you can change this as described below.

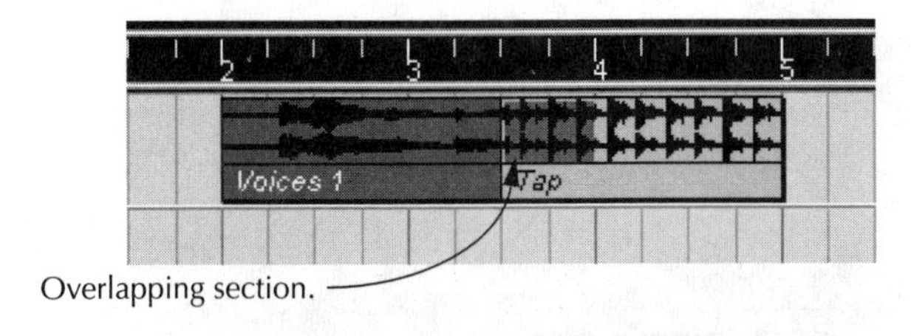

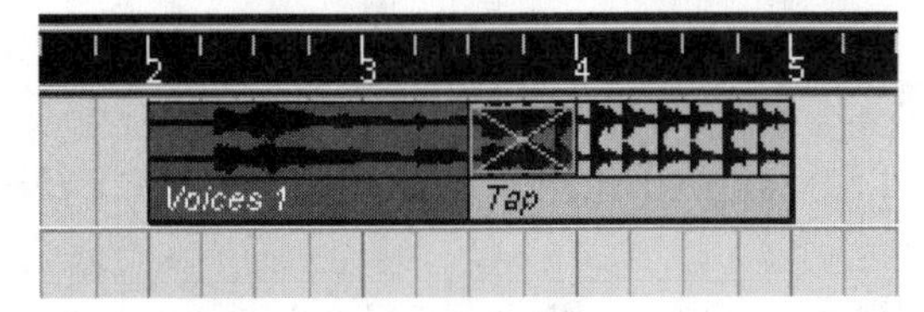

- **If the events don't overlap but are directly consecutive (lined up end-to-start, with no gap) it's still possible to crossfade them—provided that their respective audio clips overlap! In this case, the two events are resized so that they overlap, and a crossfade of the default length and shape is applied.**

  The default crossfade length and shape are set in the Crossfade dialog (see page 178).

An example:

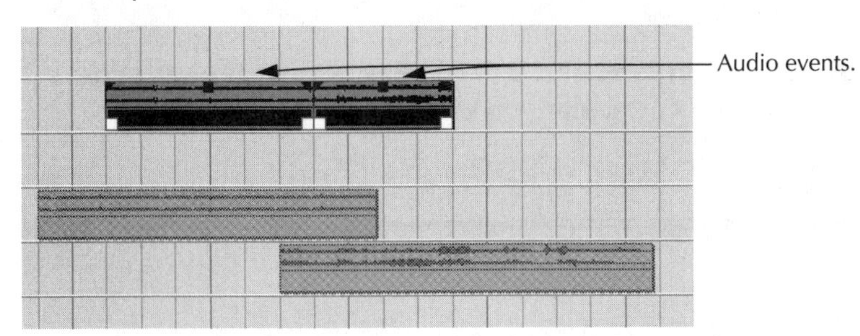

Audio clips.

The events in themselves do not overlap, but their clips do. Therefore, the events can be resized so that they overlap, which is required for a crossfade to be created.

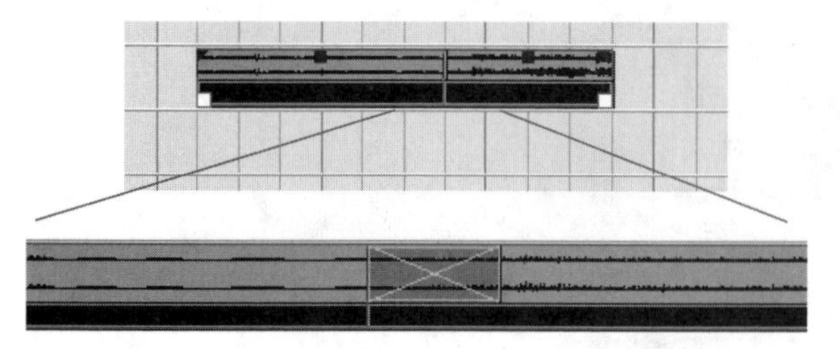

When you select the Crossfade function, the two events are resized so that they overlap, and a default crossfade is created in the overlapping section.

- **If the events don't overlap, and cannot be resized enough to overlap, a cross-fade cannot be created.**
- **Once you have created a crossfade, you can edit it by selecting one or both crossfaded events, and selecting "Crossfade" from the Audio menu again (or by double clicking in the crossfade zone).**

  This opens the Crossfade dialog, as described below.

8.3.1 Removing Crossfades

To remove a crossfade, select the events and select "Remove Fades" from the Audio menu, or use the Range Selection tool:

1. **Drag the Range Selection tool in the Project window, so that the selection encloses all of the fades and crossfades you wish to remove.**
2. **Select "Remove Fades" from the Audio menu.**

8.4 The Crossfade Dialog

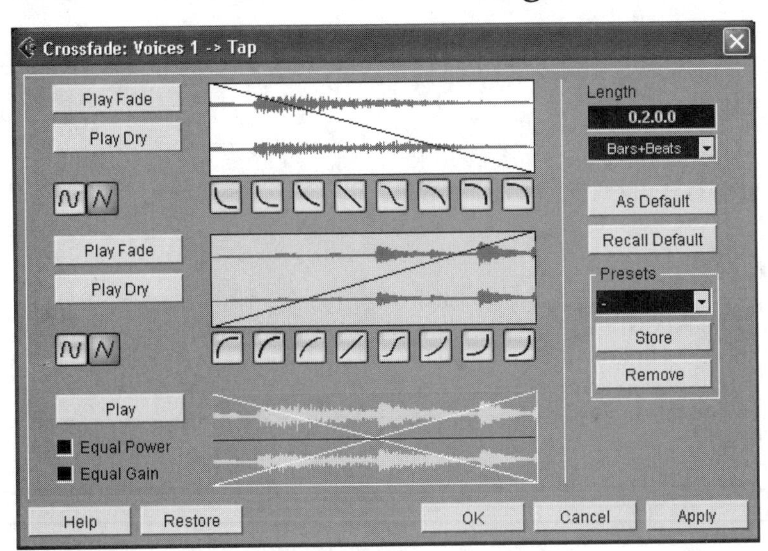

The Crossfade dialog contains separate settings for the fade-in and fade-out curve in the crossfade, as well as common settings.

The left part of the Crossfade dialog contains two sections with settings for the fade-in and fade-out curves in the crossfade. These two sections have identical settings.

Play Buttons

The "Play Fade" and "Play Dry" buttons allow you to audition the fade-in or fade-out part, with or without the crossfade.

The "Play" button plays back the whole crossfade. Playback will continue repeatedly until you click the button again (the button will be labeled "Stop" during playback).

Curve Kind Buttons

These buttons determine whether the corresponding fade curve should consist of spline curves (left button) or linear segments (right button).

Fade Displays

Shows the shape of the fade-out and fade-in curve, respectively. You can click on the curve to add points, and click and drag existing points to change the shape. To remove a point from the curve, drag it outside the display.

Curve Shape Buttons

These buttons give you quick access to some common curve shapes.

Crossfade Display

The bottom display shows the shape of the whole crossfade curve and the resulting waveform. You cannot edit the curve in this display.

Equal Power and Gain

If you activate the "Equal Power" checkbox, the fade curves are adjusted, so that the energy (power) of the crossfade will be constant all along the crossfade region.

- Equal Power curves have only one editable curve point. You cannot use the Curve kind buttons or the presets when this mode is selected.

If you activate the "Equal Gain" checkbox, the fade curves are adjusted so that the summed fade-in and fade-out amplitudes will be the same all along the crossfade region. This is often suitable for short crossfades.

Length Settings

You can adjust the length of the crossfade area numerically in the "Length" field. Use the pop-up menu in the field below to select a time format (see page 116).

- The specified length is applied when you click "Apply" or "OK".
- If possible, the length change will be applied equally to "both sides" of the crossfade (i.e. Cubase SX/SL tries to "center" the crossfade).

- To be able to resize a crossfade this way, it must be possible to resize the corresponding event. For example, if the left crossfaded event already plays its audio clip to the end, its endpoint cannot be moved any further to the right.

Default Buttons

Clicking the "As Default" button stores all of the current settings as the default crossfade. These settings will then be used whenever you create new crossfades.

- **The Crossfade Length setting is included in the Default settings. However, it is only applied if the events to be crossfaded don't overlap—otherwise the crossfade will be in the overlap area (see page 174).**

Clicking the "Recall Default" button copies the curves and settings in the Default crossfade to the Crossfade dialog.

Presets

If you have set up a crossfade shape that you may want to apply to other events, you can store it as a preset by clicking the Store button.

- **To apply a stored preset, select it from the pop-up menu.**
- **To rename the selected preset, double click on the name and type a new one.**
- **To remove a stored preset, select it from the pop-up menu and click Remove.**

Restore

Restores the crossfade curve to the shape it had when you opened the dialog.

OK

Applies the settings to the crossfade and closes the dialog.

Cancel

Closes the dialog without applying any changes.

Apply

Applies the settings to the crossfade without closing the dialog.

8.5 Auto Fades and Crossfades

Cubase SX/SL features an Auto Fade function that can be set both globally, i.e. for the entire project, and separately for each audio track. The idea behind the Auto Fade function is to create smoother transitions between events by applying short (1—500 ms) fade-ins and fade-outs.

- Note that Auto Fades are not applied to the audio events, but calculated in real time during playback. This means that the larger the number of audio tracks with Auto Fades activated in a project, the more the playback performance will be negatively affected.

8.5.1 Making Global Auto Fade Settings

1. **To make Auto Fades settings globally for the project, select "Auto Fades Settings..." from the Project menu.**

   This opens the Auto Fades dialog for the project.

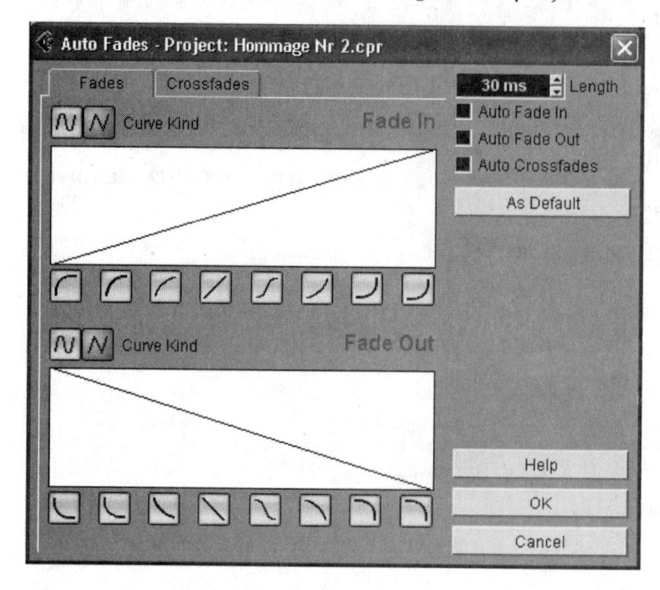

2. **Use the checkboxes in the upper right corner to activate or deactivate Auto Fade In, Auto Fade Out and Auto Crossfades, respectively.**
3. **Use the Length value field to specify the length of the auto fade or crossfade (1—500 ms).**
4. **To adjust the shapes of Auto Fade In and Auto Fade Out, select the "Fades" tab and make settings as in the regular Fade dialogs.**
5. **To adjust the shape of the Auto Crossfade, select the "Crossfades" tab and make settings as in the regular Crossfade dialog.**
6. **If you want to use the settings you have made in forthcoming new projects, click the "As Default" button.**

   The next time you create a new project, it will use these settings by default.
7. **Click OK to close the dialog.**

8.5.2 Making Auto Fade Settings for a Separate Track

By default, all audio tracks will use the settings you have made in the Project Auto Fades dialog. However, since Auto Fades use computing power, a better approach may be to turn Auto Fades off globally, and activate them for individual tracks, as needed:

1. **Right-click the track in the track list and select "Auto Fades Settings..." from the context menu (or select the track and click the "Auto Fades Settings" button in the Inspector).**

   The Auto Fades dialog for the track appears. This is identical to the Project Auto Fades dialog, with the addition of a "Use Project Settings" option.

2. **Deactivate the "Use Project Settings" option.**

   Now, any settings you make will be applied to the track only.

3. **Set up the Auto Fades as desired and close the dialog.**

Reverting to Project Settings

If you want a track to use the global Auto Fade settings, open the Auto Fades dialog for the track and activate the "Use Project Settings" checkbox. This makes the track use the Auto Fade settings you have made for the project.

9 The Mixer

9.1 About this Chapter

This chapter contains detailed information about the elements used when mixing audio and MIDI in the Mixer. Some mixing-related features are *not* described in this chapter. These are the following:

- **Setting up and using audio effects.**

  See page 221.

- **Setting up and using MIDI effects.**

  See page 436.

- **Surround Sound.**

  See page 277.

- **Automation of all Mixer parameters.**

  See page 291.

- **How to mix down several audio tracks (complete with automation and effects if you wish) to a single audio file.**

  See page 601.

9.2 Overview

The Mixer offers a common environment for controlling levels, pan, solo/mute status etc. for all channel types.

- The picture above shows the Mixer in Cubase SX—the expanded upper pane is not available in Cubase SL (see page 198).

9.2.1 Opening the Mixer

- **To open the Mixer, select it from the Devices menu.**

  Each audio, MIDI and group channel track in the Project window is also represented by a "channel strip" in the Mixer.

- **The order of the audio and MIDI channel strips (from left to right) in the Mixer corresponds to the Project window Track list.**

  If you reorder audio and MIDI tracks in the Track list, this will be reflected in the Mixer (if the Mixer is open when reordering tracks it will have to be closed and opened again to reflect the changes). Group channels in the Mixer cannot be reordered, see below.

9.2.2 What Channel Types Can Be Shown in the Mixer?

- **In addition to the aforementioned audio, MIDI and group channels, any activated ReWire (see page 649) and VST Instrument (see page 241) channels are also shown in the Mixer.**

  These cannot be reordered, and appear to the right of the audio and MIDI channels in the Mixer, ReWire channels first, then VST Instrument (VSTi) channels. Group channels always appear to the right of other channel types in the Mixer.

- Folder, marker and automation tracks are not shown in the Mixer.

9.2.3 View Options

The Mixer can be configured in various ways to suit your needs and to save screen space. Here follows a runthrough of the various view options:

Selecting What Channel Types to Show/Hide

You can specify what channel types to show/hide in the Mixer. Proceed as follows:

1. **Open the Mixer.**

   The leftmost strip is called the Common panel and is always shown in the Mixer. This contains various global settings and options relating to the Mixer.

2. **Click the View Options pop-up in the Common panel.**

   A pop-up menu appears and the last five items on the menu are the channel types. By default all channel types are viewable (i.e. ticked).

Clicking here...

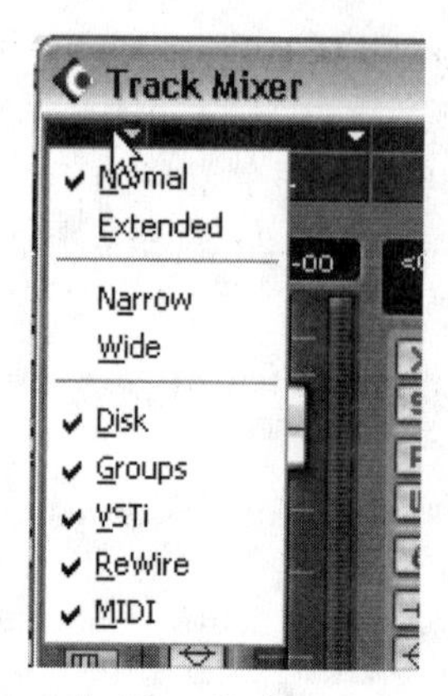

...opens the View Options pop-up.

3. **You can now untick the channel type(s) that you wish to hide from view by unticking the corresponding item(s) from the menu.**

   Regular audio tracks are named "Disk" channels on the menu.

- **This can also be done using the Channel type show/Hide indicators at the bottom of the Common panel.**

  These are lit for visible channel types. Click on the corresponding channel type indicator to hide or show the corresponding channel type in the Mixer.

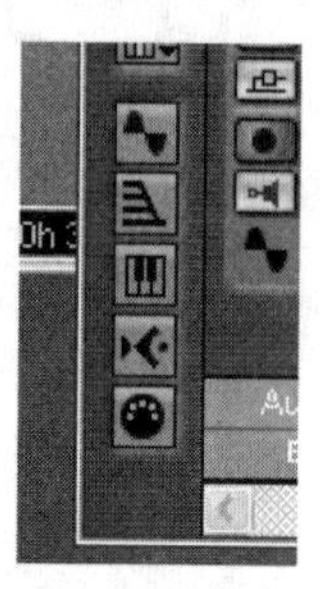

The Channel type show/hide indicators. From top to bottom Disk, Group, VSTi, ReWire and MIDI channels.

Normal vs. Extended Channel Strips (Cubase SX only)

Also on the Common panel View Options pop-up, you have the option of selecting Normal or Extended channel strips. Alternatively, click the button directly below the down arrow symbol of the pop-up menu. Normal channel strips only show the fader panels with the associated vertical row of buttons. Extended channel strips will show an extra panel above the fader panel.

Normal and extended channel strip.

Selecting What to Display in the Extended Channel Strip (Cubase SX only)

You can select what to display in the extended channel strip individually for each channel from the View Options pop-up at the top of each channel strip, or globally from the View Options pop-up on the Common panel.

- See page 198 for a description of the various options for audio channels.
- See page 210 for a description of the various options for MIDI channels.

Setting the Width of Channel Strips

Each channel strip's width can be sized to either "Wide" or "Narrow" mode from the View Options pop-up at the top of each channel strip.

- **Narrow channel strips contain a narrow fader, miniature buttons, plus the View Options pop-up.**

  Only a blank panel is shown in the extended section for narrow channel strips. If you select to show parameters in the extended section of a narrow strip, the channel strip will automatically be resized to wide.

Wide and narrow channel strips.

- **When selecting wide or narrow channel strips from the Common panel View Options pop-up, all channel strips are affected.**

9.3 The Audio Channel Strips

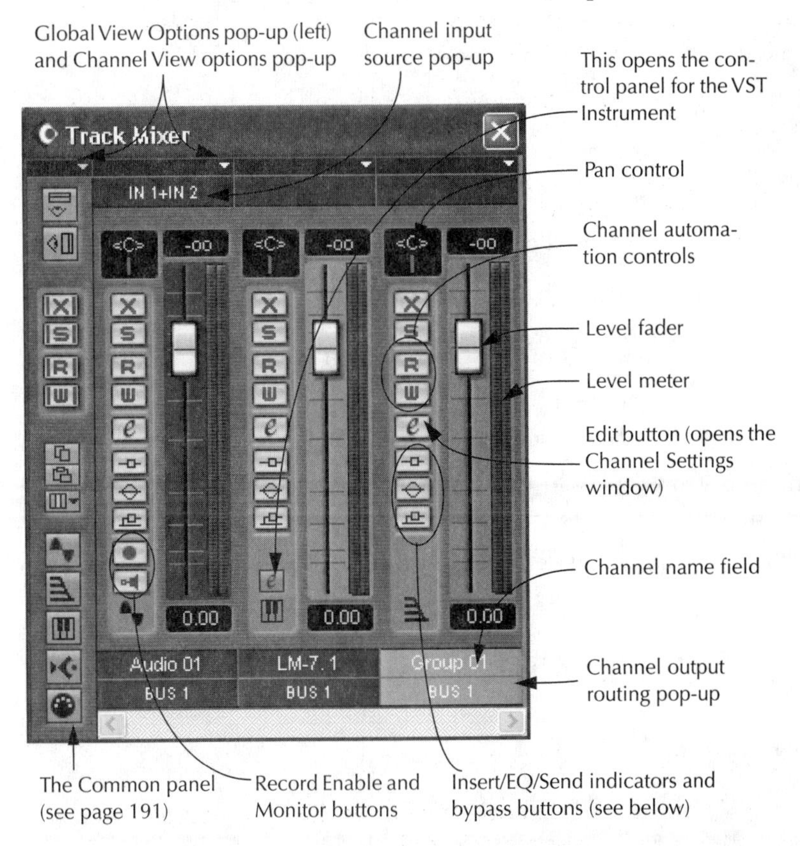

The Mixer in normal mode (no extended channel strips), showing (from left to right) the Common panel, a stereo audio channel, a VST Instrument channel, and a group channel strip.

All audio related channel types (audio, group, VST Instrument or ReWire) basically have the same channel strip layout. Only audio track (disk) channels have an Input source pop-up, a Record Enable and Monitor button (since audio inputs are never routed to group or VST Instrument channels). VST Instrument channels have an additional Edit button for opening the instrument's control panel.

About the Insert/EQ/Send Indicators and Bypass Buttons

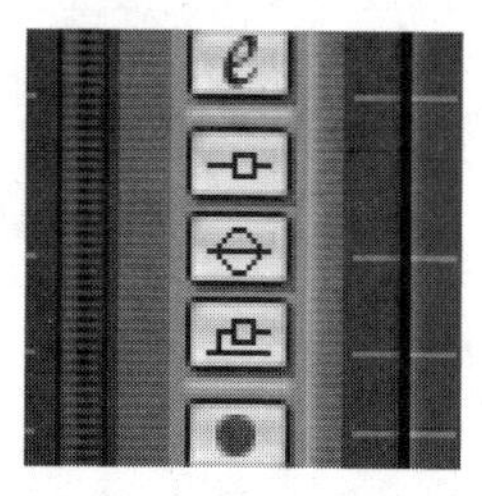

The three indicator buttons in each audio channel strip have the following functionality:

- **If an Insert or Send effect or EQ module is activated for a channel, the corresponding button is lit.**

  The effect indicators will be blue, the EQ indicator will be green.

- **By clicking these buttons when lit, the corresponding EQ or effects section will be bypassed.**

  Bypass is indicated by yellow buttons. Clicking the button again deactivates bypass.

9.4 The MIDI Channel Strips

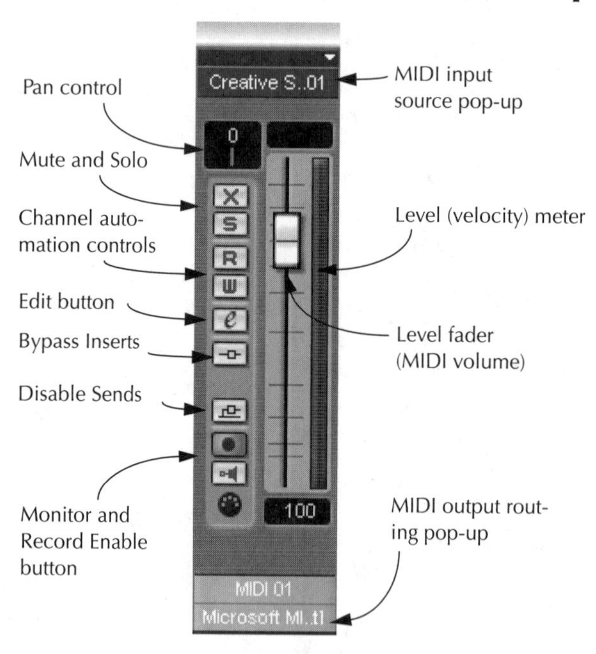

The MIDI channel strips allow you to control volume and pan in your MIDI instrument (provided that they are set up to receive the corresponding MIDI messages). The settings here are also available in the Inspector for MIDI tracks (see page 429).

9.5 The Common Panel

The Common panel appears to the left in the Mixer and Channel settings windows and contains settings for changing the look and behavior of the Mixer, as well as global settings for all channels.

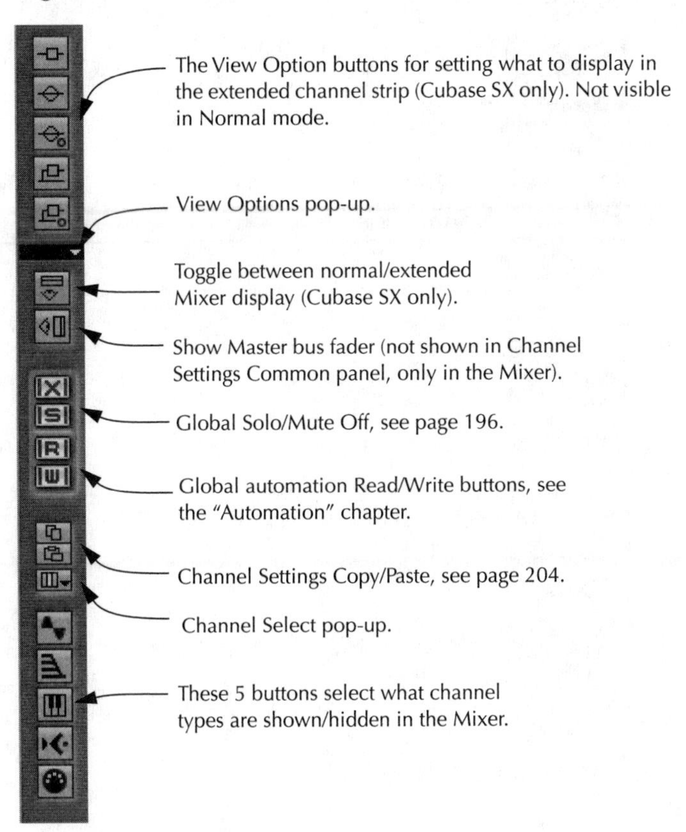

9.6 The Master Section

The Master section allows you to control the output level of the Master bus (the main output bus). With the Mixer in extended mode (Cubase SX only), the Master section will also contain the Master effect slots. This section can be shown or hidden in the Mixer by clicking the Show Master button in the Common panel.

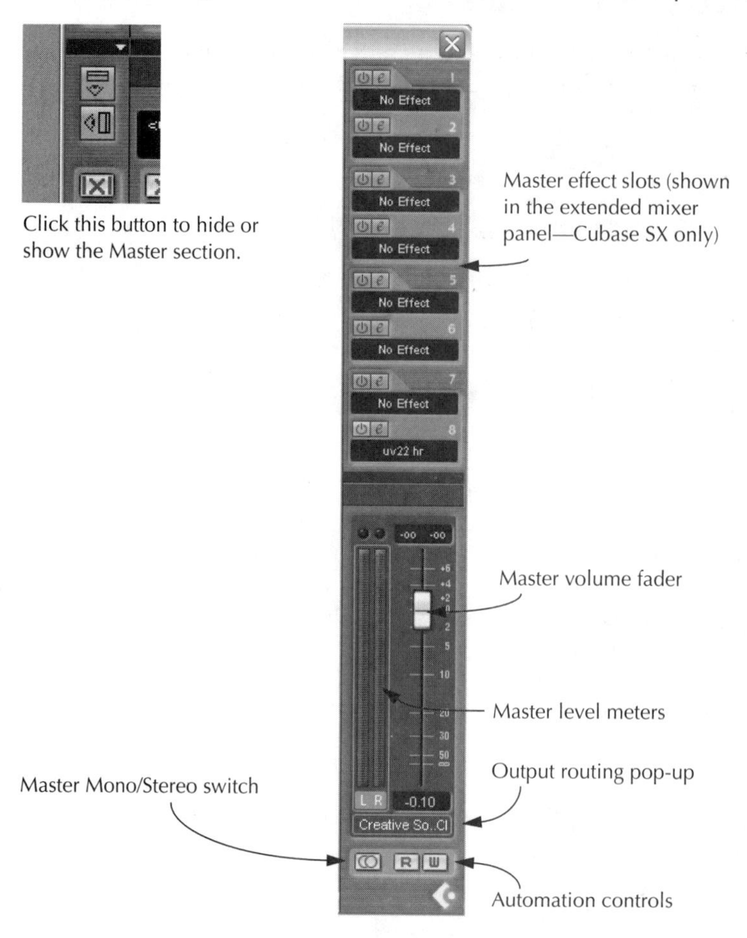

9.7 The VST Outputs Window

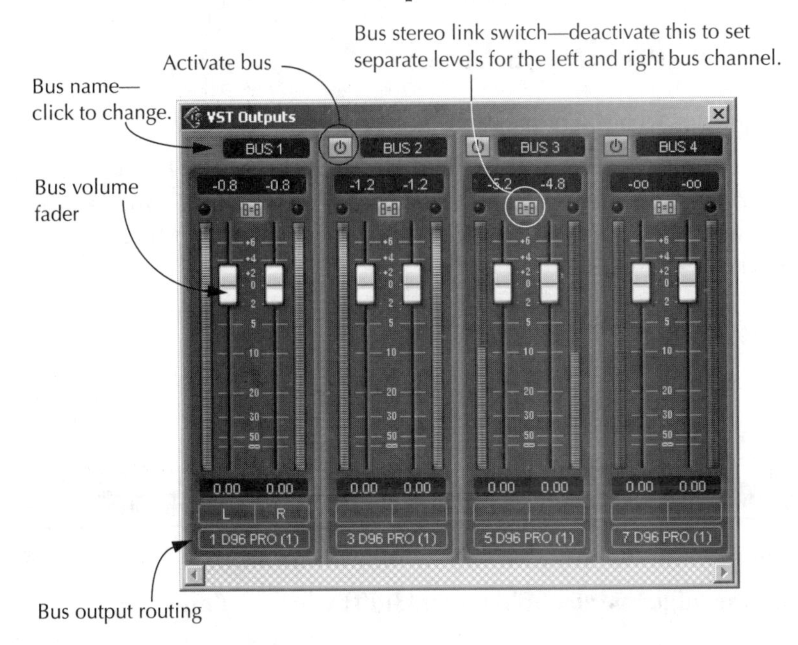

This is a separate window, opened from the Devices menu. If your audio hardware has several outputs (more than a single stereo pair), the VST Outputs window will show one stereo bus for each stereo output pair. Use the settings in the window to activate or deactivate buses, route each bus to the desired output on your audio hardware and control the bus volumes.

9.8 Basic Mixing Procedures

9.8.1 Setting Volume in the Mixer

In the Mixer, each channel strip has a fader for volume control.

- **For audio channels, the faders control the volume of the channels before they are routed directly or via a group channel to a stereo output bus, with separate faders for the left and right outputs. The Master Gain fader in the Mixer determines the output level of the Master bus.**
- **MIDI channels handle fader volume changes in the Mixer by sending out MIDI volume messages to the connected instrument(s).**

  Connected instruments must be set to respond to MIDI messages (such as MIDI volume in this case) for this to function properly.
- **The fader settings are displayed numerically below the faders, in dB for audio channels and in the MIDI volume 0 to 127 value range for MIDI channels.**

  You can click in the fader value fields and enter a volume setting by typing.
- **To make fine volume adjustments, hold down [Shift] when you move the faders.**
- **If you hold down [Ctrl] and click on a fader, it will automatically be set to position 0.0 dB for audio channels, or MIDI volume 100 for MIDI channels.**
- **Audio Output bus faders normally move together (move one and the other follows), but if you deactivate the Fader Link switch you can change either independently.**

  You can also hold down [Alt] and move faders separately.

You can use the faders to set up a volume balance between the audio and MIDI channels and perform a manual mix, by moving the faders and other controls while playing back. By using the Write function (see page 299), you can automate the levels and most Mixer actions.

● It is also possible to adjust the volume of a selected audio event in the Project window or Audio Part Editor, by making volume settings on the info line, or by using the volume handle (see page 170).

About MIDI Tracks Set to the Same MIDI Channel

If you have several MIDI tracks/Mixer channels set to the same MIDI channel (and routed to the same MIDI output), making volume settings for one of these MIDI tracks/ Mixer channels will also affect all other Mixer channels set to the same MIDI channel/ output combination.
This also applies to pan settings.

About the Level Meters for Audio Channels

When playing back audio in Cubase SX/SL, the level meters in the Mixer show the level of each audio channel. If the peak level of the audio goes above 0dB, the numerical level indicator will then show a positive value (i.e. a value above 0dB).

Cubase SX/SL uses 32 bit floating point processing internally, so there is virtually limitless headroom—signals can go way beyond 0dB without introducing distortion. Therefore:

- Having higher levels than 0 dB for individual channels and groups is not a problem in itself. The audio quality will not be degraded by this.

This is however not the case for the buses in the VST Outputs window (including the Master bus, which can be shown in the Mixer as well)! In the output buses, the floating point audio is converted to the resolution of the audio hardware. In the audio domain, the maximum level is 0dB. Levels higher than 0 dB will cause the clip indicators above the meters for each bus to light up. If the clip indicators light up for a bus, this indicates actual clipping—digital distortion which should be avoided.

- If the Clip indicator lights up for the Master bus or any other output bus, reset the clip indicator by clicking on it, and lower the level until the indicator doesn't light up.

About Level Meters for MIDI Channels

The level meters for MIDI channels do not show volume levels. Instead, they indicate the *velocity* values of the notes played back on MIDI tracks.

- Therefore, if you pull down a fader for a MIDI channel that is playing, the meter will still show the same "level", although the actual volume will change (given that the connected MIDI device is set to respond to MIDI volume).

9.8.2 Using Solo and Mute

The Mute (top) and Solo buttons.

You can use the Mute and Solo buttons to silence one or several audio or MIDI channels. The following applies:

- The Mute button silences the selected channel.
  Clicking the Mute button again un-mutes the channel. Several channels can be muted simultaneously. A muted channel is indicated by a lit Mute button, and also by the lit Global Mute indicator on the Common panel.

A Muted Channel in the Mixer.

A lit Global Mute indicator on the Common panel shows that one or more channels are muted.

- Clicking the Solo button for a channel mutes all other channels.
  A soloed channel is indicated by a lit Solo button, and also by the lit Global Solo indicator on the Common panel. Click the Solo button again to turn off Solo.
- Several channels can be soloed at the same time.
  However, if you press [Ctrl] and click the Solo button for a channel, any other soloed channels will automatically be un-soloed (i.e. this Solo mode is exclusive).
- [Alt]-clicking a Solo button activates "Solo Defeat" for that channel.
  In this mode (indicated by a red solo button without any other channels being muted) the channel will not be muted if you solo another channel (see page 233 for a practical use of this). To turn off Solo Defeat, [Alt]-click the Solo button again.
- You can un-mute or un-solo all channels by clicking the Mute or Solo indicator on the Common panel.

9.8.3 Setting Pan in the Mixer

The pan control

The Pan controls in the Mixer are used to position a channel between the left and right side of the stereo spectrum. For stereo audio channels, Pan controls the balance between the left and right channels.

- **To make fine pan adjustments, hold down [Shift] when you move the pan control.**
- **To select center pan position, hold down [Ctrl] and click on the pan control.**

For audio channels, the output bus faders determine the levels of each "side" in the stereo output. There are no pan controls for VST output buses or the Master bus.

- For MIDI channels, the Pan control sends out MIDI Pan messages.
  The result depends on how your MIDI instrument is set to respond to pan—check your documentation for details.

About the "Stereo Pan Law" Preference (Audio Channels only)

In the Project Setup dialog there is a pop-up menu named "Stereo Pan Law", on which you can select one of three pan modes. This is all related to the fact that without power compensation, the power of the sum of the left and right side will be higher (louder) if a channel is panned center than if it's panned left or right.

To remedy this, the Stereo Pan Law setting allows you to attenuate signals panned center, by -6 or -3dB (default). Selecting the 0dB option effectively turns off "constant-power panning". Experiment with the modes to see which fits best in a given situation.

9.9 Audio Specific Procedures

This section describes basic procedures for audio channels in the Mixer.

9.9.1 Selecting What to Show in the Extended Audio Channel Strip (Cubase SX only)

When using the extended channel strip view option (see page 185), the upper panel can be set to show different views for each audio channel strip. You select what to display for each channel by using the View Options pop-up menu at the top of each channel strip. The following views are possible:

- **The 8 insert effect slots.**

  The inserts can also be found in the Inspector and the Channel Settings window, see page 200.

- **The 8 effect sends, either with parameter dials ("Sends +" menu item) or pop-ups and send level value sliders.**

  These two views have exactly the same controls but different graphic layouts. The sends can also be found in the Inspector and the Channel Settings window, see page 200.

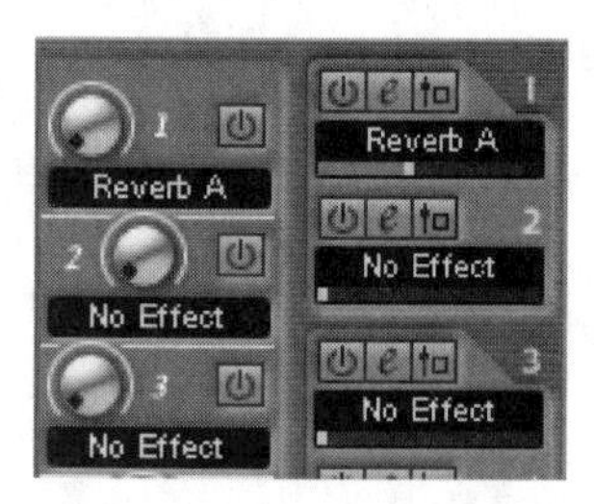

Send dials and Send level sliders.

- **The EQ section, either with parameter dials ("EQ +" menu item) or value sliders.**

  These two views have exactly the same controls but different graphic layouts. The EQ section is also available in the Channel Settings window. For EQ parameter descriptions, see page 201.

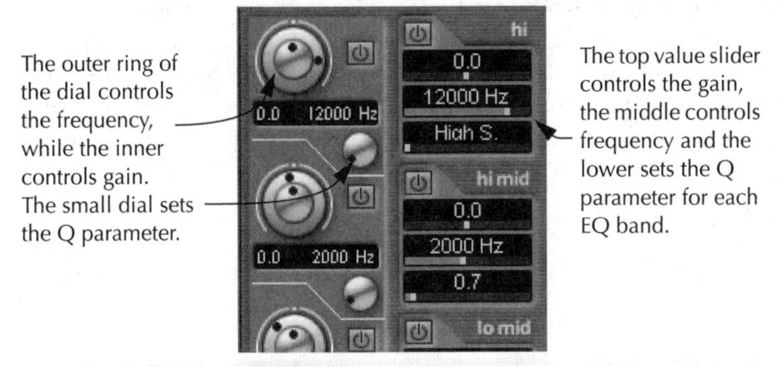

EQ dials and EQ value fields.

- **Selecting either Wide or Narrow from the View Options pop-up menu will display a blank panel in the upper section for the channel strip.**
- **By selecting from the View Options pop-up in the Common panel, you can set the view for all channels in the Mixer.**

  Selecting EQ will not change the view for MIDI channels.

- **If the Common panel is extended, you can also set the view for all channels in the Mixer by clicking the corresponding button in the upper half of the Common panel strip.**

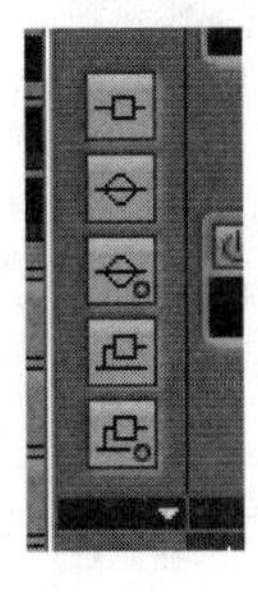

9.9.2 Using Channel Settings

For each audio channel strip in the Mixer (and in the Inspector for each audio track) there is an edit button ("E").

Clicking this opens the VST Channel Settings window. This window contains the Common panel, a duplicate of the Mixer channel strip, a section with eight insert effect slots (only five slots in Cubase SL), see page 225, 4 EQ modules and an associated EQ curve display (see page 201) and a section with eight effect sends (see page 222). Every channel has its own channel settings (although you can view each in the same window if you like—see below).

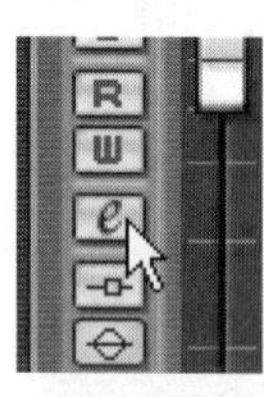

Click the Edit button to open the Channel Settings window:

The Channel Settings window is used for the following operations:

- Apply Equalization, see page 201.
- Apply Send Effects, see page 221.
- Apply Insert Effects, see page 225.
- Copy complete Channel Settings and apply them to any other channel, see page 204.

● All channel settings are applied to both sides of a stereo channel.

Changing Channels in the Channel Settings Window

You can view any channel's settings from a single window.

If the option "Mixer Selection Follows Project" is activated in the Preferences (Editing page), this can be done "automatically":

- **Open the Channel Settings window for a track and position it so that you can see both the Project window and the Channel Settings window.**

Selecting a track in the Project window automatically selects the corresponding channel in the Mixer (and vice versa). If a Channel Settings window is open, this will immediately switch to show the settings for the selected channel. This allows you to have a single Channel Settings window open in a convenient position on the screen, and use this for all your EQ and channel effect settings.

You can also select a channel manually (thereby changing what is shown in the open Channel Settings window). Proceed as follows:

1. **Open the Channel Settings window for any channel.**
2. **Open the Channel Select pop-up on the Common panel.**

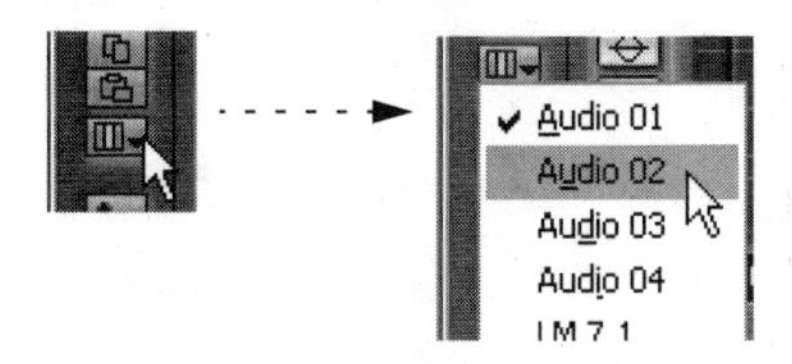

3. **Selecting a channel from the pop-up replaces the previous Channel Settings in the window with the selected channel's settings.**

You can also open channel settings in separate windows should you so wish:

- **If you have a Channel Settings window open, you can open another Channel Settings window by [Alt]-clicking the Edit button for another channel.**

Making EQ Settings

You can set EQ for a channel through the extended channel strip in the Mixer (SX only) or via the Channel Settings window. The parameters are the same in both cases, but there are no EQ presets nor a Reset function in the Mixer.

1. **Click the Edit button for the channel you want to apply EQ to.**

   The Channel Settings window opens.

2. **Activate as many EQ modules as you need (up to four).**

   This can be done in two ways:

- **By clicking on their "On" buttons.**
- **By double-clicking (or clicking and dragging) in the EQ curve display.**

  Each time you double-click (or click and drag) a new point is added (up to four). The preset frequency ranges (Lo, Hi Mid etc.) are taken into account when you click in the EQ curve display, i.e. clicking in the 10 to 20kHz area activates the "Hi" EQ module and so on.

As soon as any of the EQ modules are activated, the "EQ" button indicator in the channel strip is lit, and there will be a point added in the EQ curve display for each activated module.

The EQ section with three modules activated.

3. **Set the parameters for the activated EQ module(s).**

   This can be done in several ways:

- **By using the dials.**

  The outer ring of the Frequency/Gain dials sets the frequency, and the inner sets the gain.

- **By clicking and entering values numerically.**
- **By using the mouse to drag points in the EQ curve display window.**

  By using this method, you control both the Gain and Frequency parameters simultaneously. The knobs turn accordingly when you drag points.

- If you press [Ctrl] while dragging, only the Gain parameter will be set.
- If you press [Alt] while dragging, only the Frequency parameter will be set.

- If you press [Shift] while dragging, only the "Q" parameter will be set.

Each EQ module contains a fully parametric one band equalizer, with the following parameters:

Parameter	Description
Gain	Governs the amount of boost or attenuation around the set frequency. The range is ± 24dB.
Frequency	The center frequency for the equalization. Around this frequency, the sound will be boosted or attenuated according to the Gain setting. The range is 20Hz to 20kHz.
Q	Determines the width of the frequency band around the center frequency to be affected. The narrower the frequency band, the more drastic the effect of the boost or attenuation. For the leftmost and rightmost EQ modules, the following special modes are available: • If the Q-value for the leftmost EQ module is set to minimum, it will act as a low shelving filter. • If the Q-value for the leftmost EQ module is set to maximum, it will act as a high-pass filter. • If the Q-value for the rightmost EQ module is set to minimum, it will act as a high shelving filter. • If the Q-value for the rightmost EQ module is set to maximum, it will act as a low-pass filter.

- **To deactivate an EQ module, click its "On" button, double click its point in the EQ curve display or drag its point outside the display.**

EQ Bypass

By clicking the EQ button for a channel in the Mixer or in the Track list you can momentarily turn the EQ for a channel on and off, to compare the sound with and without EQ.

When the EQ is in Bypass mode, the EQ button is yellow.

EQ Reset

The Reset button in the lower left corner of the EQ section will reset all EQ parameters to their default values.

Using EQ Presets

Some useful basic presets are included with the program. You can use them as they are, or as a starting point for further "tweaking". To call up a preset, pull down the presets pop-up menu, and select one of the available presets.

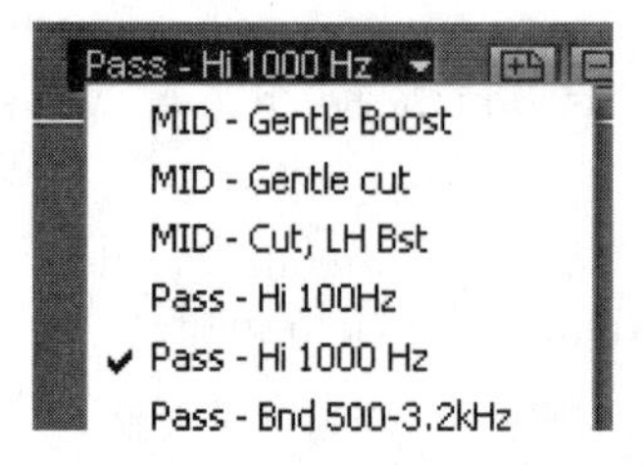

Storing and Removing EQ Presets

If you have made EQ settings you wish to store for use elsewhere in a project, you can store them in a preset. Proceed as follows:

1. **After making settings, click on the store button (plus sign) to the right of the presets field.**

   The settings are stored with the default name "Preset" and a number.

2. **Double click in the preset pop-up field and type in a new name if you wish.**

- To remove a preset, simply select it and click the remove (minus sign) button.

9.9.3 Copying Settings between Audio Channels

It is possible to copy all channel settings for an audio channel and paste them onto another channel. This applies to all audio channel types. For example, you can copy EQ settings from an audio channel and apply these to a group or VST Instrument channel, if you want them to have the same sound. Proceed as follows:

1. **Select the channel you want to copy settings from by clicking its channel name field (a highlighted name indicates a selected channel).**

   You can also select channels with the Channel Select pop-up menu—see page 201.

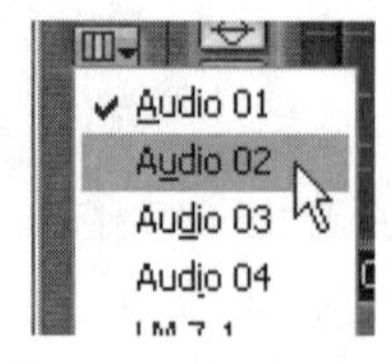

Selecting a channel in the channel strip (left), and in the Common panel (right).

2. **Click the "Copy" button in the Common panel.**

3. **Select the channel you want to copy the settings to and click the Paste button.**

   The settings are applied to the selected channel.

4. **To copy the same settings to several channels, repeat step 3.**

   The copied settings are retained in memory until you copy new channel settings, or close the project.

- Channel settings can be copied from stereo channels and pasted to mono channels and vice versa.

9.9.4 Initialize Channel

The Initialize Channel button can be found at the bottom of the Channel Settings Common panel. It resets the selected channel to the default setting. Default settings are:

- All EQ, Insert and Send effect settings are deactivated and reset.
- Solo/Mute is deactivated.
- The fader is set to 0dB.
- Pan is set to center position.

9.9.5 Changing the Meter Characteristics

You can change the Mixer's level meters characteristics for audio channels: right-click anywhere on the Mixer panel to bring up the Mixer context menu. On the menu there are two options for Meter characteristics: "VU-Meter Fast" and "VU-Meter Hold".

- **If "Fast" is activated (ticked), the meters respond very quickly to level peaks.**

  If "Fast" is deactivated, the meters respond more like standard VU meters.

- **If "Hold" is activated (ticked), the highest registered peak levels are "held" and are shown as static horizontal lines in the meter.**

  You can specify for how long the peak levels will be held. This is done with the parameter "VU-Meter Peak's Hold Time" in the Preferences dialog (VST page). The peak hold time can be between 500 and 30000ms.

Hold activated

9.9.6 Using Group Channels

You can route the outputs from multiple audio channels to a group. This enables you to control the channel levels using one fader, apply the same effects and equalization to all of them etc. To create a group channel, proceed as follows:

1. **Select Add Track from the Project menu and select "Group Channel" from the submenu that appears.**

   A group channel track is added to the Track list and a corresponding group channel strip is added to the Mixer, identical to an audio channel strip except for the lack of an Input pop-up, Record Enable and Monitor buttons. By default the first group channel strip is labeled "Group 01", but you can rename it just like any channel in the Mixer.

2. **Pull down the Output routing pop-up for a channel you want to route to a group channel, and select the group channel option.**

   The output of the audio channel is now redirected to the selected group.

3. **Repeat the previous step for the other channels you wish to route to a group.**

Settings for Group Channels

The group channel strips are (almost) identical to audio channel strips in the Mixer. The descriptions of the mixer features earlier in this chapter apply to group channels as well. Some things to note:

- **Group channels are always stereo.**
- **You can route the output of a group to an output bus or to another group with a higher number.**

  You cannot route a group to itself or to groups to the left of it in the Mixer. Routing is done with the pop-up menu at the bottom of each channel strip.
- **There are no Monitoring or Record Enable buttons for group channels.**

  This is because inputs are never connected directly to a group.
- **Solo and Mute functionality is automatically linked for a channel routed to a group and the group channel itself, in the following way:**

  If you mute or solo a group channel, all channels routed to the group are automatically muted or soloed as well.

9.9.7 Activating and Routing Buses

The number of buses shown in the VST Outputs window depends on the number of physical outputs you have on your audio hardware. As with inputs, you need to activate the buses you want to use, and assign each bus to an output pair on your audio hardware. This is done in the VST Outputs window:

1. **Pull down the Devices Menu and select VST Outputs.**

   The window will contain a number of stereo "channel strips", one for each bus:

2. **Activate the buses you need by clicking on their "On" buttons.**

   The indicator in the button lights up to show that the bus is active.

   To conserve processor power, you should avoid activating buses that you don't need to use.

- The Master bus (Bus 1) is always available and activated. This is why it doesn't have an "On" button. By default, all audio channels are assigned to the Master bus.

- The bus settings are saved with the project. However, if you select another ASIO Device and then open the project, you will be alerted that the bus settings saved will be ignored.

3. **Use the pop-up menus at the bottom of the window to route each active bus to an output pair on your audio hardware.**

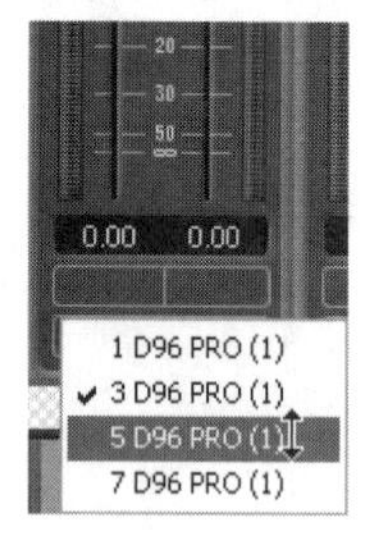

4. **To rename a bus, click on its label and type in a new name.**

5. Set the output levels for each active bus.

Dragging one of the faders for a bus will automatically move the other fader as well. To move the left or right fader for a bus independently, hold down [Alt] and drag, or deactivate the stereo link switch for the fader pair.

Routing Audio Channels to Buses

To route the output of an audio (or group/VST Instrument/ReWire) channel to one of the active buses, proceed as follows:

1. Open the Mixer.

2. Pull down the output routing pop-up menu, at the bottom of the channel strip and select one of the buses.

This pop-up menu contains the activated output buses, as well as the available group channels.

- A group channel cannot be routed to itself.

- On the output routing pop-up you also have the option to route the output to various surround channels (SX only). See page 280.

Routing an Effect Send to a Bus or Group

The eight effect sends for each audio channel or group can be routed directly to one of the buses, for use with external effects, etc. This is determined by the send routing pop-up menus in the Channel Settings window:

1. Open the Channel Settings window.

2. Activate a send.

3. Click in the name field to pull down the send routing pop-up menu.

4. Select the bus or group to which you want to route the send.

- If you route a send from a stereo channel to a bus or group, the send will be stereo. See page 232 for a practical example covering how this function can be used for setting up a flexible effect routing system.

Using the Master Gain Fader

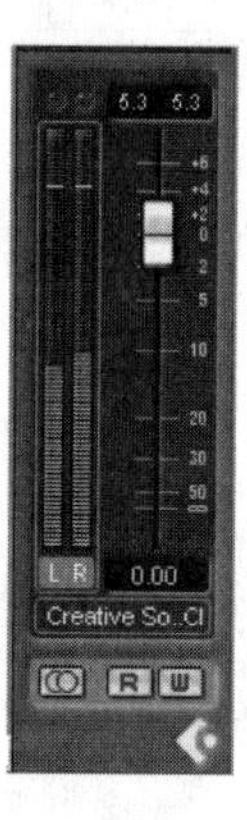

The Master Gain fader in the Master Section (to the right in the Mixer) controls the output level of the Master bus. The Master bus may be in stereo or have several channels, depending on the configuration chosen in the VST Master Setup (Cubase SX only), see page 281. It is connected to the corresponding number of VST Output buses.

- You can hide or show the Master Section with the Show Master button on the Common panel.
- Up to eight Master insert effects can be applied to the Master bus.
  See page 227.

9.10 MIDI Specific Procedures

This section describes basic procedures for MIDI channels in the Mixer.

9.10.1 Selecting What to Show in the Extended MIDI Channel Strip (Cubase SX only)

When using the extended channel strip view option (see page 185), the upper panel can be set to show different views for each MIDI channel strip. You select what to display for each channel by using the View Options pop-up menu at the top of each channel strip. The following views are possible:

- **The MIDI insert effects.**

  The MIDI inserts can also be found in the Inspector and the Channel Settings window for MIDI channels. How to use MIDI insert effects is described in the chapter "MIDI realtime parameters and effects"—see page 436.

- **The MIDI send effects.**

  The sends can also be found in the Inspector and the Channel Settings window for MIDI channels. How to use MIDI send effects is described in the chapter "MIDI realtime parameters and effects"—see page 436.

  Selecting either Wide or Narrow from the View Options pop-up menu will display a blank panel in the upper section for the channel strip.

- **By selecting from the View Options pop-up in the Common panel, you can set the view for all channels in the Mixer.**

  Selecting EQ (which applies to audio channels only) will not change the view for MIDI channels. Selecting Inserts or Send effects from the Common panel will change the view for all channel types.

9.10.2 Using Channel Settings

For each MIDI channel strip in the Mixer (and MIDI track in the Track list or the Inspector) there is an Edit ("E") button.

Clicking this opens the MIDI Channel Settings window. This window contains a duplicate of the Mixer channel strip, a section with four MIDI inserts and a section with four MIDI send effects. Every MIDI channel has its own channel settings.

The MIDI Channel Settings window.

9.11 Utilities

9.11.1 Link/Unlink Channels

This function is used to "link" selected channels in the Mixer so that any change applied to one channel will be mirrored by all channels in that link group. You can link as many channels as you like, and you can also create as many groups of linked channels as you like. To link channels in the Mixer, proceed as follows:

1. **Press [Shift] and click on the channel name field for all the channels that you want to Link.**

   Selected channels are indicated by highlighted name fields.

2. **Right click somewhere on the grey Mixer panel.**

   The Mixer context menu appears.

3. **Select "Link Channels" from the context menu.**

What Will Be Linked?

The following rules apply for linked channels:

- **Fader levels will be "ganged".**

  The relative level offset between channels will be kept if you move a linked channel fader.

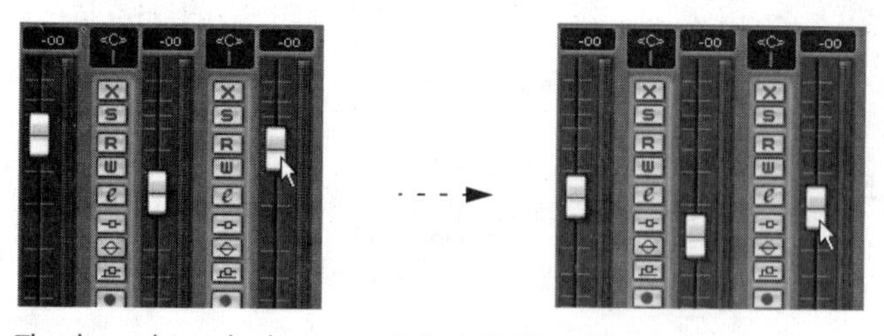

The three channels shown are linked. Pulling down one fader changes the levels for all three channels, but keeps the relative level mix.

- **Any individual channel settings you have made before linking will remain until you alter the same setting for any of the linked channels.**

  For example, if you link three channels, and one of them was muted at the time you applied the Link Channel function, this channel will remain muted after linking. However, if you mute another channel then *all* linked channels will be muted. Thus, the individual setting for one channel is lost as soon as you change the same parameter setting for any of the linked channels.

- **Channel settings you make after linking the channels will affect all linked channels of the same channel type.**

  This does not apply to settings between linked MIDI and audio channels.

- **Only Level, Mute, Solo, Select, Monitor and Record Enable will be linked between MIDI channels or MIDI and audio channels.**
- **By holding down [Alt], you can change parameter settings separately for channels that are linked.**

The above applies to all "linkable" functions.

The following settings are *not* affected by the Link Channel function (i.e. they remain individual for each channel):

- Insert effect settings
- Pan
- Input and output routing for audio and MIDI channels

● Linked channels can also have individual Automation subtracks. These are completely independent, and are not affected by the Link function.

Unlinking Channels

- **To unlink channels, simply click the channel name field for any linked Channel to select it, and select "Unlink Channels" from the Mixer context menu.**

  The channels are unlinked. Note that you do not need to select all the channels that are linked, only one of them.

● It is not possible to remove individual channels from Link status. If you want to make individual settings to a linked channel, press [Alt] when changing the setting.

9.11.2 Saving Mixer Settings

- Saving/Loading Mixer settings does not apply to MIDI channels in the Mixer—only audio related channels (group, disk, VSTi and ReWire) are saved with this function!

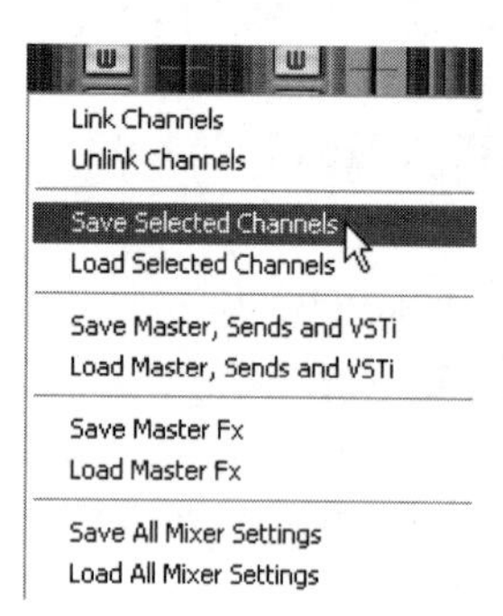

It is possible to save complete Mixer settings for selected or all audio channels in the Mixer. These can then later be loaded into any project. Channel settings are saved as Mixer settings files. These have the extension ".vmx".

Right-clicking somewhere on the Mixer panel or in the Channel Settings window brings up the Mixer context menu where four Save/Load items can be found. The following options are available:

- **"Save Selected Channels" will save all channel settings and the output bus routing for the selected channels.**

  Effects loaded in the VST Send Effects panel will not be saved. Thus, the send routing assigned for the selected channel(s) will not be saved, although the send levels, pre/post and on/off settings are. Insert effects settings are saved.

- **"Save Master, Sends and VSTi" will save the Master setup, VST output bus levels and active status, Master mix level, and all assignments and settings in the VST send effects, VST Instruments and Master effects panels.**

  You do not have to select channels for this operation.

- **"Save Master Fx" will save the current Master effects configuration and settings.**

- **"Save All Mixer Settings" saves everything.**

  This is the same as using "Save Selected Channels" with all channels selected, and using "Save Master, Sends and VSTi" and "Save Master Fx", all in one go.

When you select any of the above options, a standard file dialog opens where you can select a name and storage location on your disk for the file.

9.11.3 Loading Mixer Settings

Load Selected Channels

To load Mixer settings saved for selected channels, proceed as follows:

1. **Select the same number of channels in the new project to match the number of channels you saved settings for in the previous project.**

   For example, if you saved settings for six channels, then select six channels in the Mixer.

- **Mixer settings will be applied in the same order as they appear in the Mixer, when saved.**

  Thus, if you save settings from channels 4, 6 and 8 and apply these settings to channels 1, 2 and 3, the settings saved for channel 4 would be applied to channel 1, the settings saved for channel 6 to channel 2 and so on.

2. **Right-click the mixer panel to open the context menu, and select "Load Selected Channels".**

   A standard file dialog appears, where you can locate the saved file.

3. **Select the file and click "Open".**

   The channel settings and their corresponding output bus routing is applied to the selected channels.

- If you select to apply Mixer settings to fewer channels than you saved, the order of the saved channels in the Mixer applies—i.e. the saved channels that are "left over" and not applied will be the channels with the highest channel numbers (or furthest to the right in the Mixer).

Load Master, Sends and VSTi

As these settings are global for the whole Mixer, no channels need to be selected.

1. **Right-click the mixer panel to open the context menu and select "Load Master, Sends and VSTi".**

   A standard file dialog appears, where you can locate the saved file.

2. **Select the file and click "Open".**

   The Master setup, Master mix level, VST output levels, VST instruments and all send and Master effect assignments and settings are applied to the project.

Load Master Fx

This item allows you to load Master effect combinations and settings.

1. **Right-click the mixer panel to pull down the context menu, and select "Load Master Fx".**

   A standard file dialog appears, where you can locate the saved file.

2. **Click "Open" to recall the saved Master Effects.**

Load All Mixer Settings

Selecting "Load All Mixer Settings" from the context menu allows you to open a saved Mixer Settings file, and have the stored settings applied to all channels for which there is information included in the file. If the file was created with the "Save All Mixer Settings" function, all channels, master settings, VST Instruments, sends and master effects will be affected.

- **Please note that if the saved Mixer settings were 24 channels, and the Mixer you apply it to currently contains 16 Channels, only the settings for channels 1 to 16 will be applied—this function will not automatically add channels.**

9.11.4 About the VST Performance Window

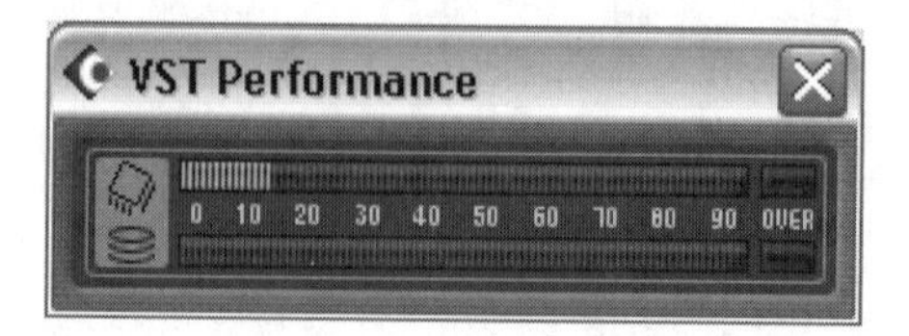

The VST Performance window is opened by selecting it from the Devices menu. It indicates the current load on the CPU and the hard disk transfer rate. It is recommended that you check this from time to time, or keep it open always. Even though you have been able to activate a number of audio channels in the project without getting any warning, you may possibly run into performance problems when adding EQ or effects.

- **The upper bar graph shows the CPU (processor) load.**

  If the red Overload indicator lights up, you need to decrease the number of EQ modules, active effects and/or audio channels playing back simultaneously.

- **The lower bar graph shows the hard disk transfer load.**

  If the red overload indicator lights up, the hard disk is not supplying data fast enough to the computer. You might then try going into the Device Setup and VST Multitrack dialog, and raise the number of disk buffers and the disk block buffer size. If this doesn't help, you need a faster hard disk. The overload indicator may occasionally blink. This is normal and nothing to worry about.

10 Audio Effects

10.1 Background

Cubase SX/SL comes with a number of effect plug-ins included. This chapter contains general details about how to assign, use and organize effect plug-ins. In addition, there are links to desciptions of all included effects.

- This chapter describes audio effects, i.e. effects that are used to process audio, group, VST Instrument and ReWire channels. MIDI effects are described in the chapter »MIDI Realtime Parameters and Effects«.

10.1.1 About VST 2.0 and Tempo Sync

Version 2.0 of the VST plug-in standard (and later) allows plug-ins to receive MIDI from the host application (in this case, Cubase SX/SL). A typical use for this feature is tempo-based effects (such as delays, auto-panning, etc.), but it is also used in other ways for certain plug-ins.

- **MIDI Timing information is automatically provided to any VST 2.0 plug-in that "requests it".**

  You don't need to make any special settings for this.

- **In many cases you set up tempo sync by specifying a base note value and a multiplier. The resulting timing interval is the base note value multiplied with the multiplier value.**

  For example, if you set the base note value to 1/16 (a sixteenth note) and the multiplier to 3, the resulting timing is 3/16. In the case of a delay effect, this means the interval between each delay repeat will be three sixteenth notes.

- **When MIDI receive is available (or neccessary) for other purposes than timing, the setting up and operation is described in the documentation for the corresponding effect.**

10.1.2 The Three Effect Types

In addition to the EQ, Cubase SX/SL provides three effect types:

- **Send effects**

  Up to eight send effects can be used. When you use send effects, audio is routed through the effect processors via independent effect sends for each channel, just like on a "real" physical mixer. The output from each effect processor is then routed to one of the buses or the master fader, where it is mixed with the "dry" signal, if any. Send effects are mono in—stereo out.

- **Insert effects**

  An insert effect is inserted into the signal chain of an audio channel, which means that the whole channel signal passes through the effect. This makes inserts suitable for effects for which you don't need to mix dry (direct) and wet (processed) sound, e.g. distortion, filters or other effects that change the tonal or dynamic characteristics of the sound. You can have up to eight different insert effects per channel (five in Cubase SL).

- **Master effects**

  Up to eight effect processors (four in Cubase SL) can be added to the signal on the Master bus, the final mix. Please note that there is no mixing of the dry/fx signals as there is with the send effects (except if included in the parameters of the individual effects). Typical uses for master effects would be compressor/limiter effects, noise suppression units, etc.

  The last two Master effect slots are post-master gain (Cubase SL only has one post-master gain slot—slot 4). Dithering for example, should always be assigned to a post-master gain effect slot, see page 228.

10.2 Using Effects

10.2.1 Using Send Effects

This procedure is divided into three steps: Activating effects, setting up the send section and making effect settings.

- Note that it's also possible to route sends to groups, and use the insert effects for the groups as additional effect racks. See page 232.

Activating Send Effects

1. **Pull down the Devices menu and select VST Send Effects.**

   The VST Send Effects panel opens. You can have up to eight separate "processors" arranged on top of each other. If no effect is selected for a slot, it will be labeled "No Effect".

2. **Pull down the pop-up menu by clicking in the "No Effect" slot.**

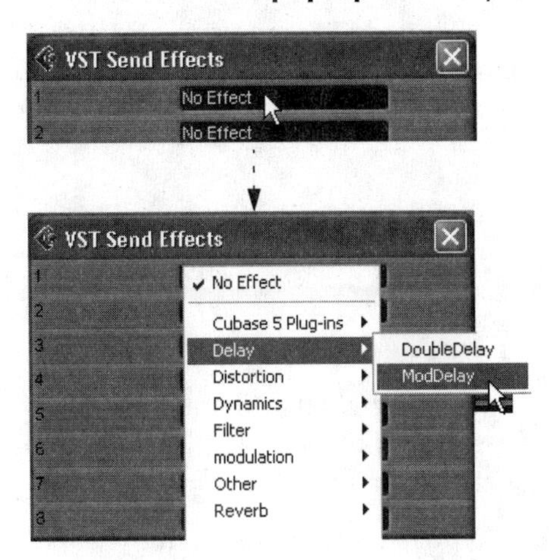

   The pop-up menu will list all effects included with Cubase SX/SL (see page 234) as well as effects installed separately. By default the included effects are sorted in hierarchical submenus according to effect type, but you can rearrange them as you see fit (see page 236).

3. **Select an effect from the list.**

   When you select an effect, an effect panel opens in the slot.

4. **By default, the effect processor is activated when selected. This is indicated by the On button. Make sure this is lit.**

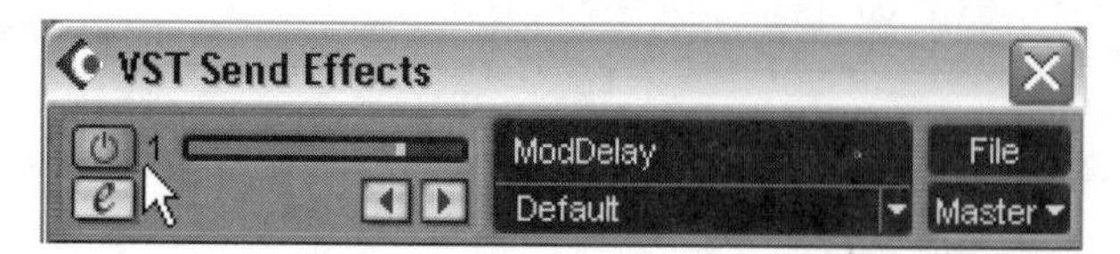

5. **Make sure the effect output is routed to the desired output bus, by checking the Bus pop-up (below the File pop-up).**

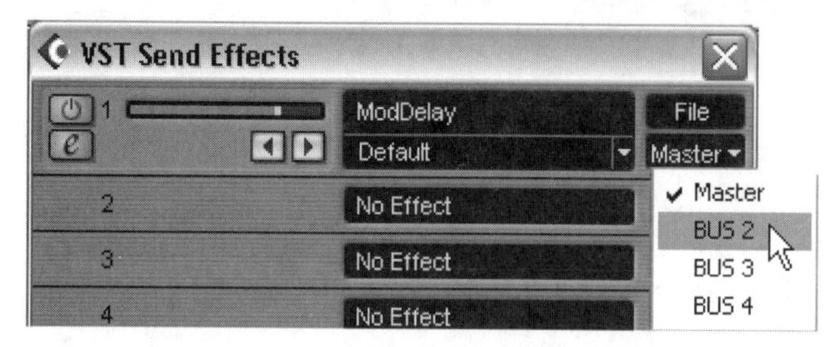

6. **If you wish to activate more effects, repeat steps 2 to 5.**

   Remember that the effects rely heavily on the CPU power in your computer. The more activated effect units, the more computer power will be used for effects.

- To turn off an effect completely, pull down the effect type pop-up menu and select "No Effect".
  You should do this for all effects that you don't intend to use, to minimize unnecessary CPU load.

Setting Up the Sends

This can be done in the Mixer (in extended mode—SX only), in the Channel Settings window or in the Inspector for the audio track. The figures below show the Channel Settings window, but the procedures are similar for all three sections:

1. **Bring up the Channel Settings window, the "Sends" or "Sends+" pane in the extended Mixer (SX only) or the Sends section in the Inspector.**

   Each of the eight sends has the following controls and options:

- A send on/off switch
- A send level slider
- A pre/post fader switch (not available in the Sends+ Mixer pane)
- An Edit button (not available in the Sends+ Mixer pane)

2. **Click the on button for one of the effect sends and set the corresponding send level slider (or dial) to a moderate value.**

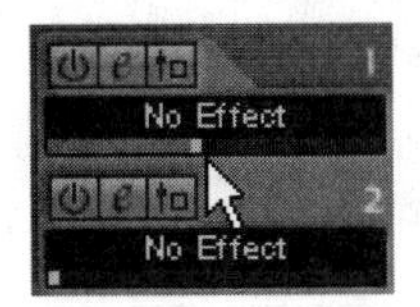

Setting the Send level.

3. **Pull down the pop-up menu for the send.**

   This is the Send Routing pop-up menu, used for routing the send to the desired effect processor.

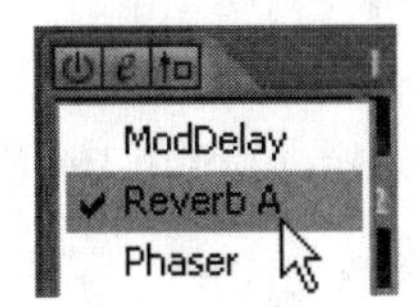

   The first items on this menu correspond to the activated internal effects (up to eight) while the following items route the send to buses and groups. A practical application of routing a send to a group is described on page 233.

4. **Select an effect from the pop-up menu.**
5. **If you want the signal to be sent to the effects before the fader, click on the Pre/Post button for the send.**

   With pre-fader effect sends, the amount of effect for the channel is not affected by the volume fader. With post-fader effect sends (Pre/Post button not pressed), the amount of effect is proportional to the channel volume, and will change with the volume fader movements.

6. **If you want to use several effects for this audio channel, repeat steps 3 to 6 above for the other effect sends.**

- When one or several sends are activated for a channel, the Send Effects buttons light up in blue in the Mixer and Track list. Click the button for a channel to bypass (disable) all its effect sends.
  When the sends are bypassed, the buttons are yellow. Click the button again to enable the sends.

Making Settings for the Effects

1. **Open the VST Send Effects window and use the Effects Master slider to the left on the processor panel to set the input level to an effect processor.**

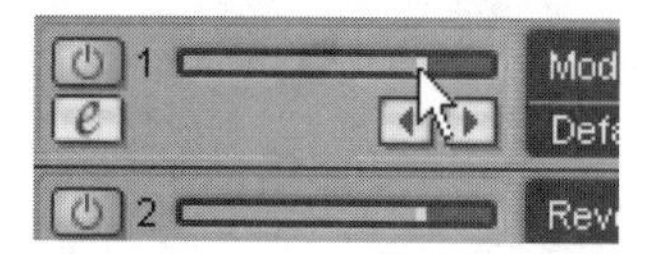

2. **Use the send level slider in the Channel Settings, Inspector, or the extended part of the Mixer (Cubase SX only) to control the amount of effect for the audio channel.**

3. **You can switch between different effect program presets by pulling down the Program pop-up in the VST Send effects panel.**

   The number of program locations depends on the selected effect type.

Clicking here...

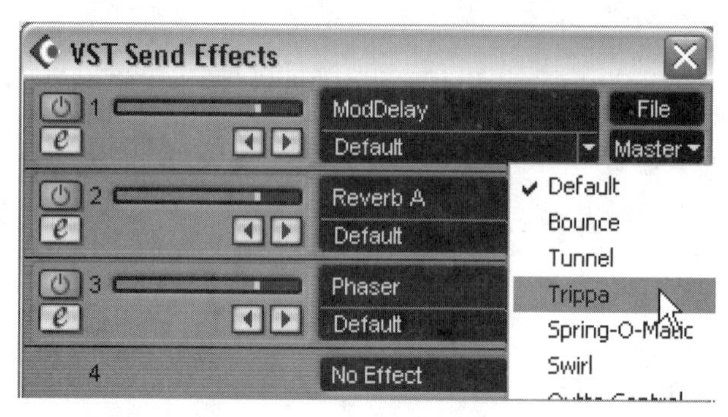

...opens the Program pop-up.

4. **If you have several effects activated, repeat steps 1 to 3 for these.**

- You can also edit the effect parameters. See page 230.

10.2.2 Using Insert Effects

- **You can apply up to eight (five in Cubase SL) different insert effects per channel.**
- **The signal passes through the effects in series from the top downwards.**
- **Each audio, group, VST Instrument and ReWire channel has its own set of insert effects.**

  Each audio channel can have up to eight (five in Cubase SL) insert effects which are totally independent of the other channels.

● Insert effects require the same processing power as any other effect type. This means that applying insert effects on many channels uses up far more processing power than the send effects (eight in total for the whole program). Remember that you can use the VST Performance window to keep an eye on the CPU load.

Which Effect Plug-ins Can I Use as Insert Effects?

Most effect plug-ins will work fine as insert effects. In general, the only restrictions are with the number of inputs and outputs in the effects:

- **For a plug-in to be usable as an insert effect, it has to have 1 or 2 inputs and 1 or 2 outputs.**

  The number of inputs and outputs is determined by whether you use the insert effects on a single (mono) audio channel or on a stereo channel pair:

- **For stereo audio channels, you need to use an effect with stereo inputs.**

  It is possible to use a mono-input effect with a stereo channel pair, but then only the left channel in the pair will be processed, which is probably not what you want.

- **For mono audio channels, you can use mono- or stereo-input effects.**

  However, since the audio channel is in mono, the output of the effect will also be in mono. For stereo output effects, the left channel will then be used.

Routing an Audio Channel through Insert Effects

Insert effect settings are available in the Mixer (in extended mode—Cubase SX only), the Channel Settings window and the Inspector. The figures below show the Channel Settings window, but the procedures are similar for all three send sections:

1. **Bring up the Channel Settings window, the "Inserts" pane in the extended Mixer or the Inserts section in the Inspector.**

   In the Channel Settings, the inserts are located to the right of the channel strip.

2. **Pull down the effect type pop-up for one of the insert slots, and select an effect.**

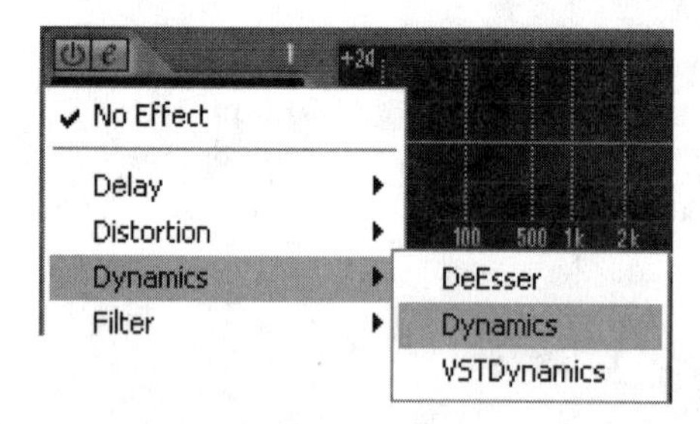

- **If you hold down [Ctrl] while selecting an insert effect, this effect will be selected in the same insert slot for all Mixer channels.**

3. **Make sure that the effect is activated (the on button for the insert slot should be lit).**

4. **If required, open the effect's control panel by clicking the Edit button and use the Mix parameter (if available) to adjust the balance between dry and effect signal.**

   See page 230 for details about editing effects.

- When one or several insert effects are activated for a channel, the Insert Effects buttons light up in blue in the Mixer and Track list. Click the button for a channel to bypass (disable) all its inserts.
  When the inserts are bypassed, the buttons are yellow. Click the button again to enable the inserts.

- To turn off an effect completely, pull down the effect type pop-up menu and select "No Effect".
  You should do this for all effects that you don't intend to use, to minimize unnecessary CPU load.

10.2.3 Using Master Effects

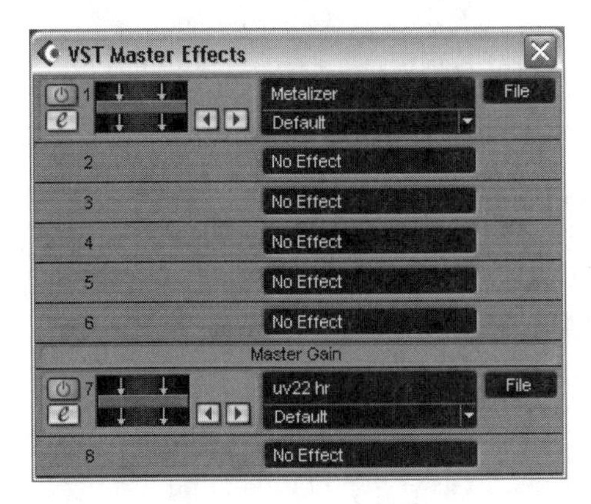

There are eight Master effect slots (four in Cubase SL), available in a separate window or in the Master section in the extended Mixer (Cubase SX only). To select and activate Master effects, proceed as follows:

1. **Either select the "Extended" mode for the Mixer (Cubase SX only) and show the Master section, or pull down the Devices menu and select "VST Master Effects" to bring up the Master effect window.**
2. **Pull down the pop-up menu for one of the Master effect slots and select an effect.**

- Note that the two last Master effect slots are "post master gain fader" (Cubase SL has one such slot—slot 4), i.e. they appear after the Master Gain fader in the signal path.
  These are typically used for effects such as dithering—see page 228.

3. **To make settings for the effect, click the Edit button to bring up its control panel.**

   See page 230.

- To turn off a Master effect, select "No Effect" for the corresponding slot.

● Master effect plug-ins must be at least stereo in/out. If you have a plug-in in your VST Plug-ins folder that you can't assign as a master effect, the reason is probably that it is a mono plug-in.

10.2.4 Dithering

- Cubase SX and Cubase SL come with different versions of the Apogee dithering plug-in; "UV22 HR" for SX, and "UV22" for SL.

Dithering is a method for controlling the noise produced by quantization errors in digital recordings. The theory behind this is that during low level passages, only a few bits are used to represent the signal, which leads to quantization errors and hence distortion.

For example, when "truncating bits", as a result of moving from 24- to 16-bit resolution, quantization errors are added to an otherwise immaculate recording. By adding a special kind of noise at an extremely low level, the effect of these errors is minimized. The added noise could be perceived as a very low-level hiss under exacting listening conditions. However, this is hardly noticeable and much preferred to the distortion that otherwise occurs.

- **The Apogee UV22 HR dither plug-in included with SX offers very high quality dithering with support for multiple resolutions.**
- **The Apogee UV22 dither included with SL has the same high quality, but always dithers to 16 bit resolution.**

When Should I Use Dither?

- **When converting files to a lower bit resolution.**
- **When processing using Master effects during Export Audio Mixdown.**

Internally Cubase SX/SL uses 32-bit float resolution. Whenever you are exporting to a lower bit resolution than this, you should use dither, especially when exporting/converting to 16-bit resolution for audio CD-burning.

Applying Dithering

1. **Bring up the Master Effects window of the effect slots in the Master section in the Mixer.**
2. **Pull down the pop-up menu in slot 7 or 8 (or slot 4 in Cubase SL).**

- These two last Master effect slots are post-fader (Cubase SL has one post-fader slot—slot 4), which is crucial for a dithering plug-in. The reason is that any master gain change applied after dithering would bring the signal back to the internal 32 bit float domain, thus rendering the dithering settings useless.

3. **Select the UV22 HR/UV22 plug-in from the pop-up menu.**

   By default, this is placed on the "Other" submenu. If you have another dithering plug-in that you prefer, you can select this instead.

4. **Click the On button for the slot to activate the dithering effect.**

5. **Click the Edit button for the slot to bring up the control panel for the dithering effect and adjust its settings to your liking.**

Apogee UV22 HR/UV22 Parameters

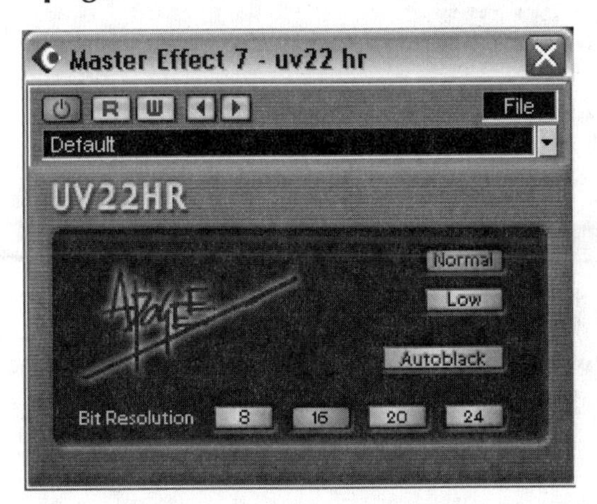

The UV22 HR/UV22 are dithering plug-ins based on an advanced algorithm developed by Apogee. You can use the UV22 HR/UV22 plug-in for all dithering situations.

The following options can be set in the control panel (the parameters are identical for UV22 HR/UV22 apart from the Bit Resolution parameter):

Option	Description
Normal	Try this first, it is the most "all-round" setting.
Low	This applies a lower level of dither noise.
Autoblack	When this is activated, the dither noise is gated (muted) during silent passages in the material.
Bit resolution 8/16/20/24 (UV22 HR only)	Specifies the resulting bit resolution of the dithering process. Make sure to set this according to the selected resolution when you export audio (as set in the Export Audio Mixdown dialog—see page 601). UV22 included with Cubase SL always dithers to 16 bits.

10.2.5 Editing Effects

All inserts, master effect slots and effect sends (except in the "Sends+" pane in the extended Mixer—Cubase SX only) have an Edit ("E") button. Clicking this opens the selected effect's control panel in which you can make parameter settings.

The contents, design and layout of the control panel depends on the selected effect. However, all effect control panels have a On/Off button, Read/Write automation buttons (for automating effect parameter changes—see page 306), a program selection pop-up menu and a File pop-up menu for saving or loading programs.

The Rotary effect control panel.

- **Please note that all effects can be edited using a simplified control panel (horizontal sliders only, no graphics) if you prefer this. To edit effects using this "basic" control panel instead, press [Ctrl]+[Shift] and click on the Edit button for the effect send or slot.**

Making Settings

Effect control panels may have any combination of knobs, sliders, buttons and graphic curves. For specifics about the included effects, please refer to page 234.

Naming Effects

If you edit the parameters for an effect, these settings are saved automatically in the project. If you want to name the current settings, the following points apply:

- **The basis for the current settings may have been a preset effect program, in which case there is a name in the Program Name field.**
- **The basis for the current settings may have been a default setting program location in which case "Init" is displayed in the Program Name field.**

In both cases, if you have changed any effect parameter settings, these are already saved! To name the current settings, click the Name field, type in a new name and press [Return]. The new name replaces the previous name on the Program pop-up menu.

Saving Effects

You can save your edited effects for further use (e.g. in other projects) by using the File pop-up menu to the right of the Name field.

1. **Pull down the File pop-up menu.**
- **If you want to save the current program only, select "Save Effect".**

  Effect Programs have the extension "fxp".
- **If you want to save all programs for the effect type, select "Save Bank".**

  Effect Banks have the extension "fxb".

2. **In the file dialog that appears, select a name and location for the file and click Save.**

   It might be a good idea to prepare a special folder for your effects.

Loading Effects

1. **Pull down the File pop-up menu.**
2. **Select "Load Effect" or "Load Bank".**
3. **In the file dialog that opens, locate the file and click Open.**

   If you loaded a Bank, it will replace the current set of all effect programs. If you loaded a single effect, it will replace the currently selected effect program only.

10.2.6 Effect Routing—a Few Tips

A Note about Stereo Effects

Several of the VST plug-in effects affect the stereo image, in the form of panning, stereo enhancement or stereo ambience. However, for this to be heard, the output of the effect must be routed to a stereo channel or bus (since otherwise, the output will be mixed to mono). In short: Stereo image effects will not be heard if the effect is used as an insert effect for a mono audio channel.

- **For example, if you want to apply auto-panning to a mono audio channel, there are two ways to do this:**

  1) Use a send effect (you would probably want to activate the Pre-fader Send switch and turn down the volume fader for the audio channel).
  Or
  2) Route the mono audio channel to a group channel and apply the effect as an insert effect for the group channel.

About Group Channels and Effects

There are certain factors to consider when using send effects from channels routed to groups. If a channel routed to a group uses send effects, the effect return signal will still be audible if you mute or pull down the fader for the group channel, which might be undesirable. There is a method you can use to remedy this:

- **You can remove the send routing from the channels being routed to a group, and apply the effects to the group channel instead.**

  This works well if you want all channels routed to the group processed by the same effect(s) and by the same amount. See below for a practical example on how you can set up a more flexible effects routing system using groups.

Using Stereo Sends and Insert Effects

Send effects are practical because you can control the dry/effect balance individually for each channel. Insert effects offer the advantage of "chaining" effects, meaning that the output of an effect can be further processed by another effect. If you route a channel send directly to a group channel, this allows you to use insert effects (applied to the group channel) much like "send effects".

This method has several advantages:

- You can take advantage of effects with stereo inputs, since the sends will be stereo. If you route a stereo channel send to an effect, as opposed to a group, the send will be mono, regardless of the chosen effect.
- You can set up insert effect chains for a group, and then control how much the individual channels are processed by this effect chain.
  For example, you could have the output of a reverb sent to an EQ and then on to a compressor. If you simply routed several channel *outputs* to a group and then applied insert effects (to the group), you would have no way of controlling the dry/effect balance for the individual channels, only for the group as a whole.

An Example

The following example describes how to route a stereo send to a group with an insert effect.

The example assumes that you have access to a stereo audio channel, some audio events to play through it, and an unused group channel in the Mixer. Proceed as follows:

1. **Open the Channel Settings for the stereo audio channel, and route one of the sends directly to the group channel.**

   As it is a stereo channel, the send will be stereo. Note that the channel itself should not be routed to this group, only one of its sends (see page 222). The channel output routing could be any bus, or another group—it doesn't matter.

2. **Activate the send, and drag the corresponding Send level slider to a moderate value.**

   The send's "Pre/Post" button should not be activated.

3. **Activate an insert effect for the group channel.**

   Choose a typical "send effect" like reverb for this example.

4. **Open the effect's control panel by clicking the Edit button and use the Mix parameter to adjust the balance between "dry" and effect signal, to 100% effect.**

   This is because the effect/dry balance can now be controlled using a combination of send level and the group channel fader—see below.

5. **Press [Alt] and click on the Solo button for the group channel to activate Solo Group.**

   In this mode, the group channel will not be muted if you solo another channel in the mixer (see below).

6. **Play back a recording via the audio channel.**

The following is now possible:

- **By adjusting the send level you will control the amount of channel signal sent to the "effect" (or to be accurate, the group channel).**
- **The level fader for the group channel now serves as effect return level control, allowing you to set the dry/effect balance.**

  If you pull down the group channel fader, you should now hear the recorded signal with no effect.

- **Since Solo Group is activated for the group channel, you can solo any of the audio channels without having the effect return (the group) muted.**

  If you need to turn off Solo Group, [Alt]-click the Solo button for the group channel again.

- **Adding more insert effects to the group allows you to process the effect output further.**
- **Simply repeat steps 1—2 for all (stereo) channels you wish to process using this method.**
- **You can of course add more group channels for a project, set up different Insert effect chains for these, and assign other sends to them.**

10.2.7 Automating Effect Parameters

Effects parameters can be automated. This is described on page 306.

10.3 The Included Effects

The list below shows the effects sorted according to category, as is the default arrangement when you install Cubase SX/SL.

Delay

DoubleDelay (page 713)

ModDelay (page 714)

Distortion

Datube (page 716)

Overdrive (page 717)

Quadrafuzz (page 718)

Dynamics

SPL DeEsser (Cubase SX only; page 722)

Dynamics (page 724)

MIDI Gate (page 731)

VST Dynamics (page 729)

Filter

StepFilter (page 734)

Modulation

Chorus (page 737)

Flanger (page 738)

Metalizer (page 739)

Phaser (page 741)

Ringmodulator (page 742)

Rotary (page 744)

Symphonic (page 746)

Tranceformer (page 748)

Other

Bitcrusher (page 750)

Chopper (page 751)

Grungelizer (page 752)

Vocoder (page 753)

UV22 HR/UV22 dither plug-in (page 229)

SMPTE Generator (Cubase SX only; page 758)

Reverb

Reverb A (page 760)

Reverb B (page 761)

Surround

Mix6To2 (Cubase SX only; page 762)

During the installation process you also had the option of installing effects that were part of Cubase 5.1 and previous versions—see page 237.

10.4 Installing and Managing Effect Plug-ins

There is a wide range of additional effect plug-ins available in the two formats supported by Cubase SX/SL (VST and DirectX). The two formats are handled differently when it comes to installation and organizing:

10.4.1 VST Plug-ins

VST-native plug-ins are usually installed simply by dragging the files (with the extension ".dll") into the Vstplugins folder in the Cubase SX/SL application folder, or into the Shared VST Plug-in folder—see below. When you launch Cubase SX/SL again, the new effects will appear on the Effect pop-up menus.

- If the effect plug-in comes with its own installation application, you should use this. Generally, always read the documentation or readme files before installing new plug-ins.
- If you want to install and use plug-ins from the manufacturer Waves Ltd. you should activate the option Preload Waves Plugins on Startup.
  These plug-ins are really DirectX plug-ins being used as VST plug-ins by means of a dll file called Waveshell. Activating the Preload option allows you to choose a Waves VST plug-in directly from any effect menu, instead of having to load the Waveshell first and then pick the desired plug-in.
  For more information, please refer to http://www.waves.com/

Organizing VST Plug-ins

If you have a large number of VST plug-ins, having them all on a single pop-up menu in the program may become unmanageable. For this reason, the plug-ins installed with Cubase SX/SL are placed in appropriate subfolders according to the effect type. You can rearrange this by moving, adding or renaming subfolders within the Vstplugins folder if you like.

- **When you launch the program and pull down an Effects pop-up menu, the subfolders will be represented by hierarchical submenus, each listing the plug-ins in the corresponding subfolder.**

About Shared VST Plug-ins

While Cubase SX/SL's own plug-ins reside in the Vstplugins folder within the Cubase SX/SL program folder, the program can also access plug-ins in an additional location, called the shared VST plug-ins folder. This lets you use plug-ins installed by other VST compatible applications, etc. You can change what folder is considered the "shared" vstplugin folder at any time in the Plug-In Information window, see page 238.

About the "Earlier VST Plug-ins" and "Cubase 5 Plug-ins" Subfolders

When installing Cubase SX/SL, you were asked whether you wanted to install the effects from previous versions of Cubase. If you chose to do so, the Cubase 5 effects will be installed in a separate "Cubase 5 Plug-ins" subfolder within the Vstplugins folder, and thus appear on a submenu to the effect pop-up menus. If you chose to install the earlier (pre-Cubase 5) plug-ins as well, these will be installed in an "Earlier VST PlugIns subfolder within the "Cubase 5 Plug-ins" folder (and appear on a submenu to the "Cubase 5 Plug-ins" submenu).

The foremost reason for installing these earlier plug-ins is backwards compatibility, allowing you to import old Cubase Songs and get the correct effect settings. However, you may also find some very useful effects among the older plug-ins. For descriptions of these older effects please see the chapter "Parameters of Cubase 5 Effect Plug-ins" on page 763 and the chapter "Parameters of Earlier VST Effect Plug-ins" on page 789.

10.4.2 DirectX Plug-ins

To be able to use DirectX plug-ins, you must have Microsoft DirectX installed on your computer (Version 8.1 recommended and included on the Cubase SX/SL CD).

DirectX plug-ins should *not* be placed in the Vstplugins folder, as these are installed under the operating system rather than for Cubase SX/SL exclusively. Rather, you should follow the installation instructions included with the plug-ins. See also page 240.

- On the effect menus, all DirectX plug-ins are listed on the DirectX submenu at the bottom.
  Selecting, activating and editing them are done as with VST effects.

10.4.3 The Plug-in Information Window

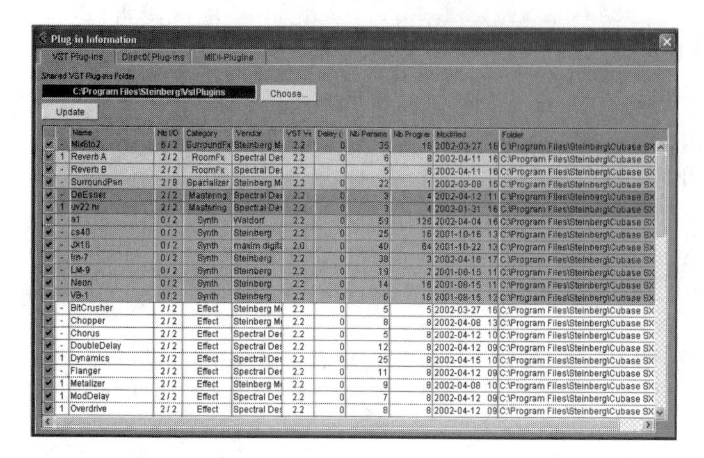

On the Devices menu, you will find an item called "Plug-in Information". Selecting this opens a dialog listing all the available VST and DirectX compatible plug-ins in your system (including VST Instruments), along with all MIDI plug-ins (see page 462).

Managing and Selecting VST Plug-ins

To see which VST plug-ins are available in your system, click the "VST Plug-ins" tab at the top of the window. The window now displays all plug-ins in the Cubase SX/SL and the shared vstplugins folder.

- To enable a plug-in (make it available for selection), click in the left column. Only the currently enabled plug-ins (shown with a check sign in the left column) will appear on the Effect menus.
- The second column indicates how many instances of the plug-in are currently used in Cubase SX/SL.
  Clicking in this column for a plug-in which is already in use produces a pop-up showing exactly where each use occurs.

● Please note that a plug-in may be in use even if it isn't enabled in the left column. You might for example have opened a Song containing effects that currently are disabled on the menu. The left column purely determines whether or not the plug-in will be visible on the Effect menus.

- All columns can be resized by using the divider in the column header.

The rest of the columns show the following information about each plug-in:

Column	Description
Name	The name of the plug-in.
Nb I/O	This column shows the number of inputs and outputs for each plug-in.
Category	This indicates the category of each plug-in (such as VST Instruments, Surround Effects, etc.).
Vendor	The manufacturer of the plug-in.
VST Version	Indicates with which version of the VST protocol each plug-in is compatible.
Delay (sample)	This shows the delay (in samples) that will be introduced if the effect is used as an Insert. This is however automatically compensated for by Cubase SX/SL.
Nb Params	The number of parameters for the plug-in.
Nb Programs	The number of programs for the plug-in.
Modified	The last modification date of the plug-in file.
Folder	The path and name of the folder in which the plug-in file is located.

Update Button

Pressing this button will make Cubase SX/SL re-scan the designated Vstplugins folders for updated information about the plug-ins.

Changing the Shared Plug-ins Folder

If you like, you can change what folder is to be the "shared" Vstplugins folder. For example, if you have Steinberg's Cubase VST 5.0 installed on your computer, you can get access to the Cubase VST 5.0-specific plug-ins in Cubase SX/SL by switching to the Vstplugins folder within the Cubase VST 5.0 folder.

The currently selected Shared Folder is displayed in the text field at the top of the window. Clicking the "Choose..." button opens a file dialog where you can browse to another Vstplugins folder on your hard drive. Clicking OK selects the new folder as the shared VST plug-ins folder.

● After selecting a new shared plug-ins folder, you need to restart Cubase SX/SL for the effects in the new folder to become available.

Managing and Selecting DirectX Plug-ins

To see which DirectX plug-ins are available in your system, click the "DirectX Plug-ins" tab at the top of the window.

- **To enable a plug-in (make it available for selection), click in the left column.**

  Only the currently enabled plug-ins (shown with a check sign in the left column) will appear on the Effect menus.

The idea here is that there could be a variety of DirectX plug-ins in your system, many of which are not intended for musical audio processing. Disabling these helps you keep the Effect menus in Cubase SX/SL more manageable.

- **The second column indicates how many instances of the plug-in are currently used in Cubase SX/SL.**

  Clicking in this column for a plug-in which is already in use produces a pop-up showing exactly where each use occurs.

● Please note that a plug-in may be in use even if it isn't enabled in the left column. You might for example have opened a Song containing effects that currently are disabled on the menu. The left column purely determines whether or not the plug-in will be visible on the Effect menus.

11 VST Instruments

11.1 Introduction

VST Instruments are software synthesizers (or other sound sources) that are contained within Cubase SX/SL. They are played internally via MIDI, and their audio outputs appear on separate channels in the Mixer, allowing you to add effects or EQ, just as with audio tracks.

Some VST Instruments are included with Cubase SX/SL, others can be purchased separately from Steinberg and other manufacturers. This chapter describes the general procedures for using VST Instruments, along with descriptions of the included VST Instruments.

The following VST Instruments are included and installed with Cubase SX/SL:

- **A1—a software synthesizer powered by Waldorf.**

  See page 245.

- **VB-1—a virtual bass instrument built on real-time physical modelling principles.**

  See page 256.

- **LM-7—a 24 bit drum machine.**

  See page 257.

- During the installation process you also had the option of installing VST instruments that were part of Cubase 5.1 and previous versions. These are described from page 260 onwards.

11.2 Activating and Using Instruments in Cubase SX/SL

1. **Pull down the Devices menu and select VST Instruments.**

   The VST Instruments panel appears with 32 slots (Cubase SL has 16 slots).

2. **Pull down the pop-up menu for an empty slot in the panel and select the desired instrument.**
3. **Select an unused MIDI track in the Project window.**
4. **Pull down the Output pop-up menu for the MIDI track in the Track list or in the Inspector.**

   The pop-up menu will now contain an additional item, with the name of the activated VST Instrument.

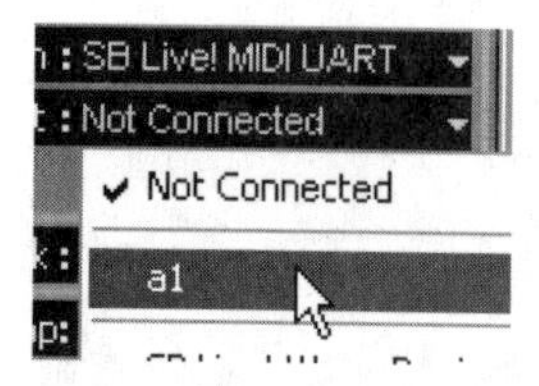

5. **Select the VST Instrument on the MIDI Output pop-up menu.**

   The MIDI Output from the track is now routed to the selected Instrument.
6. **Depending on the selected Instrument, you may also need to select a MIDI channel for the track.**

   Check the Instrument's documentation for details on its MIDI implementation. For example, multi-timbral VST Instruments are able to play back different sounds on different MIDI channels.

7. **Make sure the option "MIDI Thru Active" is activated in the Preferences dialog (MIDI page).**

8. **Click the Monitor button for the MIDI track (in the Track list, Inspector or Mixer).**

   When this is activated (or when the track is Record Enabled, see page 93) incoming MIDI is passed on to the selected MIDI Output (in this case the VST Instrument).

9. **Open the Mixer.**

   You will find an additional channel strip for the instrument's audio outputs. VST Instrument channel strips have the same features and functionality as group channel strips, with the addition of an Edit button at the bottom of the strip for opening the VST Instrument control panel.

10. **Use the pop-ups at the bottom of the channel strips to route the Instrument audio to the desired output or group.**

11. **Play the Instrument from your MIDI keyboard.**

    You can use the Mixer settings to adjust the sound, add EQ or effects, etc.—just as with regular audio channels. Of course, you can also record or manually create MIDI parts that play back sounds from the VST Instrument.

- You can have up to 32 VST Instruments activated at the same time (16 in Cubase SL), different models or several instances of the same instrument. However, software synthesizers can consume quite a lot of CPU power—keep an eye on the VST Performance window to avoid running out of processor power.

About Latency

Depending on your audio hardware and its ASIO driver, the latency (the time it takes for the Instrument to produce a sound when you press a key on your MIDI controller) may simply be too high to allow comfortable real-time VST Instrument playback from a keyboard.

If this is the case, a workaround is to play and record your parts with another MIDI Sound Source selected, and then switch to the VST Instrument for playback.

11.2.1 Selecting Patches and Making Settings

- **To select a patch for a VST Instrument, use its patch pop-up menu in the VST Instruments window.**

  The available patches depends on the VST Instrument. Not all VST Instruments come with pre-made patches.

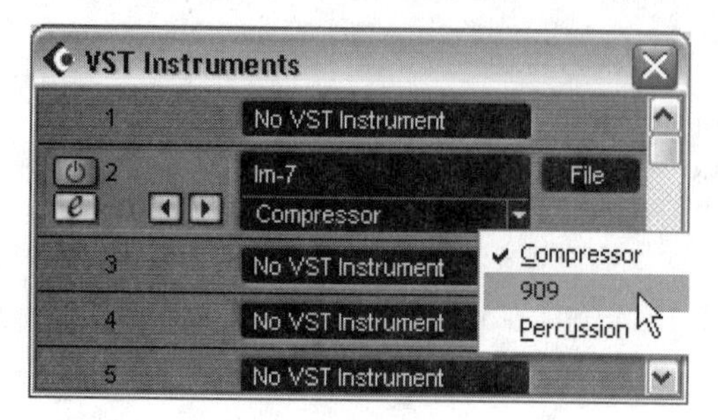

Selecting a patch for the LM-7.

- **To access the parameters for the VST Instrument, click the Edit button in the VST Instruments window or in its channel strip (at the bottom of the fader strip) in the Mixer.**

  This opens a "control panel" for the VST Instrument.

Selecting Patches from the Project Window

When a VST Instrument is selected as MIDI output for a track, you can also select patches by name, using the Program pop-up menu in the track list or Inspector. Although this is set up automatically and transparently, there are a couple of things to note:

- If the VST Instrument supports the VST 2.1 standard (or later), selecting a patch will cause Cubase SX/SL to send MIDI Program Change and Bank Select messages to the VST Instrument, just as with "real" physical MIDI instruments.
  A consequence of this is that you can enter Program Change events in MIDI parts anywhere on the track, having the VST Instrument change patch at the desired locations ("automating" the patch selection).

- If the VST Instrument supports the original VST 2.0 standard only, only limited support of patch selection is offered.
  In this case, selecting a patch will actually ask the VST Instrument to change "Plug-in Program", which is *not* the same as selecting a "Patch" by sending MIDI Program Change and Bank Select messages.

11.2.2 Automating a VST Instrument

- **Automation of the VST Instrument channel settings is done in the same way as automating regular channels.**
- **Automation of the specific parameters for a VST Instrument is done in the same way as automating VST effect parameters**

See the chapter "Automation" (page 291).

11.3 A1 Synthesizer

The A1 is a dual oscillator software synthesizer with the following main features:

- **The A1 is polyphonic with up to 16 voices.**
- **Multimode filter.**

  Lowpass, bandpass, highpass and notch filter types are available.
- **PWM (Pulse Width Modulation).**
- **FM (Frequency Modulation).**
- **Ring Modulator.**
- **Built-in stereo chorus/flanger effect.**
- **The A1 receives MIDI in Omni mode (on all MIDI channels).**

  You don't need to select a MIDI channel to direct MIDI to the A1.
- **The A1 responds to MIDI Controller messages.**

  See page 255.

11.3.1 A1 Parameters

Oscillator 1 and 2 Section

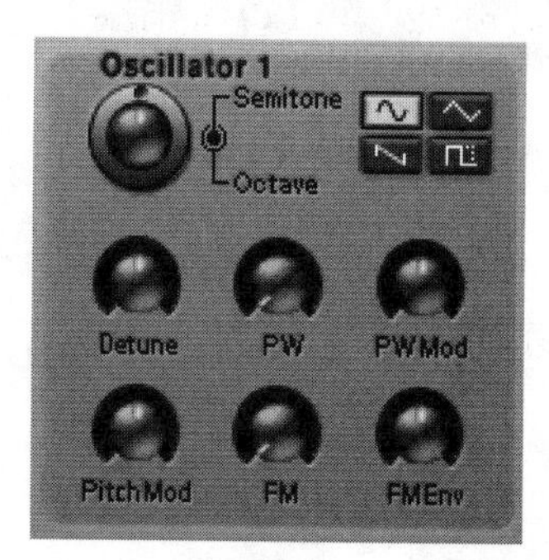

This section contains parameters affecting the oscillators.

Parameter	Values	Description
Octave	128' to 1/2' (feet)	Clicking on the outer ring of the dial allows you to tune the oscillator in octave steps.
Semitone	+/- 12 Semitones	Clicking on the inner ring of the dial allows you to tune the oscillator in semitone steps.
Detune	-100/+100 Cent	Tunes the oscillator in cent (100th of a semitone) steps.
Shape	Sine, triangle, sawtooth or pulse.	This sets the waveform for the oscillator.
PW	50%—100%	Sets the width of the waveform when a Pulse waveform is selected. Turning the dial clockwise gradually produces a narrower pulse waveform. Note that a PW setting of 100% will lead to complete cancellation of the waveform (i.e. silence), if no modulation (see PW Mod) is applied.
PW Mod	-100 to 100	This parameter determines the amount of Pulse Width Modulation (PWM) by the LFO. Positive and negative values can be set. A Pulse waveform must be selected for PW Mod to function.

Parameter	Values	Description
Pitch Mod	-100 to 100	This parameter determines the amount of oscillator 1 pitch modulation (or vibrato) by the LFO. Positive and negative values can be set.
FM (Oscillator 1 only)	0—100%	Governs the amount of frequency modulation. See page 255.
FM Env (Oscillator 1 only)	-100 to 100	This governs how much the Filter Envelope parameters affects the FM amount. Positive and negative values can be set. See page 255.

LFO Section

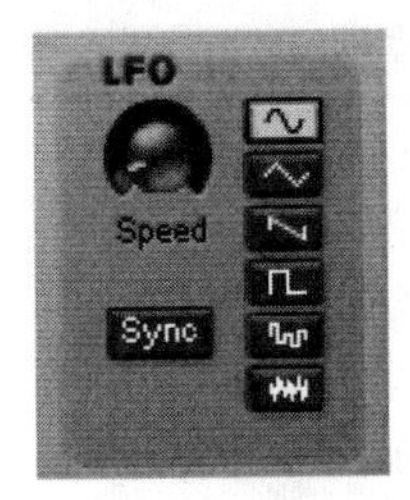

This section contains the LFO (Low Frequency Oscillator) parameters. LFOs are used to modulate parameters like pitch (vibrato) or the filter cutoff.

Parameter	Values	Description
LFO Wave	Sine/Saw/S&H/ Triangle/Square/ Random	This sets the LFO waveform for modulating parameters: Sine and triangle waves have a smooth waveform, suitable for normal vibrato. Saw produces a ramp up or down cycle. S&H produces stepped random modulation. Square waves produce cycles that abruptly change between two values. Random produces smooth random modulation.
LFO Sync	On/Off	If this is activated, the LFO rate will be synchronized to the sequencer tempo in various bar/beat divisions that can be set with the LFO Speed parameter.

Parameter	Values	Description
LFO Speed	0.010—1000 Hz	Governs the modulation rate of the LFO.
LFO Speed (tempo sync on)	8 Bars to 1/64T	If the "LFO Sync" parameter is activated, the LFO rate will be synchronized to the sequencer tempo, according to the different beat divisions that can be specified here.

Filter Section

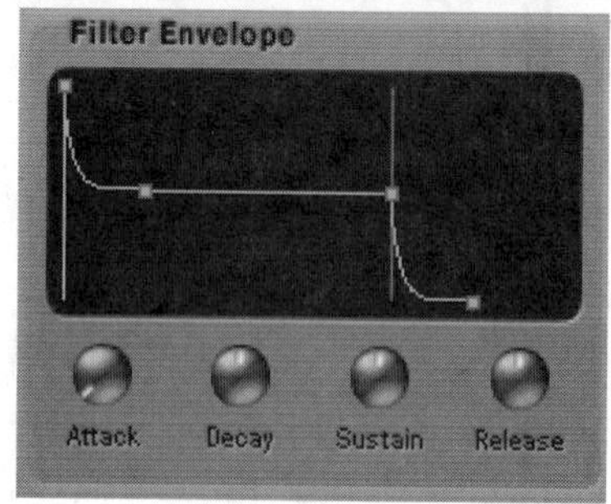

This section contains the filter parameters:

Parameter	Values	Description
Filter type	Lowpass/Highpass /Bandpass/Notch	Sets the filter type to either lowpass, high-pass, bandpass or notch. The filter types are described on page 254.
Cutoff	10.91Hz— 17740Hz	Controls the filter frequency or "cutoff". If a lowpass filter is used, it could be said to control the opening and closing of the filter, producing the classic "sweeping" synthe-sizer sound. How this parameter operates is governed by the filter mode (see page 254).

Parameter	Values	Description
Resonance	0—100%	The Resonance control for the filter. Raise this for a more pronounced filter sweep effect.
Drive	0—100%	This parameter can overdrive the filter to produce distortion effects.
Filter Envelope	-100/+100	Controls how much the filter cutoff should be affected by the Filter Envelope parameters. Negative values will invert the filter envelope settings.
Filter Velocity	-100/+100	Determines how the filter cutoff will be affected by velocity, i.e. how hard or soft you strike a key. Positive values will increase the cutoff frequency the harder you strike a key. Negative values will invert this relationship.
Filter Envelope Attack/Decay/ Sustain/Release	0—60s (Attack/ Decay/Release) and 0—100% (Sustain)	The Filter Envelope Attack, Decay, Sustain and Release parameters. Use these parameters to determine how the filter cutoff should open and close with time, when a note is played. Values can be changed using the dials or by dragging the breakpoints in the graphic display.
Cutoff Mod	-100/+100	This controls how much the filter cutoff is modulated by the LFO (low frequency oscillator).
Keytrack	-100/+100	If this parameter is set to values over 0, the filter cutoff frequency will increase the further up on the keyboard you play. Negative values invert this relationship.

Amplifier Section

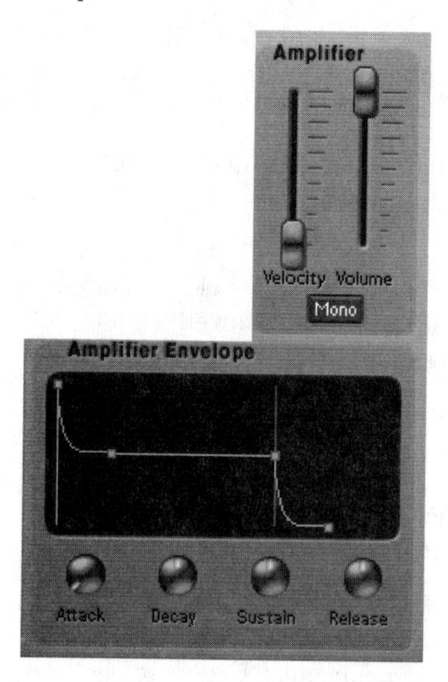

This section contains the Amplifier parameters:

Parameter	Values	Description
Amplifier Attack/ Decay/Sustain/ Release	0—60s (Attack/ Decay/Release parameters) and 0—100% (Sustain parameter)	The Amplifier Attack, Decay, Sustain and Release parameters. Use these parameters to determine how the volume should change with time, when a note is played. Values can be changed using the dials or by dragging the breakpoints in the graphic display.
Velocity	0—100%	This determines how much the Amplifier Envelope should be affected by velocity, i.e. by how hard or soft you strike a note on the keyboard.
Mono	On/Off	When this is activated, the A1 will be monophonic, i.e. only play one voice at a time.

The Chorus/Flanger Section

Adding chorus will introduce a wide stereo effect and generally "fatten" sounds. With higher Feedback settings, more metallic sounding flanging effects are produced. The section contains the following parameters.

Parameter	Values	Description
Speed	0—100	Controls the modulation rate of the effect.
Feedback	-100/+100	Increasing the Feedback parameter value results in a more pronounced sweeping metallic sound. Positive and negative feedback values can be set.
Depth	0—100	Controls the depth of the modulation.
Quad	On/Off	Adds more delay taps, producing richer chorus/flanger effects.
On	On/Off	This turns the chorus/flanger effect on or off.

The Glide Section

This section contains the glide parameters.

Parameter	Values	Description
On	On/Off	If set to "On" the pitch will glide up or down between notes played.
Speed	0—60s	Controls the time it takes for the pitch to glide from one note to the next when using Glide.

The Mixer Section

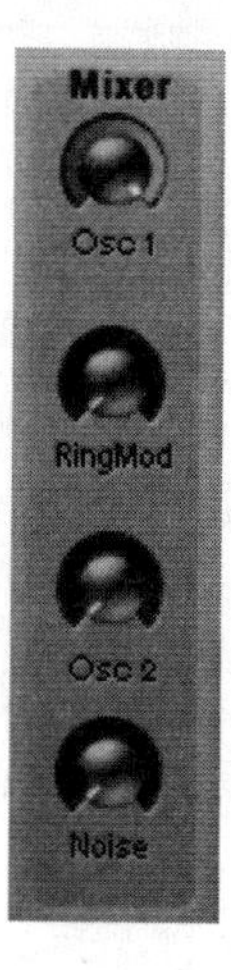

This section controls the relative levels of Oscillator 1 and 2. Here you also set the levels of the Ring Modulator and Noise Generator outputs.

Parameter	Values	Description
Osc 1	0—100%	Sets the volume of oscillator 1.
Ring Mod	0—100%	Controls the level of the ring modulator. See page 255.
Osc 2	0—100%	Sets the volume of oscillator 2.
Noise	0—100%	Noise is commonly used to create wind and percussion type sounds. To hear the noise generator output on its own, turn down the osc 1 and 2 output in the Mixer.

Mod Wheel Section

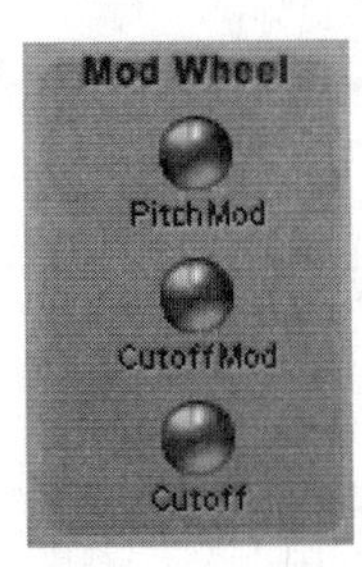

This section controls how the modulation wheel affects certain parameters. Positive and negative values can be set. For example, this can be used to set up so that moving the mod wheel gradually removes Filter Cutoff LFO modulation and instead introduces vibrato.

Parameter	Values	Description
Pitch Mod	-100/+100	Governs the amount of LFO modulation of the oscillator frequency (vibrato) using the mod wheel.
Cutoff Mod	-100/+100	Governs the amount of LFO modulation of the Filter Cut-off parameter using the mod wheel.
Cutoff	-100/+100	Governs how much the mod wheel affects the Filter Cut-off frequency. Positive values raise the cutoff frequency when moving the mod wheel forward. Negative values invert this relationship.

11.3.2 The Parameter Display

The Parameter display is located in the middle of the A1 panel. The Parameter display shows information about any A1 parameter control when you point at it with the mouse. The information is presented in the following way (from left to right):

- "Section" shows what A1 section the parameter belongs to.
- "Parameter" shows the name of the parameter.
- "Value" shows the current value of the parameter.
- "Ctrl" shows the MIDI Controller number assigned to the parameter, see page 255.

11.3.3 Setting the Number of Voices

A1 can have up to 16 voices, but you can freely set the number of voices for each program by changing the value in the "Voices" field.

11.3.4 Keyboard Section

The keyboard shows incoming MIDI note data as played by "invisible hands". The keyboard can be "played" by clicking on it with mouse. Note that the velocity produced will be fixed and that you cannot record anything by clicking the keyboard.

- **"Bend Range" is the only parameter that can be set in this section.**

  A value of "1" equals a semitone bend range, "2" equals a range of two semitones etc.

11.3.5 About the Filter Types

The A1 features a multimode filter. The various filter modes are selected with the Filter Type buttons, and are as follows:

- **Lowpass**

  Lowpass filters let low frequencies pass and cuts out the high frequencies. This is the most commonly used filter type in analog synthesizers.

- **Bandpass**

  A bandpass filter cuts frequencies above and below the cutoff frequency, allowing a specific range of frequencies to pass while attenuating all others.

- **Highpass**

  A highpass filter is the opposite of a lowpass filter, cutting out the lower frequencies and letting the high frequencies pass.

- **Notch**

  A notch filter cuts out frequencies in a narrow midrange band, letting the frequencies below and above through.

Filter Slope

You can also select between 12 or 24 dB filter slopes for all filter types. A 12 dB Lowpass filter leaves more of the harmonics in the filtered sound compared to a 24 dB Lowpass filter.

11.3.6 Ring Modulator

Ring modulators basically multiply two audio signals together. In the A1, Oscillator 1 is multiplied with Oscillator 2 to produce sum and difference frequencies. Ring modulation can be used to create complex, bell-like sounds.

- **To hear the output of Ring Modulator on its own, turn down the osc 1 and 2 output in the Mixer.**
- **If the oscillators are tuned to the same frequency, and no modulation is applied to either the oscillator 1 or 2 frequency, the ring modulated output will sound fairly similar to the "normal" sound of the oscillators. It is when the frequencies of osc 1 and osc 2 *differ,* that you get the more complex timbres associated with ring modulation.**

11.3.7 About FM

Frequency Modulation, or FM, is when the frequency of one oscillator (called the "carrier") is modulated by the frequency of another oscillator (called the "modulator"). Using FM can produce a wide range of harmonic and non-harmonic timbres.

- **In the A1, Oscillator 1 is the carrier and Oscillator 2 the modulator.**

  When using FM, you should turn the master volume for Oscillator 2 down to zero in the Mixer to hear the "pure" sound of FM. The output of oscillator 2 is internally routed to oscillator 1 anyway when using FM.

- **Changing the frequency of Oscillator 2 also changes the timbre of the FM sound.**

  The waveform selected for both oscillators also affects the timbre.

11.3.8 MIDI Controller Messages

The A1 responds to MIDI Controller Messages. All A1 parameters are assigned controller numbers. To find out what controller number is assigned to a parameter, simply point at the parameter and you can see the associated controller number assigned to it in the Parameter display (see page 253).

11.4 VB-1 Bass Synth

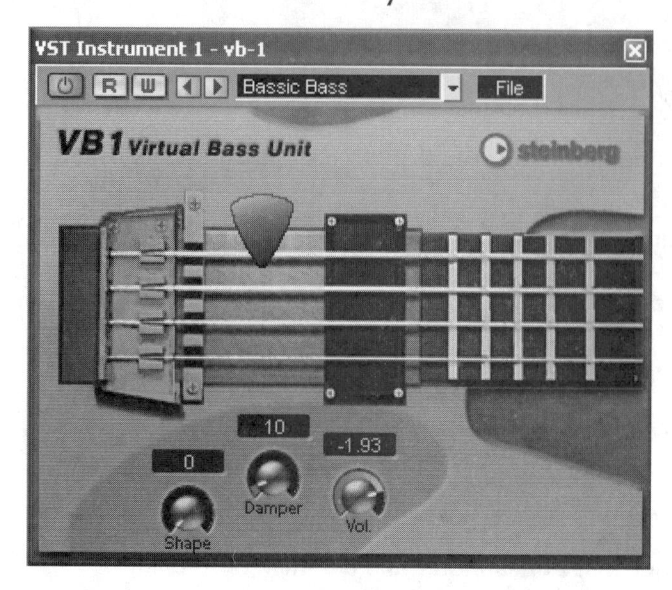

The VB-1 is a virtual bass instrument built on real-time physical modelling principles. It has the following properties:

- **VB-1 is polyphonic with up to 4 voices.**
- **VB-1 receives MIDI In Omni mode (on all MIDI channels).**

  You don't need to select a MIDI channel to direct MIDI to the VB-1.
- **VB-1 responds to the following MIDI messages:**

  MIDI Note On/Off (velocity governs volume), Volume and Pan.

VB-1 Parameters

Parameter	Description
Pick-up	To change the Pick-up position, click and drag the lower end of the Pick-up. Positioning the pick-up position towards the left produces a hollow sound that emphasizes the upper harmonics of the plucked string. When placed towards the right position, the tone is fuller and warmer.
Pick	This determines where along the length of the string the initial pluck is made. This controls the "roundness" of the tone, just like on a real bass. Click-drag the Pick to change position.

Parameter	Description
Shape	This knob selects the basic waveform used to drive the plucked string model. This parameter can drastically change the sound character. The control smoothly morphs through the waves. It is possible to create sounds that have no relation to a bass guitar with this control.
Volume	This knob regulates the VB-1 volume.
Damper	This parametercontrols the length of time the string vibrates after being plucked.

11.5 LM-7 Drum Machine

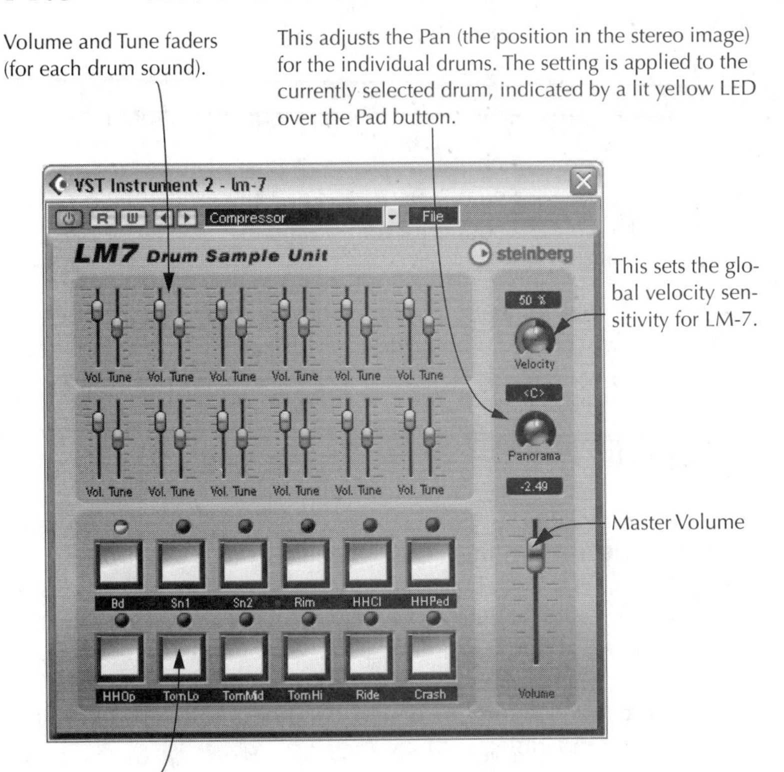

Pad (one for each drum sound). Press to audition the drum sound assigned to the Pad, or to select a sound for adjusting pan.

The LM-7 is a 24-bit drum machine. It has the following properties:

- **LM-7 is polyphonic with up to 12 voices.**

- **LM-7 receives MIDI in Omni mode (on all MIDI channels).**

  You don't need to select a MIDI channel to direct MIDI to LM-7.

- **LM-7 responds to the following MIDI messages:**

  MIDI Note On/Off (velocity governs volume).

11.5.1 LM-7 Parameters

Parameter	Description
Velocity	This sets the global velocity sensitivity for LM-7. The higher the value, the more sensitive LM-7 will be to incoming velocity data. If set to "0", the sounds will play back with a fixed velocity value.
Volume sliders	The volume sliders are used to adjust the volume for each individual drum sound.
Tune sliders	The tune sliders are used to tune each individual drum sound, up or down 1 octave.
Pad	The Pads are used for two things: To audition the individual drum sounds, and to select a sound for adjusting pan.
Panorama	This is used to position an individual sound in the stereo image. The setting applies to the currently selected sound, indicated by a lit yellow LED over the Pad button.

11.5.2 Drum Sounds

LM-7 comes with six sets of drum sounds. "Compressor", "909" and "Percussion" are loaded as the default sounds when launching LM-7. "Modulation", "Fusion" and "DrumNbass" can be loaded by selecting "Load Bank" from the File menu and opening the lm7_second_set.fxb file (which is located in the Vstplugins/Drums subfolder). Compressor features samples of an acoustic drum kit, 909 features classic analog drum machine sounds and Percussion not surprisingly features various percussion sounds. The table below shows how the drum sounds are assigned to note values on your MIDI keyboard. The mapping is GM compatible:

Drum sound	Note value	Comment
Bd	C1	
Rim	C#1	Compressor only.
Snare	D1	
Clap	D#1	909 only.
Hi-Hat	F#1	
O-Hi-Hat	A#1	
Tom 1	A1	
Tom 2	B2	
Tom 3	D2	
Crash	C#2	
Ride	D#2	Compressor only.
Tambourine	F#2	Percussion only.
Cowbell	G#2	Percussion only.
Hi Bongo	C3	Percussion only.
Lo Bongo	C3#	Percussion only.
Conga Mute	D3	Percussion only.
Conga Open	D#3	Percussion only.
Conga Lo	E3	Percussion only.
Timbale Lo	G3	Percussion only.
Timbale Hi	G#3	Percussion only.
Cabasa	A3	Percussion only.

11.5.3 Switching the Sets

Use the pop-up menu to switch between the three supplied drum sets, just like you switch between effect programs.

11.6 JX16 Synthesizer

- The JX-16 synthesizer can be found in the Cubase 5 Instruments subfolder of your VST plug-ins if you chose to install Cubase 5 Instruments during the Cubase SX/SL installation.

The JX16 is a dual oscillator software synthesizer with the following main features:

- **The JX16 is polyphonic with up to 16 voices.**

  The polyphony setting for each patch is user programmable.

- **Low CPU load and high quality sound (low aliasing distortion).**
- **Multimode Filter.**

  Lowpass, Bandpass and Hipass filter modes are available.

- **Oscillator Lock function enables the creation of pulse and square waveforms with classic PWM (Pulse Width Modulation).**

  See page 267.

- **Built-in stereo chorus effect.**
- **The JX16 receives MIDI in Omni mode (on all MIDI channels).**

  You don't need to select a MIDI channel to direct MIDI to the JX16.

- **The JX16 responds to MIDI Controller messages.**

  See MIDI Controller Messages.

- All parameters can be automated.

11.6.1 JX16 Parameters

Osc 1+2 Section

This section contains parameters affecting both oscillators.

Parameter	Values	Description
Octave	-2/+2	Tunes the oscillators in octave steps.
Fine Tune	-100/+100 Cent	Tunes the oscillators in cent (100th of a semitone) steps.
Vibrato	0—100	Governs how much the LFO should modulate the pitch of the oscillators (vibrato). The Vibrato parameter is also controllable via MIDI by using the Mod Wheel.
Noise	0—100	This parameter produces white noise mixed with the oscillators. By using the "OSC lock" parameter you can "cancel out" the oscillators and use pure noise as the sound source. This is described on About the "Oscillator Lock" Parameter.
OSC lock	0—95/Free	See About the "Oscillator Lock" Parameter.

The Oscillator 2 Section

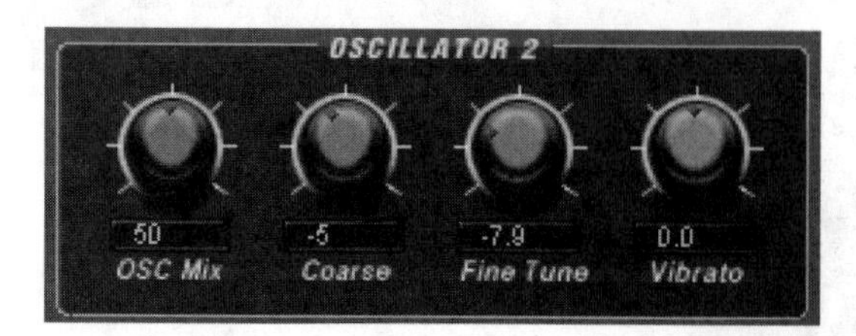

This section contains parameters that affect oscillator 2 only.

Parameter	Values	Description
OSC Mix	0—100	Controls the level of oscillator 2. 100 produces equal level to oscillator 1, which has a fixed output level.
Coarse	-24/+24 Semitones	Tuning of Oscillator 2, in semitone steps.
Fine Tune	-50/+50 Cent	Fine tuning of Oscillator 2, in cent (=100th of a semitone) steps.
Vibrato	-100/100	This lets you apply vibrato on the second oscillator only. This can be useful for creating PWM effects—see About the "Oscillator Lock" Parameter for a further description. Both positive and negative values can be set.

The Glide/Chorus Section

This section contains Glide parameters, and also the Polyphony and Chorus parameters.

Parameter	Values	Description
Mode	Off/Held/On	If set to "On", the pitch will glide up or down between notes played. If set to "Held", Glide will only be applied when you press a key while another key is held.
Rate	0—100	Controls the time it takes for the pitch to glide from one note to the next when using Glide. If Bend (see below) is used, this parameter controls the time it takes for the pitch bend to "land" at the correct pitch.
Bend	-36/+36 Semitones	Applies an initial pitch bend to the notes played. Negative values causes the pitch to slide up to the pitch of the note played, and vice versa.
Polyphony	1 to 16	This sets the polyphony, i.e. the number of voices a patch can use.
Chorus	OFF/I/II/III/IV	This adds a stereo chorus effect. The values set different modulation rates and depths for the effect.

The LFO Section

This section contains the LFO (Low Frequency Oscillator) parameters. LFOs are used to modulate parameters like pitch (vibrato) or the filter cutoff.

Parameter	Values	Description
LFO Wave	Sine/Square/Saw+/Saw-/Random	This sets the LFO waveform for modulating parameters: Sine waves have a smooth waveform, suitable for normal vibrato. Square waves produce cycles that abruptly change between two values. Saw+ produces a ramp up cycle. Saw- produces a ramp down cycle. Random produces random stepped modulation.
LFO Sync	On/Off	If this is activated, the LFO rate will be synced to the sequencer tempo in various beat divisions that can be set with the LFO Rate parameter.
LFO Rate	0.018—54.598 Hz	Governs the modulation rate of the LFO.

Parameter	Values	Description
LFO Rate (tempo sync on)	8 to 1/8 Beats 1 Beat=1/4 note	If the "LFO Sync" parameter is activated, the LFO rate will be synced to the sequencer tempo, according to the different beat divisions that can be specified here.
LFO Velocity	0—100	This allows you to control the LFO Rate parameter with velocity, i.e. by how hard or soft you strike a note on the keyboard. The harder you play the faster the LFO rate.

The VCF Section

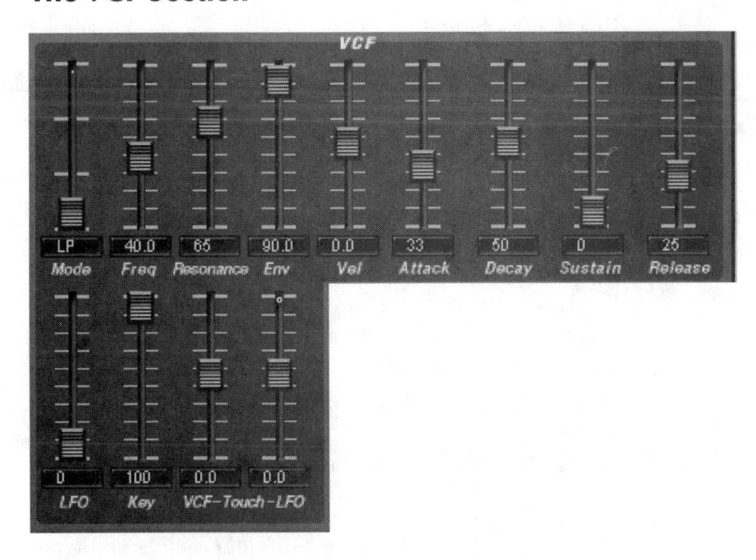

This section contains the filter parameters:

Parameter	Values	Description
VCF Mode	LP/HP/BP/Off	Sets the filter mode to either lowpass (LP), highpass (HP), bandpass (BP) or off. The filter modes are described on About the Filter Types.
VCF Freq (Cutoff)	0—100	Controls the filter frequency or "cutoff". If a lowpass filter is used, it could be said to control the opening and closing of the filter, producing the classic "sweeping" synthesizer sound. How this parameter operates is governed by the filter mode (see About the Filter Types).

Resonance	0—100	The Resonance control for the filter. Raise this for a more pronounced filter sweep effect. If set to 100, the filter will self-oscillate and produce a pitch. See the "VCF Key" parameter below for a description of how this can be used.
VCF Env	-100/+100	Controls how much the filter cutoff should be affected by the VCF Envelope parameters. Negative values will invert the filter envelope settings.
VCF Vel	-100/+100	Determines how the filter cutoff will be affected by velocity, i.e. how hard or soft you strike a key. Positive values will increase the cutoff frequency the harder you strike a key. Negative values will invert this relationship.
VCF Att/Dec /Sus/Rel	0—100	The Filter Envelope Attack, Decay, Sustain and Release parameters. Use these parameters to determine how the filter cutoff should open and close with time, when a note is played.
VCF LFO	0—100	This controls how much the filter cutoff is modulated by the LFO (low frequency oscillator).
VCF Key	0—100	If this parameter is set to values over 0, the filter cutoff frequency will increase the further up on the keyboard you play. If set to 100, it will track the notes on the keyboard, enabling you to "play" the filter as an extra sound source, as the filter self-oscillates and produces a pitch when the resonance is set to 100.
VCF Touch	-100/+100	This sets the amount the VCF cutoff parameter should be affected by Aftertouch. If positive values are set, the filter cutoff is raised the harder you press. Negative values invert this relationship.
LFO Touch	-100/+100	This sets the amount the VCF LFO parameter should be affected by Aftertouch. If positive values are set, the modulation increases the harder you press. Negative values invert this relationship.

The VCA Section

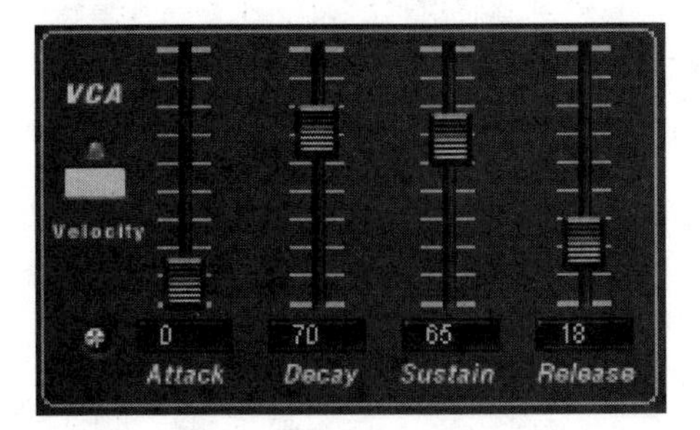

This section contains the VCA Envelope parameters:

Parameter	Values	Description
VCA Att/Dec/Sus/ Rel	0—100	The VCA Attack, Decay, Sustain and Release parameters. Use these parameters to determine how the volume should change with time, when a note is played.
VCA Velocity	On/Off	This determines whether the VCA Envelope should be affected by velocity, i.e. by how hard or soft you strike a note on the keyboard.

11.6.2 About the "Oscillator Lock" Parameter

JX16 features two oscillators per voice, with fixed sawtooth waveforms. You can, however, generate square waves and PWM (pulse width modulation) with the JX16, by combining the two oscillators using the "OSC lock" and Oscillator 2 "Vibrato" parameters. The following applies:

- **"OSC lock" allows the phase of Oscillator 2 to be fixed relative to OSC 1, producing pulse waves when Oscillator 2 has the same pitch and level as OSC 1.**
- **If the oscillators are tuned to the same pitch and level, an "OSC lock" setting of 50% produces a square wave with higher and lower settings producing progressively narrower pulse waveforms.**

  With an "OSC lock" setting of 0% the two oscillators cancel out completely, which is useful if you only want to use the noise generator as a sound source.

- **By applying the Oscillator 2 "Vibrato" parameter when OSC lock is set to around 50%, classic PWM is produced.**

  You can also detune Oscillator 2 for even richer modulation effects.

- **In "Free" mode the oscillator phase is allowed to drift, producing a random timbre change.**

By experimenting with these parameters, many different timbres and modulation effects can be produced.

11.6.3 About the Filter Modes

The JX16 features a multimode filter. The various filter modes are selected with the VCF Mode parameter, and are as follows:

- **Lowpass (LP)**

  A lowpass filter lets low frequencies pass and cuts out the high frequencies. This is the most commonly used filter type in analog synthesizers.

- **Bandpass (BP)**

  A bandpass filter cuts frequencies above and below the cutoff frequency, allowing a specific range of frequencies to pass while attenuating all others.

- **Highpass (HP)**

  A highpass filter is the opposite of a lowpass filter, cutting out the lower frequencies and letting the high frequencies pass.

11.6.4 MIDI Controller Messages

The JX16 responds to the following MIDI Controller Messages:

Controller	Parameter/Value
Pitch Bend	+/- 2 Semitones
CC1 (Mod Wheel)	Vibrato
Aftertouch	Can control filter cutoff and filter cutoff modulation (by the VCF LFO).
CC2	Increase filter cutoff
CC3	Decrease filter cutoff
CC7	Volume
CC16	Increase filter resonance
Program Change #	1—64

11.7 CS40 Synthesizer

● The CS40 synthesizer can be found in the Cubase 5 Instruments subfolder of your VST plug-ins if you chose to install Cubase 5 Instruments during the Cubase SX/SL installation.

The CS40 is a straightforward software synthesizer with the following main features:

- **The CS40 is polyphonic with up to 6 voices.**
- **The CS40 receives MIDI in Omni mode (on all MIDI channels).**

  You don't need to select a MIDI channel to direct MIDI to the CS40.
- **The CS40 responds to the following MIDI messages:**

  MIDI Note On/Off (velocity governs volume).
  Volume.
  Pan.
  Pitch Bend (± 2 semitones).
  Modulation (vibrato).

11.7.1 CS40 Parameters

Parameter	Description
Oscillator 1 Range	Selects an octave range for oscillator 1; 32, 16, 8 or 4 feet.
Oscillator 1 Waveform	The basic waveform for oscillator 1; Triangle, Sawtooth, Square or Pulse.
Oscillator 1 Tune	Detunes Oscillator 1 ± 7 semitones.
Oscillator 2 Range	Same as Oscillator 1.
Oscillator 2 Waveform	Same as Oscillator 1.
Oscillator 2 Tune	Same as Oscillator 1.
Oscillator Blend	Adjusts the relative volume mix between oscillator 1 and 2.
LFO Speed	Governs the speed of the LFO. If LFO Sync is activated, this parameter sets the LFO speed in various beat increments to the sequencer tempo.
LFO Sync	If activated, the LFO speed will be synced to the set sequencer tempo.
LFO Amount	This governs the amount of LFO modulation applied to the destination parameters.
LFO Destination	This sets the destination parameter(s) for the LFO. Options are as follows: Off—No modulation VCF—modulation of the VCF cutoff frequency. VCA—amplitude modulation (tremolo). Both—modulation of both the VCF and VCA.
Vibrato Speed	Governs the speed of the Vibrato LFO. The Vibrato amount is controlled by the Mod Wheel.
VCF Cutoff	The Cutoff Frequency for the filter, governing the amount of high frequencies in the sound.
VCF Resonance	The Resonance control for the filter. Raise this for a more hollow, pronounced filter effect.
Filter Mod ADSR	This controls how much the VCF cutoff is affected by the VCF Envelope. Negative values invert the Envelope settings.

Parameter	Description
VCF Attack, Decay, Sustain, Release	The Filter Envelope. Use these parameters to determine how the filter should open and close with time, when a note is played.
VCA Attack, Decay, Sustain, Release	The Amplitude Envelope. Use these parameters to determine how the amplitude (volume) should change with time, when a note is played.
MonoMode	When activated the CS40 will be monophonic.
Volume	Governs the overall volume.

11.8 The Neon Synthesizer

- The Neon synthesizer can be found in the Cubase 5 Instruments subfolder of your VST plug-ins if you chose to install Cubase 5 Instruments during the Cubase SX/SL installation.

The Neon is a simple software synthesizer. It has the following properties:

- **The Neon is polyphonic with up to 16 voices.**

  However, since each added voice consumes CPU power, the maximum polyphony may be limited by the speed of your computer.

- **The Neon receives MIDI in Omni mode (on all MIDI channels).**

  You don't need to select a MIDI channel to direct MIDI to the Neon.

- **The Neon responds to the following MIDI messages:**

  MIDI Note On/Off (velocity governs volume).
  Volume.
  Pan (remember to pan the two Instrument channels hard Left/Right if you want to use MIDI Pan messages).
  Pitch Bend (± 2 semitones).
  Modulation (vibrato).

11.8.1 Neon Parameters

Parameter	Description
Range	Selects an octave range for the oscillators, 16, 8 or 4 feet.
Waveform	The basic waveform for the oscillators, Triangle, Sawtooth or Square.
LFO Speed	Governs the speed of the vibrato. The vibrato depth is controlled via MIDI Modulation messages (for example, using the Mod Wheel on your MIDI controller).
Osc 2 Detune	Allows you to detune the "second oscillator" ± 7 semitones. By setting this to a value close to "twelve o'clock", you will get fine detuning, for a warmer, fatter sound.
VCF Cutoff	The Cutoff Frequency for the filter, governing the amount of high frequencies in the sound. On the Neon, the Cutoff control also serves as a Depth control for the Filter Envelope (VCF Attack, Decay, Sustain, Release), so that the lower the setting of the Cutoff parameter, the more will the filter be affected by the Filter Envelope.
VCF Resonance	The Resonance control for the filter. Raise this for a more hollow, pronounced filter effect.
VCF Attack, Decay, Sustain, Release	The Filter Envelope. Use these parameters to determine how the filter should open and close with time, when a note is played.
VCA Attack, Decay, Sustain, Release	The Amplitude Envelope. Use these parameters to determine how the amplitude (volume) should change with time, when a note is played.

11.9 LM-9 Drum Machine

Volume fader (one for each drum sound).

This sets the global velocity sensitivity for LM-9.

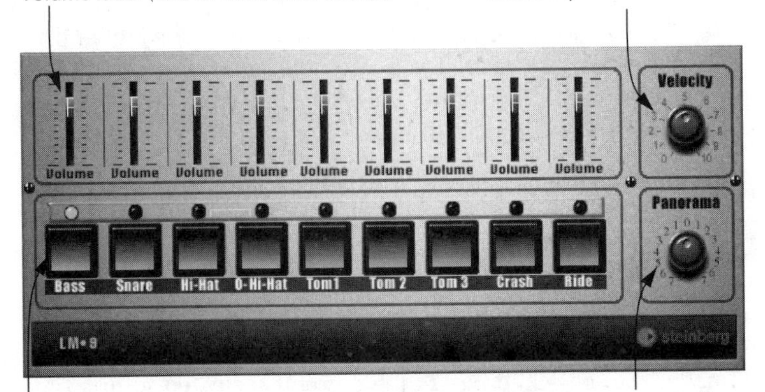

Pad (one for each drum sound). Click to audition the drum sound assigned to the Pad, or to select a sound for adjusting pan.

This adjusts the Pan (the position in the stereo image) for the individual drums. The setting is applied to the currently selected drum, indicated by a lit yellow LED over the Pad button.

- The LM-9 drum machine can be found in the Cubase 5 Instruments subfolder of your VST plug-ins if you chose to install Cubase 5 Instruments during the Cubase SX/SL installation.

The LM-9 is a simple drum machine. It has the following properties:

- **LM-9 is polyphonic with up to 9 voices.**
- **LM-9 receives MIDI in Omni mode (on all MIDI channels).**

  You don't need to select a MIDI channel to direct MIDI to LM-9.
- **LM-9 responds to the following MIDI messages:**

  MIDI Note On/Off (velocity governs volume).

Furthermore, all parameters can be automated.

11.9.1 LM-9 Parameters

Parameter	Description
Velocity	This sets the global velocity sensitivity for LM-9. The higher the value, the more sensitive LM-9 will be to incoming velocity data. If set to "0", the sounds will play back with a fixed velocity value.
Volume sliders	The volume sliders are used to adjust the volume for each individual drum sound.
Pad	The Pads are used for two things: To audition the individual drum sounds and to select a sound for adjusting pan.
Panorama	This is used to position an individual sound in the stereo image. The setting applies to the currently selected sound, indicated by a lit yellow LED over the Pad button.

11.9.2 Drum Sounds

LM-9 comes with two sets of drum sounds: "Acoustic" and "Beat Box". Acoustic features samples of an acoustic drum kit and Beat Box features classic analog drum machine sounds.

- **Use the Program button to switch between the two supplied drum sets, just like you switch between effect programs.**

The table below shows how the drum sounds are assigned to note values on your MIDI keyboard. The mapping is GM compatible:

Drum sound	Note value
Bass	C1
Snare	D1
Hi-Hat	F#1
O-Hi-Hat	A#1
Tom 1	D2
Tom 2	B1
Tom 3	A1

Drum sound	Note value
Crash	C#2
Ride	D#2

12 Surround Sound (Cubase SX only)

12.1 Background

12.1.1 What Is Surround Sound?

Surround is a common name for various techniques for positioning audio in reference to the listener. Whereas regular stereo is limited to left/right positioning, within a relatively narrow field, surround sound opens possibilities of positioning an audio source anywhere around the listener.

Surround sound comes in many flavors, from the ill-fated Quadraphonic format for vinyl discs launched in the 70s, to today's more successful incarnations.

The differences between the formats are in two areas:

- The number of speakers.
  This varies from two speakers up to six.
- The intended final coding format.
  This depends on the media the audio will be "stored" on: film, broadcast video or DVD, for example.

Surround sound is a large topic, there are entire books and regular publications devoted to the subject. This chapter will not provide an in-depth introduction to surround sound as such. Instead it will concentrate on the specific implementation in Cubase SX.

12.1.2 Surround Sound in Cubase SX

Cubase SX has integrated surround sound features with support for several formats. This support goes all the way through the audio path:

- Audio Mixer channels can be routed freely to surround channels.
- The special SurroundPanner function in the Mixer allows you to graphically position channels in the surround field.
- Cubase SX is ready for surround specific plug-ins, that is plug-ins with multi channel support specifically designed for surround sound mixing tasks (the included "Mix6to2" plug-in is an example of this).
  There are also surround *aware* plug-ins, which are not designed specifically for Surround but which due to their multi-channel support work well in a Surround configuration. An example of such a plug-in is the UV22 HR dithering plug-in.
- The VST Master Setup window allows you to select and define surround speaker configurations and to map surround channels to physical outputs.

12.1.3 Requirements for Using Surround

The following additional equipment is required for taking advantage of Cubase SX's surround sound implementation:

- An audio card with more than two outputs.
  The card must have as many outputs as the surround format you plan to select.
- A matching amplifier/speaker configuration.

12.1.4 Encoding

The result of a surround mix in Cubase SX is either a number of audio channels in the project, or (if you use the Export audio feature) a number of related audio files on your hard disk. These are technically not different from regular stereo mixes (except they contain more channels).

To get from this step to the final product (surround sound on DVD disc, DTS etc.) requires special software and possibly hardware. This equipment will encode the signal into the desired format, possibly compress the audio (for example using MPEG encoding) and store it on the final media.

Exactly what type of software and/or hardware you need depends on what kind of format you are mixing for and is not dependent on Cubase SX in any way.

12.2 Window Overview

12.2.1 VST Master Setup

In this window you can select a surround sound configuration. Apart from the "Label" and "Name" entries, the configurations cannot be edited.

Label and Name represent the channel names as they will appear in the SurroundPan and the bus output pop-up in the Mixer, respectively.

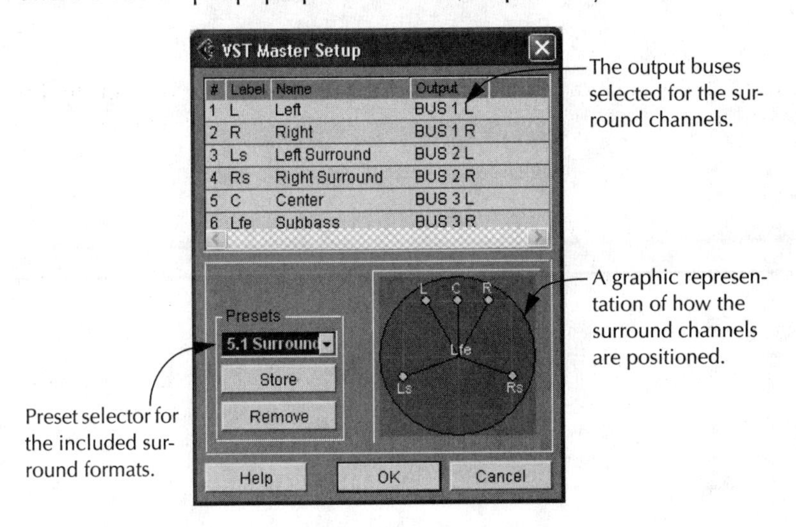

12.2.2 Surround in the Mixer

There are two ways to route audio to surround channels in the mixer:

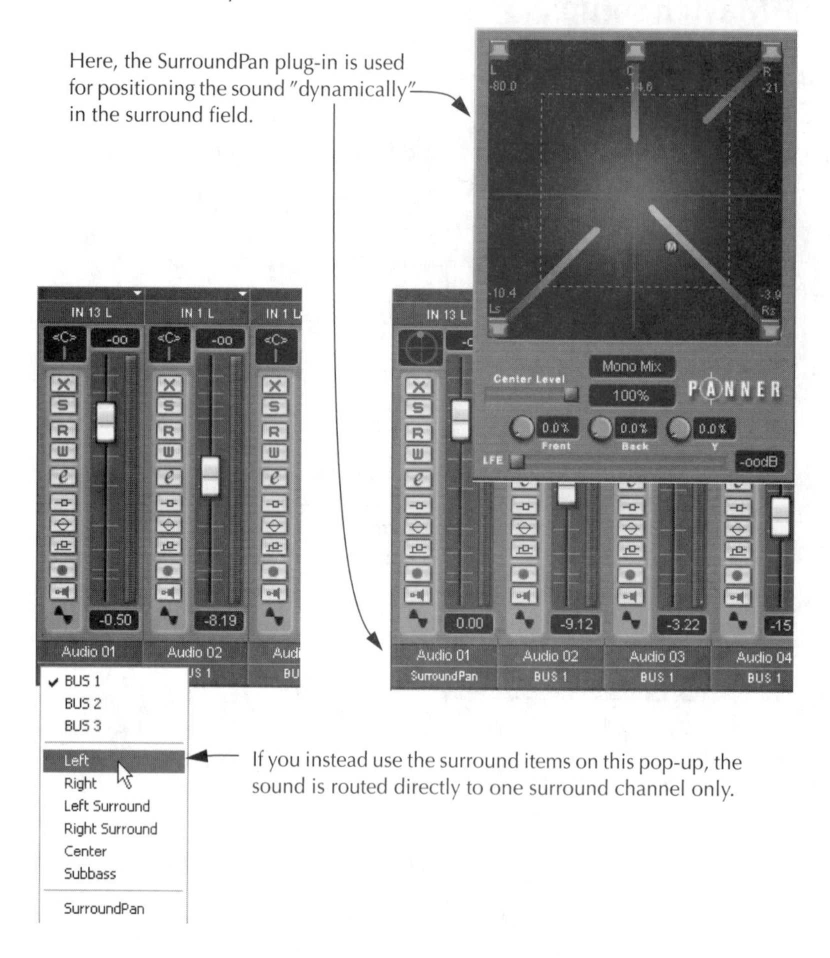

12.2.3 The VST Output Section

In the VST Outputs window you can adjust master levels for surround channels and route the surround channels to physical outputs on your audio card.

Here, three stereo buses are activated, in a 5.1 surround sound configuration.

12.3 Operations

12.3.1 Choosing a Type of Surround

To select your preferred surround configuration, open the VST Master Setup window and select a preset from the Presets pop-up.

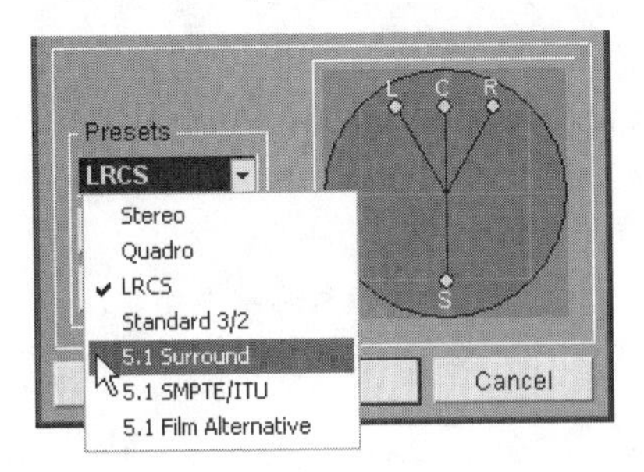

The following surround configurations are included:

Format	Description
Stereo	Not a surround format but rather standard stereo (Left/Right).
Quadro	The original Quadraphonic format for music, with one speaker in each corner. This format was intended for vinyl record players.
LRCS	LRCS refers to Left Center Right Surround, where the surround speaker is center-rear positioned. This is the original surround format that first appeared as Dolby Stereo in cinema and later as the home cinema format Dolby ProLogic.
Standard 3/2	This is the same as 5.1 (see below) but without the LFE channel. The LFE channel is optional in 5.1 and if you don't plan to use it, you might find this option more convenient.
5.1 Surround	This format is one of the most popular in cinema and DVD. In its various cinema and DVD encoding implementations (established by different manufacturers) it is referred to as Dolby Digital, AC-3, DTS and MPEG 2 Multichannel. 5.1 has one center speaker (mainly used for speech) and four surround speakers (for music and sound effects). Additionally a subchannel (LFE—Low Frequency Emitter) with lower bandwidth is used for special low frequency effects.
5.1 SMPTE/ITU 5.1 Film Alternative	These are alternative versions of 5.1 Surround, in which the order of the speakers is changed.

- **The graph shows you how the speakers are positioned in the "room".**

  The graph indicates a room, where the listener is facing the upper quadrants.
- **The Output column indicates to which bus each channel will be routed.**

When you are done, click OK to close the dialog.

12.3.2 Mapping Surround Outputs to Audio Outputs

As indicated in the list in the VST Master Setup window, the surround channels are routed to the outputs/buses in the VST Outputs window, in pairs of two. In order to use the outputs they need to be activated and mapped to a physical output (pair) on your audio card.

- **To activate a bus, open the VST Outputs window and click the Active buttons for the channels you need to use.**

  The exact number of output buses required depends on the surround format chosen, for example 5.1 (a six channel format) requires three (stereo) buses.

- **To map a bus to an output pair, use the pop-up menu at the bottom of the window.**

  Read more about the VST Outputs window on page 207.

12.3.3 Positioning Channels in the Surround Field

There are basically two ways you can route a mixer audio channel to a surround channel:

Using the Surround Pan Plug-in

Cubase SX has a special feature for graphically positioning a sound source in a surround field. This is actually a special plug-in which distributes the audio from the channel in various proportions to the surround channels.

1. **Open the Mixer and locate the channel.**
2. **From the output routing pop-up menu, select SurroundPan.**

   A miniature graph of the surround plug-in interface appears at the top of the channel strip.

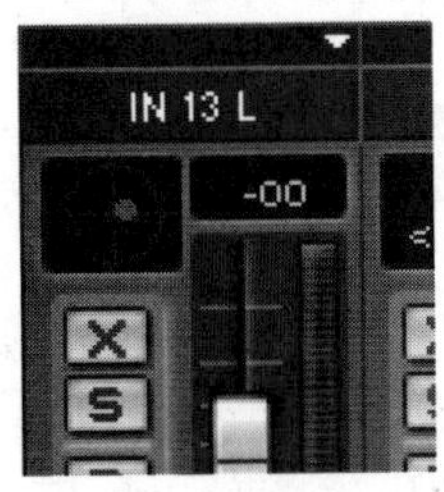

When SurroundPan is selected, the channel strip shows a miniature surround control.

3. **Click and drag directly in the miniature image to move the sound in the surround field.**

   To move the sound to the front center position, hold down [Ctrl] and click.

- **You can double click on the miniature image to open the full plug-in interface in a separate window, where the sound source can be positioned just as in the miniature.**

  The exact controls in this window are described below.

Routing Channels Directly to Surround Buses

Sometimes you may want to route a channel directly to a surround channel. This may for example be true for pre-mixed material or multi-channel recordings that don't require panning.

Also please note that LFE channels are not shown in the SurroundPan. To route low frequency effect sounds to the LFE channel you *must* use the method described below:

1. **Open the Mixer and locate the channel.**

   Please note that this may very well be a group channel, that is a mix of a number of channels that should all be routed to a special surround channel.

2. **From the output routing pop-up menu, select the corresponding surround channel, from the section just above the SurroundPan option.**

   The names of the channels, as they appear here, are defined in the VST Master Setup window, see page 279.

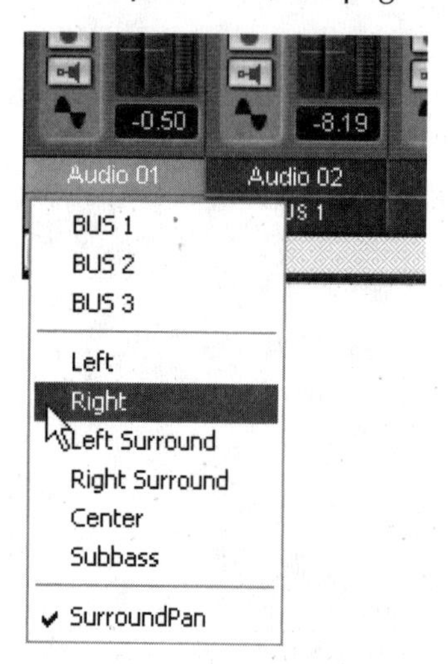

The lower section of the Output routing pop-up contains the surround outputs.

12.3.4 The SurroundPan Controls

The SurroundPan plug-in interface.

The SurroundPan plug-in allows you to position your audio in the surround field. It consists of an image of the speaker arrangement, as defined in the VST Master Setup window, with the sound source indicated as a grey ball.

The following options and methods are available:

Speakers

The speakers in the panel represent the speakers defined in the VST Master Setup window.

- **The speakers in the front are aligned, as they would normally be in a cinema-type situation.**

  This means that the front speakers are at a varying distance from the center, allowing you to move sources between speakers without level attenuation.

- **The LFE channel will not be visible.**
- **You can turn speakers on and off by clicking them with [Alt] pressed. When a speaker is turned off, no audio will be routed to that surround channel.**

Positioning and Levels

- The text below assumes mono/stereo pop-up is set to "Mono Mix". For more information on the other modes, see below.

A sound source is positioned either by clicking or dragging the grey "ball" around in the panel (or by using key commands, see below). By dragging during playback you can record automation, see page 299.

Exactly how levels are handled may require some explanation:

- **When you move a source around, a number will indicate the loudness in each speaker.**

  This is a value in dB (decibel) and is relative to the nominal level of the source. In other words, 0.0 (dB) represents full level.

- **If you position the source far enough away from a speaker, its level will drop to zero (indicated by an infinity symbol).**
- **The signal levels from the individual speakers are indicated by colored lines from the speakers to the center of display.**
- **You can use modifier keys to restrict movement in various ways:**

Key	Movement restriction
[Shift]	Horizontally only
[Ctrl]	Vertically only
[Alt]	Diagonally (up left, down right)
[Ctrl]+[Alt]	Diagonally (up right, down left)

There is a also special set of key commands for working in the SurroundPan window.

● For a complete list of the available key commands, click on the "Panner" logo in the lower right corner and then click again!

The LFE Slider

If the selected Master Setup includes an LFE (Low Frequency Emitter) channel, a separate LFE level slider will be available at the bottom of the SurroundPan window. Use this to set the signal amount sent to the LFE channel.

Mono/Stereo Pop-up

If you have a mono channel this is by default set to Mono Mix. The panner will then behave as described above.

If you have a stereo channel, you have the option of using one of the three Mirror modes. Two grey balls will then appear, one for each channel (L/R). This will allow you to move the two channels symmetrically, by just dragging one of them. The three modes allow you to select which axis should be used for mirroring.

- **The default mode for stereo channels is the Y-Mirror mode.**
- **If you run a stereo signal through the panner in Mono Mix mode, the two channels will be mixed together before entering the plug-in.**
- **If you run a mono signal through the plug-in in one of the stereo modes, the signal will be split before entering the plug-in.**

Additional Parameters

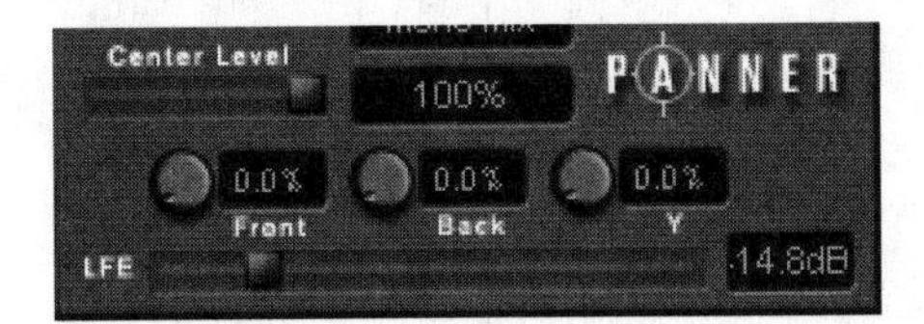

- **Center Level.**

  This determines how center source signals should be reproduced by the front speakers. With a value of 100%, the center speaker will provide the center source. With a value of 0%, the center source will be provided by the ghost image created by the left and right speakers. Other values will produce a mix between these two methods.

- **Divergence Controls.**

  The three divergence controls determine the attenuation curves used when positioning sound sources, for X-axis front, X-axis back and Y-axis, respectively. If all three Divergence values are 0% (default), positioning a sound source on a speaker will set all other speakers to zero level (-∞) (except for the center speaker which depends on the center level). With higher values, the other speakers will receive a percentage of the sound source.

Automation

All parameters in the SurroundPan plug-in can be automated, just as with any other plug-in. See page 299.

12.3.5 Exporting a Surround Mix

A surround mix can be exported to audio files, just as any other mix. There are special features on the Channels pop-up in the Export Audio Mixdown dialog for this purpose. See page 604.

12.3.6 Using Master Plug-ins in Surround Configurations

- For general instructions on how to use Master plug-ins, see page 227. The following text only describes the specifics of using master plug-ins in surround configurations.

Cubase SX introduces a special surround format for VST plug-ins, that is plug-ins that can process more than two channels. An example of such a plug-in is the included Mix6to2.

Still, many stereo plug-ins might be useful as master effects even in a surround configuration.

In the upper left corner of the plug-in panel in the Master Effects window you will see a miniature signal diagram displaying graphics corresponding to the number of master channels in the current configuration, see below.

Applying a Surround-aware Master Plug-in

This is not different from applying a regular plug-in. The only difference is that the plug-in panel may have controls for more than two channels.

Using a Stereo Plug-in in a Surround Configuration

Normally, when you apply a stereo plug-in to a surround sound configuration, the first two channels (often L and R) are routed through the plug-in's two channels, and other channels are left unprocessed. This is indicated by the signal diagram in the upper left corner of the Master Effects window.

However, you may want to use the plug-in on other channels. To do so, click on the small signal diagram to open up an editor window.

● Changes you make in this window do not take effect until you click OK!

- The columns in the diagram represent the channels in the current surround configuration.
- At the top are audio channels from the Mixer. In the middle is the plug-in itself. At the bottom is the output to the output buses (or to the input of the next Master Insert plug-in). Audio flows from top to bottom.
- The square brackets on the in- and outputs to the plug-in represent just that, the in- and outputs to the plug-ins.
- An arrow that ends at a plug-in input indicates that the audio from this surround channel arrives at that plug-in's input.
- An arrow that starts at the output of a plug-in indicates that audio from this plug-in channel is routed to that output channel.
- An arrow that passes above the plug-in indicates a bypass connection (audio passes to the output bus without passing through the effect).

A plug-in input.

A "broken connection". No audio from the "S" channel will be sent into the plug-in.

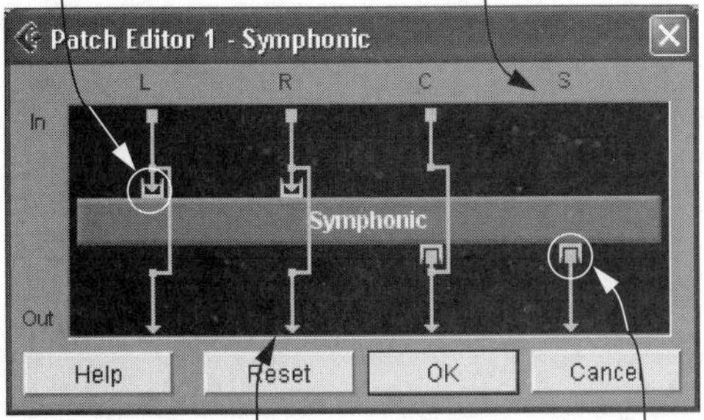

Patch Editor 1 - Symphonic

L R C S

In

Symphonic

Out

Help Reset OK Cancel

This channel includes both a direct and a bypass connection.

A plug-in output.

In this case, the output from the Symphonic plug-in will be routed to the "C" and "S" Output Buses, or (if you have another Master plug-in below this one), to the "C" and "S" inputs of the next plug-in.

Operations

- **You can drag arrows that are connected to the plug-in inputs and outputs sideways to route the audio to/from other audio channels than the standard configuration.**
- **By dragging both the upper and lower arrows to another channel, you route the audio from that channel right through the plug-in. Any other combination will make the audio from an input appear on another output channel.**
- **For channels with a "broken connection" (see illustration above), you can click on the plug-in to add a bypass connection. Click again to remove.**

- **You can set things up so that you both have a bypass connection and an input or output connection for a channel.**
- **Clicking Reset gets you back to the original standard connection.**

13 Automation

13.1 Background

Cubase SX/SL has very comprehensive automation features. Virtually every Mixer and effect parameter can be automated.

There are two main methods you can use to automate parameter settings:

- **By manually drawing curves on automation subtracks in the Project window.**

  See page 303.

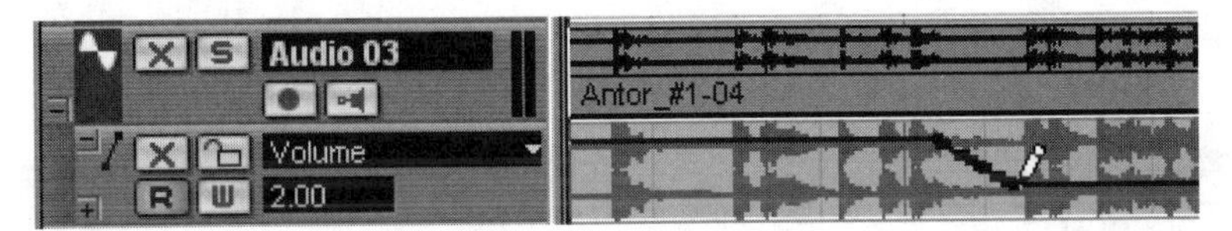

- **By using the Write/Read function and adjusting parameters in the Mixer.**

  See page 299.

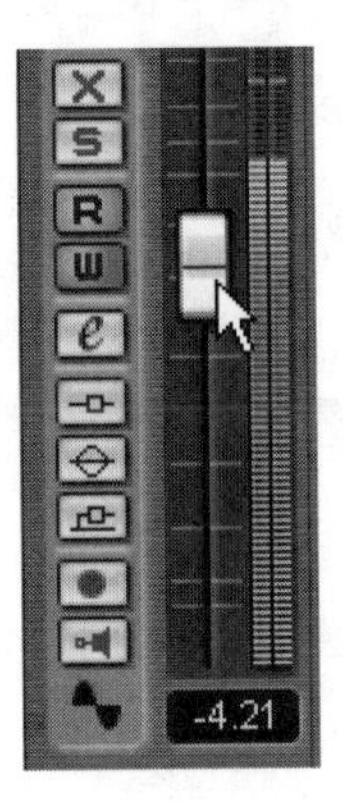

The methods are not different in terms of how the automation data is applied—they only differ in the way the automation events are created, either by manually drawing them or recording them. Any applied automation data will be reflected in both the Mixer (a fader will move for example) and in a corresponding automation track curve (although this may be hidden).

13.1.1 What Can Be Automated?

Mixing in Cubase SX/SL can be completely automated. The following parameter settings can be recorded automatically—or manually drawn in—on automation subtracks:

For Each Audio and Group Track

- Volume
- Pan Left—Right
- Pan Front—Rear
- Mute
- EQ Master Bypass
- FX Send Bypass
- Settings for 4 EQ modules (Enable/Freq/Quality/Gain)
- 8× effect Send on/off switches
- 8× effect Send levels
- 8× effect Send pre/post switches
- SurroundPan parameters (if used—Cubase SX only)
- 8× (5× in Cubase SL) Insert effect program selection and effect parameters (if insert effects are used)

Global for All Audio and Group Tracks

From the Master automation track:

- Master Gain
- L and R levels for all output buses
- Send effects "master" input levels

For Each Plug-in Automation Track (if Audio Effects Are Used):

- Send effect program selection and effect parameters
- Master effect program selection and effect parameters
- VST Instrument program selection and parameters

- There is one Plug-in automation track for each automated Send effect, Master effect and VST Instrument.

For Each MIDI Track

- Volume
- Pan
- Mute

- Track Parameters on/off switch
- Transpose
- Vel. shift
- Random 1—2 Min/Max/Target
- Range 1—2 Min/Max/Target
- 4x Insert effect on/off switches
- 4x Send effect on/off switches
- 4x MIDI Insert effect parameters (if used)
- 4x MIDI Send effect parameters (if used)

13.1.2 About Automation Tracks

There are three types of automation tracks available:

- **Channel automation tracks**

  There is one automation track for every audio, group, and MIDI track, and also for each activated ReWire and VST Instrument channel. This automation track has a number of automation subtracks, one for each channel setting available. Each channel's insert effect program selection and effect parameter settings are handled by the Channel automation track. For MIDI tracks, all Track parameters, MIDI send and insert effect parameter settings (if used) are also handled by the Channel automation track.

- **Plug-in automation tracks**

  There is one Plug-in automation track for each automated Send and Master effect, and for each automated VST Instrument. These tracks have a number of automation subtracks, one for every parameter of each automated effect and VST Instrument.

- **Master automation track**

  There is only one Master automation track for a project. This track can, just like for a single audio track, have any number of automation subtracks, for the Master Gain parameter, all the bus output levels and the send effects "master" input levels.

● Automation subtracks are not separate tracks, but rather separate "views" of the same automation track, showing one automation parameter at a time.

13.2 Automation Subtrack Operations

13.2.1 Opening Automation Subtracks

Opening a Channel Automation Subtrack

Every track/channel has its own automation track, and each automation subtrack shows one automation parameter. There are two ways you can open a Channel automation subtrack:

- **By right-clicking the track in the Track list and selecting "Show Automation" from the pop-up that appears.**
- **By clicking on the "Show/Hide Automation" button (the plus sign) in the Track list for the channel.**

  An automation subtrack opens in the Track list, and a straight black horizontal line is shown as well as a greyed out mirror image of the audio events' waveform (or MIDI events for MIDI tracks) in the event display. By default, the first subtrack is assigned the Volume parameter.

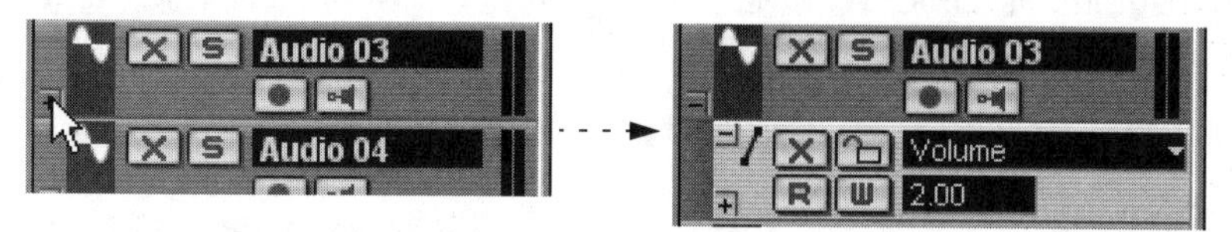

Click the plus button to open an automation subtrack.

- **If you click on the "Show/Hide Automation" button (the plus sign) for an automation subtrack, the next parameter in the Add Parameter list (see page 295) is shown in a separate subtrack.**

Opening a Plug-in Automation Subtrack

- **Plug-in automation tracks are automatically created when the Write button is activated on an effect (Send/Master) or VST instrument control panel.**

  There is one Plug-in automation track for each automated effect or VST Instrument, containing subtracks for all parameters for the effect or VST Instrument.

Opening a Master Automation Subtrack

- **Select "Add Track" from the Project menu, and select "Master Automation" from the submenu.**

  A Master automation subtrack is added to the Track list. By default, the Master Gain parameter is assigned.

13.2.2 Assigning a Parameter to an Automation Subtrack

All parameters are actually already "assigned" to the automation track. To select what parameter an open subtrack should display, proceed as follows:

1. **If none exists, open a Channel automation subtrack using one of the methods described previously.**
2. **Click in the parameter display for the automation subtrack.**

   A pop-up list is shown containing some of the automation parameters plus the item "More..." at the bottom of the list.

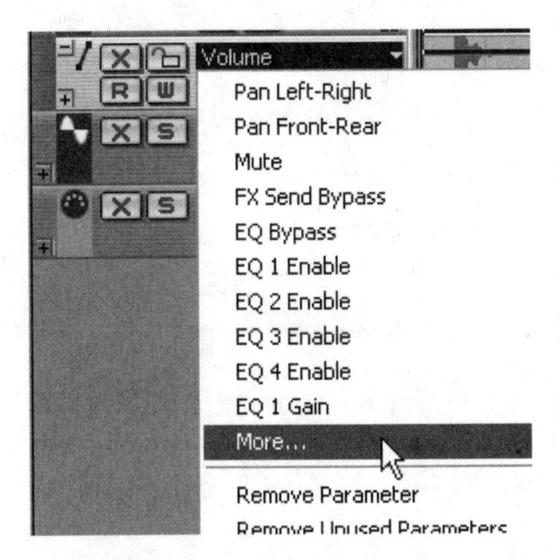

- **If the parameter you wish to automate is on the pop-up you can select it directly.**

  The parameter will then replace the current parameter in the automation subtrack.

If you wish to add several items or to view all parameters that can be automated, go on to the next step.

3. Select "More...".

The Add Parameter dialog appears. This list contains all parameters that can be automated for the selected channel, including the parameters for any assigned insert effects. The available parameters are identical for all audio related channel types. MIDI tracks have different parameters.

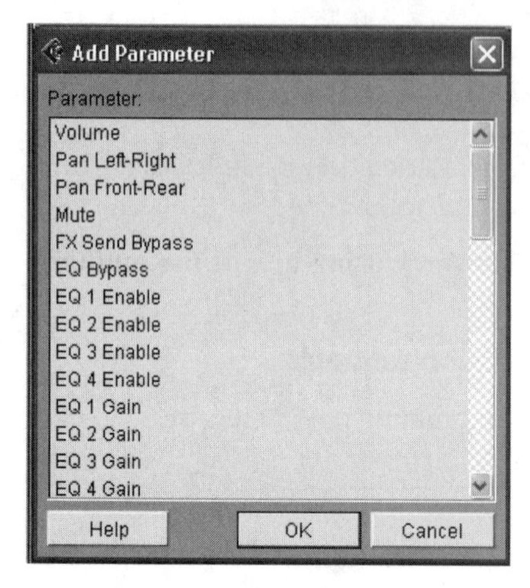

The Add Parameter dialog for an audio track.

4. Select a parameter from the list, and click OK.

The parameter will then replace the current parameter in the automation subtrack.

- Note that the "replacing" of the parameter displayed in the subtrack is completely non-destructive.
  For example, if the replaced subtrack had contained any automation data, this data would still be there, although it would not be visible in the current subtrack. If you click in the parameter display you can switch back to the replaced parameter. All automated parameters are indicated with an asterisk (*) after the parameter name on the pop-up menu.

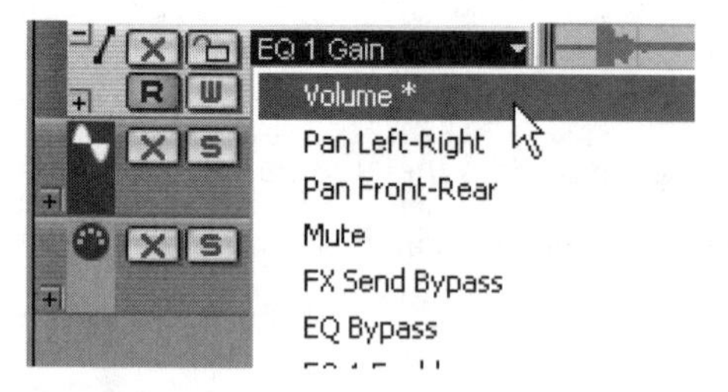

The Volume parameter is automated.

- **You can select any number of parameters at the same time from the Add Parameter dialog using standard selection methods.**

  The parameters selected in the dialog will then appear on the parameter display pop-up menu.

  Before selecting parameters in the dialog, the pop-up shows the first number of parameters, in the order they appear in the Add Parameter list. By selecting parameters you can temporarily "reorder" the list so that they become available on the pop-up.

- **If you click on the plus sign for the first subtrack (and then for each following subtrack), all the parameter subtrack(s) you added will appear, in the order that they originally appeared in the Add Parameter list.**

- **Automation subtracks that contain automation events are indicated by an asterisk after the name on the parameter display pop-up menu.**

13.2.3 Removing Automation Subtracks

To remove automation subtracks from the Track list, proceed as follows:

- **To remove a single parameter, click in the parameter display on a subtrack and select "Remove Parameter" from the pop-up menu.**

  Note that this will also delete any automation events on the subtrack, and the subtrack will be closed.

- **To remove all currently unused subtracks from a track in the Track list, select "Remove Unused Parameters" from a subtrack.**

  All subtracks that do not contain automation events will be closed for the selected track.

13.2.4 Hiding Automation Subtracks

- **To hide a single automation subtrack, click the "Hide Automation" button (the minus sign) in the Track list.**

- **To hide all automation subtracks for a track, right-click the track for which you wish to hide the automation subtracks, and select "Hide Automation" from the pop-up menu that appears.**

- **To hide all automation subtracks for all tracks in the Track list, right-click any track and select "Hide All Automation" from the pop-up menu that appears.**

  This option is also available on the Project menu.

13.2.5 Showing Only Used Automation Subtracks

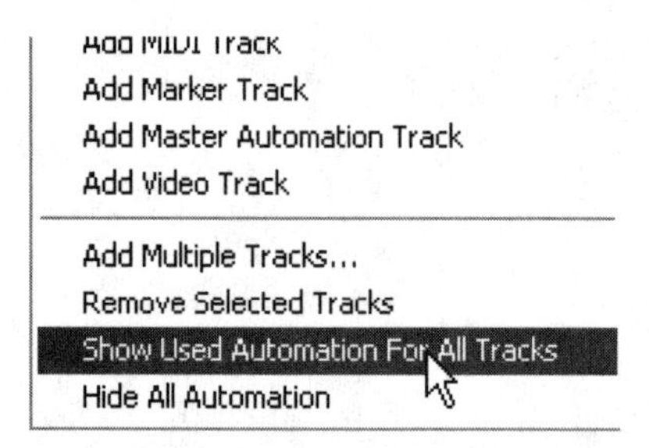

If a lot of automation subtracks are used, it may be impractical to have them all open in the Track list. If you want to bring back all hidden automation tracks that are currently used (e.g. there are automation events on the subtrack), this can be done using the following methods:

- **Right-clicking any audio or MIDI track in the Track list allows you to select the option "Show Used Automation for All Tracks" from the pop-up menu.**

  This will open all automation subtracks that contain automation events for all tracks. This option is also available on the Project menu.

- **Right-clicking a specific track allows you to select the option "Show Used Automation" from the pop-up menu.**

  This will open all automation subtracks that contain automation events for the selected track.

13.2.6 Muting Automation Subtracks

You can Mute individual automation subtracks by clicking their Mute buttons in the Track list. While clicking the Read (R) button (see page 299) for an automation subtrack will activate or deactivate Read mode for *all* automated parameters of the track, using the Mute button allows you to turn off automation for a single parameter.

13.3 Using Write/Read Automation

Write (W) and Read (R) buttons can be found for each channel in the Mixer, for each MIDI, audio and group track (including subtracks) in the Track list, on the control panels for all plug-in effects and VST Instruments and for the Master fader.

The Write and Read buttons for a channel in the Mixer, and for an automation subtrack in the Track list.

- If you activate Write for a channel, all mixer parameters you adjust during playback for that specific channel will be recorded as automation events.
- If you activate Read for a channel, all your recorded mixer actions for that channel will be performed during playback, just like you performed them in Write mode.
- The W and R buttons for a track in the Track list are mirrors of the W and R buttons in the corresponding channel strip in the Mixer.
- The first time you activate the Write button on the control panel for a send effect or master effect, a plug-in automation track is created for the effect plug-in.
  You can then proceed with automating the parameters of the plug-in (by editing the automation subtracks or by writing, as described below). To play back the plug-in automation, make sure the Read button for the plug-in is activated.

There are also global Read All and Write All buttons in the Mixer's Common panel:

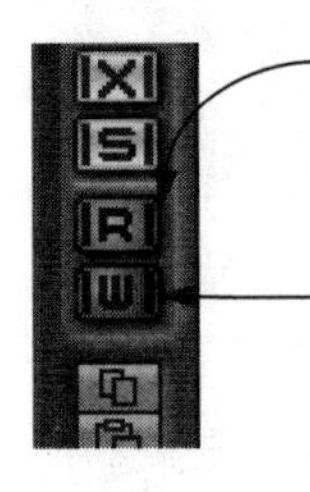

13.3.1 About the Three Automation Modes (Cubase SX only)

- In Cubase SL the automation mode is always "Touch Fader".

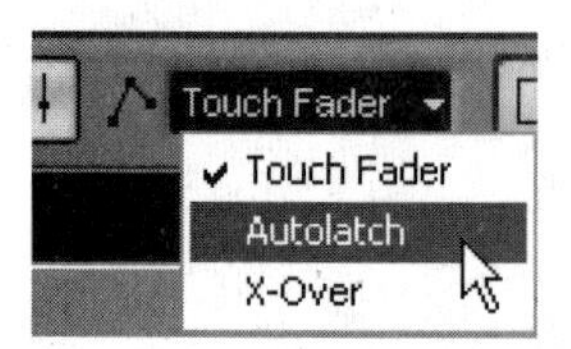

When recording automation, you can choose one of three automation modes (available on the Project window toolbar):

- When Touch Fader mode is selected, the program starts writing the automation as soon as you click the control and stops writing when you release the mouse button.
- When Autolatch mode is selected, the program starts writing the automation as soon as you click the control and stops writing when you turn off the Write function.
  This means that the last automation value will be continuously written until you turn off Write.

The Autolatch mode is useful if you want to overwrite a long section of previous automation, and also when you are recording automation from a remote device (because then there is no way for the program to know when you "release" the control). However, make sure you only touch the desired control(s) when recording automation in Autolatch mode—and remember to stop playback when you're done!

- X-Over mode works like Autolatch mode, but with one difference: As soon as you "cross" any existing (previous) automation curve, the writing is automatically turned off.

13.3.2 Recording Your Actions—an Example

If the settings in your current project are crucial, you may not want to "experiment" with automation until you know more about how it all fits together. If so, you can open up a new project for the following example. It doesn't even have to contain any audio events, just a few audio tracks. Proceed as follows:

1. **Open the Mixer.**
2. **Click the "Write All" button in the Mixer Common Panel.**

   Cubase SX/SL is now in Global Write mode.

3. **Start playback, and adjust some volume faders and/or other parameter settings in the Mixer or perhaps in a Channel Settings window.**

   Stop playback when you are done, and return to the position where playback was activated.

4. **Deactivate Write mode, and click the "Read All" button in the Mixer Common panel.**

   Cubase SX/SL is now in Global Read mode.

5. **Start playback, and watch the Mixer window.**

   All your actions performed during the previous playback will be reproduced exactly.

6. **If you wish to redo anything that was recorded, activate Write mode again, and start playback from the same position.**

- **You may have Write and Read activated simultaneously, if you want to watch and listen to your recorded mixer actions while you're recording fader movements for another mixer channel, etc.**

13.3.3 Where Did the Automation Data I Recorded End Up?

When using "Write All" automation, you can write automation data on all channels' automation tracks. In the previous Write operation, you probably added automation events for many different channels and parameters.

- **To view all the automation events you recorded during the operation, select "Show Used Automation" from the Project menu.**

  Now the automation data for every channel parameter that you adjusted in the Mixer during Write mode is shown on corresponding subtracks in the Project window. The automation events recorded are shown as points in the automation curves.

13.4 Working with Automation Curves

13.4.1 About Automation Curves

There are two kinds of automation curves, "Ramp" and "Jump":

- **Jump curves are created for any parameter that only has on/off values, like a Mute button, for example.**
- **Ramp curves are created for any parameter that generates continuous multiple values, such as fader or dial movements etc.**

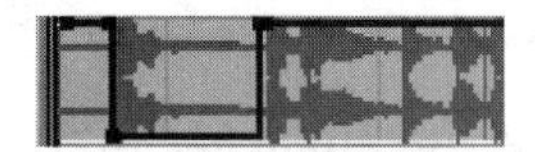

Examples of Jump (top subtrack) and Ramp automation curves shown in the event display.

13.4.2 About the Static Value Line

When you first open an automation subtrack for a parameter, it doesn't contain any automation events (unless you have previously adjusted that parameter with Write automation activated), and this is reflected in the event display as a straight horizontal black line, the "static value" line. This line represents the current parameter setting.

In the following description it is assumed that you have a Volume subtrack open showing a static value line with neither Read nor Write automation activated.

- **If you click and hold the static value line with the Arrow tool, you can drag it up or down.**

  The corresponding fader in the mixer moves with the static value line and vice versa.

- **If you have manually added any automation events or used Write automation for the corresponding parameter, and then deactivate Read mode, the automation curve will be greyed-out in the automation subtrack event display and the static value will be used instead.**

  As soon as Read mode is activated the greyed-out automation curve will become active.

13.4.3 Editing Automation Events

Drawing Automation Events

By using Write automation in the Mixer, you generate automation events by moving parameter dials and fader settings in the Mixer. You can also add them manually, by drawing automation curves on an automation subtrack. Proceed as follows:

1. **Open a Channel Volume automation subtrack for an audio track by clicking the plus sign.**

   The static value line is shown in the event display.

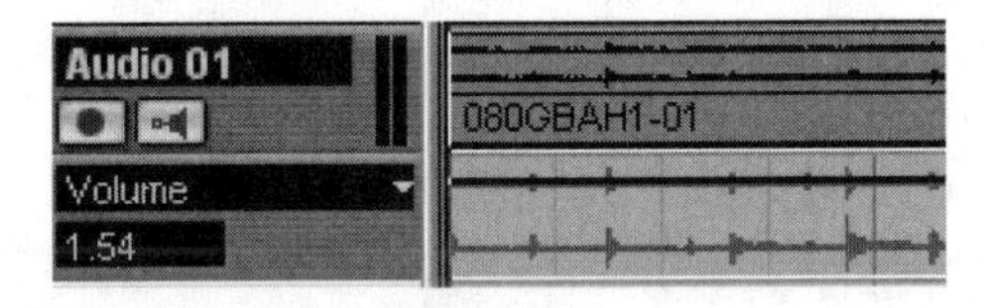

2. **Select the Pencil tool.**

   You could also use the Pencil tool in other modes for drawing curves, see below.

3. **If you click on the static value Line, an automation event is added, Read automation mode is automatically activated, and the static value line changes to a blue automation curve.**

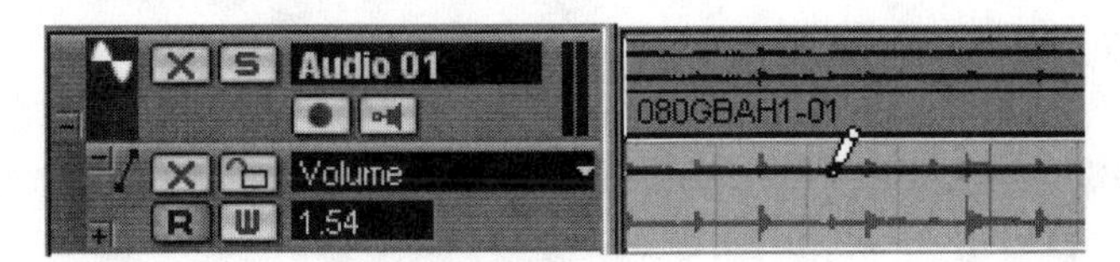

4. **If you click and hold, you can draw a curve, by adding a multitude of single automation events.**

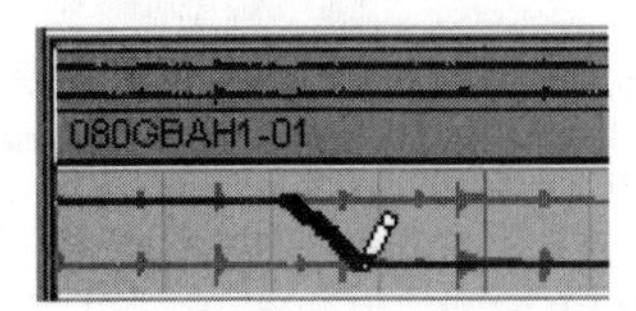

5. **When you release the mouse button, the number of automation events are reduced to a few events, but the basic shape of the curve still remains.**

   This "thinning" of events is governed by the Reduction setting in the Preferences, see page 309.

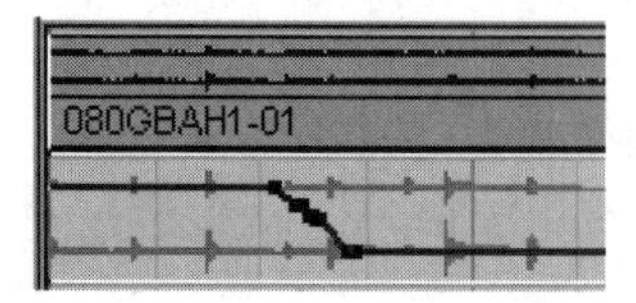

6. **If you now activate playback, the Volume will change with the automation curve.**

   In the Mixer the corresponding fader moves accordingly.

7. **Simply redo the operation if you are not happy with the result.**

   If you draw over existing events, a new curve is created.

- **If the automation subtrack is in Read mode already, you can also add automation events by clicking with the Arrow tool.**

  If you are trying to add a point between two existing points and the new point doesn't deviate from the existing curve, it will be removed by Reduction (see page 309) as soon as you release the mouse button.

Using the Pencil Tool in Other Modes to Draw Automation Curves

Other Pencil tool modes can be very useful for drawing automation events. The various modes are accessed by clicking on the Pencil tool on the toolbar and selecting from the pop-up that appears.

- Clicking and dragging with the Pencil tool in Line mode shows a line in the automation subtrack, and creates automation events aligned with this line.
  This is a quick way to create linear fades, etc.

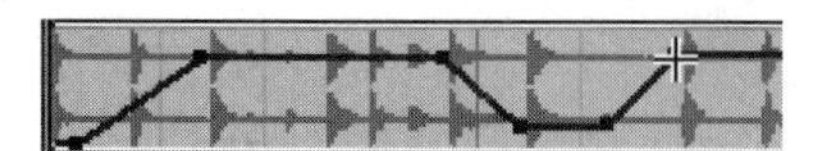

- The Parable mode works in the same way, but aligns the automation events with a parable curve instead, giving more "natural" curves and fades.
  Note that the result depends on from which direction you draw the parable.

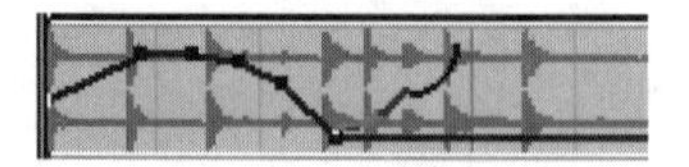

- The Sine, Triangle and Square modes create automation events aligned with continuous curves.
  If snap is activated and set to Grid, the period of the curve (the length of one curve "cycle") is determined by the grid setting. If you press [Shift] and drag, you can set the period length manually, in multiples of the grid value.

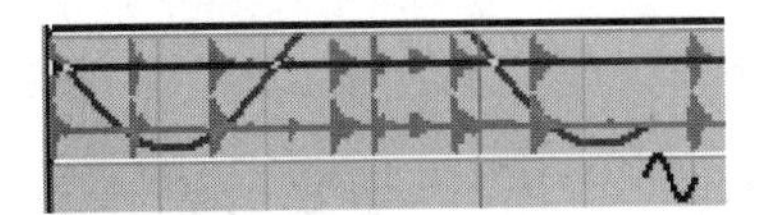

Selecting Automation Event Points

- **To select a single automation event point, click on it with the Arrow tool.**

  The point turns red, and you can drag it in any horizontal or vertical direction between two points.

- **To select multiple curve points, you can either [Shift]-click or drag a selection rectangle with the Arrow tool.**

  All events inside the selection rectangle will become selected.

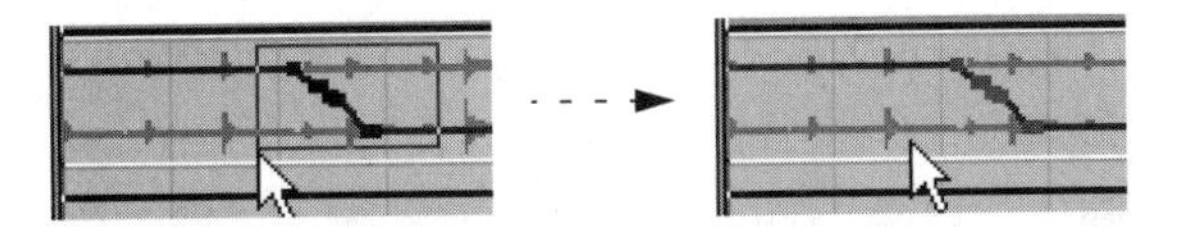

Draw a selection rectangle around some points to select them.

When selected, several points can be moved in all directions as "one", i.e. the curve shape formed by the selected event points remains intact.

- **To select all automation events on a subtrack, right-click the automation subtrack in the Track list and choose "Select All Events" from the context menu.**

Removing Automation Events

There are several ways to remove event points:

- **By selecting points and pressing [Backspace] or [Delete].**
- **By clicking on a point with the Eraser tool.**

- **By clicking in the parameter display on a subtrack and selecting "Remove Parameter" from the pop-up.**

  This will remove all automation events from the subtrack, and the subtrack will be closed.

Editing Automation Events

You can cut/copy automation events and paste them in at the current project cursor position. However, most items on the Edit menu are not applicable to automation events.

13.4.4 Using Plug-in Automation

Each parameter for every assigned effect or VST Instrument can be automated. Proceed as follows:

- Channel Insert Effects are automated using the respective Channel automation track.

Using Write/Read Automation

All effects have Write/Read buttons on their control panels. These work exactly like the corresponding buttons in the Mixer or in the Inspector, but the recorded data ends up on separate Plug-in automation tracks, one for each automated effect.

Opening Plug-in Automation Subtracks

Plug-in automation tracks are created automatically when a Write button is activated for a Send or Master effect or an VST Instrument. Each automated effect or VST Instrument will have its own Plug-in automation track, containing subtracks for all parameters for that effect or VST Instrument. The track will get the same name as the effect or VST Instrument.

Assigning a Parameter to a Plug-in Automation Subtrack

To select which parameter is currently shown in the Plug-in automation track, proceed as follows:

1. **Click in the parameter display for a Plug-in automation subtrack.**

   The parameter display pop-up list is shown containing the automation parameters for the plug-in. The automated parameter(s) are indicated by an asterisk after the parameter name in the list. If there are more parameters than can fit on the pop-up menu, the item "More..." is shown at the bottom of the list. Selecting "More" opens the Add Parameter dialog window for the Plug-in automation track, showing all the parameters for the selected effect or VST Instrument.

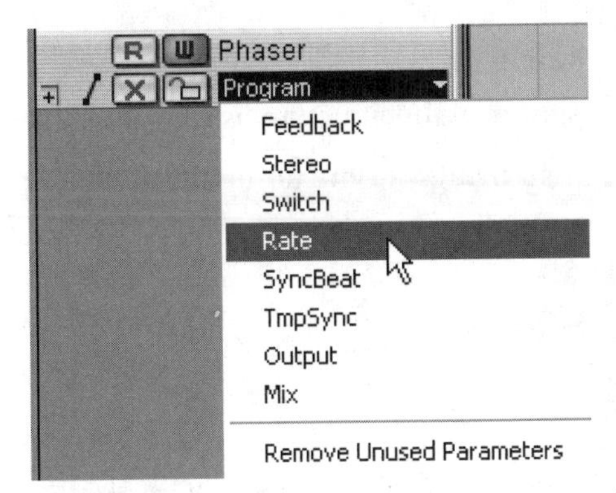

The Phaser parameters.

2. **Select the parameter you wish to view directly from the parameter display pop-up or from the Add Parameter dialog.**

- All procedures for editing Plug-In automation events is identical to Channel automation tracks.

13.4.5 Using Master Automation

The procedure for using Master automation is as follows:

- **To open a subtrack for the Master automation track, select "Master Automation" from the Project menu's "Add Track" submenu.**

  A subtrack named "Mixer" is added to the Track list, with the first parameter by default being the Master Gain Parameter.

13.4.6 Editing Automation Events in the Project Browser

You can also edit automation events in the Project Browser. Proceed as follows:

1. **Open the Project Browser by selecting it from the Project menu.**

   The Browser window opens. The window is divided into two sections, the Structure list to the left, and the event display to the right.

2. **Click on the plus sign for a track in the Structure list.**

   Tracks have two subitems: Track data and automation. The automation item corresponds to the automation subtrack in the Project window, and contains the track's automation events.

3. **Click on the plus sign for the Automation item.**

   All automated parameters for the track are shown in the Structure list.

4. **Clicking on a parameter in the Structure list, brings up the automation events in the event display.**

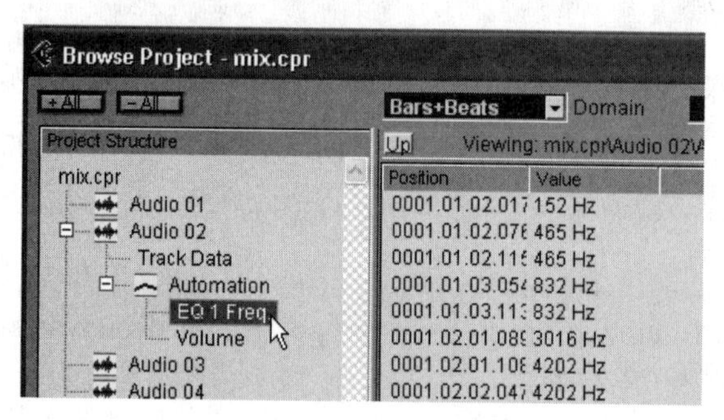

The following parameters are available for all automation tracks and subtracks, including the group channel tracks:

Parameter	Description
Position	The position of the automation event.
Value	The value (0.000—1.000) of the automation event.

13.5 Tips and Common Methods

There are no hard and fast rules when it comes to describing which automation method you should use. You could for example never even open an automation subtrack, and stick with Write automation throughout a project. On the other hand, you could stick to drawing automation curves to automate settings in a project. Both methods have their advantages, but it is of course up to you to decide what to use and when.

- **Editing curves on automation subtracks offers a graphical overview in relation to the track contents and the time position.**

  This makes it easy to quickly change parameter values at specific points, without having to activate playback. For example, this method gives you a good overview if you have a voice-over or a dialog on one track and a music bed on another track, the level of which needs to be lowered with a specific amount every time the dialog occurs.

- **By using Write automation in the Mixer you don't have to manually select parameter subtracks from the Add Parameter list.**

  You can work much like you would using a "real" physical mixer. Every action you perform is automatically recorded on subtracks for the parameters you change which you can later open for viewing and editing.

These are just two examples of advantages for each method. Generally, editing curves and using Write automation are two methods that complement each other, and depending on the nature of your projects you will probably work out what method works best for a given situation.

13.6 Options and Settings

13.6.1 About the "Reduction" Preference

This item can be found on the Editing page in the Preferences dialog. Reduction reduces the number of automation events *after* you have used Write automation or added automation events manually. When you Write (or draw with the Pencil tool) automation events, these are added as a continuous stream of densely packed events. This is necessary because the program cannot "guess" what you will be doing next! However, when you are done, the Reduction function will remove all superfluous event points and the automation curve now contains only the event points necessary to reproduce your actions.

For example, all event points that might exist between two other points, but do not deviate from the curve, will be automatically removed by reduction.

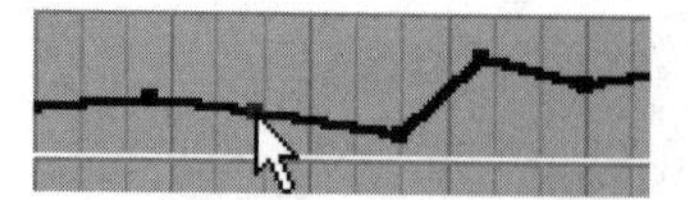

If you try to add an event that doesn't deviate from the existing curve between two existing points...

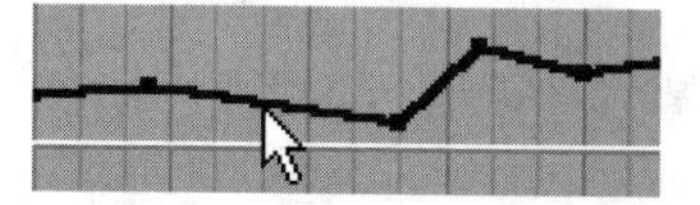

...it will be removed when the mouse is released. If you had moved the selected event by any amount so that the resulting curve wouldn't be a straight line, the event would of course be added.

- **If you feel you need a lower (or higher) reduction level of events than the default setting of roughly 75% reduction, you can change it, but normally the default setting works well.**
- **A minimum reduction level setting is not recommended as this will simply retain a lot of unnecessary events.**

14 Remote Controlling the Mixer

14.1 Background

It is possible to control the Cubase SX/SL Mixer via MIDI. Currently, the following MIDI control devices are supported:

- Steinberg Houston
- CM Automation Motor Mix
- JL Cooper CS-10
- JL Cooper MCS-3000
- Radikal SAC-2k
- Roland MCR8
- Tascam US-428
- Yamaha 01V

There is also a Generic Remote Device, allowing you to use any MIDI controller to remote control Cubase SX/SL.

14.2 Operations

14.2.1 Selecting a Remote Device

1. **Make sure the MIDI control device is connected to your MIDI interface.**

   You need to connect the MIDI Out on the remote unit to a MIDI In on your MIDI interface. Depending on the remote unit model, you may also need to connect a MIDI Out on the interface to a MIDI In on the remote unit (this is necessary if the remote unit features "feedback devices" such as indicators, motorized faders, etc). See the MIDI control device specifications on the following pages for details.

2. **Pull down the Devices menu and select Device Setup.**

   A dialog window opens with a list of devices shown in the left part of the window.

3. **If you can't find the remote device you are looking for, click on the Add/ Remove tab and select it from the Device Classes menu.**

   Click "Add" to add it to the Devices list.

- **Note that it is possible to select more than one remote device of the same type.**

  If you have more than one remote device of the same type, these will be numbered in the Device list.

4. **Now click the Setup tab and select your MIDI control device model from the Devices list.**

   Depending on the selected device, either a list of programmable function commands or a blank panel is shown in the right half of the dialog window.

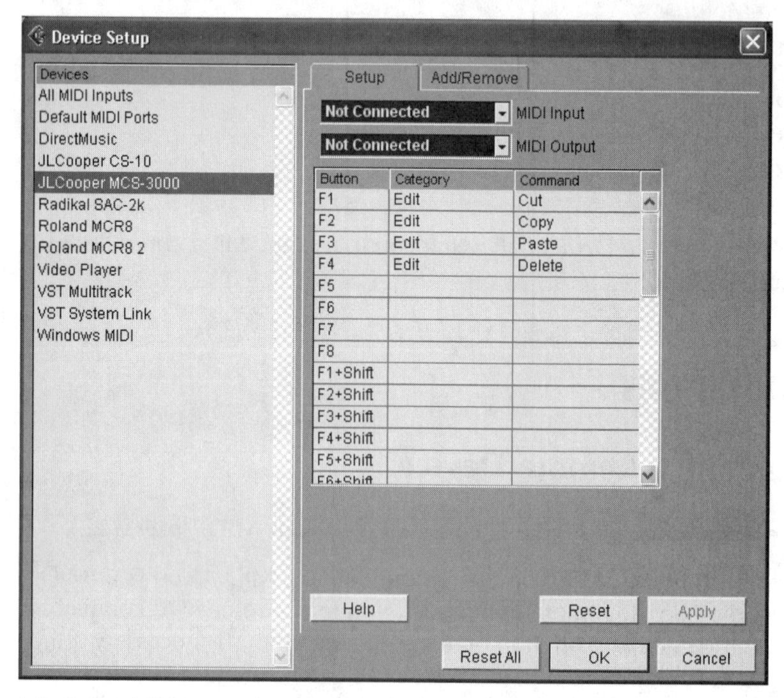

A JL Cooper MCS-3000 selected as remote control device.

5. **Select the correct MIDI input from the pop-up menu.**
6. **If necessary, select the correct MIDI output from the pop-up menu.**
7. **Click OK to close the dialog.**

   You can now use the MIDI control device to move faders and knobs, activate mute and solo, etc. The exact parameter configuration depends on which external MIDI control device you are using.

14.2.2 Writing Automation Using Remote Controls

Automating the Mixer using a remote control device is basically done in the same way as when you operate on-screen controls in Write mode. However, when it comes to *replacing* existing automation data, there is one important difference:

- **If you activate Write mode and move a control on the remote control device, all data for the corresponding parameter is replaced from the position where you moved the control, up until the position where playback is stopped!**

  In other words, as soon as you have moved a control in Write mode, it remains "active" until you stop playback. The reason for this is explained below.

As a consequence, an additional precaution must be taken:

- **Make sure you move only the controller you want to replace!**

In order to replace existing automation data for a control, the computer needs to know how long the user actually "grabbed" or used the control. When doing this "on screen", the program simply detects when the mouse button is pressed and released. When you are using an external remote control device, however, there is no mouse button involved, and Cubase SX/SL cannot tell whether you "grab and hold" a fader, or simply move it and release it. Instead, you have to indicate that you have "released" the control by stopping playback.

● The above does not apply to the MCS 3000. This device has touch sensitive faders, which means that it stops writing as soon as you release the fader.

● This is only relevant when you are using a remote control device and Write mode is activated in the Mixer.

14.2.3 Assigning Remote Key Commands

For some of the supported remote devices, you can assign any Cubase SX/SL function (that can be assigned a key command) to generic buttons, wheels or other controls. As of this writing, these devices are:

- JL Cooper MCS 3000
- JL Cooper CS-10
- CM Automation Motor Mix

Proceed as follows:

1. **Open the Device Setup and select one of the remote devices that support this feature.**

   On the right side of the window there are three columns. This is where you assign commands.

2. **Use the "Button" column to locate a Remote device control or button to which you wish to assign a Cubase SX/SL function.**
3. **Click in the "Category" column for the control, and select one of the Cubase SX/SL function categories from the pop-up menu that appears.**
4. **Click in the "Command" column, and select the desired Cubase SX/SL function from the pop-up menu that appears.**

   The available items on the pop-up menu depend on the selected category.

5. **Click "Apply" when you are done.**

The selected function is now assigned to the button or control on the remote device.

14.2.4 Remote Controlling MIDI Tracks

While most remote control devices will be able to control both MIDI and audio track channels in Cubase SX/SL, the parameter setup may be different. For example, audio-specific controls (such as EQ) will be disregarded when controlling MIDI channels.

14.3 Remote Control Device Specifics

14.3.1 Steinberg Houston

Houston is a MIDI/USB remote control device designed especially for use with VST audio applications such as Cubase SX/SL. With clearly laid out controls (including touch sensitive motorized faders, rotary knobs, transport controls and a jog/shuttle wheel) Houston allows you to control virtually every Mixer parameter in Cubase SX/SL, without having to use the computer keyboard or mouse.

- **For details about parameters and hands-on mixing techniques, please see the Houston documentation.**

14.3.2 CM Automation Motor Mix

The CM Motor Mix can control any number of channels in groups of 8.

- **Fader level, mute, solo control the equivalent Cubase SX/SL functions.**
- **Left and right View buttons: select channels 1—8, 9—16 etc.**
- **Top button row (above the rotary knobs) selects channel.**
- **The two rows of buttons on each side of the faders can be assigned functions in the Device Setup dialog.**

  All except the Shift button, which acts like [Shift] on your computer keyboard.
- **The rotary knobs are multi-functional, depending on the selected Rotary setting.**

The following parameters can be remote controlled with the 8 rotary knobs:

- Pan
- Effect sends 1—8
- EQ Enable
- EQ Freq
- EQ Gain
- EQ Q

- **The first two rows of buttons below the rotary knobs are also multi-functional, depending on the status of the buttons to the left and right of these two rows.**

  Note that the "Group" button is not assigned any parameter.

The following parameters can be remote controlled with the 8 buttons on the first row below the rotary knobs:

- EQ Master Bypass
- Insert On

The following parameters can be remote controlled with the 8 buttons on the second row below the rotary knobs:

- Record Enable
- Monitor
- Write Automation
- Read Automation

14.3.3 JL Cooper CS-10

The CS-10 can remote control 32 channels (in groups of 8). The following CS-10 controls will remote control the following parameter for each channel strip:

- Fader: volume
- Solo and Mute: solo and mute
- Sel: select channel for editing

The following parameters can be remote controlled for each *selected* channel using the six rotary knobs on the CS-10:

Dial	Parameter
Send 1	Effect send 1
Send 2	Effect send 2
Pan	Pan
Boost/cut	EQ 1 Gain
Frequency	EQ 1 Frequency
Bandwidth	EQ 1 Q Factor

- **The CS-10 function keys 1—4 are used to select channels 1—32 in groups of 8.**

  Function key 1 selects channels 1—8, function key 2 selects channels 9—16, and so on.

- **If you hold down the function key "Shift" and then move a fader, the two indicators beside the fader will indicate whether the fader position is below or above the current fader level in Cubase SX/SL.**

  If the upper indicator is lit, the fader position on the panel is above the fader level in Cubase SX/SL and vice versa. When both indicators are dark, the fader positions are matched for that channel.

- **The CS-10 Play, Stop, Record, Rewind and Fast Forward transport controls will have the equivalent functionality in Cubase SX/SL.**

● The CS-10 supports "MIDI Feedback", allowing the mute, solo and selection status of the channels in Cubase SX/SL to be indicated on the panel. For this (and the fader position indication described above) to work, you need a two-way MIDI connection between the CS-10 and Cubase SX/SL.

14.3.4 JL Cooper MCS-3000

The MCS-3000 can control 32 Mixer channels remotely (in groups of 8). The following MCS-3000 controls will remote control the following Mixer parameter for each channel strip:

- **Fader: volume**
- **Solo and Mute: solo and mute**
- **Sel: Select channel for editing**

  These parameters can be remote controlled for each *selected* channel using the dials on the MCS-3000 and switching between Pages 1—4:

Page 1		**Page 2**	
Dial	**Parameter**	**Dial**	**Parameter**
1	Pan	1	EQ 1 Gain
2	Effect send 1	2	EQ 1 Freq
3	Effect send 2	3	EQ 1 "Q"
4	Effect send 3	4	EQ 1 Low Limit
5	Effect send 4	5	EQ 1 High Limit

Page 3		**Page 4**	
Dial	**Parameter**	**Dial**	**Parameter**
1	EQ 2 Gain	1	EQ 3 Gain
2	EQ 2 Freq	2	EQ 3 Freq
3	EQ 2 "Q"	3	EQ 3 "Q"
4	EQ 2 Low Limit	4	EQ 3 Low Limit
5	EQ 2 High Limit	5	EQ 3 High Limit

- **The MCS-3000 bank keys 1—4 are used to select channels 1—32 in groups of 8.**

  Bank key 1 selects channels 1—8, bank key 2 selects channels 9—16 and so on.

- **You can create markers by pressing the "Set Locate" key on the MCS-3000, typing in a marker ID and pressing [Return].**
- **To locate to a marker, press "Locate", type in a marker ID and press [Return].**
- **The MCS-3000 Play, Stop, Record, Rewind and Fast Forward transport controls will have the equivalent functionality in Cubase SX/SL.**

● The MCS-3000 supports "MIDI Feedback", allowing fader settings and channel mute, solo and selection status to be indicated on the panel. For this to work, you need a two-way MIDI connection between the MCS-3000 and Cubase SX/SL.

14.3.5 Roland MCR-8

● Before you can initiate remote control operation, the MCR-8 "Mode" switch must be set to "4".

The Roland MCR-8 can control 16 Mixer channels, plus transport control. The "A/B switch" is used to switch between controlling channels 1—8 and 9—16. The following MCR-8 parameters control the equivalent parameters for each channel strip:

- **Fader level, mute, solo and pan.**

The following MCR-8 transport controls control the equivalent Cubase SX/SL functions:

- **Play, Stop, Record, Rewind, Fast Forward.**

● The MCR-8 does not support "MIDI feedback", that is, the current status of parameters in Cubase SX/SL is not indicated on the MCR-8. Therefore, you only need a one-way MIDI connection between the MCR-8 and Cubase SX/SL.

14.3.6 Radikal Technologies SAC-2K

The SAC-2K can control 32 channels (in groups of 8). The following SAC-2K parameters control the equivalent parameters for each channel strip:

- **Fader: volume**
- **Solo and Mute: solo and mute (depending on the solo/mute state switch)**
- **Select: select channel for editing in Channel Strip mode**

Encoder Operation Modes and Display Layout

The SAC-2K supports two operation modes for the encoder dials and the display. Mixer Mode will assign the same parameter for each channel strip to the encoder dials, e.g. EQ1-Gain for each channel. Channel Strip mode will assign a parameter set for one selected channel to the encoder dials, e.g. all 8 send levels for the selected channel.

The first row of the displays above the channel strips will display the name of the channels. The second row will display the value of the parameter assigned to the encoder dials. The first row of the rightmost display will show the name of the selected channel, the assignment for the encoder dials and the channel range. The second row will display any value of the parameter assigned to the encoder dials in Channel Strip mode:

- **Display for encoder operation in Mixer mode "Pan":**

Chn1	Chn2	Chn3	Chn4	Chn5	Chn6	Chn7	Chn8	Chn1	Pan	VST 1—8	
Pan	Pan	Pan	Pan	Pan	Pan	Pan	Pan				

- **Display for encoder operation in Channel Strip mode "EQs":**

Chn1	Chn2	Chn3	Chn4	Chn5	Chn6	Chn7	Chn8	Chn1	EQ	VST 1—8	
Freq1	Freq2	Freq3	Freq4	Freq5	Freq6	Freq7	Freq8	Q1	Q2	Q3	Q4

In order to access all parameters of a parameter set with the encoder dials, the parameter set buttons need to be pressed repeatedly to cycle through the parameter assignments.

When pressing an encoder dial the currently selected band of EQ or FX-Send will be activated or deactivated.

Assignment mapping for the Mixer mode buttons:

Mode	Assignment
Pan	Pan
High	EQ4 Gain, EQ4 Freq, EQ4 On, EQ4 Q
HiMid	EQ3 Gain, EQ3 Freq, EQ3 On, EQ3 Q
LowMid	EQ2 Gain, EQ2 Freq, EQ2 On, EQ2 Q
Low	EQ1 Gain, EQ1 Freq, EQ1 On, EQ1 Q
Snd/Ins1	Send1 Level, Send1 On, Send1 Pre, Send1 Bus
Snd/Ins2	Send2 Level, Send2 On, Send2 Pre, Send2 Bus

Mode	Assignment
Snd/Ins3	Send3 Level, Send3 On, Send3 Pre, Send3 Bus
Snd/Ins4	Send4 Level, Send4 On, Send4 Pre, Send4 Bus

Assignment mapping for the Channel Strip buttons:

Mode	Assignment
EQs	EQs
Inserts/Sends	Send Level, Send On, Send Pre, Send Bus

- **The buttons "1-8", "9-16", "17-24" and "25-31" will switch to the according channels.**
- **You can create Markers by pressing the "Store Marker" key on the SAC-2K and pressing a number key between "1" and "9" or "To" and "From".**
- **To locate to a Marker, press "Recall Marker" and press a number key between "1" and "9" or "To" and "From".**
- **The SAC-2K Play, Stop, Record, Rewind and Fast Forward transport controls control the equivalent functions in Cubase SX/SL.**
- **The following buttons of the Mixer-Mode section have no assignment: "Snd/Ins", "MIDI", "Input", "Inst", "Group" and "Bus".**
- **The following buttons of the Channel Strip section have no assignment: "Dynamics", "MIDI" and "Instruments".**

● The SAC-2K supports "MIDI Feedback", allowing fader settings and channel mute, solo and selection status to be indicated on the panel. For this to work, you need a two-way MIDI connection between the SAC-2K and Cubase SX/SL.

14.3.7 Tascam US-428

The US-428 can remote control up to 64 Mixer channels and 1 or 2 DSP Factory cards (if installed).

- **When the Tascam US-428 device is added in the Device Setup dialog, you can open the Remote Status window by selecting "Tascam US-428" from the Devices menu.**

  This indicates which bank (group of eight channels in Cubase SX/SL) is currently being controlled by the remote device. To select another bank, use the pop-up menu in the window or use the Bank Left/Right buttons on the remote device.

The Remote Status window

- **The US-428 Transport keys will have the equivalent functionality in Cubase SX/SL.**
- **To set markers, hold down "Set" while pressing a locator key.**
- **If you hold down the function key [Null] and then move a fader, the Select and Rec indicators above the fader will indicate whether the fader position is below or above the current fader level in Cubase SX/SL.**

  If the upper indicator is lit, the fader position on the panel is above the fader level in Cubase SX/SL and vice versa. When both indicators are dark, fader positions are matched for that channel.

- **The US-428 supports "MIDI Feedback", allowing for mute/solo, channel selection, EQ band, Aux 1 to 4 and Transport status to be indicated on the panel. For this (and the fader position indication described above) to work, you need to select the "US-428 Control" port as input and output.**

Cubase SX/SL Mixer

The following US-428 controls will remote control the following Mixer parameter for each channel strip:

- Fader: volume
- Mute/Solo: mute and solo (selected via the Solo switch)
- Select: selects channel for editing
- Pan-Dial: pan

- EQ-Gain
  Controls the EQ gain for each band selected with the Low, LoMid, HiMid and High buttons. These correspond to the four EQ bands in Cubase SX/SL, starting from the leftmost band.
- EQ-Freq
  Controls the EQ frequency for each band selected with the Low, LoMid, HiMid and High buttons. These correspond to the four EQ bands in Cubase SX/SL, starting from the leftmost band.
- EQ-"Q"
  Controls the EQ "Q" for each band selected with the Low, LoMid, HiMid and High buttons. These correspond to the four EQ bands in Cubase SX/SL, starting from the leftmost band.
- Aux 1 to Aux 4 and shuttle wheel:
  The effect send levels for sends 1 to 4.
- The shuttle wheel will act as position shuttle if no Aux send button is selected. Press the activated button to deselect it.
- Holding down the "Asgn" button and pressing the Low, LoMid, HiMid and High EQ buttons switches the corresponding EQ band "On" button status.
- Holding down the "Asgn" button and pressing the Aux1 to Aux4 buttons switches the corresponding Effect Send 1-4 "On" button status.

DSP Factory

The following US-428 controls will remote control the following DSP Factory parameter for each channel strip:

- **Fader: volume**
- **Mute/Solo: mute and solo (selected via the Solo switch)**
- **Select: selects channel for editing**
- **Pan-Dial: pan**
- **EQ-Gain**

  Controls the corresponding EQ gain for each band selected with the Low, LoMid, HiMid and High buttons.
- **EQ-Freq**

  Controls the corresponding EQ frequency for each band selected with the Low, LoMid, HiMid and High buttons.

- **EQ-"Q"**

  Controls the corresponding EQ "Q" for each band selected with the Low, LoMid, HiMid and High buttons.

- **Aux 1 to Aux 4 and shuttle wheel:**

  Control the effect send levels for sends 1/2 and 5/6.

- **Holding down the "Asgn" button and pressing the Low, LoMid, HiMid and High EQ buttons switches the corresponding EQ band "Bypass" button status.**

- **Holding down the "Asgn" button and pressing the Aux1 to Aux4 buttons switches the effect sends 1/2 and 5/6 "On" button status.**

14.3.8 Yamaha 01V

The Yamaha 01V can remote control either the Cubase SX/SL Mixer or the Yamaha DSP Factory if installed. Before you can initiate remote control operation, the 01V must be setup in the following way:

- **MIDI Parameter Change and Receive must be enabled.**
- **MIDI Control Change and Receive must be disabled.**
- **Device ID / MIDI Channel Receive must be set to "1".**
- **Local Control should be set to "Off".**

  As soon as Local Control is set to "Off", remote control of the Mixer is enabled.

The 01V remote operation of the Cubase SX/SL Mixer is very straightforward, with (almost) every parameter having the equivalent parameter controller in the 01V mixer. The current status of all controllable parameters is fed back to the 01V and indicated on the panel, using the motorized faders, indicators, etc. (for this to work, you need a two-way MIDI connection between the 01V and Cubase SX/SL).

To facilitate 32 channel remote control, two separate control "Layouts" are used, each controlling 16 Mixer channels. The "Memory" button on the 01V is used to switch between VST layout 1 and 2. Page 1 displays VST Layout 1, page 2 VST Layout 2, page 3 DSP Factory Layout 1 and page 4 DSP Factory Layout 2.

The following parameters are remote controllable for Channels 1—32 in the Mixer:

● The value ranges for the parameters in the 01V may not match the ranges for the corresponding parameters in all cases.

- **Fader level, mute and pan.**

  01V controls for these parameters control the equivalent Cubase SX/SL parameters.

- **Effect sends 1—6.**

  01V Aux 1—4 control effect send 1—4, 01V effect 1 and 2 control effect send 5 and 6.

- **EQ Frequency, Gain and Q (4 Bands).**

  01V controls for these parameters control the equivalent Cubase SX/SL parameters.

- **Stereo Master Volume.**

  The 01V control for this parameter controls the equivalent Cubase SX/SL parameter.

- **Send effects master volume 1—4 are controlled by 01V Aux Master 1—4. Send effects master 5 and 6 are controlled by 01V effect master 1 and 2.**

With Layout 1 the 01V controls the following channels:

- **Channel 1—12, 13/14 and 15/16 will control channels 1—14.**
- **01V Return 1 and 2 will control channels 15 and 16.**

With Layout 2 the 01V controls the following channels:

- **Channel 1—12, 13/14 and 15/16 will control channels 17—30.**
- **01V Return 1 and 2 will control channels 31 and 32.**

14.3.9 The Generic Remote Device

If you have a generic MIDI controller, you can use this for remote control of Cubase SX/SL by setting up the Generic Remote device:

1. **Open the Device Setup dialog on the Devices menu.**

   If the Generic Remote device isn't on the Devices list, you need to add it:

2. **Click the "Add/Remove" tab and select the "Generic Remote" device in the list to the right.**
3. **Click the Add button.**

- **When the Generic Remote device is added in the Device Setup dialog, you can open the Remote Status window by selecting "Generic Remote" from the Devices menu.**

The Remote Status window

4. Click the Setup tab and select the Generic Remote device in the Devices list to the left.

The settings for the Generic Remote are displayed, allowing you to specify which control on your device should control which parameter in Cubase SX/SL.

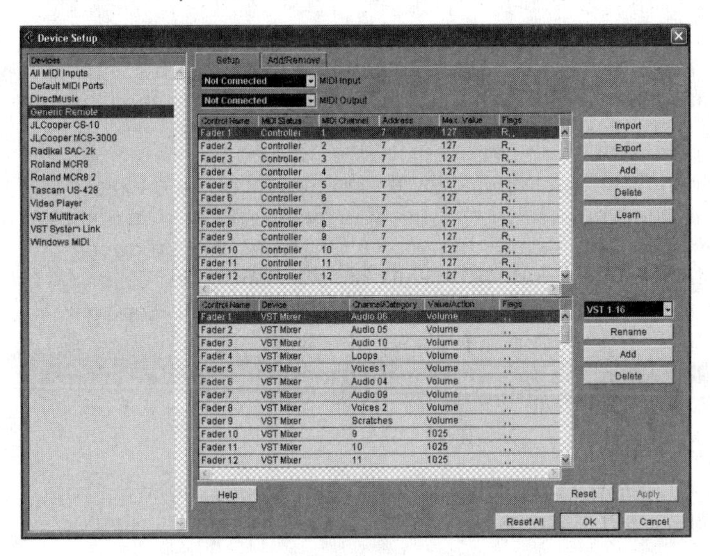

5. Use the MIDI Input and Output pop-up menu to select the MIDI Port(s) to which your remote device is connected.

6. Use the pop-up menu to the right to select a bank.

The concept of banks is based on the simple fact that most MIDI devices can control a limited number of channels at a time (often 8 or 16). For example, if your MIDI control device has 16 volume faders, and you are using 32 Mixer channels in Cubase SX/SL, you would need two banks of 16 channels each. When the first bank is selected you control channel 1 to 16; when the second Bank is selected you control channel 17 to 32. Since you can control Transport functions as well, you may need several banks.

7. **Set up the upper table according to the controls on your MIDI control device.**

The columns have the following functionality:

Column	Description
Control Name	Double clicking this field allows you to enter a descriptive name for the control (typically a name written on the console). This name is automatically reflected in the Control Name column in the lower table.
MIDI Status	Clicking in this column pulls down a pop-up menu, allowing you to specify the type of MIDI message sent by the control. The options are Controller, Program Change, Note On, Note Off, Aftertouch and Polyphonic Pressure. Also available are Continuous Control NRPN and RPN, a way to extend the available control messages. The "Ctrl JLCooper" option is a special version of a Continuous Controller where the 3rd byte of a MIDI message is used as address instead of the 2nd byte (a method supported by various JL-Cooper remote devices).
MIDI Channel	Clicking in this column pulls down a pop-up menu, allowing you to select the MIDI channel on which the controller is transmitted.
Address	The Continuous Controller number, the pitch of a note or the address of a NRPN/RPN Continuous Controller.
Max. Value	The maximum value the control will transmit. This value is used by the program to "scale" the value range of the MIDI controller to the value range of the program parameter.
Flags	Clicking in this column pulls down a pop-up menu, allowing you to activate or deactivate three flags: Receive—activate this if the MIDI message should be processed on reception. Transmit—activate this if a MIDI message should be transmitted when the corresponding value in the program changes. Relative—activate this if the control is an "endless" dial, which reports the number of turns instead of an absolute value.

- **If you find that the upper table holds too many or too few controls, you can add or remove controls with the Add and Delete buttons to the right of the upper table.**

- **If you are uncertain of which MIDI message a certain controller sends, you can use the Learn function:**

  Select the control in the upper table (by clicking in the Control Name column), move the corresponding control on your MIDI device and click the Learn button to the right of the table. The MIDI Status, MIDI Channel and Address values are automatically set to those of the moved control.

8. **Use the lower table to specify which Cubase SX/SL parameters you want to control.**

   Each row in the table is associated to the controller in the corresponding row in the upper table (as indicated by the Control Name column). The other columns have the following functionality:

Column	Description
Device	Clicking in this column pulls down a pop-up menu, used for determining which device in Cubase SX/SL should be controlled. The special option "Command" allows you to perform certain command actions by remote control. One example of this is the selection of remote banks. If you have a Yamaha DSP Factory card installed, this will also appear as an option on the Device pop-up menu.
Channel/Category	This is where you select the channel to be controlled or, if the "Command" Device option is selected, the Command category.
Value/Action	Clicking in this column pulls down a pop-up menu, allowing you to select the parameter of the channel to be controlled (typically, if the "VST Mixer" Device option is selected you can choose between volume, pan, send levels, EQ, etc.). If the "Command" Device option is selected, this is where you specify the "Action" of the category.

Column	Description
Flags	Clicking in this column pulls down a pop-up menu, allowing you to activate or deactivate three flags: Push Button—When activated, the parameter is only changed if the received MIDI message shows a value unequal to 0. Toggle—When activated, the parameter value is switched between minimum and maximum value each time a MIDI message is received. The combination of Push Button and Toggle is useful for remote controls which do not latch the state of a button. One example is controlling mute status with a device on which pressing the Mute button turns it on, and releasing the Mute button turns it off. If Push Button and Toggle are activated, the Mute status will change between on and off whenever the button is pressed on the console. Not Automated—When activated, the parameter will not be automated.

9. **If needed, select another bank and make settings for this.**

   Note that you only need to make settings in the lower table for this—the upper table is already set up according to the MIDI remote device.

- **If you need, you can add banks by clicking the Add button below the Bank pop-up.**

  Clicking the Rename button allows you to assign a new name to the currently selected bank, and you can remove an unneeded bank by selecting it and clicking the Delete button.

10. **When you are finished, close the Generic Remote Setup window.**

    Now, you can control the specified Cubase SX/SL parameters from the MIDI remote device. To select another bank, use the pop-up menu in the Remote Status window (or use a control on the MIDI remote device, if you have assigned one for this).

Importing and Exporting Remote Setups

The Export button in the upper right corner of the Generic Remote Setup window allows you to export the current setup, including the Control configuration (the upper table) and all banks. The setup is saved as a file (with the extension ".xml"). Clicking the Import button allows you to import saved Remote Setup files.

- **The last imported or exported Remote Setup will automatically be loaded when the program starts or the Generic Remote control is added in the Device Setup dialog.**

15 Audio Processing and Functions

15.1 Background

Audio processing in Cubase SX/SL can be called "non-destructive", in the sense that you can always undo changes or revert to the original versions. This is possible because processing affects *audio clips* rather than the actual audio files, and because audio clips can refer to more than one audio file. This is how it works:

1. **If you process an event or a selection range, a new audio file is created in the Edits folder, within your project folder.**

   This new file contains the processed audio, while the original file is unaffected.

2. **The processed section of the audio clip (the section corresponding to the event or selection range) is then made to refer to the new, processed audio file.**

   The other sections of the clip will still refer to the original file.

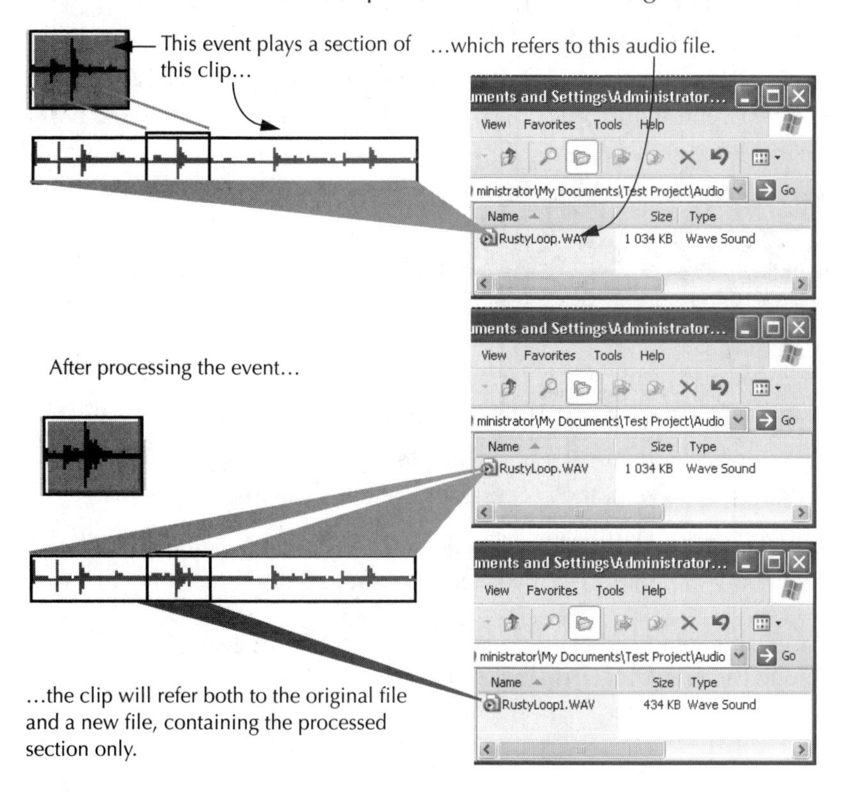

- **Since all edits are available as separate files, it is possible to undo any processing, at any point and in any order!**

  This is done in the Offline Process History dialog, as described on page 349.

- **Furthermore, the original, unprocessed audio file can still be used by other clips in the project, by other projects or by other applications.**

15.2 Audio Processing

Basically, you apply processing by making a selection and selecting a function from the Process submenu on the Audio menu. Processing is applied according to the following rules:

- Selecting events in the Project window or the Audio Part Editor will apply processing to the selected events only.
  Processing will only affect the clip sections that are referenced by the events.
- Selecting an audio clip in the Pool will apply processing to the whole clip.
- Making a selection range will apply processing to the selected range only.
  Other sections of the clip are not affected.

If you attempt to process an event that is a shared copy (i.e. the event refers to a clip that is used by other events in the project), you are asked whether you want to create a new version of the clip or not.

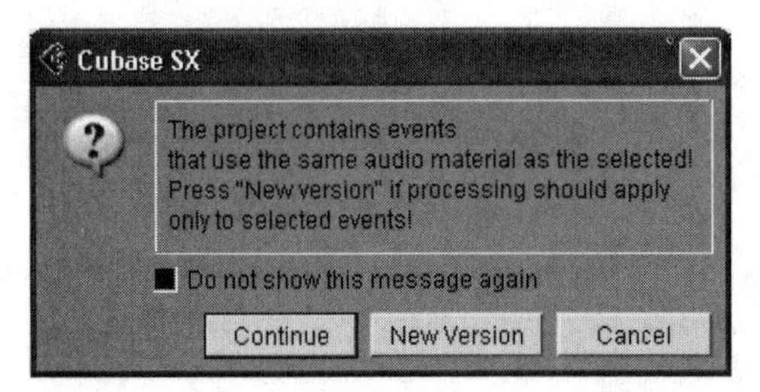

Select "New Version" if you want the processing to affect the selected event only.
Select "Continue" if you want the processing to affect all shared copies.

- If you activate the "Do not show this message again" option, any and all further processing you do will conform to the selected method ("Continue" or "New Version").
  You can change this setting at any time by using the "On Processing Shared Clips" pop-up menu in the Preferences dialog (Audio page).

15.2.1 Common Settings and Features

If there are any settings for the selected Audio processing function, these will appear in a dialog when you select the function from the Process submenu. While most settings are specific for the function, there are some features and settings that work in the same way for several functions:

The Preview, Process and Cancel Buttons

These buttons have the following functionality:

Button	Description
Preview	Allows you to listen to the result of the processing with the current settings. Playback will continue repeatedly until you click the button again (the button is labeled "Stop" during Preview playback). You can make adjustments during Preview playback, but the changes are not applied until the start of the next "lap". Some changes may automatically restart the Preview playback from the beginning.
Process	Performs the processing and closes the dialog.
Cancel	Closes the dialog without processing.

The "More..." Button

If the dialog has a lot of settings, some options may be hidden when the dialog appears. To reveal these, click the "More..." button.

To hide the settings, click the button again (now labeled "Less...").

Pre/Post Crossfade

Some processing functions allow you to gradually mix the effect in or out. This is done with the pre and post crossfade parameters. If you activate Pre-crossfade and specify a value of e.g. 1000 ms, the processing will be applied gradually from the start of selection, reaching full effect 1000 ms after the start. Similarly, if you activate post-crossfade, the processing will gradually be removed, starting at the specified interval before the end of the selection.

- The sum of the pre- and post-crossfade times cannot be larger than the length of the selection.

15.2.2 Envelope

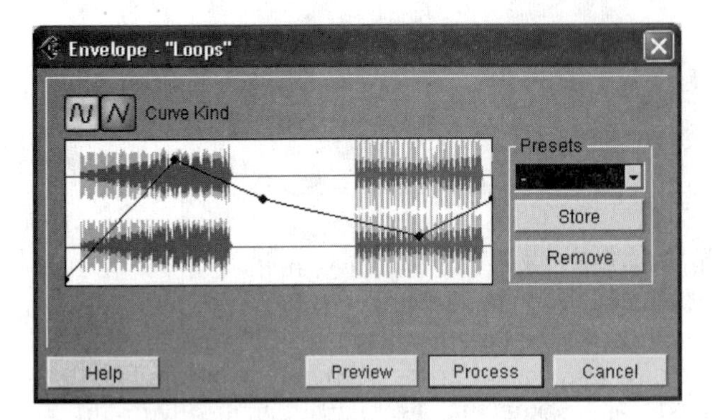

The Envelope function allows you to apply a volume envelope to the selected audio. The dialog contains the following settings:

Curve Kind Buttons

These determine whether the envelope curve should consist of spline curve segments (left button) or linear segments (right button).

Fade Display

Shows the shape of the envelope curve. The resulting waveform shape is shown in dark grey, with the current waveform shape in light grey. You can click on the curve to add points, and click and drag existing points to change the shape. To remove a point from the curve, drag it outside the display.

Presets

If you have set up an envelope curve that you may want to apply to other events or clips, you can store it as a Preset by clicking the Store button.

- **To apply a stored Preset, select it from the pop-up menu.**
- **To rename the selected Preset, double click on the name and type a new one in the dialog that appears.**
- **To remove a stored Preset, select it from the pop-up menu and click Remove.**

15.2.3 Fade In and Fade Out

These function are described in the chapter "Fades and Crossfades" (see page 169).

15.2.4 Gain

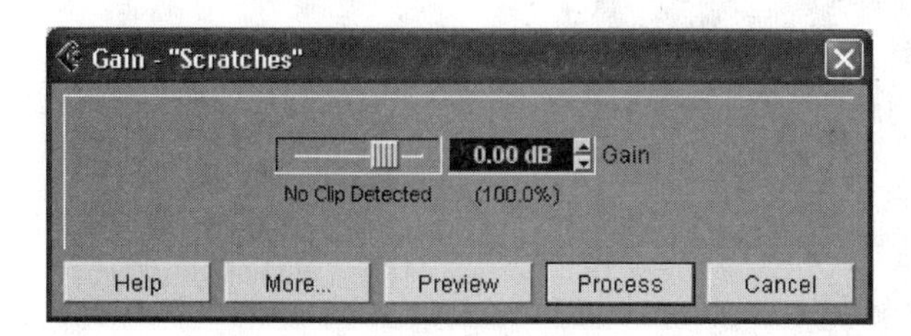

Allows you to change the gain (level) of the selected audio. The dialog contains the following settings:

Gain

This is where you set the desired gain, between -50 and +20dB. The setting is also indicated below the Gain display as a percentage.

Clip Detection Text

If you use the Preview function before applying the processing, the text below the slider indicates whether the current settings result in clipping (audio levels above 0 dB). If that is the case, lower the Gain value and use the Preview function again.

- **If you want to increase the level of the audio as much as possible without causing clipping, you should use the Normalize function instead (see page 336).**

Pre- and Post-Crossfade

See page 331.

15.2.5 Merge Clipboard

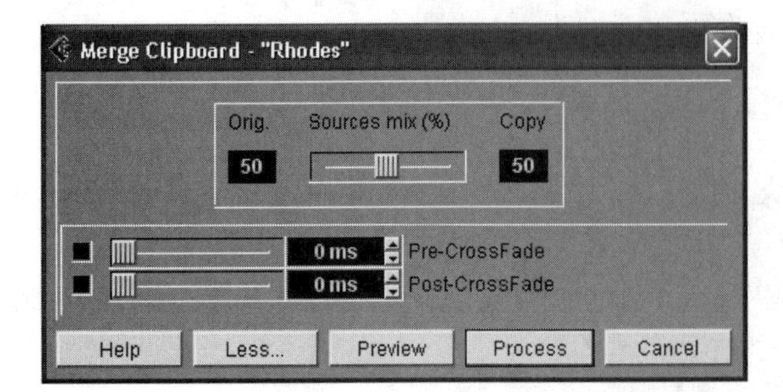

This functions mixes the audio from the clipboard into the audio selected for processing, starting at the beginning of the selection.

- For this function to be available, you need to have Cut or Copied a range of audio in the Sample Editor first.

The dialog contains the following settings:

Sources Mix

Allows you to specify a mix ratio between the Original (the audio selected for processing) and the Copy (the audio on the clipboard).

Pre- and Post-Crossfade

See page 331.

15.2.6 Noise Gate

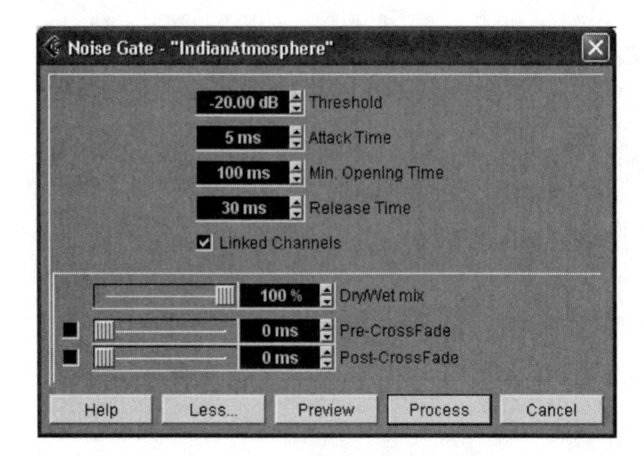

Scans the audio for sections weaker than a specified threshold level, and replaces them with silence. The dialog contains the following settings:

Threshold

The level below which you want audio to be silenced. Levels below this value will close the gate.

Attack Time

The time it takes for the gate to open fully after the audio level has exceeded the threshold level.

Min. Opening Time

This is the shortest time the gate will remain open. If you find that the gate opens and closes too often when processing material that varies rapidly in level, you should try raising this value.

Release Time

The time it takes for the gate to close fully after the audio level has dropped below the threshold level.

Linked Channels

This is available for stereo audio only. When it is activated, the Noise Gate is opened for both channels as soon as one or both channels exceed the Threshold level. When Linked Channels is deactivated, the Noise Gate works independently for the left and right channel.

Dry/Wet Mix

Allows you to specify a mix ratio between "dry" and processed sound.

Pre- and Post-Crossfade

See page 331.

15.2.7 Normalize

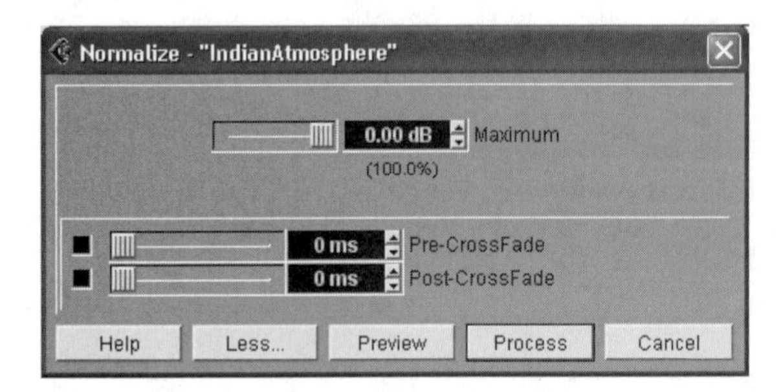

The Normalize function allows you to specify the desired maximum level of the audio. It then analyzes the selected audio and finds the current maximum level. Finally it subtracts the current maximum level from the specified level, and raises the gain of the audio by the resulting amount (if the specified maximum level is lower than the current maximum, the gain will be lowered instead). A common use for Normalizing is to raise the level of audio that was recorded at too low an input level. The dialog contains the following settings:

Maximum

The desired maximum level for the audio, between -50 and 0dB. The setting is also indicated below the Gain display as a percentage.

Pre- and Post-Crossfade

See page 331.

15.2.8 Phase Reverse

Reverses the phase of the selected audio, turning the waveform "upside down". The dialog contains the following settings:

Phase Reverse on

When processing stereo audio, this pop-up menu allows you to specify which channel(s) should be phase reversed.

Pre- and Post-Crossfade

See page 331.

15.2.9 Pitch Shift

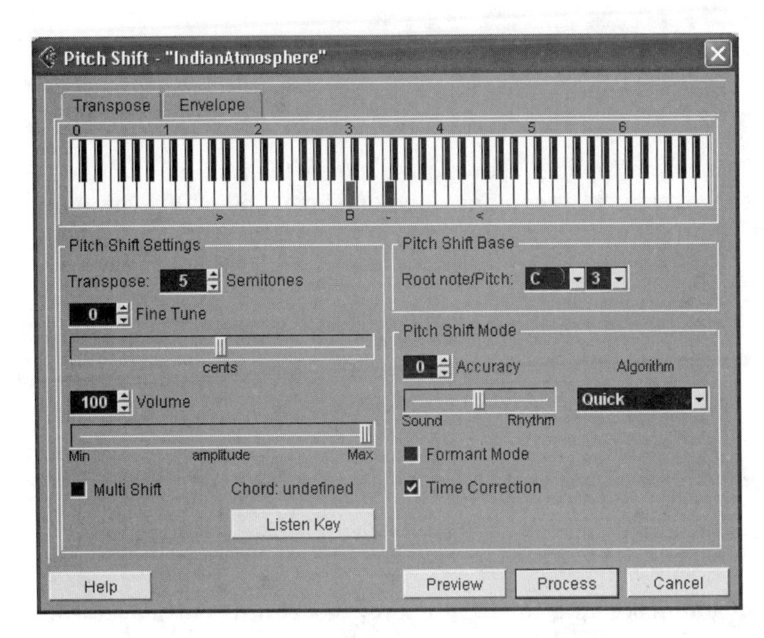

This function allows you to change the pitch of the audio with or without affecting its length. You can also create "harmonies" by specifying several pitches, or apply pitch shift based on a user specified envelope curve.

When the "Transpose" tab is selected, the dialog contains the following parameters:

Keyboard Display

This offers a way to specify the transpose interval in semitones, and gives a graphic overview of the transposition setting.

- **The "root note" is indicated in red.**

  This has nothing to do with the actual key or pitch of the original audio, it just provides a way to display transpose intervals. If you like, you can change the root note by using the settings to the right below the keyboard display, or by pressing [Alt] and clicking in the keyboard display.

- **To specify a transpose interval, click on one of the keys.**

  The key is indicated in blue, and the program plays test tones in the base pitch and transpose pitch, to give you an audible confirmation.

- **If "Multi Shift" is activated (see below), you can click on several keys to create "chords".**

  Clicking on a blue (activated) key removes it.

Transpose Settings

The "Semitones" and "Fine tune" settings allow you to specify the amount of pitch shift. You can transpose the audio ±16 semitones, and fine tune it by ±200 cents (hundredths of semitones).

Volume

Allows you to lower the volume of the pitch shifted sound.

Multi Shift

When this is activated, you can add more than one transpose value, creating multi-part harmonies. This is done by adding intervals in the keyboard display, as described above.

- **If the intervals you add make up a standard chord, this chord is displayed to the right.**

  Note however, that to include the base pitch (the original, untransposed sound) in the processed result, you need to click the base key in the keyboard display as well, so that it is displayed in blue.

Listen Key/Chord Button

Clicking this button plays a test tone, pitched according to the activated interval key on the keyboard display. If "Multi Shift" is activated, this button is called "Listen Chord", and plays all activated intervals, as a chord.

Pitch Shift Base

This allows you to set the root note (the red key in the keyboard display). This has no actual relation to the pitch of the audio material, but should be viewed as an aid for easily setting up intervals and chords.

Accuracy

Set this parameter according to whether the rhythmic feel of the audio material has a high priority or not. If you set this to a high value (drag the slider to the right), the timing and rhythmic feel will be preserved as accurately as possible. If you set it to a low value, the tonal quality gets priority, allowing slight changes in timing. This parameter is not available if the MPEX algorithm is used (only Cubase SX, see below).

Algorithm

Allows you to select one of four Quality modes: Quick, Standard, High and MPEX (only Cubase SX, see below). Generally, the higher the quality, the slower the processing.

- **About the MPEX mode (only Cubase SX):**

  The MPEX Quality mode is based on Prosoniq's proprietary MPEX (Minimum Perceived Loss Time Compression/Expansion) algorithm. This algorithm (which is also used in Prosoniq's TimeFactory™ application) uses an artificial neural network for time series prediction in the scale space domain to achieve high end time and pitch scaling. This gives the best possible audio quality result.
  Note that the Accuracy parameter isn't available in MPEX mode. Furthermore, you should not use the Preview function in MPEX Quality mode, since the MPEX algorithm isn't designed for real time processing.

Formant Mode

If you are processing vocal material, you should activate this option in order to preserve the vocal characteristics of the pitch shifted audio.

Time Correction

When this is activated, the pitch shift process will not affect the length of the audio. When this is deactivated, raising the pitch will shorten the audio section and vice versa, much like changing the playback speed on a tape recorder.

Using Envelope Based Pitch Shift

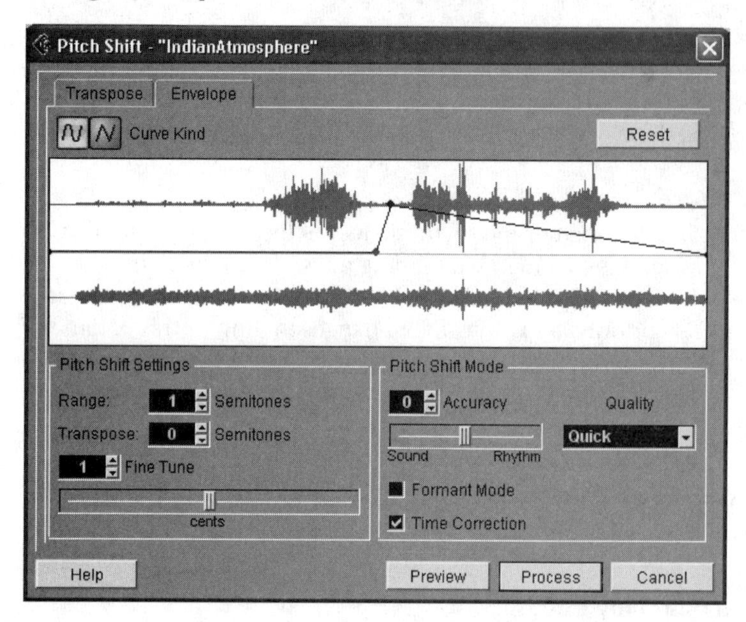

When the "Envelope" tab is selected, you can specify an envelope curve on which the pitch shift should be based. This allows you to create pitch bend effects, pitch shift different sections of the audio by different amounts, etc.

Envelope Display

Shows the shape of the envelope curve, over the waveform image of the audio selected for processing. Envelope curve points above the center line indicate positive pitch shift, while curve points below the center line indicate negative pitch shift. Initially, the envelope curve will be a horizontal, centered line, indicating zero pitch shift.

- **You can click on the curve to add points, and click and drag existing points to change the shape. To remove a point from the curve, drag it outside the display.**

Curve Kind

These buttons determine whether the envelope curve should consist of spline curve segments (left button) or linear segments (right button).

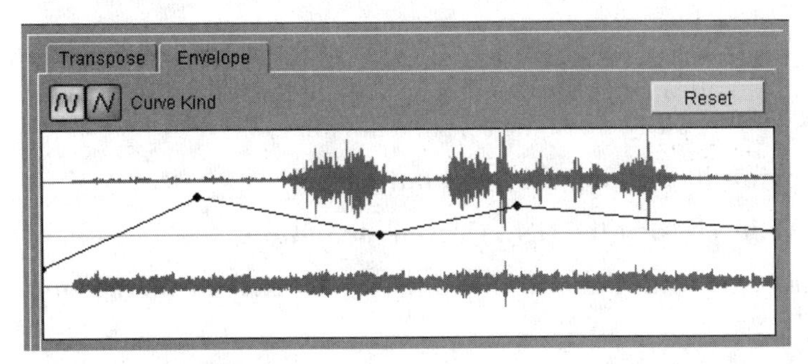

Linear segment envelope.

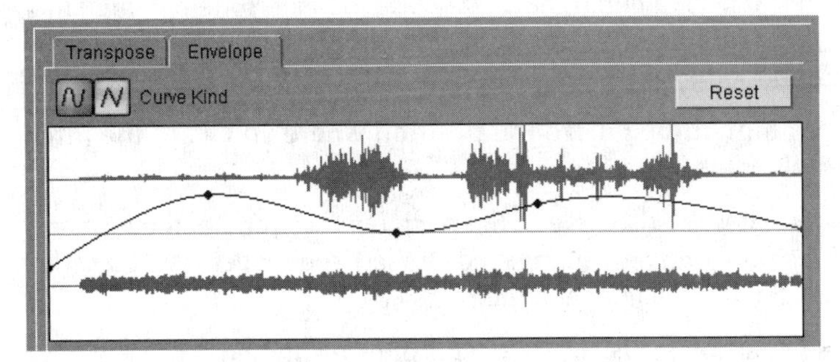

The same envelope with spline curve segments selected.

Range

This parameter determines the vertical pitch range of the envelope. If this is set to "4", moving a curve point to the top of the display corresponds to pitch shifting by + 4 semitones. The maximum range is +/- 16 Semitones.

Transpose and Fine Tune

Allows you to adjust the value of a curve point numerically:

1. **Click on a curve point to select it.**

   The selected point is shown in red.

2. **Adjust the Transpose and Fine Tune parameters to change the pitch of the curve point in semitones and cents, respectively.**

Pitch Shift Mode

These are the same parameters as on the Transpose tab, see page 339.

Example

Let's say that you wish to create a pitch bend effect, so that the pitch is raised linearly by exactly 2 semitones in a specific part of the selected audio.

1. **Remove all curve points by clicking the Reset button.**
2. **Select a linear curve by clicking the right Curve Kind button.**
3. **Create a point where you want the pitch bend to start by clicking on the envelope line.**

   Since this is the starting point for the pitch bend, you want its pitch to be zero (the envelope line should still be straight). If necessary, use the Fine Tune parameter to set the curve point to 0 cents, because this point governs the start point, where you want the pitch transition to begin.
4. **Create a new curve point at the horizontal position where you want the pitch bend to reach the full value.**

   This curve point determines the rise time of the pitch bend effect, i.e. the further away from the starting point the new point is positioned, the longer it will take for the pitch bend to reach the full value, and vice versa.
5. **Make sure the Range parameter is set to 2 semitones or higher.**
6. **With the second point still selected, use the Transpose and Fine Tune parameters to set the pitch to exactly 2 semitones.**
7. **Create a new curve point to set the duration of the pitch bend, i.e. the time the pitch should remain transposed by 2 semitones.**
8. **Finally, create a point where you want the pitch bend to end.**

   You don't need to create a new point if this should be the end of the audio file being processed. There is always an end point at the right side of the waveform display.
9. **If necessary, make additional settings in the Pitch Shift Mode section.**
10. **Click Process.**

    The pitch bend is applied according to the specified settings.

15.2.10 Remove DC Offset

This function will remove any DC offset in the audio selection. A DC offset is when there is too large a DC (direct current) component in the signal, sometimes visible as the signal not being visually centered around the "zero level axis". DC offsets do not affect what you actually hear, but they affect zero crossing detection and certain processing, and it is recommended that you remove them.

- It is recommended that this function is applied to complete audio clips, since the DC offset (if any) is normally present throughout the entire recording.

There are no parameters for this function. Note that you can check for DC Offset in an audio clip using the Statistics function (see page 357).

15.2.11 Reverse

Reverses the audio selection, as when playing a tape backwards. There are no parameters for this function.

15.2.12 Silence

Replaces the selection with silence. There are no parameters for this function.

15.2.13 Stereo Flip

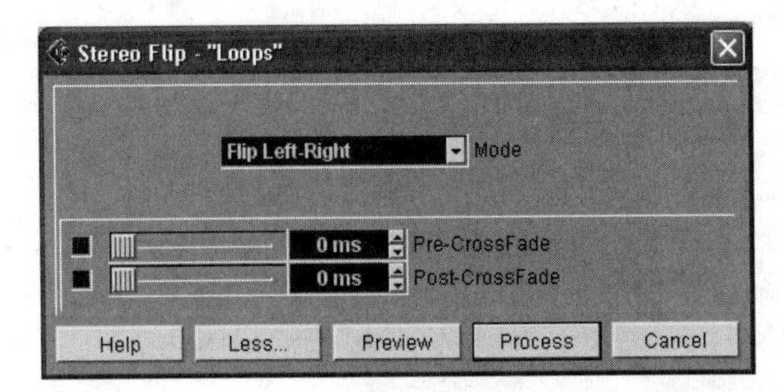

This function works with stereo audio selections only. It allows you to manipulate the left and right channel in various ways. The dialog contains the following parameters:

Mode

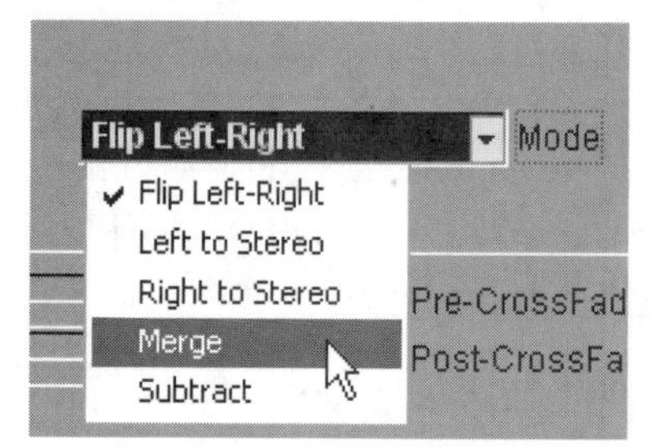

This pop-up menu determines what the function does:

Option	Description
Flip Left-Right	Swaps the left and right channel.
Left to Stereo	Copies the left channel sound to the right channel.
Right to Stereo	Copies the right channel sound to the left channel.
Merge	Merges both channels on each side, for mono sound.
Subtract	Subtracts the left channel information from the right and vice versa. This is typically used as a "Karaoke effect", for removing centered mono material from a stereo signal.

15.2.14 Time Stretch

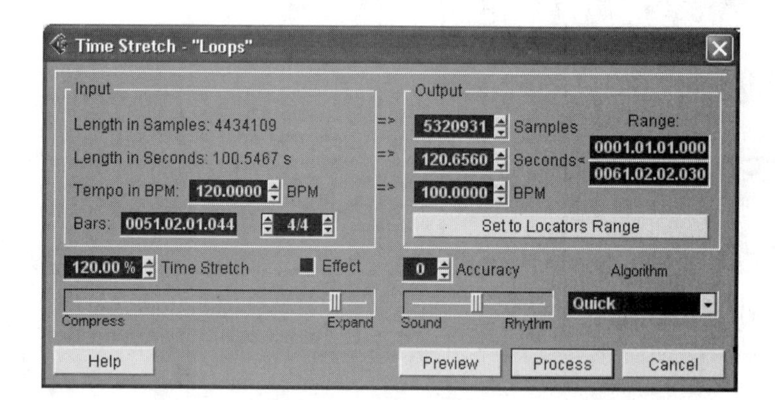

This function allows you to change the length and "tempo" of the selected audio, without affecting the pitch. The dialog contains the following parameters:

Input Section

This section contains information and settings regarding the "input", the audio selected for processing:

Parameter	Description
Length in Samples	The length of the selected audio, in samples.
Length in Seconds	The length of the selected audio, in seconds.
Tempo in BPM	If you are processing music, and know the actual tempo of the audio, you can enter it here as beats per minute. This makes it possible to time stretch the audio to another tempo, without having to compute the actual time stretch amount.
Bars	If you use the tempo setting, you need to specify the length of the selected audio here, as bars, beats, 1/16-notes and ticks (with 120 ticks per 1/16-note).
Time Signature	If you use the tempo setting, you need to specify the time signature here.

Output Section

These settings are used if you want to stretch the audio to fit within a specific time span or tempo. The values will change automatically if you adjust the Timestretch amount (see below).

Parameter	Description
Samples	The desired length in samples.
Seconds	The desired length in seconds.
BPM	The desired tempo (beats per minute). For this to work, you have to know the actual tempo of the audio, and specify this (along with time signature and length in bars) in the Input section to the left.
Range	Allows you to specify the desired length as a range between two time positions.
Set to Locators Range	Clicking this button sets the Range values to the length of the Cycle.

Timestretch

The Timestretch parameter determines the amount of timestretch, as a percentage of the original length. If you use the settings in the Output section to specify the amount of timestretch, this value will change automatically.

The possible timestretch range depends on the "Effect" option:

- **If the "Effect" checkbox is deactivated, the range is 75 to 125%.**

  This is the preferred mode if you want to preserve the character of the sound.

- **If the "Effect" checkbox is activated, you can specify values between 10 and 1000%.**

  This mode is mainly useful for special effects, etc.

Accuracy

Set this parameter according to whether the rhythmic feel of the audio material has a high priority or not. If you set this to a high value (drag the slider to the right), the timing and rhythmic feel will be preserved as accurately as possible. If you set it to a low value, the tonal quality gets priority, allowing slight changes in timing. This parameter is not available if the MPEX algorithm is used (only Cubase SX, see below).

Algorithm

Allows you to select one of five Quality modes: Quick, Standard, High MPEX (only Cubase SX, see below) and Drum (see below). Generally, the higher the Quality, the slower the processing.

- **MPEX mode (only Cubase SX):**

  The MPEX Quality mode is based on Prosoniq's proprietary MPEX (Minimum Perceived Loss Time Compression/Expansion) algorithm. This algorithm (which is also used in Prosoniq's TimeFactory™ application) uses an artificial neural network for time series prediction in the scale space domain to achieve high end time and pitch scaling. This gives the best possible audio quality result.
  Note that the Accuracy parameter isn't available in MPEX mode. Furthermore, you should not use the Preview function in MPEX Quality mode, since the MPEX algorithm isn't designed for real time processing.

- **Drum mode:**

  This is special algorithm developed by Spectral Design, optimized for processing rhythmic material. By default, the Close Gaps function (see page 396) uses this algorithm. The Accuracy parameter and Preview function are not available in Drum mode.

15.3 Applying Plug-ins (Cubase SX only)

As described in the chapter "Audio Effects", you can add VST and DirectX plug-in effects in real-time during playback. However, sometimes it's useful to "permanently" apply effects processing to one or several selected events. This is done in the following way:

1. **Make a selection in the Project window, the Pool or an editor.**

   Effects are applied according to the same rules as Processing (see page 331).

2. **Select "Plugins" from the Audio menu.**
3. **Select the desired effect from the submenu that appears.**

   The Process Plug-in dialog appears.

About Stereo and Mono

If you are applying an effect to mono audio material, only the left side of the effect's stereo output will be applied.

15.3.1 The Process Plug-in Dialog

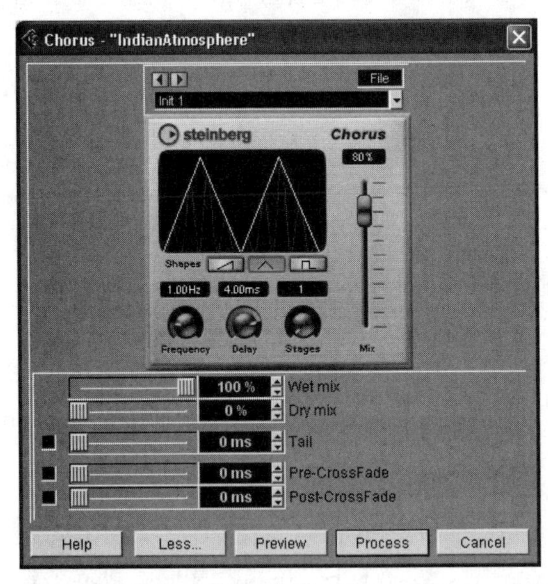

The Process Plug-in dialog for the Chorus effect.

The upper section of the Process Plug-in dialog contains the actual effect parameters of the selected plug-in. For details on the included plug-ins' parameters, see page 234.

The lower section of the dialog contains settings for the actual processing. These are common to all plug-ins.

- **If the lower section is hidden, click the "More..." button to display it.**

  Clicking the button again (now labeled "Less...") will hide the lower section.

The following settings and functions are available in the common, lower section of the dialog:

Wet Mix/Dry Mix

These two sliders allow you to specify the balance between wet (processed) and dry (original) signal in the resulting clip.

Normally the two sliders are "reverse-ganged", so that raising the Wet mix slider lowers the Dry mix slider by the same amount. However, if you press [Alt] and drag a slider, you can move it independently. This allows you to set e.g. 80% dry and 80% wet signal. Be careful to avoid distortion.

Tail

This parameter is useful if you are applying an effect that adds material after the end of original audio (such as reverb and delay effects). When the checkbox is activated, you can specify a tail length using the slider. The tail time is included when playing back with the Preview function, allowing you to find the appropriate tail length.

Pre/Post Crossfade

These settings allow you to gradually mix the effect in or out. If you activate Pre-Crossfade and specify a value of e.g. 1000 ms, the effect will be applied gradually from the start of selection, reaching full effect 1000 ms after the start. Similarly, if you activate Post-Crossfade, the processing will gradually be removed starting at the specified interval before the end of the selection.

- The sum of the Pre- and Post-Crossfade times cannot be larger than the length of the selection.

Preview Button

Allows you to listen to the result of the processing with the current settings. Playback will continue repeatedly until you click the button again (the button is labeled "Stop" during Preview playback). You can change the effect settings during Preview playback if needed.

Process Button

Applies the effect and closes the dialog.

Cancel Button

Closes the dialog without applying the effect.

15.4 The Offline Process History Dialog

15.4.1 Procedures

If you find you want to remove some or all processing from a clip, this can be done in the Offline Process History dialog. Processing that can be modified in the Offline Process History dialog includes the functions on the Process menu, any applied plug-in effects, and Sample Editor operations such as Cut, Paste, Delete and drawing with the Pencil tool.

- Due to the clip-file relationship (see page 329), it is even possible to modify or remove some processing "in the middle" of the Process History, while keeping later processing! This feature depends on the type of processing performed (see page 350).

Proceed as follows:

1. **Select the clip in the Pool or one of its events in the Project window.**

   You can see which clips have been processed by checking the Status column in the Pool—the waveform symbol indicates that processing or effects have been applied to the clip (see page 350).

2. **Select "Offline Process History..." from the Audio menu.**

   The Offline Process History dialog appears.

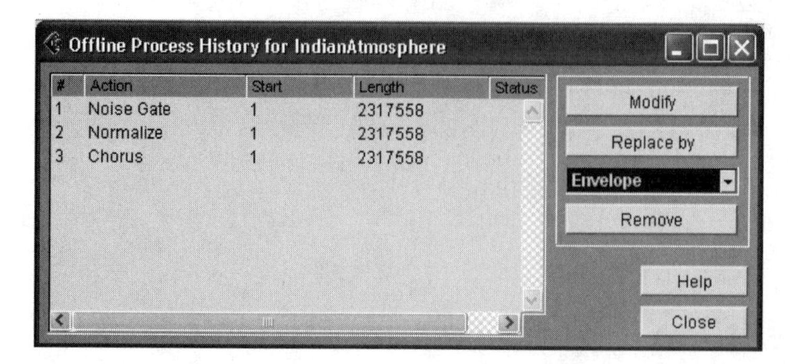

The left part of the dialog contains a list of all processing you have added to the clip, with the most recent operations at the bottom of the list. The "Start" and "Length" columns indicate which section of the clip was affected by each operation. The "Status" column indicates if the operation can be modified or removed.

3. **Locate the operation you want to edit and select it by clicking on it in the list.**

- **To modify the settings of the selected processing, click the "Modify" button.**

  This opens the dialog for the processing function or applied effect, allowing you to change the settings. This works just as when you applied the processing or effect the first time.

- **To replace the selected operation with another processing function or effect, select the desired function from the pop-up menu and click the "Replace by" button.**

  If the selected function has settings, a dialog will appear as usual. The original operation will then be removed and the new processing will be inserted in the Offline Process History.

- **To remove the selected operation, click the "Remove" button.**

  The processing is removed from the clip.

4. **Click "Close" to close the dialog.**

15.4.2 Restrictions

- If there are no settings for the processing function, you can't modify it.

- If you have applied processing that changes the length of the clip (such as Cut, Insert or Time Stretch), you can only remove this if it is the most recent processing in the Offline Process History (at the bottom of the list in the dialog). If an operation can not be removed or modified, this is indicated by an icon in the "Status" column. Also, the corresponding buttons will be greyed out.

15.4.3 Freeze Edits

The Freeze Edits function on the Audio menu allows you to make all processing and applied effects permanent for a clip:

1. **Select the clip in the Pool or one of its events in the Project window.**
2. **Select "Freeze Edits..." from the Audio menu.**

- **If there is only one edit version of the clip (no other clips refer to the same audio file), the following dialog will appear:**

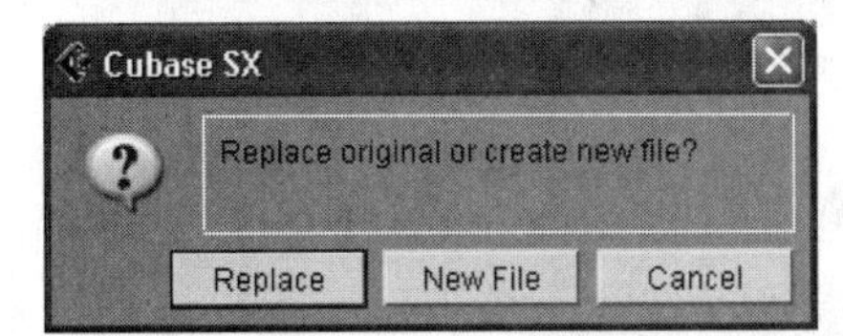

If you select "Replace", all edits will be applied to the original audio file (the one listed in the clip's Path column in the Pool). If you select "New File", the Freeze Edits operation will create a new file in the Audio folder within the project folder (leaving the original audio file unaffected).

- **If the selected clip (or the clip played by the selected event) has several edit versions (i.e. there are other clips referring to the same audio file), the following alert will appear:**

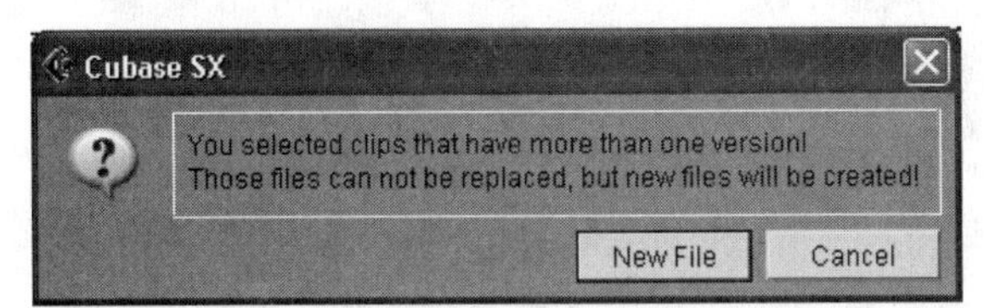

As you can see, you don't have the option to Replace the original audio file in this case. This is because that audio file is used by other clips. Select "New File" to have a new file created in the Audio folder within the project folder.

- Now, the clip refers to a new, single audio file. If you open the Offline Process History dialog for the clip, the list will be empty.

15.5 Detect Silence

The Detect Silence function on the Audio menu isn't really a processing function, since it doesn't actually affect the audio clip. Instead, it searches for silent sections in an event, and either splits the event, removing the silent parts from the project, or creates regions corresponding to the non-silent sections. Proceed as follows:

1. **Select the event in the Project window or the Audio Part Editor.**

   You can select several events if you like, in which case you will be allowed to make separate settings for each selected event.

2. **Select "Detect Silence" from the Audio menu.**

   The Detect Silence dialog appears.

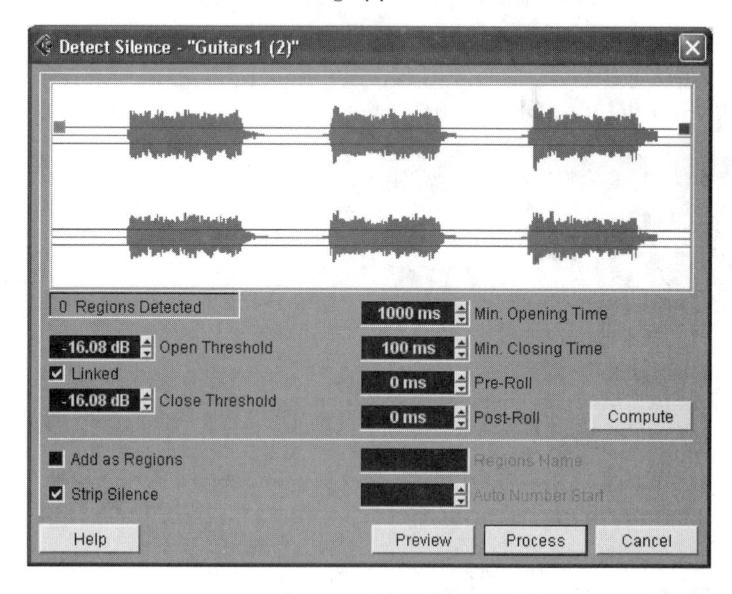

3. **Adjust the settings in the area below the waveform display.**

   They have the following functionality:

Setting	Description
Open Threshold	When the audio level exceeds this value, the function will "open", i.e. let the sound through. Set this low enough to open when a sound starts, but high enough to remove unwanted noise during "silent" sections.
Close Threshold	When the audio level drops below this value, the function will "close". This value cannot be higher than the Open Threshold value. Set this high enough to remove unwanted noise during "silent" sections.
Linked	If this checkbox is ticked, Open and Close Threshold will have the same value.
Min. Opening Time	Determines the minimum time that the function will remain "open" after the audio level has exceeded the Open Threshold value. If the audio contains repeated short sounds, and you find that this results in too many short "open" sections, try raising this value.
Min. Closing Time	Determines the minimum time that the function will remain "closed" after the audio level has dropped below the Close Threshold value. Usually you would want to set this to a low value, to avoid removing sounds.
Pre-Roll	Allows you to have the function "open" slightly before the audio level exceeds the Open Threshold value. In other words, the start of each "open" section is moved to the left according to the time you set here. This is useful to avoid removing the attack of sounds.
Post-Roll	Allows you to have the function "close" slightly after the audio level drops below the Close Threshold value. This is useful to avoid removing the natural decay of sounds.

4. **Click the "Compute" button.**

   The audio event is analyzed, and the waveform display is redrawn to indicate which sections will be considered "silent", according to your settings.

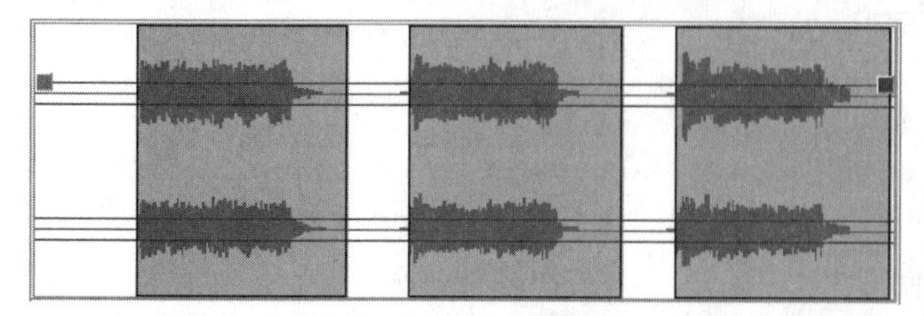

- **If you like, you can use the Preview function to listen to the result.**

  The event is played back repeatedly in its entire length, but with the "closed" sections silenced.

5. **Repeat steps 3 and 4 until you are satisfied with the result.**
6. **Select what you want the function to do, by activating either the "Add as Regions" checkbox, the "Strip Silence" checkbox, or both.**

   "Add as Regions" will create regions according to the non-silent sections. "Strip Silence" will split the event at the start and end of each non-silent section, and remove the silent sections inbetween.

7. **If you activated "Add as Regions", you can specify a name for the Regions in the Regions Name field.**

   In addition to the name, the regions will be numbered, starting with the number specified in the Auto Number Start field.

8. **Click "Process".**

   The event is split and/or regions are added.

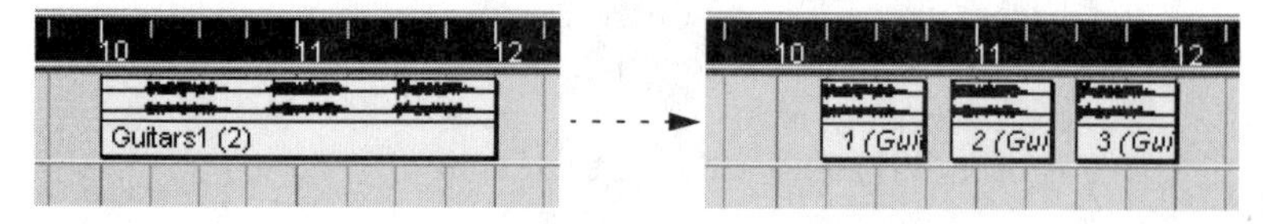

The result of the "Strip Silence" option.

- **If you selected more than one event in step 1 above, the dialog will appear again, allowing you to make separate settings for each selected event.**

15.6 The Spectrum Analyzer (Cubase SX only)

This function analyzes the selected audio, computes the average "spectrum" (level distribution over the frequency range) and displays this as a two-dimensional graph, with frequency on the x-axis and level on the y-axis.

1. **Make an audio selection (a clip, an event or a range selection).**
2. **Select "Spectrum Analyzer" from the Audio menu.**

   A dialog with settings for the analysis appears.

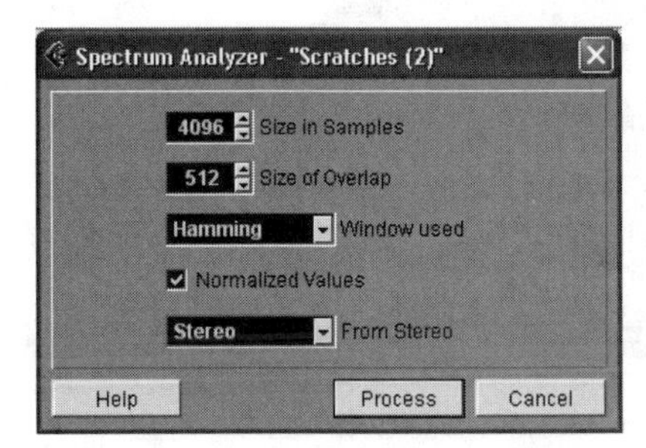

The default values are chosen to give good results in most situations, but you can adjust the settings if you like:

Setting	Description
Size in Samples	The function divides the audio into "analysis blocks", the size of which is set here. The larger this value, the higher the frequency resolution of the resulting spectrum.
Size of Overlap	The overlap between each analysis block.
Window used	Allows you to select which window type should be used for the FFT (Fast Fourier Transform, the mathematical method used for computing the spectrum).
Normalized values	When this is activated, the resulting level values are scaled, so that the highest level is displayed as "1" (0 dB).
From Stereo	When analyzing stereo material, there is a pop-up menu with the following options: Mono mix—the stereo signal is mixed to mono before analyzing. Mono left—the left channel signal is used for the analysis. Mono right—the right channel signal is used for the analysis. Stereo—both channels are analyzed (two separate spectrums will be displayed).

3. Click the "Process" button.

The spectrum is computed and displayed as a graph.

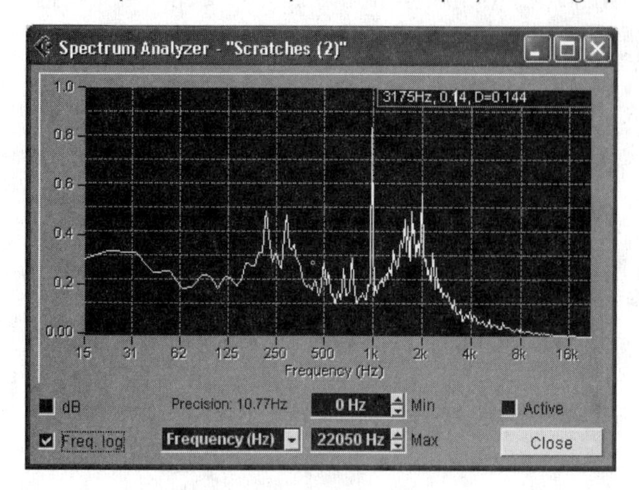

4. You can adjust the display with the settings in the display window:

Setting	Description
dB	When this is activated, the vertical axis shows dB values. When it is deactivated, values between 0 and 1 are shown.
Freq. log	When this is activated, frequencies (on the horizontal axis) are displayed on a logarithmic scale. When it is deactivated, the frequency axis is linear.
Precision	Indicates the frequency resolution of the graph. This value cannot be changed here, but is governed by the Size in Samples setting in the previous dialog.
Frequency/Note	Allows you to select whether you want the frequencies to be displayed in Hertz or with note names.
Min.	Sets the lowest frequency shown in the graph.
Max.	Sets the highest frequency shown in the graph. By adjusting the Min and Max values, you can take a closer look at a smaller frequency range.
Active	When this is activated, the next Spectrum Analysis will appear in the same window. When deactivated, new Spectrum Analysis results will appear in separate windows.

5. **If you move the mouse pointer over the graph, a crosshair cursor follows the graph curve and the display in the upper right corner shows the frequency/ note and level at the current position.**

   To compare the level between two frequencies, move the pointer to one of the frequencies, right click once and move the pointer to the second frequency. The delta value (the difference in level between the current position and the right-click position) is displayed in the upper right corner (labeled "D").

- **If you analyzed stereo audio and selected the "Stereo" option in the first dialog, the graphs for the left and right channel are superimposed in the display, with the left channel graph in white and the right channel graph in yellow.**

  The display in the upper right corner shows the values for the left channel—to see the right channel values, hold down [Shift]. An "L" or "R" is displayed to indicate which channel values are shown.

6. **You can leave the window open or close it by clicking the "Close" button.**

   If you leave it open and the "Active" checkbox is ticked, the result of the next Spectrum Analysis will be displayed in the same window.

15.7 Statistics (Cubase SX only)

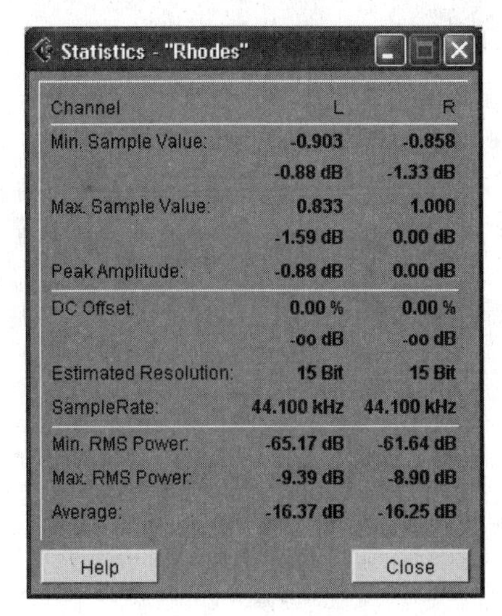

The Statistics function on the Audio menu analyzes the selected audio (events, clips or range selections) and displays a window with the following information:

Item	Description
Min. Sample Value	The lowest sample value in the selection, as a value between -1 and 1 and in dB.
Max. Sample Value	The highest sample value in the selection, as a value between -1 and 1 and in dB.
Peak Amplitude	The largest sample value (in absolute numbers) in the selection, in dB.
DC Offset	The amount of DC Offset (see page 343) in the selection, as a percentage and in dB.
Estimated Resolution	Even though an audio file is in 16 or 24 bits, it may have been converted from a lower resolution. The Estimated Resolution value makes an educated guess about the actual resolution of the audio selection, by computing the smallest level difference between two samples.
Sample Rate	The sample rate of the audio selection.
Min. RMS Power	The lowest loudness (RMS) measured in the selection.
Max. RMS Power	The highest loudness (RMS) measured in the selection.
Average	The average loudness over the whole selection.

16 The Sample Editor

16.1 Background

The Sample Editor allows you to view and manipulate audio at the audio clip level, by cutting and pasting, removing or drawing audio data or applying effects. This editing can be called "non-destructive", in the sense that you can undo changes or revert to the original versions at any point, using the Offline Process History.

For details, see the section about non-destructive processing on page 329 and the description of the Offline Process History on page 349.

16.2 Opening the Sample Editor

You open the Sample Editor by double clicking an audio event in the Project window or the Audio Part Editor, or by double clicking an audio clip in the Pool. You can have more than one Sample Editor open at the same time.

- **Note that double clicking on an audio part in the Project window will open the Audio Part Editor, even if the part only contains a single audio event.**

  See page 377.

16.3 Window Overview

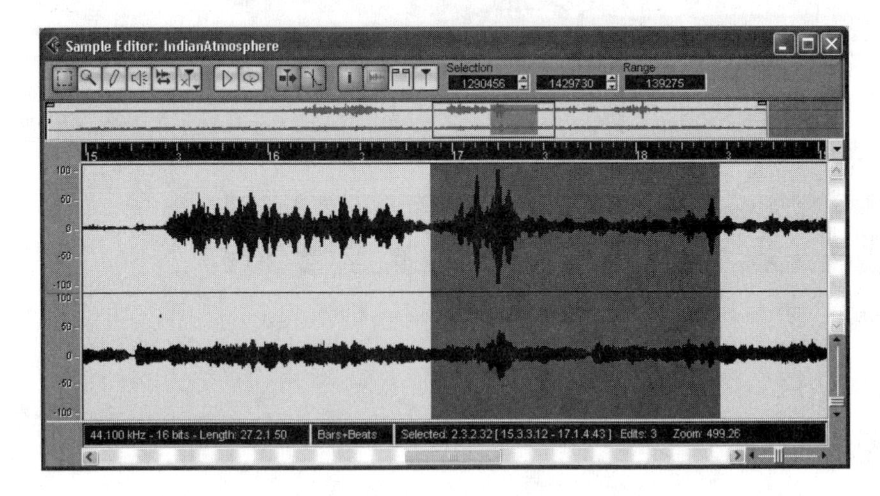

16.3.1 The Elements Menu

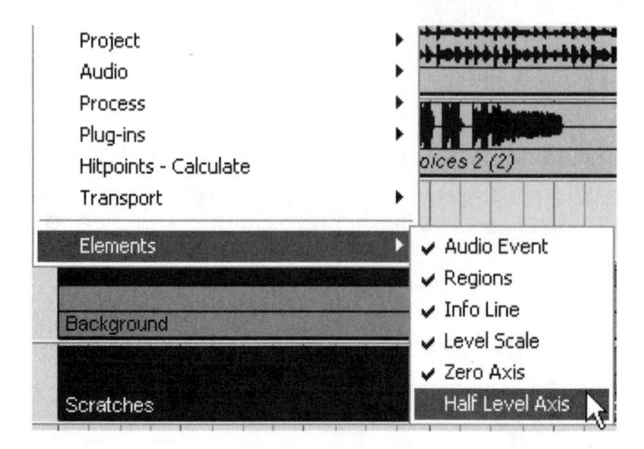

If you right-click in the Sample Editor to bring up the Quick menu, you will find a sub-menu called "Elements". By activating or deactivating options on this submenu, you can decide what you want shown in the Editor window. Some of these options are also available as icons on the toolbar.

16.3.2 The Toolbar

The toolbar contains tools and various settings:

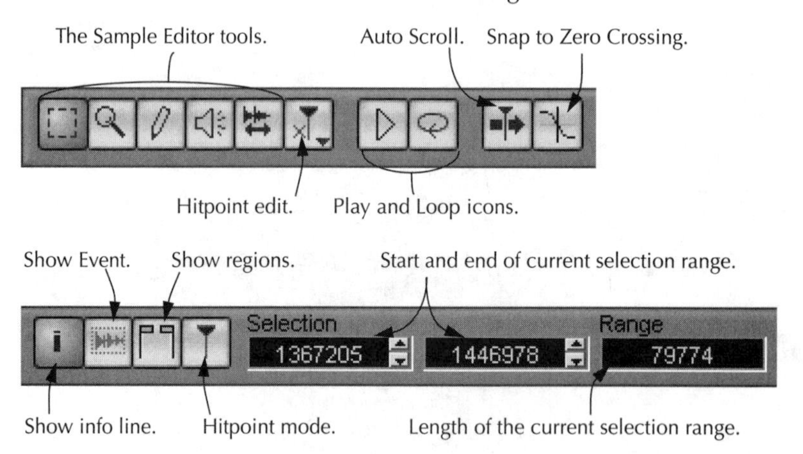

16.3.3 The Thumbnail Display

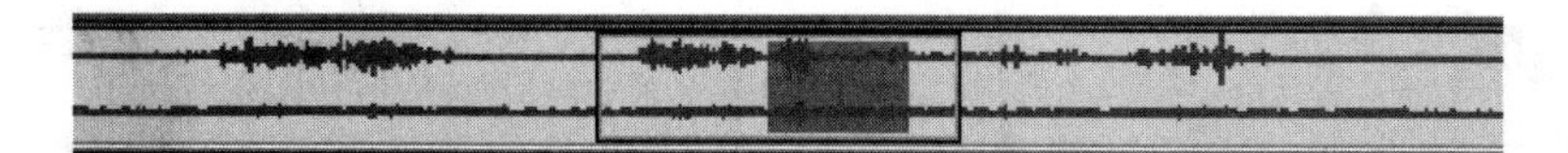

The thumbnail display provides an overview of the whole clip. The section currently shown in the Sample Editor's main Waveform display is indicated by a blue rectangle in the thumbnail, while the current selection range is shown in blue-grey.

- **You can move the blue rectangle in the thumbnail to view other sections of the clip.**

  This is done by clicking in the lower half of the rectangle and dragging it to the left or right.

- **You can resize the blue rectangle (by dragging its left or right edge) to zoom in or out, horizontally.**
- **You can define a new viewing area by clicking in the upper half of the overview and dragging a rectangle with the pointer.**

16.3.4 The Ruler

The Sample Editor ruler is located between the thumbnail and the Waveform display. It shows the timeline in the display format specified in the Project Setup dialog (see page 117). If you like, you can select an independent display format for the ruler by clicking on the arrow button to the right of it and selecting an option from the pop-up menu that appears (this affects the values in the info line too). For a list of the display format options, see page 116.

16.3.5 The Waveform Display and the Level Scale

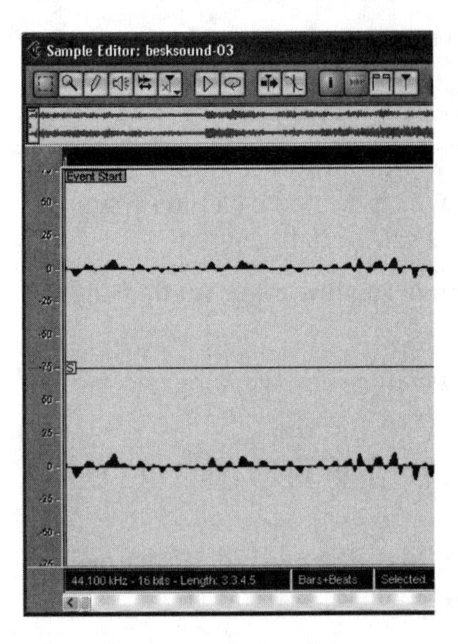

The Waveform display shows the waveform image of the edited audio clip—in the style selected in the Preferences dialog (Event Display—Audio page), see page 123. To the left of it, a level scale can be shown, indicating the amplitude of the audio.

- **When the level scale is shown, you can select whether the level should be shown as a percentage or in dB.**

  This is done by right-clicking the level scale and selecting an option from the pop-up menu that appears. This also allows you to hide the level scale.

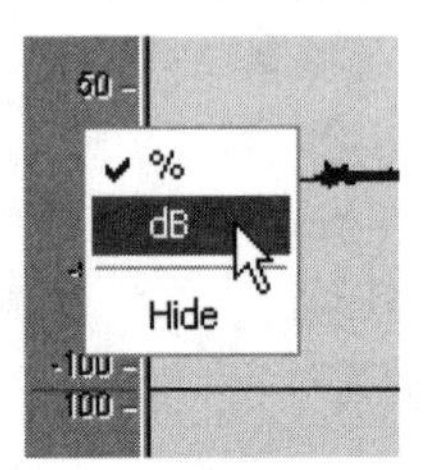

- **To display the level scale after hiding it, right-click to bring up the Quick menu and activate "Level Scale" on the Elements submenu.**

  This submenu also allows you to select whether you want the zero axis and/or the half level axis indicated in the Waveform display.

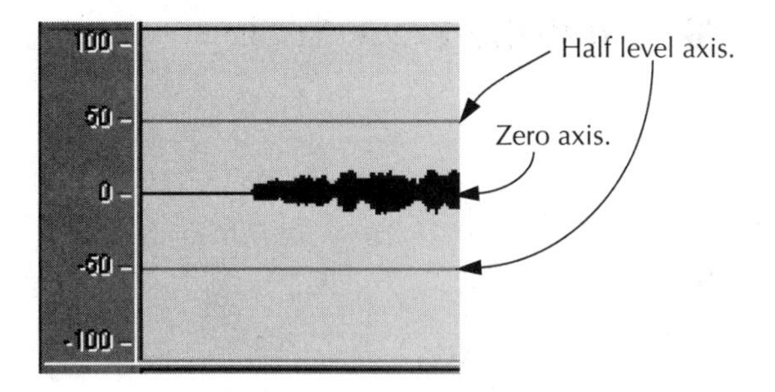

16.3.6 The Info Line

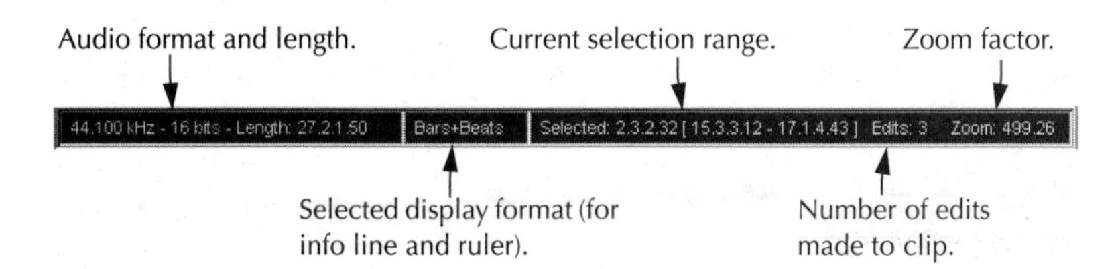

The info line at the bottom of the window shows information about the edited audio clip. You cannot edit the values on the info line.

- **To hide or show the info line, click the "i" icon on the toolbar.**
- **Initially, length and position values are displayed in the format specified in the Project Setup dialog (see page 117), but you can change this by clicking in the middle field of the info line and selecting another display format from a pop-up menu.**

  This selection affects the Sample Editor ruler as well.

16.4 Operations

16.4.1 Zooming

Zooming in the Sample Editor is done according to the standard zoom procedures, with the following special notes:

- **The vertical zoom slider changes the vertical scale relative to the height of the Editor window, in a way similar to the waveform zooming in the Project window (see page 119).**

- **The following options relevant to the Sample Editor are available on the Zoom submenu on the Edit menu:**

Option	Description
Zoom In	Zooms in one step, centering on the position cursor.
Zoom Out	Zooms out one step, centering on the position cursor.
Zoom Full	Zooms out so that the whole clip is visible in the editor.
Zoom to Selection	Zooms in so that the current selection fills the screen.
Zoom to Event	Zooms in so that the editor shows the section of the clip corresponding to the edited audio event. This is not available if you opened the Sample Editor from the Pool (in which case the whole clip is opened for editing, not an event).
Zoom In/Out Vertical	This is the same as adjusting the vertical zoom slider (see above).

- **You can also zoom by resizing the blue rectangle in the thumbnail display.**

  See page 361.

- **The current zoom setting is shown in the info line, as a "samples per screen pixel" value.**
- **Note that you can zoom in horizontally to a scale with less than one sample per pixel!**

  This is required for drawing with the Pencil tool (see page 373).

- **If you have zoomed in to one sample per pixel or less, the appearance of the samples depend on the option "Interpolate Audio Images" in the Preferences dialog (Event Display—Audio page).**

  If the option is deactivated, single sample values are drawn as "steps". If the option is activated they are interpolated to "curves" form.

16.4.2 Auditioning

While you can use the regular play commands to play back audio when the Sample Editor is open, it is often useful to listen to the edited material only. This can be done in the following ways:

- When auditioning, audio will be routed directly to Bus 1, bypassing the audio channel's settings, effects and EQs.

By Using the Speaker Tool

If you click somewhere in the Waveform display with the Speaker tool and keep the mouse button pressed, the clip will be played back from the position at which you clicked. Playback will continue until you release the mouse button.

By Using the Play Icon

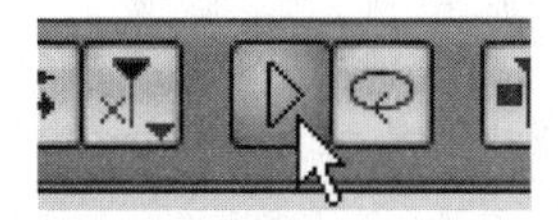

Clicking the Play icon on the toolbar plays back the edited audio, according to the following rules:

- If you have made a selection, this selection will be played back.
- If there is no selection, but the option "Show Event" is activated (see page 374), the section of the clip corresponding to the event will be played back.
- If there is no selection, and "Show Event" is deactivated, the playback will start at the cursor position (if the cursor is outside the display, the whole clip is played back).
- If the Loop icon is activated, playback will continue repeatedly until you deactivated the Play icon. Otherwise, the section will be played back once.

16.4.3 Scrubbing

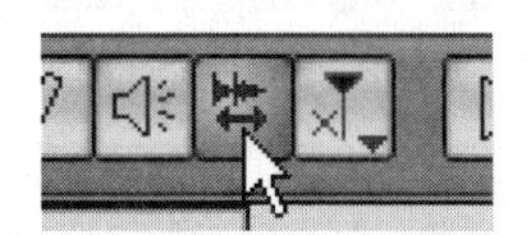

The Scrub tool allows you to locate positions in the audio by playing back, forwards or backwards, at any speed:

1. **Select the Scrub tool.**
2. **Click in the Waveform display and keep the mouse button pressed.**

   The project cursor is moved to the position at which you click.

3. Drag to the left or right.

The project cursor follows the mouse pointer and the audio is played back. The speed and pitch of the playback depends on how fast you move the pointer.

16.4.4 Adjusting the Snap Point

The snap point is a marker within an audio event (or clip—see below). This is used as a reference position when you are moving events with snap activated, so that the snap point is "magnetic" to whatever snap positions you have selected.

By default, the snap point is set at the beginning of the audio event, but often it is useful to move the snap point to a "relevant" position in the event, such as a downbeat, etc:

1. Activate the "Audio Event" option so that the event is displayed in the editor.

2. Scroll so that the event is visible, and locate the "S" flag in the event.

If you haven't adjusted this previously, it will be located at the beginning of the event.

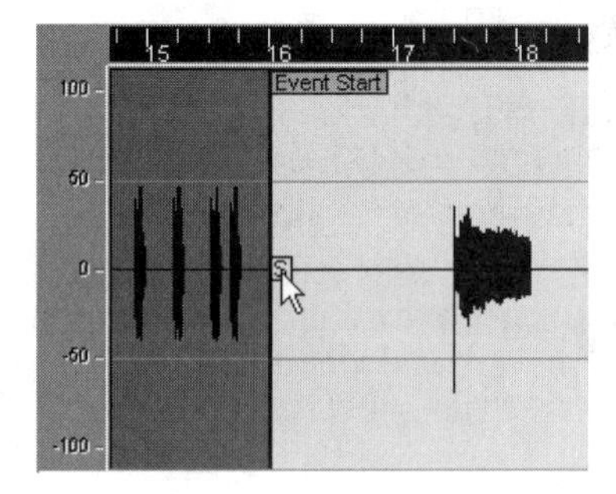

3. Click on the "S" flag and drag it to the desired position.

You can also adjust the snap point by setting the project cursor:

1. Place the cursor at the desired position (intersecting the event).

You may want to do this by scrubbing, to spot the right position exactly.

2. Pull down the Audio menu and select "Snap Point To Cursor".

The snap point will be set to the position of the cursor. This method can also be used in the Project window and the Audio Part Editor.

- **It is also possible to define a snap point for a clip (for which there is no event yet).**

  To open a clip in the Sample Editor, double click it in the Pool (or drag it from the Pool to the Sample Editor). After having set the snap point using the procedure described above, you can insert the clip into the project from the Pool or the Sample Editor, taking the snap point position into account.

16.4.5 Making Selections

To select an audio section in the Sample Editor, you click and drag with the Range Selection tool.

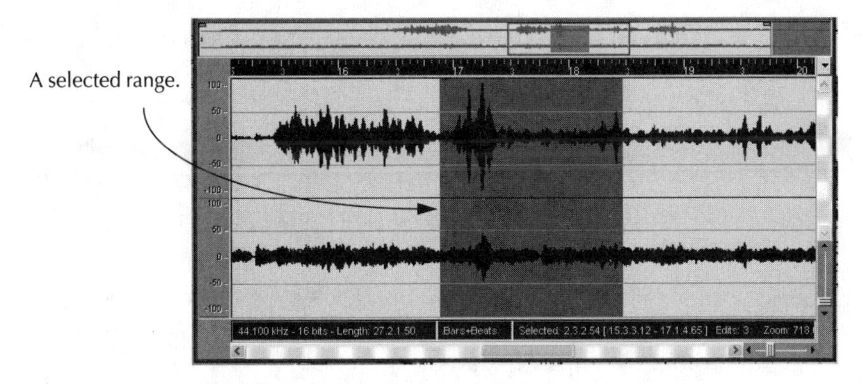

- **If Snap to Zero Crossing is activated on the toolbar, the start and end of the selection will always be at zero crossings (see page 374).**
- **You can resize the selection by dragging its left and right edge or by [Shift]-clicking.**
- **The current selection is indicated to the right on the toolbar.**

  You can fine-tune the selection by changing these values numerically. Note that the values are relative to the start of the clip, rather than to the project timeline.

Using the Select Menu

The Select submenu on the Edit menu contains the following selection functions:

Function	Description
All	Selects the whole clip.
None	Selects no audio (the selection length is set to "0").
In Loop	Selects all audio between the left and right locator.
From Start to Cursor	Selects all audio between the start of the clip and the project cursor.
From Cursor to End	Selects all audio between the project cursor and the end of the clip. For this to work, the project cursor must be within the clip boundaries.
Select Event	Selects the audio that is included in the edited event only. This is not available if you opened the Sample Editor from the Pool (in which case the whole clip is opened for editing, not an event).
Left Selection Side to Cursor	Moves the left side of the current selection range to the project cursor position. For this to work, the cursor must be within the clip boundaries.
Right Selection Side to Cursor	Moves the right side of the current selection range to the project cursor position (or the end of the clip, if the cursor is to the right of the clip).

16.4.6 Editing Selection Ranges

Selections in the Sample Editor can be manipulated in several ways. Please note:

- **If you attempt to edit an event that is a shared copy (i.e. the event refers to a clip that is used by other events in the project), you are asked whether you want to create a new version of the clip or not (if you haven't made a "permanent" choice already—see below).**

  Select "New Version" if you want the editing to affect the selected event only. Select "Continue" if you want the editing to affect all shared copies.
  Note: If you activate the option "Do not show this message again" in the dialog, any and all further editing you do will conform to the selected method ("Continue" or "New Version"). You can change this setting at any time with the "On Processing Shared Clips" pop-up menu in the Preferences dialog (Audio page).

- **Any changes to the clip will appear in the Offline Process History, making it possible to undo them at a later point (see page 349).**

Cut, Copy and Paste

The cut, copy and paste commands on the Edit menu work according to the following rules:

- **Selecting copy copies the selection to the clipboard.**
- **Selecting cut removes the selection from the clip and moves it to the clipboard.**

  The section to the right of the selection is moved to the left to fill out the gap.
- **Selecting paste copies the data on the clipboard into the clip.**

  If there is a selection in the editor, this will be replaced by the pasted data. If there is no selection (if the selection length is "0"), the pasted data will be inserted starting at the selection line. The section to the right of the line will be moved to make room for the pasted material.

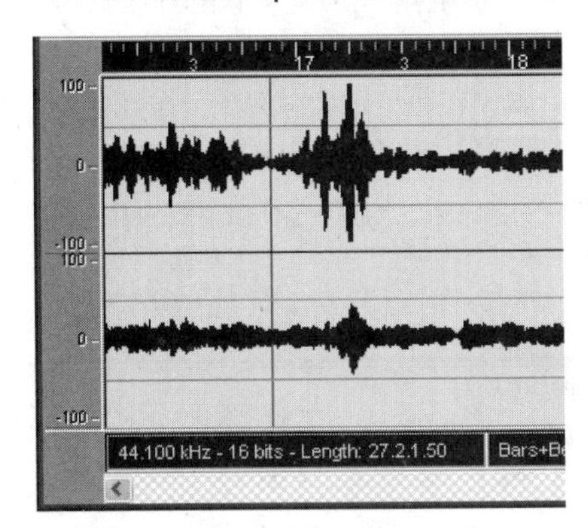

The pasted data will be inserted at the selection line.

Insert Silence

Selecting "Insert Silence" from the Range submenu on the Edit menu will insert a silent section with the same length as the current selection, at the selection start.

- **The selection will not be replaced, but moved to the right to make room.**

  If you want to replace the selection, use the "Silence" processing function instead (see page 343).

Delete

Selecting Delete from the Edit menu (or pressing [Backspace]) removes the selection from the clip. The section to the right of the selection is moved to the left to fill out the gap.

Processing

The functions on the Process submenu on the Audio menu can be applied to selections in the Sample Editor, as can the effects on the Plug-ins submenu. See the chapter "Audio Processing and Functions".

Creating a New Event from the Selection

You can create a new event that plays only the selected range, using the following method:

1. **Make a selection range.**
2. **Press [Ctrl] and drag the selection range to the desired audio track in the Project window.**

Creating a New Clip or Audio File from the Selection

You can extract a selection from an event and either create a new clip or a new audio file, in the following way:

1. **Make a selection range.**
2. **Select "Bounce Selection" from the Audio menu.**

   You are asked whether you want to create a new edit version (clip) or a new audio file.

- **If you select "Edit Version", a new clip is created and added to the Pool.**

  The new clip will refer to the same audio file as the original clip, but will only contain the audio corresponding to the selection range.

- **If you select "File", a new file is created, containing the selected audio.**

  A new clip will also be added to the Pool, referring to the new audio file.

  Regardless of which option you choose, a new Sample Editor opens with the new clip.

16.4.7 Working with Regions

Regions are sections within a clip. One of the main uses for regions is Cycle recording, in which the different "takes" are stored as regions (see page 90). You can also use this feature for marking important sections in the audio clip. Regions can be dragged into the Project window from the Editor or the Pool, to create new audio events. You can also export a region to disk as a new audio file, from the Pool.

Regions are best created, edited and managed in the Sample Editor:

Creating a Region

1. **Select the range you want to convert to a region.**
2. **Click the "Show Regions" icon on the toolbar, or activate the "Regions" option on the Elements submenu on the Quick menu.**

   The regions list is displayed to the right in the Sample Editor window.

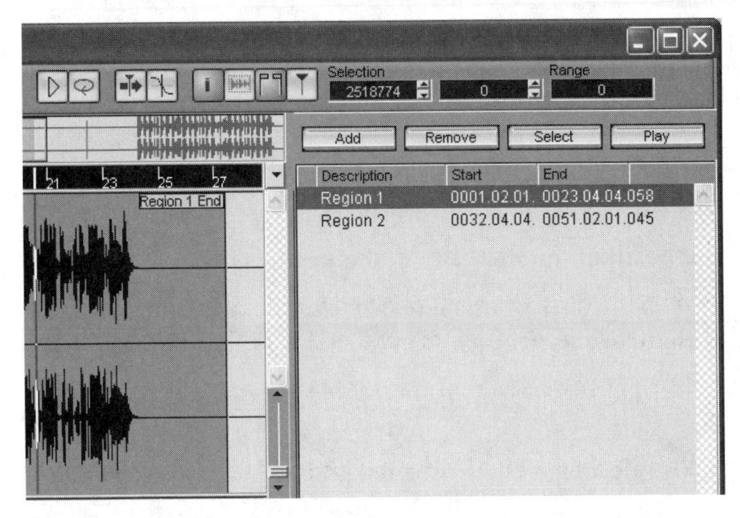

3. **Click the Add button above the Regions list (or select "Create Region(s)" from the Audio menu).**

   A region is created, corresponding to the selected range.
4. **To name the region, click on it in the list and type in a new name.**

   Regions can be renamed at any time, using this procedure.

- **When a region is selected in the Region list, it is instantly displayed and selected in the Sample Editor.**

Editing Regions

The region selected in the list is displayed in grey in the Waveform display and thumbnail.

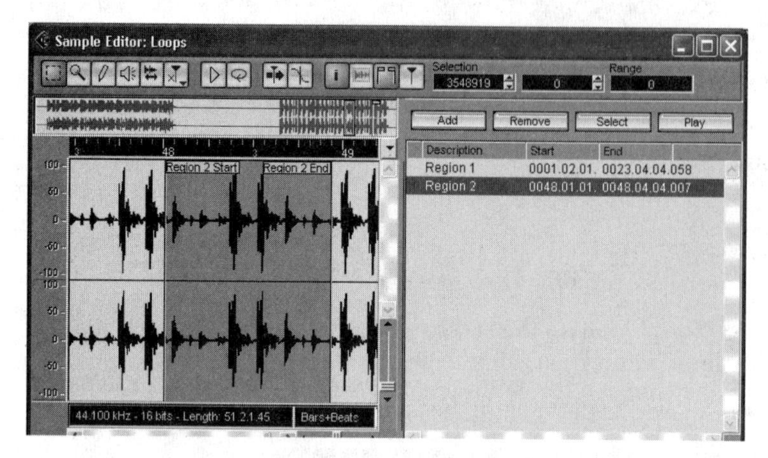

There are two ways to edit the start and end position of a region:

- **Click and drag its start and end handles in the Waveform display (with any tool).**

  When you move the pointer over the handles, it will automatically change to an arrow pointer, to indicate that you can drag the handles.

- **Edit the Start and End positions numerically in the Regions list.**

  The positions are shown in the display format selected for the ruler and info line, but are relative to the start of the audio clip, rather than the project timeline.

Auditioning Regions

You can listen to a region by selecting it in the list and clicking the Play button. The region will play back once or repeatedly, depending on whether the Loop icon on the toolbar is activated or not.

Making Selections from Regions

If you select a region in the list and click the Select button above, the corresponding section of the audio clip is selected (as if you had selected it with the Range Selection tool). This is useful if you want to apply processing to the region only, etc.

- **Note that you can also double click a region in the Pool, to have its audio clip open in the Sample Editor with the area of the region automatically selected.**

Creating New Events from Regions

You can create new audio events from regions, using the following method:

1. **Click in the Region's leftmost column in the list and keep the mouse button pressed.**
2. **Move the pointer to the desired audio track and position in the Project window.**
3. **Release the mouse button.**

   A new event is created.

- **You can also use the function "Events from Regions" for this (see page 148).**

Removing Regions

To remove a region from a clip, select it in the list and click the Remove button.

Exporting Regions as Audio Files

If you create a region in the Sample Editor, the region can then be exported to disk as a new audio file. This is done from the Pool, and is described on page 413.

16.4.8 Drawing in the Sample Editor

It is possible to edit the audio clip at sample level, by drawing with the Pencil tool. This can be useful if you need to manually edit out a spike or click, etc.

1. **Zoom in to a zoom value lower than 1.**

   This means that there is more than one screen pixel per sample.
2. **Select the Pencil tool.**
3. **Click and draw at the desired position in the Waveform display.**

   When you release the mouse button, the edited section is automatically selected.

- Any changes created by drawing will appear in the Offline Process History, making it possible to undo them at a later stage (see page 349).

16.5 Options and Settings

16.5.1 Show Audio Event

- This is only available if you opened the Sample Editor by double clicking on an audio event in the Project window or the Audio Part Editor.

When the option "Audio Event" is activated on the Elements submenu on the Quick menu (or the Show Audio Event button is activated on the toolbar), the section corresponding to the edited event is shown with a white background in the Waveform display and Thumbnail. The sections of the audio clip that are "outside" the event are shown with a grey background.

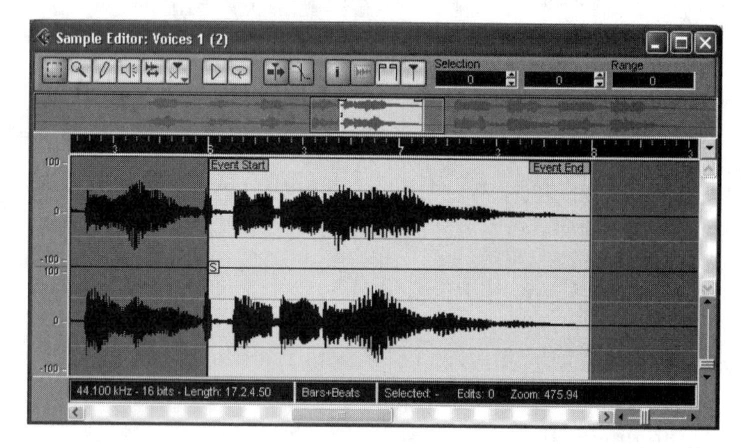

- **In this mode, you can adjust the start and end of the event in the clip, by dragging the event handles in the Waveform display.**

  When you move the pointer over the event handles (no matter what tool may be selected), it takes on the shape of an arrow, to indicate that you can click and drag.

16.5.2 Snap to Zero Crossing

Snap to Zero Crossing activated.

When this option is activated, all audio edits are done at zero crossings (positions in the audio where the amplitude is zero). This helps you avoid pops and clicks which might otherwise be caused by sudden amplitude changes.

- **This setting is global for the project, which means that if you activate it in the Sample Editor, it will also be activated in the Project window and Audio Part Editor (and vice versa).**

16.5.3 Auto Scroll

Auto Scroll activated.

When this option is activated, the Waveform display will scroll during playback, keeping the project cursor visible in the editor.

17 The Audio Part Editor

17.1 Background

The Audio Part Editor allows you to view and edit the events inside an audio part. Essentially, this is the same type of editing that you do in the Project window, which means that this chapter contains a lot of references to the chapter "The Project Window".

Audio parts are created in the Project window, in one of the following ways:

- **By selecting one or several audio events on the same track, and selecting "Events to Part" from the Audio menu.**
- **By gluing together two or more audio events on the same track with the Glue Tube tool.**
- **By drawing an empty part with the Pencil tool.**
- **By double clicking between the left and right locator on an audio track.**

  With the last two methods, an empty part is created. You can then add events to the part by pasting, or by using drag and drop from the Pool.

17.2 Opening the Audio Part Editor

You open the Audio Part Editor by double clicking on an audio part in the Project window. You can have more than one Audio Part Editor open at the same time.

- **If the part you double click on is a shared copy (i.e. you have previously copied the part by [Alt]-dragging), any editing you perform will affect all shared copies of this part.**

  To indicate that it is a shared copy the part name is in italics and an icon is displayed in the lower right corner of the part in the Project window. (see page 135).

- **Note that double clicking on an audio event in the Project window will open the Sample Editor (see page 359).**

17.3 Window Overview

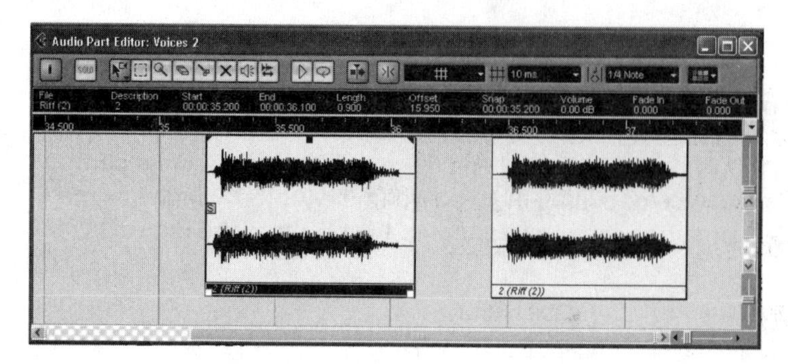

17.3.1 The Toolbar

The tools, settings and icons on the toolbar have the same functionality as in the Project window, with the following differences:

- A Solo button (see page 381).
- Separate tools for audition (Speaker) and scrubbing (see page 382).
- No Pencil or Glue Tube tool.
- Play and Loop icons (see page 381).

17.3.2 The Ruler and Info Line

These have the same functionality and appearance as their counterparts in the Project window.

- **Note that you can select a separate display format for the Audio Part Editor ruler by clicking on the arrow button to the right of it and selecting an option from the pop-up menu that appears.**

  For a list of the available formats, see page 116.

17.3.3 About Lanes

If you make the Editor window larger, this will reveal additional space below the edited events. This is because an audio part is divided vertically in *lanes*.

Lanes can make it easier to work with several audio events in a part:

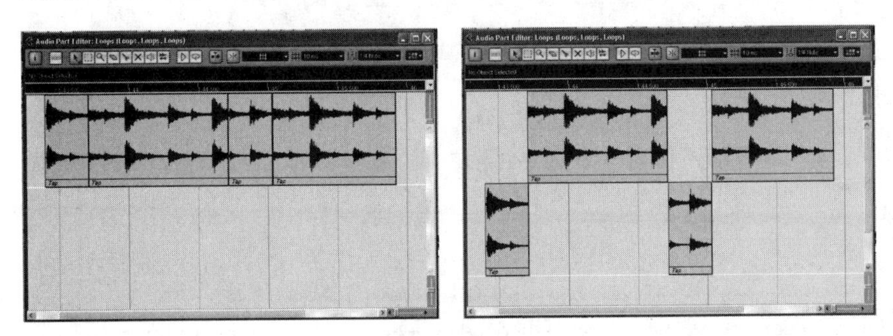

In the left figure it is unnecessarily hard to discern, select and edit the separate events. In the right figure, some of the events have been moved to a lower lane, making selection and editing much easier.

- **To move an event to another lane without accidentally moving it horizontally, press [Ctrl] and drag it up or down.**

  This is the default modifier key for this—you can adjust this in the Preferences if you like.

Overlapping Events

Only one event per track can be played back at the same time! This means that if you have overlapping events, on the same lane or different lanes, these will cut each other off, according to the following rules:

- **For events on the same lane, the ones that are on top (visible) will be played.**

  To move overlapping events to the front or back, use the Move to Front and Move to Back functions on the Edit menu.

- **For events on different lanes, the event on the lowest lane gets playback priority.**

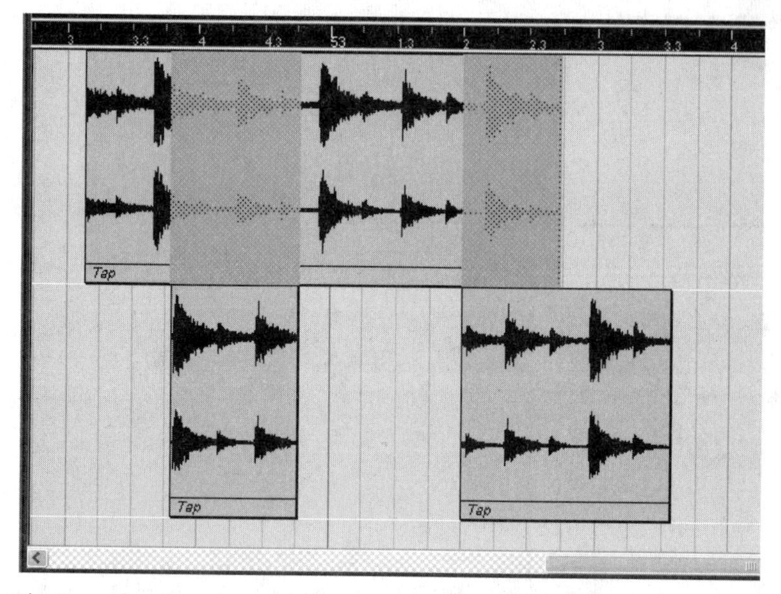

The "greyed-out" sections of the upper event will not be played since the event on the lower lane has playback priority! Note that in the actual program, playback priority between lanes is not indicated by event sections being greyed out.

17.4 Operations

- Zooming, selecting and editing in the Audio Part Editor is done just as in the Project window (see page 117).

17.4.1 Auditioning

There are three ways to listen to the events in the Audio Part Editor:

By Using Regular Playback

You can of course use the regular playback controls while in the Audio Part Editor. Furthermore, if you activate the Solo button on the Toolbar, only the events in the edited part will be played back.

By Using the Speaker Tool

If you click somewhere in the editor's event display with the Speaker tool and keep the mouse button pressed, the part will be played back from the position at which you clicked. Playback will continue until you release the mouse button.

- With the Speaker tool, audio will be routed directly to Bus 1, bypassing the audio channel's settings, effects and EQs.

By Using the Play Icon

The Play and Loop icons.

Clicking the Play icon on the toolbar plays back the edited audio, according to the following rules:

- If you have selected events in the part, only the section between the first and last selected event will be played back.
- If you have made a range selection, only this section will be played back.
- If there is no selection, the whole part will be played back. Note that if the project cursor is within the part, playback starts from the current cursor position. If the project cursor is outside the part, playback starts from the beginning of the part.

- If the Loop icon is activated, playback will continue until you deactivate the Play icon. Otherwise, the section will be played back once.

17.4.2 Scrubbing

In the Audio Part Editor, the Scrub tool has a separate icon on the toolbar. Apart from that, scrubbing works exactly as in the Project window (see page 132).

17.5 Common Methods

17.5.1 Assembling a "Perfect Take"

When you record audio in Cycle mode, either an event or a Region (or both) is created for each recorded lap (see page 90). These events and Regions are named "Take X", where "X" is the number of the take. You can create a perfect take by putting together sections of the different takes in the Audio Part Editor. First, you have to create an audio part from the takes.

Creating an Audio Part

This procedure is slightly different depending on whether you choose to create events or Regions.

From Events

1. **In the Project window, use the Object Selection tool to draw a rectangle around the recorded events.**

   This is necessary, since clicking on the event may just select the event on top (the last take). If in doubt, check the Info line—it should say "Multiple Objects Selected".

2. **Pull down the Audio menu and select "Events to Part".**

   The events are converted to an audio part.

- **Note that the events cycle record mode also makes it easy to combine different takes in the Project Window—see page 90.**

From Regions

1. **In the Project window, select the event you recorded in Cycle mode.**

   After recording, this will play the last take.

2. **Pull down the Audio menu and select "Events to Part".**

   You are asked whether you want to "Create Part using Regions".

3. **Click "Regions".**

   The regions are converted to an audio part.

Assembling a Take

1. **Double click the part to open the Audio Part Editor.**

   Now, the different takes will be placed on different lanes, with the last take at the bottom.

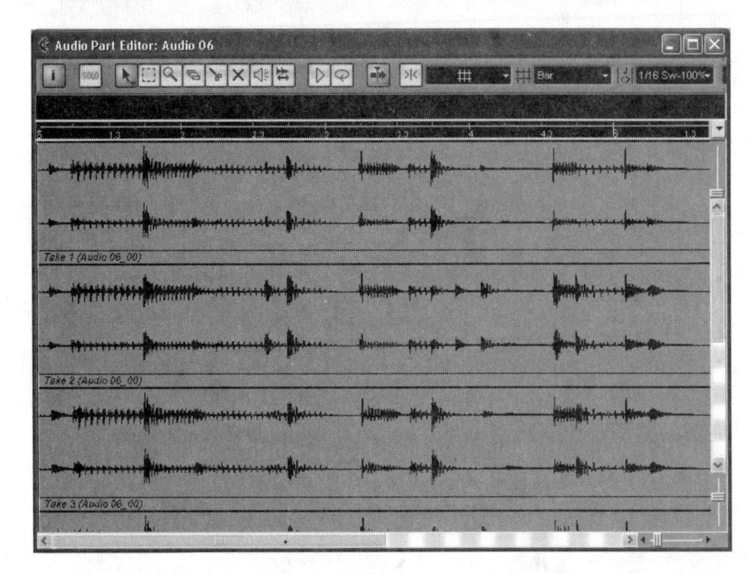

2. **Use the tools to cut out pieces of the takes and assemble the final result.**

   This could include splitting with the Scissors tool, resizing events with the Arrow tool, muting events with the Mute tool or deleting with the Eraser tool.

- **Remember that the events on the lowest lane have playback priority.**

  Use the Play icon to audition the result.

3. Close the Audio Part Editor.

You have now assembled a "perfect take!"

17.6 Options and Settings

The following options and settings are available in the Audio Part Editor:

- **Snap**

  You can specify an independent Snap mode (and snap value for the Grid mode) in the editor. The functionality is exactly the same as in the Project window.

- **Snap to Zero Crossing**

  The Snap to Zero Crossing setting is global for the project, which means that if you activate it in the Audio Part Editor, it will also be activated in the Project window and Sample Editor (and vice versa). For a description of this setting, see page 151.

- **Auto Scroll**

  When Auto Scroll is activated on the toolbar, the window will scroll during playback, keeping the project cursor visible in the Editor. This setting can be activated or deactivated individually for each window.

18 Working with Hitpoints and Slices

18.1 Background

Hitpoint detection is a special feature of the Sample Editor. It automatically detects attack transients in an audio file, and then adds a type of marker, a "hitpoint", at each transient. These hitpoints allow you to create "slices", where each slice ideally represents each individual sound or "beat" in a loop (drum or other rhythmic loops work best with this feature). When you have successfully sliced the audio file, you can do a number of useful things with it:

- Change the tempo without affecting pitch.
- Extract the timing (a groove map) from a drum loop. This can then be applied to quantize other events.
- Replace individual sounds in a drum loop.
- Edit the actual playing in the drum loop without affecting the basic feel.
- Extract sounds from loops.

- Note that the term "loop" is used throughout this chapter. Loops in this context usually means an audio file with a musical timebase, i.e. the length of the loop represents a certain number of bars and/or beats at a certain tempo. Playing the loop back at the right tempo in a cycle set to the correct length will produce a continuous loop, without gaps.

18.2 Using Hitpoints

The basic functionality of using hitpoints to slice up a loop is to make a loop fit the tempo of a song, or alternatively to create a situation that allows the song tempo to be changed whilst retaining the timing of a rhythmic audio loop, just like when using MIDI files.

18.2.1 What Audio Files Can Be Used?

Here are some guidelines to what type of audio files will render the best results when slicing files using hitpoints:

- **Each individual sound in the loop should have some kind of noticeable attack.**

  Slow attacks, legato playing etc. may not produce the desired result.

- **Poorly recorded audio might be difficult to slice correctly.**

  Normalizing a file first can improve the performance.

- **There may be problems with sounds drowned in smearing effects, like short delays.**

18.2.2 Calculating Hitpoints and Slicing a Loop—a Quick Tutorial

Before proceeding, find a suitable loop using the above mentioned criteria. At this point it doesn't matter whether you know the original tempo of the loop, as this will be automatically detected. Proceed as follows:

1. **Create a new empty project.**
2. **Create an audio track.**
3. **Place a suitable audio file at the start of a measure on the audio track.**

   Any type of drumloop should work well.
4. **Select the audio event and select "Locators to Selection" from the Transport menu.**

   This sets the left and right locators to encompass the selection.
5. **Double click the event to open the Sample Editor.**

   Here you can check if you need to adjust the event start and end points to make the file loop seamlessly, by activating Cycle mode in the editor, and playing it back using the Play button in the Sample Editor.
6. **Click the Hitpoint Mode button on the Sample Editor toolbar.**

   The program calculates the hitpoints in the event.

The Hitpoint Mode button.

7. **As you now can see, hitpoints have been set at the beginning of each sound in the loop (or at least at most sounds), and the right half of the toolbar now shows the Sensitivity slider and additional pop-ups.**

   Make sure that the "Use" pop-up is set to "Sense".

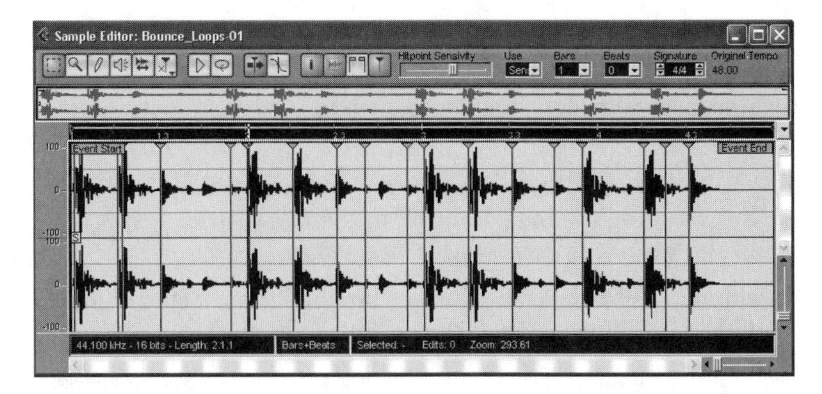

8. If you now move the Hitpoint Sensitivity slider to the left, this gradually hides the hitpoints. Moving the slider to the right increases the sensitivity to reveal additional hitpoints detected during the calculate process.

The basic aim is to add, remove or in various other ways edit the hitpoints so that one individual sound is played between each hitpoint. This is described in detail starting on page 388.

9. Once the hitpoints have been set correctly, enter the length of the loop (using the Bars and/or Beats value fields) and the time signature.

The "original" tempo of the loop is now diplayed to the right on the Sample Editor toolbar. This tempo is based on the length specified for the loop. Note however that the loop will adapt to the tempo set in Cubase SX/SL in the next step.

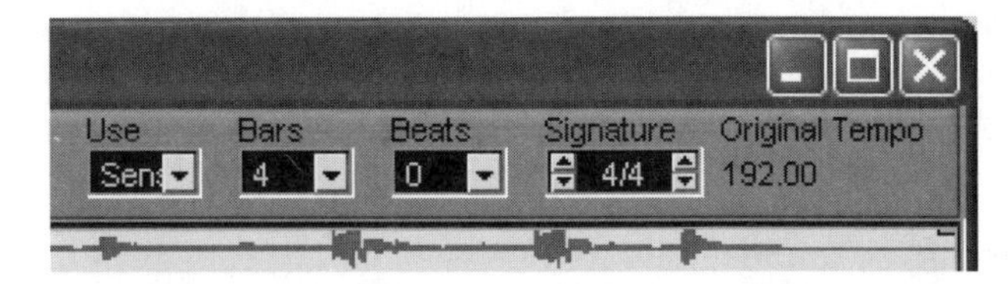

10. Pull down the Audio menu, and select "Create Slices" from the Hitpoints sub-menu.

Now the following happens:

- The Sample Editor closes.
- The audio event is "sliced" so that there is a separate event for each hitpoint.
- The audio event is replaced by an audio part, containing the slices (double click the part to view the slices in the Audio Part Editor).
- The loop is automatically adapted to the set tempo in Cubase SX/SL.

11. If you activate cycle playback on the transport, the loop should now play back seamlessly at the tempo set in the program!

If the loop was two bars long, the loop will be adapted to this length in the Project window, whatever the tempo setting.

12. To make the loop follow any further tempo changes, make sure it's set to "Musical time base" by using the toggle button in the Track list or Inspector (the button should show a note symbol—see page 127).

- **Note that if the tempo in Cubase SX/SL is lower than the loop's original tempo, there may be audible gaps between each slice event in the part.**

  This can be remedied by using the Close Gaps function on the Audio menu—see page 396.

18.3 Editing Hitpoints

In this section, we go back a bit and look at what can be done with hitpoints in the Sample Editor. There are three ways to invoke the hitpoint calculation:

- Select Calculate from the Hitpoints submenu on the Audio menu.
- Click the Hitpoint Mode button in the Sample Editor toolbar.
- Select the Hitpoint Edit tool from the toolbar or Quick menu.
  The last two methods will calculate hitpoints if they haven't already been calculated.

As outlined in the previous section, this makes the program calculate (or detect) hitpoints in the audio event, and you can use the Sensitivity slider to change how many hitpoints are shown.

For some loops, this may be all that is needed to set the hitpoints so that each slice to be created will contain a single "hit" or sound. However there will almost certainly be cases when the automatic calculation may add a hitpoint where there shouldn't be one, and fail to add a hitpoint where one is needed, even if the Sensitivity slider is set to maximum. If there are too many or too few hitpoints in a loop, it will most probably not play back properly.

When this occurs, you have to edit the hitpoints manually in the Sample Editor.

18.3.1 Auditioning Slices

A slice is a section of the waveform, from one hitpoint to the next.

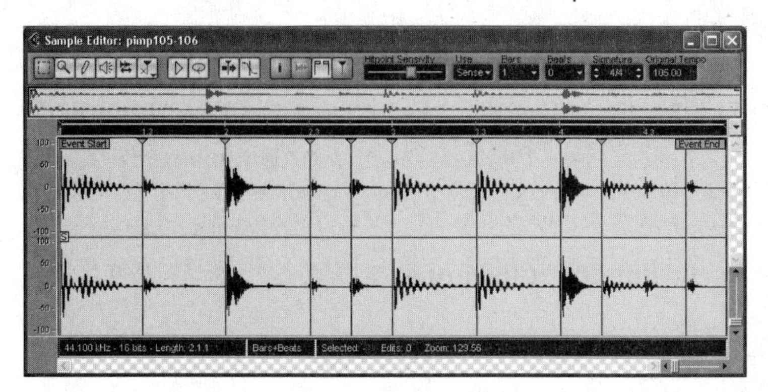

The first thing you should do before editing hitpoints is to listen to each slice in the Sample Editor, to determine what they contain. The aim is basically to avoid "double hits", like a snare hit being followed by a hi-hat hit within the same slice. You also want to determine whether any hitpoints have been added that should be removed:

1. **Open a loop in the Sample Editor.**

   If you have already created slices you can open them in the Sample Editor by double-clicking any event in the Audio Part Editor. If it is a new loop, follow the instructions in the tutorial.

2. **Select the Speaker tool.**
3. **Now you can simply point and click on any slice and it will be played back.**

   Listen for "double hits" and slices that contain parts of a single sound.

If you find hitpoints that need to be removed or instances where a hitpoint needs to be added, the first thing to try is to change the sensitivity setting—see the following section.

18.3.2 Setting the Sensitivity

The loop is first analyzed to determine where hitpoints should appear (where the individual "beats" in the loop are), then you manually set the sensitivity with the Sensitivity slider to determine how many hitpoints there should be.

- **Try raising the sensitivity to add "missing" hitpoints, and lowering it to remove unwanted hitpoints.**

  This may or may not work, depending on the situation, but as a general rule you should try this first.

- **Audition the slices again to determine if changing the sensitivity has improved matters.**

How Many Slices Do I Need?

If your main reason for slicing the loop is to change the tempo, you generally need as many slices as you can get, but never more than one per individual "beat" in the loop.

If you want to create a groove (see page 395), you should try to get approximately one slice per eighth note, sixteenth note or whatever the loop requires.

Setting Hitpoints According to Note Values

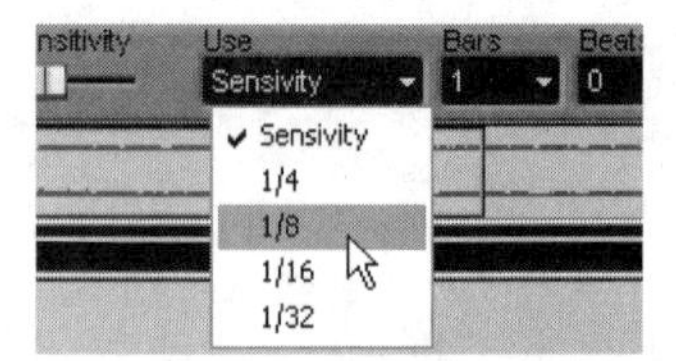

The "Use" pop-up menu on the Sample Editor toolbar also features different note values for setting hitpoints. 1/4, 1/8, 1/16 and 1/32 notes can be selected. Only hitpoints that are close to the selected note value positions within the loop (e.g. close to exact sixteenth note positions, if you have selected the 1/16 option) will be shown—all other hitpoints will be disabled.

- For this to work properly, you must have specified the correct length (bars and beats) and time signature of the loop in the toolbar.

This is useful if you know the loop consists of exact note values with no timing variations (e.g. a loop from a drum machine) or if you're only interested in hits around certain note values (e.g. if you're creating grooves—see page 395).

18.3.3 Disabling Slices

You might run into situations where there are too many slices—a single sound may have been split into two slices for example. You could of course reduce the sensitivity to get rid of the hitpoints you don't want, but then other hitpoints could disappear too, which may be undesirable. What you need to do in a situation like this is to disable an individual slice, using the Hitpoint Edit tool in Disable mode:

1. **Select the Hitpoint Edit tool and click the tool icon on the toolbar again.**

   A pop-up menu appears, listing the three modes of the Hitpoint Edit tool.

2. **Select the Disable mode.**

   The pointer turns into a cross in the Sample Editor window.

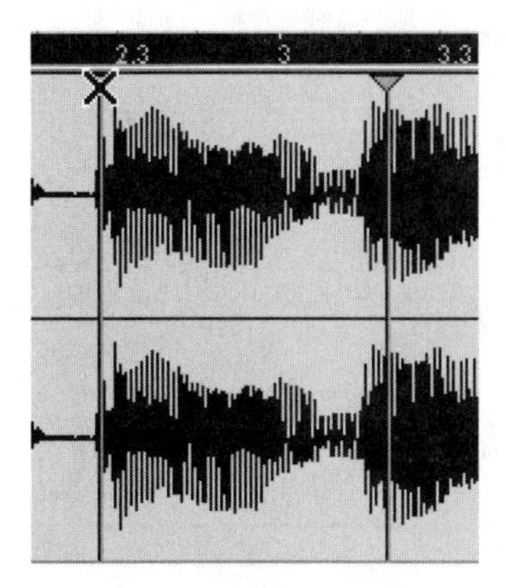

3. **Click on the handle (the triangle) of the hitpoint you wish to disable.**

   The hitpoint handle is diminished and its line disappears to indicate that it is disabled.

4. **Now, the hitpoint won't be taken into account when you create slices.**
5. **To reactivate a disabled hitpoint, click on the hitpoint handle with the Disable tool.**

18.3.4 Locking Slices

If you lock a hitpoint, by clicking on its handle with the Hitpoints Edit tool in Lock mode, it will stay even if you drag the Sensitivity slider all the way to zero. This can be used in situations where one or several slices contain double hits, but raising the sensitivity adds a lot of unwanted slices.

1. **Find the place where you hear double hits when auditioning.**
2. **Remember the current slider setting.**
3. **Raise the sensitivity slider to a higher value so that a hitpoint appears, separating the two sounds.**

   Most likely this will add a lot of other unwanted hitpoints as well.

4. **Audition to make sure you got what you wanted.**
5. **Select the Hitpoint Edit tool and click the tool icon again to select Lock mode.**

   A lock icon is shown beside the pointer in the Sample Editor window.

6. **Lock the new slice by clicking on its handle.**

7. **Drag the sensitivity slider to the original setting.**

   The locked hitpoint will remain shown.

- **You can unlock a locked hitpoint by clicking it again with the Hitpoint Edit tool in Lock mode.**

18.3.5 Setting Hitpoints Manually

If you cannot get the desired result by adjusting sensitivity, disabling or locking, you can add, move and delete hitpoints manually.

- Note that you should always try to use the hitpoints found by the Calculate function before manually moving or adding hitpoints.

Adding Hitpoints

Manually adding hitpoints can be done in situations where a hitpoint is missing at a specific point, but doesn't appear even if the sensitivity is set to full.

1. **Zoom in on the waveform at the point where you wish to add a hitpoint.**
2. **Audition the area with the Speaker tool to make sure that the start of the sound is in view.**
3. **Activate Snap to Zero Crossing on the Sample Editor toolbar.**

   By finding zero crossings in the waveform (positions where the amplitude is close to zero), manually added slices won't introduce any clicks or pops. All hitpoints found by the Calculate function are automatically placed at zero crossings.

4. **Select the Pencil tool from the Sample Editor toolbar and click just before the start of the sound.**

   A new hitpoint appears. Manually added hitpoints are locked by default.

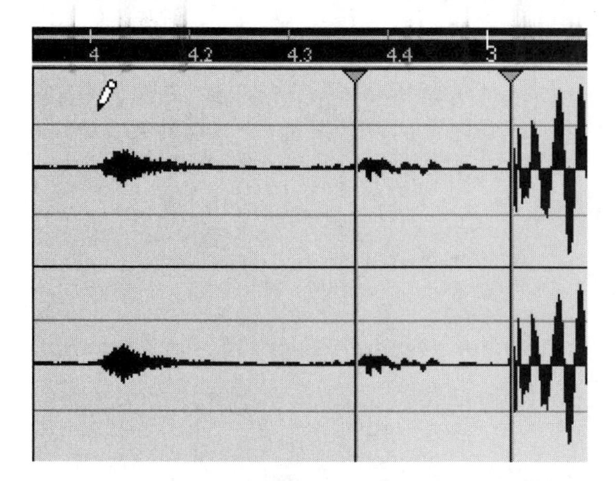

- **If you click and keep the mouse button pressed, you can adjust the position of the new hitpoint by dragging.**

  Releasing the mouse button adds the hitpoint.

5. **Audition the new slice with the Play tool to make sure you got what you wanted.**

Moving Hitpoints

If you manually added a hitpoint, and it was either placed too far away from the start of the sound, or too far into the sound, you can manually move the hitpoint.

1. **Make sure Snap to Zero Crossing is activated on the Sample Editor toolbar.**
2. **Select the Hitpoint Edit tool and click the tool icon again to select the Move mode.**
3. **Click on the tool handle and drag it to the new position.**

Deleting Hitpoints

To delete a hitpoint, select the Move tool and drag it out of the Sample Editor window.

- Don't delete hitpoints that were found by the Calculate function—it is better to disable them.

18.4 Creating Slices

After you have specified the correct loop length and time signature and worked on the hitpoints in the Sample Editor so that one sound per slice is heard, it is time to actually slice the file. This is done by selecting "Create Audio Slices" from the Hitpoints submenu on the Audio menu.

Now the following happens:

- **The Sample Editor closes.**
- **The audio event is "sliced" so that there is a separate event for each hitpoint.**

  In other words, the sections between the hitpoints become separate events, all referring to the same original file.
- **The audio event is replaced by an audio part, containing the slices.**
- **The loop is automatically adapted to the tempo set in Cubase SX/SL.**

  This takes the loop length settings you made into account: if the loop was e.g. one bar long, the part is resized to fit exactly one bar in the Cubase SX/SL tempo, and the slices are moved accordingly—keeping their relative positions intact within the part.

Now, you can change the tempo and have the loop automatically follow (provided that the track is set to musical time base—see page 127). Furthermore, you can double click the part to edit the slices in the Audio Part Editor:

- Remove or mute slices.
- Change the loop by reordering, replacing or quantizing slices.
- Apply processing or effects to individual slices.
- Create new files from individual slices using the "Bounce Selected" function on the Audio menu.

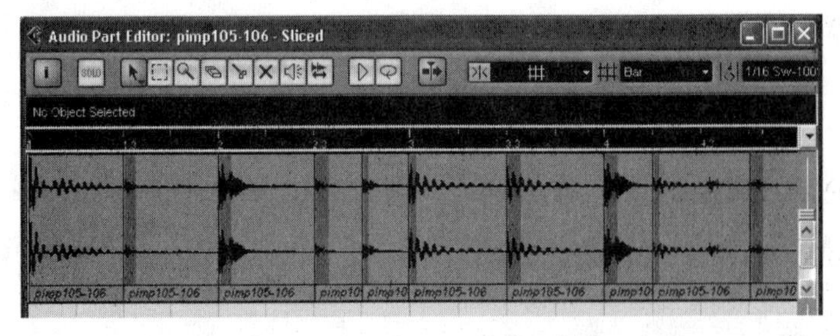

18.5 Creating Groove Quantize Maps

You can generate groove quantize maps based on the hitpoints you have created in the Sample Editor. Groove quantizing is not meant for correcting errors, but for creating rhythmic feels. This is done by comparing your recorded music with a "groove" (a timing grid generated from the file) and moving the appropriate notes so that their timing matches the one of the groove. In other words, you can extract the timing from an audio loop and use it for quantizing MIDI parts (or other audio loops, after slicing them).

Proceed as follows:

1. **Create and edit hitpoints as described earlier in this chapter.**

   You don't have to create slices—just set up the hitpoints.

- **You should try to get approximately one slice per eighth note, sixteenth note or whatever the loop requires when setting hitpoints for extracting a groove. Therefore it can make sense to use note value-based hitpoints.**

  Pull down the "Use" pop-up menu in the Sample Editor toolbar and instead of the regular "Sense" option, select the note value that is most suited as a base for quantizing. 1/4, 1/8, 1/16 and 1/32 notes can be selected. What to choose depends on the loop; typically, rock, pop and dance loops are based on 1/16 or 1/8 notes.

2. **When you have finished setting the hitpoints, select "Create Groove Quantize" from the Hitpoints submenu on the Audio menu.**

   The groove is extracted.

3. **If you now pull down the Quantize pop-up in the Project window you will find an additional item at the bottom of the list, with the same name as the file from which you extracted the groove.**

   This groove can now be selected as a base for quantizing, just like any other quantize value. See page 468.

18.6 Divide Audio Events

This Hitpoints submenu item can be used when you simply wish to create separate events according to the hitpoints for a file. This means that you do not have to make the same considerations as when slicing for tempo changes. You can use any method you like to set hitpoints, use sensitivity, note values, manually or any combination.

- **The slices created will appear in the Project window as separate events.**

18.7 Using the Close Gaps Function

If you have sliced a loop for tempo changes, lowering the tempo below the loop's original tempo will create gaps between the slices. The lower the tempo in relation to the original tempo, the wider the gaps will be. This can be fixed using the "Close Gaps" function on the Audio menu:

1. **Set the desired tempo.**
2. **Select the part in the Project window.**
3. **Pull down the Audio menu and select "Close Gaps".**

   Now time stretch is applied on each slice to close the gaps. Depending on the length of the part, this can take a little while.

4. **The waveform is redrawn and the gaps are now closed!**

- **Note that this feature creates new clips in the Pool, one for each slice.**

● Close Gaps should only be used when you are certain that you wish to permanently adapt the loop to a lower tempo. If you decide to raise the tempo again, you should start over again, using the original unstretched file.

---

19 The Pool

19.1 Background

19.1.1 What Is the Pool?

Every time you record on an audio track, a file is created on your hard disk. A reference to this file—a clip—is also added to the Pool. Two general rules apply to the Pool:

- **All clips, Audio or Video, that belong to a project are listed in the Pool.**
- **There is a separate Pool for every project.**

The way the Pool displays folders and their contents is similar to the way the Windows Explorer displays folders and lists of files.

19.1.2 What Can You Do in the Pool?

In the Pool you can, amongst other things, perform the following operations:

Operations that affect files on disk

- Import clips (audio files can automatically be copied and/or converted).
- Convert file formats.
- Rename clips (this will also rename the referred files on disk).
- Delete clips (if you select the "Move to Trash" option and empty the Trash folder—see page 404).
- Prepare File Archives for backup.
- Minimize Files.

Operations that only affect clips

- Copy clips.
- Audition clips.
- Organize clips.
- Apply audio processing to clips.
- Save or import complete Pool files.

19.1.3 Opening the Pool

You open the Pool in any of the following ways:

- By clicking the Pool icon in the Project window.

- By selecting "Pool" on the Project menu.
- By using a key command (by default [Ctrl]-[P]).

The content of the Pool is divided into three main folders:

- **The Audio folder**

  This contains all audio clips and regions currently in the project.

- **The Video folder**

  This contains all video clips currently in the project.

- **The Trash folder**

  Unused clips can be moved to the Trash folder for later permanent removal from the hard disk.

These folders cannot be renamed or deleted from the Pool, but any number of subfolders can be added (see page 414).

19.2 Window Overview

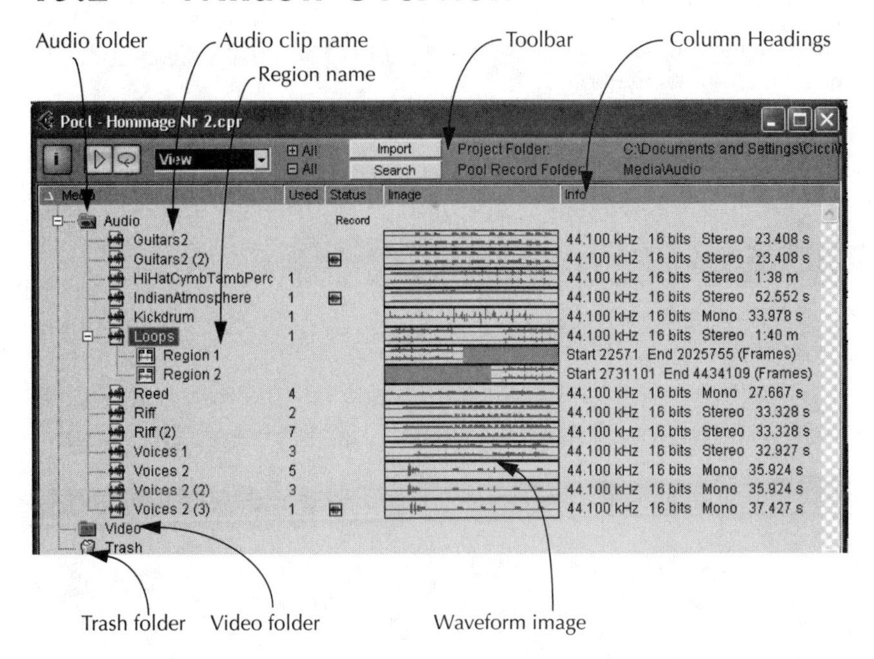

19.2.1 Toolbar Overview

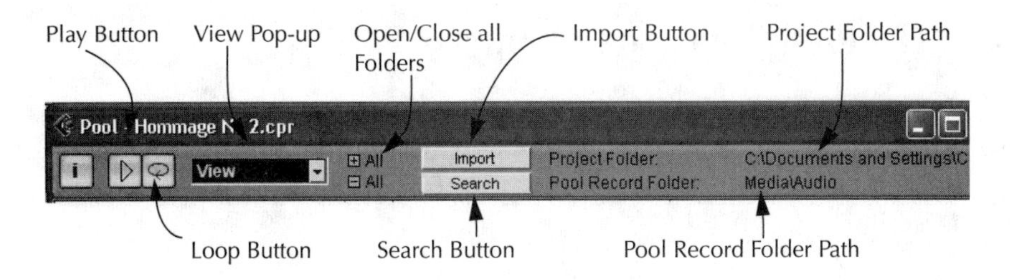

19.2.2 The Info Line

Click the i button on the toolbar to show or hide the info line at the bottom of the Pool window. It shows the following information:

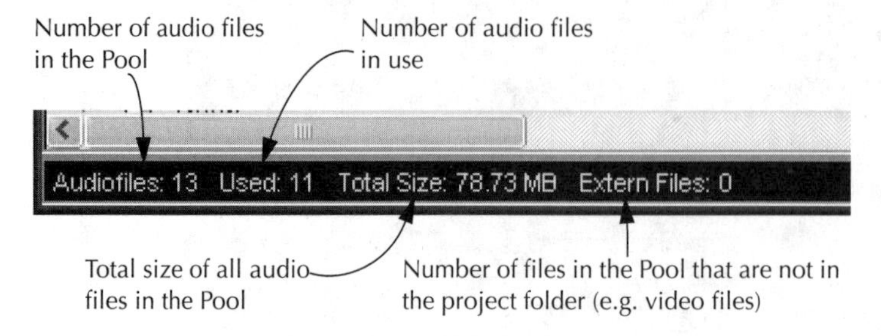

19.2.3 How Clips and Regions Are Displayed in the Pool

- Audio clips are represented by a waveform icon followed by the clip name.

- Audio regions are represented by a region icon followed by the region name.

- Video clips are represented by a camera icon followed by the clip name.

19.2.4 The Pool Window Columns

Various information about the clips and regions can be viewed in the Pool window columns. The columns contain the following information:

Column	Description
Media	This column contains the Audio, Video and Trash folders. If the folders are opened, the clip or region names are shown and can be edited. This column is always shown.
Used	This column displays the number of times a clip is used in the project. If a column row is empty, the corresponding clip is not used.
Image	This column displays waveform images of audio clips or regions.
Status	This column displays various icons that relate to the current Pool and clip status. See page 401 for a description of the icons.

Column	Description
Info	This column shows the following information for audio clips: The sample rate, bit resolution, number of channels and the length in seconds. For regions, it displays start and end times in frames, and for video clips the frame rate, number of frames, and length in seconds.
Type	This column shows the file format of the clip.
Date	This column shows the date when the clip was created.
Origin Time	This column shows the original start position where a clip was recorded in the project. As this value can be used as a basis for the "Insert into Project" Pool menu item (and other functions), you can change it if the Origin Time value is redundant. This can either be done by editing the value in the column, or by selecting the corresponding clip in the Pool, moving the project cursor to the new desired position and selecting "Update Origin" from the Pool menu.
Path	This column shows the path to the location of a clip on the hard disk.

About the Status Column Symbols

The Status column can display various symbols that relate to the clips status. The following symbols can be shown:

Symbol	Description
Record	This indicates the current Pool Record folder (see page 413).
	This symbol is shown if a clip has been processed.
?	The question mark indicates that a clip is referenced to the project but is missing from the Pool (see page 408).
	This indicates that the clip file is external, i.e. located outside the current Project Audio folder.
R	This indicates that the clip has been recorded in the currently open version of the project. This is useful for finding recently recorded clips quickly.

Sorting the Pool Contents

You can sort the clips in the Pool by name, date etc. This is done by clicking on the corresponding column heading. Clicking again on the same heading switches between ascending and descending sort order.

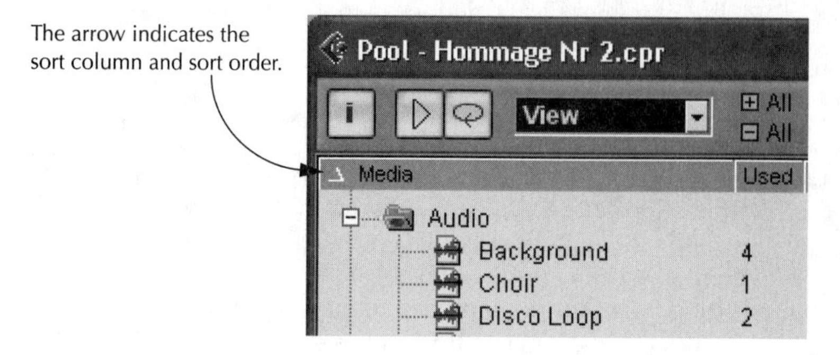

19.3 Operations

19.3.1 Renaming Clips in the Pool

Renaming a clip in the Pool is done in the following way:

- **Select and click on the existing name, type in a new name and press [Return].**

- Renaming a clip in the Pool is much preferred to renaming it outside Cubase SX/SL (for example on the computer desktop). This way Cubase SX/SL already "knows" about the change, and won't lose track of the clip the next time you open the project. See page 408 for details about lost files.

19.3.2 Copying Clips in the Pool

To make a duplicate clip, proceed as follows:

1. **Select the clip you wish to copy.**
2. **Select "New Version" on the Pool menu.**

   A new version of the clip appears in the same Pool folder, with the same name but with a "version number" after it, to indicate that the new clip is a duplicate. The first copy made of a clip will logically get the version number "2" and so on.

● Note: Copying a clip does not create a new file on disk, but just a new edit version of the clip (referring to the same original file).

19.3.3 Inserting Clips into a Project

Using Menus

1. **Select the clip(s) you want to insert into the project.**
2. **Pull down the Pool menu and select one of the "Insert into Project" options:**

Option	Description
At Cursor	The clip(s) will be inserted at the current project cursor position.
At Origin	The clip(s) will be inserted at their Origin Time position.

- **Note that the clip will be positioned so that its Snap point is aligned with the selected insert position.**

  You can also open the Sample Editor for a clip by double clicking it, and perform the insert operation from there. This allows you to set the Snap point for a clip before inserting it.

3. **The clip is inserted on a new audio track, created automatically, or on a selected track.**

   If several tracks are selected, the clip will be inserted on the first selected track.

By Drag and Drop

You can use drag and drop to insert clips into the Project window. You can also use drag and drop from the Sample Editor for a clip by making a selection range and pressing [Ctrl] while dragging. Note:

- **Snap is taken into account if activated.**
- **While you drag the clip in the Project window, its position will be indicated by a marker line and a numerical position box.**

  Note that these indicate the position of the Snap point in the clip. For example, if you drop the clip at the position 22.00, this will be where the Snap point ends up. See page 366 for info about how to set the Snap point.

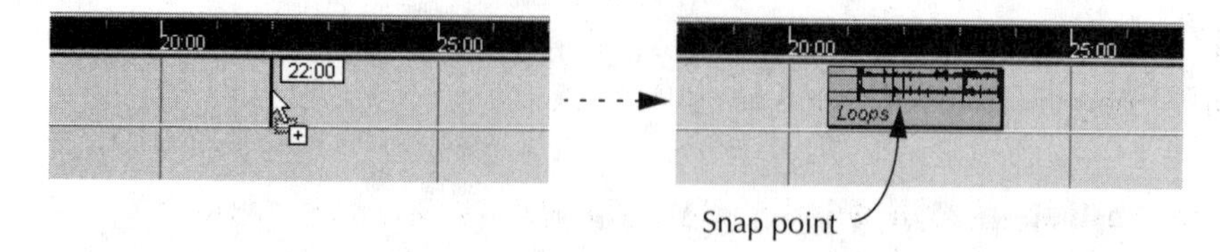

- **If the destination track is empty, it is automatically set to stereo or mono depending on the clip.**

  This works just as when importing audio files from disk into the Project window (see page 129).

- **You can position it in an empty area in the event display (i.e below existing tracks), and a new track is created for the inserted event.**

19.3.4 Deleting Clips

Removing Clips from the Pool

To remove a clip from the Pool *without* deleting it from the hard disk, proceed as follows:

1. **Select the file(s) and select "Delete" from the Edit menu (or press [Backspace] or [Delete]).**

- If you try to delete a clip that is used by one or more events, the program will ask you if you want to remove these events from the project.

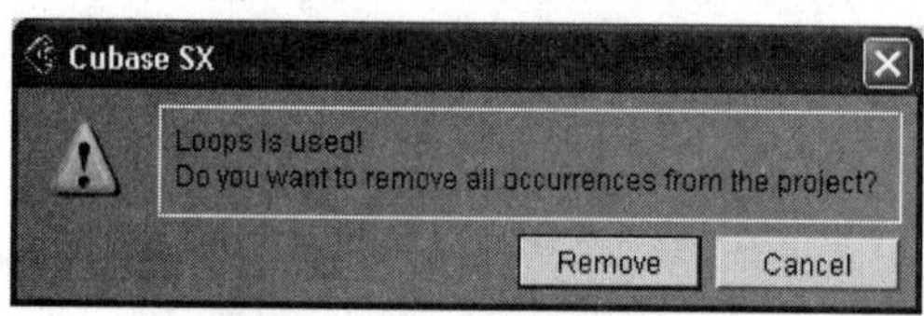

  Canceling this operation means that neither the clip nor the associated events are deleted.

2. **Click Remove.**

   A new prompt asks whether you want to move the clip to the Trash or remove it from the Pool.

3. **Select "Remove from Pool".**

   The clip is no longer associated with the project, but still exists on the hard disk, and can be used in other projects etc. This operation can be undone.

Deleting from the Hard Disk

To delete a file permanently from the hard disk, it must first be moved to the Trash folder:

- **Follow the instructions for deleting clips (see above), and select "Trash".**

When clips are in the Trash folder they can be removed permanently.

- **Select "Empty Trash" on the Pool menu.**

  A dialog box asks you if you are sure you want to follow through. Remember that this operation cannot be undone!

● Before you permanently delete audio files from the hard disk, you should make sure that these aren't used by another project!

Removing Unused Clips from the Pool

This function finds all clips in the Pool that are not used in the project, and either moves them to the Pool Trash folder where they can be permanently deleted, or removes them from the Pool:

1. **Select "Remove Unused Media" on the Pool menu.**

   A prompt appears with the text "Move to Trash or Remove From Pool?"

2. **Make your selection.**

19.3.5 Locating Events Referring to a Clip in the Pool

If you want to find out which events in the project refer to a particular clip in the Pool, proceed as follows:

1. **Select the clip in the Pool.**
2. **Select "Select in Project" on the Pool menu.**

   All events that refer to the selected clip are now selected in the Project window.

19.3.6 Locating Clips or Regions in the Pool

You can perform a search of the Pool to locate particular clips or regions, in the following way:

1. Select "Find in Pool" from the Pool menu.

This opens the Find Media window, in which you can specify various criteria to match. You can search by any one (or a combination) of the following properties:

- Name.
- Size (in seconds, minutes, frames or bytes).
- Bitsize.
- Channels (stereo or mono).

2. Tick the box beside the property you would like to search by, and enter the desired name or value.

For the "Size" property, you can search for sizes smaller or greater than a value, or between two values. This is determined by the second pop-up menu.

3. Press Start.

The search result appears in the lower half of the window.

- **To select the found clips or regions in the Pool, click the "Select in Pool" button.**
- **To insert a found clip or region directly into the project, select it in the list in the dialog and select one of the "Insert into Project" options from the Pool menu.**

The options are described on page 403.

● The "Find in Pool" command is also accessible from the Project window—the Pool window does not have to be open.

Locating Selected Events

If you quickly want to find the clip for an event in the Project window, you can also use the following method:

1. Select one or several events in the Project window.

2. Pull down the Audio menu and select "Find Selected in Pool".

The corresponding clip(s) will be located and highlighted in the Pool. If the Pool window isn't already open it will be opened.

19.3.7 Searching for Audio Files on Disk

The Pool can help you locate audio files on your hard disk or other media. This works much like the regular file search under Windows, but with a couple of extra features:

1. **Click the Search button in the toolbar.**

   A lower pane appears in the window, displaying the search functions.

2. **Use the Folder pop-up menu to specify where to search.**

   The pop-up menu will list all your local drives and removable media.

- **If you want to limit the search to certain folders, choose "Select Search Path" and select the desired folder in the dialog that appears.**

  The search will include the selected folder and all subfolders. Note also that folders you have recently selected using the "Select Search Path" function will appear on the pop-up menu, allowing you to quickly select any of them.

3. **Specify the name of the file(s) to search for in the Name field.**

   You can use partial names or wildcards (*), if you like. Note however, that the function only searches for audio files of the supported formats.

4. **Click the Search button in the search pane.**

   The search is started and the Search button is labeled Stop—click this to cancel the search if needed.

When the search is finished, the found files are listed to the right.

- **To audition a file, select it in the list and use the playback controls to the left.**

  If Auto Play is activated, selected files will automatically be played back.

- **To import a found file into the Pool, select it in the list and click the Import button in the search pane.**

5. **To close the search pane, click the Search button in the toolbar again.**

19.3.8 About Missing Files

When you open a project, you may get a warning that one or more files are "missing". If you click Close in the warning dialog, the project will open anyway, without the missing files. In the Pool you can check which files are considered missing. This is indicated by a question mark in the Status column.

A file is considered missing under one of the following conditions:

- **The file has been moved or renamed outside the program since the last time you worked with the project, and you ignored the Resolve Missing files dialog when you opened the project for the current session.**
- **You have moved or renamed the file outside the program during the current session.**
- **You have moved or renamed the folder in which the missing files are located.**

Locate Missing Files

1. **Select "Find Missing Files" from the Pool menu.**

   The Resolve Missing Files dialog opens.

2. **In the dialog that appears, decide if you want the program to try to find the file for you (Search), if you want to do it yourself (Locate) or if you want to specify in which directory the program should search for the file (Folder).**

- **If you select Locate, a file dialog opens, allowing you to locate the file manually.**

  Click "Open" when you have located the file.

- **If you select Folder, a dialog opens to let you specify the directory in which the missing file can be found.**

  This might be the preferred method if you have renamed or moved the folder containing the missing file, but the file still has the same name. Once you select the correct folder, the program finds the file and you can close the dialog.

- **If you select Search, the program will scan your hard disks for a file with the proper name and display them in a list.**

  The dialog allows you to specify which folder or disk should be scanned. Click the Search Folder button, select a directory or a disk and then click the Start button. If found, select the file from the list and click "Accept". Afterwards Cubase SX/SL tries to map all other missing files automatically.

Reconstructing Missing Edit Files

If a missing file cannot be found (e.g. if you have accidentally deleted it from the hard disk) it will normally be indicated with a question mark in the Status column in the Pool. However, if the missing file is an edit file (a file created when you process audio, stored in the Edits folder within the project folder), it may be possible for the program to reconstruct it by recreating the editing to the original audio file:

1. **Open the Pool and locate the clip(s) for which files are missing.**
2. **Check the Status column—if this says "Reconstructible", the file can be reconstructed by Cubase SX/SL.**
3. **Select the reconstructible clips and select "Reconstruct" from the Pool menu.**

   The editing is performed and the edit files are recreated.

Removing Missing Files from the Pool

If the Pool contains audio files that cannot be found or reconstructed, you may want to remove these:

- **Select "Remove Missing Files" from the Pool menu to remove all missing files from the Pool (and remove their corresponding events from the Project window).**

19.3.9 Auditioning Clips in the Pool

There are two methods you can use to audition clips in the Pool:

- **By selecting a clip and activating the Play button.**

  The whole clip will play back, unless you stop playback by clicking the Play button again.

The Play button.

- **By clicking somewhere in the waveform image for a clip.**

  The clip will play from the position in the waveform you click until the end of the clip, unless you stop playback by clicking the Play button, or by clicking anywhere else in the pool window.

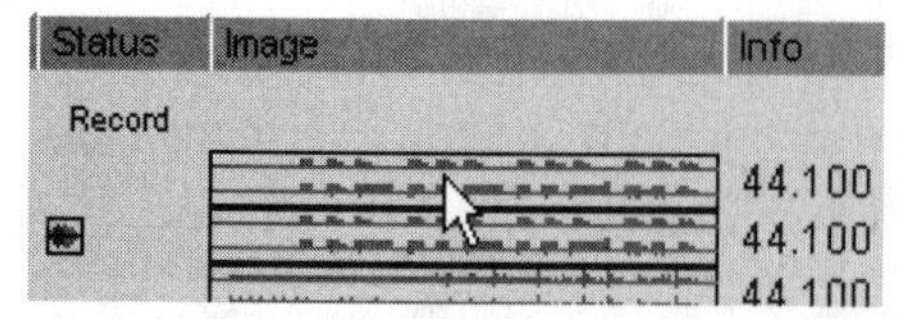

Clicking in the waveform image to audition a clip.

If you have activated the Loop button before you audition, the following will happen:

The Loop button.

- **If you activate the Play button to audition a clip, the clip will repeat indefinitely, until you stop playback by clicking the Play or Loop button again.**
- **If you click in the waveform image to audition, the section from the point you clicked to the end of the clip will repeat indefinitely until you stop playback.**

19.3.10 Opening Clips in the Sample Editor

The Sample Editor allows you to perform detailed editing on the clip (see the Sample Editor chapter for details). You can open clips in the Sample Editor directly from the Pool in the following ways:

- **If you double click on a clip waveform icon, the clip will open in the Sample Editor.**
- **If you double click on a region in the Pool, its clip will open in the Sample Editor with the region selected.**

One practical use for this is to set a Snap point for a clip (see page 366). When you later insert the clip from the Pool into the project, you can have it properly aligned according to the set Snap point.

19.3.11 Import Medium...

The Import Medium dialog is used for importing files directly into the Pool. It is opened by using the Pool menu or by using the Import button in the Pool window.

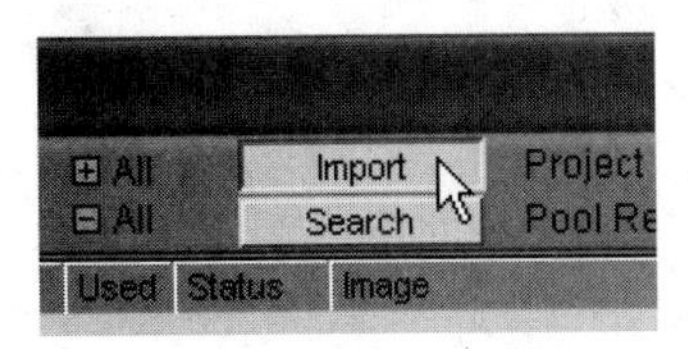

Clicking the Import button...

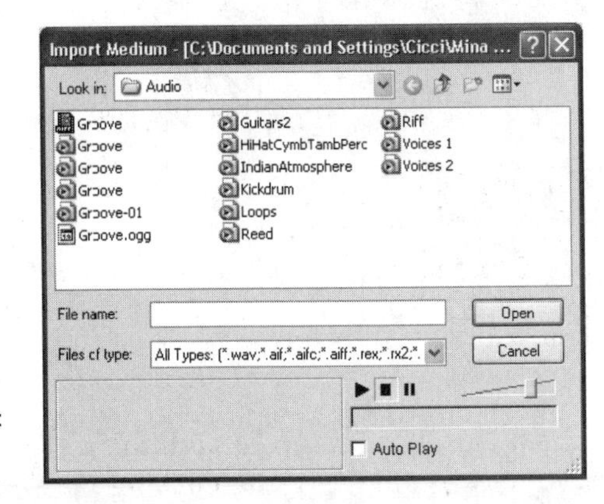

...opens the Import dialog:

The Import Medium dialog is a standard file dialog, where you can navigate to other folders, audition files etc. The following audio file formats can be imported:

- Wave (Normal or Broadcast, see page 611)
- AIFF
- AIFC (Compressed AIFF)
- REX or REX 2 (see page 666)
- MPEG Layer 2 and Layer 3 (mp2 and mp3 files—see page 667)
- Ogg Vorbis (ogg files—see page 667)
- Windows Media Audio (wma files—see page 667)
- Stereo or mono
- Any sample rate (although files with another sample rate than the one used in the project will play back at the wrong speed and pitch—see below).
- 8, 16, 24 bit or 32 bit float resolution

In addition, AVI, QuickTime and MPEG video files can be imported into the Pool.

- It is also possible to use the commands on the Import submenu on the File menu to import audio or video files into the Pool.

When you select a file in the Import Medium dialog and click Open, the Import Options dialog will appear.

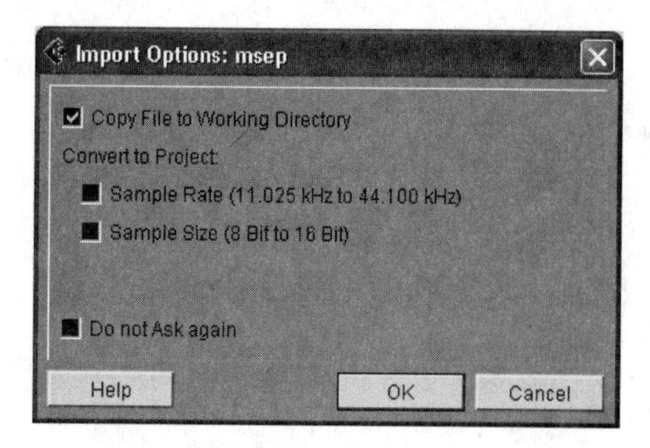

It contains the following options:

- Copy File to Working Directory.
  Activate this if you want a copy of the file to be made in the Project Audio folder, and have the clip refer to this copy. If the option is deactivated, the clip will refer to the original file in the original location (and will thus be marked as "external" in the Pool—see page 401).
- Convert to Project.
  Here you can choose to convert the sample rate and/or the sample size (resolution) to the current format used in the project. The options will only be available if necessary (if the sample rate is different than the one set for the project and/or if the sample size is *lower* than the record format used in the project).
  Note that if you are importing several audio files in one go, the Import Options dialog will instead contain a "Convert if needed" checkbox. When this is activated, the imported files will be converted only if the sample rate is different or the sample size is lower than the project's.
- Do not Ask again.
  If this is ticked, you will always import files according to the settings you have made, without this dialog appearing. This can be reset again in the Preferences—Audio dialog.

● You can always convert later should you so wish, by using the Convert Files (see page 416) or Conform Files (see page 417) options.

19.3.12 Importing Audio CD Tracks (Cubase SX only)

You can import tracks (or sections of tracks) from an audio CD directly into the Pool by using the "Import Audio CD" function on the Pool menu. This opens a dialog in which you can specify which tracks should be grabbed from the CD, converted to audio files and added to the Pool.

For details about the Import Audio CD dialog, see page 663.

19.3.13 Exporting Regions as Audio Files

If you have created regions within an audio clip (see page 371) these can be exported as separate audio files. To create a new audio file from a region, proceed as follows:

1. **In the Pool, select the region you wish to export.**
2. **Pull down the Audio menu and select "Bounce Selection".**

   A browser dialog opens.
3. **Select the folder in which you want the new file to be created.**

   A new audio file is created in the specified folder. The file will have the name of the region and will automatically be added to the Pool.

19.3.14 Changing the Pool Record Folder

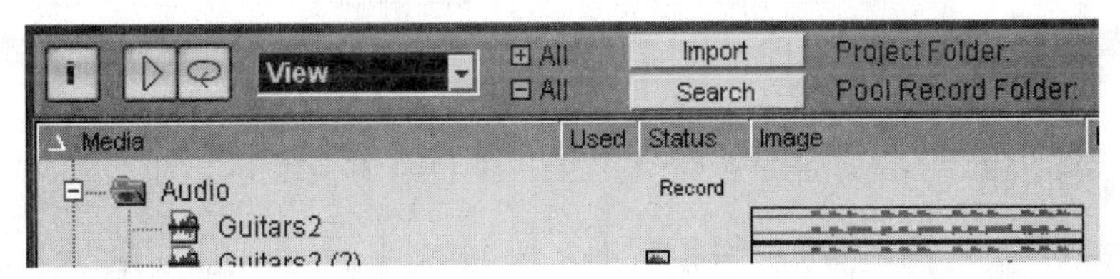

The Pool Record folder.

The Pool Record folder is where all audio clips that you record in the project will end up. The Pool Record folder is indicated by the "Record" symbol shown in the Status column, and by a red dot on the folder itself, as shown in the picture above. By default, this is the main Audio folder. You can, however, at any time create a new Audio subfolder and designate this as your Pool Record folder. Proceed as follows:

1. **Select the Audio folder or any audio clip.**

   You cannot designate the Video folder (or a subfolder in it) as the Pool Record folder.
2. **Select "Create Folder" on the Pool menu.**

   A new empty audio subfolder appears in the Pool.
3. **Select the new folder.**
4. **Select "Set Pool Record Folder" on the Pool menu, or click in the new folders Status column.**

   The new folder now becomes the Pool Record folder, and any audio recorded in the project will from this point on end up in this folder.

19.3.15 Organizing Clips and Folders

If you accumulate a large number of clips in the Pool, it may sometimes be difficult to quickly find specific items. In such cases, organizing clips in new subfolders with suitable names that reflect the content can be a solution. For example, you could put all sound effects in one folder, all lead vocals in another etc. Proceed as follows:

1. **Select the type of folder, audio or video, in which you want to create a subfolder.**

   You cannot put audio clips in a video folder and vice versa.

2. **Select "Create Folder" on the Pool menu.**

   A new empty subfolder named "New Folder" appears in the Pool.

3. **Click on the name and type in a new appropriate name for the folder.**
4. **Select and drag the clips you wish to move to the new folder.**
5. **Repeat steps 1 to 4 as necessary.**

19.3.16 Applying Processing to Clips in the Pool

You can apply audio processing to clips from within the Pool, just like you can to events in the Project window. Simply select the clip(s) and select a processing method from the Audio menu. To find out more about audio processing, see page 330.

19.3.17 Freeze Edits

If you have applied processing to a clip, either in the Project window or in the Pool, this is indicated by the red and grey waveform symbol in the Status column. This processing can always be undone using the Offline Process History (see page 349). You can also use the Freeze Edits function to create a new file with processing applied or replace the original with a processed version—see page 351.

19.3.18 Prepare Archive

This Pool menu command should be used when you want to archive a project. It checks that every clip referenced in the project is located in the same folder. To be more precise, it does the following:

- **Any files that are located outside the current project folder will be copied to it.**

- **If any processing has been applied, you will be asked whether you want to Freeze Edits.**

  If you do this, you don't have to archive the Edit folder. Everything belonging to the project will be contained in the project file and the Audio folder.

- **Once you have performed a Prepare Archive, you can copy the project file and the Audio folder to backup disks, etc.**

  It is not necessary to archive the Images or Fades folders, since these can be recreated by Cubase SX/SL. You may also find a file with the extension ".csh" in the project folder. This contains image information for edited clips and other data that can be recreated, and can safely be deleted.

● Video clips are always referenced, and are not stored in the project folder.

19.3.19 Minimize File

This item on the Pool menu allows you to change the size of audio files according to the audio clips referenced in a project. The files produced using this option will only contain the audio file portions actually used in the project, which can significantly reduce the size of the project (given that large portions of the audio files are unused).

- **This operation will permanently alter the selected audio files in the Pool (the process is undoable), so be careful with this command!**

  If this is not what you want, you can use the "Save Project to New Folder" File menu item instead. This function also has the option of minimizing files, but copies all files into a new folder, leaving the original project untouched. See page 657.

It is useful for archiving purposes. If you have completed a project and wish to minimize the project size as much as possible, use this function.

Proceed as follows:

1. **Select the file(s) you wish to minimize in the Pool.**
2. **Select "Minimize File" from the Pool menu.**

   An alert appears informing you that the entire Edit History will be cleared. You will at this point have the option of cancelling or continuing the operation.

3. **After the operation is finished, another alert asks you to save the project, to update the new file references.**

   Do so.

The audio file(s) in the Pool Record folder will now be cropped so that only the audio actually used in the project remains in the corresponding audio file.

19.3.20 Importing Pool Files

Steinberg's Nuendo application can export the Pool as a separate file (file extension ".npl"). Such Pool files can be imported into Cubase SX/SL, by using the Import Pool command on the Pool menu. When you import a Pool file, the file references in it are "added" to the current Pool.

- The audio and video files themselves are not saved in the Pool file, only a reference to them. For there to be any point in importing a Pool file, you need access to all reference files (which preferably should have the same file paths as when the Pool was saved).

19.3.21 Convert Files

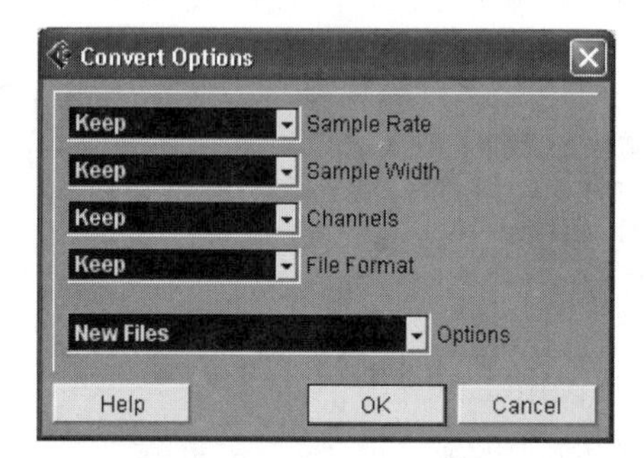

Selecting Convert Files on the Pool menu opens the Convert Options dialog which operates on selected files. Use the pop-up menus to specify which audio file attributes you want to keep and which you want to convert. The options are:

- **Sample Rate.**

  Keep the sample rate as is, or convert to a sample rate between 8.000 and 96.000 kHz.

- **Sample Width.**

  Keep the sample width (resolution) as is, or convert to 16 bit, 24 bit or 32 Bit float.

- **Channels.**

  Keep as is, or convert the file to Mono or Stereo Interleaved.

- **File Format.**

  Keep the current format, or convert to AIFF, Wave or Broadcast Wave format.

Options

When you convert a file, you can use the Options pop-up to set one of the following options regarding what to do with the new file:

Option	Description
New Files	This creates a copy of the file in the audio folder and converts this new file according to the chosen attributes. The new file is added to the Pool, but all clip references will still point to the original, unconverted file.
Replace Files	This converts the original file, without changing clip references.
New + Replace in Pool	This creates a new copy with the chosen attributes, replaces the original file with the new one in the Pool and redirects the current clip references from the original file to the new file. This is the option to select if you want your audio clips to refer to the converted file, but still want to keep the original file on disk (e.g. if the file is used in other projects).

19.3.22 Conform Files

By using this Pool menu command, you will change all selected files that have different file attributes to what is specified for the project, to conform to this standard. Proceed as follows:

1. **Select all clips in the Pool.**
2. **Select "Conform Files" on the Pool menu.**

   A dialog opens allowing you to choose between keeping or replacing the original unconverted files in the Pool. The following applies:

- Clip/event references in the pool are always redirected to the conformed files.
- If any 'keep' option is selected, original files remain in the Project Audio folder and new files are created.
- If you select the 'Replace' option, files in the Pool and in the Project Audio folder are replaced.

19.4 Options and Settings

Customizing the View

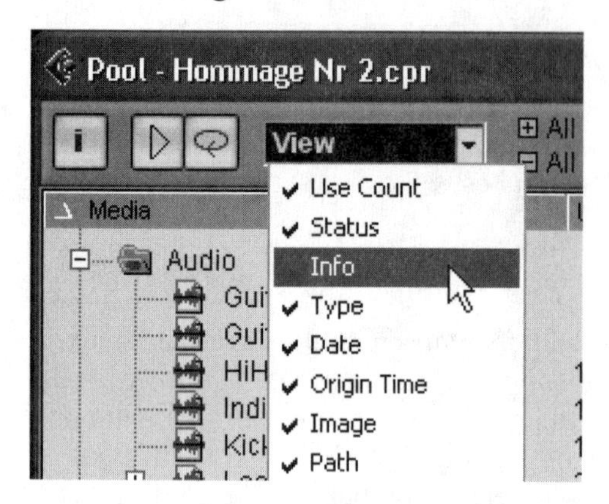

- **You can specify which of the columns should be shown or hidden by selecting the View pop-up on the toolbar and ticking items on or off.**
- **You can rearrange the order of the columns by clicking on a column heading and dragging the column to the left or to the right.**

  The mouse pointer changes to a hand when you place it on the column heading.
- **The width of a column can also be adjusted by placing the pointer between two column headers and dragging left or right.**

  The pointer changes to a divider when you place it between two column headers.

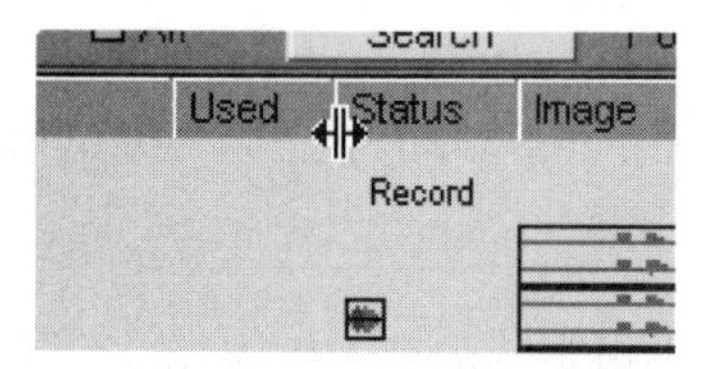

20 MIDI Devices and Patches

20.1 About Program Change and Bank Select

To instruct a MIDI instrument to select a certain patch (sound), you send a MIDI Program Change message to the instrument. Program Change messages can be recorded or entered in a MIDI part like other events, but you can also enter a value in the Program (prg) field in the Inspector for a MIDI track (see page 430). This way, you can quickly set each MIDI track to play a different sound.

With Program Change messages, you are able to select between 128 different patches in your MIDI device. However, many MIDI instruments contain a larger number of patch locations. To make these available from within Cubase SX/SL, you need to use Bank Select messages, a system in which the programs in a MIDI instrument are divided into banks, each bank containing 128 programs. If your instruments support MIDI Bank Select, you can use the Bank (bnk) field in the Inspector to select a bank, and then the Program field to select a program in this bank.

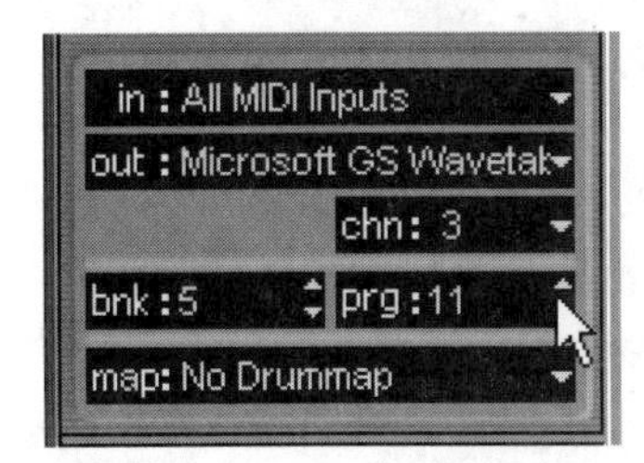

Unfortunately, different instrument manufacturers use different schemes for how Bank Select messages should be constructed, which can lead to some confusion and make it hard to select the correct sound. Also, selecting patches by numbers this way seems unnecessarily cumbersome, when most instruments use names for their patches nowadays.

To help with this, Cubase SX/SL features the MIDI Device Manager. This allows you to specify which MIDI instruments you have connected, by selecting from a vast list of existing devices or by specifying the details yourself. Once you have specified which MIDI devices you're using, you can select to which particular device each MIDI track should be routed. It is then possible to select patches by name in the track list or Inspector.

20.2 Opening the MIDI Device Manager

Select MIDI Device Manager from the Devices menu to bring up the following window:

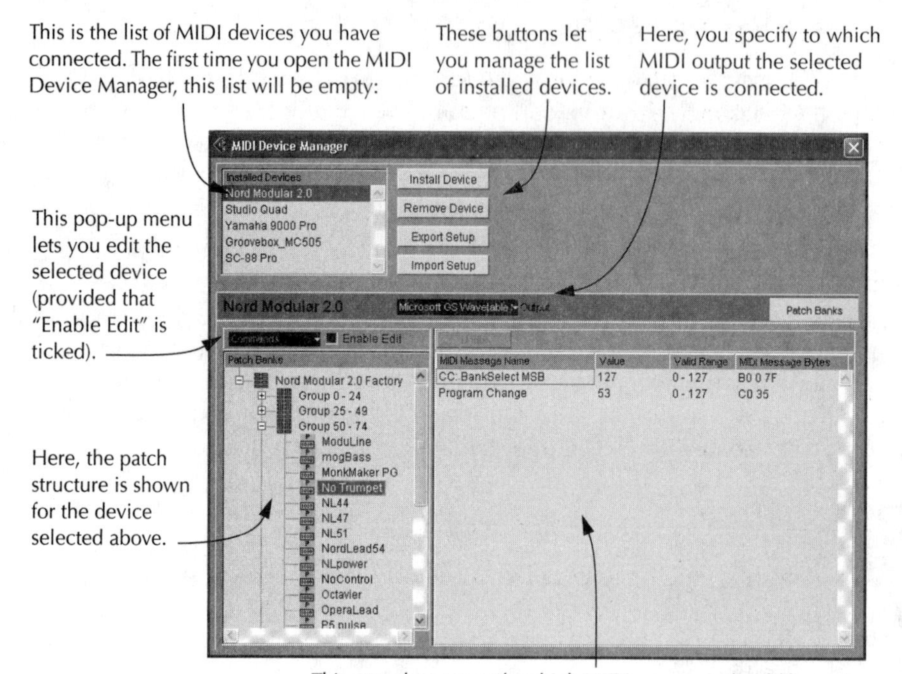

This area shows exactly which MIDI messages should be sent out to select the patch highlighted in the list to the left.

When you open the MIDI Device Manager for the first time, it will be empty (because you haven't installed any devices yet). On the following pages we describe how to add a pre-configured MIDI device to the list, how to edit the settings and how to define a device from scratch (only necessary if a MIDI device isn't included among the pre-configured devices).

20.3 Installing a MIDI Device

In this case "install" means "add to the Installed Devices" list, i.e. specify that a certain device is part of your MIDI system. Proceed as follows:

1. **Click the Install Device button.**

   A dialog appears listing all pre-configured MIDI devices. For now we assume that your MIDI device is included in this list.

2. **Locate and select the device in the list and click OK.**

- **If your MIDI device isn't included in the list but is compatible with the GM (General MIDI) or XG standards, you can select the generic GM or XG Device options at the top of list.**

  When you select any of these options, a name dialog will appear. Enter a name for the instrument and click OK.

Now the device appears in the Installed Devices list to the left.

3. **Make sure that the new device is selected in the list and pull down the Output pop-up menu.**

4. **Select the MIDI output that is connected to the device.**

When the device is selected in the Installed Devices list, the Patch Banks list below shows the patch structure of the device. This could simply be a list of patches, but it's usually one or several layers of banks or groups containing the patches (much like a folder structure on a hard disk for example).

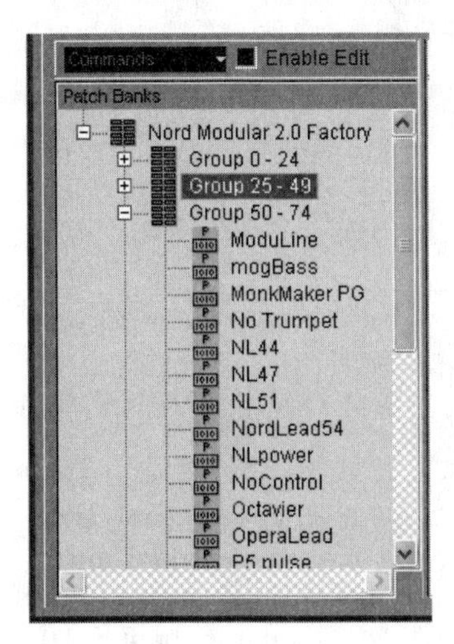

- You can rename a device in the Installed Devices list by double clicking and typing. This is useful if you have several devices of the same model, and want to separate them by name instead of by a number.
- To remove a device from the Installed Devices list, select it and click Remove Device.

20.3.1 About Patch Banks

Depending on the selected device, you may find that the Patch Banks list is divided in two or more main banks. Typically, these are called Patches, Performances, Drums etc. The reason for having several patch banks is that different "types" of patches are handled differently in the instruments. For example, while "patches" typically are "regular" programs that you play one at the time, "performances" may be combinations of patches, which could e.g. be split across the keyboard, layered or used for multitimbral playback.

For devices with several banks, you will find an additional button to the right, labeled Bank Assignment. Clicking this opens a dialog in which you can specify for each MIDI channel which bank it should use.

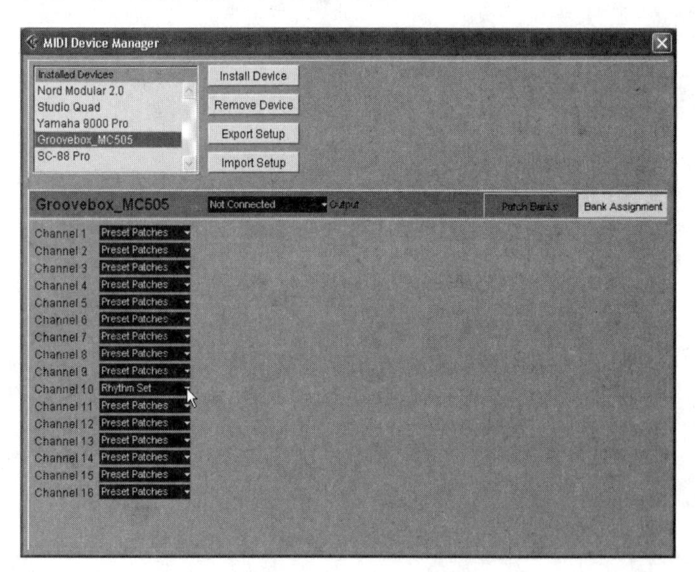

The selection here will affect which bank is displayed when you select programs by name for the device in the track list or Inspector (see below). For example, many instruments use MIDI channel 10 as a exclusive drum channel, in which case you would want to select the "Drums" (or "Rhythm Set", "Percussion", etc.) bank for channel 10 in this list. This would then let you select between different drum kits in the track list or Inspector.

20.4 Selecting a Patch for an Installed Device

If you return to the Project window at this point, you will find that the installed device has been added to the MIDI Output menus (in the track list and the Inspector). Now you can select patches by name, in the following way:

1. **Pull down the Output menu (in the track list or Inspector) for a track that you want to play the installed device, and select the device.**

   This directs the track to the MIDI output specified for the device in the MIDI Device Manager. The bank and program fields in the track list and Inspector are replaced by a single "prg" field.

2. **Click the "prg" field to display a pop-up menu, hierarchically listing all the patches in the device.**

   The list is similar to the one displayed in the MIDI Device Manager. You can scroll the list up and down (if required), click the plus/minus signs to show or hide sub-groups, etc.

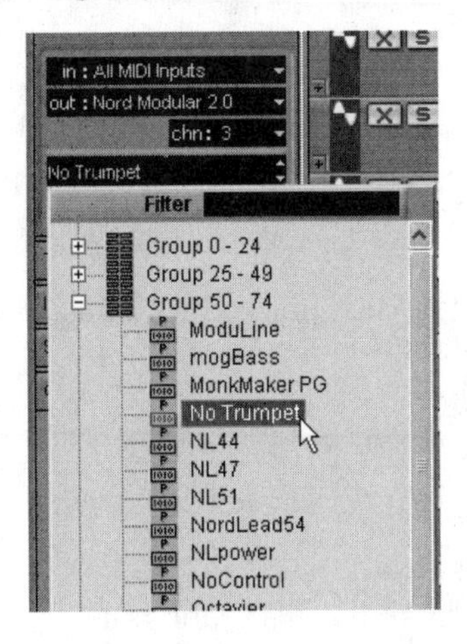

3. **Click a patch in the list to select it.**

   This sends the appropriate MIDI message to the device. You can also scroll the program selection up or down, as with any value.

20.5 Renaming Patches in a Device

The pre-configured devices list the factory-preset patches, i.e. the patches included in the device when you first bought it. If you have replaced some of the factory presets with your own patches, you need to modify the device so that the patch name list matches the actual device:

1. **In the MIDI Device Manager, select the device in the Installed Devices list.**
2. **Activate the Enable Edit checkbox.**

   When this is turned off (default) you cannot edit the pre-configured devices.
3. **Use the Patch Banks display to locate and select the patch you want to rename.**

   In many instruments, the user-editable patches are located in a separate group or bank.
4. **Click on the selected patch in the Patch Banks list to edit its name.**
5. **Type in the new name and click OK.**
6. **Rename the desired patches in this way, and finish by deactivating Enable Edit again (to avoid modifying the device by accident).**

- It's fully possible to make more radical changes to the patch structure in a device as well (adding or deleting patches, groups or banks).
  For example, this would be useful if you expanded your MIDI device by adding extra storage media such as RAM cards, etc. The available editing functions are described in the section "Defining a new device" below.

20.6 Defining a New Device

If your MIDI device is not included in the list of pre-configured devices (and not a "plain" GM or XG device), you need to define it manually to make it possible to select patches by name:

1. **In the MIDI Device Manager, click the Install Device button.**

   The Add MIDI Device dialog appears.
2. **Select "Define New..." and click OK.**

   A name dialog appears.
3. **Enter the name of the device and click OK.**

   The device appears in the Installed Devices list.

4. **Select the device in the list.**

   As you can see, it currently contains only an Empty Bank item.

5. **Make sure the Enable Edit checkbox is activated.**

   Now you can use the functions on the Commands pop-up menu to the left to organize the patch structure of the new device.

A patch structure is made out of the following components:

- Banks are the main categories of sounds—typically patches, performances and drums, as described above.
- Each bank can contain any number of groups, represented by folders in the list.
- The individual patches, performances or drum kits are represented by presets in the list.

The Commands pop-up menu contains the following items:

Create Bank

Creates a new bank at the highest hierarchical level of the Patch Banks list. You can rename this by clicking on it and typing a new name.

New Folder

Creates a new subfolder in the selected bank or folder. This could correspond to a group of patches in the MIDI device, or just be a way for you to categorize sounds, etc. When you select this item, a name dialog will appear, allowing you to name the folder. You can also rename the folder afterwards by clicking it and typing in the list.

New Preset

This adds a new preset in the selected bank or folder.

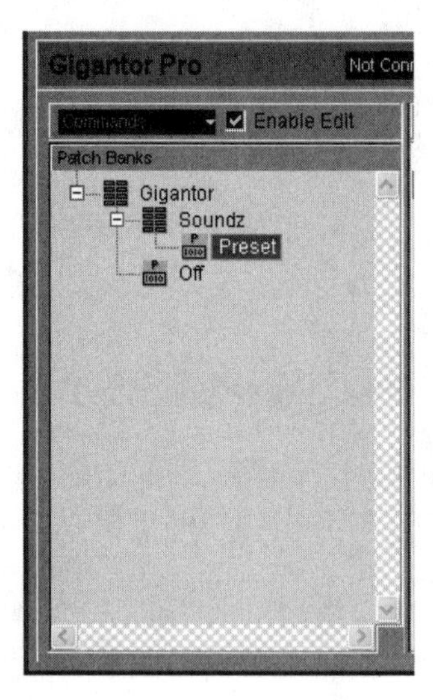

You can rename the preset by clicking it and typing a new name.

When the preset is selected, its corresponding MIDI events (Program Change, Bank Select, etc.) are shown in the event display to the right. The default setting for a new preset is Program Change 0—to change this, use the following procedures:

- For details on which MIDI events are used for selecting patches in the MIDI device, consult its documentation.

- **To change which Program Change value should be sent out to select the patch, adjust the number in the Value column for the Program Change event.**
- **To add another MIDI event (e.g. Bank Select) click immediately below the last event in the list and select a new event from the pop-up menu that appears.**

  After adding a new event, you need to set its value in the Value column, as with Program Change.
- **To replace an event, click on it and select another event from the pop-up menu.**

  For example, a MIDI device may require that a Bank Select message is sent first, followed by a Program Change message, in which case you would need to replace the default Program Change message with a Bank Select message and add a new Program Change after that.
- **To remove an event, click to select it and press [Del].**

- Different devices use different schemes for Bank Select. When you insert a Bank Select event, you should check the device's documentation to find whether to choose "CC: BankSelect MSB", "Bank Select 14 Bit", "Bank Select 14 Bit MSB-LSB Swapped" or possibly some other option.

Add Multiple Presets

This opens a dialog, allowing you to set up a range of presets to be added in the selected bank or folder.

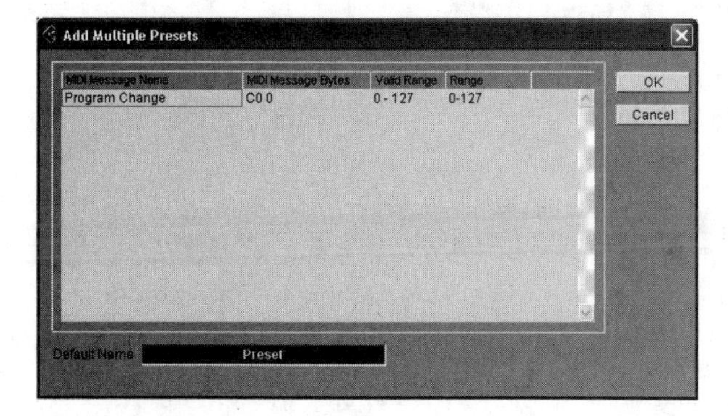

Proceed as follows:

1. **Add the event types required for selecting a patch in the MIDI device.**

   This is done just as when editing the settings for a single event: clicking in the event display brings up a pop-up menu from which you can select an event type.

2. **Use the Range column to set up either a fixed value or a range of values for each event type in the list.**

   This requires some explanation:
   If you specify a single value in the Range column (e.g. 3, 15 or 127), all added presets will have an event of this type set to the same value.
   If you instead specify a value range (a start value and an end value, separated by a dash sign, e.g. 0—63), the first added preset will have an event set to the start value, the next will have this value incremented by one and so on, up to and including the end value.

- The number of added presets depends on the Range setting.

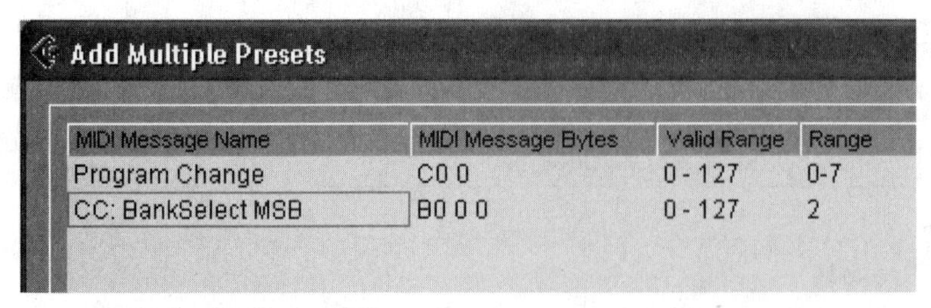

This example will generate eight presets, each with a Bank Select event set to 2, but with different Program Change events (ranging from 0 to 7).

3. **Specify a Default Name below the event display.**

   The added events will get this name, followed by a number. You can rename presets manually in the Patch Banks list later.

4. **Click OK.**

   A number of new presets are now added in the selected bank or folder, according to your settings.

Other Editing Functions

- You can move presets between banks and folders by dragging them in the Patch Banks list.
- You can remove a bank, folder or preset by selecting it in the Patch Banks list and pressing [Backspace].
- If you specify more than one bank, a Bank Assignment button will appear to the right above the event display. Use this to assign banks to the different MIDI channels (see page 422).

20.7 Exporting and Importing Device Setups

Clicking the Export Setup button allows you to export your complete MIDI device setup as a separate file. The file can then be imported using the Import Setup button. This is useful if you move your instruments to another studio, install the program on a new computer, etc.

- When you import a stored setup with the Import Setup function, a dialog will appear, listing all devices included in the stored setup.
  Select the device(s) you wish to import and click OK.

- Importing will not overwrite any currently installed devices.
  If the current list contains a device with the same name as a device to be imported, a number will be added to the name of imported device.

21 MIDI Realtime Parameters and Effects

21.1 Introduction

For each MIDI track, you can set up a number of track parameters and MIDI effects. These affect how the MIDI data is played back, "transforming" MIDI events in real time before they are sent to the MIDI outputs.

On the following pages, the available parameters and effects are described. Keep in mind:

- The actual MIDI events will not be affected—the changes happen "on the fly".
- Since the track parameter settings don't actually change the MIDI data on the track, they will not be reflected in the MIDI editors. To convert the settings to "real" MIDI events, you need to use the Merge MIDI in Loop function (see page 464).

21.2 The Inspector—General Handling

The track parameters and effects are set up in the Inspector (although some settings are available in the Mixer as well, see page 190). Here's a brief rundown on how to handle the Inspector:

- **To show or hide the Inspector, click the Inspector icon on the Project window's toolbar.**

- **The Inspector for a MIDI track is divided into five sections. You can fold or unfold the sections individually by clicking the tabs in their upper right corners.**

  Clicking the tab for a hidden section brings it to view and hides the other sections. [Ctrl]-clicking the tab allows you to hide or show a section without affecting other sections. Finally, [Alt]-clicking a tab shows or hides all sections in the Inspector.

- Folding a section does not affect the functionality but merely hides the section from view.
  In other words, if you have set up a track parameter or activated a MIDI effect, your settings will still be active even if you fold the Inspector settings.

21.3 Basic Track Settings

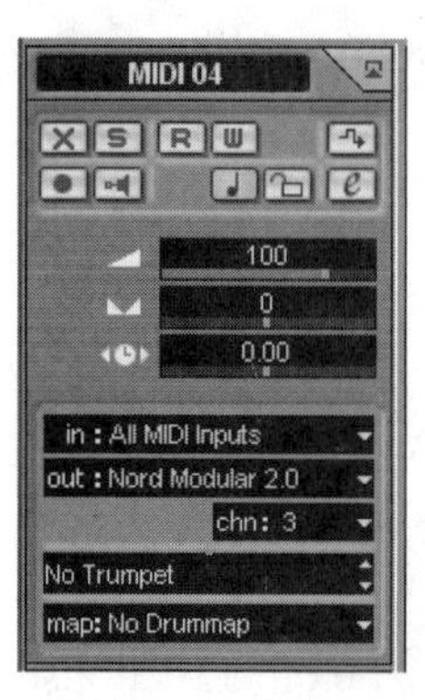

The topmost Inspector section contains the basic settings for the selected MIDI track. These are not really "realtime track parameters" as described above, but rather settings that either affect the basic funtionality for the track (mute, solo, enable record, etc.) or send out additional MIDI data to the connected devices (program change, volume, etc.).

The section contains all settings in the track list (see page 110), with the following additional parameters:

Parameter	Description
Toggle Timebase button	Switches between musical (tempo related) and linear (time related) time base for the track. See page 127.
Edit button	This normally opens the channel settings window for the track (a window showing a channel strip with volume fader and other controls, along with effect settings—see page 211). However, if the MIDI track is routed to a VST instrument, clicking the Edit button opens the control panel for the VST instrument instead. To bring up the channel settings window in that case, [Alt]-click the Edit button.
Volume	Use this to adjust the level for the track. Changing this setting will move the track's fader in the Mixer window, and vice versa. See page 194 for more about setting levels.
Delay	This adjusts the playback timing of the MIDI track. Positive values delay the playback while negative values cause the track to play earlier. The values are set in milliseconds.
Pan	Use this to adjust the panning of the track. As with the Volume setting, this corresponds to the Pan setting in the Mixer.
Input transformer button	Opens the Input Transformer dialog, allowing you to transform incoming MIDI events in real time (e.g. change events of one type to another). See page 568.

- Note that the functionality of the "Programs" settings (used for selecting sounds in the connected MIDI instrument) depends on to which instrument the MIDI output is routed, and how you have set up this in the MIDI Device Manager.
  As described on page 420, the MIDI Device Manager allows you to specify which MIDI instruments and other devices are connected to the various MIDI outputs, thus making it possible to select patches by name.
- Many of the basic track settings are duplicated in "mixer channel strip form", in the Channel section at the bottom of the Inspector.
  See page 463.

21.4 Track Parameters

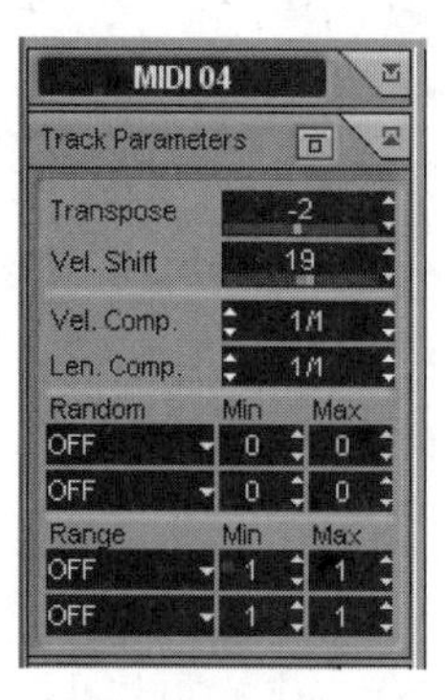

The following settings will affect the MIDI events on the track in real time during playback. They will also be in effect if you play "live" with the track selected and record enabled (provided that "MIDI Thru Active" is activated on the Preferences—MIDI page). This makes it possible to e.g. transpose or adjust the velocity of your live playing.

- If you want to compare the result of your track parameters with the "unprocessed" MIDI, you can use the Bypass button in the Track Parameters section.
  When this is activated, the Track Parameter settings will be temporarily disabled. A bypassed section is indicated by its Inspector tab turning yellow.

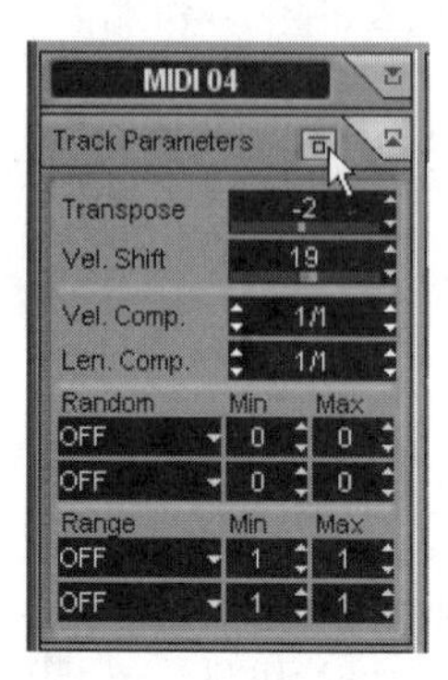

21.4.1 Transpose

This allows you to transpose all notes on the track in semitones. The available range is -127 to +127 semitones, but remember that the total range of MIDI note numbers is 0 to 127. Furthermore, not all instruments can play back notes over the whole range. Therefore, extreme transpositions can give rather strange and unwanted results.

21.4.2 Velocity Shift

This settings lets you change the dynamics of all notes on the track. The value in this field is added to the velocity of each note message that is sent out (use negative values to lower the velocities). The range is -127 to +127 with 0 representing no change in velocity.

Note that the effects of changing the velocity depends on the sound and instrument.

21.4.3 Velocity Compression

This function multiplies the velocity values with the factor you specify. This factor is set using a numerator (left value) and a denominator (right value), resulting in a fractional number (1/2, 3/4, 3/2 etc.). For example, if you set the factor to 3/4, the velocities will be three quarters of their original values. The point is, that this will also affect the *difference* in velocity between the notes, thereby compressing or expanding the velocity scale. Typically, you would combine this setting with the Velocity Shift parameter. An example:

Let's say you have three notes with the velocity values 60, 90 and 120, and wish to "even out" the velocity differences somewhat. If you set the Velocity Compression value to 1/2, the notes will play back with the velocities 30, 45 and 60. By adding 60 in the Velocity Shift field, you will have the notes playing back with the velocities 90, 105 and 120, meaning you have in effect compressed the velocity range.

In a similar way, you can use Velocity Compression values greater than 1/1 together with negative values in the Velocity Shift field, to expand the velocity range.

- Remember that the maximum velocity is always 127 no matter how much you try to expand.

21.4.4 Length Compression

This value adjusts the lengths of all notes on the track. As with Velocity Compression, the value is set with a numerator and denominator. For example, the value 2/1 means that all note lengths will be doubled, while 1/4 means all note lengths will be quarter of the actual lengths.

21.4.5 Random

The Random settings let you introduce random variations to various properties of MIDI notes. Anything from very subtle variations to dramatic changes can be applied. There are two separate "Random generators", each of which are set up in the following way:

1. **Pull down the Random pop-up menu and select which note property should be randomized.**

   The options are position, pitch, velocity and length.

- Keep in mind that depending on the content of the track, certain parameter changes might not be immediately noticeable, or have any effect at all (as would be the case if applying random length to a percussion track playing "one-shot" samples for example).
  To best audition the random changes choose a track with clearly defined rhythm and note content, if possible (as opposed to a string pad).

2. **Set the desired range of random deviation by entering values in the two number fields.**

   The two values govern the limits of the randomization, so that the values will vary between the left value and the right value (you cannot set the left value higher than the right value). The maximum random range for each property is listed in the table below:

Property	Range
Position	-500 to +500 ticks
Pitch	-100 to +100 semitones
Velocity	-100 to +100
Length	-500 to +500 ticks

Note again that you can make independent settings for the two random generators.

- **To deactivate the Random function, pull down the Random pop-up menu(s) and select "OFF".**

21.4.6 Range

The Range function lets you specify a note (pitch) or velocity range and either force all notes to fit within this range, or exclude all notes outside this range from playback. As with the Random function, there are two separate Range settings. Set them up as follows:

1. Pull down the Range pop-up menu and select one of the following four modes:

Mode	Description
Vel. Limit	This function affects all velocity values *outside* the specified range. Velocity values below the Min setting (the lower limit of the range) are set to the Min value, and velocity values above the Max setting are set to the Max value. Notes with velocity values within the set range are not affected. Use this if you want to force all velocity values to fit within a certain range.
Vel. Filter	Velocity Filter works by *excluding* all notes with velocity values outside the specified range. Notes with velocity values below the Min setting or above the Max setting will not be played back. Use this to "isolate" notes with certain velocity values.
Note Limit	This function allows you to specify a pitch range, and forces all notes to fit within this range. Notes outside the specified range are transposed up or down in octave steps until they fit within the range. Note: If the range is too "narrow", so that some notes cannot be fit within the range by octave-transposing, these notes will get a pitch in the middle of the range. For example, if you have a note with a pitch of F3, and the range is C4—E4, that note will be transposed to D4.
Note Filter	Note Filter works by *excluding* all notes with pitches outside the specified range. Notes lower than the Min setting or higher than the Max setting will not be played back. Use this to "isolate" notes with certain pitches.

2. Use the two fields to the right to set the min and max values.

These values will be shown as numbers (0—127) for the velocity modes and as note numbers (C-2 to G8) for the pitch modes.

Note again that you can make independent settings for the two Range functions.

- **To deactivate the Range function, pull down the Range pop-up menu(s) and select "OFF".**

21.5 MIDI Effects

Cubase SX/SL comes with a number of MIDI effect plug-ins, capable of transforming the MIDI output from a track in various ways.

Just like the MIDI track parameters, MIDI effects are applied in real time to the MIDI data played back from the track (or to MIDI you play live "thru" the track).

21.5.1 What Are MIDI Effects?

Although a MIDI effect can be similar to an audio effect, it's important to remember that you're not processing the *sound* resulting from MIDI playback, but the MIDI data (the "instructions" for how the music should be played back).

A MIDI effect will change properties of the MIDI events (e.g. change the pitch of notes) and/or generate new MIDI events (for example, a MIDI delay may add new MIDI notes, "echoing" the original notes).

21.5.2 Insert and Send Effects

As with audio effects, there are two ways to route the MIDI events on a track to an effect:

- If you add an insert effect, the MIDI events will be sent to the effect, which will process the data and pass it on to the track's MIDI output (or to another insert effect). In other words, the MIDI events will be routed "through" the insert effect.
- If you use a send effect, the MIDI events will be sent both to the track's MIDI output and to the effect.
  That is, you will get both the unprocessed MIDI events and the output of the MIDI effect. Note that the effect can send its processed MIDI data to any MIDI output—not necessarily to the one used by the track.

There are separate sections in the Inspector for Inserts and Sends:

Inserts Section

This allows you to add up to four MIDI insert effects. The section contains the following items:

Item	Description
Edit button	Opens the Channel Settings window for the MIDI track.
Bypass button	Click this to temporarily disable all insert effects for the track (useful for comparing with the unprocessed MIDI, etc.).
Inserts section tab	This lights blue if any insert effect is activated. A yellow tab means that the insert section is bypassed.
Effect selection pop-up menu (×4)	Selecting an effect from this pop-up menu automatically activates it and brings up its control panel (which can be a separate window or a number of settings below the insert slot in the Inspector). To remove an insert effect completely, select "No Effect".
On button (×4)	Allows you to turn the selected effect on or off.
Edit button (×4)	Click this to bring up the control panel for the selected effect. Depending on the effect, this may appear in a separate window or below the insert slot in the Inspector. Clicking the button again hides the control panel.

- Effects that display their controls in the Inspector can be forced to appear in a separate control panel window by pressing [Alt] and double clicking the Edit button.

Sends Section

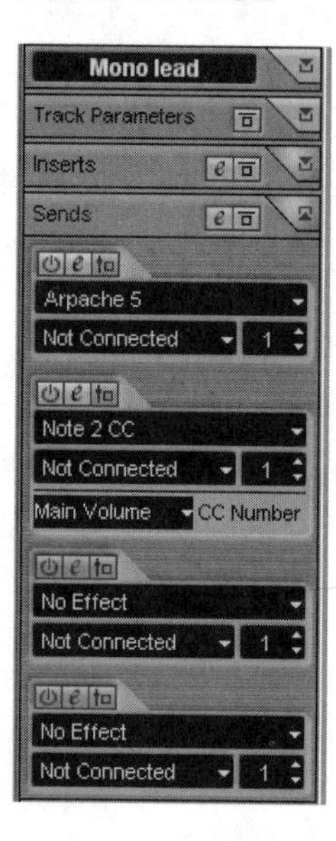

This allows you to add up to four MIDI send effects. Unlike audio send effects, you can select and activate send effects individually for each track. The section contains the following items:

Item	Description
Edit button	Opens the Channel Settings window for the MIDI track.
Bypass button	Click this to temporarily disable all send effects for the track (useful for comparing with the unprocessed MIDI, etc.).
Sends section tab	This lights blue if any send effect is activated. A yellow tab means that the send section is bypassed.
Effect selection pop-up menu (x4)	Selecting an effect from this pop-up menu automatically activates it and brings up its control panel (which can be a separate window or a number of settings below the send slot in the Inspector). To remove a send effect completely, select "No Effect".
On button (x4)	Allows you to turn the selected effect on or off.
Edit button (x4)	Click this to bring up the control panel for the selected effect. Depending on the effect, this may appear in a separate window or below the sends slot in the Inspector. Clicking the button again hides the control panel.

Item	Description
Output pop-up menu (×4)	This determines to which MIDI output the effect should send the processed MIDI events.
Channel setting (×4)	This determines on which MIDI channel the effect should send the processed MIDI events.
Pre button (×4)	If this is activated, the MIDI signals will be sent to the send effects before the track parameters and insert effects.

- Effects that display their controls in the Inspector can be forced to appear in a separate control panel window by pressing [Alt] and double clicking the Edit button.

21.6 The Available Effects

21.6.1 About Presets

Several of the MIDI plug-ins come with a number of presets for instant use. The controls for handling presets consist of a Presets pop-up menu along with Store [+] and Remove [-] buttons.

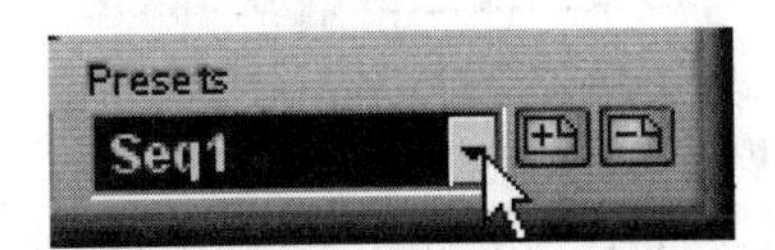

- To load a preset, select it from the Presets pop-up menu.
- To store your current settings as a preset, click the [+] button to the right.
  A dialog appears, asking you to specify a name for the preset. The stored preset will then be available for selection from the pop-up menu for all instances of that MIDI plug-in, in all projects.
- To remove a stored preset, select it and click the [-] button to the right.

21.6.2 Arpache

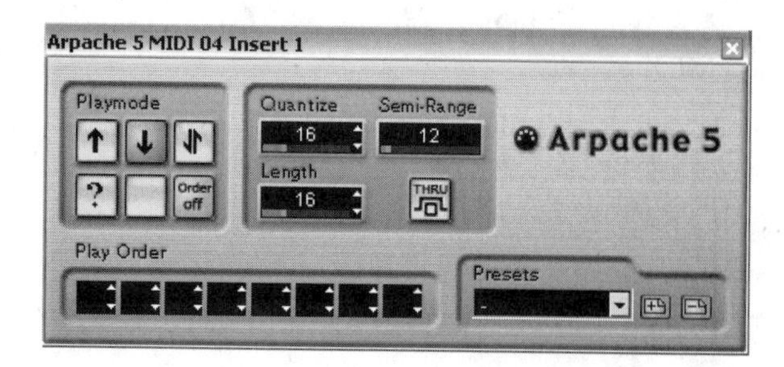

A typical arpeggiator accepts a chord (a group of MIDI notes) as input, and plays back each note in the chord separately, with the playback order and speed set by the user. The Arpache 5 arpeggiator does just that, and more. Before describing the parameters, let's look at how to create a simple, typical arpeggio:

1. **Select a MIDI track and activate monitoring (or record enable it) so that you can play "thru" the track.**

   Check that the track is properly set up for playback to a suitable MIDI instrument.

2. **Select and activate the arpeggiator.**

   For now, use it as an insert effect for the selected track.

3. **In the arpeggiator panel, use the Quantize setting to set the arpeggio speed.**

   The speed is set as a note value, relative to the project tempo. For example, setting Quantize to "16" means the arpeggio will be a pattern of sixteenth notes.

4. **Use the Length setting to set the length of the arpeggio notes.**

   This allows you to create staccato arpeggios (Length smaller than the Quantize setting) or arpeggio notes that overlap each other (Length greater than Quantize).

5. **Set the Semi-Range parameter to 12.**

   This will make the notes arpeggiate within an octave.

6. **Play a chord on your MIDI instrument.**

   Now, instead of hearing the chord, you will hear the notes of the chord played one by one, in an arpeggio.

7. **Try the different arpeggio modes by clicking the Playmode buttons.**

   The symbols on the buttons indicate the playback order for the notes (up, down, up+down, etc.). The Play Order settings are described below.

Parameters

The Arpache 5 has the following settings:

Setting	Description
Playmode buttons	Allows you to select the playback order for the arpeggied notes. The options are down+up, up+down, up, down, random ("?" button) and "Order off", in which case you can set the playback order manually with the Play Order fields below.
Quantize	Determines the speed of the arpeggio, as a note value related to the project tempo. The range is 32T (1/32 note triplets) to 1. (one and a half bar).
Length	Sets the length of the arpeggio notes, as a note value related to the project tempo. The range is the same as for the Quantize setting.
Semi-Range	Determines the arpeggiated note range, in semitones counted from the lowest key you play. This works as follows: - Any notes you play that are outside this range will be transposed in octave steps to fit within the range. - If the range is more than one octave, octave-transposed copies of the notes you play will be added to the arpeggio (as many octaves as fits within the range).
Thru	If this is activated, the notes sent to the arpeggiator (i.e. the chord you play) will be passed through the plug-in (sent out together with the arpeggiated notes).
Play Order	If the "Order on" playmode is selected, you can use these "slots" to specify a custom playback order for the arpeggio notes: Each slot corresponds to a position in the arpeggio pattern. For each slot, you specify which note should be played on that position by selecting a number. The numbers correspond to the keys you play, counted from the lowest pressed key. So, if you play the notes C3-E3-G3 (a C major chord), "1" would mean C3, "2" would mean E3, and "3" would mean G3. Note that you can use the same number in several slots, creating arpeggio patterns that are not possible using the standard play modes.  Play Order 1 2 3 2 2 2 4 6

21.6.3 AutoPan

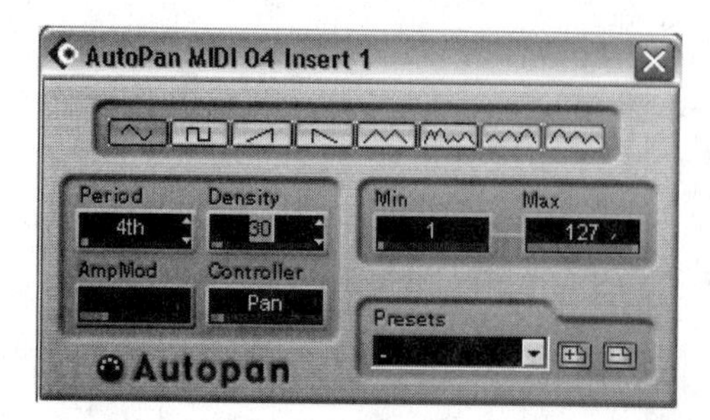

This plug-in works a bit like an LFO in a synthesizer, allowing you to send out continuously changing MIDI controller messages. One typical use for this is automatic MIDI panning (hence the name), but you can select any MIDI Continuous Controller event type. The AutoPanner has the following parameters:

Waveform Selectors

These determine the shape of the controller curves sent out. The results of most of these waveforms are obvious from looking at the buttons, but a few of them require some extra explanations:

This generates a "random" controller curve.

These generate curves with a "periodical envelope". This means the amplitude of the curve will gradually increase or decrease over a set time, set with the Period parameter (see below).

Density

This determines the density of the controller curves sent out. The value can be set ticks (1/480ths of quarter notes), or as rhythmically exact note values (by clicking the arrow buttons next to the value). The higher the note value, the smoother the controller curve. For example, if you set this to 60 (shown as "32th") a new controller event will be sent out every 60th tick (at every 1/32 note position).

- You should probably avoid extremely low Density values, as these will generate a very large number of events (which may cause the MIDI instrument to "choke", delaying notes etc.).

Period

This is where you set the speed of the Autopanner, or rather the length of a single controller curve cycle. The value can be set ticks (1/480ths of quarter notes), or as rhythmically exact note values (by clicking the arrow buttons next to the value). The lower the note value, the slower the speed. For example, if you set this to 240 ("8th") the waveform will be repeated every eighth note.

AmpMod

This is only used for the two waveforms with "periodical envelopes". The period value (set in beats) determines the length of the envelope. In the following figure, Period is set to 4th and the AmpMod is 4 beats. This results in a quarter note-based curve in which the top amplitude decreases gradually, repeated each bar:

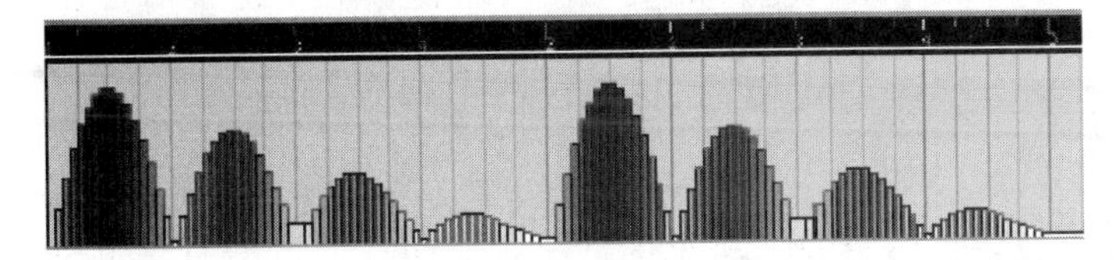

Controller

Determines which Continuous Controller type is sent out. Typical choices would include pan, volume and brightness but your MIDI instrument may have controllers mapped to various settings, allowing you to modulate the synth parameter of your choice—check the MIDI implementation chart for your instrument for details!

Min and Max

These determines the minimum and maximum controller values sent out, i.e. the "bottom" and "top" of the controller curves.

21.6.4 Chorder

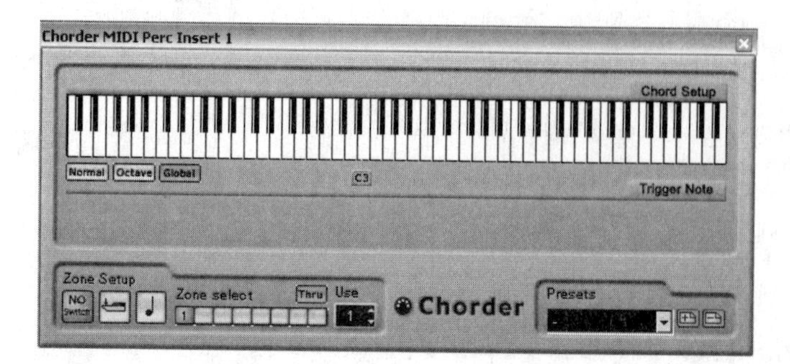

The Chorder is a MIDI chord processor, allowing you to assign complete chords to single keys in a multitude of variations. There are three main modes of operation: Normal, 1Oct and Global.

Normal Mode

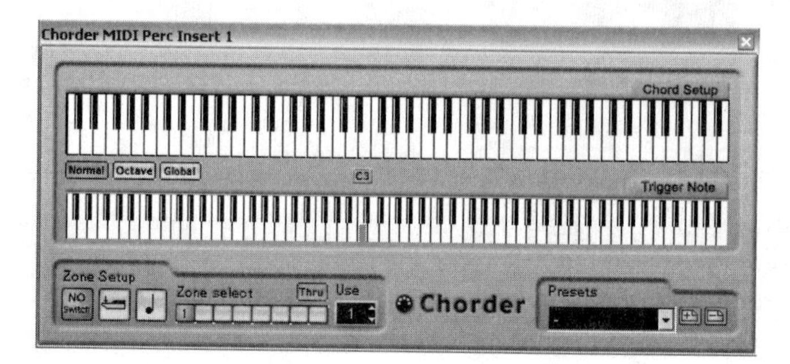

In this mode, you can assign a different chord to each single key on the keyboard. Proceed as follows:

1. **Select the key to which you want to assign a chord, by clicking in the lower "Trigger Note" keyboard display.**
2. **Set up the desired chord for that key by clicking in the upper "Chord Setup" keyboard display.**

   Clicking a key adds it to the chord; clicking it again removes it.
3. **Repeat the above with any other keys you wish to use.**

If you now play the keys you have set up, you will instead hear the assigned chords.

1Oct Mode

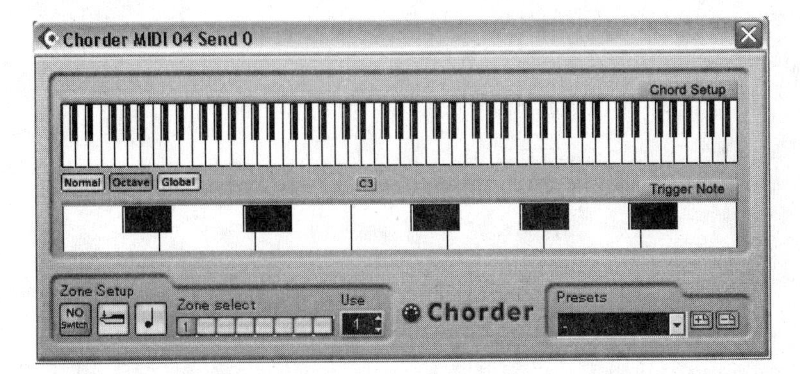

The 1 Octave mode is similar to the Normal mode, but you can only set up one chord for each key in an octave (that is, twelve different chords). When you play a C note (regardless of whether it's a C3, C4 or any other octave) you will hear the chord set up for the C key.

Global Mode

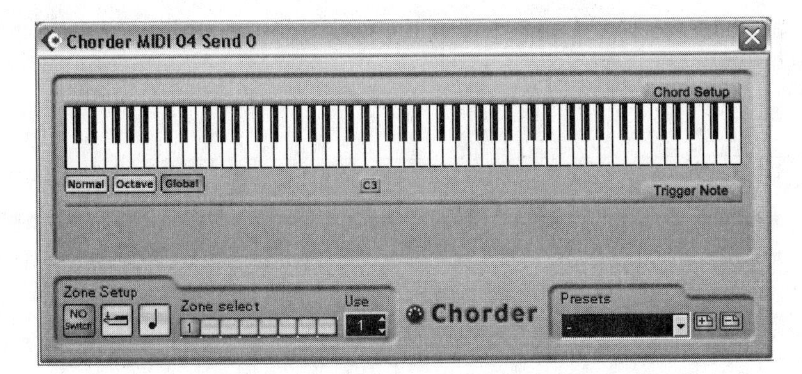

In the Global mode, you only set up a single chord, using the Chord Setup keyboard display (the lower keyboard display is hidden). This chord is then played by all keys on the keyboard, but transposed according to the note you play.

Using Switches

The Switch Setup section at the bottom of the panel allows you to set up variations to the defined chords. This works with all three modes and provides a total of eight variations for each assignable key (that is, a maximum of 8 different chords in Global mode, 12 × 8 chords in 1Oct mode and 128 × 8 chords in Normal mode).

The variations can be controlled by velocity or note range. Here's how you set it up:

1. **Select one of the two switch modes: velocity or note.**

   How to use these is explained below.

The velocity switch mode selected.

2. **Specify how many variations you want to use with the Use value box.**
3. **Click the first Switch Select button and set up the chord(s) you want for the first variation.**
4. **Click the next Switch Select button and set up the chord(s) you want for that variation.**
5. **Repeat this for the number of variations you specified with the Use setting.**

   Each Switch Select button corresponds to a variation.

6. **Now you can play the keyboard and control the variations according to the selected switch modes.**

   These work as follows:

Switch mode	Description
Velocity	The full velocity range (1—127) is divided into "zones", according to the number of variations you specified. For example, if you're using two variations (Max is set to 2) there will be two velocity "zones": 1—63 and 64—127. Playing a note with velocity at 64 or higher will trigger the second variation, while playing a softer note will trigger the first variation.
Note	In this mode, the chorder will play one chord at a time—you cannot play several different chords simultaneously. When the Note switch mode is selected, you play a key to determine the base note for the chord, then press a higher key to select a variation. The variation number will be the difference between the two keys. To select variation 1, press a key one semitone higher than the base note, for variation 2, press a key two semitones higher, and so on.

- **To turn the variation switch feature off, select the "No Switch" mode.**

21.6.5 Compress

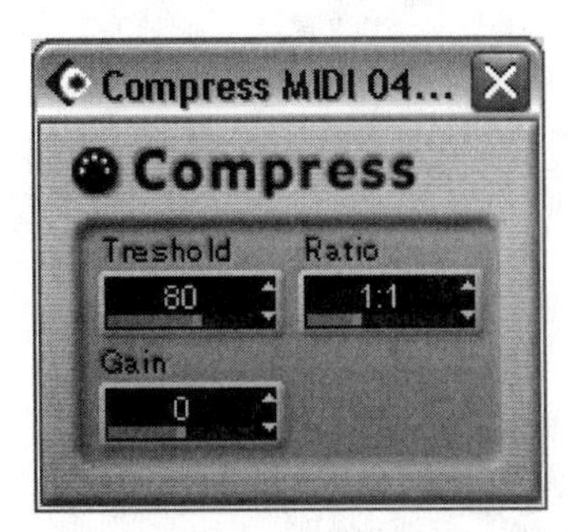

This MIDI Compressor is used for evening out or expanding differences in velocity. Though the result is similar to what you get with the Velocity Compression track parameter, the Compress plug-in presents the controls in a manner more like regular audio compressors. The parameters are:

Parameter	Description
Threshold	Only notes with velocities over this value will be affected by the compression/expansion.
Ratio	This determines the rate of compression applied to the velocity values above the threshold level. Ratios greater than 1:1 result in compression (i.e. less difference in velocity) while ratios lower than 1:1 result in expansion (i.e. greater difference in velocity). What actually happens is that the part of the velocity value that is above the threshold value is divided by the ratio value.
Gain	This adds or subtracts a fixed value from the velocities. Since the maximum range for velocity values is 0—127, you may need to use the Gain setting to compensate, keeping the resulting velocities within the range. Typically, you would use negative Gain settings when expanding and positive Gain settings when compressing.

21.6.6 Control

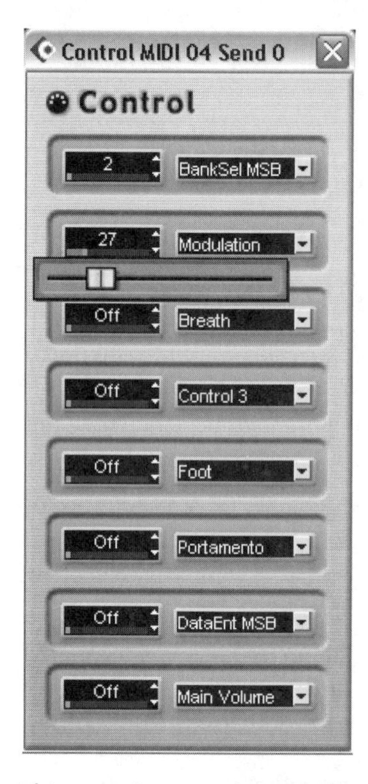

This generic control panel allows you to select up to eight different MIDI controller types, and use the value fields/sliders to set values for these. A typical use for this would be if you're using a MIDI instrument with parameters that can be controlled by MIDI controller data (e.g. filter cutoff, resonance, levels, etc.). By selecting the correct MIDI controller types, you can use the plug-in as a control panel for adjusting the sound of the instrument from within Cubase SX/SL, at any time.

- To select a controller type, use the pop-up menus to the right.
- To deactivate a controller slider, set it to "Off" (drag the slider all the way to the left).

21.6.7 Density

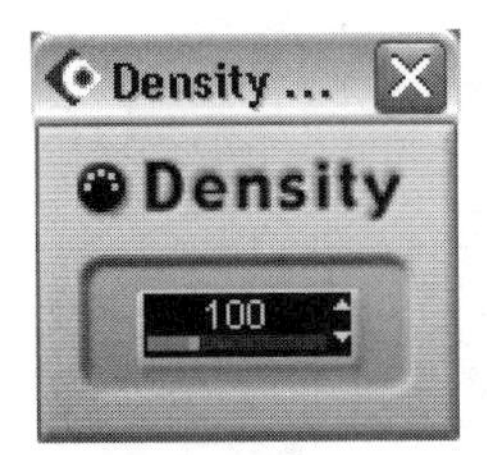

This affects the "density" of the notes being played from (or thru) the track. When this is set to 100%, the notes are not affected. Lowering the Density setting below 100% will randomly filter out or "mute" notes. Raising the setting above 100% will instead randomly add new notes.

21.6.8 Micro Tuner

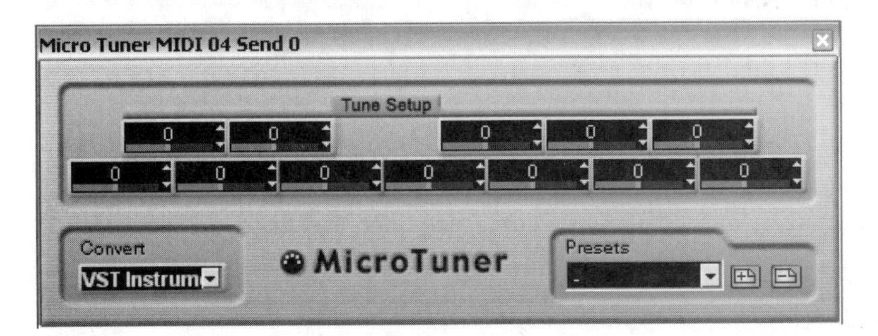

The Micro Tuner lets you set up a different microtuning scheme for the instrument, by detuning each key.

- Each Detune field corresponds to a key in an octave (as indicated by the keyboard display). Adjust a Detune field to raise or lower the tuning of that key, in cents (hundreds of a semitone).
- Set the Convert setting according to whether the track is routed to a VST instrument or a "real" standard MIDI instrument (capable of receiving microtuning information).

The Micro Tuner comes with a vast number of presets, including both classical microtuning scales and experimental ones.

21.6.9 MIDIEcho

This is an advanced MIDI Echo, which will generate additional echoing notes based on the MIDI notes it receives. It creates effects similar to a digital delay, but also features MIDI pitch shifting and much more. As always it is important to remember that the effect doesn't "echo" the actual audio, but the MIDI notes which will eventually produce the sound in the synthesizer.

The following parameters are available:

Velocity Decay

This parameter allows you to add or subtract to the velocity values for each repeat so that the echo fades away or increases in volume (provided that the sound you use is velocity sensitive). For no change of velocity, set this to 0 (middle position).

Pitch Decay

If you set this to a value other than 0, the repeating (echoing) notes will be raised or lowered in pitch, so that each succesive note has a higher or lower pitch than the previous. The value is set in semitones.

For example, setting this to -2 will cause the first echo note to have a pitch two semitones lower than the original note, the second echo note two semitones lower than the first echo note, and so on.

Repeat Rate

This is the number of echoes (1 to 12) you get from each incoming note.

Quantize

The echoed notes will be moved in position to a quantizing grid, as set up with this parameter. You can either use the slider or type to set the value in ticks (1/480 ticks of quarter notes) or click the arrow buttons to step between the "rhythmically exact" values (displayed as note values—see the table below). This makes it easy to find rhythmically relevant quantize values, but still allows experimental settings in between.

An example: setting this to "16th" will force all echo notes to be played on exact 16th note positions, regardless of the timing of the original notes and the Echo-Quant. setting.

- To disable quantizing, set this parameter to its lowest value (1).

Length

This sets the length of the echoed notes. This can either be the same length as their respective original notes (parameter set to its lowest value, "Source") or the length you specify manually. You can either set the length in ticks or click the arrow buttons to step between the "rhythmically exact" lengths (displayed as note values—see the table below).

- The length can also be affected by the Length Decay parameter.

Echo-Quant.

The Echo-Quant. parameter sets the delay time, i.e. the time between a played note and its first echo note. You can either use the slider or type to set the value in ticks (1/480 ticks of quarter notes) or click the arrow buttons to step between the "rhythmically exact" delay times (displayed as note values—see the table below).

For example, setting this to "8th" will cause the echo notes to sound an eighth note after their original notes.

- The echo time can also be affected by the Echo Decay parameter.

Echo Decay

This parameter lets you adjust how the echo time should be changed with each successive repeat. The value is set as a percentage.

- When set to 100% (middle position) the echo time will be the same for all repeats (as set with the Echo-Quant. parameter).
- If you raise the value above 100, the echoing notes will play with gradually longer intervals (i.e. the echo will become slower).

- If you lower the value below 100, the echoing notes will come gradually faster, like the sound of a bouncing ball.

About Ticks and Note Values

The timing- and position-related parameters (Echo-Quant., Length and Quantize) can all be set in ticks. There are 480 ticks to each quarter note. While the parameters allow you to step between the rhythmically relevant values (displayed as note values), the following table can also be of help, showing you the most common note values and their corresponding number of ticks:

Note Value	Ticks
1/32 note	60
1/16 note triplet	90
1/16 note	120
1/8 note triplet	160
1/8 note	240
Quarter note triplet	320
Quarter note	480
Half note	960

21.6.10 Note to CC

This effect will generate a MIDI continuous controller event for each incoming MIDI note. The value of the controller event corresponds to the note number (pitch) and the single parameter allows you to select which MIDI controller should be sent out (by default controller 7, MIDI volume). The incoming MIDI notes pass through the effect unaffected.

For example, if MIDI volume (controller 7) is selected, notes with low note numbers (pitches) will lower the volume in the MIDI instrument, while higher note numbers will raise the volume. This way you can create "keyboard tracking" of volume or other parameters.

- Note that a controller event is sent out each time a new note is played. If high and low notes are played simultaneously, this could lead to somewhat confusing results. Therefore, the Note to CC effect is probably best applied to monophonic tracks (playing one note at the time).

21.6.11 Quantizer

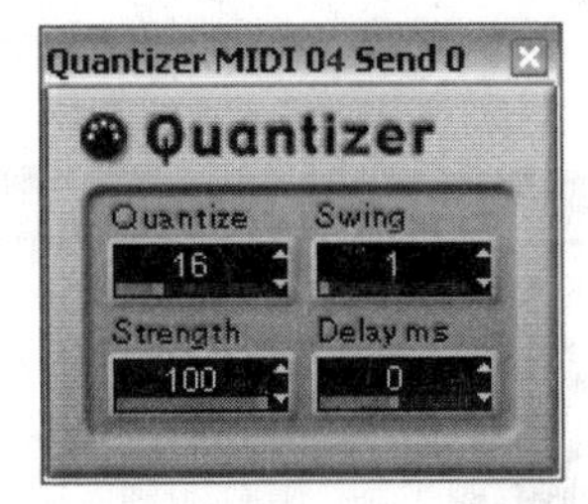

Quantizing is a function that changes the timing of notes by moving them towards a "quantize grid". This grid may consist of e.g. straight sixteenth notes (in which case the notes would all get perfect sixteenth note timing), but could also be more loosely related to straight note value positions (applying a "swing feel" to the timing, etc.).

- The main Quantize function in Cubase SX/SL is described on page 468.

While the Quantize function on the MIDI menu applies the timing change to the actual notes on a track, the Quantizer effect allows you to apply quantizing "on the fly", changing the timing of the notes in real time. This makes it easier to experiment with different settings when creating grooves and rhythms. Note however, that the main Quantize function contains settings and features that are not available in the Quantizer.

The Quantizer has the following parameters:

Parameter	Description
Quantize Note	This sets the note value on which the quantize grid is based. Straight notes, triplets and dotted notes are available. For example, "16" means straight sixteenth notes and "8T" means eighth note triplets.

Parameter	Description
Swing	The Swing parameter allows you to offset every second position in the grid, creating a swing or shuffle feel. The value is a percentage—the higher you set this, the farther to the right every even grid position is moved. See page 470.
Strength	This determines how close the notes should be moved to the quantize grid. When set to 100%, all notes will be forced to the closest grid position; lowering the setting will gradually loosen the timing.
Delay	This delays (positive values) or advances (negative values) the notes in milliseconds. Unlike the Delay setting in the Track Parameters, this delay can be automated.

21.6.12 Step Designer

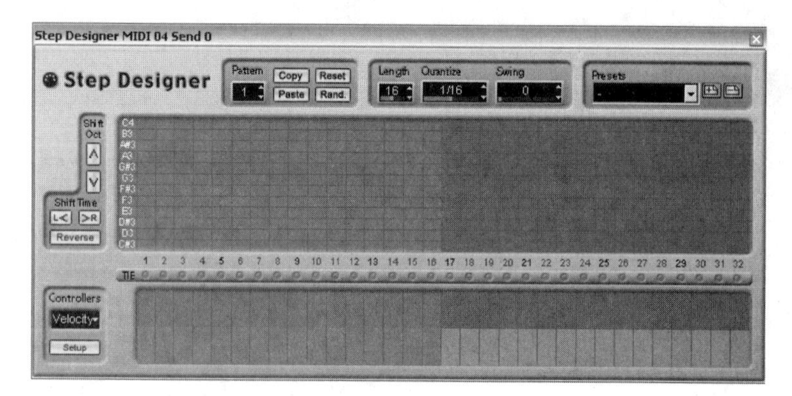

The Step Designer is a MIDI pattern sequencer, that sends out MIDI notes and additional controller data according to the pattern you set up. It does not make use of the incoming MIDI, other than automation data (such as recorded pattern changes).

Creating a Basic Pattern

1. **Use the Pattern selector to choose which pattern to create.**

   Each Step Designer can hold up to 100 different patterns.

2. **Use the Quantize setting to specify the "resolution" of the pattern.**

   In other words, this setting determines how long each step is. For example, if Quantize is set to "16th" each step will be a sixteenth note.

3. **Specify the number of steps in the pattern with the Length setting.**

   As you can see in the note display, the maximum number of steps is 32. For example, setting Quantize to 16 and Length to 32 would create a two bar pattern with sixteenth note steps.

4. **Click in the note display to insert notes.**

   You can insert notes on any of the 32 steps, but the Step Designer will only play back the number of steps set with the Length parameter.

- **The display spans one octave (as indicated by the pitch list to the left). You can scroll the displayed octave up or down by clicking in the pitch list and dragging up or down.**

  This way you can insert notes at any pitch. Note though that each step can contain one note only—the Step Designer is monophonic.

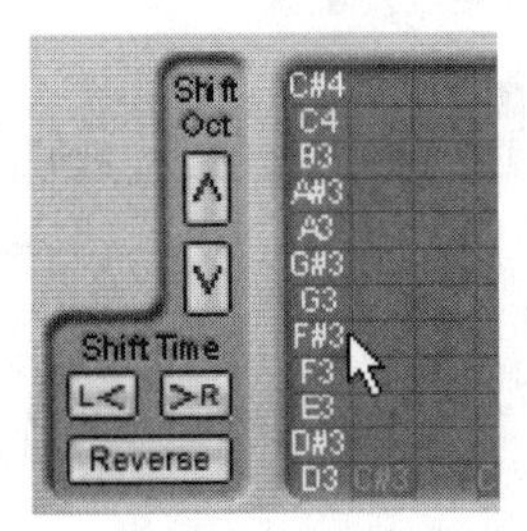

Click and drag to view other octaves.

- **To remove a note from the pattern, click on it again.**

5. **Select "Velocity" on the Controllers pop-up menu.**

   This pop-up menu determines what is shown in the lower controller display.

6. **Adjust the velocity of the notes by dragging the velocity bars in the controller display.**

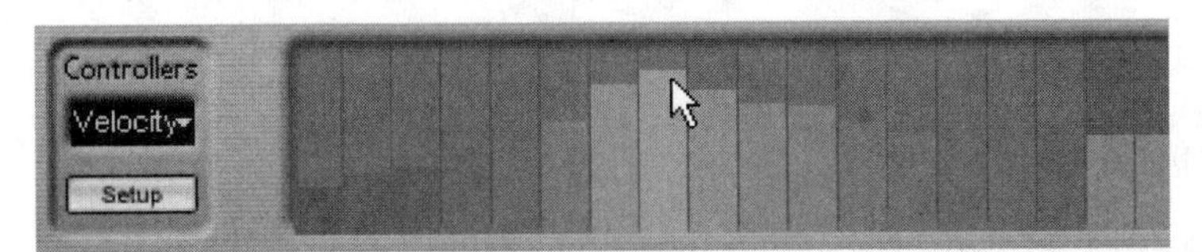

7. **To make notes shorter, select "Gate" on the Controllers pop-up menu and lower the bars in the controller display.**

   When a bar is set to its maximum value (fully up), the corresponding note will be the full length of the step (as set with the Quantize parameter).

8. **To make notes longer, you can tie two notes together. This is done by inserting two notes and clicking the Tie button below the second note.**

   When the Tie button is lit for a note, it won't retrigger—instead the previous note will be lengthened. Also, the tied (second) note will automatically get the same pitch as the first note. You can add more notes and tie them in the same way, creating longer notes.

9. **If you now start playback in Cubase SX/SL, the pattern will play as well, sending out MIDI notes on the track's MIDI output and channel (or, if you have activated the Step Designer as a send effect, on the MIDI output and channel selected for the send in the Inspector).**

Adding Controller Curves

The Controllers pop-up menu holds two more items: two controller types.

- **You can select which two controller types (filter cutoff, resonance, volume, etc.) should be available on the pop-up menu by clicking the Setup button and selecting controllers from the lists that appears.**

  This selection is global to all patterns.

- **To insert controller information in a pattern, select the desired controller from the pop-up menu and click in the controller display to draw events.**

  The MIDI controller events will be sent out during playback along with the notes.

- If you drag a controller event bar all the way down, no controller value will be sent out on that step.

Other Pattern Functions

The following functions make it easier to edit, manipulate and manage patterns:

Function	Description
Shift Oct	These buttons allow you to shift the entire pattern up or down in octave steps.
Shift Time	Moves the pattern one step to the left or right.

Function	Description
Reverse	Reverses the pattern, so that it plays backwards.
Copy/Paste	Allows you to copy the current pattern and paste it in another pattern location (in the same Step Designer or another).
Reset	Clears the pattern, removing all notes and setting controller values to default.
Random	Generates a completely random pattern—useful for experimenting.
Swing	The Swing parameter allows you to offset every second step, creating a swing or shuffle feel. The value is a percentage—the higher you set this, the farther to the right every even step is moved.
Presets	Presets are handled as described on page 439. Note that a stored Preset contains all 100 patterns in the Step Designer.

Automating Pattern Changes

You can create up to 100 different patterns in each Step Designer—just select a new pattern and add notes and controllers as described above.

Typically, you want the pattern selection to change during the song. You can accomplish this by automating the Pattern selector, either in real time by activating the Write automation and switchin patterns during playback or by drawing in the automation subtrack for the Step Designer's MIDI track.

21.6.13 Track Controls

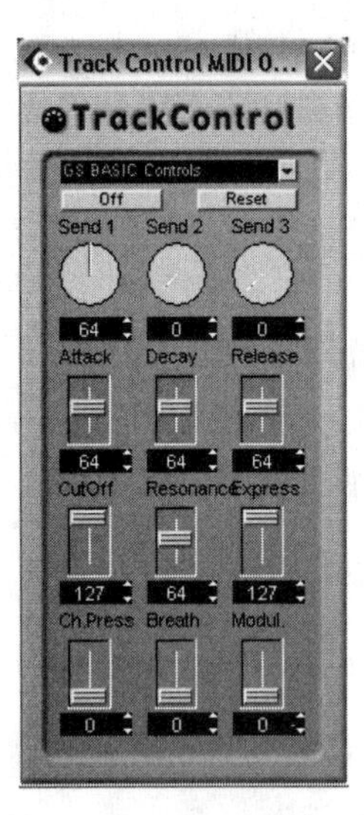

The Track Control effect contains three ready-made control panels for adjusting parameters on a GS or XG compatible MIDI device. The Roland GS and Yamaha XG protocols are extension of the General MIDI standard, allowing for more sounds and better control of various instrument settings. If your instrument is compatible with GS or XG, the Track Controls effect allows you to adjust sounds and effects in your instrument from within Cubase SX/SL.

Selecting a Control Panel

At the top of the Track Controls effect window you will find a pop-up menu. This is where you select which of the available control panels to use:

Control panel	Description
GS Basic Controls	Effect sends and various sound control parameters for use with instruments compatible with the Roland GS standard.
XG Effect + Sends	Effect Sends and various sound control parameters for use with instruments compatible with the Yamaha XG standard.
XG Global	Global settings (affecting all channels) for instruments compatible with the Yamaha XG standard.

About the Reset and Off Buttons

Regardless of the selected mode, you will find two buttons labelled "Off" and "Reset" at the top of the control panel. These have the following functions:

- Clicking the Off button will set all controls to their lowest value, without sending out any MIDI messages.
- Clicking the Reset button will set all parameters to their default values, and send out the corresponding MIDI messages.
  For most parameters, the default values will be zero or "no adjustment", but there are exceptions to this. For example, the default Reverb Send settings are 64.

GS Basic Controls

The following controls are available when the GS Basic Controls mode is selected:

Control	Description
Send 1	Send level for the reverb effect.
Send 2	Send level for the chorus effect.
Send 3	Send level for the "variation" effect.
Attack	Adjusts the attack time of the sound. Lowering the value shortens the attack, while raising it gives a slower attack. Middle position (64) means no adjustment is made.
Decay	Adjusts the decay time of the sound. Lowering the value shortens the decay, while raising it makes the decay longer.
Release	Adjusts the release time of the sound. Lowering the value shortens the release, while raising it makes the release time longer.
Cutoff	Adjusts the filter cutoff frequency.
Resonance	Adjusts the filter resonance.
Express	Allows you to send out expression pedal messages on the track's MIDI channel.
Press.	Allows you to send out aftertouch (channel pressure) messages on the track's MIDI channel. This is useful if your keyboard cannot send after-touch, but you have sound modules that respond to aftertouch. The default value for this parameter is zero.
Breath	Allows you to send out breath control messages on the track's MIDI channel.

Control	Description
Modul.	Allows you to send out modulation messages on the track's MIDI channel (just as you would normally do with a modulation wheel on a MIDI keyboard).

XG Effects + Sends

The following controls are available when the XG Effects + Sends mode is selected:

Control	Description
Send 1	Send level for the reverb effect.
Send 2	Send level for the chorus effect.
Send 3	Send level for the "variation" effect.
Attack	Adjusts the attack time of the sound. Lowering this value shortens the attack, while raising it gives a slower attack. Middle position means no adjustment is made.
Release	Adjusts the release time of the sound. Lowering this value shortens the release, while raising it makes the release time longer. Middle position means no adjustment is made.
Harm.Cont	Adjusts the harmonic content of the sound.
Bright	Adjusts the brightness of the sound.
CutOff	Adjusts the filter cutoff frequency.
Resonance	Adjusts the filter resonance.

XG Global Settings

In this mode, the parameters affect global settings in the instrument(s). Changing one of these settings for a track will in fact affect all MIDI instruments connected to the same MIDI Output, regardless of the MIDI Channel setting of the track. Therefore, to avoid confusion it might be a good idea to create an empty track and use this only for these global settings. The following controls are available:

Control	Description
Eff. 1	This allows you to select which type of reverb effect should be used: No effect (the reverb turned off), Hall 1-2, Room 1-3, Stage 1-2 or Plate.
Eff. 2	This allows you to select which type of chorus effect should be used: No effect (the chorus turned off), Chorus 1-3, Celeste 1-3 or Flanger 1-2.
Eff. 3	This allows you to select one of a large number of "variation" effect types. Selecting "No Effect" is the same as turning off the variation effect.
Reset	Sends an XG reset message.
MastVol	This is used to control the Master Volume of an instrument. Normally you should leave this in its highest position and set the volumes individually for each channel (with the volume faders in the Cubase SX/SL mixer or in the Inspector).

21.6.14 Track FX

This plug-in is essentially a duplicate of the Track Parameter section (see page 432). This can be useful if you e.g. need extra Random or Range settings, or if you prefer to have your track parameters in a separate window (to get this, [Alt]-click the Edit button for the effect).

The Track FX also includes an additional function that isn't available among the track parameters:

Scale Transpose

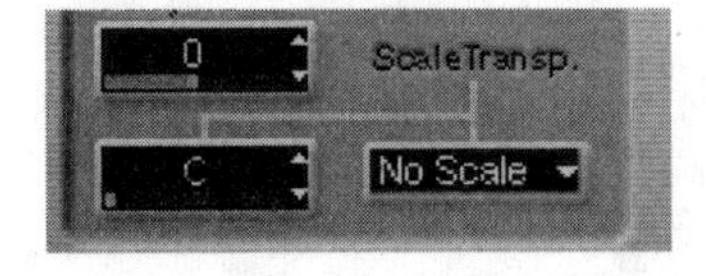

This allows you to transpose each incoming MIDI note, so that it fits within a selected musical scale. The scale is specified by selecting a key (C, C#, D, etc.) and a scale type (major, melodic or harmonic minor, blues, etc.).

- To turn Scale Transpose off, select "No Scale" from the scale type pop-up menu.

21.6.15 Transformer

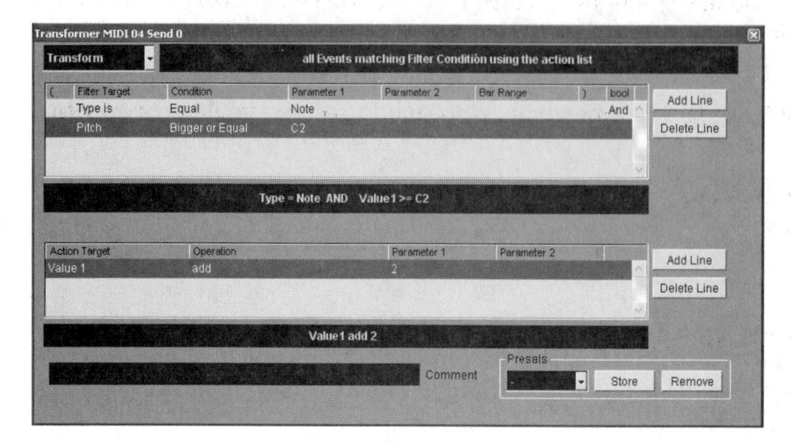

The Transformer is a real-time version of the Logical Editor. With this you can perform very powerful MIDI processing on the fly, without affecting the actual MIDI events on the track.

The Logical Editor is described in a separate chapter (see page 549). There you will also find the few differences between the Logical Editor and the Transformer clearly stated.

21.7 Managing Plug-ins

Selecting Plug-in Information from the Devices menu opens a window in which all loaded plug-ins, audio and MIDI, are listed.

- **To view the MIDI effect plug-ins, click the MIDI Plug-ins tab.**

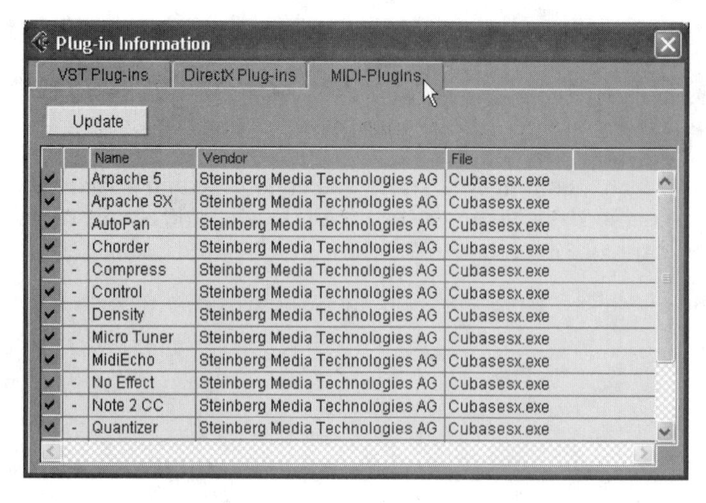

		Name	Vendor	File
✔	-	Arpache 5	Steinberg Media Technologies AG	Cubasesx.exe
✔	-	Arpache SX	Steinberg Media Technologies AG	Cubasesx.exe
✔	-	AutoPan	Steinberg Media Technologies AG	Cubasesx.exe
✔	-	Chorder	Steinberg Media Technologies AG	Cubasesx.exe
✔	-	Compress	Steinberg Media Technologies AG	Cubasesx.exe
✔	-	Control	Steinberg Media Technologies AG	Cubasesx.exe
✔	-	Density	Steinberg Media Technologies AG	Cubasesx.exe
✔	-	Micro Tuner	Steinberg Media Technologies AG	Cubasesx.exe
✔	-	MidiEcho	Steinberg Media Technologies AG	Cubasesx.exe
✔	-	No Effect	Steinberg Media Technologies AG	Cubasesx.exe
✔	-	Note 2 CC	Steinberg Media Technologies AG	Cubasesx.exe
✔	-	Quantizer	Steinberg Media Technologies AG	Cubasesx.exe

- **The leftmost column allows you to deactivate plug-ins.**

  This is useful if you have plug-ins installed that you don't want to use in Cubase SX/SL. Only plug-ins that are activated (ticked checkbox) will appear on the MIDI effect pop-up menus.

- **The second column shows how many instances of each plug-in are currently used in the project.**

- **The remaining columns show various information about each plug-in and cannot be edited.**

21.8 The Channel Section

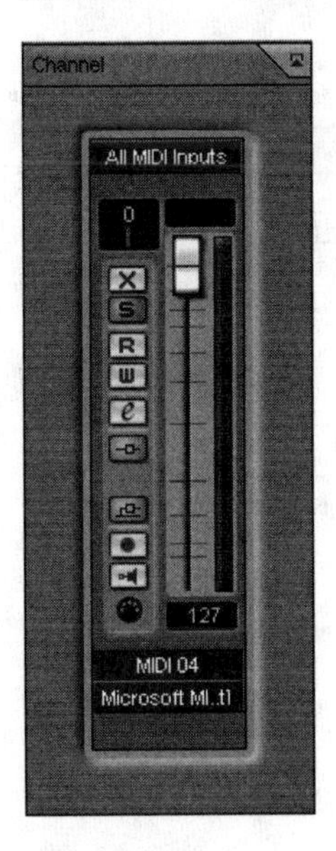

At the bottom of the Inspector, you will find a section labeled "Channel". This contains a single channel strip, allowing you to set volume, pan, mute/solo and other parameters for the track.

- This is a "mirror" of the track's channel strip in the Cubase SX/SL mixer—for details see page 190.

21.9 Merge MIDI in Loop

As mentioned, the parameters and effects described in this chapter do not change the MIDI events themselves, but work rather like "filters", affecting the music on playback. However, sometimes you may want to make these settings permanent, i.e. convert them to "real" MIDI events on the track. You might for example want to transpose a track and then edit the transposed notes in a MIDI editor. For this, you need to use the Merge MIDI in Loop function on the MIDI menu. This combines all MIDI events on all unmuted tracks, applies track parameters and effects and generates a new MIDI part, containing all the events as you would hear them play back.

1. **Make sure only the desired MIDI track(s) are unmuted.**

   If you only want to include events from a single track in the Merge operation, you may want to solo the track.

2. **Set up the left and right locator around the area you want to merge.**

   Only events starting within this cycle area will be included.

3. **Select the track on which you want the new part to be created.**

   This could be a new track or an existing track. If there are data in the cycle area on the track, you can choose whether this should be kept or overwritten (see below).

4. **Select Merge MIDI in Loop from the MIDI menu.**

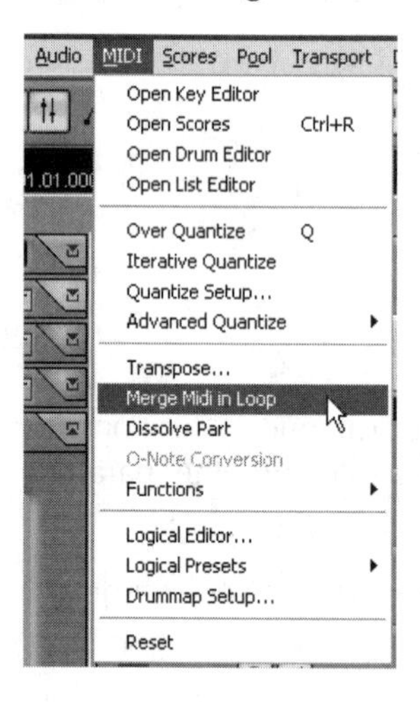

5. **Fill in the dialog that appears.**

   The options in the dialog are:

Option	Description
Include Inserts	If this is activated, any MIDI insert effects activated for the track(s) will be applied.
Include Sends	If this is activated, any MIDI send effects activated for the track(s) will be applied.
Erase Destination	If this is activated, all MIDI data between the left and right locator on the destination track will be deleted.

6. **Click OK.**

   A new part is created between the locators on the destination track, containing the processed MIDI events.

Applying Effects to a Single Part

Normally, the MIDI track parameters and effects affect a whole MIDI track. This may not always be what you want—you may want to apply some MIDI effects to a single part for example (without having to create a separate track for that part only). The Merge MIDI in Loop function can help:

1. **Set up your track parameters and MIDI effects the way you want them for the part.**

   This will of course affect the whole track, but focus on the part for now.

2. **Set the locators to encompass the part.**

   This is easiest done by selecting the part and selecting Locators to Selection from the Transport menu (or using the corresponding key command, by default [P]).

3. **Make sure the track holding the part is selected in the track list.**

4. **Select Merge MIDI in Loop.**

5. **In the dialog that appears, activate the desired effect options, make sure that Erase Destination is activated and click OK.**

   Now a new part is created on the same track, containing the processed events. The original part is deleted.

6. **Turn off or reset all track parameters and effects, so that the track plays back as usual.**

22 MIDI Processing and Quantizing

22.1 Introduction

This chapter describes the various MIDI processing functions available on the MIDI menu. These offer various ways to change MIDI notes and other events, in the Project window or within a MIDI editor.

MIDI Functions versus Track Parameters

In some cases, the result of a MIDI function can also be obtained by using MIDI track parameters and effects (see page 429). For example, the MIDI functions transpose and quantize are also available as a track parameter and a MIDI effect, respectively. The main difference is that track parameters don't affect the actual MIDI events on the track in any way, while MIDI functions change the events "permanently" (although recent changes can be undone). Use the following guidelines to decide which path to choose:

- If you want to adjust a few parts or events only, use MIDI functions. The track parameters and effects affect the output of the whole track (although they can be made permanent in a specific area with the Merge MIDI in Loop function).
- If you want to experiment with different settings, track parameters can be the best way to go.
- Track parameter settings are not reflected in the MIDI editors, since the actual MIDI events aren't affected. This can be potentially confusing; if you've e.g. transposed notes using track parameters, the MIDI editors will still show the notes with their original pitch (but they will play back at their transposed pitch). MIDI functions can be a better way in those cases.

Of course, there are also MIDI functions that have no track parameter counterpart, and vice versa.

What Is Affected by the MIDI Functions?

Which events are affected when you use a MIDI function depends on the function, the active window and the current selection:

- A MIDI function may only apply to MIDI events of a certain type.
  For example, quantization affects notes only, while the Delete Controllers function obviously applies to MIDI controller events.
- In the Project window, the MIDI functions apply to all selected parts, affecting all events (of the relevant types) in them.

- In the MIDI editors, the MIDI functions apply to all selected events. If no events are selected, all events in the edited part(s) will be affected.

22.2 Quantizing

22.2.1 What Is Quantizing?

Quantizing in its fundamental form is a function that automatically moves recorded notes, positioning them on exact note values:

For example, if you record a series of eighth notes, some of them may end up slightly beside the exact eighth note positions.

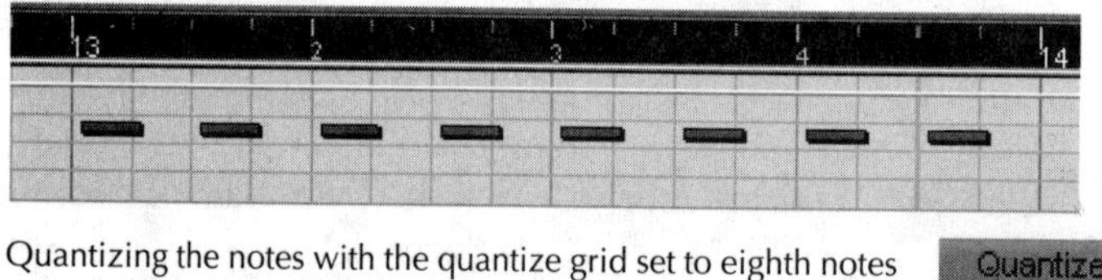

Quantizing the notes with the quantize grid set to eighth notes will move the "misplaced" notes to exact positions.

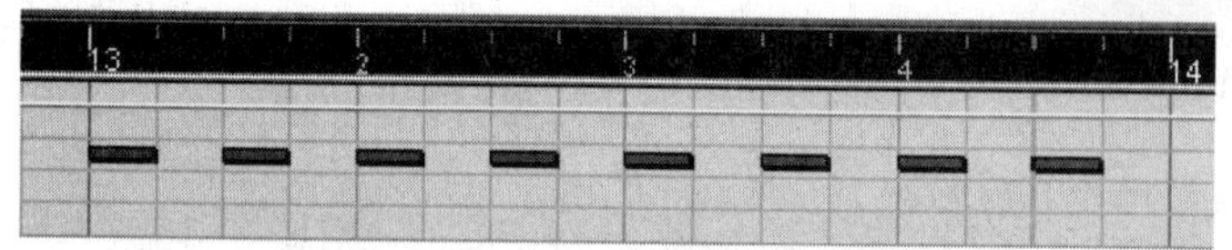

However, quantizing is not only a method of correcting errors, it can also be used creatively in various ways. For example, the "quantize grid" does not have to consist of perfectly straight notes, some notes can automatically be excluded from quantizing, etc.

- When quantizing MIDI, only the notes are affected (not other event types).
  It is also possible to quantize audio events, which is especially useful when working with Cubase SX/SL's loop splicing features—see page 385.

22.2.2 Setting Up

At its most basic, setting up quantizing consists of selecting a note value from the Quantize pop-up menu on the toolbar (in the Project window or a MIDI Editor).

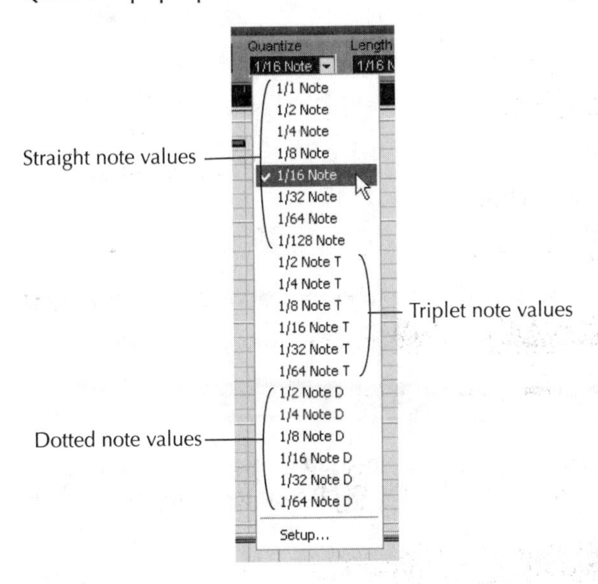

By default, this allows you to quantize to exact note values (straight, triplet or dotted notes) only. If you want more options, select "Quantize Setup..." from the MIDI menu (or "Setup..." from the Quantize pop-up menu) to open the Quantize Setup dialog.

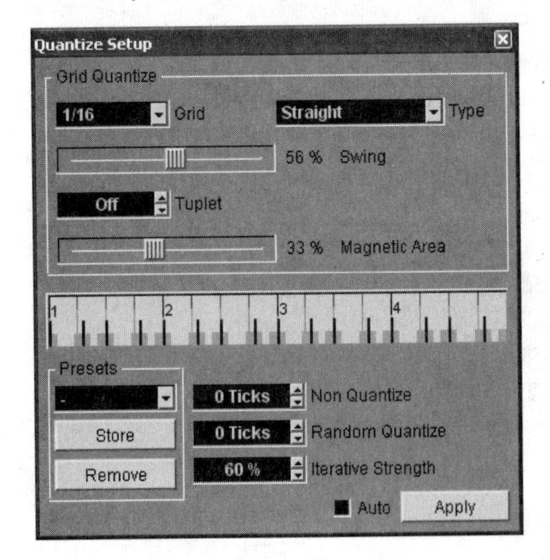

- Any settings you make in the dialog are immediately reflected in the Quantize pop-up menus. However, if you want your settings permanently available on the Quantize pop-up menus, you have to use the Presets functions (see page 471).

The dialog contains the following settings:

Grid Display

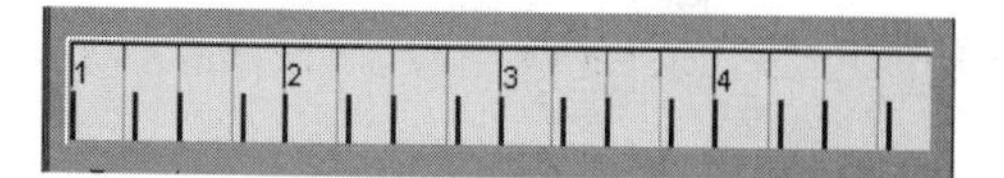

The grid display shows one bar (four beats), with blue lines indicating the quantize grid (the positions that notes will be moved to).

The Grid and Type Pop-ups

These are used to determine the basic note value for the quantizing grid. In other words, these have the same functionality as the Quantize pop-up menu on the Toolbar.

Eighth note triplets selected as quantizing grid.

Swing

The Swing slider is only available when a straight note value is selected for the grid and Tuplet is off (see below). It allows you to offset every second position in the grid, creating a swing or shuffle feel. When you adjust the Swing slider, the result is shown in the grid display below.

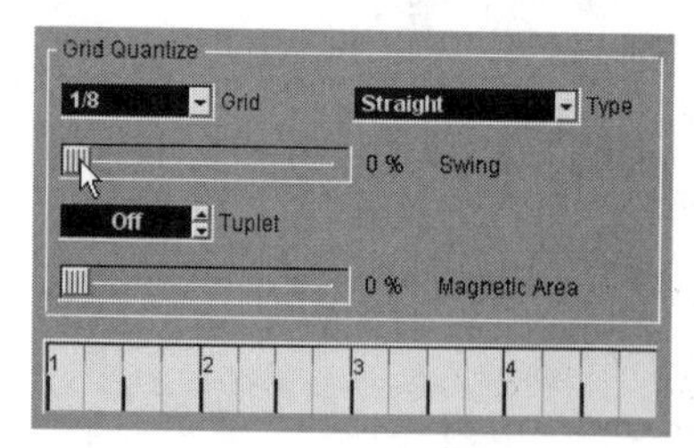

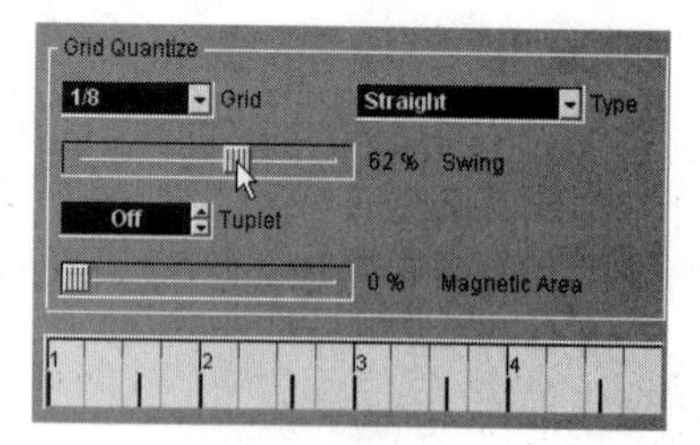

A straight eighth note grid compared with a grid with 62% swing.

Tuplet

Allows you to create more rhythmically complex grids, by dividing the grid into smaller steps.

Magnetic Area

This allows you to specify that only notes within a certain distance from the grid lines should be affected by quantizing.

- **When the slider is set to 0%, the Magnetic Area function is deactivated, i.e. all notes are affected by quantizing.**

  If you move the slider gradually to the right, you will note how the magnetic areas are shown around the blue lines in the grid display.

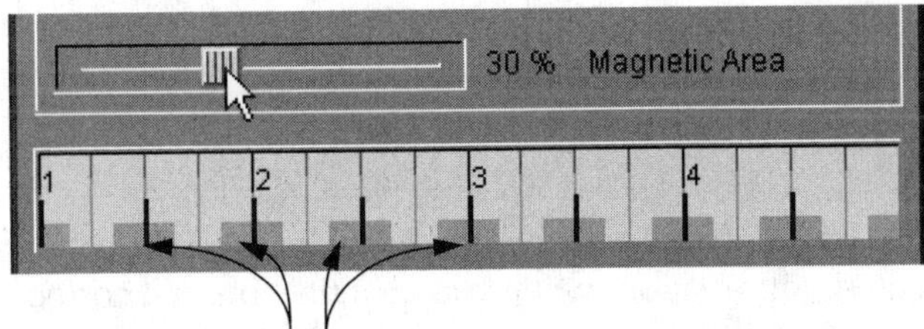

Only notes within the indicated zones will be affected by quantizing.

Presets

The controls in the lower left corner of the dialog allow you to store the current settings as a Preset, available on the Quantize menus in the Toolbars. The usual Preset procedures apply:

- **To store the settings as a Preset, click the Store button.**
- **To "load" a stored Preset, showing the stored settings in the dialog, just select it from the pop-up menu.**

  This is useful if you want to modify an existing Preset.

- **To rename the selected Preset, double click on the name and type a new one.**
- **To remove a stored Preset, select it from the pop-up menu and click Remove.**
- You can also create Presets by having the program analyse an audio event and extract the groove in the audio.
  See page 395.

Auto and Apply

These functions allow you to apply quantizing directly from the dialog, as described below.

- If you don't want to apply the quantizing you have set up in the dialog, you can close the window by clicking its standard close box. You can also leave the dialog open while you continue working.

The Non Quantize Setting

This is an additional setting that affects the result of the quantizing. It allows you to set a "distance" in ticks (120ths of sixteenth notes).

Events that already are within the specified distance from the quantize grid will not be quantized. This allows you to keep slight variations when you quantize, but still correct notes that are too far from the grid.

The Random Quantize Setting

This is an additional setting that affects the result of the quantizing. It allows you to set a "distance" in ticks (120ths of sixteenth notes).

Events will be quantized to random positions within the specified "distance" from the quantize grid, thus creating a more "loose" quantizing. Much like the Non Quantize setting, this allows for slight variations, while at the same time keeping notes from ending up too far from the grid.

The Iterative Strength Setting

This affects the results of the Iterative Quantize function, as described below.

22.2.3 Applying Quantize

There are several ways to apply the quantize:

- **The standard method is to select "Over Quantize" from the MIDI menu (or using a key command, by default [Q]).**

  This quantizes the selected MIDI parts or notes, according to the current Quantize pop-up menu setting.

- **You can also apply quantizing directly from the Quantize Setup dialog, by clicking the "Apply" button.**

- **If you activate the "Auto" checkbox in the Quantize Setup dialog, any change you make in the dialog is immediately applied to the selected MIDI parts or notes.**

  A great way of using this feature is to set up a playback loop, and adjust the settings in the dialog until you get the desired result.

● When you apply quantize, the result is based on the original position of the notes. Therefore, you can freely try different quantize settings with no risk of "destroying" anything. See also Undo and Freeze Quantize, below.

The Auto Quantize Function

If you activate the AQ button on the Transport panel, all MIDI recordings you make are automatically quantized according to the settings you have made in the Quantize Setup dialog.

22.2.4 Iterative Quantize

Another way to apply "loose" quantization is to use the Iterative Quantize function on the MIDI menu. It works like this:

Instead of moving a note to the closest quantize grid position, Iterative Quantize moves it only part of the way. You specify how much the notes should be moved towards the grid with the Iterative Strength setting in the Quantize Setup dialog.

Iterative Quantize is also different from "regular" quantization, in that the operation is not based on the notes' original positions but on their current, quantized position. This makes it possible to repeatedly use Iterative Quantize, gradually moving the notes closer to the quantize grid until you've find the desired timing.

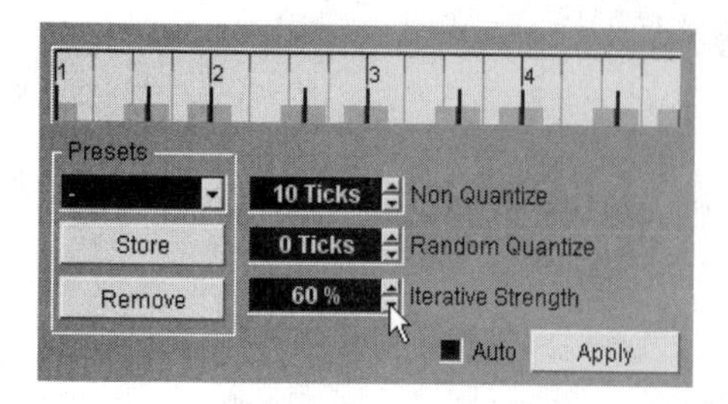

22.2.5 Quantize Lengths

- This function is only available from within the MIDI editors.

This function (on the Advanced Quantize submenu on the MIDI menu) will quantize the length of the notes, without changing their start positions. At its most basic level, this function will set the length of the notes to the Length Quantize value on the MIDI editors' toolbar. However, if you have selected the "Linked to Quantize" option on the Length Quantize pop-up menu, the function will resize the note according to the quantize grid, taking the Swing, Tuplet and Magnetic Area settings into account. An example:

1. Length Quantize set to "Linked to Quantize".

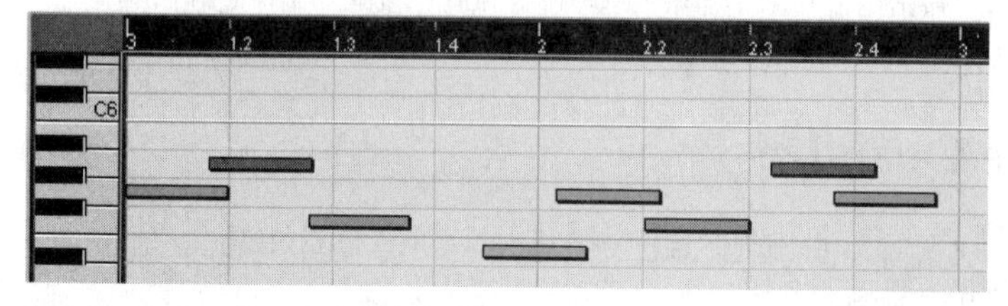

2. Some notes, all a 1/16th note of length.

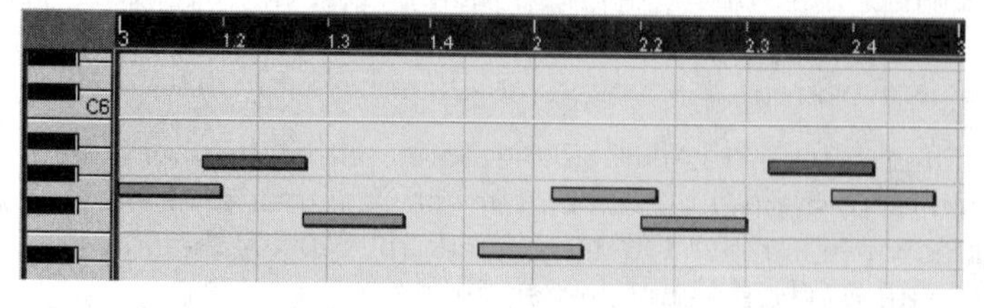

3. Here, the quantize value has been set to straight 1/16th notes with Swing at 100%. Since Snap is activated (see page 546), the quantize grid is reflected in the note display's grid.

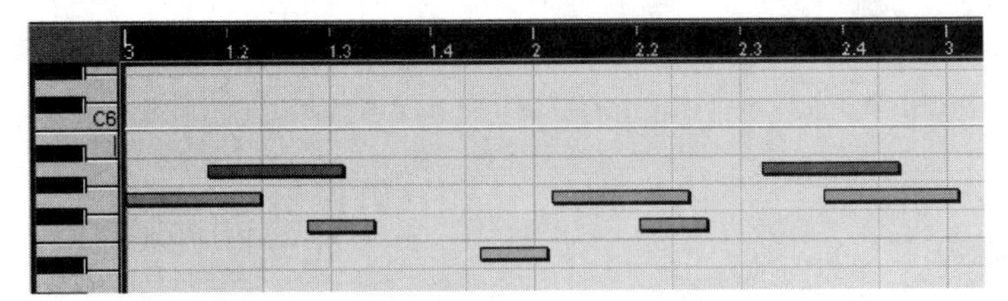

4. Selecting Quantize Lengths will adjust the note lengths according to the grid. If you compare the result to the first figure above, you will find that notes that started within the odd sixteenth note "zones" got the longer grid length, and notes in the even zones got the shorter length.

22.2.6 Quantize Ends

The Quantize Ends function on the Advanced Quantize submenu will only affect the end positions of notes. Apart from that, it works just like regular quantizing, taking the Quantize pop-up menu setting into account.

22.2.7 Undo and Freeze Quantize

As mentioned above, the original position of each quantized note is stored. Therefore, you can make the selected MIDI notes revert to their original, unquantized state at any time, by selecting Undo Quantize from the Advanced Quantize submenu. This is independent from the regular Undo History.

However, there may be situations when you want to make the quantized positions "permanent". For example, you may want to quantize notes a second time, having the results based on the current quantized positions rather than the original positions. To make this possible, select the notes in question and select "Freeze Quantize" from the Advanced Quantize submenu. This makes the quantized positions permanent.

- After you have performed a Freeze Quantize for a note, you cannot undo its quantization.

22.3 Other MIDI Menu Functions

The Transpose item and the items on the Functions submenu contain the following functions:

22.3.1 Transpose

Opens a dialog with settings for transposing the selected notes:

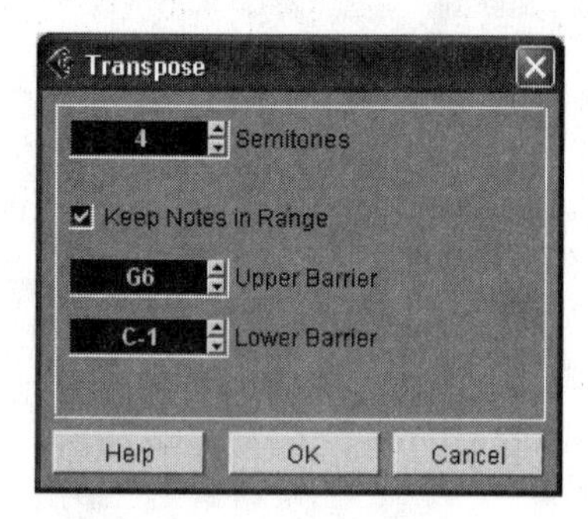

Semitones

This is where you set the amount of transposition.

Keep Notes in Range

When this checkbox is activated, transposed notes will remain within the Upper and Lower Barrier values.

- **If a note ends up outside the barriers after transposition, it will be shifted to another octave, keeping the correct transposed pitch if possible.**

  If this isn't possible (if you have set a very narrow range between the Upper and Lower Barrier), the note will be transposed "as far as possible", i.e. to the Upper or Lower Barrier note. If you set the Upper and Lower Barriers to the same value, all notes will be transposed to this pitch!

OK and Cancel

Clicking OK performs the transposition. Clicking Cancel closes the dialog without transposing.

22.3.2 Legato

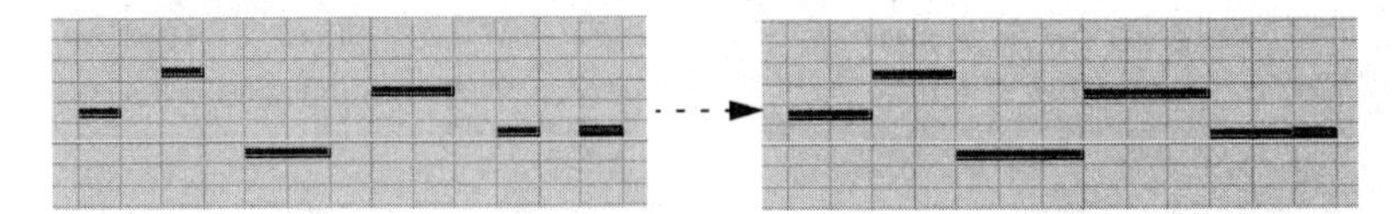

Extends each selected note so that it reaches the next note. You can specify the desired gap or overlap with the "Legato Overlap" setting in the Preferences dialog (MIDI—Function Parameters page).

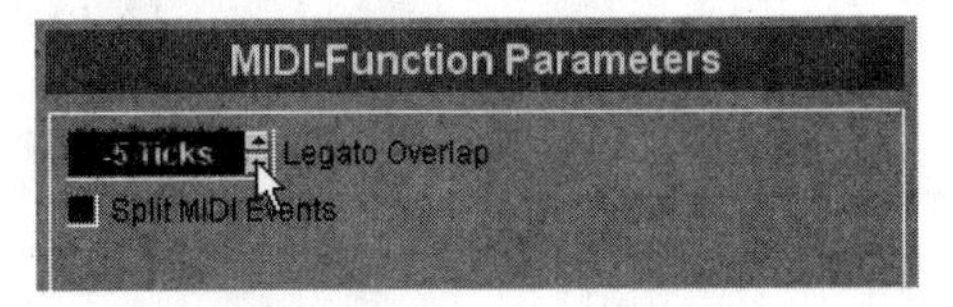

When using Legato with this setting, each note will be extended to end 5 ticks before the next note.

22.3.3 Fixed Lengths

- This function is only available from within the MIDI editors.

This function resizes all selected notes to the length set with the Length Quantize pop-up menu on the MIDI editor toolbar.

22.3.4 Delete Doubles

This function removes double notes, i.e. notes of the same pitch on the exact same position. Double notes can occur when recording in Cycle mode, after Quantizing, etc.

- This function always affects whole MIDI parts.

22.3.5 Delete Controllers

This function removes all non-note events from the selected MIDI parts.

- This function always affects whole MIDI parts.

22.3.6 Delete Notes

Allows you to delete very short or weak notes. This is useful for automatically removing unwanted "ghost notes" after recording. Selecting "Delete Notes..." opens a dialog in which you set up the criteria for the function:

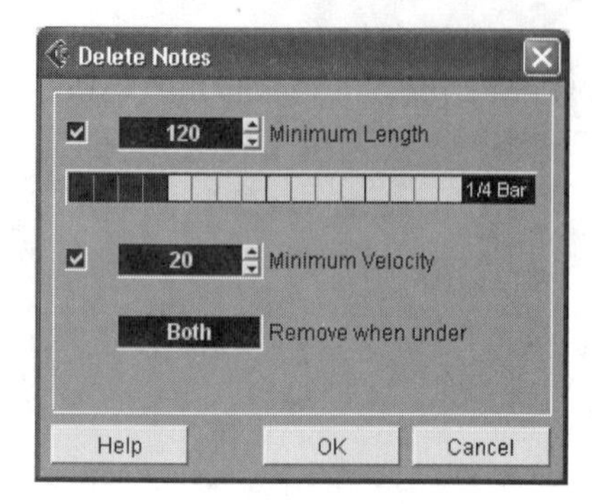

The parameters have the following functionality:

Minimum Length

When the Minimum Length checkbox is activated, the note length is taken into account, allowing you to remove short notes. You can either specify the minimum length (for notes to be kept) in the value display or by dragging the blue line in the graphical length display below.

- **The graphical length display can correspond to 1/4 bar, one bar, two bars or four bars.**

  You change this setting by clicking in the field to the right of the display.

In this case, the whole length display corresponds to 1/4 bar (one beat), and the Minimum Length is set to 1/32nd notes (60 ticks).

Minimum Velocity

When the Minimum Velocity checkbox is activated, the velocity of notes is taken into account, allowing you to remove weak notes. You specify the minimum velocity (for notes to be kept) in the value display.

Remove when under

This setting is only available when both Minimum Length and Minimum Velocity is activated. By clicking the value display, you select whether both length and velocity criteria must be met for notes to be deleted, or whether one of the criteria will suffice.

OK and Cancel

Clicking OK performs the automatic delete according to the rules set up. Clicking Cancel closes the dialog without deleting notes.

22.3.7 Restrict Polyphony

Selecting this item opens a dialog in which you can specify how many "voices" should be used (for the selected notes or parts). Restricting the polyphony this way is useful when you have an instrument with limited polyphony and want to make sure all notes will be played. The effect is achieved by shortening notes as required, so that they end before the next note starts.

22.3.8 Pedals to Note Length

This function scans for Sustain pedal on/off events, lengthens the affected notes to match the Sustain pedal off position, and then removes the Sustain Controller on/off events.

22.3.9 Delete Overlaps (mono)

This function allows you to make sure that no two notes of the same pitch overlap (i.e. that one starts before the other ends). Overlapping notes of the same pitch can confuse some MIDI instruments (a new Note On is transmitted before the Note Off is transmitted). This command can then be used to automatically rectify the problem.

22.3.10 Delete Overlaps (poly)

This function shortens notes when required, so that no note begins before another ends. This happens regardless of which pitch the notes have.

22.3.11 Velocity

This function opens a dialog that allows you to manipulate the velocity of notes in various ways.

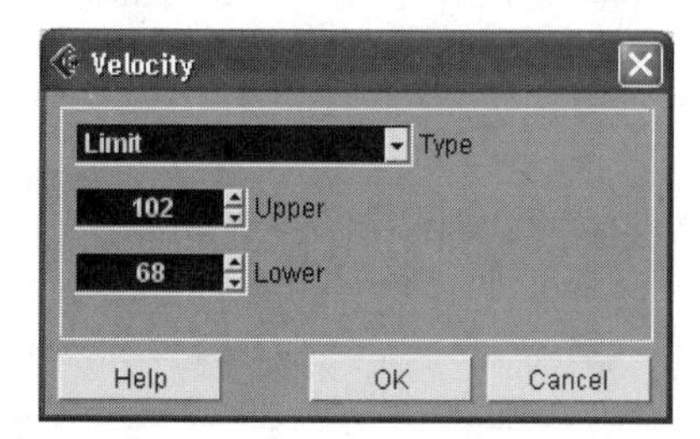

To apply the function, select one of the three processing types from the Type pop-up, adjust the settings and click OK (to close the dialog without applying, click Cancel).

The following types of velocity processing are available:

Add/Subtract

This simply adds a fixed number to the existing velocity values. You set the value (positive or negative) with the Amount parameter.

Compress/Expand

Compresses or expands the "dynamic range" of MIDI notes by scaling the velocity values according to the Ratio setting (0—300%). The principle behind this is that multiplying different velocity values with a factor higher than 1 (over 100%) will also make the differences between velocity values greater, while using a factor lower than 1 (under 100%) will make the differences smaller. In short:

- **To compress ("even out" velocity differences), use ratio values below 100%.**

  After compression, you would probably want to add a velocity amount (with the Add/Subtract function) to maintain the average velocity level.

- **To expand (create greater difference in velocity), use ratio values above 100%.**

  Before you expand, you may want to adjust the velocity with the Add/Subtract function, so that the average velocity is somewhere in the middle of the range. If the average velocity is high (near 127) or low (near 0), expansion will not work properly, simply because velocity values can only be between 0 and 127!

Limit

This function allows you to make sure that no velocity values fall outside a given range (the Lower and Upper values). Any velocity values outside this range are raised/lowered to exactly the Lower/Upper values.

22.3.12 Fixed Velocity

This function sets the velocity of all selected notes to the Insert Velocity value on the toolbar in the MIDI editors.

22.3.13 Reverse

This function inverts the order of the selected events (or of all events in the selected parts), causing the MIDI music to play backwards. Note though, that the effect is different from reversing an audio recording. With MIDI, the individual notes will still play as usual in the MIDI instrument—it's only the order of playback that is changed.

22.4 Dissolve Part

The Dissolve Part function on the MIDI menu has two separate uses:

- **When you work with MIDI parts (on MIDI channel "Any") containing events on different MIDI channels.**

  Dissolve Part separates the events according to MIDI channel.

- **When you want to separate MIDI events according to pitch.**

  A typical example would be drum and percussion tracks, where each pitch usually corresponds to a separate drum sound.

22.4.1 Dissolving Parts into Separate Channels

Setting a track to MIDI channel "Any" will cause each MIDI event to play back on its original MIDI channel, rather than a channel set for the whole track. There are two main situations when "Any" channel tracks are useful:

- **When you record several MIDI channels at the same time.**

  You may for example have a MIDI keyboard with several keyboard zones, where each zone sends MIDI on a separate channel. Recording on an "Any" channel track allows you to play back the recording with different sounds for each zone (since the different MIDI notes play back on separate MIDI channels).

- **When you have imported a MIDI file of Type 0.**

  MIDI files of Type 0 contain only one track, with notes on up to 16 different MIDI channels. If you were to set this track to a specific MIDI channel, all notes in the MIDI file would be played back with the same sound; setting the track to "Any" will cause the imported file to play back as intended.

The Dissolve Part function scans MIDI parts for events on different MIDI channels, distributes the events into new parts on new tracks, one for each MIDI channel found. This allows you to work with each musical part individually. Proceed as follows:

1. **Select the part(s) containing MIDI data on different channels.**
2. **Select "Dissolve Part" from the MIDI menu.**
3. **In the dialog that appears, select the "Separate Channels" option.**

   This is only available if the MIDI track was set to channel "Any".

Now, for each MIDI channel used in the selected part(s), a new MIDI track is created and set to the corresponding MIDI channel. Each event is then copied into the part on the track with the corresponding MIDI channel. Finally, the original part(s) are muted.

An example:

This part contains events on MIDI channel 1, 2 and 3.

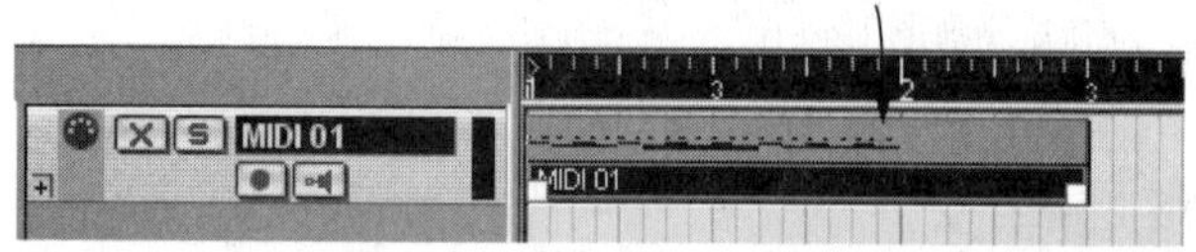

Selecting "Dissolve Part" creates new parts on new tracks, set to channel 1, 2 and 3. Each new part contains only the events on the respective MIDI channel.

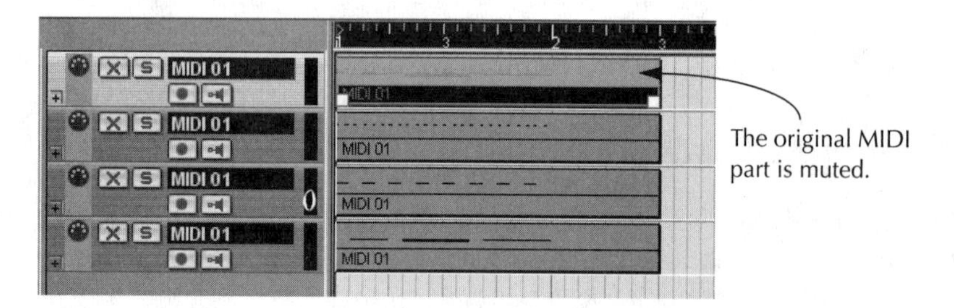

22.4.2 Dissolving Parts into Separate Pitches

The Dissolve Part function can also scan MIDI parts for events of different pitch, and distribute the events into new parts on new tracks, one for each pitch. This is useful when the different pitches are not used in a regular melodic context, but rather for separating different sounds (e.g. MIDI drum tracks or sampler sound FX tracks). By dissolving such parts, you can work with each sound individually, on a separate track. Proceed as follows:

1. **Select the part(s) containing MIDI data.**
2. **Select "Dissolve Part" from the MIDI menu.**
3. **In the dialog that appears, select the "Separate Pitches" option.**

   A new MIDI track is created for each used pitch in the selected part(s). The events are then copied into the parts on the track for the corresponding pitch. Finally, the original part(s) are muted.

23 The MIDI Editors

23.1 About Editing MIDI

There are several ways to edit MIDI in Cubase SX/SL. You can use the tools and functions in the Project window for large-scale editing, or use the functions on the MIDI menu to process MIDI parts in various ways (see page 467). For hands-on graphical editing of the contents of MIDI parts, you use the MIDI editors:

- The Key Editor is the default MIDI editor, presenting notes graphically in an intuitive piano roll-style grid.
  The Key Editor also allows for detailed editing of non-note events such as MIDI controllers.
- The Drum Editor is similar to the Key Editor, but takes advantage of the fact that with drum parts, each key corresponds to a separate drum sound.
  This is the editor to use when you're editing drum or percussion parts.
- The List Editor shows all events in a MIDI part as a list, allowing you to view and edit their properties numerically.
  Unlike the other editors, in the List Editor you can only view and edit one part at a time.
- The Score Editor shows MIDI notes as a musical score.
  If you are using Cubase SL, the Score Editor offers basic score editing and printing—see page 529 for details). Cubase SX comes with advanced tools and functions for notation, layout and printing, all described in the separate pdf document "Score Layout and Printing" (opened from the Windows Start menu or the Help menu in the program). However, even if your focus is on creating printed scores we recommend that you study this chapter as well, to get a grip on the common MIDI editing procedures.
- Finally, you can also edit MIDI in the Project Browser.
  Like the List Editor, this shows the events in a list and allows you to perform numerical editing. However, you will probably find the List Editor more suited for MIDI editing, since it has various special features and functions for this. The Project Browser is described in its own chapter, on page 583.

About this Chapter

This chapter describes how to use the Key, Drum and List Editor. Please note that a lot of features are identical in these editors (especially in the Key and Drum Editors)—they are all described in the Key Editor section. The sections about the Drum Editor (see page 509) and the List Editor (see page 522) describe the specific features of these editors only.

23.2 Opening a MIDI Editor

There are two ways to open a MIDI editor:

- Select one or several parts and select Open Key Editor, Open Drum Editor or Open List Editor from the MIDI menu (or use the corresponding key command).
  Note that the List Editor only opens a single part at a time. For details about opening the Score Editor in Cubase SL, see page 531.
- Double click a part.
  Which editor opens depends on the settings in the Preferences (Event Display—MIDI page):

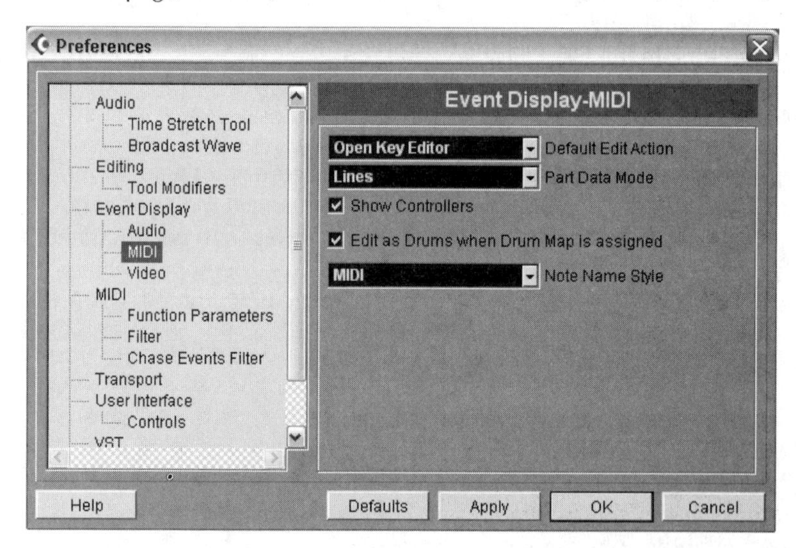

Double clicking will open the editor selected on the Default Edit Action pop-up menu. However, if the option "Edit as Drums when Drum Map is assigned" is activated and a drum map is selected for the edited track (see page 519), the Drum Editor will open. This way you can double click to open the Key Editor (or the Score or List Editor, depending on your preferences) but drum tracks will automatically open in the Drum Editor.

- If the part you open for editing is a shared copy, any editing you perform will affect all shared copies of this part.
  Shared copies are created by pressing [Alt]+[Shift] and dragging, or by using the Repeat function with the "Shared copies" option activated. In the Project window, shared copies are indicated by the part name in italics and an icon in the lower right corner of the part (see page 135).

23.3 The Key Editor—Overview

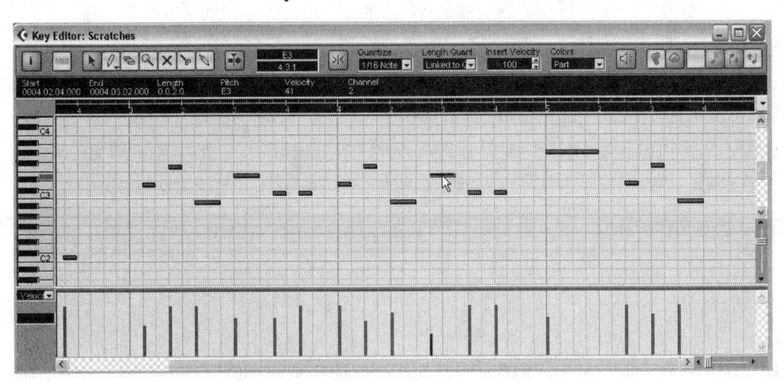

23.3.1 The Toolbar

As in other windows, the toolbar contains tools and various settings.

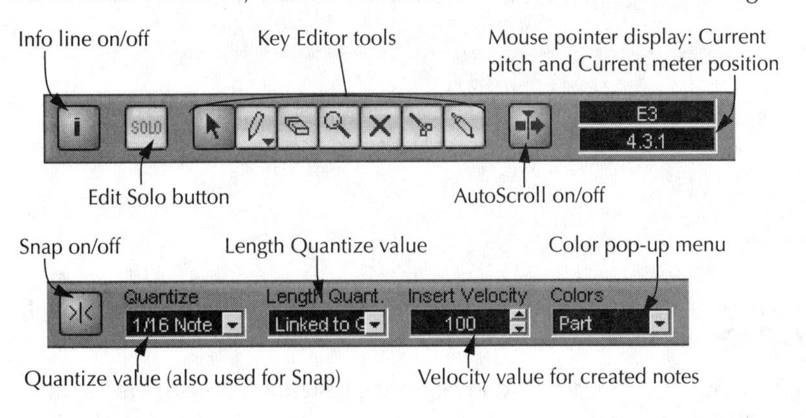

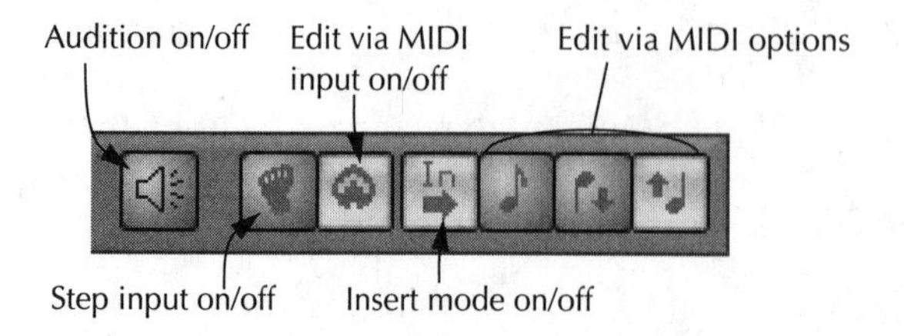

23.3.2 The Info Line

The info line shows information about selected MIDI notes. You can edit all values on the info line using regular value editing (see page 498 for details). Length and position values are displayed in the format currently selected for the ruler (see below).

- **To hide or show the info line, click the "i" icon in the toolbar.**

23.3.3 The Ruler

The ruler shows the time line, by default in the display format selected on the Transport panel. You can select a separate format for a MIDI editor ruler by clicking the arrow button to the right of it and selecting an option from the pop-up menu that appears. For a list of the available formats, see page 116.

At the bottom of the pop-up menu there are two additional items:

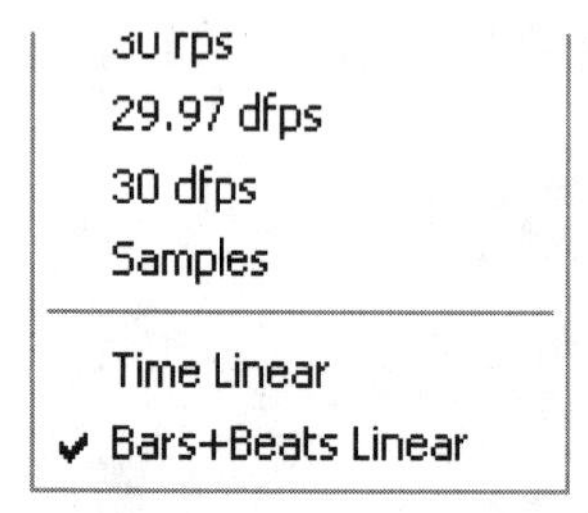

- **If "Time Linear" is selected, the ruler, note display and controller display will be linear in relation to time.**

  This means that if the ruler shows bars and beats, the distance between the bar lines will vary depending on the tempo.

- **If "Bars+Beats Linear" is selected, the ruler, note display and controller display will be linear in relation to tempo.**

  This means that if the ruler shows bars and beats, the distance between beats will be constant.

In most cases, you would probably set the display format to "Bars+Beats" in "Bars+Beats Linear" mode when editing MIDI.

23.3.4 The Note Display

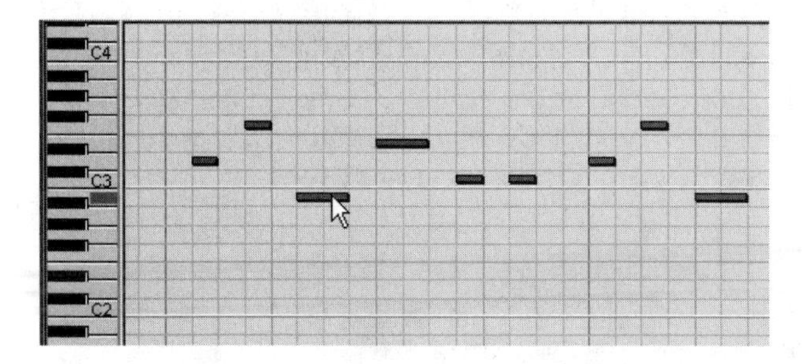

The note display is the main area in the Key Editor. It contains a grid, in which MIDI notes are shown as boxes. The width of a box corresponds to the note length, and the vertical position of a box corresponds to the note number (pitch), with higher notes higher up in the grid. The piano keyboard to the left serves as a guide for finding the right note number.

23.3.5 The Controller Display

The area at the bottom of the Key Editor window is the controller display. This consists of one or several controller lanes, each showing one of the following properties or event types:

- Velocity values of the notes.
- Pitch Bend events.
- Aftertouch events.
- Poly Pressure events.
- Program Change events.
- Any type of continuous controller event.

Velocity values are shown as vertical bars in the controller display, with higher bars corresponding to higher velocity values:

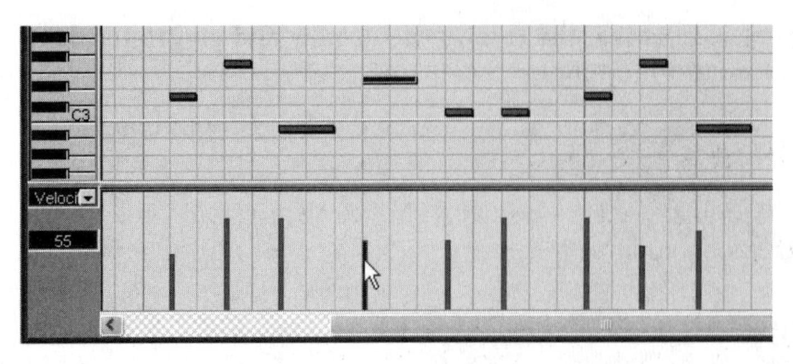

Each velocity bar corresponds to a note in the note display.

Events in the controller display (that is, anything other than velocity values) are shown as "blocks", the heights of which correspond to the "values" of the events. However, events that have been recorded (or drawn with a low quantize value) may appear more like "filled curves", simply because they are positioned very closely:

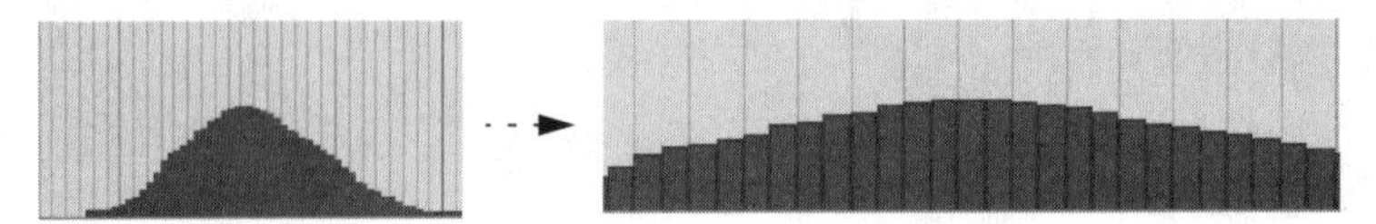

If you zoom in on this "curve", you will find that it consists of separate events:

- Unlike notes, events in the controller display have no length. The value of an event in the display will be "valid" until the start of the next event:

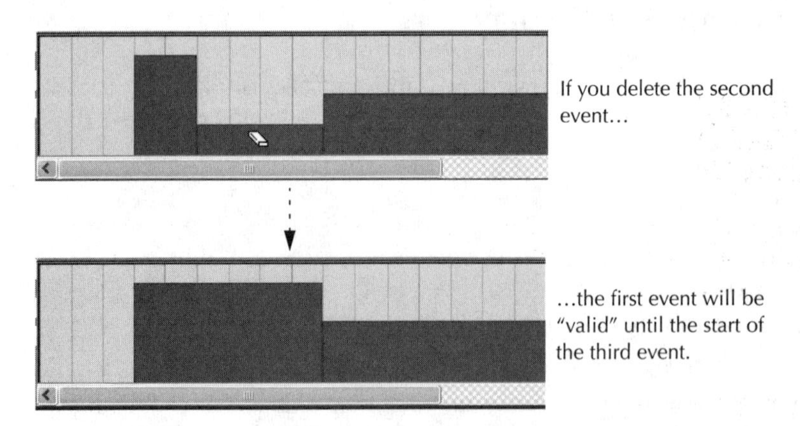

If you delete the second event...

...the first event will be "valid" until the start of the third event.

- **To change the size of the controller display, drag the divider between the controller display and the note display.**

  This will make the controller display larger and the note display smaller, or vice versa.

For a description of editing in the controller display, see page 501.

23.4 Key Editor Operations

23.4.1 Zooming

Zooming in the Key Editor is done according to the standard zoom procedures, using the zoom sliders, the Magnifying Glass tool or the Zoom submenu on the Edit menu.

23.4.2 Playing Back

You can play back your music as usual when working in a MIDI editor. There are a couple of features making it easier to edit during playback:

Solo Button

If you activate the Solo button, only the edited MIDI parts will be heard during regular playback.

Autoscroll

As described on page 152, the Autoscroll function makes the window "follow" the project cursor during playback, so that the current play position is visible at all times. However, when you are working in a MIDI editor, you may want to deactivate Autoscroll—this way, the events you are working with will stay visible.

The Autoscroll button on the toolbar of each MIDI editor is independent for the editor. For example, this means you can have Autoscroll deactivated in the Key Editor and activated in the Project window, should you so like.

23.4.3 Auditioning

If the speaker icon on the toolbar is activated, individual notes will automatically be played back (auditioned) when you move or transpose them, or when you create new notes by drawing. This makes it easier to hear what you're doing.

23.4.4 Creating and Editing Notes

Drawing Notes

To draw new notes in the Key Editor, you use the Pencil tool. In the default "Draw" mode (see below), you insert single notes by clicking with the Pencil tool at the desired time position and pitch (height).

- **When you move the pointer in the note display, its bar position is indicated in the toolbar, and its pitch is indicated both in the toolbar and on the piano keyboard to the left.**

  This makes it easy to find the right note and insert position.

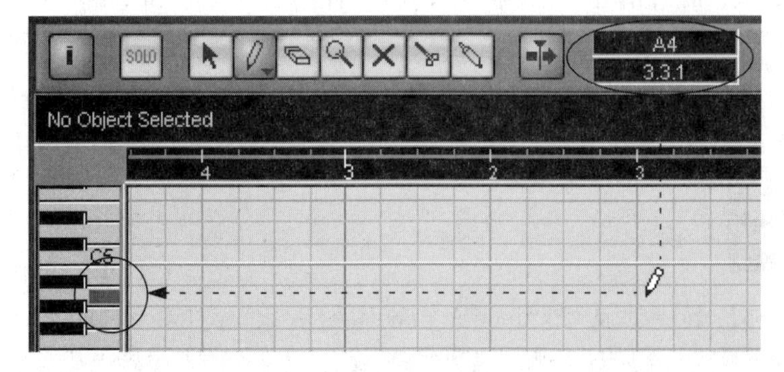

- **If Snap is activated, this determines the start position of the created note (see page 546).**

- **If you just click once, the created note will get the length set on the Length Quantize pop-up menu on the toolbar.**

  You can create a longer note by clicking and dragging the pointer with the mouse button pressed. The length of the created note will be a multiple of the Length Quantize value.

- **The notes will get the Insert Velocity value set on the toolbar.**
- Just like the Arrow tool in the Project window, the Pencil tool has several different modes.
  To select one of the modes, click on the Pencil tool icon on the toolbar when the tool is already selected. This opens a pop-up menu from which you can select one of the Pencil modes.

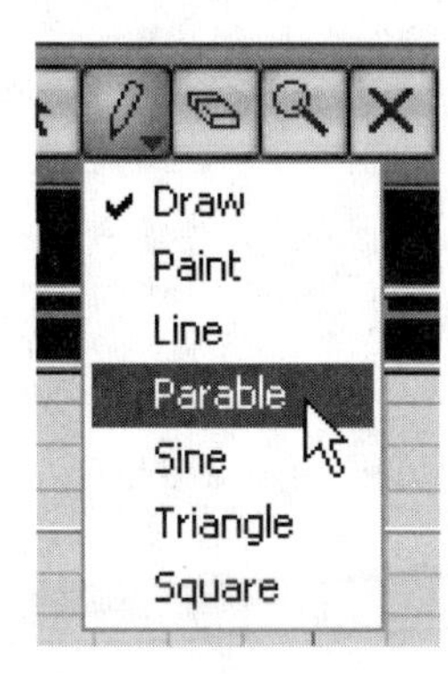

The tool icon will change appearance according to the selected mode.

Mode	Description
Draw	This inserts single notes, as described above.
Paint	Allows you to insert multiple notes by dragging with the mouse button pressed. If Snap is activated, the notes will be positioned and sized according to the Quantize and Length Quantize values. If you press [Ctrl] while painting, movement will be restricted to horizontal only (i.e. the painted notes will have the same pitch).
Line	When this mode is selected, you click and drag to create a straight line, in any angle. When you release the mouse button a series of notes will be created, aligned with the line. If Snap is activated, the notes will be spaced and sized according to the Quantize value.
Parable, Sine, Triangle, Square	These modes insert events along different curve shapes. While they can be used for creating notes, they're probably best suited for controller editing (see page 504).

Selecting Notes

Selecting notes is done using any of the following methods:

- **Use the Arrow tool.**

  The standard selection techniques apply.

- **Use the Select submenu on the Quick menu.**

  The options are:

Option	Description
All	Selects all notes in the edited part.
None	Deselects all events.
In Loop	Selects all notes that are partially or completely inside the boundaries of the left and right locators.
From Start to Cursor	Selects all notes that begin to the left of the project cursor.
From Cursor to End	Selects all notes that end to the right of the project cursor.

- **You can also use the left and right arrow keys on the computer keyboard to step from one note to the next or previous.**

  If you press [Shift] and use the arrow keys, the current selection will be kept, allowing you to select several notes.

- **To select all notes of a certain pitch, press [Ctrl] and click on the desired key in the keyboard display to the left.**

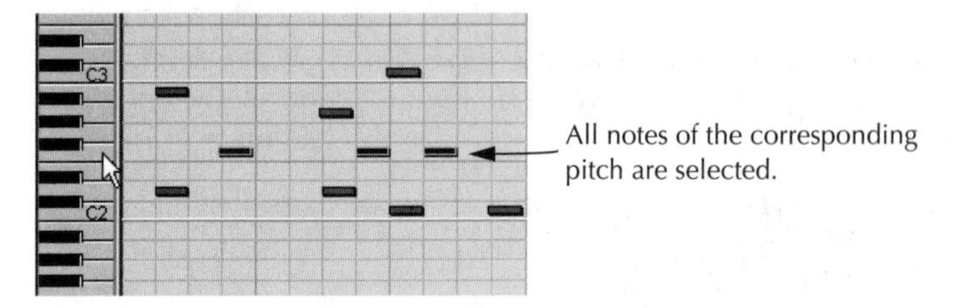

  You can also press [Shift] and double click on a note to select all the *following* notes of the same pitch.

- **If the option "Auto Select Events under Cursor" is activated in the Preferences dialog (Editing page), all notes currently "touched" by the project cursor are automatically selected.**

Moving and Transposing Notes

To move notes in the editor, use any of the following methods:

- **Click and drag to a new position.**

  All selected notes will be moved, maintaining their relative positions. If Snap is activated, this determines to which positions you can move the notes, see page 546.

- Note also that you can restrict movement to horizontal or vertical only by holding down [Ctrl] while dragging.

- **Use the up and down arrow keys on the computer keyboard.**

  This method allows you to transpose the selected notes, without risking to move them horizontally. You can also use the Transpose function (see page 476) or the info line (see page 488) for this. Note that pressing [Shift] and using the up and down arrow keys will transpose notes in steps of one octave.

- **Use the Move to Cursor function on the Edit menu.**

  This moves the selected notes to the project cursor position.

- **Select a note and adjust its position or pitch on the info line.**

  See page 498.

You can also adjust the position of notes by quantizing (see page 468).

Duplicating and Repeating Notes

Notes are duplicated much in the same way as events in the Project window:

- **Hold down [Alt] and drag the note(s) to a new position.**

  If Snap is activated, this determines to which positions you can copy the notes (see page 546).

- **Selecting "Duplicate" from the Edit menu creates a copy of the selected note and places it directly after the original.**

  If several notes are selected, all of these are copied "as one unit", maintaining the relative distance between the notes.

- **Selecting "Repeat" from the Edit menu opens a dialog, allowing you to create a number of copies of the selected note(s).**

  This works just like the Duplicate function, except that you can specify the number of copies.

Using Cut and Paste

You can use the Cut, Copy and Paste functions on the Edit menu to move or copy material within a part or between different parts. When you paste copied notes, you can either use the regular Paste function or the Paste Time function on the Edit menu's Range submenu.

- "Paste" inserts the copied notes at the project cursor position, without affecting existing notes.
- "Paste Time" inserts at the project cursor position, but moves (and if necessary, splits) existing notes to make room for the pasted notes.

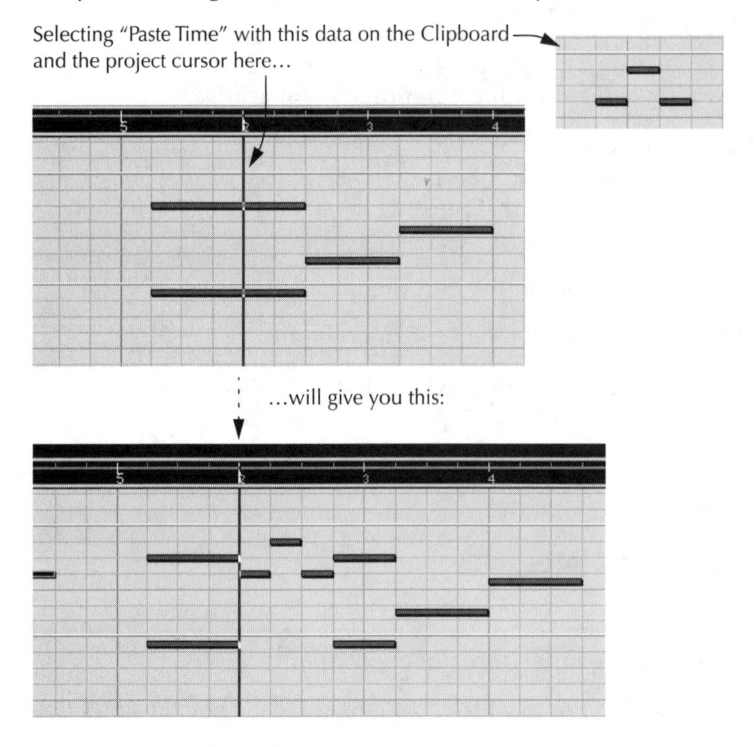

Resizing Notes

To resize a note, use one of the following methods:

- **Position the arrow tool at the start or end of the note, so that the pointer takes on the shape of a small double arrow. Click and drag to the left or right to resize the note.**

  This method allows you to resize the note from either direction.

- **Click with the Pencil tool within the note box and drag to the left or the right (to make the note shorter or longer, respectively).**

With both these methods, the resulting length will be a multiple of the Length Quantize value on the toolbar.

- **Select the note and adjust its length on the info line.**

  See page 498 for details on info line editing.

Splitting Notes

There are three ways to split notes:

- **Clicking on a note with the Scissors tool splits the note at the position you pointed (taking the Snap setting into account if activated).**

  If several notes are selected, they are all split at the same position if applicable.

- **If you select "Split at Cursor", all notes that are intersected by the project cursor are split at the cursor position.**
- **If you select "Split Loop", all notes that are intersected by the left or right locator are split at the locator positions.**

Gluing Notes

Clicking on a note with the Glue tube tool will "glue it together" with the next note of the same pitch. The result will be one long note spanning from the start of the first note to the end of the second note, and with the properties (velocity, etc.) of the first note.

Muting Notes

Individual notes can be muted in the Key Editor, as opposed to muting an entire MIDI part in the Project window. This allows you to exclude notes from playback, but keep the option to bring them back again at any time. To mute a note, use one of the following methods:

- Click on it with the Mute tool.
- Select the Mute tool and drag a rectangle, enclosing all notes you want to mute.
- Select the note(s) and choose Mute from the Edit menu.
  The default key command for this is [Shift]+[M].

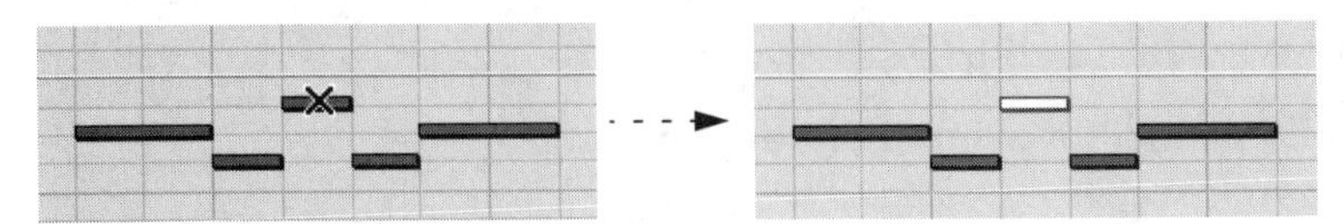

Muted notes are "dimmed" in the note display.

To unmute a note, either click it or enclose it with the Mute tool, or select it and choose Unmute from the Edit menu. The default key command for this is [Shift]+[U].

Deleting Notes

To delete notes, either click on them with the Eraser tool or select them and press [Backspace].

23.4.5 Editing on the Info Line

The info line shows the values and properties of the selected event(s). If a single event is selected, its values are displayed in light blue on the info line. If several events are selected, the info line shows the values of the first of these events, in yellow.

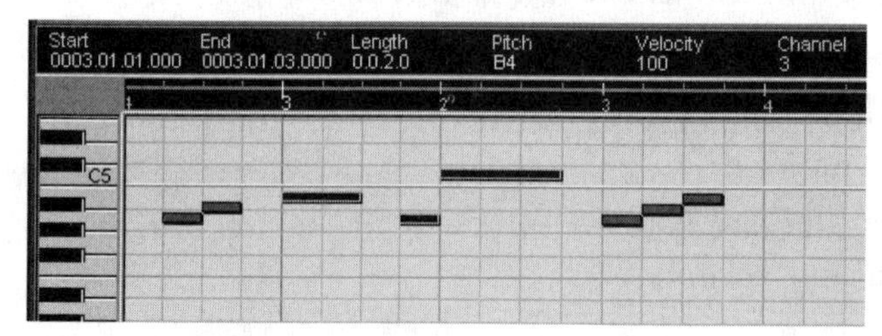

Several events selected.

You can edit the values on the info line using regular value editing. This allows you to move, resize, transpose or change velocity of events in a very precise manner.

- If you have several events selected and change a value, all selected events will be changed relatively.
  In other words, the value will be changed by an equal amount for all selected events.
- If you have several events selected, hold down [Ctrl] and change a value, the change will be absolute.
  In other words, the value setting will be the same for all selected events.

23.4.6 Editing Notes via MIDI

You can change the properties of notes via MIDI. For example, this can be a fast way to get the right velocity value, since you will hear the result even as you edit:

1. **Select the note you want to edit.**
2. **Click on the MIDI connector symbol on the toolbar.**

The symbol should be lit. This enables editing via MIDI.

3. **Use the note buttons on the toolbar to decide which properties should be changed by the MIDI input.**

   You can enable editing of pitch, note-on and/or note-off velocity.

With this setting, the edited notes will get the pitch and velocity values of the notes input via MIDI, but the note-off velocities will be kept as they are.

4. **Play a note on your MIDI instrument.**

   The note selected in the editor will get the pitch, velocity and/or note-off velocity of the played note.

The next note in the edited part is automatically selected, making it easy to quickly edit a series of notes.

- **If you want another try, select the note again (easiest by pressing the [←] key on the computer keyboard) and again play a note on your MIDI instrument.**

23.4.7 Step Input

Step input, or step recording, is when you enter notes one at a time (or one chord at a time) without worrying about the exact timing. This is useful e.g. when you know the part you want to record but are not able to play it exactly as you want it.

Proceed as follows:

1. **Click the "foot button" on the toolbar to activate Step input mode.**

2. **Use the note buttons to the right to decide which properties should be included when you input the notes.**

   For example, you may not want to include the velocity and/or note-off velocity of the played notes. It's also possible to turn off the pitch property, in which case all notes will get the pitch C3, no matter what you play.

3. **Click anywhere in the note display to set the start position (the desired position of the first note or chord).**

   The step input position is shown as a blue line in the note display, and in the lower mouse pointer display in the toolbar.

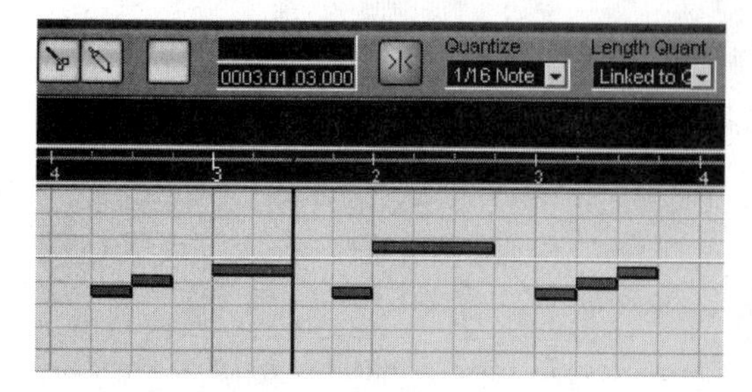

4. **Specify the desired note spacing and length with the Quantize and Length Quantize pop-up menus.**

   The notes you input will be positioned according to the Quantize value and have the length set with the Length Quantize value. For instance, if you set Quantize to 1/8 notes and Length Quantize to 1/16 note, the notes will be sixteenth notes, appearing on each eighth note position.

5. **Play the first note or chord on your MIDI instrument.**

   The note or chord appears in the editor and the step input position advances one quantize value step.

- If Insert mode is activated, all notes to the right of the step input position will be moved to "make room" for the inserted note or chord.

Insert mode activated.

6. **Continue in the same way with the rest of the notes or chords.**

   You can adjust the Quantize or Length Quantize value as you go along, to change the timing or note lengths. You can also move the step input position manually by clicking anywhere in the note display.

- **To insert a "rest", press the right arrow key on the computer keyboard.**

  This advances the step input position one step.

7. **When you're done, click the foot button to deactivate step input.**

23.4.8 Editing in the Controller Display

About Controller Lanes

By default, the controller display has a single lane, showing one event type at a time. However, you can easily add lanes by right-clicking in the display and selecting "Create new controller lane" from the Quick menu. This allows you to view and edit different controllers at the same time.

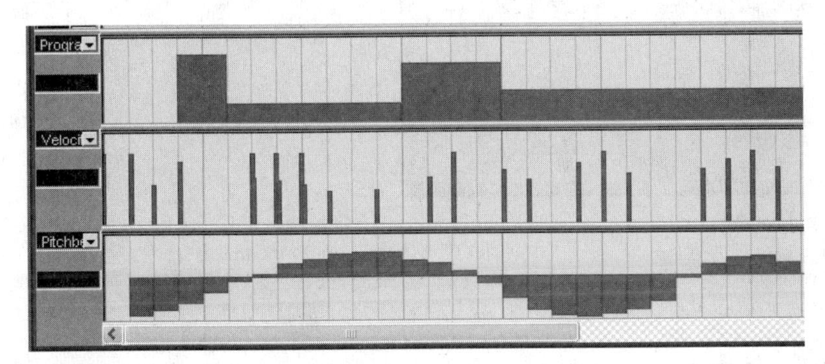

The controller display with three lanes set up.

- To remove a lane, right-click in it and select "Remove this Lane" from the Quick menu.
  This hides the lane from view—it doesn't affect the events in any way.
- If you remove all lanes, the controller display will be completely hidden.
  To bring it back again, select "Create new controller lane" from the Quick menu.

Selecting Event Type

Each controller lane shows one event type at a time. To select which event type should be displayed, use the pop-up menu to the left of the lane.

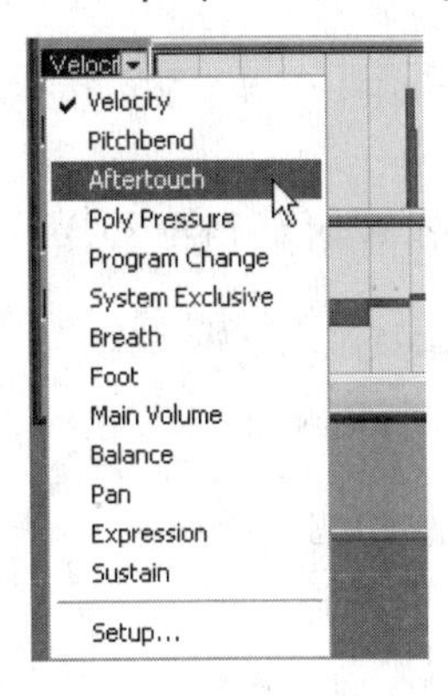

- **Selecting "Setup..." opens a dialog in which you can specify which Continuous Controller event types you want available on the pop-up menu.**

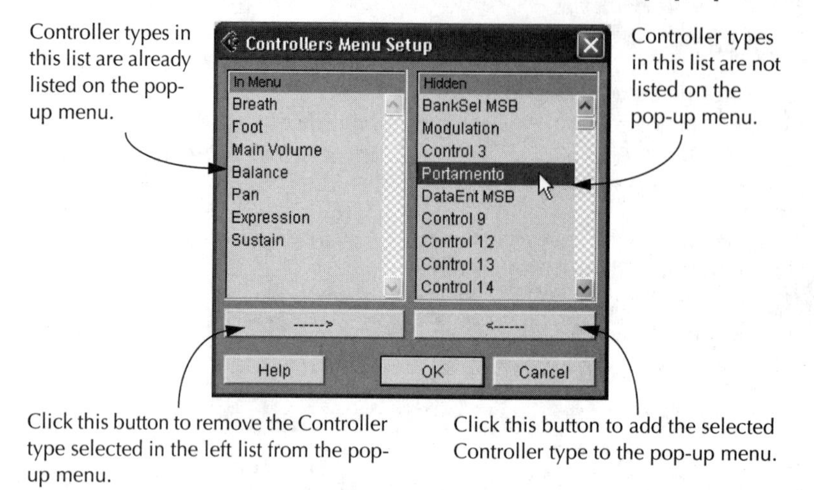

Editing Velocity Values

When "Velocity" is selected for viewing, the lane shows the velocity of each note as a vertical bar.

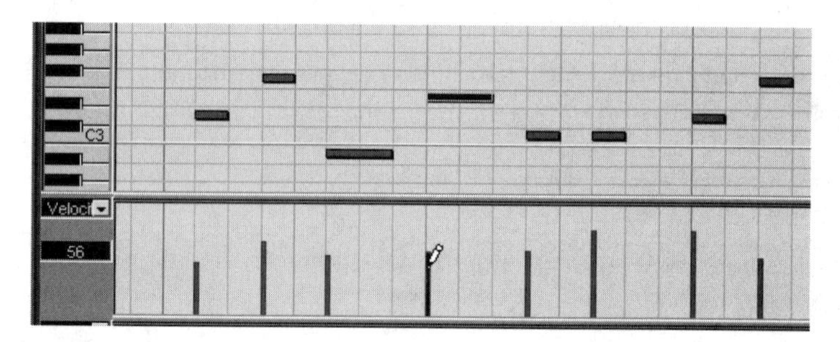

Velocity values are edited with the Pencil tool. The different Pencil tool modes offer the following possibilities:

- In Draw mode, you can use the Pencil tool to change the velocity of a single note: click on its velocity bar and drag the bar up or down.
  While you drag, the current velocity value is shown in the display to the left.
- You can use Draw mode or Paint mode to change the velocity values of several notes by painting a "freehand curve".
  When editing velocity, these two modes have the same functionality.

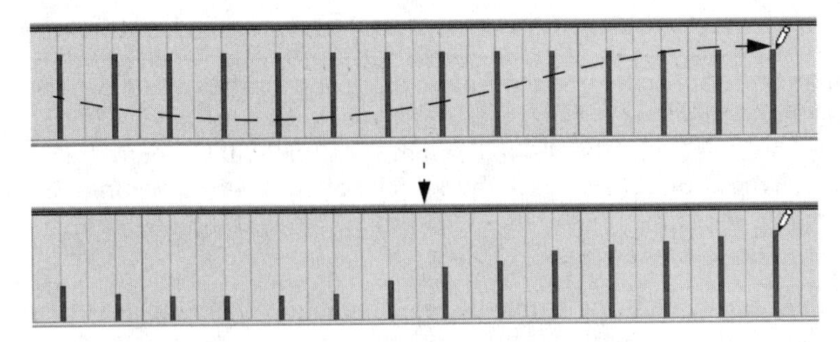

- Use Line mode for creating linear velocity ramps.
  Click where you want the ramp to start and drag the cursor to where you want the ramp to end. When you release the mouse button, the velocity values are aligned with the line between the two points.

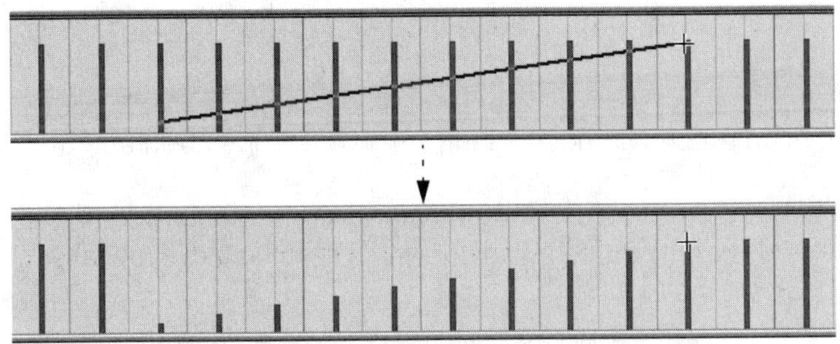

- Parable mode works in the same way, but aligns the velocity values with a parable curve instead.
  Use this for smooth, "natural" velocity fades, etc.

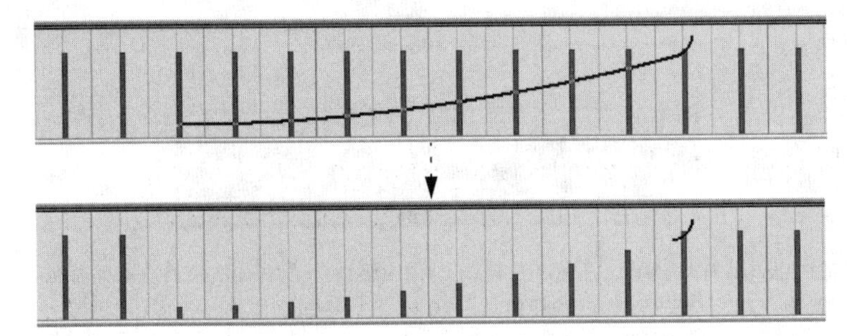

- The remaining three modes align the velocity values with continuous curve shapes (see below).

Note:

- If there is more than one note on the same position (e.g. a chord), their velocity bars will overlap in the controller lane.
  If none of the notes are selected, all notes at the same position will be set to the same velocity value when you draw. To edit the velocity of only one of the notes at the same position, first select the note in the note display. Now, editing will only affect the velocity of the selected note.

You can also adjust the velocity of a single note by selecting it and changing its velocity value on the info line.

Adding and Editing Events in the Controller Display

When any option other than "Velocity" is selected for viewing in a controller lane, you can create new events or edit the values of existing events using the Pencil tool in its various modes:

- Clicking with the Pencil tool in Draw mode or Paint mode creates a new event.
- To modify the value of an event (without creating a new one), press [Alt] and use the Pencil tool.
  Note that you can click and drag to change or add multiple events, draw controller curves, etc. You can press or release [Alt] while drawing, switching dynamically between "edit mode" and "create mode".

If you want to enter or adjust a single event, click once with the Pencil:

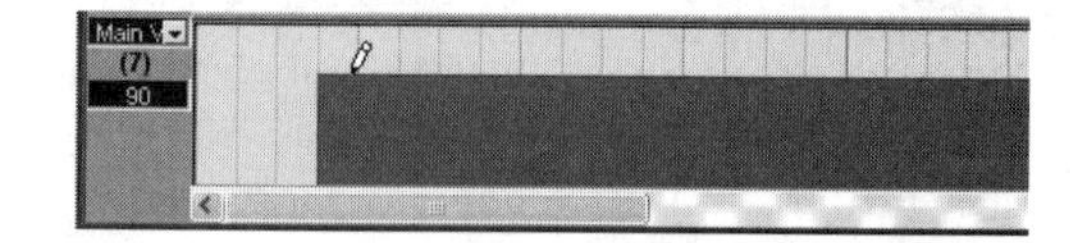

If you want to "paint a curve", drag the Pencil (with the mouse button pressed):

When you move the pointer in the controller lane, the corresponding value is displayed in this field.

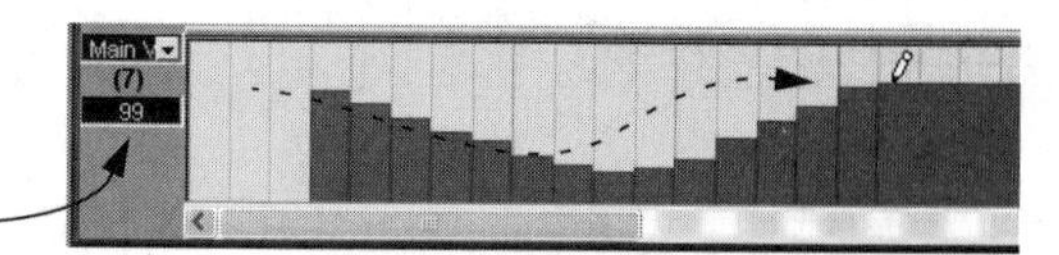

- Clicking and dragging with the Pencil tool in Line mode shows a line in the controller lane, and creates events with values aligned with this line.
  This is the best way to draw linear controller ramps. If you press [Alt], no new events are created—use this mode for modifying existing controller curves.

Converting a Controller curve to a ramp using the Line tool:

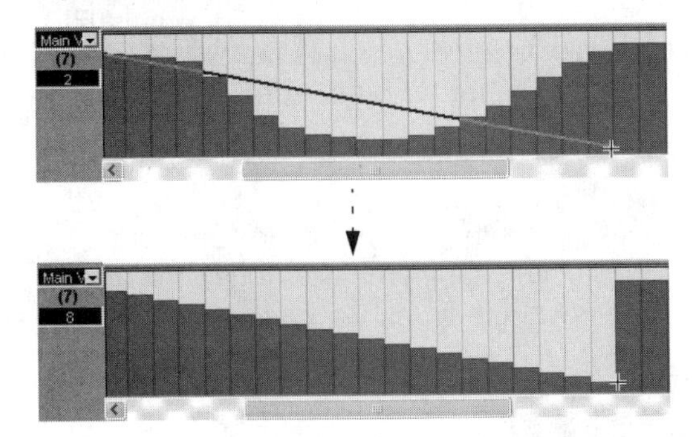

- The Parable mode works in the same way, but aligns the values with a parable curve instead, giving more "natural" curves and fades.
  Note that the result depends on from which direction you draw the parable:

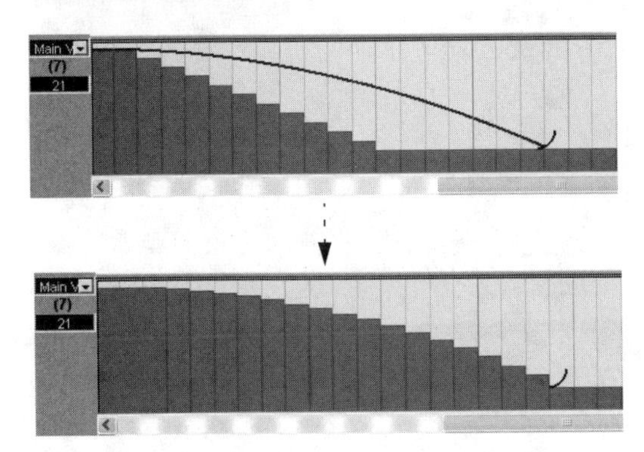

- In Parable mode you can use modifier keys to determine the shape of the parable curve.
  If you press [Ctrl] the parable curve will be reversed, if you press [Alt]+[Ctrl] while snap is activated you can change the position of the whole curve (in both cases the snap value for the positioning will be a quarter of the Quantize value). If you press [Shift], the exponent will be increased or decreased.

- For the above modes, the Length Quantize value on the toolbar determines the "density" of created controller curves (if Snap is activated).
  For very smooth curves, you should use a small Length Quantize value or turn off Snap. However, please note that this creates a very large number of MIDI events, which can cause MIDI playback to "stutter" in some situations. A medium-low density is often sufficient.

- The Sine, Triangle and Square modes create events with values aligned to continuous curves.
  In these modes, the Quantize value determines the period of the curve (the length of one curve "cycle") and the Length Quantize value determines the density of the events (the lower the Length Quantize note value, the smoother the curve).
- In Sine, Triangle and Square mode you can also use modifier keys to determine the shape of the curve.
  If you press [Ctrl] you can change the phase of the beginning of the curve, if you press [Alt]+[Ctrl] while snap is activated you can change the position of the whole curve (in both cases the snap value for the positioning will be a quarter of the Quantize value).

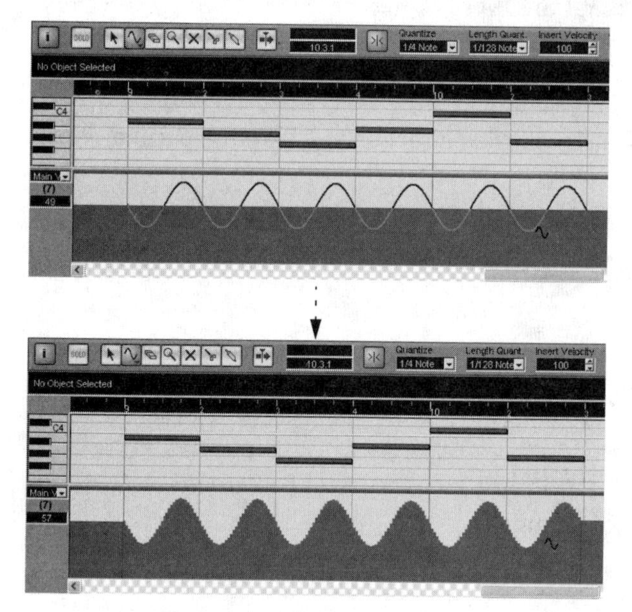

- You can also set the curve period freely by holding down [Shift] when you insert events in Sine, Triangle or Square mode.
  Activate Snap, [Shift]-click and drag to set the length of one period. The period length will be a multiple of the Quantize value.
- In Triangle and Square mode you can press [Shift]+[Ctrl] to change the maximum position of the triangle curve (to create sawtooth curves) or the pulse of the square curve. As in other modes, you can press [Alt] if you want to change the existing events rather than creating new ones. Again, the snap value for the positioning will be a quarter of the Quantize value.

Moving and Copying Events

You can move or duplicate events in a controller lane, much like you can with notes:

1. **Use the Arrow tool to select the events you want to cut or copy.**

   To select more than one event, [Shift]-click or drag a selection rectangle, according to the standard selection procedures.

2. **Click and drag the events to move them.**

   If Snap is activated, this determines to which positions you can move the events (see page 546).

- **If you hold down [Alt] and drag, the events will be copied rather than moved.**

- If there already is an event of the same type at the exact same position, this will be replaced by the moved event.

- Remember that a non-note event doesn't have a length—it's "valid" until the next event (see page 490).

Using Cut, Copy, and Paste

You can use the standard Cut, Copy and Paste functions on the Edit menu to move or copy events in the controller display:

1. **Select the notes you want to cut or copy.**
2. **Select Cut or Copy from the Edit menu.**
3. **If you want to paste the events into another MIDI part, open that part in a Key Editor.**
4. **Position the project cursor where you want to paste the events.**
5. **Select Paste from the Edit menu.**

   The events on the Clipboard are added, starting at the project cursor position, maintaining their relative positions. If a pasted event ends up at the same position as an existing event of the same type, the old event is replaced.

Deleting Events in the Controller Display

You delete events by clicking with the Eraser tool or by selecting them and pressing [Backspace]. Please note:

- **Deleting a controller event makes the last event before this valid up until the next event. It does not "zero" any Controller changes. See page 490.**
- **You can delete notes by deleting their velocity bars in the controller display.**

  Please be aware that if there is more than one note on the same position, there may still only be one velocity bar visible—make sure you delete only the desired notes!

Adding and Editing Poly Pressure Events

Poly Pressure events are special, in that they "belong to" a specific note number (key). That is, each Poly Pressure event has two editable values: the note number and the amount of pressure. Therefore, when Poly Pressure is selected on the event Type pop-up menu, there are two value fields to the left of the controller display, one for the note number and one for the amount:

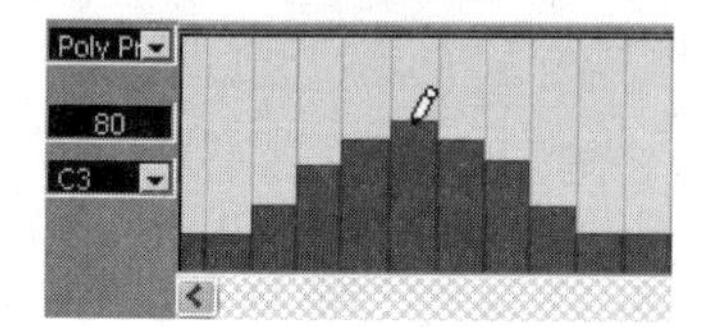

To add a new Poly Pressure event, proceed as follows:

1. **Select Poly Pressure on the event type pop-up menu.**
2. **Set the note number by clicking on the keyboard display.**

   Note that this only works for the topmost lane. If you have selected "Poly Pressure" for several controller lanes, you have to type in the desired note number directly in the lower value field to the left of each lane. The selected note number is displayed in the lower value field to the left of the controller display.
3. **Use the Pencil tool to add a new event, just as when adding regular Controller events.**

To view and edit existing Poly Pressure events, proceed as follows:

1. **Select Poly Pressure on the event type pop-up menu.**
2. **Click on the arrow button next to the note number field to the left of the controller lane.**

   A pop-up menu appears, listing all note numbers for which there already are Poly Pressure events.

3. **Select a note number from the pop-up menu.**

   The Poly Pressure events for the selected note number are shown in the controller lane.

4. **Use the Pencil tool to edit the events as usual.**

   Press [Alt] to edit existing events without adding any new ones.

- **Poly Pressure events can also be added and edited in List Edit.**

23.5 The Drum Editor—Overview

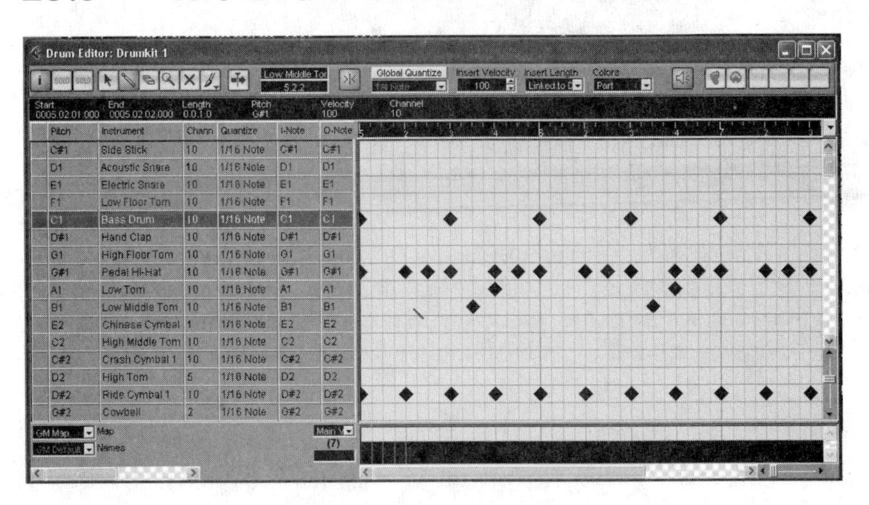

23.5.1 The Toolbar and Info Line

These are much the same as the toolbar and info line in the Key Editor, with the following differences:

- The Drum Editor has no Pencil tool—instead there is a Drumstick tool (for inputting and removing notes) and a Paint tool with various line and curve modes (for painting several notes in one go or editing controller events).
- There are no Scissors and Glue Tube tools in the Drum Editor.
- As in the Key Editor, the mouse pointer display in the toolbar shows the pitch and position of the pointer, but the pitch is shown as a drum sound name rather than a note number.

- The Global Quantize button allows you to select which value should be used when Snap is on—the global quantize value on the toolbar or the individual quantize values for the drum sounds.
- Instead of a Length Quantize setting, there is an Insert Length pop-up menu. It is used in much the same way, as described on the following pages.

23.5.2 The Drum Sound List

Pitch	Instrument	Chann	Quantize	I-Note	O-Note	Mute	Output
C#1	Side Stick	10	1/16 Note	C#1	C#1		Default
D1	Acoustic Snare	10	1/16 Note	D1	D1		Default
E1	Electric Snare	10	1/16 Note	E1	E1		Default
F1	Low Floor Tom	10	1/16 Note	F1	F1		Default
C1	Bass Drum	10	1/16 Note	C1	C1		Default
D#1	Hand Clap	10	1/16 Note	D#1	D#1		Default
G1	High Floor Tom	10	1/16 Note	G1	G1		Default
G#1	Pedal Hi-Hat	10	1/16 Note	G#1	G#1		Default
A1	Low Tom	10	1/16 Note	A1	A1		Default
B1	Low Middle Tom	10	1/16 Note	B1	B1		Default

The purpose of the Drum Editor is to edit MIDI tracks where each note (pitch) plays a separate sound, as is typically the case with a MIDI drum kit. The drum sound list to the left lists all drum sounds by name (according to the selected drum map or name list—see below), and lets you adjust and manipulate the drum sound setup in various ways.

Note:

- The number of columns in the list depends on whether there's a drum map selected for the track or not.
  See page 514.
- You can reorder the columns by dragging the column headings, and resize the columns by dragging the dividers between the column headings.

23.5.3 The Note Display

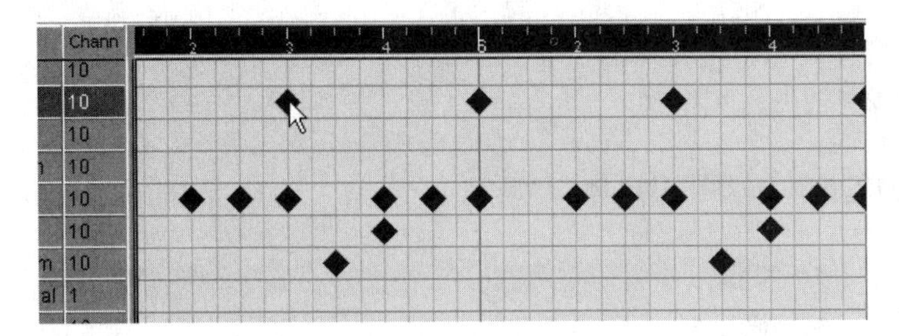

The Drum Editor's note display displays notes as diamond symbols. The vertical position of the notes corresponds to the drum sound list to the left, while the horizontal position corresponds to the note's position in time, just as in the Key Editor. Note however, that the diamond symbols don't indicate the length of the notes. This makes sense, since drum sounds most often are "one-shot" samples that play to their end regardless of the note lengths.

23.5.4 Drum Map and Name Pop-up Menus

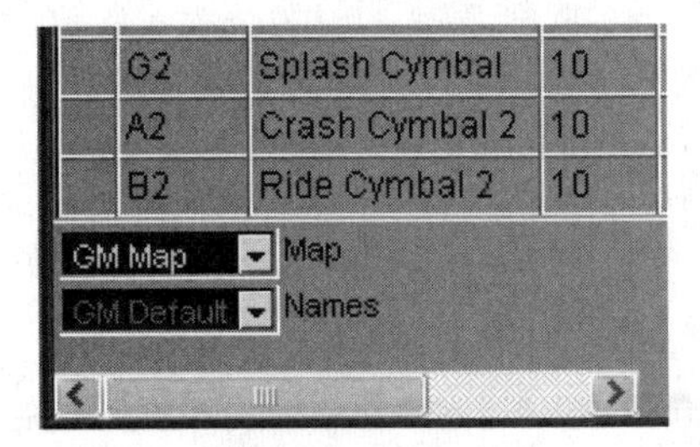

Below the drum sound list you will find two pop-up menus, used for selecting a drum map for the edited track or (if no drum map is selected) a list of drum sound names. For an explanation of drum maps, see page 514.

23.5.5 Controller Display

The controller display in the Drum Editor is exactly the same as in the Key Editor. You can add or remove controller lanes from the Quick menu, and create and edit events as described on page 501.

23.6 Drum Editor Operations

The basic handling (zooming, playback, auditioning, etc.) is the same as in the Key Editor (see page 491). The following sections describe the procedures and features that are specific to the Drum Editor.

23.6.1 Creating and Editing Notes

The standard way of entering notes in the Drum Editor is to click with the Drumstick tool.

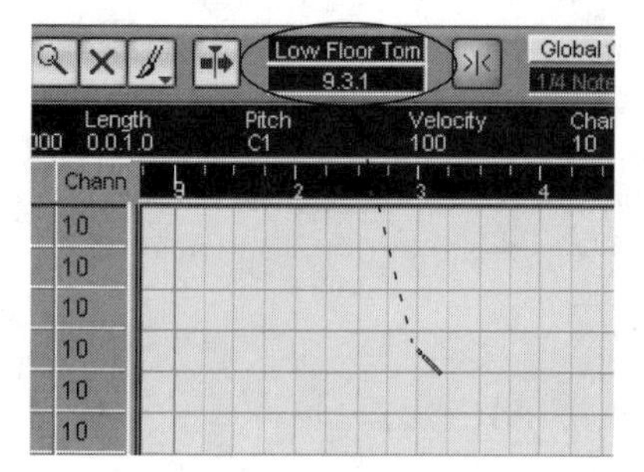

When you move the pointer in the note display, its bar position and drum sound is indicated in the toolbar, making it easy to find the right sound and position.

The position of the created note depends on the following factors:

- If Snap is deactivated on the toolbar, the note will appear exactly where you clicked.
  In this mode, notes can be positioned freely.
- If Snap is activated and Global Quantize is deactivated on the toolbar, the note will snap to positions according to the Quantize value set for the sound in the drum sound list.
  You can set up different Quantize values for different drum sounds. You may for example want hi-hat notes snap to sixteenth notes, but snare and bass drum snap to eighth notes.
- If both Snap and Global Quantize are activated, the note will snap to positions according to the Quantize value on the toolbar (below the Global Quantize button).

The length of the inserted note is determined by the Insert Length setting on the toolbar. However, if this is set to "Linked to drum map", the note will get the length of the Quantize value for the drum sound.

The notes will get the Insert Velocity value set on the toolbar.

- You can quickly audition the drum sounds by clicking in the leftmost column in the drum sound list.
  This plays the corresponding note.
- Clicking with the Drumstick tool on an existing note will remove it.
  This makes drum pattern editing very quick and intuitive.

Selecting Notes

Selecting notes is done by any of the following methods:

- **Use the Arrow tool.**

  The standard selection techniques apply.
- **Use the Select submenu on the Quick menu (see page 494).**
- **Use the left and right arrow keys on the computer keyboard to step from one note to the next or previous note.**

  If you press [Shift] and use the arrow keys, the current selection will be kept, allowing you to select several notes.
- **You can also press [Shift] and double click on a note to select all the following notes for the same drum sound.**
- **If the option "Auto Select Events under Cursor" is activated in the Preferences dialog (Editing page), all notes currently "touched" by the project cursor are automatically selected.**

Moving, Duplicating or Repeating Notes

To move or copy notes in the editor (to other positions or other drum sounds), you use the same methods as in the Key Editor: click and drag, use the arrow keys or Edit menu functions, etc.—see page 495. There is one thing to note:

When you are moving or copying several selected notes by dragging them and Snap is activated but Global Quantize turned off, the notes will snap to positions according to the quantize values for the drum sounds. If the moved/copied notes have different quantize values, the largest value will determine snapping. For example, if you are moving two notes, with the quantize values 1/16 and 1/4 respectively, the notes will snap to quarter notes (1/4).

- You can also adjust the position of notes by quantizing (see page 468).
  Again, which quantize value is used depends on whether Global Quantize is on or off.

Muting Notes and Drum Sounds

You can mute individual notes by clicking or enclosing them with the Mute tool or by using the Mute function on the Edit menu (see page 497).

Furthermore, if a drum map is selected (see page 519), the drum sound list will have a Mute column. Click in the Mute column for a drum sound to mute that sound. Finally, clicking the Drum Solo button will mute all drum sounds other than the selected one.

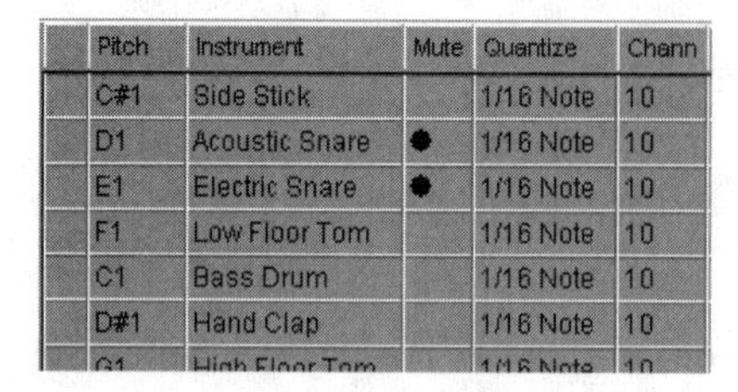

Pitch	Instrument	Mute	Quantize	Chann
C#1	Side Stick		1/16 Note	10
D1	Acoustic Snare	●	1/16 Note	10
E1	Electric Snare	●	1/16 Note	10
F1	Low Floor Tom		1/16 Note	10
C1	Bass Drum		1/16 Note	10
D#1	Hand Clap		1/16 Note	10
G1	High Floor Tom		1/16 Note	10

Muted drum sounds

- Please note that the mute state for drum sounds is part of the drum map, so any other tracks using the same map will also be affected.

Deleting Notes

To delete notes, click on them with the Drumstick tool or Eraser tool or select them and press [Backspace].

23.6.2 Other Editing Methods

As in the Key Editor, you can edit notes on the info line or via MIDI, and enter notes using step input. Please refer to page 498.

23.7 Working with Drum Maps

23.7.1 Background

As discussed earlier, a drum kit in a MIDI instrument is most often a set of different drum sounds with each sound placed on a separate key (i.e. the different sounds are assigned to different MIDI note numbers). One key plays a bass drum sound, another a snare and so on.

Unfortunately, different MIDI instruments often use different key assignments. This can be troublesome if you have made a drum pattern using one MIDI device, and then want to try it on another. When you switch device, it is very likely that your snare drum becomes a ride cymbal, or your hi-hat becomes a tom, etc.—just because the drum sounds are distributed differently in the two instruments.

To solve this problem, and simplify several aspects of MIDI drum kits (like using drum sounds from different instruments in the same "drum kit"), Cubase SX/SL features so-called drum maps. A drum map is basically a list of drum sounds, with a number of settings for each sound. When you play back a MIDI track for which you have selected a drum map, the MIDI notes are "filtered" through the drum map before being sent to the MIDI instrument. Among other things, the map determines which MIDI note number is sent out for each drum sound, and so which sound is played in the receiving MIDI device.

A solution to the problem above would therefore be to make up drum maps for all your instruments. When you want to try your drum pattern on another instrument, you simply switch to the corresponding drum map and your snare drum sound will remain a snare drum sound.

23.7.2 Drum Map Settings

A drum map consists of settings for 128 drum sounds (one for each MIDI note number). To get an overview of these settings, open the Drum Editor and use the Map pop-up menu below the drum sound list to select the "GM Map" drum map.

This drum map is set up according to the General MIDI standard. For information on how to load, create and select other drum maps, see page 519.

Now, take a look at the drum sound list (you may have to drag the divider between the list and the note display to the right to see all columns). The columns show the settings of the drum map for each sound.

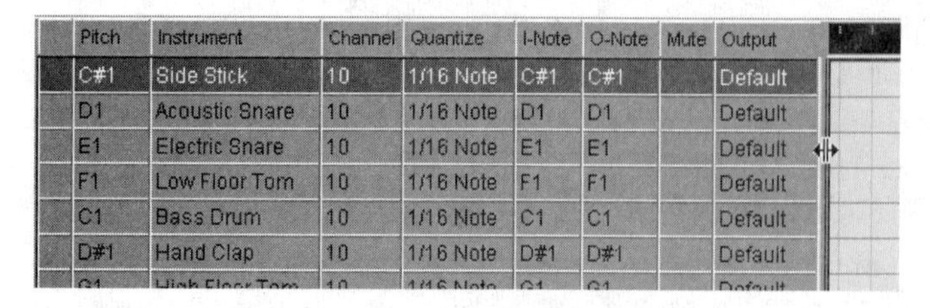

Pitch	Instrument	Channel	Quantize	I-Note	O-Note	Mute	Output
C#1	Side Stick	10	1/16 Note	C#1	C#1		Default
D1	Acoustic Snare	10	1/16 Note	D1	D1		Default
E1	Electric Snare	10	1/16 Note	E1	E1		Default
F1	Low Floor Tom	10	1/16 Note	F1	F1		Default
C1	Bass Drum	10	1/16 Note	C1	C1		Default
D#1	Hand Clap	10	1/16 Note	D#1	D#1		Default

Here's a brief description (details follow below):

Column	Description
Pitch	The actual note number of the drum sound. This is what links notes on a MIDI track to drum sounds. For example, with the above drum map, all MIDI notes with the pitch C1 would be mapped to the Bass Drum sound. More on this below.
Instrument	The name of the drum sound.
Quantize	This value is used when entering and editing notes as described on page 512 and page 513.
Mute	Allows you to mute a drum sound, excluding it from playback. See page 514.
I-note	This is the "input note" for the drum sound. When this MIDI note is sent into Cubase SX/SL, (i.e. played by you), the note will be mapped to the corresponding drum sound (and automatically transposed according to the Pitch setting for the sound). See below.
O-note	This is the "output note", i.e. the MIDI note number that is sent out every time the drum sound is played back. See below.
Channel	The drum sound will be played back on this MIDI channel.
Output	The drum sound will be played back on this MIDI output. If you set this to "Default", the MIDI output selected for the track will be used.

- All settings in a drum map (except the Pitch setting) can be changed directly in the drum sound list, or in the Drum Map Setup dialog (see page 519).
  Note that the changes you make will affect all tracks that use the drum map.

23.7.3 About Pitch, I-Note and O-Note

This can be a somewhat confusing area, but once you've grasped how it all works it's not very complicated. Going through the following "theory" will help you make the most out of the drum map concept—especially if you want to create your own drum maps.

As we said earlier, a drum map is a kind of "filter", transforming notes according to the settings in the map. It does this transformation twice; once when it receives an incoming note (i.e. when you play a note on your MIDI controller) and once when a note is sent from the program to the MIDI sound device.

In the following example, we have modified the drum map, so that the Bass Drum sound has different Pitch, I-note and O-note values.

Pitch	Instrument	Channel	Quantize	I-Note	O-Note	Mu
F1	Low Floor Tom	10	1/16 Note	F1	F1	
C1	Bass Drum	10	1/16 Note	A1	B0	
D#1	Hand Clap	10	1/16 Note	D#1	D#1	

I-Notes

Let's look at what happens on input: When you play a note on your MIDI instrument, the program will look for this note number among the I-notes in the drum map. In our case, if you play the note A1, the program will find that this is the I-note of the Bass Drum sound.

This is where the first transformation happens: the note will get a new note number according to the Pitch setting for the drum sound. In our case, the note will be transformed to a C1 note, because that is the Pitch of the Bass Drum sound. If you record the note, it will be recorded as a C1 note.

O-Notes

The next step is the output. This is what happens when you play back the recorded note, or when the note you play is sent back out to a MIDI instrument in real time (MIDI Thru):

The program checks the drum map and finds the drum sound with the Pitch of the note. In our case, this is a C1 note and the drum sound is the Bass Drum. Before the note is sent to the MIDI output, the second transformation takes place: the note number is changed to that of the O-note for the sound. In our example, the note sent to the MIDI instrument will be a B0 note.

Usage

So, what's the point of all this? Again, the purposes are different for I-notes and O-notes:

- Changing the I-note settings allows you to choose which keys will play which drum sounds, when playing or recording from a MIDI instrument.
  For example, you may want to place some drum sounds near each other on the keyboard so that they can be easily played together, move sounds so that the most important sounds can be played from a short keyboard, play a sound from a black key instead of a white, and so on.
  If you never play your drum parts from a MIDI controller (but draw them in the editor) you don't need to care about the I-note setting.

- The O-note settings let you set things up so that the "Bass Drum" sound really plays a bass drum.
  If you're using a MIDI instrument in which the bass drum sound is on the C2 key, you set the O-note for the "Bass Drum" sound to C2. When you switch to another instrument (in which the bass drum is on C1) you want the Bass Drum O-note set to C1. Once you have set up drum maps for all your MIDI instruments, you don't have to care about this anymore—you just select another drum map when you want to use another MIDI instrument for drum sounds.

23.7.4 The Channel and Output Settings

You can set separate MIDI channels and/or MIDI outputs for each sound in a drum map. The following rules apply:

- When a drum map is selected for a track, the MIDI channel settings in the drum map override the MIDI channel setting for the track.
  In other words, the MIDI channel setting you make in the Track list or Inspector for the track is normally disregarded. If you want a drum sound to use the channel of the track, set it to channel "Any" in the drum map.

- If the MIDI output is set to "default" for a sound in a drum map, the sound will use the MIDI output selected for the track.
  Selecting any other option allows you to direct the sound to a specific MIDI output.

By making specific MIDI channel and output settings for all sounds in a drum map, you can direct your drum tracks directly to another MIDI instrument simply by selecting another drum map—you don't need to make any channel or output changes for the actual track.

- To select the same MIDI channel for all sounds in a drum map, click the Channel column, press [Ctrl] and select the desired channel.
  All drum sounds will be set to this MIDI channel. The same procedure can be used for selecting the same MIDI output for all sounds as well.

It can also be useful to select different channels and/or outputs for different sounds. This allows you to construct drum kits with sounds from several different MIDI devices, etc.

23.7.5 Managing Drum Maps

Selecting a Drum Map for a Track

To select a drum map for a MIDI track, use the Map pop-up menu in the Inspector or in the Drum Editor:

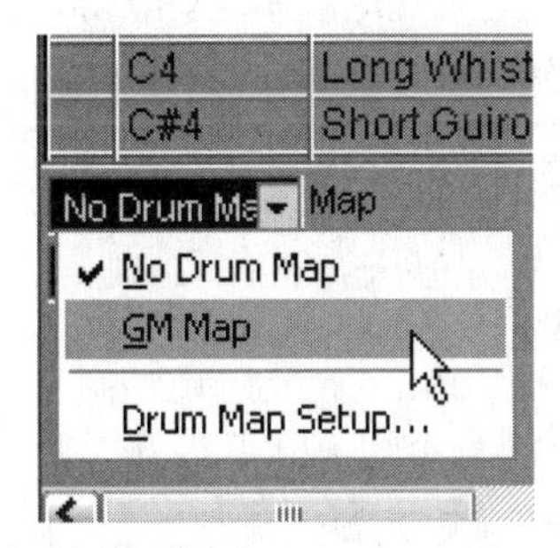

Selecting "No Drum Map" turns off the drum map functionality in the Drum Editor. Even if you don't use a drum map, you can still separate sounds by name using a name list (see page 522).

- Initially, the Map pop-up menu will only contain one map: "GM Map". However, you will find a number of drum maps included on the program CD—how to load these is described below.

The Drum Map Setup Dialog

To set up and manage your drum maps, select "Drum Map Setup" from the Map pop-up menus or the MIDI menu. This opens the following dialog:

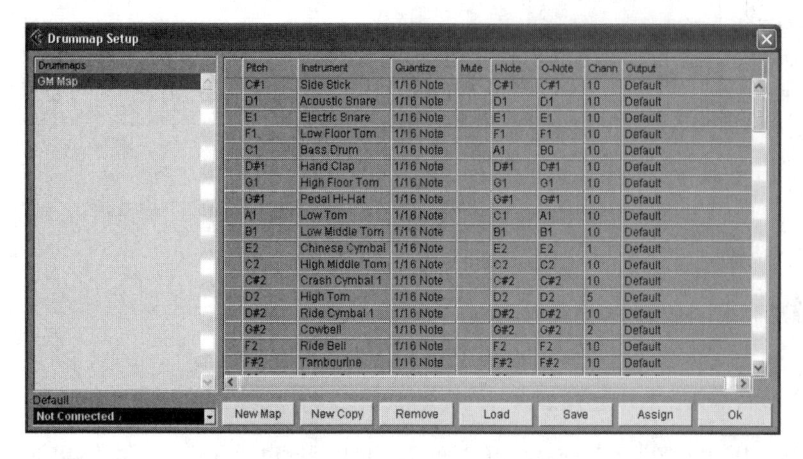

This is where you load, create, modify and save drum maps. The list to the left shows the currently loaded drum maps; selecting a drum map in the list displays its sounds and settings to the right.

- The settings for the drum sounds are exactly the same as in the Drum Editor (see page 515).
  As in the Drum Editor, you can click the leftmost column to audition a drum sound. Note: if you audition a sound in the Drummap Setup dialog, and the sound is set to MIDI output "Default", the output selected on the Default pop-up menu in the lower left corner will be used. When auditioning a Default output sound in the Drum Editor, the MIDI output selected for the track will be used, as described on page 518.

Below the drum sound list you will find a number of buttons, with the following functionality:

Button	Description
New Map	Click this to add a new drum map to the project. The drum sounds will be named "Sound 1, Sound 2" and so on, and have all parameters set to default values. The map will be named "Empty Map", but you can rename it by clicking and typing in the list.
New Copy	Adds a copy of the currently selected drum map. This is probably the quickest way to create a new drum map: select the map that is similar to what you want, create a copy, change the desired drum sound settings and rename the map in the list.
Remove	Removes the selected drum map from the project.

Button	Description
Load	Opens a file dialog, allowing you to load drum maps from disk. On the Cubase SX/SL CD you will find a number of drum maps for different MIDI instruments—use this function to load the desired maps into your project.
Save	Opens a file dialog for saving the drum map selected in the list. If you have created or modified a drum map, you should use this function to save it as a file on disk—this allows you to load it into other projects. Drum map files have the extension ".drm".
Assign	Click this button to assign the selected drum map to the current MIDI track (only available if a MIDI track was selected when you opened the Drum Map Setup dialog). This is the same as selecting the drum map from the Map pop-up menu.
OK	Closes the dialog.

- Drum maps are saved with the project files. If you have created or modified a drum map, you should use the Save function to store it as a separate file, available for loading into other projects.
  If you always want to have the same drum map(s) included in your projects, you may want to load these into the default project—see page 657.

O-Note Conversion

This function on the MIDI menu goes through the selected MIDI part(s) and sets the actual pitch of each note according to its O-note setting. This is useful if you want to convert the track to a "regular" MIDI track (with no drum map) and still have the notes play back the correct drum sound. A typical application is if you want to export your MIDI recording as a standard MIDI file (see page 660)—by first performing an O-Note Conversion you make sure that your drum tracks play back as they should when they are exported.

23.8 Using Drum Name Lists

Even if no drum map is selected for the edited MIDI track, you can still use the Drum Editor if needed. As previously mentioned, the drum sound list will then only have four columns: Audition, Pitch, Instrument (drum sound names) and Quantize. There will be no I-note and O-note functionality.

In this mode, the names shown in the Instrument column depend on the selection on the Names pop-up menu, just below the Map pop-up in the Drum Editor.

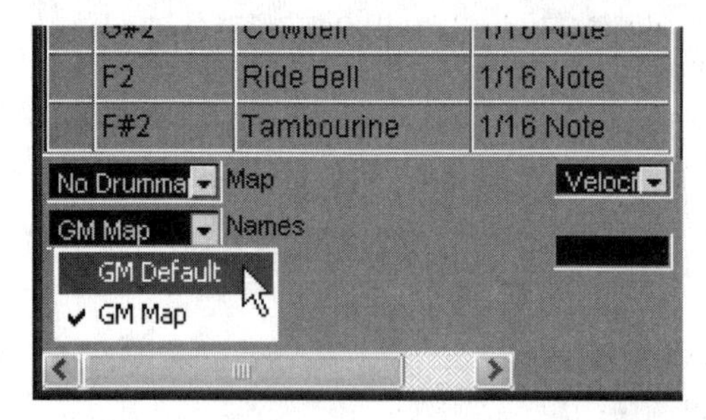

The options on this pop-up menu are the currently loaded drum maps plus a "GM Default" item which is always available. This means you can use the drum sound names in any loaded drum map without using I-notes and O-notes, should you so like.

23.9 The List Editor—Overview

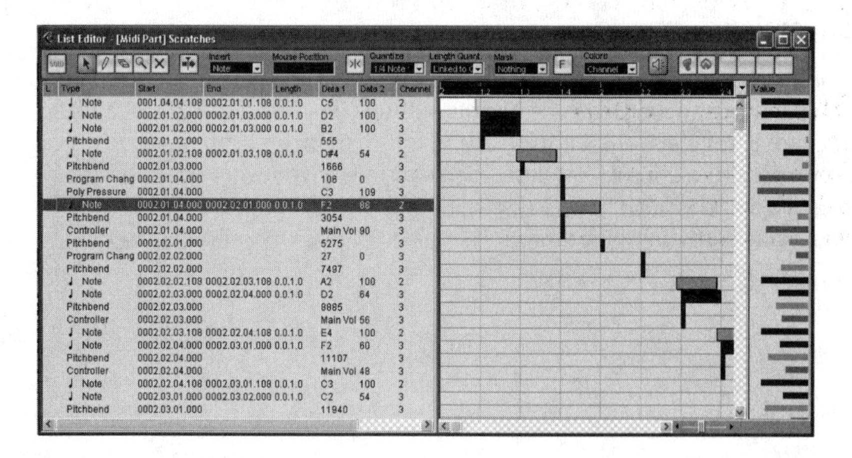

23.9.1 The Toolbar

The toolbar contains several items that are the same as in the Key Editor (edit solo, Snap, Quantize settings, etc.). These are described earlier in this chapter. The following toolbar items are unique to the List Editor:

- The Insert pop-up menu is used when creating new events.
  This is where you determine what type of event to add (see page 524).
- The Mask pop-up menu and Filter bar (F button) allow you to hide events from view, based on their type and other properties.
  See page 526.

The List Editor has no info line (numerical editing is available in the list instead).

23.9.2 The List

This lists all events in the currently selected MIDI part, in the order (from top to bottom) they are played back. You can edit the event properties by using regular value editing, as described on page 525.

23.9.3 The Event Display

This shows the events graphically. The vertical position of an event in the display corresponds to its entry in the list (i.e. to the playback order), while the horizontal position corresponds to its actual position in the project. This is where you add new parts or events, drag to move them, etc.

23.9.4 The Value Display

This display shows the "value" of each event, allowing for easy viewing and graphical editing. Typically, the value shown is the "Data 2" or "Value 2" property (amounts for MIDI controller events, velocity for notes, etc.).

23.10 List Editor Operations

23.10.1 Customizing the View

You can click and drag the divider between the list and the event display to make one area wider and the other narrower. Furthermore, the list can be customized in the following ways:

- You can change the order of the columns by dragging the column headings.
- You can resize columns by dragging the dividers between the column headings.

Setting the Display Format

Just like in the Project window, you set the display format (bars+beats, seconds, etc.) by right-clicking in the ruler and selecting an option from the pop-up menu. This setting affects both the ruler and all start, end and length values shown in the list.

Zooming

You can change the horizontal magnification in the event display by using the zoom slider below the display or the Magnification glass tool.

23.10.2 Adding Events

To add a new event to the edited part, proceed as follows:

1. Use the Insert pop-up menu on the toolbar to select the event type.

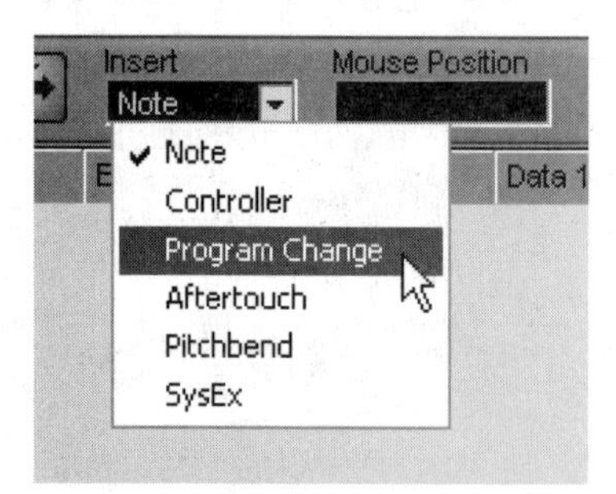

2. Select the Pencil tool and click in the event display, at the desired position (relative to the ruler).

If you are creating note events, you can click and drag to set the length of the note.

The new event appears in the list and in the display. Its properties will be set to default values, but can easily be adjusted in the list.

23.10.3 Editing in the List

The list allows you to perform detailed numerical editing of the events' properties. The columns have the following functionality:

Column	Description
Type	The event type. This cannot be changed.
Start	The start position of the event, shown in the format selected for the ruler. Changing this is the same as moving the event. Note that moving the event past any other event in the list will re-sort the list (the list always shows the events in the order they are played back).
End	This is only used for note events, allowing you to view and edit the end position of a note (thereby resizing it).
Length	This is only used for note events. It shows the length of the note—changing this resizes the note and automatically changes the End value as well.
Data 1	This is the "data 1" or "value 1" property of the event. The content of this depends on the event type—for notes, this is the pitch, for example. Where applicable, the values are shown in the most relevant form. For instance, the Data 1 value for notes is shown as a note number in the format selected in the Preferences dialog (Event Display—MIDI page). See also the table on page 528.
Data 2	This is the "data 2" or "value 2" property of the event. The content of this depends on the event type—for notes, this is the velocity value, for example. See the table on page 528.
Channel	The MIDI channel of the event. Note that this setting is normally overridden by the channel setting for the track. To make a MIDI event play back on "its own" channel, set its track to channel "Any" in the Project window.
Comment	This column is used for some event types only, providing an additional comment about the event.

- For SysEx (system exclusive) events, you can only edit the position (Start) in the list. However, clicking the Comment column opens the SysEx Editor, in which you can perform detailed editing of system exclusive events. This and other aspects of working with system exclusive messages are described in a separate chapter—see page 598.

23.10.4 Editing in the Event Display

The event display allows you to edit the events graphically using the tools on the toolbar.

- **To move an event, click and drag it to a new position.**

  Note that moving the event past any other event in the display will re-sort the list (the list always shows the events in the order they are played back). As a result, the vertical position of the event in the display will change as well.

- **To make a copy of an event, press [Alt] and drag it to a new position.**
- **To resize a note, select it and drag its end points with the Arrow tool as in the Project window.**

  This only works with notes.

- **To mute or unmute an event, click on it with the Mute tool.**

  You can mute or unmute several events in one go by enclosing them in a selection rectangle with the Mute tool.

- **You can select a color scheme for the events with the Colors pop-up menu on the toolbar.**

  This affects how all MIDI events are shown in the Project Browser and works as in the other MIDI editors—see page 546.

- **To delete an event, select it and press [Backspace] or [Delete], or click on it with the Eraser tool in the event display.**

23.10.5 Filtering

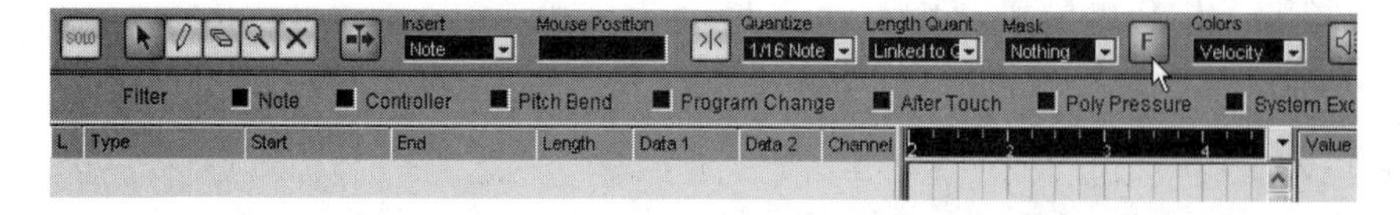

Clicking the F button on the toolbar makes an additional filter bar appear. This allows you to hide some event types from view. For example, it may be hard to find note events if the part contains a lot of controller events—by hiding these the list becomes more manageable.

To hide an event type, tick its checkbox on the filter bar. Note:

- The event types remain hidden even if you close the filter bar.
  To make sure you see all events, open the filter bar and check that all checkboxes are deactivated.

- The filter bar does not remove, mute or in any other way change the events.

23.10.6 Masking

The Mask function is similar to the filter bar but allows you to hide events based on some other criteria as well. Proceed as follows:

1. **Select an event of the type you want to view.**
2. **Pull down the Mask pop-up menu on the toolbar and select one of the options.**

   The results are as follows:

Option	Description
Event Types	Only events with the type of the selected event will be shown. This does the same as the filter bar but is quicker if you only want to view a single event type.
Controller and Event Types	Only events with the type of the selected event will be shown. Furthermore, if the selected event is a controller, only controllers of the same type (with the same "Data 1" value) will be shown.
Event Channels	Only events with the same channel as the selected event will be shown.

- **To deactivate the Mask function, select "Nothing" from the Mask pop-up menu.**

The most typical usage of the Mask function is to view a certain type of controller only (e.g. Modulation, Breath Control, etc.). Since these are all the same event types (controller), this would not be possible with the filter bar. With the "Controllers and Event Types" option on the Mask pop-up menu, it is!

23.10.7 Editing in the Value Display

The value display to the right of the event display is a tool for quick viewing and editing of multiple values, e.g. velocities or controller amounts. The values are shown as horizontal bars, with the bar length corresponding to the value.

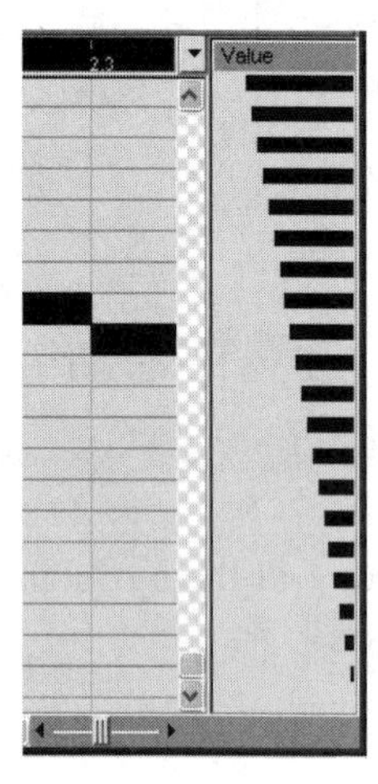

A velocity ramp in the value display.

You edit the values by clicking and dragging. Note that the pointer automatically takes on the shape of the Pencil tool when you move it into the value display—you don't have to select the Pencil tool for this.

Exactly which value is shown for an event depends on the event type. The following table shows what is displayed and edited in the Data columns and the value display:

Event type	Data 1	Data 2	Value display
Note	Pitch (note number)	Velocity	Velocity
Controller	Controller type	Controller amount	Controller amount
Program Change	Program number	Not used	Program number
Aftertouch	Aftertouch amount	Not used	Aftertouch amount
Pitch Bend	Bend amount	Not used	Bend amount
SysEx	Not used	Not used	Not used

23.11 The Score Editor—Overview (Cubase SL only)

- This section describes the Score Editor in Cubase SL. If you are using Cubase SX, please refer to the separate pdf document "Score Layout and Printing" (opened from the Windows Start menu or the Help menu in the program).

The Score Editor shows the MIDI notes as a musical score. The window contains the following sections and items:

23.11.1 The Toolbar

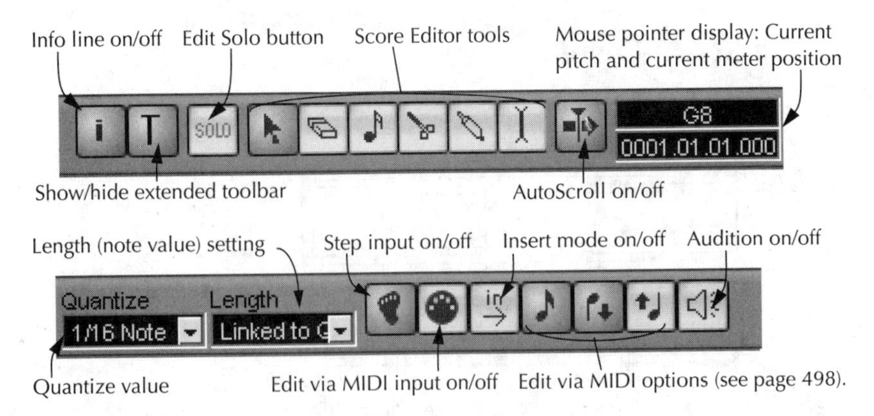

The Score Editor toolbar is similar to the toolbar in the Key Editor, with the addition of a button for showing or hiding the extended toolbar (see below).

23.11.2 The Info Line

The info line shows information about selected MIDI notes, just like in the Key and Drum Editors. You can edit all values on the info line using regular value editing (see page 498 for details).

- **To hide or show the info line, click the "i" icon in the toolbar.**

23.11.3 The Extended Toolbar

The extended toolbar (shown or hidden by clicking the T button on the main toolbar) contains the following items:

Note Value Buttons

Click one of these to select a note value for input. The "T" and "." options are for triplet and dotted note values. You can also press [Ctrl] and click one of the note value buttons—this will resize all selected notes to the note value you choose.

Enharmonic Shift

Allows you to manually select whether a note should be shown with flat or sharp accidentals. See page 543.

23.11.4 The Score Display

The main area of the Score Editor window shows the notes in the edited parts one one or several staves.

- If you are editing one or several parts on the same track, as much of them as possible is shown on several staves—one above the other—just as with a score on paper.

- If you are editing parts on several tracks, they are put on a grand staff (multiple staves, tied together by bar lines).
- The number of measures across the screen depends on the size of the window and the number of notes in each measure.
  The maximum number of bars across the page is four.
- The end of the last part is indicated by a double bar line.
- Unlike the other MIDI editors, the Score Editor does not have a ruler.
  A conventional ruler would not make sense, since there is no exact relationship between a note's horizontal position in the score and its musical position in the Project.

23.12 Score Editor Operations (Cubase SL only)

23.12.1 Opening the Score Editor

To open one or several parts in the Score editor you proceed much as with the other editors: select the parts (on the same or different tracks), and select "Open Score Editor" from the Scores submenu on the MIDI menu. The default key command for this is [Ctrl]-[R].

- **You can also select the Score editor as your default editor, allowing you to open it by double clicking parts.**

  This is done with the Default Edit Action pop-up menu in the Preferences dialog (event Display—MIDI page).

About Editing Parts on Different Tracks

If you have selected parts on two or more tracks and open the Score editor, you will get one staff for each track (although you can split a staff in two, e.g. when scoring for piano). The staves are tied together by bar lines and placed in the order of the tracks in the Project window.

- **If you need to rearrange the staves: close the editor, go back into the Project window, drag the tracks to the order you want them, and open the Score Editor again.**

The Active Staff

Just as in the other editors, all MIDI input (as when recording from your instrument) is directed to one of the tracks, here called the Active staff. The Active staff is indicated by a black rectangle in the left part of the first visible bar.

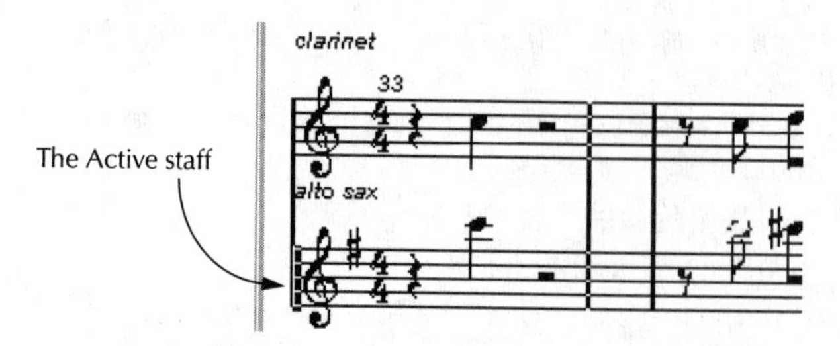

To change Active staff, click in the staff you want to activate.

23.12.2 Getting the Score Displayed Correctly

When you open the Score Editor for a part recorded in real time, the score may not look as legible as you would first expect. The Score Editor can ignore the minor time variances in performance and make a neater score almost instantly. To achieve this, there are a number of *Staff Settings* that determine how the program displays the music.

- Note that the time signature follows the time signature(s) on the Tempo track and are common to all tracks/staves in the score.

There are two ways to open the Staff Settings dialog:

- **Double click in the white area to the left of the staff.**
- **Activate a staff by clicking in it, and select "Staff Settings" from the Scores submenu on the MIDI menu.**

  The Staff Settings dialog appears.

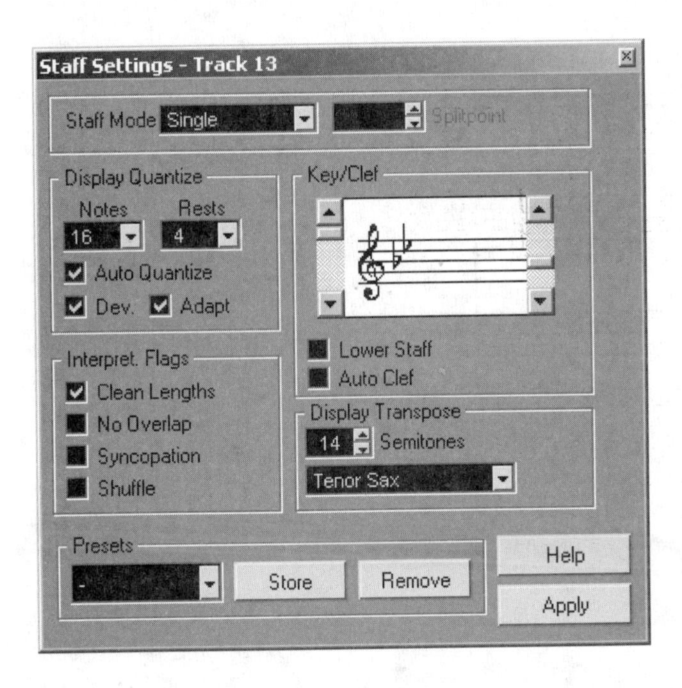

- The settings you make in this dialog are independent for each staff (track), but common for a piano staff which you have created by choosing the "Split" Staff Mode option (see below).

Staff Mode

This pop-up determines how the staff should be shown:

- **When set to "Single", all notes in the part are shown in the same staff.**
- **When set to "Split", the part is split on the screen into a bass and treble clef, as in a piano score.**

  You use the Splitpoint value field to set the note where you want the split to occur. Notes above and including the split note will appear on the upper staff, and notes below the split note will appear on the lower staff.

Before and after setting a split at C3.

Display Quantize

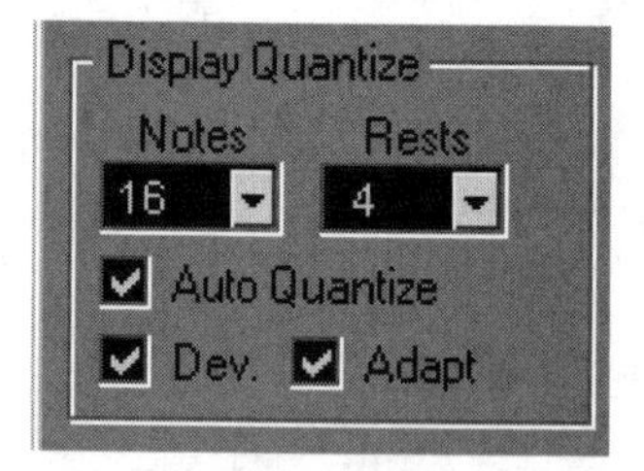

Notes are not an absolute language, and you must give the program a few hints on how the score should be displayed. This is done using the Display Quantize section of the Staff Settings dialog.

- These are only display values used for the graphics in the Score Editor. They do not affect the actual playback in any way.

Here is a description of the functions:

Parameter	Description
Notes	Determines the smallest note value to be displayed and the "smallest position" to be recognized and properly displayed. Set this to the smallest significant note position used in your music. For example, if you have notes on odd sixteenth note positions, you should set this value to 16. The "T" values are for triplet note values. This setting is partly overridden by Auto Quantize (see below).
Rests	This value is used as a "recommendation"—the program will not display rests smaller than this value, except where necessary. In effect, this setting also determines how the length of notes should be displayed. Set this value according to the smallest note value (length) you want to be displayed for a single note, positioned on a beat.
Auto Quantize	Generally, if your music contains mixed triplets and straight notes, try activating this checkbox. Otherwise, make sure it is deactivated. Auto Quantize uses involved methods to make your score look as legible as possible. Auto Quantize allows you to mix straight notes with tuplets (triplets) in a part. But, Auto Quantize also uses the (display) Quantize value. If it can't find an appropriate note value for a certain note or group of notes, it will use the set Quantize value to display it. If the part is imprecisely played and/or complex, Auto Quantize may have a problem "figuring out" exactly what you "mean".
Dev	This option is only available if Auto Quantize is on. When Dev (Deviation) is activated, triplets/straight notes will be detected even if they are not exactly "on the beat". However, if you know your triplets/straight notes are perfectly recorded (quantized or entered by hand), turn this off.
Adapt	This option is only available if Auto Quantize is on. When Adapt is activated, the program "guesses" that when one triplet is found, there are probably more triplets surrounding it. Turn this on if not all of your triplets are detected.

Key and Clef

The correct Key and Clef are set using the two scroll bars in the Key & Clef section.

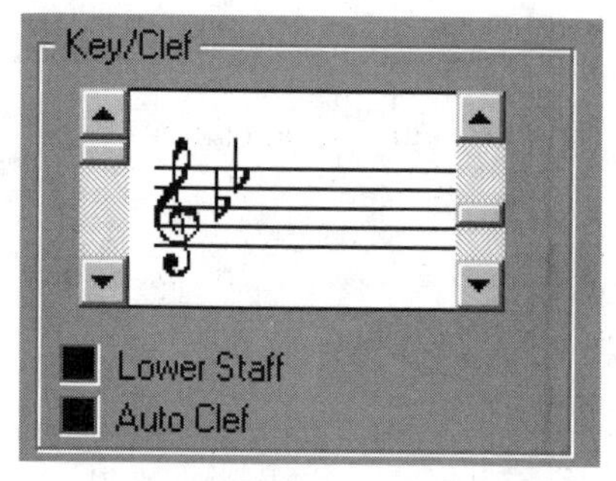

If you activate the "Auto Clef" checkbox, the program attempts to guess the correct clef, judging from the pitch of the music.

- **To set the clef and key for the lower staff, activate the "Lower Staff" checkbox in the Key/Clef section.**

Display Transpose

Some instruments, for example a lot of brass instruments, are scored transposed. For this purpose, the Staff Settings dialog allows you to specify a separate Display Transpose setting for each staff (track). This transposes the notes in the score (i.e. how they are displayed) without affecting how the notes play back. This allows you to record and play back a multi staff arrangement, and still score each instrument according to its own transposition.

- **Use the pop-up menu to select the instrument for which you are scoring.**

  You can also manually set a display transpose value with the Semitones box above.

Flags

These provide additional options for how the score should be displayed:

Parameter	Description
Clean Lengths	When this is activated, notes that are considered to be chords will be shown with identical lengths. This is done by showing the longer notes as shorter than they are. When Clean Lengths is turned on, notes with very short overlaps are also cut off; a bit as with No Overlap (see below), but with a more subtle effect.
No Overlap	When this is activated one note will never be shown as overlapping another, lengthwise. This allows long and short notes starting at the same point to be displayed without ties; the long notes are cut off in the display. This will make the music more legible.  An example measure with No Overlap deactivated...  ...and with No Overlap activated.
Syncopation	When this function is activated, syncopated notes are shown in a more legible way.  This is a dotted quarter at the end of a bar when Syncopation is Off...  ...and when it is On.
Shuffle	Activate this function when you have played a shuffle beat and want it displayed as straight notes (not triplets). This is very common in jazz notation.

Applying Your Settings

After you've made your settings, click Apply to apply them to the active staff. You can select another staff in the score and make settings for that, without having to close the Staff Settings dialog first—just remember to click Apply before you change staff, otherwise your changes will be lost.

- **As in many other dialogs and property windows in Cubase SX/SL, you can store your settings as presets.**

  This is done according to the usual procedures: click Store to store the current settings as a preset, select a preset from the pop-up menu to load it into the dialog or use the Remove button to remove the currently selected preset.

23.12.3 Entering Notes with the Mouse

To enter notes into a part in the Score Editor, you use the Note tool. However, first you need to make some settings for note value (length) and spacing:

Selecting a Note Value for Input

This can be done in two ways:

- By clicking the note symbols on the extended toolbar.
  You can select any note value from 1/1 to 1/64th and turn on and off the dotted and triplet options by clicking the two buttons to the right. The selected note value is displayed in the Length value field on the toolbar and in the Note tool cursor shape.
- By selecting an option from the Length pop-up menu on the toolbar.

Selecting a Quantize Value

When you move the mouse pointer over the score, you will see that the position box on the toolbar tracks your movement and shows the current position in bars, beats, sixteenth notes and ticks.

Positioning on screen is controlled by the current Quantize value. If you for example set this to "1/8 Note" you can only insert and move notes to eighth note positions, at quarter notes, at half bars or at bar positions. It is a good strategy to set the Quantize value to the smallest note value in the piece. This doesn't stop you from inputting notes at "coarser" positions. However, if you set the Quantize value to too small a note value, it is easier to make mistakes.

With the Quantize value set to "1/8 Note", you can only input notes at eighth note positions.

The Quantize value is set with the Quantize pop-up menu on the toolbar.

- **You can also assign key commands to the different Quantize values.**

  This is done in the Key Commands dialog on the File menu, under the heading "MIDI Quantize".

- **Just like in the other MIDI editors, you can use the Quantize Setup dialog to create other quantize values, irregular grids, etc.**

  However, this is not often used when entering score notes.

Entering a Note

To add a note to the score, proceed as follows:

1. **Make the staff active.**

   Notes are always put in on the active staff.

2. **Select the type of note by selecting a note value.**

   This is described in detail above.

3. **If you selected the note value by clicking on a symbol on the extended toolbar, the Note tool was automatically selected—otherwise select the Note tool from the toolbar or Quick menu.**

4. **Select a Quantize value.**

   As described above, the Quantize value will determine the spacing between notes. If you have Quantize set to "1/1 Note" you will only be able to add notes at down-beats. If you set Quantize to "1/8 Note" you will be able to add notes at all eighth note positions etc.

5. **Click in the staff and keep the mouse button pressed.**

   A note appears under the mouse pointer.

6. **Move the mouse horizontally to find the correct position.**

   Check the lower mouse position box on the toolbar—the position is "magnetically" attracted to the grid defined by the current Quantize value. This allows you to easily find the correct position.

7. **Move the mouse vertically to find the correct pitch.**

   The upper mouse position box shows the pitch at the pointer position, making it easy to find the right pitch.

8. **Release the mouse button.**

   The note appears in the score.

23.12.4 Selecting Notes

There are several ways to select notes in the Score Editor:

By Clicking

To select a note, click on its note head with the Arrow tool. The note head gets inverted to indicate that it is selected.

- **To select more notes, hold down [Shift] and click on them.**
- **To deselect notes, hold [Shift] down and click on them again.**
- **If you hold down [Shift] and double click on a note, this note *and all the following notes in the same staff* are selected.**

Using a Selection Rectangle

1. **Press the mouse button with the Arrow tool in some free (white) space in the score.**
2. **Drag the mouse pointer.**

   A rectangle appears. You can drag to select voices on several voices or staves if you wish.

3. **Release the mouse button.**

   All notes with their note heads inside the rectangle get selected.

If you want to deselect one or more of the notes, hold down [Shift] and click as described above.

Using the Keyboard

By default, you can step through the notes in the staff using the left and right arrow keys. If you press [Shift], you will select the notes as you step through them.

- **If you want to use other keys for selecting notes, you can customize the settings in the Key Commands dialog on the File menu (in the Navigate category).**

Deselecting Everything

To deselect everything, simply click with the Arrow tool in some "free" (white) space in the score.

23.12.5 Deleting Notes

Notes can be deleted in two ways:

Using the Eraser Tool

1. **Select the Eraser tool from the toolbar or Quick menu.**
2. **Click on the Note(s) you want to erase, one at a time or drag over them with the mouse button pressed.**

Using the Keyboard or Delete Menu Item

1. **Select the notes you want to delete.**
2. **Select Delete from the Edit menu, or press [Delete] or [Backspace] on the computer keyboard.**

23.12.6 Moving Notes

To move or transpose notes, proceed as follows:

1. **Set the Quantize value.**

   The Quantize value will restrict your movement in time. You can not place the notes on positions smaller than the Quantize value. If Quantize for example is set to "1/8 Note", you will not be able to move the notes to a sixteenth note position. However, you will be able to put them on any eighth note, quarter note, half note or whole note position.

2. **If you want to hear the pitch of the note while moving, activate the speaker icon on the toolbar.**

   When it is on, you will hear the current pitch of the "dragged" note.

3. **Select the note(s) you plan to move.**
4. **Click one of the selected notes and drag it to a new position and/or pitch.**

   The horizontal movement of the note is "magnetically attracted" to the current Quantize value. The position boxes on the toolbar show what the new position and pitch for the dragged note will be.

5. **Release the mouse.**

   The notes appear at their new position.

- **If you press [Ctrl] and drag, movement is restricted to vertical or horizontal only (depending on in which direction you drag).**
- **You can also move selected notes by using key commands, as assigned in the Nudge category in the Key Commands dialog.**

  When moving notes to the left or right using key commands, the notes will be moved in steps according to the current Quantize value. The keys assigned for up/down nudging will transpose notes in semitones steps.

23.12.7 Duplicating Notes

1. **Set the Quantize value and select the notes, as for moving.**
2. **Press [Alt] and drag the notes to their new position.**

- **If you want to restrict movements to one direction only, press [Ctrl].**

  This works just as for moving, as described above.

- **[Alt] is the default modifier key for copying/duplicating. If you like, you can change this in the Preferences dialog (Editing—Tool Modifiers page).**

  The entry for this is found in the Drag & Drop category ("Copy").

23.12.8 Changing the Length of Notes

As described earlier in this section (see page 532), the displayed length of a note isn't necessarily the actual note length, but also depends on the Note and Rest Display Quantize settings in the Staff Settings dialog. This is important to remember when you change the length of a note, since it can give rise to confusing ressults.

There are several ways to change the length of a note in the Score Editor:

By using the Note Tool

1. **Select a Note value that you wish to apply to the Note.**

   This can be done by clicking a note value icon in the extended toolbar or by selecting a new Length value.

2. **Select the Note tool if it isn't already selected.**
3. **Hold down [Alt] and click on the notes you wish to set to this length.**

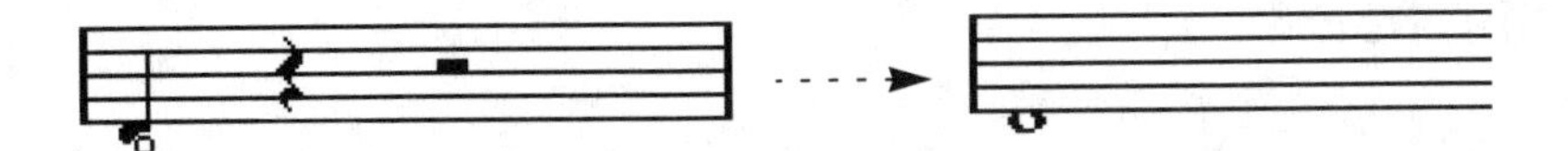

By using the note value icons on the extended toolbar

Using the extended toolbar is another quick way to set a number of notes to the same length:

1. **Select the notes you want to change.**
2. **Hold down [Ctrl] and click on one of the note icons on the extended toolbar.**

   All the selected notes are now given the length of the clicked note.

By using the info line

You can also edit length values numerically on the info line, just like in the Key and Drum Editors (see page 498).

23.12.9 Splitting and Gluing Notes

- **If you have two notes strung together by a tie, and click on the "tied" note head with the Scissors tool, the note will be divided into two, with the respective length of the "main" and the tied note.**
- **Conversely, if you click on a note with the Glue Tube tool it will be joined to the next note with the same pitch.**

23.12.10 Enharmonic Shift

The buttons to the right on the extended toolbar allow you to shift the display of selected notes so that for example an F# (F sharp) is instead shown as a Gb (G flat) and vice versa:

1. **Select the note(s) you want to affect.**
2. **Click on one of the buttons to display the selected note(s) a certain way.**

The "off" button resets the notes to original display. The other five options are double flats, flats, No, sharps and double sharps.

23.12.11 Flip Stems

Normally the direction of the note stems is automatically selected according to the note pitches, but you can change this manually if you like:

1. **Select the notes for which you want to change (flip) the stem direction.**
2. **Pull down the MIDI menu and select Flip Stems from the Scores submenu.**

23.12.12 Working with Text

You can use the Text tool to add comments, articulation or instrumentation advice and other text strings anywhere in the score:

Adding a Text String

1. **Select the Text tool from the toolbar or Quick menu.**

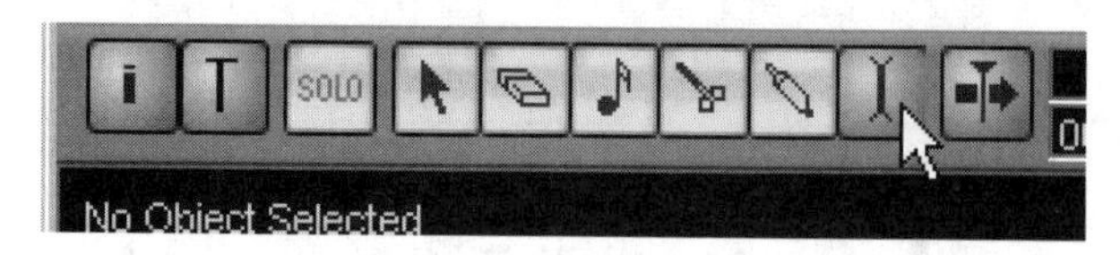

2. **Click anywhere in the score.**

   A text input line dialog box appears.

3. **Enter the text and press [Return].**

Editing Text

To edit an already added text string, double click it with the Arrow tool. This opens the text for editing, and you can use the arrow keys to move the cursor, delete characters with the [Delete] or [Backspace] keys and type new text as usual. Finish by pressing [Return].

- **To delete a text block, select it with the Arrow tool and press [Backspace] or [Delete].**
- **You can move or duplicate text blocks by dragging (or [Alt]-dragging) them, just as with notes.**

Changing the Text Font, Size and Style

To change the font settings for the text you have added, proceed as follows:

1. **Select the text block by clicking it with the Arrow tool.**
2. **Pull down the MIDI menu and select "Set Font" from the Scores submenu.**

   A Font Settings dialog appears, containing the following settings:

Item	Description
Font	This is where you specify the font for the text. Which fonts are available on the pop-up menu depends on which fonts you have installed on you computer. You probably don't want to use the "Steinberg" fonts—these are special fonts used by the program (e.g. for score symbols) and not suited for common text.
Size	Sets the size of the text.
Frame	Allows you to encase the text in a rectangular (box) or oval frame.
Text style options	These checkboxes determine whether the text should be bold, italic, and/or underlined.

3. **When you've made your settings, click Apply.**

   If you like, you can leave the Font Settings dialog open, select another text block and adjust the settings for that—just remember to click Apply before you select a new text block.

- If you make settings in the Font Settings dialog with no text block selected, the settings will be used as default for all new text.
  In other words, all text you enter from then on will get the settings you have specified (although you can of course change this manually for each text block as usual).

23.12.13 Printing

To print your score, proceed as follows:

1. **Open the parts you want to print in the Score Editor.**

   Printing is only available from within the Score Editor.

2. **Select Page Setup from the File menu and make sure all your Printer settings are correct.**

   This includes paper size and margins.

3. **Close the Page Setup dialog and select Print from the File menu.**
4. **The standard Print dialog appears. Fill out the options as desired.**
5. **Click Print.**

23.13 Common MIDI Editor Options and Settings

23.13.1 Snap

Snap activated on the toolbar.

The Snap function helps you to find exact positions when editing in a MIDI editor. It does this by restricting horizontal movement and positioning to certain positions. Operations affected by Snap include moving, duplicating, drawing, sizing, etc.

- When the "Bars+Beats" display format is selected in the ruler, the Quantize value on the toolbar determines the Snap value.
  This makes it possible to Snap not only to straight note values but also to Swing grids set up in the Quantize Setup dialog (see page 468).
- When any time-based display format is selected in the ruler, editing snaps to whole seconds.

23.13.2 Coloring Notes and Events

By using the Colors pop-up menu on the toolbar, you can select a color scheme for the events in the editor. The following options are available:

Option	Description
Velocity	The notes get different colors depending on their velocity values.
Pitch	The notes get different colors depending on their pitch.

Option	Description
Channel	The notes get different colors depending on their individual MIDI channel values.
Part	The notes get the same color as their respective part in the Project window. Use this option when you are working with two or more tracks in an editor, to see better which notes belong to which track.

When any of the first three options is selected, you can select "Setup" from the Colors pop-up menu. This opens a dialog in which you can specify which colors should be associated with which velocities, pitches or channels, respectively.

24 The Logical Editor, Transformer and Input Transformer

24.1 Introduction

Most of the time you will probably perform your MIDI editing graphically, from one of the main graphic editors. But there are times when you want more of a "search and replace" function on MIDI data, and that's where the Logical Editor comes in.

The principle for the Logical Editor is this:

- You set up *filter conditions* to find certain events.
  This could be events of a certain type, with certain attributes or values or on certain positions, in any combination. You can combine any number of filter conditions and make composite conditions using AND/OR operators.

- You select the basic *function* to be performed.
  The options include Transform (changing properties of the found events), Delete (removing the events), Insert (adding new events based on the found events' positions) and more.

- You set up a list of *actions*, which specify exactly what should be done.
  This is not necessary for all functions. For example, the Delete function does not require any additional action specifications—it simply removes all found events. The Transform function on the other hand, requires that you specify which properties should be changed and in which way (transpose notes by a certain amount, adjust velocity values, etc.).

By combining filter conditions, functions and the specific actions, you can perform very powerful processing.

To master the Logical Editor you need some knowledge about how MIDI messages are built up. However, the Logical Editor also comes with a rich selection of presets, allowing you to access its processing powers without delving into its more complicated aspects, see page 551.

● Studying the included presets is an excellent way to learn the workings of the Logical Editor! Many of them can also be used as starting points when you set up your own Logical editing tasks.

About the Transformer MIDI Effect

The Transformer effect is a real-time version of the Logical Editor, allowing you to apply logical editing to the events played back from a track "on the fly". The Transformer contains virtually the same settings and functions as the Logical Editor—where there are differences between the two, this is clearly stated on the following pages.

About the Input Transformer

Again, this is very similar to the Logical Editor. Just like the Transformer effect, the Input Transformer works in real time. However, the Input Transformer filters out and transforms MIDI data *as it is recorded.* In other words, the settings you make in the Input Transformer will affect the actual MIDI events you record.

The Input Transformer is described on page 568. However, we recommend that you make yourself familiar with the Logical Editor first, since they share many features and principles.

24.2 Opening the Logical Editor

1. **Select the desired parts or events.**

   What will be affected by the operation depends on the current selection:

- In the Project window, Logical editing is applied to all selected parts, affecting all events (of the relevant types) in them.
- In the MIDI editors, Logical editing is applied to all selected events. If no events are selected, all events in the edited part(s) will be affected.

You can change the selection while the Logical Editor window is open, if needed.

2. **Select "Logical Editor..." from the MIDI menu.**

- For details on how to open the Transformer (and other MIDI effects) see page 436.

24.3 Window Overview

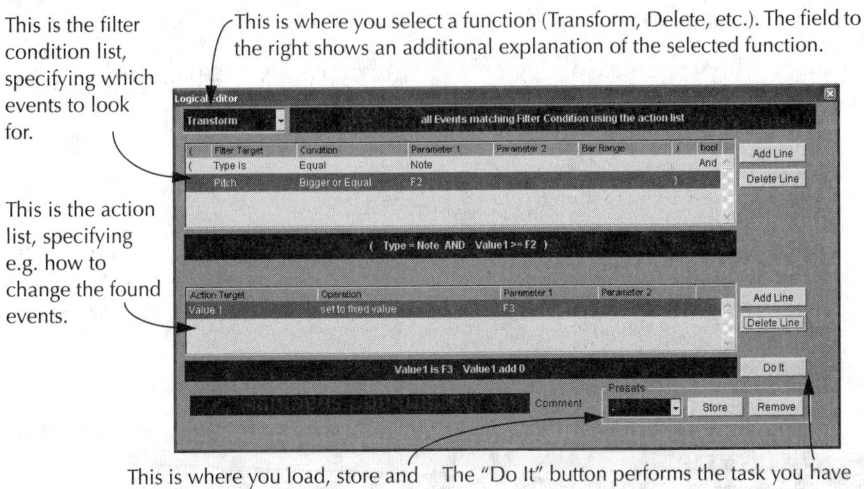

24.4 Selecting a Preset

To come to terms with the Logical Editor, it might be a good idea to start with exploring the included presets. These are found on the pop-up menu at the bottom of the window, to the right.

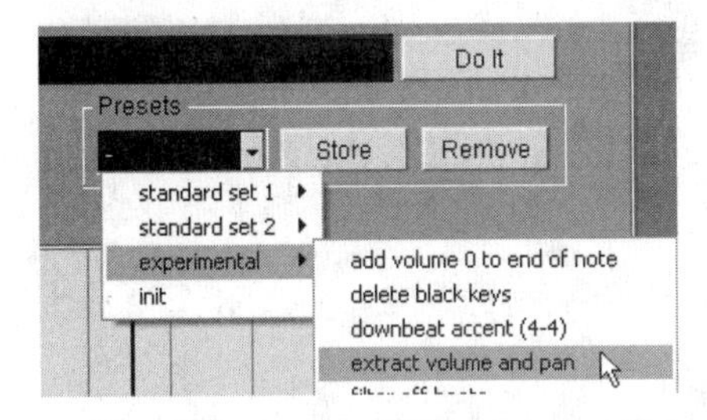

- **To load a preset, select it from the Presets pop-up menu.**

  The window will show the settings stored in the preset. As the preset is not applied to the MIDI events yet, you can load different presets just to study them without affecting any events. You can also edit the preset before performing the Logical editing, if needed.

- **To apply the loaded preset (perform the Logical editing), click Do It.**

- You can also select Logical Presets directly from the MIDI menu.
  This allows you to apply a preset to the selected MIDI part directly, without having to open the Logical Editor.

For information on how to create and handle your own presets, see page 567.

24.5 Setting Up Filter Conditions

24.5.1 General Procedure

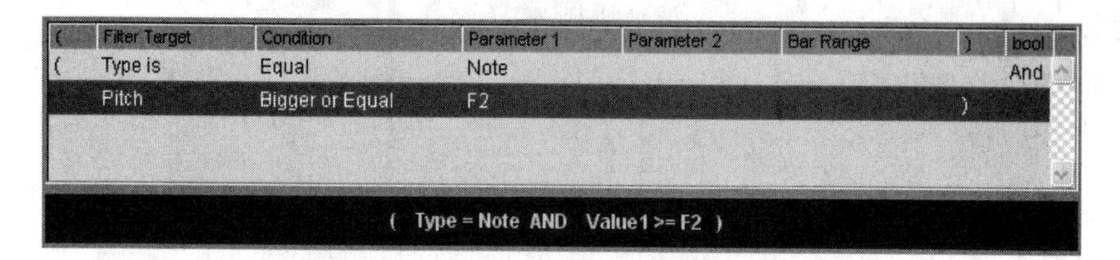

The upper list is where you set up the filter conditions, determining which events to find. The list contains one or several conditions, each on a separate line.

- If you want to start from scratch (as opposed to basing your settings on an existing preset) you may want to initialize the settings by selecting the Init option from the Presets pop-up menu.

- **To add a new line (condition) click the Add Line button to the right.**

  The new line is added at the bottom of the list. If there are many lines, you may need to use the scrollbar to the right to view them.

- **To remove a line, click anywhere on it to select it and click the Delete Line button to the right.**

You set up a filter condition line by clicking in the columns and selecting options from the pop-up menus that appear. Here is a brief description of the columns:

Column	Description
Left bracket	This is used for "bracketing" several lines together when creating conditions with multiple lines and the boolean operators And/Or. See page 559.
Filter Target	Here you select which property to look for when finding events. Your choice here affects the available options in the other columns as well, see below!
Condition	This determines how the Logical Editor should compare the property in the Filter Target column to the values in the Parameter columns (Equal, Unequal, Bigger, etc.—see the separate table below). The available options depend on the Filter Target setting.
Parameter 1	Here you set which value the event properties should be compared to (a numeric value, a position or a choice from a pop-up menu, depending on the Filter Target). For example, if the Filter Target is "Position" and Condition is "Equal", the Logical Editor will look for all events starting at the position you specify in the Parameter 1 column.
Parameter 2	This column is only used if you have selected one of the "Range" options in the Condition column. Typically, this allows you to find all events with values within (or outside) the range between Parameter 1 and Parameter 2.
Bar Range	This column is only used if the Filter Target is "Position" and one of the "Bar Range" options is selected in the Condition column. In these cases, you use the Bar Range column to specify "zones" within each bar (allowing you to find e.g. all events on or around the first beat of every bar). See page 555.
Right bracket	This is used for "bracketing" several lines together. See page 559.
bool	This allows you to insert the boolean operators And/Or, when creating conditions with multiple lines. See page 559.

Conditions

The options in the Condition column have the following meaning (please note that the available Condition options depend on the Filter Target setting):

Condition	Events will be found if their Filter Target property...
Equal	...has the exact same value as set up in the Parameter 1 column.
Unequal	...has any value other than the one set up in the Parameter 1 column.
Bigger	...has a value higher than the one set up in the Parameter 1 column.
Bigger or Equal	...has a value that is the same as or higher than the one set up in the Parameter 1 column.
Less	...has a value lower than the one set up in the Parameter 1 column.
Less or Equal	...has a value that is the same as or lower than the one set up in the Parameter 1 column.
Inside Range	...has a value that is between the values set up in the Parameter 1 and Parameter 2 columns. Note that Parameter 1 should be the lower value and Parameter 2 the higher.
Outside Range	...has a value that is not between the values set up in the Parameter 1 and Parameter 2 columns.
Inside Bar Range	...is within the "zone" set up in the Bar Range column (Position only), in each bar within the current selection.
Outside Bar Range	...is outside the "zone" set up in the Bar Range column (Position only), in each bar within the current selection.
Note is equal to	...is the note specified in the Parameter 1 column, regardless of octave (Pitch only). Lets you find e.g. all C notes, in all octaves.

- The Conditions for the "Property" filter target are different, see page 558.

Below, the different Filter Targets (and their corresponding Condition and Parameter options) are described in more detail.

24.5.2 Searching for Events at Certain Positions

Selecting Position in the Filter Target column lets you find events starting at certain positions, either relative to the start of the song or within each bar.

- If you select any Condition other than the Range or Bar Range options, you set up a specific position (in bars, beats, sixteenth notes and ticks) in the Parameter 1 column.

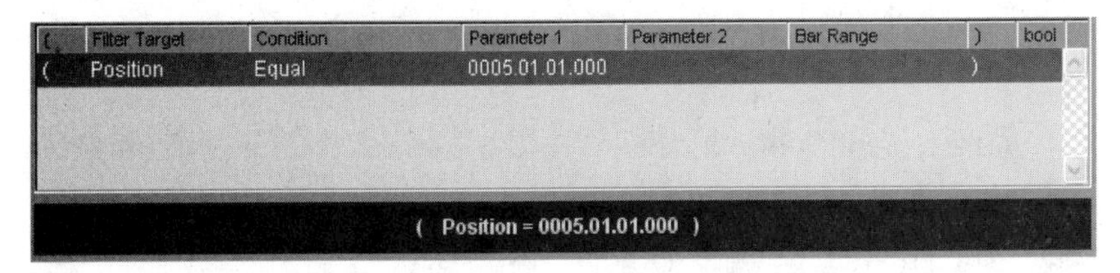

Here, the Logical Editor will find all events at 5.1.1 in the project.

- If you select the Inside or Outside Range option in the Condition column, you set the start position of the range in the Parameter 1 column and the end position in the Parameter 2 column.
  The Logical Editor will then find all events inside or outside this position range.
- If you select one of the Bar Range options in the Condition column, the Bar Range column will show a graphic bar display. You specify the range within the bar by clicking and dragging in the bar display (the specified Bar Range is indicated in blue).
  The Logical Editor will then find all events starting inside or outside this Bar Range, in all bars (within the current selection).

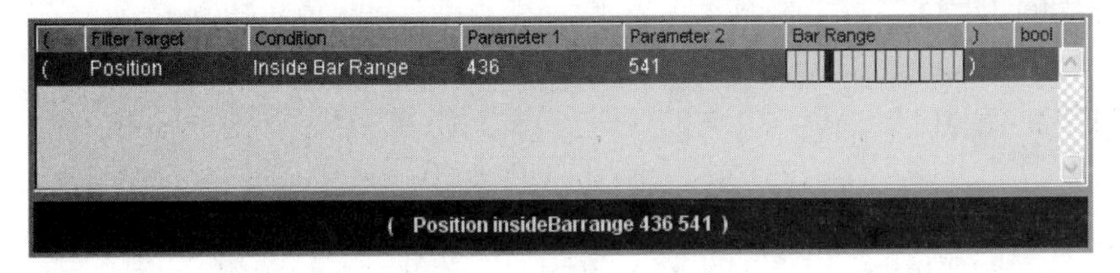

Here, the Logical Editor will find events starting around the second beat in each bar.

24.5.3 Searching for Notes of Certain Lengths

Only note events have lengths (actually, a note is made up of separate note-on and note-off events but in Cubase SX/SL it's considered as a single event with a length). Therefore, the "Length" Filter Target is only valid if you're specifically searching for notes—there has to be another condition line with the Filter Target "Type", Condition "Equal" and Parameter 1 set to "Note". See page 559 for more about using multiple filter conditions.

24.5.4 Searching for Value 1 or Value 2

A MIDI event is composed of several values. The meanings of value 1 and 2 depend on the type of event:

Event type	Value 1	Value 2
Notes	The Note Number/Pitch.	The velocity of the note.
PolyPressure	The key that was pressed.	The amount of pressure for the key.
Controller	The type of Controller, displayed as a number.	The amount of Control Change.
Program Change	The Program Change number.	Not used.
Aftertouch	The amount of pressure.	Not used.
Pitchbend	The "fine tune" of the bend. Not always used.	The coarse amount of bend.

- System Exclusive events are not included in the table above, since they don't use value 1 and 2.

Since value 1 and 2 have different meanings for different events, searching for e.g. value 2 = 64 would both find notes with the velocity 64 and controllers with the amount 64, etc. If this is not what you want, you can add an additional filter condition line with the Filter Target "Type", specifying which type of events to find (see below).

- This is particularly useful when searching for note pitch or velocity values, as described below.

The general procedures when searching for value 1 or 2 are:

- If you select any Condition other than the Range options, you set up a specific value in the Parameter 1 column.

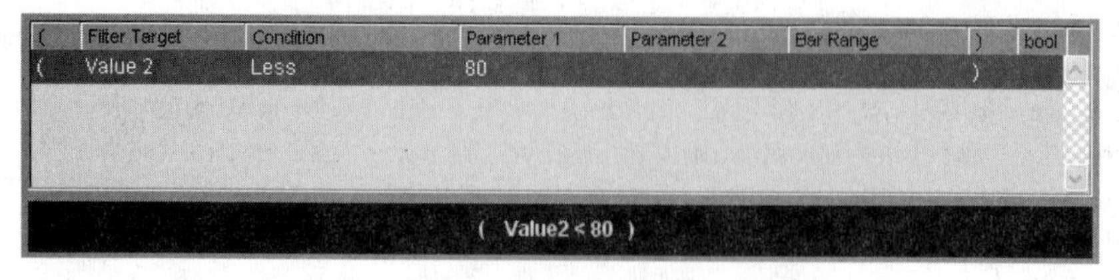

Here, the Logical Editor will find all events with a value 2 less than 80.

- If you select the Inside or Outside Range option in the Condition column, the range consists of the values between Parameter 1 and Parameter 2.
  Note that Parameter 1 should have the lower value.

Searching for Note Pitch or Velocity

If you add another condition line with the Filter Target "Type", Condition "Equal" and Parameter 1 set to "Note", the Logical Editor will "know" you are searching for pitch or velocity. This has the following benefits:

- The Filter Targets Value 1 and Value 2 will be displayed as "Pitch" and "Velocity" respectively, making it easier to grasp the function of the filter condition.
- Pitch values in the Parameter columns will be displayed as note names (C3, D#4, etc.). When entering pitch values you can either type a note name or a MIDI note number (0—127).
- When Value 1 (pitch) is selected as Filter Target, an additional option appears in the Condition column: "Note is equal to". When this is selected, you specify a note name in the Parameter 1 column but without any octave number (C, C#, D, D#, etc.). The Logical Editor can then find all notes of a certain key, in all octaves.

See page 559 for more info on working with multiple filter condition lines.

Searching for Controllers

There is similar extended functionality when searching for controllers: If you've added an additional "Type = Controller" condition line, the Logical Editor will "know" you are searching for controllers. The Parameter 1 column will then show the names of the MIDI controllers (Modulation, Volume, etc.) when Value 1 is selected as Filter Target.

24.5.5 Searching for MIDI Channels

Each MIDI event contains a MIDI channel setting (1—16). Normally, these settings are not used, since the MIDI event plays back on the MIDI channel set for its track. However, you can come across MIDI parts with events set to different channels in the following scenarios for example:

- If you have recorded MIDI from an instrument sending on several different channels (e.g. a master keyboard with different key zones).
- If you have imported a MIDI file of type 0 (with a single track, containing MIDI events with different channel settings).

Searching for MIDI channel values is straightforward; you select a Condition and enter a MIDI channel (1—16) in the Parameter 1 column (and, if you've selected one of the Range Conditions, a higher channel in the Parameter 2 column, creating a value range).

24.5.6 Searching for Event Types

Selecting the Filter Target Type allows you to find events of a certain type only.

- The Condition column contains three options only: Equal, Unequal and All Type.
- Clicking the Parameter 1 column displays a pop-up menu, listing the available event types (Note, PolyPressure, Controller, etc.).

The Logical Editor will find all events matching or not matching the selected type (depending on the Condition).

- As mentioned above, selecting Type = Note or Type = Controller adds some additional functionality to the Logical Editor. You should make it a habit to add a Type condition when applicable.

24.5.7 Searching for Properties

On the Filter Target pop-up menu you will find an option called Property. This allows you to search for properties that are not part of the MIDI standard but rather event-specific Cubase SX/SL settings.

When the Property option is selected, the Condition column has two options: "Property is set" and "Property is not set". Which property to look for is selected in the Parameter 1 column. The options are "muted", "selected" and "locked". Two examples:

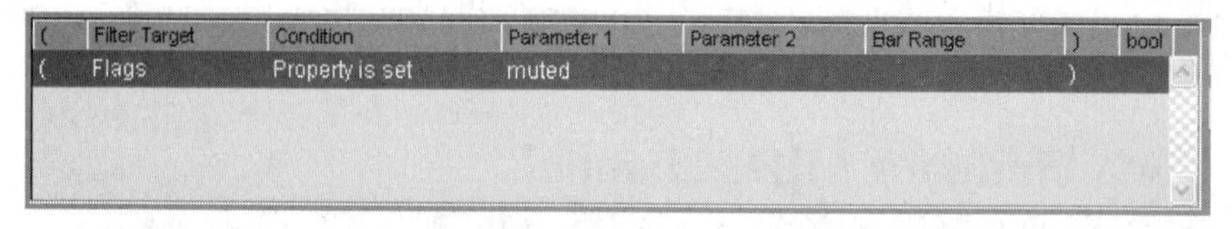

Here, the Logical Editor will find all muted events.

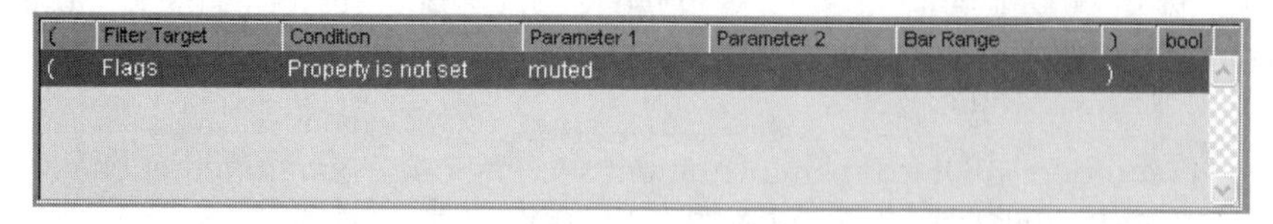

Here, the Logical Editor will find all events that are selected but not muted.

24.5.8 Combining Multiple Condition Lines

As described above, you can add condition lines by clicking the Add Line button to the right of the list. The result of combining condition lines depends on the boolean And/ Or operators and the brackets.

The Bool Column

By clicking in the boolean column to the right in the list, you can select a boolean operator: And or Or. A bool operator separates two condition lines and determines the result in the following way:

- If two condition lines are separated by a boolean And, both conditions must be fulfilled for an event to be found.

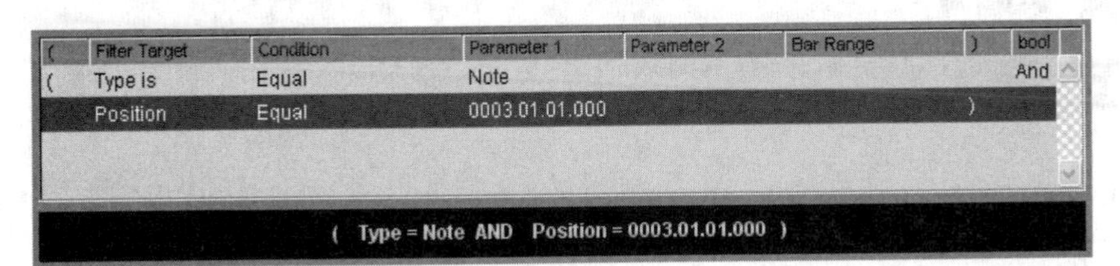

The Logical Editor will only find events that are notes and start at the beginning of the third bar.

- If two condition lines are separated by a boolean Or, one of the conditions (or both) must be fulfilled for an event to be found.

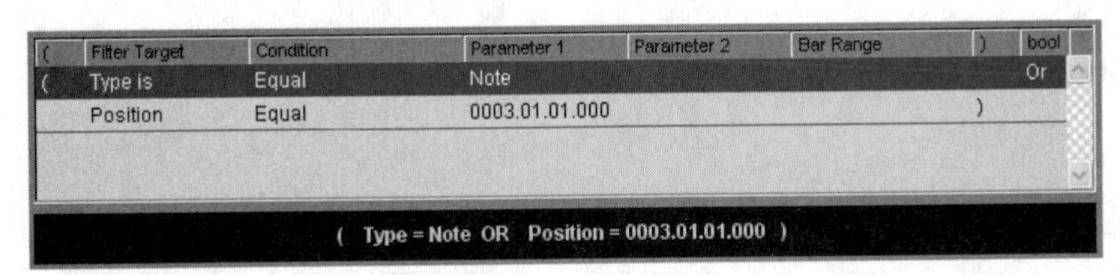

The Logical Editor will find all events that are notes (regardless of their position) and all events starting at the beginning of the third bar (regardless of their type).

- When you add a new condition line, the boolean setting defaults to And. Therefore, if all you want to do is set up two or more conditions that all must be met for an event to be found, you don't have to think about the boolean column—just add the required lines and make the usual filter settings.

Using Brackets

The bracket (parenthesis) columns let you enclose two or more condition lines, dividing the conditional expression into smaller units. This is only relevant when you have three or more condition lines and want to use the boolean Or operator. This is how it works:

- Without brackets, the conditional expressions are evaluated according their order in the list.

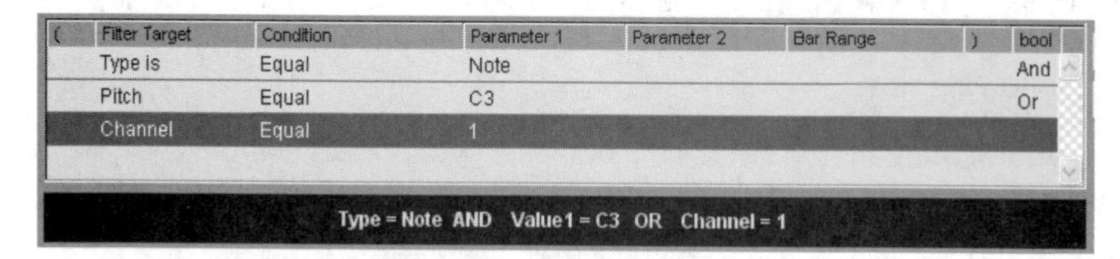

In this case we have the expression Type = Note AND Pitch = C3 OR Channel = 1, without brackets. This means that the Logical Editor will find all MIDI notes with the pitch C3, as well as all events (regardless of their type) set to MIDI channel 1.

Maybe you wanted to find all notes that either had the pitch C3 or the MIDI channel 1 (but no non-note events)? Then you need to add some brackets:

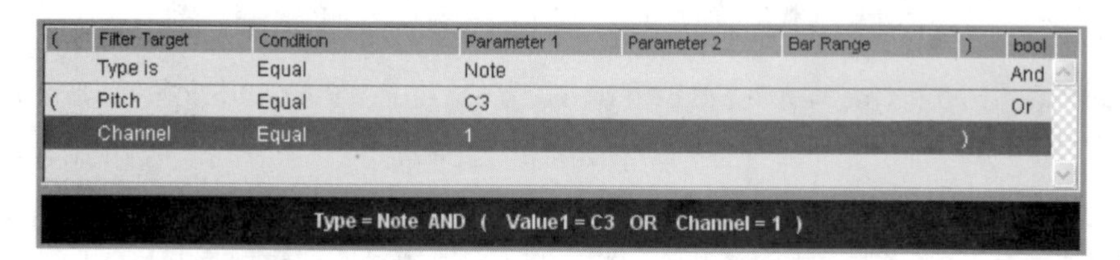

Here the expression is Type = Note AND (pitch = C3 OR Channel = 1), which will find what you want. The rule behind this is:

- Expressions within brackets are evaluated first.
  If there are several layers of brackets, these are evaluated "from the inside out", starting with the innermost brackets.

You add brackets by clicking in the bracket columns and selecting an option. Up to triple brackets can be selected.

24.5.9 Editing Filter Conditions as Text

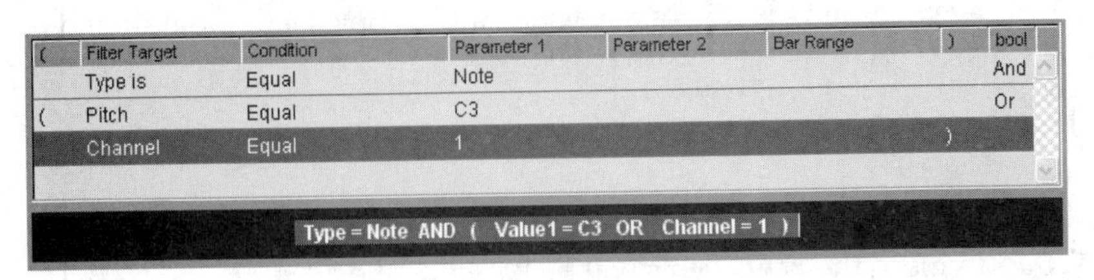

The area directly below the filter condition list shows you the current filter conditions as text. It also allows you to enter and edit the filter conditions in textual form. For tips on the syntax, please study the included presets.

- There is no additional functionality involved when editing filter conditions as text; it is simply another way to make settings.
  When you enter something in the text field you will see the corresponding settings appear in the filter condition list (provided that you have used the correct syntax).

24.6 Selecting a Function

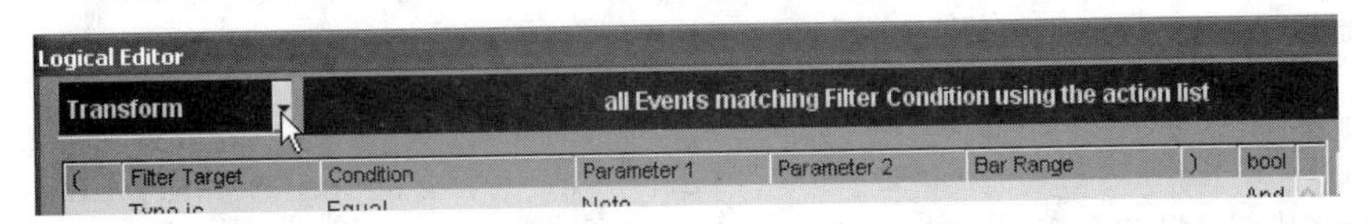

The pop-up menu in the upper left corner of the Logical Editor is where you select the function—the basic type of editing to be performed. When you select an option from the pop-up menu, the field to the right displays a clarifying text, making it easier to see what the function does.

- Note: In the Logical Editor, processing isn't performed until you click the Do It button. When using the Transformer MIDI effect there is no Do It button—the current settings are automatically applied in real time during playback or live playing.

Below, the available options are listed. Note that some options are available in the Logical Editor only—not in the Transformer effect.

Delete

Deletes all events found by the Logical Editor. In the case of the Transformer, this function will remove (or "mute") all found events from the "output stream"—the actual events on the track are not affected.

Transform

Changes one or several aspects of the found events. You set up exactly what should be changed in the action list, as described on page 563.

Insert

This will create new events and insert these into the part(s) (Logical Editor) or the output stream (Transformer). The new events will be based on the events found by the Logical Editor's filter conditions, but with any changes you have set up in the action list applied.

Another way of expressing this is that the Insert function copies the found events, transforms them according to the action list and inserts the transformed copies among the existing events.

Insert Exclusive

This will transform the found events according to the action list. Then, all events that were *not* found (that didn't fit the filter conditions) are deleted (Logical Editor) or removed from the output stream (Transformer).

Copy (not available in the Transformer)

This will copy all found events, transform them according to the action list and paste them into a new part on a new MIDI track. The original events are not affected.

Extract (not available in the Transformer)

This works like Copy, but will cut the found events instead. Or in other words, Extract will transform all found events and move them to a new part on a new MIDI track.

Select (not available in the Transformer)

This will simply select all found events, highlighting them for further work in the regular MIDI editors.

24.7 Specifying Actions

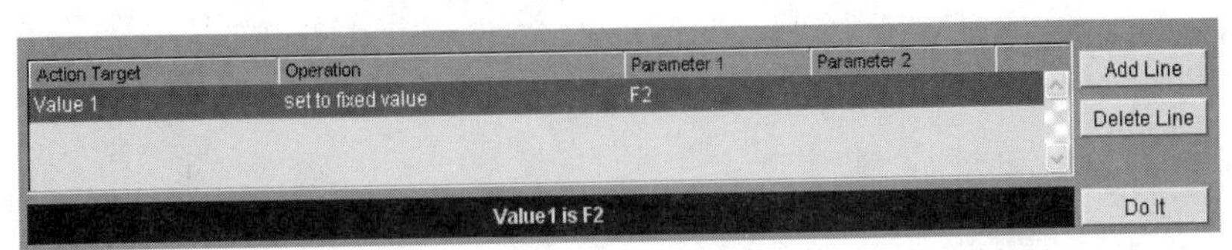

The lower list in the Logical Editor window is the action list. This is where you specify any changes that should be made to the found events (relevant for all function types except Delete and Select).

The handling of the action list is similar to the filter condition list, but without the brackets and booleans. You simply add lines by clicking the Add Line button to the right, and fill out the columns as required. To remove a superfluous action line, select it and click the Delete Line button.

Below, the four list columns are described:

24.7.1 Action Target

This is where you select the property that should be changed in the events:

Option	Description
Position	Adjusting this value will move the events.
Length	Lets you resize the events (notes only)
Value 1	This adjusts value 1 in the events. As described on page 556, the meaning of value 1 depends on the event type. For notes, value 1 is the pitch.
Value 2	This adjusts value 2 in the events. As described on page 556, the meaning of value 2 depends on the event type. For notes, value 2 is the velocity value.
Channel	Allows you to change the MIDI channel setting. See page 557.
Type	Allows you to change an event from one type to another, e.g. transform aftertouch events to modulation events.
Value 3	This adjusts value 3 in the events. At the time of this writing, this option is only implemented for notes and corresponds to the note off value.

24.7.2 Operation

This setting determines what to do with the Action Target. The options on this pop-up menu are different depending on the selected Action Target. Below, all available operations are listed:

Add

Adds the value specified in the Parameter 1 column to the Action Target.

Subtract

Subtracts the value specified in the Parameter 1 column from the Action Target.

Multiply by

Multiplies the Action Target value with the value specified in the Parameter 1 column.

Divide by

Divides the Action Target value with the value specified in the Parameter 1 column.

Round by

This "rounds" the Action Target value with the value specified in the Parameter 1 column. In other words, the Action Target value is changed to the closest value that can be divided by the Parameter 1 value.

For example, if the Action Target value is 17 and Parameter 1 is 5, the result of rounding will be 15 (the closest value that can be divided by 5). Another word for this type of operation would be "quantizing", and it's actually possible to use it for this, by setting the Action Target to "Position" and specifying a quantize value with Parameter 1 (in ticks, with 480 ticks per quarter note).

Set Random Values between

This will set the Action Target value to a random value within the range specified with Parameter 1 and 2.

Set Relative Random Values between

This will *add* a random value to the current Action Target value. The added random value will be within the range specified with Parameter 1 and 2. Note that these can be set to negative values.

For example, if you set Parameter 1 to -20 and Parameter 2 to +20, the original Action Target value will get a random variation, never exceeding ±20.

Set to fixed value

This sets the Action Target to the value specified in the Parameter 1 column.

Add Length

This is only available when Action Target is set to Position. Furthermore, it is only valid if the found events are notes (and thus have a length). When Add Length is selected, the length of each note event will be added to the Position value. This can be used for creating new events (using the Insert function) positioned relative to the end positions of the original notes.

Transpose to Scale

This is only available when Action Target is set to Value 1, and when the filter conditions are specifically set up to find notes (a "Type = Note" filter condition line has been added). When Transpose to scale is selected, you can specify a musical scale using the Parameter 1 and 2 columns. Parameter 1 is the key (C, C#, D, etc.) while Parameter 2 is the type of scale (major, melodic or harmonic minor, etc.).

Each note will be transposed to the closest note in the selected scale.

Use Value 2

This is only available when Action Target is set to Value 1. If this option is selected, the Value 2 setting in each event will be copied to the Value 1 setting.

For example, this would be useful if you are transforming all Modulation controllers to Aftertouch events (since controllers use Value 2 for their amount, while Aftertouch use Value 1—see the table on page 556).

Use Value 1

This is only available when Action Target is set to Value 2. If this option is selected, the Value 1 setting in each event will be copied to the Value 2 setting.

Mirror

This is only available when Action Target is set to Value 1 or Value 2. When this option is selected, the values will be "mirrored" or "flipped" around the value set in the Parameter 1 column.

In the case of notes, this will invert the scale, with the key set in the Parameter 1 column as "center point".

Linear Change in Loop Range

This will affect events within the cycle loop range (between the left and right locators) only. It will create a linear "ramp" of values (replacing the original values) starting at the value in the Parameter 1 column and ending at the Parameter 2 value.

This can be used for creating linear controller sweeps, velocity ramps, etc.

Relative Change in Loop Range

As with the previous option, this will create a ramp of values, affecting events in the cycle loop range only. However, here the changes are "relative", meaning that values will be added to the existing values.

In other words, you set up a value ramp starting at Parameter 1 and ending at Parameter 2 (note that the Parameter values can be negative). The resulting value ramp is then added to the existing values for the events within the cycle loop range.

For example, if you apply this to note velocities with Parameter 1 set to 0 and Parameter 2 set to -127, you would create a velocity fade-out, keeping the original velocity relations:

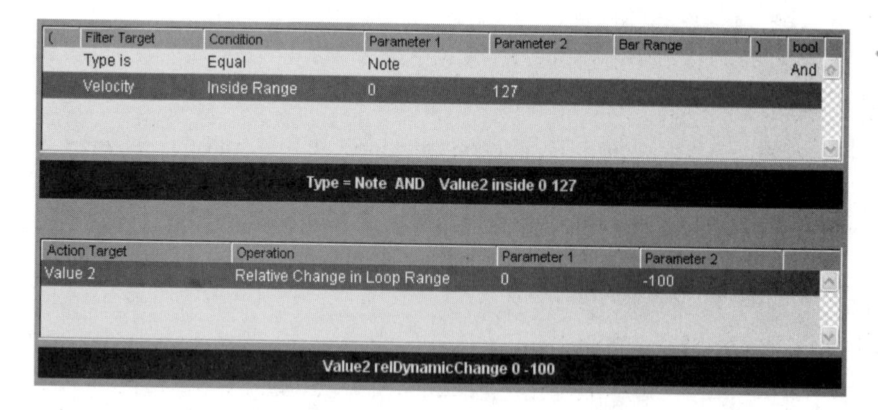

24.8 Performing the Logical Editing

Once you have set up filter conditions, selected a function and set the required actions (or loaded a preset), you perform the Logical editing by clicking the Do It button.

Logical editing can be undone just like any other editing.

- Again, when using the Transformer MIDI effect there is no Do It button. The processing is applied to the events played back from the track (or played live "thru" the track) as soon as you set it up.
  Since no existing events on the track are affected by the Transformer setting, there is no need for undo.

24.9 Working with Presets

The Presets section in the lower right area of the window allows you to load, store and manage Logical Editor presets. A preset contains all settings in the window, which means you can perform Logical editing by simply loading a preset and clicking Do It.

- To load a preset, select it from the Presets menu.

Storing Your Own Settings as a Preset

If you have made Logical Editor settings that you may want to use again, you can store them as a preset:

1. **If you like, enter some explanatory text in the Comment field.**

   An extra description of the preset can be useful, especially if the settings are complex.

2. **Click the Store button in the Presets section.**

   A name dialog appears.

3. **Enter a name for the preset and click OK.**

   The preset is stored.

- To remove a preset, load it and click the Remove button.

Organizing and Sharing Presets

The Logical Editor presets are stored as individual files within the Cubase SX/SL program folder, in the presets\Logical Edit subfolder. While these files cannot be edited "manually", you can reorganize them (e.g. putting them in subfolders) like any files.

This also makes it easy to share presets with other Cubase SX/SL users, by transferring the individual preset files.

- The list of presets is read each time the Logical Editor is opened.

24.10 The Input Transformer

This function allows you to selectively filter out and change MIDI data coming to a MIDI track, before it is recorded. The Input Transformer is very similar to the Transformer MIDI effect, but contains four independent "modules", for which you can set up different filtering and actions if you like. You can activate any or all of these four modules.

Here are some of the things the Input Transformer allows you to do:

- Make up split keyboard combinations for recording left and right hands separately.
- Turn a controller like a foot pedal into MIDI notes (for playing bass drum the right way).
- Filter out one specific type of MIDI data on one MIDI channel only.
- Turn aftertouch into any controller (and vice versa).
- Invert velocity or pitch.

And again: four of these things can be done at the same time.

Opening the Input Transformer

To open the Input Transformer for a MIDI track, select the track and click the Input Transformer button in the Inspector.

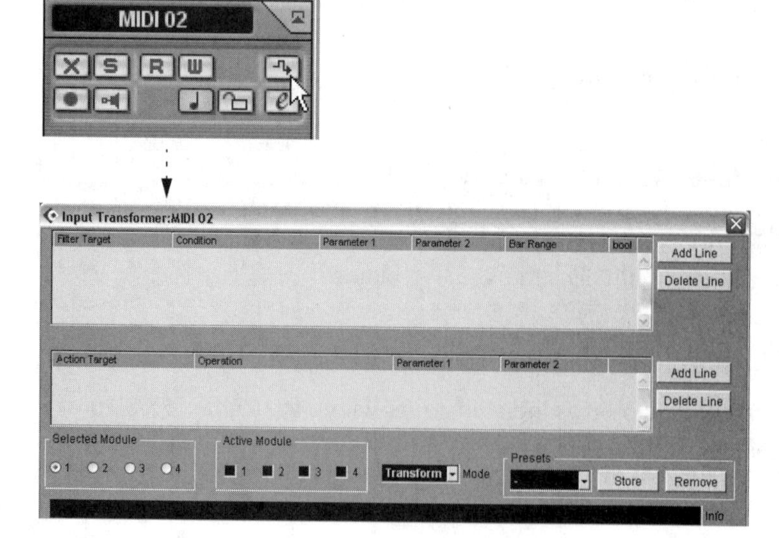

Handling the Four Modules

The Input Transformer is really four separate transformers, or modules.

- **You select which module to view and make settings for by clicking its button in the Selected Module section.**

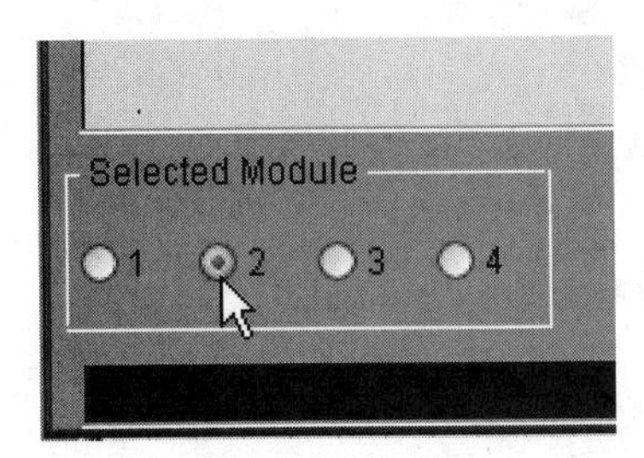

Module 2 selected for viewing and editing.

- **The checkboxes in the Active Module section determine which module(s) are active.**

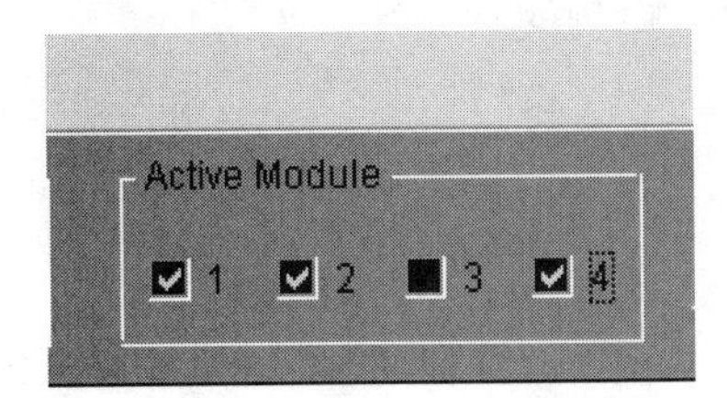

Here, modules 1, 2 and 4 are active.

The Two Modes

The Mode pop-up menu contains two modes: Filter and Transform.

- **In the Filter mode, only the filter conditions (the upper list) are taken into account. All events matching the conditions set up will be filtered out (excluded from the recording).**
- **In the Transform mode, events matching the filter conditions will be transformed according to the settings in the action list (the lower list).**

Setting Up Filtering and Actions

This is done just like in the Logical Editor. Here is a brief rundown:

- **Click the Add Line buttons to add lines to the filter condition list or action list.**

  To remove a line, click it to select it and click the Delete Line button to the right.

- **Clicking the columns in the filter condition list brings up pop-up menus, allowing you to specify the conditions to match.**
- **Clicking the columns in the action list brings up pop-up menus, allowing you to specify what should be done to the found events (when Transform mode is selected).**

For detailed descriptions of the filter conditions and action columns, see page 552.

- **Selecting the Init option from the Presets pop-up menu will reset the selected module, removing all filter condition and target list lines.**
- **The Input Transformer has no "Do It" button—the settings are active as soon as you activate an Active Module checkbox.**

  The settings made in the activated modules will affect all MIDI data you record on the track.

- Closing the Input Transformer window does *not* turn it off—you need to deactivate all Active Module checkboxes for this!
  A lit Input Transformer button in the Inspector indicates that one or more modules are active.

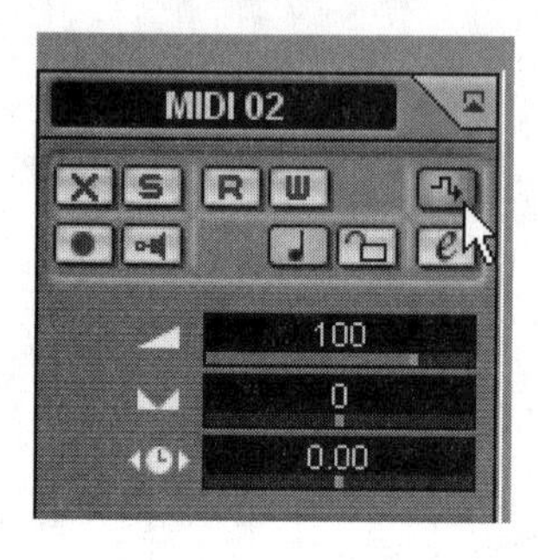

25 The Tempo Track Editor

25.1 Background

For each audio or MIDI track in Cubase SX/SL, you can specify whether it should be time based or tempo based (see page 127). For tempo based tracks, the tempo can either be fixed through the whole project (this is called "Rehearsal tempo") or follow the Tempo track (this is called "Master tempo"), which may contain tempo changes.

- **To switch between Rehearsal mode and Master Tempo track mode, use the Master button on the Transport bar or in the Tempo Track Editor.**

  When the Master button is activated, the tempo follows the Tempo track, when it is deactivated, the Rehearsal Tempo is used (see page 578).

The Tempo track also contains time signature events. These are always active, regardless of whether Rehearsal mode or Master mode is selected.

About Tempo Based Audio Tracks

For tempo based tracks, the start time position of audio events depends on the current tempo setting. However, it is important to realize that the actual audio ("within" the events) will play back as recorded, regardless of any tempo changes you make. Therefore, it's good practice to make the proper tempo and time signature settings before you start recording tempo based audio.

- To make an already recorded audio track follow the tempo changes, you can use the Hitpoints and Slicing features, as described on page 385.
  How well this works depends on the character of the audio recordings, since the Hitpoint detection feature works best with fairly rhythmical material.

25.2 Opening the Tempo Track Editor

To make changes to the actual Tempo track, you need to open the Tempo Track Editor. This is done by selecting "Tempo track" on the Project menu.

25.3 Window Overview

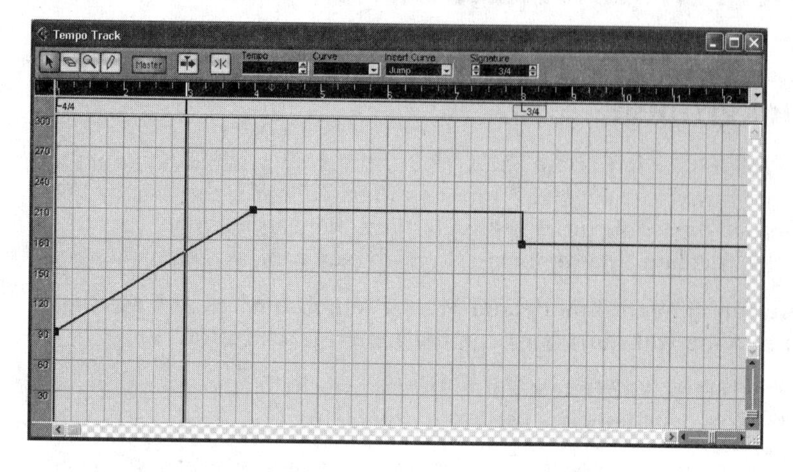

25.3.1 The Toolbar

The toolbar contains various tools and settings. The Tempo and Signature displays to the right allow you to view and edit the value of the selected tempo curve point or time signature event, much like the info line in other editors.

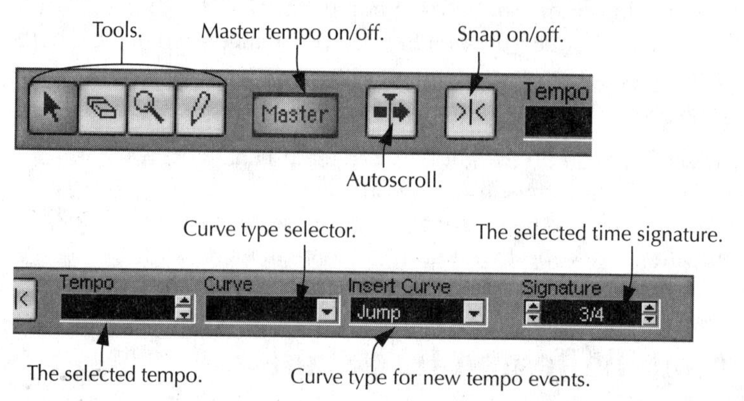

25.3.2 The Ruler

The ruler in the Tempo Track Editor shows the timeline. As in other windows, you can select a display format by clicking on the arrow button to the right of the ruler, and selecting an option from the pop-up menu that appears.

The two additional items at the bottom of the menu have the following functionality:

• **If "Time Linear" is selected, the ruler, time signature area and tempo curve display will be linear in relation to the timeline.**

  This means that if the ruler shows bars and beats, the distance between the bar lines will vary depending on the tempo.

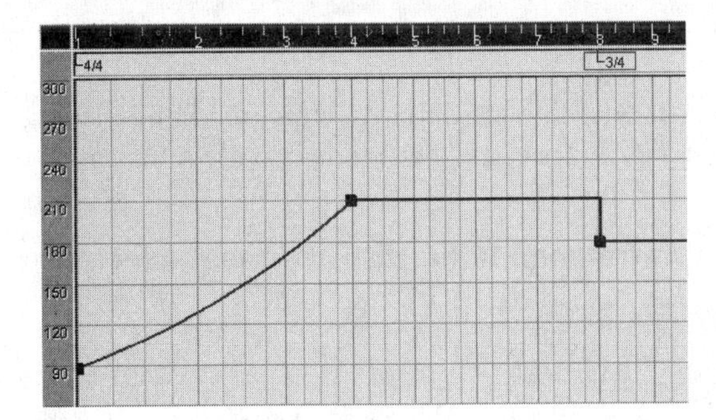

• **If "Bars+Beats Linear" is selected, the ruler, time signature area and tempo curve display will be linear in relation to beats.**

  This means that if the ruler shows bars and beats, the distance between beats will be constant.

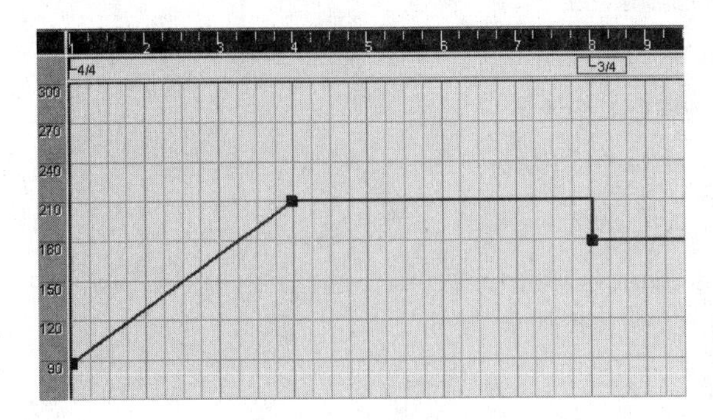

25.3.3 The Time Signature Area

The area below the ruler contains time signature events.

25.3.4 The Tempo Curve Display

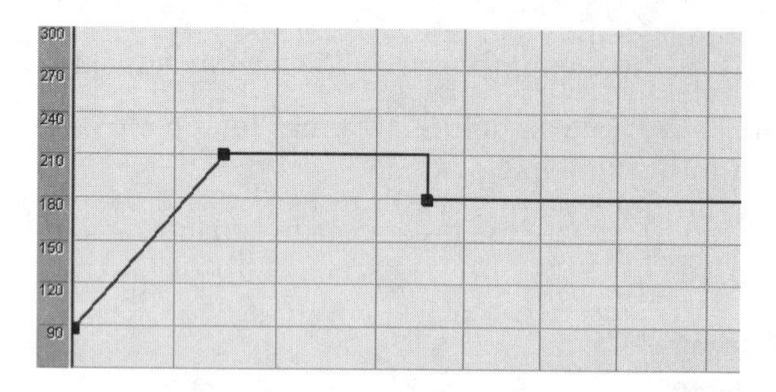

The main display shows the tempo curve (or, if Rehearsal mode is selected, the Rehearsal tempo—see page 578). To the left of the display is a tempo scale to help you quickly locate the desired tempo.

- **Note that the vertical "grid lines" correspond to the display format selected for the ruler.**

25.4 Operations

25.4.1 Zooming

Changing the magnification is done using any of the following methods:

- **By using the zoom sliders in the lower right corner of the window.**
- **By using the Magnifying Glass tool.**

  This works according to the standard procedures.
- **By using the Zoom submenu on the Edit menu.**

  The options on the menu work as in other windows.

25.4.2 Editing the Tempo Curve

- This section assumes that you are working in Tempo track mode, i.e. the Master button is activated.

Adding Tempo Curve Points

1. **Use the "Insert Curve" pop-up menu in the toolbar to select whether you want the tempo to change gradually from the previous curve point to the new one ("Ramp") or change instantly to the new value ("Jump").**
2. **Select the Pencil tool.**
3. **Click at the desired time position in the tempo curve display, and keep the mouse button pressed.**

   If Snap is activated on the toolbar, this determines at which time positions you can insert tempo curve points, see page 579.

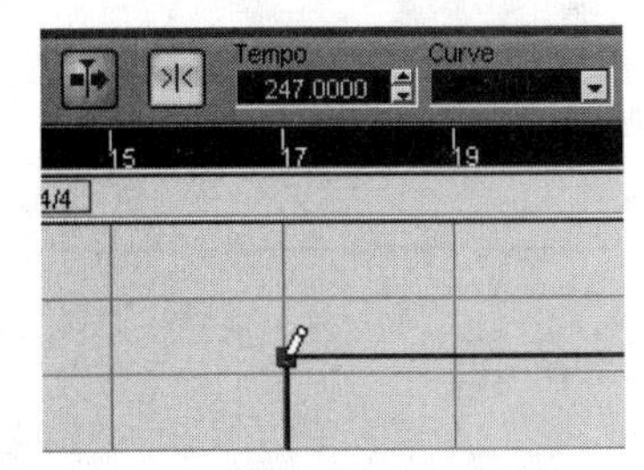

When you click, the Tempo Display in the toolbar shows the tempo value.

4. **Drag the curve point to the desired tempo value (indicated in the Tempo Display), and release the mouse button.**

   The tempo curve point is inserted. The result depends on whether you selected "Ramp" or "Jump" in step 1 above:

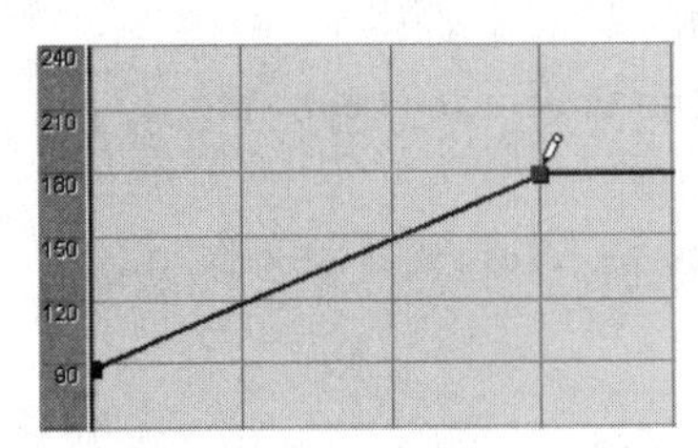

Insert Curve set to "Ramp".

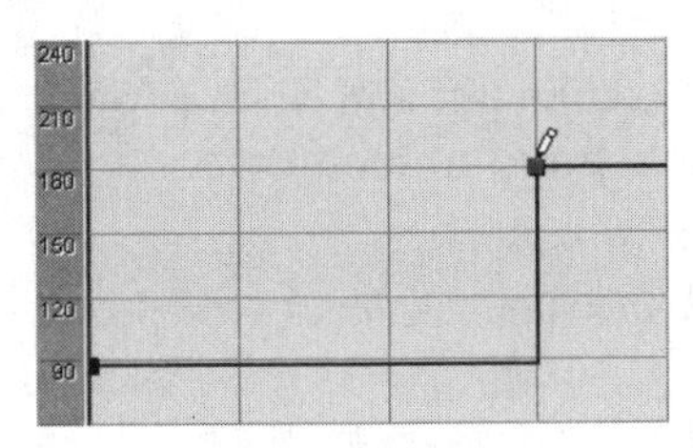

Insert Curve set to "Jump".

- **You can also just click and draw a tempo curve with the Pencil tool, having curve points automatically inserted as you draw.**

  You would probably want to select the "Ramp" Insert Curve mode when doing this.

- **Instead of using the Pencil tool, you can press [Alt] and use the Arrow tool.**

  This will only insert a single point (i.e. you cannot draw a curve with the Arrow tool).

● You can also have tempo values automatically inserted by the Beat Calculator, see page 580.

Selecting Tempo Curve Points

Selecting curve points is done using any of the following methods:

- **Use the Arrow tool.**

  The standard selection techniques apply.

- **Use the Select submenu on the Edit menu.**

  The options are:

Option	Description
All	Selects all curve points on the Tempo track.
None	Deselects all curve points.
In Loop	Selects all curve points between the left and right locator.
From Start to Cursor	Selects all points to the left of the project cursor.
From Cursor to End	Selects all points to the right of the project cursor.

- **You can also use the left and right arrow keys on the computer keyboard, to go from one curve point to the next.**

  If you press [Shift] and use the arrow keys, the current selection will be kept, allowing you to select several points.

Editing Tempo Curve Points

Curve points can be edited in the following ways:

- **By clicking and dragging horizontally and/or vertically.**

  If several points are selected, all of them are moved. If Snap is activated on the toolbar, this determines to which time positions you can move curve points, see page 579.

- **By adjusting the tempo value in the Tempo Display on the toolbar.**

  For this to work, a single tempo curve point must be selected.

● Dragging tempo curve points with a time based display format (any other format than "Bars+Beats") may give confusing results. This is because moving a point will change the relationship between tempo and time. Specifically, let's say you move a tempo point to the right and drop it on a certain time position. When you release the mouse button, the mapping between tempo and time will be adjusted (since you have changed the tempo curve). As a result, the moved point will appear at another position. For this reason, we recommend that you use the Bars+Beats display format when editing tempo curves.

Adjusting the Curve Type

You can change the curve type of a tempo curve segment at any time, using the following method:

1. **Select all curve points within the segment you want to edit.**

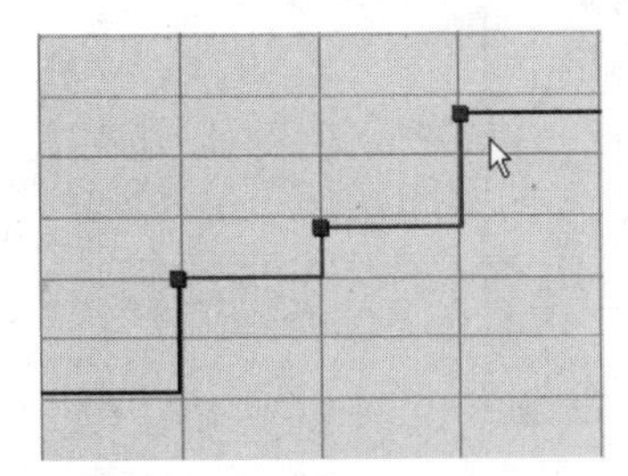

2. **Pull down the Curve pop-up menu on the toolbar and select "Jump" or "Ramp".**

   The curve sections between the selected points are adjusted.

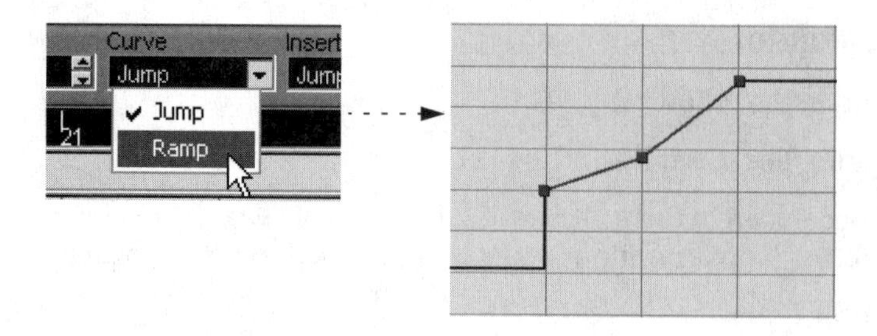

Removing Tempo Curve Points

To remove a curve point, either click on it with the Eraser tool or select it and press [Backspace]. The first tempo curve point cannot be removed.

25.4.3 Setting the Rehearsal Tempo

When the Master button is deactivated, the Tempo track curve is greyed out (but still visible). Since the Rehearsal tempo is constant throughout the whole project, there are no tempo curve points. Instead, the Rehearsal tempo is displayed as a horizontal black line in the tempo curve display.

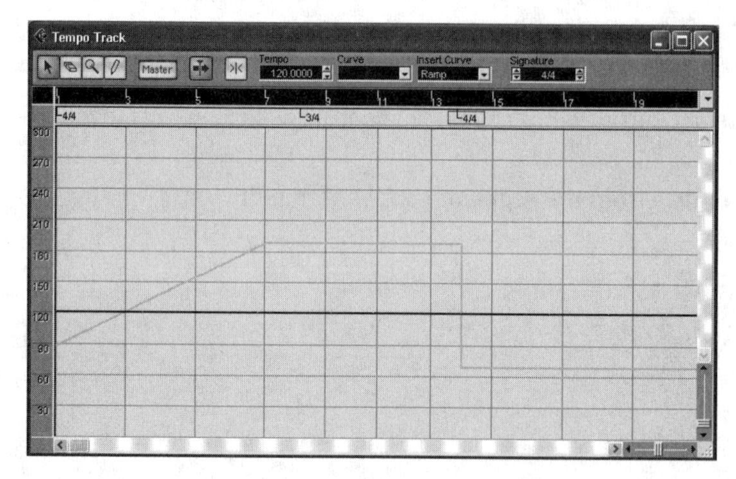

There are two ways to set the tempo in Rehearsal mode:

- **Drag the tempo line up or down with the Arrow tool.**
- **Adjust the value numerically in the Tempo Display on the toolbar.**

25.4.4 Adding and Editing Time Signature Events

- **To add a time signature event, click in the time signature area with the Pencil tool.**

  This adds a default 4/4 time signature event at the closest bar position. You can also do this by pressing [Alt] and clicking with the Arrow tool.

- **To edit the value of a time signature event, select it and adjust the value in the Signature display on the toolbar.**

  Note that there are two thumbwheel controls for the Signature display; the left adjusts the numerator and the right adjusts the denominator.

- **You can move a time signature event by clicking and dragging it with the Arrow tool.**

  Again, note that time signature events can only be positioned at the start of bars.

- **To remove a time signature, either click on it with the Eraser tool or select it and press [Backspace].**

  The first time signature event cannot be removed.

25.5 Options and Settings

25.5.1 Snap

You activate or deactivate Snap by clicking the Snap icon on the toolbar. The behavior of the function depends on the display format selected for the ruler:

- **If "Bars+Beats" is selected, tempo curve points will snap to the start of bars.**
- **If any other display format is selected, tempo curve points will snap to the vertical grid lines in the tempo curve display.**

  The spacing of the grid lines depends on the horizontal magnification.

- **Time signature events can only be positioned at the start of bars, regardless of whether Snap is activated or not.**

25.5.2 Auto Scroll

When this option is activated, the tempo curve display will scroll during playback, keeping the project cursor visible.

25.6 The Beat Calculator

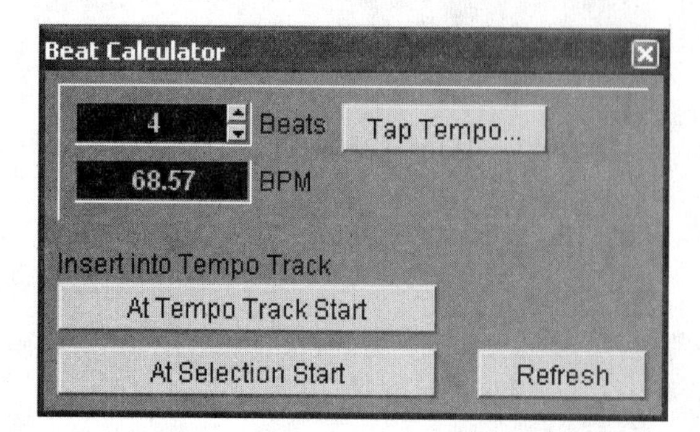

The Beat Calculator is a tool for calculating the tempo of freely recorded audio or MIDI material. It also allows you to set the tempo by tapping.

25.6.1 Calculating the Tempo of a Recording

1. **In the Project window, make a selection that covers an exact number of beats of the recording.**
2. **Select "Beat Calculator..." from the Project menu.**

   The Beat Calculator window appears.
3. **Enter the number of beats that the selection encompasses in the Beats field.**

   The corresponding tempo is calculated and displayed in the BPM field.

- **If you need to adjust the selection, you can just go back to the Project window, leaving the Beat Calculator open.**

  To re-calculate the tempo after adjusting the selection, click Refresh.

4. **If you like, you can insert the calculated tempo into the Tempo track, by clicking one of the buttons in the lower left corner of the Beat Calculator window.**

   Clicking "At Tempo Track Start" will adjust the first tempo curve point, while "At Selection Start" will add a new tempo curve point at the selection's start position, using the "Jump" curve type (see page 575).

● If Rehearsal mode is selected when you insert the calculated tempo, the Rehearsal tempo will be adjusted, regardless of which button you click.

25.6.2 Using Tap Tempo

The Tap Tempo function allows you to specify a tempo by tapping:

1. **Open the Beat Calculator.**
2. **If you want to tap the tempo to some recorded material, activate playback.**
3. **Click the Tap Tempo button.**

   The Tap Tempo window appears.

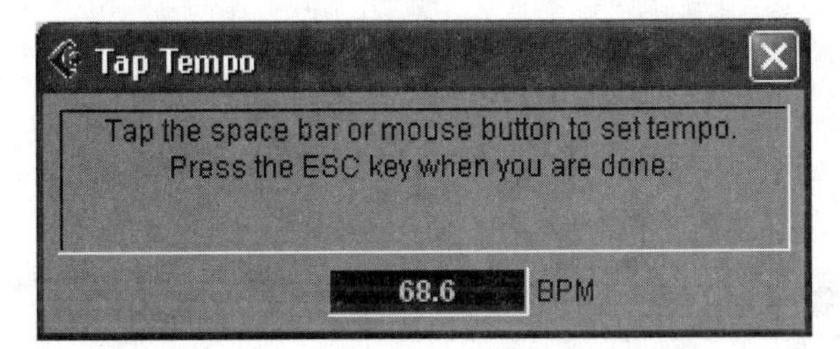

4. **Tap the tempo on the computer keyboard's space bar or with the mouse button.**

   The tempo display will update the calculated tempo between each tap.
5. **When you stop tapping, the program calculates the average timing of the taps and displays it.**
6. **Press [Esc] to close the Tap Tempo window.**

   The tapped tempo is now shown in the Beat Calculator's BPM display. If you like, you can insert it into the Tempo track as described on the previous page.

26 The Project Browser

26.1 Background

While the Project window and the editors display events and other data graphically, the Project Browser window provides a list based representation of the project. This allows you to view and edit all events on all tracks by using regular value editing in a list.

26.2 Opening the Project Browser

You open the Project Browser by selecting "Browser" from the Project menu. The Browser window can be open while you are working in other windows; any changes made in the Project window or an editor are immediately reflected in the Project Browser and vice versa.

26.3 Window Overview

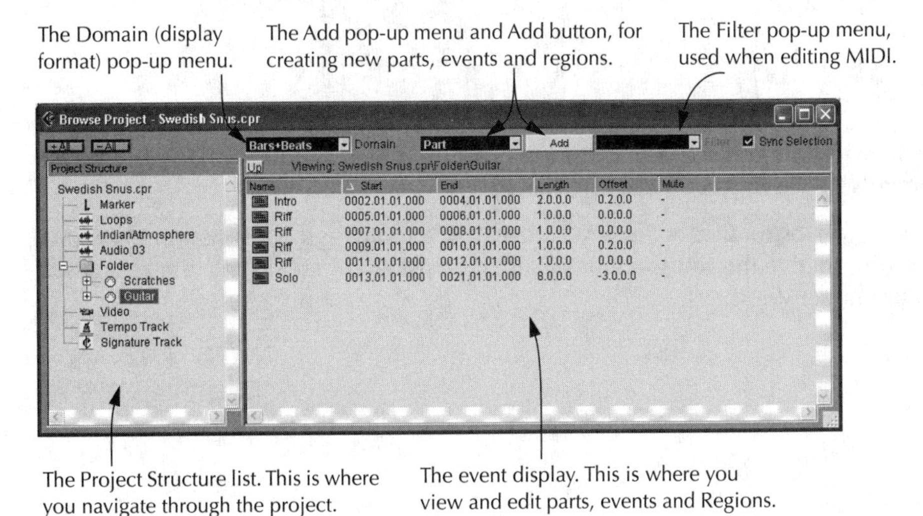

26.4 Navigating in the Browser

You use the Project Browser much like you use the Windows Explorer for browsing folders on your hard disk:

- **Click on an item in the Project Structure list to select it for viewing.**

  The contents of the item are shown in the event display.

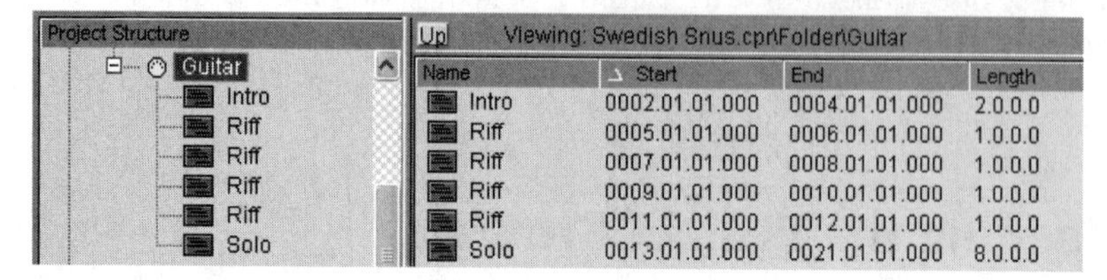

In this figure, the parts on a MIDI track are displayed.

- **Click the Up button above the event display to view the items "one step up" in the hierarchy.**

  For example, if you are viewing the contents of a MIDI part and click the Up button, the contents of the MIDI track are displayed instead.

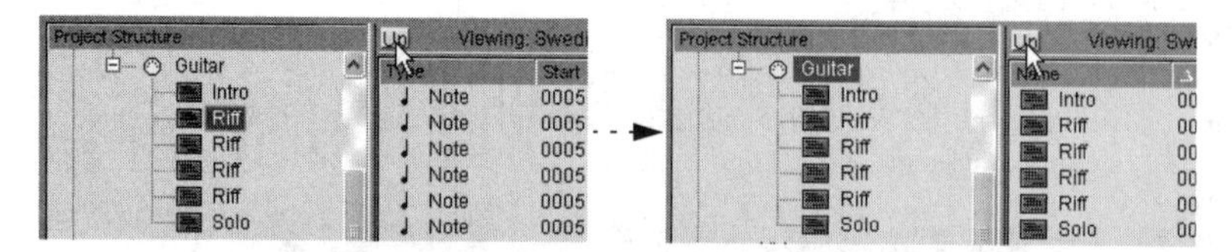

- **Items with hierarchical substructures can be folded out by clicking the plus symbols in the Project Structure list.**

  When the substructure of an item is revealed, a minus symbol is shown instead—click this to hide the substructure. Again, this is similar to revealing and hiding sub-folders under Windows.

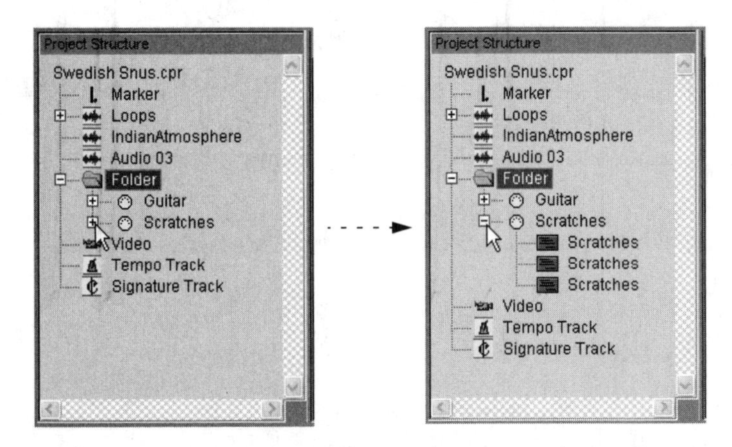

- **To reveal or hide all substructures in the Project Structure list, use the buttons "[+] All" and "[-] All" above the list.**
- **The actual editing is done in the event display, using regular value editing techniques.**

  There is one exception: You can rename items in the Project Structure list by clicking on their names and typing.

26.5 Customizing the View

You can drag the divider between the Project Structure list and the event display to make one of them wider and the other narrower. Furthermore, the event display can be customized in the following ways:

- **You can change the order of the columns by dragging the column headings to the left or right.**
- **You can resize columns by dragging the dividers between the column headings.**
- **To select a display format for all position and length values, use the Domain pop-up menu.**
- **You can sort events in the display by columns, by clicking the column heading.**

  If you for example want to sort events by their start positions, click that column heading. An arrow appears in the column heading, indicating that events are sorted by that column. The direction of the arrow indicates whether the events are sorted in ascending or descending order. To change the direction, click the column heading again.

26.6 About the Sync Selection Option

If the "Sync Selection" checkbox is activated (in the upper right corner of the Project Browser), selecting an event in the Project window automatically selects it in the Project Browser, and vice versa. This makes it easy to locate events in the two windows.

- This function is only available when a single event or part is selected.

26.7 Editing Audio Tracks

Audio tracks have two "subitems": Track Data and Automation.

- The Automation item corresponds to the Automation subtrack in the Project window, and contains the track's automation events (see page 591).
- The Track Data item corresponds to the actual audio track in the Project window. It contains audio events and/or audio parts, which in turn can contain audio events.

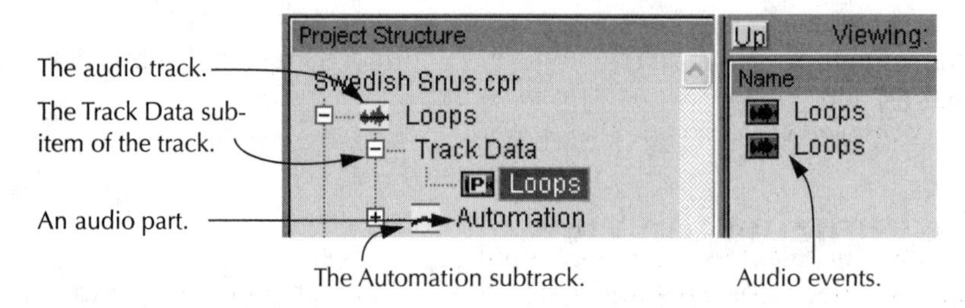

The following parameters are available for the different items:

The list columns for audio parts:

Parameter	Description
Name	The name of the part. Double clicking on the part symbol beside it opens the Audio Part Editor for the part.
Start	The start position of the part. Editing this value is the same as moving the part in the Project window.
End	The end position of the part. Editing this value is the same as resizing the part in the Project window.
Length	The length of the part. Editing this value is the same as resizing the part in the Project window.

Parameter	Description
Offset	This adjusts the start position of the events within the part. Adjusting this value is the same as sliding the contents of the part in the Project window (see page 140): setting a positive Offset value is the same as sliding the contents to the left, while a negative Offset corresponds to sliding the contents to the right.
Mute	Click in this column to mute or unmute the part.

The list columns for audio events:

Parameter	Description
Name	Allows you to enter a descriptive comment for the event. Double clicking on the waveform image beside it opens the Sample Editor for the event.
File	The name of the audio file referred by the event's audio clip.
Start	The start position of the event. If the event belongs to an audio part, you cannot move it outside the part.
End	The end position of the event.
Snap	The absolute position of the event's Snap point. Note that adjusting this value will not change the position of the Snap point within the event—instead it is another way of moving the event!
Length	The length of the event.
Offset	This determines "where in the audio clip" the event starts. Adjusting this value is the same as sliding the contents of the event in the Project window (see page 140). You can only specify positive Offset values, since the event cannot start before the start of the clip. Likewise, it cannot end after the end of the clip. If the event already plays the whole clip, the Offset cannot be adjusted at all.
Volume	The volume of the event, as set with the Volume handle or on the info line in the Project Window.
Fade In Fade Out	The length of the fade-in and fade-out areas respectively. If you use these settings to add a fade (where there previously was none), a linear fade will be created. If you adjust the length of an existing fade, the previous fade shape will be maintained.

Parameter	Description
Mute	Click in this column to mute or unmute the event.
Image	Displays a waveform image of the event inside a grey box corresponding to the clip. The image is scaled according to the width of the column. Click on the image to open the Sample Editor for the event.

Creating Audio Parts

When the "Audio" item of an audio track is selected in the Project Structure list, you can create empty audio parts on the track by clicking the Add button on the toolbar. This will insert a part between the left and right locator.

26.8 Editing MIDI Tracks

Just like audio tracks, MIDI tracks can have two "subitems": Track Data and Automation.

- The Track Data item corresponds to the actual MIDI track in the Project window and can contain MIDI parts (which in turn can contain MIDI events).
- The Automation item corresponds to the automation subtrack in the Project window, and contains the track's automation events (see page 591).

When editing the Track Data, the following parameters are available:

The list columns for MIDI parts:

Parameter	Description
Name	The name of the part.
Start	The start position of the part. Editing this value is the same as moving the part.
End	The end position of the part. Changing this is the same as resizing the part (and will automatically affect the Length value as well).
Length	The length of the part. Changing this resizes the part and automatically changes the End value.

Parameter	Description
Offset	This adjusts the start position of the events within the part. Adjusting this value is the same as sliding the contents of the part in the Project window (see page 140): setting a positive Offset value is the same as sliding the contents to the left, while a negative Offset corresponds to sliding the contents to the right.
Mute	Click in this column to mute or unmute the part.

The list columns for MIDI events:

Parameter	Description
Type	The type of MIDI event. This cannot be changed.
Start	The position of the event. Editing this value is the same as moving the event.
End	This is only used for note events, allowing you to view and edit the end position of a note (thereby resizing it).
Length	This is only used for note events. It shows the length of the note—changing this resizes the note and automatically changes the End value as well.
Data 1	The property of this value depends on the type of MIDI event: For notes, this is the note number (pitch). This is displayed and edited as a note name and an octave number, with the values ranging between C-2 and G8. For Controller events, this is the type of Controller, displayed in words. Note that you can edit this by entering a number—the corresponding Controller type is automatically displayed. For Pitch Bend events, this is the fine adjustment of the bend amount. For Poly Pressure events, this is the note number (pitch). For other event types, this is the value of the event.
Data 2	The property of this value depends on the type of MIDI event: For notes, this is the note-on velocity. For Controller events, this is the value of the event. For Pitch Bend events, this is the coarse bend amount. For Poly Pressure events, this is the amount of pressure. For other event types, this is not used.

Parameter	Description
Channel	The event's MIDI Channel. See page 98.
Comment	This column is used for some event types only, providing an additional comment about the event.

- For SysEx (system exclusive) events, you can only edit the position (Start) in the list. However, clicking the Comment column opens the SysEx Editor, in which you can perform detailed editing of system exclusive events. This and other aspects of working with system exclusive messages are described in a separate chapter—see page 595.

Filtering MIDI Events

When you are editing MIDI in the Project Browser, the large number of different MIDI events displayed can make it hard to find your way. To remedy this, the Filter pop-up menu allows you to select a single event type for display.

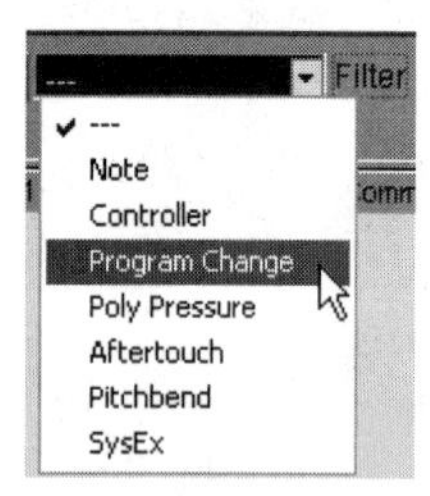

When this option is selected, only Program Change events will be shown in the event display.

To reveal all event types, select the top item ("---") from the menu.

Creating MIDI Parts

When a MIDI track is selected in the Project Structure list, you can create empty MIDI parts on the track by clicking the Add button. This will insert a part between the left and right locator.

Creating MIDI Events

You can use the Project Browser to create new MIDI events, in the following way:

1. **Select a MIDI part in the Project Structure list.**
2. **Move the project cursor to the desired position for the new event.**

3. **Use the Add pop-up above the event display to select which type of MIDI event to add.**

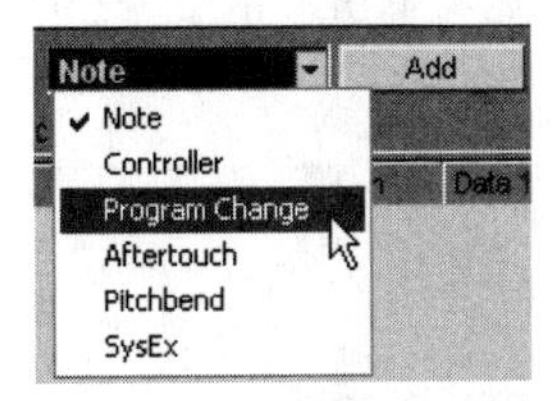

4. **Click the Add button.**

   An event of the selected type is added to the part, at the project cursor position. If the cursor is outside the selected part, the event is added at the beginning of the part.

26.9 Editing Automation Tracks

All kinds of Cubase SX/SL automation (the automation subtracks for MIDI, audio or group channel tracks, the Master automation track or the individual automation tracks for send effects, master effects and VST Instruments) are handled in the same way in the Project Browser. Each Automation item in the Project Structure list will have a number of subentries, one for each automated parameter. Selecting one of these parameters in the Project Structure list shows its automation events in the list:

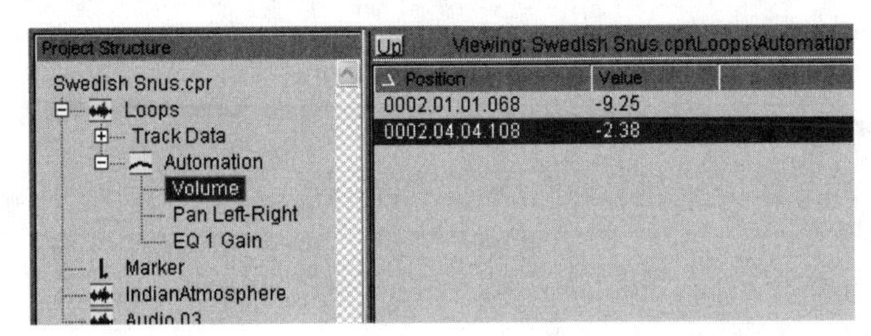

You can use the two columns in the list to edit the position of the events and their values.

26.10 Editing the Video Track

When the Video track is selected in the Project Structure list, the event display lists the video events on the track, with the following parameters:

Column	Description
Name	The name of the video clip that the event refers to.
Start	The start position of the event. Editing this value is the same as moving the event.
End	The end position of the event. Editing this value is the same as resizing the event, and will automatically change the Length value as well.
Length	The length of the event. Editing this value is the same as resizing the event, and will automatically change the End value as well.
Offset	This determines "where in the video clip" the event starts. Note that the event cannot start before the start of the clip, or end after the end of the clip. Thus, if the event already plays the whole video clip, the Offset cannot be adjusted at all.

26.11 Editing the Marker Track

Marker events have the following parameters:

Column	Description
Name	The name of the marker. This can be edited for all markers except the left and right locator.
Start	The position of "regular" markers or the start position of cycle markers.
End	The end positions of cycle markers. Editing this value is the same as resizing the cycle marker, and will automatically change the Length value as well.

Column	Description
Length	The length of cycle markers. Editing this value is the same as resizing the marker, and will automatically change the End value as well.
ID	The number of the marker. For regular (non-cycle) markers, this corresponds to the key commands used for navigating to the markers. For example, if a marker has ID 3, pressing [3] on the computer keyboard will move the song position to that marker. By editing these values, you can assign the most important markers to key commands. Note that you cannot edit the "L" and "R" marker IDs (Left and Right locator) or assign IDs 1 and 2 to markers (since these are reserved for the locators).

When the Marker track is selected, you can insert markers selecting "Marker" or "Cycle Marker" from the Add pop-up menu and clicking the Add button. Regular markers will be added at the current project cursor position while cycle markers will be added between the current left and right locator positions.

26.12 Editing the Tempo Track

When Tempo track is selected in the Project Structure list, the event display shows the events on the Tempo track, with the following parameters:

Parameter	Description
Position	The position of the Tempo event. You cannot move the first event on the Tempo track.
Tempo	The tempo value of the event.
Type	This indicates whether the tempo should jump to the value of the event ("Jump" type) or whether it should change gradually from the previous Tempo event, creating a ramp ("Ramp" type). See page 575.

You can add new Tempo events by clicking the Add button. This creates a Jump-type event with the value 120 bpm, at the project cursor position. Make sure that there is no other tempo event at the current cursor position.

26.13 Editing Time Signatures

When "Signature track" is selected in the Project Structure list, the event display shows the Time Signature events in the project:

Parameter	Description
Position	The position of the event. Note that you cannot move the first Time Signature event.
Signature	The value (time signature) of the event.

You can add new Time Signature events by clicking the Add button. This creates a 4/4 event, at the beginning of the bar closest to the project cursor position. Make sure that there is no other time signature event at the current cursor position.

27 Working with System Exclusive Messages

27.1 Introduction

System Exclusive (Sys Ex) is a special type of MIDI message used to send things that only make sense to a unit of a certain make and type. Every major MIDI manufacturer has its own Sys Ex identity code. System Exclusive messages are typically used for transmitting patch data, i.e. the numbers that make up the settings of one or more sounds in a MIDI instrument.

Cubase SX/SL allows you to record and manipulate System Exclusive data in various ways. This chapter points to various features that help you manage and create System Exclusive data.

27.2 Bulk Dumps

27.2.1 Recording a Bulk Dump in Cubase SX/SL

In any programmable device, all settings are stored as numbers in computer memory. Change those numbers, and you will change the settings.

Normally, MIDI devices allow you to dump (transmit) all or some settings in the device's memory, in the form of MIDI System Exclusive messages. Return these messages, and you get the settings back. This is (among other things) a way of making backup copies of the settings of any instrument.

If your instrument allows the dumping of a few or all of its settings via MIDI by activating some function on the front panel, this dump will most probably be recordable in Cubase SX/SL.

1. **Open the Preferences dialog from the File menu and select the MIDI-Filter page.**

   As described in the section page 101, this allows you to govern which MIDI event types should be recorded and/or thru-put.

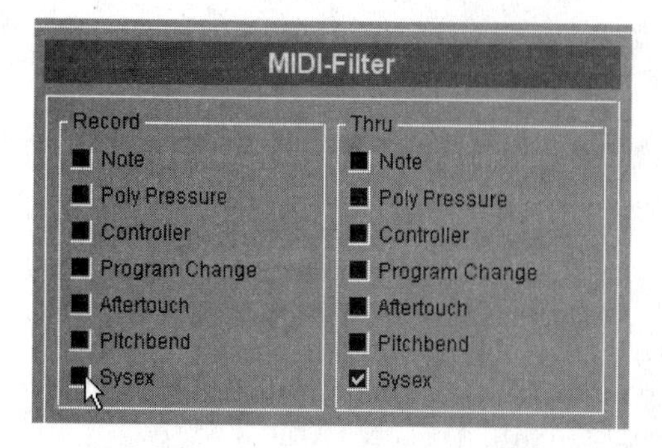

2. **Deactivate the Sysex checkbox in the Record section, but make sure the Sysex checkbox in the Thru section is activated.**

   With this setting (shown in the figure above) SysEx messages will be recorded but not echoed back out to the instrument (which could lead to strange results).

3. **Activate recording on a MIDI track and initiate the dump from the front panel of the instrument.**

4. **When done recording, select the new part and open the List Editor from the MIDI menu.**

   This allows you to check that the System Exclusive dump was recorded—there should be one or several SysEx events in the part/event list.

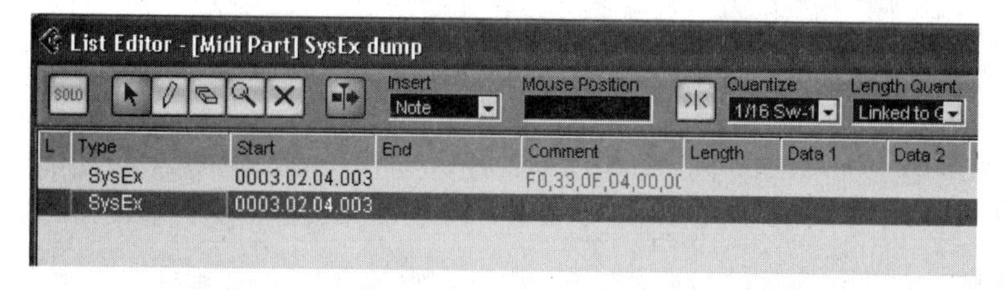

- If your MIDI instrument doesn't offer a way to initiate a dump "by itself", you have to send a Dump Request message from Cubase SX/SL to start the dump. You will then have to use the SysEx Editor (see page 598) to insert the specific Request message (see the instrument's documentation) at the beginning of a MIDI track. When you activate recording, the Request message will be played back (sent to the instrument), the dump will start and be recorded as above.

27.2.2 Transmitting a Bulk Dump Back to a Device

1. **Make sure the MIDI track with the System Exclusive data is routed to the device.**

   You may want to check your device's documentation to find details about which MIDI channel should be used, etc.

2. **Solo the track.**

   This might not be necessary, but it is a good safety measure.

3. **Make sure the device is set up to receive System Exclusive data (often, the reception of SysEx is turned off by default).**

4. **If necessary, put the device in "Standby to Receive System Exclusive" mode.**

5. **Play back the data.**

27.2.3 Some Advice

- Don't transmit more data than you need. If all you want is a single program, don't send them all, it will only make it harder to find the one you want. Usually, you can specify exactly what you want to send.
- If you want the sequencer to dump the pertinent sounds to your instrument each time you load a song, put the SysEx data in a silent "count-in" before the song itself starts.
- If the dump is very short (for instance, a single sound) you can put it in the middle of the Song to re-program a device on the fly. However, if you can achieve the same effect by using Program Change, this is definitely preferable, since less MIDI data is sent and recorded. Some devices may be set up to dump the settings for a sound as soon as you select it on the front panel.
- If you create parts with useful "SysEx dumps", you can put these on a special muted track. When you want to use one of them, drag it to an empty unmuted track and play it back from there.
- Do not transmit several SysEx dumps to several instruments at the same time.
- Make a note of the current Device ID setting of the instrument. If you change this, the instrument may refuse to load the dump later.

27.3 Recording System Exclusive Parameter Changes

Often you can use System Exclusive to remotely change individual settings in a device, open up a filter, select a waveform, change the decay of the reverb etc. Many devices are also capable of transmitting changes made on the front panel as System Exclusive messages. These can be recorded into Cubase SX/SL, and thus incorporated into a regular MIDI recording.

Here's how it works: let's say you open up a filter while playing some notes. In that case, you will record both the notes and the System Exclusive messages generated by your opening of the filter. When you play it back, the sound changes exactly like it did when you recorded it.

1. **Open the Preferences dialog from the File menu, select the MIDI-Filter page and make sure that System Exclusive gets recorded.**
2. **Make sure the instrument is actually set to transmit front panel control movements as System Exclusive data.**
3. **Record normally.**

   When you're done, you can check that the events were recorded properly in the List Editor.

27.4 Editing System Exclusive Messages

While System Exclusive events are shown in the List Editor/Project Browser, their entire content is not (only the beginning of the message is displayed in the Comment column for the event). Furthermore, you cannot edit the event (other than moving it) as you can with other event types in the List Editor.

Instead, you use the MIDI SysEx Editor for this.

- **To open the SysEx editor for an event, click in the Comments column for the event in the List Editor/Project Browser.**

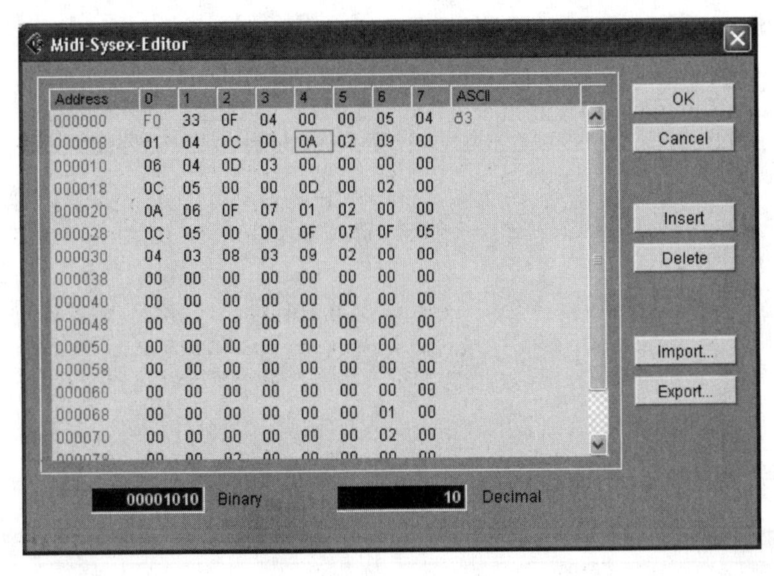

The display shows the entire message on one or several lines. All System Exclusive messages always begin with F0 and end with F7 with a number of arbitrary bytes in between. If the message contains more bytes than fit on one line, it continues on the next. The Address indication to the left helps you find out on which position in the message a certain value resides.

Selecting and Viewing Values

To select a value, either click on it or use the cursor keys. The selected byte is indicated in various formats:

- In the main display, values are shown in Hexadecimal.
- To the right of this, values are shown as ASCII.
- At the bottom of the dialog, the selected value is shown in binary and decimal formats.

Editing a Value

The selected value can be edited directly in the main display or in the decimal and binary displays. Just click on it and type in the desired value as usual.

Adding and Deleting Bytes

Using the Insert and Delete buttons, or their corresponding computer keyboard keys, you can add and delete bytes from the message. Inserted data will appear *before* the selection.

Importing and Exporting Data

The Import and Export buttons allow you to get SysEx data from disk and to export the edited data into a file. The file format used is called "Raw SysEx" (.SYX), which means that data is saved exactly as is, in a binary file. Only the first dump in a "SYX" file will be loaded.

This format should not be confused with MIDI Files.

28 Export Audio Mixdown

28.1 Background

The Export Audio Mixdown function allows you to mix down all audio tracks, complete with effects and automation, into one or several audio files, in one of several file formats. The following rules apply:

- All audio you hear on playback will be included in the mixdown file!
  You can however choose whether you want effects and automation included in the mixdown, as described below.
- Cubase SX/SL can export to a number of different file formats, each with different options.
  See page 603.
- If you are working with multi channel audio (surround—Cubase SX only), Cubase SX allows you to export all channels at once, either as separate files or as one multi channel audio file.
  The file(s) can then be imported into stand-alone encoding applications, etc. See page 604.
- MIDI tracks are not included in the mixdown!
  To make a complete mixdown containing both MIDI and audio, you first need to record all your MIDI music to audio tracks (by connecting the outputs of your MIDI instruments to your audio inputs and recording, as with any other sound source).

28.2 Mixing Down to an Audio File

1. **Set up the left and right locator to encompass the area that you want to mix down.**
2. **Set up your tracks, so that they play back the way you want.**

   This includes muting unwanted tracks or parts, making manual mixer settings and/or activating the R (Read) automation buttons for some or all mixer channels.
3. **Pull down the File menu and select "Audio Mixdown..." from the Export submenu.**

   The Export Audio Mixdown dialog appears.

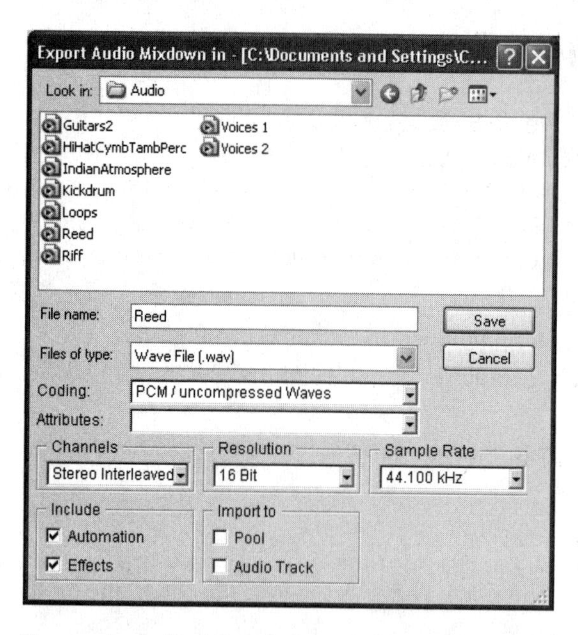

The upper half of this dialog is a standard file dialog, while the lower half contains file format options and settings for the mixdown function. Note that the available settings and options differ depending on the selected file format (see page 603).

4. **If you want to include any activated Mixer automation, activate the "Include Automation" checkbox.**

5. **If you want to include insert effects, send effects and master effects, activate the "Include Effects" checkbox.**

6. **Select a file format with the file type pop-up menu.**

7. **If you want to automatically import the resulting audio file back into Cubase SX/SL, activate the "Import to" checkboxes.**

   If you activate the "Pool" checkbox, a clip referring to the file will appear in the Pool. Activating the "Audio Track" checkbox as well will create an audio event that plays the clip, and place it on a new audio track, starting at the left locator.

- The Import options are only available if you have selected one of the following file formats: AIFF, Wave (uncompressed) or Broadcast Wave files.

---

8. **Make additional settings for the file to be created.**

   This includes selecting stereo or mono, sample rate, resolution, quality, etc. The available options depend on the selected file format—see page 603.

9. Select a folder and a name for the audio file to be created.

- With some file formats, there is a Stereo Split option (see page 604). If this is selected, two files will be created, one for each side. The two files will have the same name, but with the letter "L" appended for the left channel file and "R" for the right channel file.

10.Click Save.

A dialog with a progress bar is displayed while the audio file is created. If you change your mind during the file creation, you can click the Abort button to abort the operation.

- **If you have activated the "Import to" options, the file will be imported back into the project.**

When playing back the re-imported file in Cubase SX/SL, remember to mute the original tracks so that you really hear the true result.

28.3 File Format Specifics

The following pages describe the different export file formats, and their options and settings.

28.3.1 AIFF Files

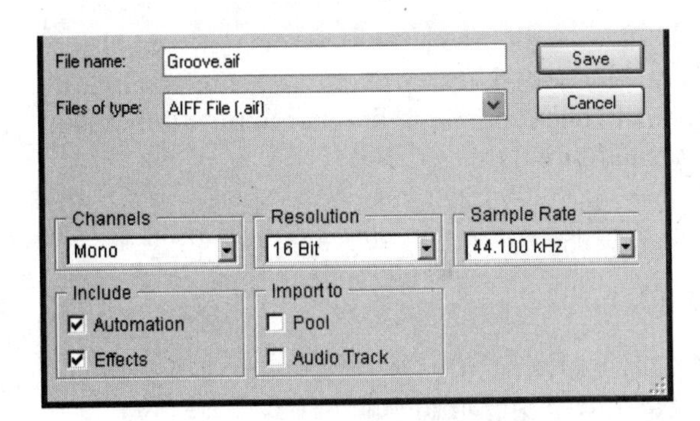

AIFF stands for Audio Interchange File Format, a standard defined by Apple Computer Inc. AIFF files have the extension ".aif" and are used on most computer platforms. When AIFF is selected as export file format, the following settings are available:

Resolution

Allows you to select 8, 16, 24 bit or 32 bit (float) files.

- If the file is an "intermediate mixdown" that you plan to re-import and continue working on in Cubase SX/SL, we recommend that you select the 32 bit (float) option.
  32 bit (float) is a very high resolution (the same resolution as used internally for audio processing in Cubase SX/SL), and the audio files will be twice the size of 16 bit files.
- If you are making a mixdown for CD burning, you should use the 16 bit option, as CD audio is always 16 bit.
  In this case, we recommend that you activate the UV-22HR/UV22 dithering plug-in (see page 229). This reduces the effects of quantization noise and artifacts from being introduced when converting the audio down to 16 bit.
- 8 bit resolution should only be used if required, since it will result in limited audio quality.
  Examples of situations when 8 bit audio may be suitable are some multimedia applications, etc.

Channels

Option	Description
Mono	The audio is mixed down to mono.
Stereo Split	Two mono files are created, one for each side of the stereo mix. The files will have the name you specify in the dialog, but with "L" and "R" added, respectively. Select this format if you plan to use the resulting file in another application, that doesn't support stereo interleaved files. If you plan to re-import the file into Cubase SX/SL, we recommend that you use the Stereo Interleaved option instead, since Cubase SX/SL doesn't automatically handle stereo split files as one entity.
Stereo Interleaved	A stereo audio file is created. This is the recommended stereo option if you want to re-import the file into Cubase SX/SL.

Option	Description
Multi Channel Split (Cubase SX only)	This option is only available if you are working with a multi channel (Surround) mix. Exporting with this option selected will create one mono audio file for each Master channel, which you later can import into other applications. For example, if you have selected the "5.1 Surround" preset in the Master Setup dialog (see page 279), there are six Master channels. This option will then be called "6 Chan. Split" and result in six mono audio files.
Multi Channel Interleaved (Cubase SX only)	This option is only available if you are working with a multi channel (Surround) mix. Exporting with this option selected will create a single audio file containing all Master channels, which you later can import into other applications. For example, if you have selected the "5.1 Surround" preset in the Master Setup dialog (see page 279), there are six Master channels. This option will then be called "6 Chan. Interleaved" and result in a single audio file, containing six channels. This is not a very common file format—make sure the receiving application can import multi-channel audio files.

Sample Rate

Allows you to select a sample rate for the exported audio file. In most cases, you should select the sample rate set for the project, since a lower sample rate will degrade the audio quality (mainly reducing the high frequency content) and selecting a higher sample rate will only increase the file size, without adding to audio quality. However, you should also consider the future usage of the file; for example, if you plan to import the file into another application, you should make sure to select a sample rate supported by that application.

- If you are making a mixdown for CD burning, you should select 44.100 kHz, since this is the sample rate used on audio CDs.

28.3.2 Wave Files

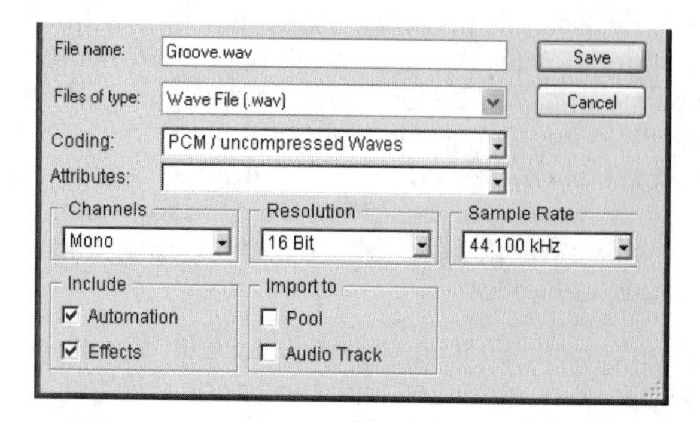

Wave files have the extension ".wav" and are the most common file format on the PC platform. Wave files can be uncompressed or compressed, as described below. For uncompressed Wave files (the most common choice), the following settings are available:

Channels

Allows you to select mono or stereo files, with the same options as for AIFF files (see page 604). You can also export multi-channel Wave files using the new multi-channel wave format extension from Microsoft, in which speaker information is included (so that a certain channel is identified as belonging to a certain speaker).

Resolution

The bit resolution of the file, with the same options as for AIFF files (see page 604).

Sample Rate

The options are the same as for AIFF files. See page 605.

Coding

The Coding pop-up menu allows you to select a compression scheme for the Wave file, creating smaller files (with a loss of audio quality).

- Which options are available depends on the installed and activated codecs in the ACM (Audio Compression Manager) under Windows.
  See the operating system documentation for details.

- When a compression option is selected, not all Channels, Resolution and Sample Rate options may be available (depending on the selected compression scheme). The Attributes pop-up menu displays the currently selected properties for the file.
- For regular, uncompressed Wave files, select "PCM / uncompressed Waves".

28.3.3 MPEG Layer 3 Files (Cubase SX only)

- Cubase SL users can export to mp3 20 times as a "trial" feature (fully functional), after which the function is disabled.
  When the mp3 format is selected, a text at the bottom of the Export Audio Mixdown dialog shows you how many remaining encodings you have left.
  You can upgrade your Cubase SL copy to include unlimited MP3 encoding by clicking the "Order now" link in the lower right corner of the dialog (this takes you to Steinberg's online store on the web—a working internet connection is required).

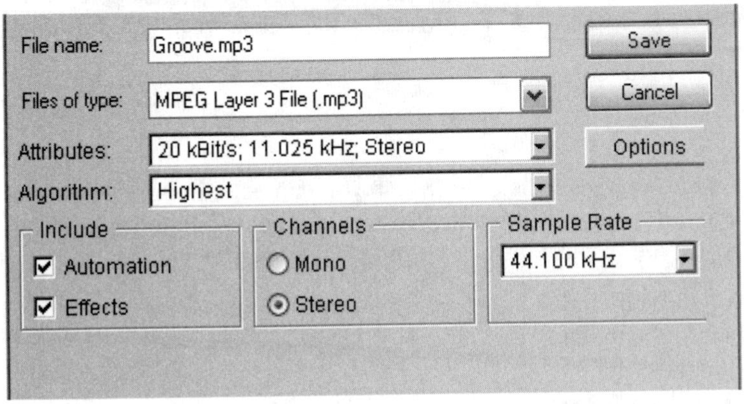

MPEG Layer 3 files have the extension ".mp3". By use of advanced audio compression algorithms, mp3 files can be made very small, maintaining good audio quality.

The following options are available for MPEG Layer 3 files:

Channels

Use the radio buttons to select mono or stereo files. This setting affects which options are available on the Attributes pop-up menu (see below).

Sample Rate

Determines the frequency range of the audio—the lower the sample rate, the lower the highest audible frequency in the audio. This setting will also affect which options are available on the Attributes pop-up menu, as described below.

Attributes

This pop-up menu allows you to select a bit rate for the mp3 file. As a rule, the higher the bit rate, the better the audio quality and the larger the file. For stereo audio, 128 kBit/s is often considered to result in "good" audio quality.

- Note that the available options on this pop-up menu depend on the Channels and Sample Rate settings.
  This is because for mono audio and/or low sample rates, there is no point in using the highest bit rates—they would simply create larger files without adding to audio quality.

Algorithm

These options determine the "depth" of the encoding algorithm and thus the quality of the resulting file. In the "Highest" mode, the encoding will take the longest time, while in the "Fast" mode, the audio quality may be lower. The file size is not affected by these options.

Options

Clicking the Options button opens a dialog in which you can enter information about the file. This additional information (called the ID3 tag) will be embedded as text strings in the file, and can be displayed by some mp3 playback applications.

- For the information to be included in the file, you need to activate the "Insert Options" checkbox in the dialog.

28.3.4 Ogg Vorbis Files

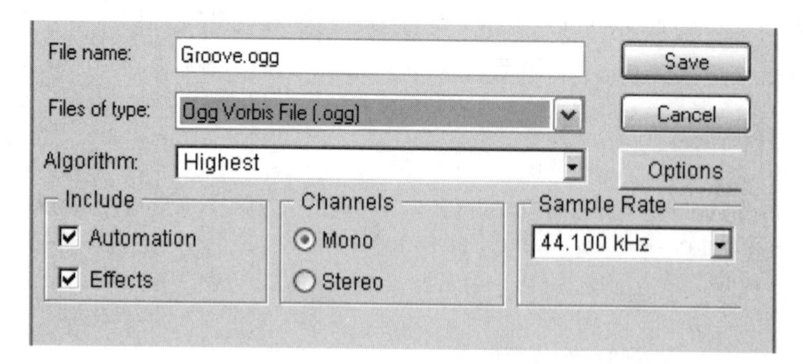

Ogg Vorbis is an open, patent-free audio encoding and streaming technology, offering compressed audio files (extension ".ogg") of small size but with comparatively high audio quality.

The following options are available for Ogg Vorbis files:

Channels

Use the radio buttons to select mono or stereo files.

Sample Rate

Determines the frequency range of the audio—the lower the sample rate, the lower the highest audible frequency in the audio.

Algorithm

These options determine the quality of the encoding. The Ogg Vorbis encoder uses variable bit rate encoding, and the Algorithm setting determines between which limits the bit rate will vary. Generally speaking the better the Algorithm setting, the higher the sound quality but also the larger the files.

Options

Clicking the Options button opens a dialog in which you can enter information about the file, as when creating mp3 files.

- For the information to be included in the file, you need to activate the "Insert Options" checkbox in the dialog.

28.3.5 Real Audio V5 and G2 Files

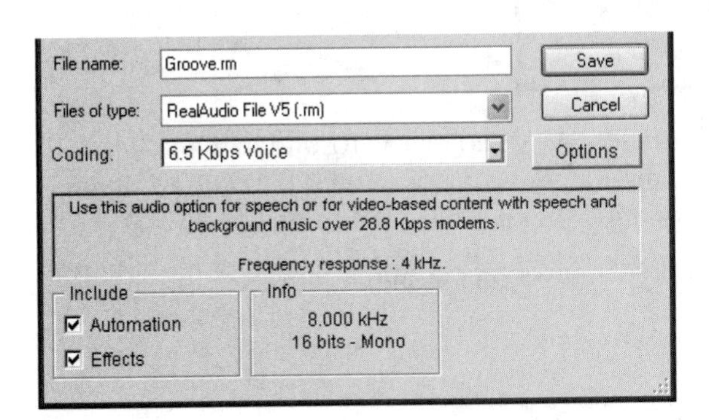

Real Audio files allow very high compression rates and can therefore be made very small. This makes the format especially useful for downloading and streaming multimedia from the internet. The files have the extension ".rm".

The following options are available for Real Audio files:

Coding and Content

By selecting an option from the Coding pop-up menu, you specify the desired audio quality for the file. In the Real Audio G2 format, this information is divided in two pop-up menus: Coding (determining the bit rate) and Content (specifying the typical audio content—voice, music, etc.)

When you select a Coding/Content, a descriptive text appears in the field below the pop-up menu, describing the suitable use of the selected format.

- Note that the choice of mono or stereo is included in the Coding/Content options.

Options

Clicking the Options button opens a dialog in which you can select one or more modes (each explained in the dialog) for the file. You can also enter information about the file. These text strings will be embedded in the file and can be displayed by some Real Audio playback applications.

28.3.6 Windows Media Audio Files

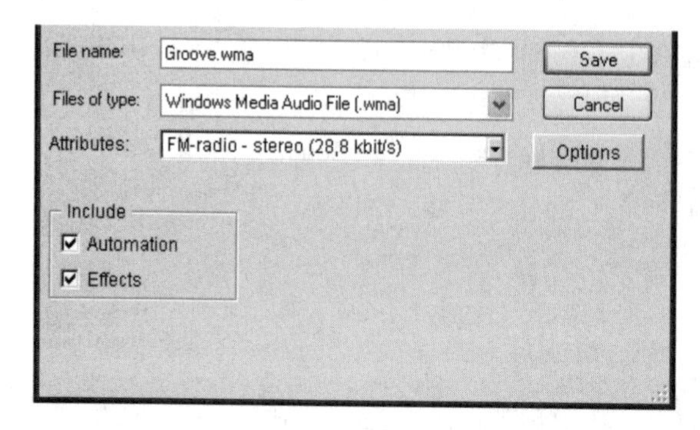

Windows Media Audio is an audio format developed by Microsoft Inc. Due to advanced audio compression algorithms, Windows Media Audio files can be made very small, maintaining good audio quality. The files have the extension ".wma".

The following options are available for Windows Media Audio files:

Attributes

This pop-up menu allows you to select a bit rate for the WMA file. As a rule, the higher the bit rate, the better the audio quality and the larger the file. For stereo audio, 96 kBit/s is often considered to give "good" audio quality.

Options

Clicking the Options button opens a dialog in which you can enter information about the title and author of the file, as well as copyright information. These text strings will be embedded in the file and can be displayed by some Windows Media Audio playback applications.

28.3.7 Broadcast Wave Files

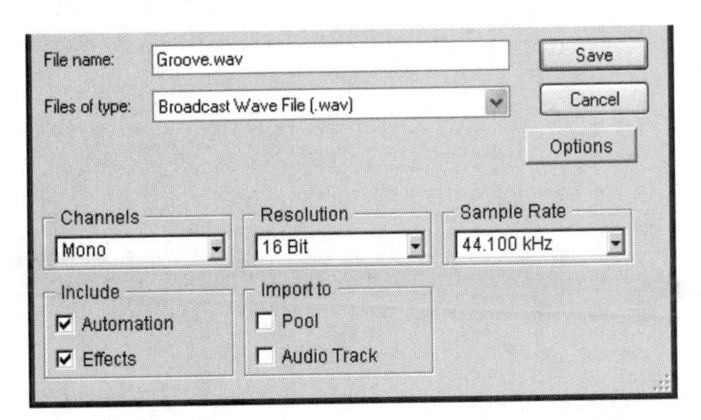

Audio-wise, Broadcast Wave files are the same as regular Wave files. They have the same options as Wave files, with the following additions:

- There are no Coding (compression) options for Broadcast Waves.
- Clicking the Options button opens a dialog in which you can specify a number of text strings to be included in the file.
  This allows you to embed information in the file, such as author, description etc. Furthermore, a Timecode position is included in the file, allowing you to insert exported audio at the correct position in other applications, video projects, etc. By default, the Timecode position is set to the start position of the exported audio in the project (i.e. the left locator position), but you can adjust this in the Options dialog if needed.

- You can enter default text strings for author, description and reference in the Preferences dialog (Audio—Broadcast Wave page).
  These will automatically appear in the Options dialog when Broadcast Wave dialog is selected. For example, this saves you from having to enter the author name each time you export, if it is the same.

29 Synchronization

29.1 Background

29.1.1 What Is Synchronization?

Synchronization is said to exist when you make two pieces of equipment agree on time or tempo. You can establish synchronization between Cubase SX/SL and a number of other types of devices, including tape recorders and video decks, but also MIDI devices that "play back", such as other sequencers, drum machines, "workstation sequencers" etc.

When you set up a synchronization system you must decide which unit is the *master*. All other devices are then *slaved* to this unit, which means they will adjust their playback speed to the master's.

Cubase SX/SL as a Slave

When a synchronization signal is coming in to Cubase SX/SL, from another device (such as a tape recorder, video recorder etc.), this device is the master and Cubase SX/SL is the slave. Cubase SX/SL will adjust its playback to the other device.

Cubase SX/SL as a Master

When you set up Cubase SX/SL to transmit synchronization information to other devices, Cubase SX/SL is the master and the other devices are the slaves; they will adjust their playback to Cubase SX/SL.

Cubase SX/SL—Both Master and Slave

Cubase SX/SL is a very capable synchronization device. It can operate as both a master and a slave at the same time. For example, Cubase SX/SL might be slaved to a tape recorder transmitting timecode, while at the same time transmitting MIDI Clock to a drum machine, acting as a master for that.

- Note: The VST System Link feature (with which you can synchronize separate computers running Cubase SX/SL or Nuendo) is described in a separate chapter. See page 629.

29.1.2 Timecode, MIDI Clock and Word Clock

Basically there are three types of synchronization signals for audio, timecode, MIDI clock and word clock:

Timecode (SMPTE, EBU, MTC, VITC etc.)

Timecode appears in a number of guises. No matter which "format" it has, it always supplies a "clock on the wall" type of synchronization, that is, a synchronization related to hours, minutes, seconds and two smaller units called "frames" and "sub-frames".

- LTC (SMPTE, EBU) is the audio version of timecode. This means that it can be recorded on the audio track of an audio or video recorder.
- VITC is the video format timecode, that is it is stored in the actual video image.
- MTC is the MIDI version of timecode, transmitted in MIDI cables.
- ADAT sync (Alesis) is only used with the ASIO Positioning Protocol, see later in this chapter.

For the ASIO Positioning Protocol, other high precision timecode formats may also be supported.

Format Recommendations for Timecode—without ASIO Positioning Protocol

When synchronizing your system to external timecode, via a synchronizer, the most common timecode format is MTC. Contrary to some reports you might have heard, MTC delivers good precision for external sync. This is due to the fact that the operating system can "time stamp" incoming MIDI messages, which increases precision.

Format Recommendations for Timecode—with ASIO Positioning Protocol

- LTC and VITC are the formats with the highest precision and are recommended when available.
- MTC is the next best option and probably the most common choice, since few audio hardware solutions have built in LTC or VITC readers. However, LTC and VITC offer even higher precision when available.

MIDI Clock

MIDI Clock is a tempo based type of synchronization signal, that is it is related to the number of "beats per minute". MIDI Clock signals are suitable for synchronizing two devices that agree on tempo, such as for example Cubase SX/SL and a drum machine.

- MIDI Clock is not suitable as a master sync source for an application like Cubase SX/SL. Therefore Cubase SX/SL will transmit MIDI Clock signals to other devices, but it will not receive MIDI Clock.

Word Clock

Word clock is basically a replacement for the sample rate clock in for example an audio card. Word clock hence runs at the same rate as the sample rate in the audio, 44.1kHz, 48kHz etc.

Word clock does not contain any position information, it is only a "simple" signal for clocking the audio at its sample rate.

Word clock comes in many formats, analog on coaxial cable, digital as part of an S/PDIF, AES/EBU or ADAT audio signal, etc.

29.1.3 Synchronizing the Transport Versus Synchronizing Audio

How Timing is Handled in a Non-synchronized System

Let's first look at the situation where Cubase SX/SL is not synchronized to any external source.

Any digital playback system has an internal clock that ultimately affects the playback speed and stability, and PC audio hardware is no exception. This clock is *extremely* stable.

When Cubase SX/SL is playing back with no external synchronization, all playback is internally synchronized to the internal digital audio clock, to ensure synchronization between digital audio and MIDI.

Synchronizing Cubase SX/SL's Playback

Let's assume now that we use external timecode synchronization, with Cubase SX/SL. For example, we might synchronize playback to a tape recorder.

Timecode coming from an analog tape recorder will always vary slightly in speed. Different timecode generators and different tape recorders will also supply timecode with slight differences in speed. In addition, the shuttling of tape mechanisms due to overdubs and re-recordings can cause the physical tape to wear and stretch, which affects the speed of the timecode.

If you set up Cubase SX/SL to sync to incoming timecode, it will vary its overall playback speed to compensate for such fluctuations in the speed of the timecode—that's the whole purpose of synchronization.

What Happens with the Digital Audio?

The fact that Cubase SX/SL's playback is synchronized to the timecode does not affect the playback of the digital audio. It still relies on the perfectly stable, built-in clock in the audio hardware.

As you may understand by now, problems will appear when the perfectly stable digital audio gets related to the slightly varying speed of a system synchronized to timecode.

The playback timing of each event will *not* be in total accordance with the tape or the MIDI playback, since the playback speed of the audio is determined by the digital audio hardware's built-in clock.

Resolving to Word Clock

The solution to this problem is to use one external clock for all components in the system. One master clock is used to derive whatever type of clock signal each component in the system needs. For example, something called a house clock can be used to generate sample rate clocks for the digital audio hardware and timecode for Cubase SX/SL. This ensures all components in the system use the same reference source for their timing.

Synchronizing digital audio to external clocks running at sample rate is often called "resolving" or "synchronizing to word clock".

If you aim to perform synchronization to external signals, we strongly recommend that you obtain proper synchronization equipment. This encompasses:

- An audio card that can be slaved to external word clock.
- A synchronizer that can read timecode (and possibly house clock) and generate the required sync signals from that, such as the Steinberg TimeLock Pro.

or…

- An audio system with complete built-in synchronization possibilities, preferably supporting the ASIO Positioning Protocol.

Using Timecode without Word Clock

Of course, it is possible to set up a synchronization system where you lock Cubase SX/SL to timecode without using word clock. However, please note that the timing of audio vs. MIDI cannot be guaranteed and that fluctuations in speed in the incoming timecode will not affect the playback of audio events. This means that synchronizing to timecode may work in the following situations:

- **When the timecode was originally generated by the audio card itself.**
- **When the source providing the timecode is extremely stable (such as a digital video system, a digital tape recorder or another computer).**
- **When you remain synchronized to that same stable source throughout the entire process, both while recording and playing back audio.**

29.1.4 About the ASIO Positioning Protocol (APP)

The ASIO Positioning Protocol is a technology that expands on the type of sync described above and makes *sample accurate positioning* possible.

When transferring audio digitally between devices, it is important that synchronization using word clock and timecode is *completely* correlated. If not, the audio will not be recorded at the exact intended (sample accurate) position, which can cause various types of problems, such as inaccurately positioned audio material, clicks and pops etc.

A typical situation is when transferring material from a digital multi-track tape recorder to Cubase SX/SL (for editing) and then back again. If you do not have sample accurate synchronization set up, you cannot be sure that the material will appear in its exact original position, when transferred back to the tape recorder.

In order to take advantage of the ASIO Positioning Protocol, your audio hardware must be suitably equipped and the functionality must be included in the ASIO driver for the hardware.

An example of a system for doing sample accurate transfers, would be transferring audio tracks from an Alesis ADAT to Cubase SX/SL. Here the ADAT will be the sync master (though it doesn't necessarily have to be). It provides both the digital audio (with an inherent word clock) and positional information (timecode) via its ADAT sync protocol. The master clock is generated by the ADAT itself.

Hardware and Software Requirements for APP

- Your computer audio hardware (in our example above this would be an ADAT card in your computer) must support all the functionality required for the ASIO Positioning Protocol. That is, it must be able to read the digital audio and the corresponding positional information from the external device.

- There must be an ASIO 2.0 driver for the audio hardware.
- For resolving to external timecode, the audio hardware must have a timecode reader/writer on-board.
- For information about which audio hardware models currently support APP, see the Steinberg web site (www.steinberg.net).

● The ASIO Positioning Protocol exploits the specific advantage of having an audio card that has a built-in timecode reader. With such a card and the ASIO Positioning Protocol, you can achieve constant sample accurate synchronization between the audio source and Cubase SX/SL.

29.1.5 Machine Control

Cubase SX/SL can control external tape transports and similar devices via MIDI Machine Control. This allows you to operate an external tape transport from Cubase SX/SL's Transport panel. That is, Cubase SX/SL can make the tape recorder locate to a certain position, start, stop, rewind etc.

About Sync and Machine Control

Controlling tape transports is a two-way process:

- Cubase SX/SL sends out machine control commands to the tape recorder, asking it to locate to a certain position and activate playback etc.
- The tape recorder locates to the requested position, starts and delivers timecode back to Cubase SX/SL, to which Cubase SX/SL is synchronized.

Even though it appears as if Cubase SX/SL is controlling the tape recorder completely, it is important to remember that in this setup, Cubase SX/SL is still being synchronized to the external tape transport, not vice versa.

Also note that the two processes of sync and machine control are completely separated, in terms of protocols used. You can for example synchronize to MTC while sending out transport commands via MMC.

About MIDI Machine Control (MMC)

This is a standard MIDI protocol for controlling tape transports. There are a number of tape recorders and hard disk recording systems on the market that support this protocol. Cubase SX/SL implements three MMC commands: Start, Stop and Locate.

29.2 Window Overview

29.2.1 The Synchronization Setup Dialog Box

This dialog box is used for setting up everything that has to do with Cubase SX/SL's synchronization to other units. You reach it from the Transport menu.

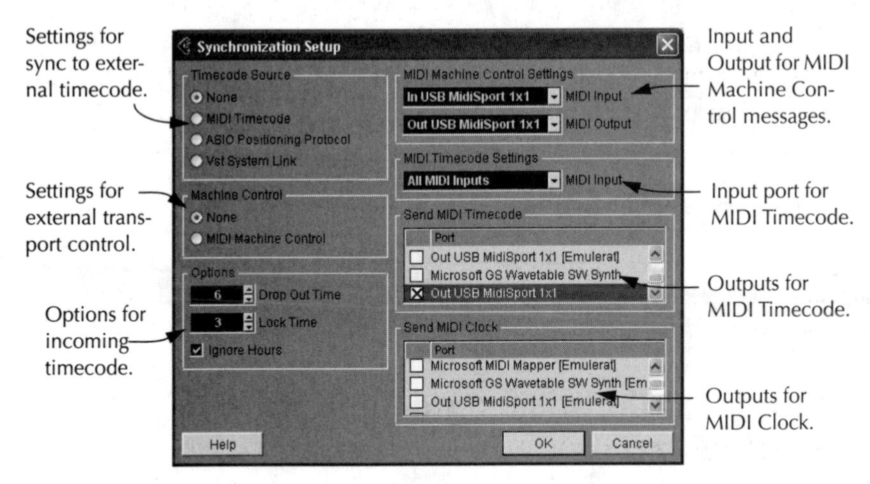

29.3 Operations

29.3.1 Making Connections and Basic Settings

- The descriptions below are for a basic setup with a separate synchronizer and audio card. Depending on your exact situation and requirements for communication with external devices, there are endless variations on this theme. Please consult your dealer for more detailed recommendations.

The following connections are required for external sync via a synchronizer, including resolving of the audio card. For details on audio card and synchronizer settings and connections, see the included manuals.

- **Route the master clock signal (LTC, VITC, etc.) to an input on the synchronizer.**
- **Connect the word clock output on the synchronizer to an input on the audio card.**

- **Connect the MIDI Timecode (MTC) on the synchronizer to the corresponding input on the computer.**
- **Set up the synchronizer and make sure the frame rate settings are in accordance with the master clock.**

  For more information on frame rates, see page 625.

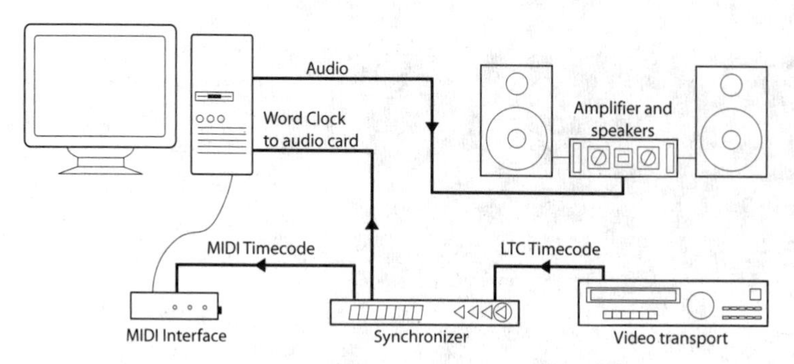

A typical synchronization setup.

29.3.2 Setting Up the Audio Card for External Synchronization

1. **Open the Device Setup dialog from the Devices menu and select the item VST Multitrack from the list to the left.**
2. **Click the Control Panel button to open the card's proprietary setup dialog.**

   If this card is accessed via a special ASIO driver (as opposed to MME or Direct X), this dialog is provided by the card, not by Cubase SX/SL. Hence the settings vary with the card brand and model.
3. **Adjust the settings as recommended by the card manufacturer, then close the dialog.**

   The dialog may also contain various diagnostic tools that allow you to verify for example whether word clock is arriving correctly.
4. **From the Clock Source pop-up, select the input to which you routed the word clock signal.**

   This pop-up may not be used if you selected an input in the Control Panel dialog instead.

29.3.3 Setting Up Cubase SX/SL for External Sync to Timecode

1. **In the Synchronization dialog, set Timecode Source to MIDI Timecode or ASIO Positioning Protocol (only if your hardware is ASIO Positioning Protocol compatible).**
2. **For MIDI Timecode, use the "MIDI Timecode Settings—MIDI Input" pop-up menu to select an input for the timecode.**

   If you are using the ASIO Positioning Protocol this is not required, since the timecode is then coming in directly via your audio hardware.

Sync to timecode activated

The MIDI Input for the timecode

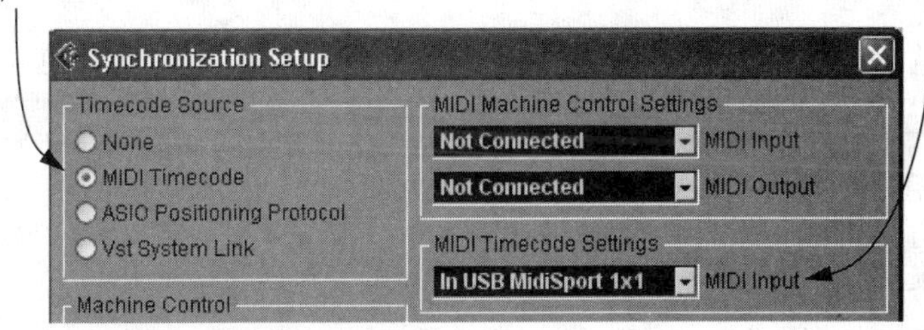

Sync settings for MIDI Timecode.

3. **Close the Synchronization Setup dialog and instead open the Project Setup dialog from the Project menu.**
4. **Use the Start value to set which frame on the external device (e.g. a video tape) should correspond to the beginning of the project.**

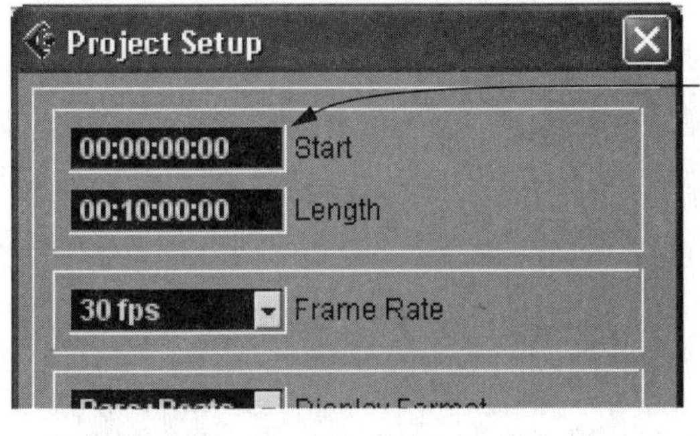

Set this to the timecode position where you want the project to start.

5. **Close the Project Setup dialog.**
6. **On the Transport panel, activate the Sync button (or select Sync Online from the Transport menu).**

7. **Start the tape (or video, or…) that contains the timecode. Cubase SX/SL starts playing when it receives timecode with a position "higher" than, or equal to, the Project Start frame.**

You can wind the device that sends the timecode to any position and start from there.

- When the device with the timecode is stopped, you can use the Cubase SX/SL transport controls as you normally do, when it is not synchronized.

You should also look into the Sync Options, see page 626.

The Sync Indicator

On the Transport panel you can check the status of incoming timecode by observing the sync indicator. It switches between "Offline" (not waiting for sync), "Idle" (ready for sync but no signal is coming in), and "Lock xx" (where xx is indicating the frame rate of the incoming signal).

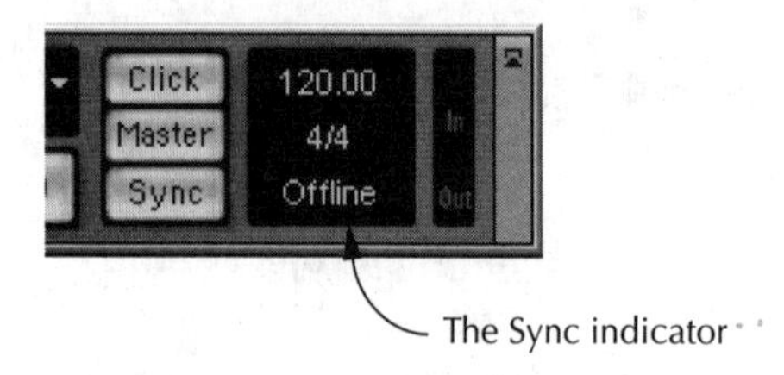

The Sync indicator

29.3.4 Synchronizing Other Equipment to Cubase SX/SL

You may have other MIDI devices that you want to synchronize to Cubase SX/SL. There are two types of synchronization that Cubase SX/SL can transmit: MIDI Clock and MIDI Timecode.

Transmitting MIDI Clock

If you transmit MIDI Clock to a device supporting this type of synchronization signal, the other device will follow Cubase SX/SL's tempo. The tempo setting in the other device is of no relevance. Instead it plays at the same tempo as Cubase SX/SL. If the device also reacts to Song Position Pointers (which Cubase SX/SL transmits) it will follow when you wind, rewind and locate using the Cubase SX/SL Transport panel.

- MIDI Clock transport commands include "Start", "Stop" and "Continue". However, some MIDI equipment (e.g. some drum machines) do not recognize the "Continue" command. If this is the case with your equipment, activate the option "Always Use MIDI Clock Start" in the Preferences (Transport page).
  When this is activated, only the Start command is used.

Transmitting MIDI Timecode

If you transmit MIDI Timecode to a device supporting this type of synchronization signal, the device will synchronize time-wise to Cubase SX/SL, that is, the time displays on Cubase SX/SL's Transport panel and on the other device will agree. When you wind and locate Cubase SX/SL and then activate playback, the other device will follow from the same position (if it has this capability and is set up for it!).

Setting Up

1. **Connect the desired MIDI Outputs from Cubase SX/SL to the device(s) that you plan to synchronize.**
2. **Open the Synchronization Setup dialog from the Transport menu.**
3. **Activate the sync outputs by using the corresponding checkboxes in the lower right part of the dialog.**

   You can output any combination of MIDI Timecode and MIDI Clock to any combination of outputs (however, you probably don't want to send MTC and MIDI Clock to the same output).

- Some MIDI Interfaces will automatically send MIDI Clock to all MIDI outputs, regardless of the MIDI Clock Port selection you make in Cubase SX/SL. If this is the case, you should only select one MIDI Clock Port (consult the documentation of the MIDI Interface if in doubt).

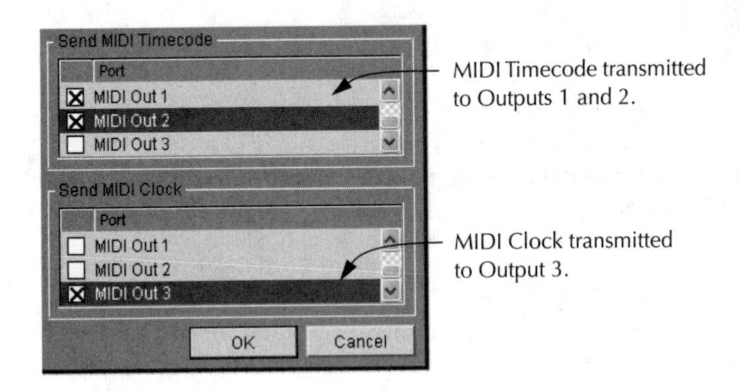

4. **Set the other device(s) to their "external synchronization" mode (or some other mode with a similar name) and activate playback on them if necessary.**
5. **Activate playback in Cubase SX/SL, and the other device(s) will follow.**

29.3.5 Machine Control

Machine control commands can be sent using the MIDI Machine Control (MMC) protocol. Proceed as follows:

1. **Set up and test basic timecode synchronization, as described earlier in this chapter.**
2. **Connect a MIDI Out on your MIDI interface to MIDI In on the tape recorder (or similar device).**

   If you have not already done so (when setting up for MIDI Timecode), also connect a MIDI cable from the MIDI Output on the tape recorder to a MIDI In on the computer.
3. **Make sure you have timecode recorded on the tape recorder, and that it is set up to utilize MMC.**
4. **Open the Synchronization Setup dialog on the Transport menu in Cubase SX/SL.**
5. **Select MIDI Machine Control from the Machine Control section of the dialog.**
6. **Select the correct MIDI In- and Outputs from the MIDI Machine Control Settings pop-ups.**

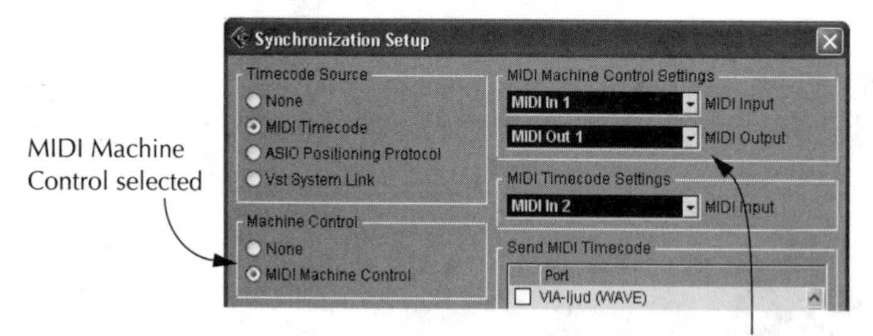

7. **Open the Preferences dialog from the File menu, select the MIDI Filter section and make sure Sysex is activated in the Thru section.**

   This is necessary since MMC uses two-way communication (the tape recorder "replies" to the MMC messages it receives from Cubase SX/SL). By filtering out Sysex Thru, you ensure that these MMC System Exclusive replies are not echoed back to the tape recorder.

8. Open the Project Setup dialog from the Project menu.

9. As when synchronizing without using transport control, use the Start value to specify which frame on the tape should correspond to the beginning of the project.

10.Close the Project Setup dialog.

11.On the Transport panel, activate the Sync button.

12.Press play on the external tape transport and let the tape roll for a few seconds, so that Cubase SX/SL can "learn" about the timecode positions on the tape. Stop the tape transport.

13.Now activate play from Cubase SX/SL.

The external tape transport should wind the tape to a position just before the project cursor in Cubase SX/SL and go into Play. After a short while, Cubase SX/SL should start, in sync.

Try to Stop, Fast Forward and Rewind from Cubase SX/SL and activate Play from different positions in the project. The tape transport should follow.

- Each time you start up your external tape transport, you may have to activate play from its front panel for a couple of seconds. If you don't, Cubase SX/SL has no chance of "knowing" where to wind the first time, since it doesn't know what timecode is recorded on the tape.

Whenever you want to turn off the synchronization between the tape recorder and Cubase SX/SL, simply deactivate Sync on the Transport panel.

29.4 Options

29.4.1 Making Project Settings

About Frame Rates

The frame rate is the number of frames per second in a film or on a video tape. Just as there is always sixty seconds to a minute, there is always a certain number of frames to each second. However, the frame rate used varies with the type of media (film or video), which country the video tape has been produced in, and other circumstances.

In the Project Setup dialog are two settings for frame rates:

- **The Frame Rate pop-up is automatically adjusted to the frame rate of the incoming timecode.**

  There is an exception to this when you are synchronizing Cubase SX/SL to MIDI Timecode: If you have selected 29.97 fps or 30 dfps as Frame Rate in Cubase SX/SL, this selection will be kept, since these frame rates are not included in the MTC format.

- **The Display Format pop-up has, in addition to various other formats, an identical set of frame rates.**

  This is the "master" setting for the display format used in the various windows' rulers and position displays. To make editing with frame accuracy correspond to the actual frame rate in an external sync source, set this pop-up to the same value as the Frame Rate pop-up.

In Cubase SX/SL there are six frame rates to choose from:

Frame Rate	Description
24 fps	The traditional frame rate of 35mm film.
25 fps	The frame rate used for all video and audio in Europe (EBU).
30 fps	Straight 30 frames per second. This is often used in the United States for audio only work.
30 dfps	Very rarely used.
29.97 fps	Straight 29.97 frames per second.
29.97 dfps	"Drop frame" code running at 29.97 frames per second, most often used in the United States of America for work with color video.

29.4.2 Sync Options

The following Options are available in the Synchronization Setup dialog:

Drop Out Time

On an analog tape with timecode, dropouts may occur. If a drop-out is very long, Cubase SX/SL may (temporarily) stop. In the Dropout Time field you can set how long a drop-out (in frames) should be tolerated until Cubase SX/SL decides that the tape isn't good enough to synchronize to. If you have a very stable timecode source, you may lower this number to make Cubase SX/SL stop more swiftly after the tape recorder has been stopped.

Lock Time

Using this field you can set how many frames of "correct" timecode Cubase SX/SL should receive before attempting to "lock" (synchronize) to incoming timecode. If you have an external tape transport with a very short start-up time, you could try lowering this number to make lock-up even faster than it already is.

Ignore Hours

When this is activated, only the "minutes:seconds:frames" part of the incoming time-code positions are used for synchronization. In other words, the "hours" part of the Start time in the Project Setup dialog is then of no relevance.

30 VST System Link

30.1 Introduction

VST System Link is a network system for digital audio that allows you to have several computers working together in one large system. Unlike conventional networks it does not require Ethernet cards, hubs, or CAT-5 cables; instead it uses the kind of digital audio hardware and cables you probably already possess in your studio.

VST System Link has been designed to be simple to set up and operate, yet give enormous flexibility and performance gains in use. It is capable of linking computers in a "ring" network (the System Link signal is passed from one machine to the next, and eventually returns to the first machine). VST System Link can send its networking signal over any type of digital audio cable, including S/PDIF, ADAT, TDIF, or AES, as long as each computer in the system is equipped with a suitable ASIO compatible audio interface.

So, why would you want to link up two or more computers? Well, the added computer power gives you vast possibilities:

- Dedicate one computer to running VST instruments while recording audio tracks on another.
- If you need lots of audio tracks, you may simply add tracks on another computer.
- You could have one computer serve as a "virtual effect rack", running CPU-intensive send effect plug-ins only.
- Since you can use VST System Link to connect different VST System Link applications on different platforms, you can take advantage of effect plug-ins and VST instruments that are specific to certain programs or platforms.

This chapter describes how to set up and use VST System Link in Cubase SX/SL.

30.2 Preparations

30.2.1 Requirements

The following equipment is required for VST System Link operation:

- **Two or more computers.**

  These can be of the same type or use different operating systems—it doesn't matter. For example, you can link an Intel-based PC to an Apple Macintosh without problems.

- **Each computer must have audio hardware with specific ASIO drivers, installed and working.**
- **The audio hardware must have digital inputs and outputs.**

  Of course, to be able to connect the computers the digital connections must be compatible (i.e. the same digital formats and connection types must be available).
- **At least one digital audio cable for each computer in the network.**
- **A VST System Link host application installed on each computer.**

  As of this writing, VST System Link is implemented for Cubase SX/SL, Nuendo 1.6 and Cubase 5.2s (System Link version). Any VST System Link applications can connect to each other.

Additionally, we recommend that you use a KVM switchbox:

Using a KVM Switchbox

If you want to set up a multi-computer network, or even a small network in a limited space, it's a good idea to invest in a KVM (Keyboard, Video, Mouse) switchbox. With one of these switchers you can use the same keyboard, monitor, and mouse to control each computer in the system, and switch between computers very rapidly. KVM switchers are not too expensive, and very easy to setup and operate. It you decide not to go this route, the network will function just the same, but you may end up doing a lot of jumping from one machine to the other while setting up!

30.2.2 Making Connections

Below, we will assume that you are connecting two computers. Should you have more than two computers, it's still best to start with two and add the others one by one once the system is working—this makes troubleshooting easier if you run into problems. For two computers, you will need two digital audio cables, one in each direction:

1. **Connect a digital audio cable from the digital output of Computer 1 to the digital input of Computer 2.**
2. **Connect the other cable from the digital output of Computer 2 into the digital input of Computer 1.**

- **If a card has more than one set of inputs and outputs, choose whichever one that suits you—for simplicity usually the first set is best.**

30.2.3 Setting Up Clock Sync

Before you proceed you need to make sure that the clock signals on your ASIO cards are synchronized correctly. This is essential when cabling any kind of digital audio system, not just VST System Link.

- All digital audio cables by definition always carry a clock signal as well as audio signals, so you don't need to use a special Word Clock input and output for this (although you may find that you get a slightly more stable audio system if you do, especially when using multiple computers).

The Clock Mode or Sync Mode is set up in the audio hardware's ASIO Control Panel. In Cubase SX/SL, you proceed as follows:

1. **Pull down the Devices menu and open the Device Setup dialog.**
2. **Select the VST Multitrack device and make sure the Setup tab is selected to the right.**

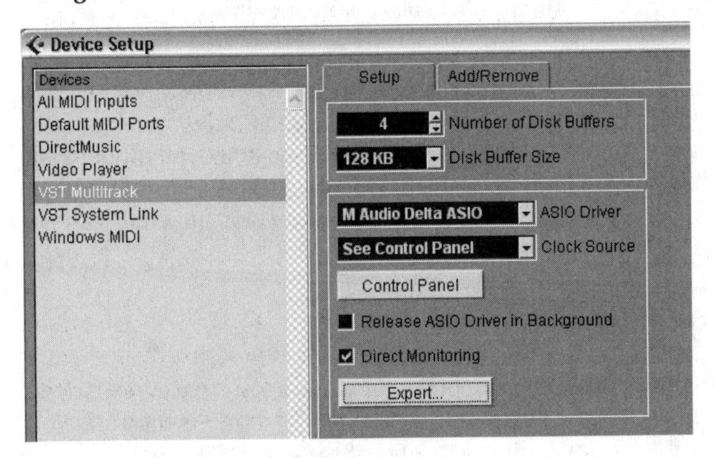

3. **Click the Control Panel button.**

   The ASIO Control Panel appears.

4. **Open the ASIO Control Panel on the other computer as well.**

   If you are using another VST System Link host application on that computer, check its documentation for details on how to open the ASIO Control Panel. Hint: in Steinberg's Nuendo 1.6, the procedure is the same as in Cubase SX/SL. In Cubase 5.2, you pull down the Options menu, select System from the Audio Setup menu and click the Control Panel button in the Audio System Setup dialog that appears.

5. **Now, you need to make sure that one audio card (and only one!) is set to be the Clock Master, and all the other cards must be set to listen for the clock signal coming from the Clock Master i.e. they must be Clock Slaves.**

   The naming and procedure for this differs depending on the audio hardware—consult its documentation if required. If you are using Steinberg Nuendo ASIO hardware, all cards default to the "AutoSync" setting—in this case you must set one of the cards (and only one) to "Master" in the Clock Mode section of the Control Panel.

- **Typically, the ASIO Control Panel for an audio card contains some indication of whether the card receives a proper sync signal or not, and the sample rate of that signal.**

  This is a good indication that you have connected the cards and set up clock sync properly. Check your audio hardware's documentation for details.

- It's very important that one and only one card is the clock master, otherwise the network cannot function correctly. Once you have set this up, all the other cards in the network will take their clock signal from this card automatically.

The only exception to this procedure is if you are using an external clock—which could be from a digital mixing desk or special Word Clock synchronizer for example. If so, you must then leave all your ASIO cards in Clock Slave or AutoSync mode, and make sure that each of them is listening for the signal coming from the synchronizer, usually passed through your ADAT cables or Word Clock connectors in a daisy chain fashion.

30.2.4 Minimizing the Latency

The general definition of latency is the amount of time it takes any system to respond to whatever messages are sent to it. For example, if your system's latency is high and you play VST instruments in real time, you will get a noticeable delay between when you press a key and when you hear the sound of the VST instrument. Nowadays, most ASIO-compatible audio cards are capable of operating with very low latencies. Also, all VST applications are designed to compensate for latency during playback, making the playback timing tight.

However, the latency time of a VST System Link network is the total latency of all the ASIO cards in the system added together. Therefore it's extra important to minimize the latency times for each computer in the network.

- The latency does *not* affect the synchronization—it's always perfectly in time. But, it can affect the time it takes to send and receive MIDI and audio signals, or make the system seem sluggish.

To adjust the latency of a system, you typically adjust the size of the buffers in the ASIO Control Panel—the lower the buffer size, the lower the latency. Generally speaking it's best to keep to fairly low latencies (buffer sizes) if your system can handle it—about 12 ms or less is usually a good idea.

30.2.5 Setting Up Your Software

Now it's time to set up your programs. The procedures below describe how to set things up in Cubase SX/SL; if you are using another program on the other computer, please refer to its documentation.

Setting the Sample Rate

The projects in both programs must be set to use the same sample rate. Select "Project Setup…" from the Project menu and make sure the sample rate is the same in both systems.

Setting Up Inputs and Outputs

1. **Open the VST Inputs window from the Devices menu.**
2. **Activate the inputs you want to use by clicking the buttons in the Active column.**

   To make it simple you will probably want to enable all inputs available in the cable you are using. For example, if you are using an ADAT connection this would mean clicking on the first four buttons (i.e. activate the first eight inputs).

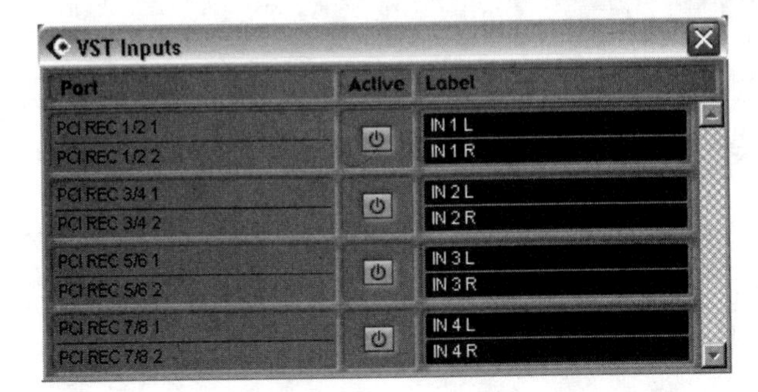

3. **Close the VST Inputs window and open the VST Outputs window from the Devices menu.**

4. **Enable the output buses you need.**

   Usually these should match up to the input buses you enabled above. In our ADAT example, this would mean the first four stereo outputs.

5. **Repeat the steps above for all computers in the network.**

- Note that at least one computer in your network needs to have more than one physical set of audio outputs, so that you can hear what's coming out of it!
  For example, if your audio card has a stereo analog out and an ADAT connector, you can use the ADAT connector for networking and the analog outs for monitoring. Make sure that the bus setup in your VST application reflects which set of outputs is doing which operation.

Once we've done this we have a set of inputs and outputs that can carry both our network commands and audio signals from one computer to another. At this point, it may be a good idea to test that everything is set up properly:

Streaming Digital Audio between Applications

1. **Set things up so that Computer 1 plays back some audio.**

   You could for example import an audio file and play this back in Cycle mode.

2. **In the Mixer, make sure the playing audio channel is routed to one of the digital outputs you have set up for the VST System Link connection.**

3. **In Computer 2, select the corresponding digital input for an audio channel and activate monitoring for the channel.**

   The audio being played back should now "appear" in the program running on Computer 2. You should now see the input level meters moving, and hear the audio.

4. **Reverse this procedure so that Computer 2 plays back and Computer 1 "listens".**

Now you have verified that the digital connection works as it should.

30.3 Activating VST System Link

After setting up the inputs and outputs, you now need to define which input/output should carry the actual VST System Link information.

The System Link networking signal is carried on only one bit of one channel. This means that if you have an ADAT based system which normally carries eight channels of 24-bit audio, once you activate VST System Link you will have seven channels of 24-bit audio and one channel of 23-bit audio (the least significant bit of this last channel is what we will use for networking). In practice this makes no discernible difference to the audio quality, since you will still have around 138dB headroom on this channel.

To set things up we need to open the VST System Link panel:

1. **Open the Device Setup dialog on the Devices menu.**

2. **Select the VST System Link device and make sure the Setup tab is selected to the right.**

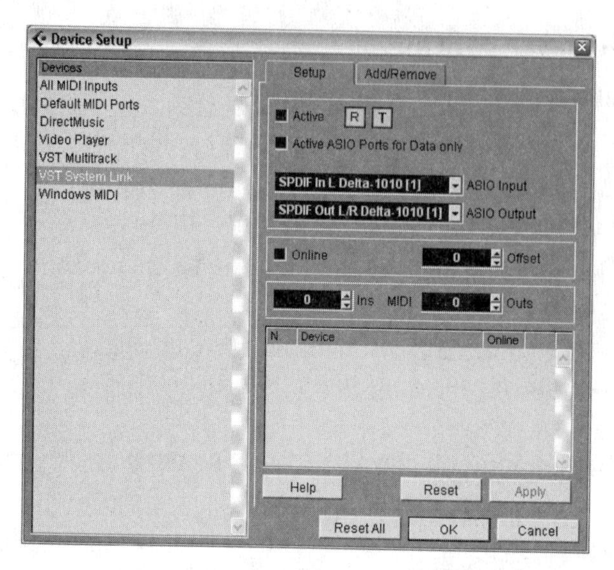

3. **Use the ASIO Input and ASIO Output pop-up menus to define which channel should be the networking channel (and thus become a 23-bit audio channel, in our example).**

   Quite often you will be able to just leave these pop-ups the way they are.

4. **Click the Active checkbox at the top of the panel.**

5. **Repeat the steps above for every computer on the network.**

As the computers are made active, you should see the small T (Transmit) and R (Receive) lights flashing on each active computer, and the name of each computer should appear in the list at the bottom of the pane. Each computer is assigned a random number—don't worry about this, it's just so the network knows internally which one is which.

- **You can double click on the name in bold (which is the name of the computer you're currently working on) and set it to whatever other name you wish.**

  This name will appear in the System Link window of every computer on the network.

- If you don't see the name of each computer appearing once you have made it active, you may have to check your settings.
  Go through the procedure above again and make sure that all ASIO cards are listening to the digital clock signals correctly, and that each computer has the correct inputs and outputs assigned to the System Link network.

30.3.1 Putting the Network Online

After each computer's name you will see whether it is online or not. When a computer is online, that means it receives transport and timecode signals, and its sequencer application can be started and stopped by remote control. If it is off-line it can only be started from its own keyboard—it is effectively an independent machine, although it is still on the network.

- Note that any computer can control any and all of the others—VST System Link is a peer to peer network and there is no absolute "master" computer.
  However, most users do like to think of one machine as the master (in a one person/two computer network, this would be the machine you actually sit behind most of the time).

For now, let's put all computers online:

1. Activate the Online checkbox in the VST System Link panel for all computers.

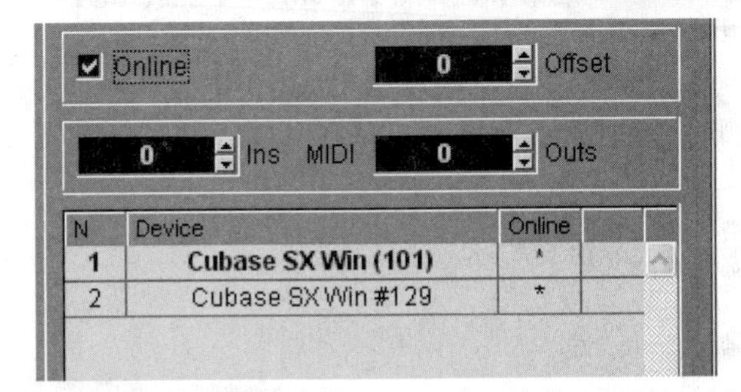

2. Check that the system is working by pressing Play on one computer—all computers should start almost instantly and play perfectly in time, with sample accurate precision.

- **The Offset setting to the right allows you to adjust whether one machine will play back slightly ahead or behind the rest.**

  This is normally not needed, but occasionally with some hardware you may find that the lock is a few samples out. In that case you can adjust the lock with the Offset value. For now, leave it set to 0—it will most likely be what you want.

VST System Link sends and understands all transport commands, so you can play, stop, fast forward, rewind etc. the entire network from one computer without a problem—try it! If you jump to a locator point on one machine, all other machines will also instantly jump to that locator point.

- Don't forget to make sure that all computers have their tempos set to the same value, otherwise your synchronization will be seriously skewed.

30.3.2 Using MIDI

As well as supplying transport and sync control, VST System Link also supplies up to 16 MIDI ports, each with 16 channels. You set this up as follows:

1. **Use the MIDI Ins and Outs value boxes to specify the number of MIDI ports you need.**

   The default value is 0 MIDI In and 0 MIDI Out ports.

2. **Create a MIDI track in the Project window and open the Inspector (top section).**

3. **If you now pull down the "in" or "out" pop-ups, you will find the specified System Link ports added to the list of MIDI Inputs and Outputs.**

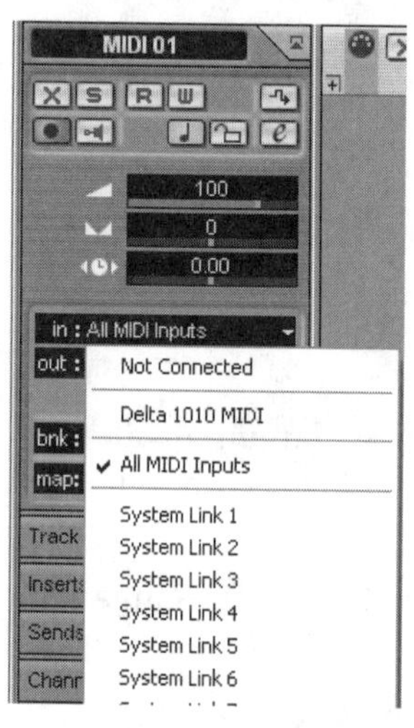

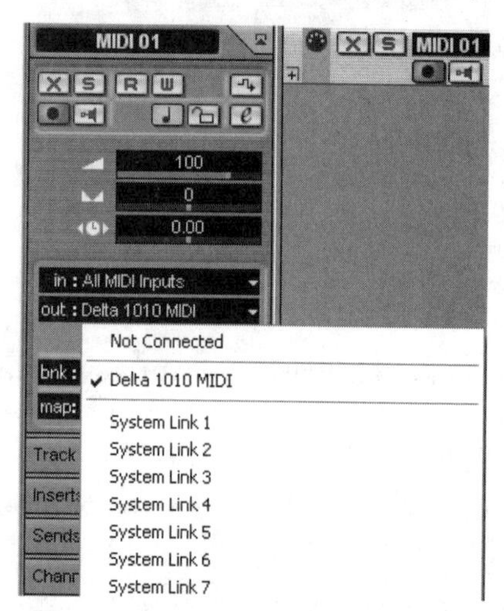

This allows you to route MIDI tracks to VST instruments running on another computer, as described in the application examples (see page 641).

The "Active ASIO Ports for Data only" Setting

If you are sending huge amounts of MIDI data at once, there is a small possibility that you might run out of bandwidth on your VST System Link network. This will manifest itself by notes "choking" or timing becoming erratic.

If this happens, you can devote more bandwidth to MIDI by selecting Active ASIO Ports for Data only in the VST System Link Setup panel. When this is active, the VST System Link information will be sent on the entire channel instead of just one bit, more than enough for all the MIDI you could ever hope to use. The downside is that you can no longer use this ASIO channel for audio transfer (do not connect it to a speaker!), thus leaving you only 7 channels of audio in our ADAT cable example. Depending on how you work this might be a reasonable compromise.

30.3.3 Hearing the Network Audio

If you are using an external mixing desk, hearing your audio really isn't an issue—just plug the outputs of each computer into the desired channels on the external mixing desk, press Play on one of the computers, and you're good to go.

However, many people prefer to mix internally inside the computer and just use a desk for monitoring (or maybe not use any external mixer at all). In this case you'll need to select one computer to be your "main mix computer" and send the audio from your other computers into this.

In the following example, we assume you are using two computers, with Computer 1 as your main mix computer and Computer 2 running two additional audio tracks, a reverb plug-in and a VST instrument plug-in with stereo outputs.

1. **First you want to set things up so that you can listen to the audio playback from Computer 1.**

   In other words, you need an unused set of outputs, e.g. an analog stereo output, connected to your monitoring equipment.

2. **Go to Computer 2 and assign each of the two audio tracks to a separate VST System Link output bus.**

   For example, assign the audio tracks to Bus 1 and 2.

3. **Assign the output of the reverb to another bus (e.g. Bus 3).**

   This is done using the output routing pop-up menu in the VST Send Effects window.

4. **Assign the VST instrument stereo channel to yet another bus (e.g. Bus 4).**

5. **Go back to Computer 1 and add four new stereo audio tracks.**

   These should be routed to the bus you use for listening, e.g. to the analog stereo outputs.

6. **Use the Input pop-up menus in the Mixer to select the four VST System Link buses (one for each track).**

7. **Activate monitoring for the four tracks.**

If you now start playback, the audio from Computer 2 will be sent "live" to the new tracks on Computer 1, allowing you to hear them together with any tracks you play back on Computer 1.

Adding More Tracks

OK, but if you have more audio tracks than you have VST System Link buses (physical outputs)? Then you just use the VST Outputs window on Computer 2 as a small sub-mixer: Assign several audio tracks to the same Output bus and then set the fader in the VST Output window to make sure you are sending the right level to your main mix computer.

Note also that if your audio cards have multiple sets of input and output connections you can link up e.g. multiple ADAT cables and send audio via any of the buses on any of the cables.

Internal Mixing and Latency

One problem with mixing inside the computer is the latency issue we mentioned earlier. The VST engine always compensates for record latencies, but if you are monitoring through Computer 1 you will hear a processing delay while you listen to signals coming from your other computers (*not* on your recording!). If your audio card in Computer 1 supports ASIO Direct Monitoring you should definitely turn this on—you'll find the setting in the VST Multitrack Device Setup panel (see page 88). Most modern ASIO cards support this function. If yours doesn't you may want to change the Offset value in the VST System Link Setup panel to compensate for any latency issues.

30.3.4 Setting Up a Larger Network

This is not much more difficult than a two computer network. The main thing to remember is that VST System Link is a daisy chain system. In other words, the output of Computer 1 goes to the input of Computer 2, the output of Computer 2 goes to the input of Computer 3, and so on around the chain. The output of the last computer in the chain must always go back into the input of Computer 1, to complete the ring.

Once you've done this, the transmission of all the transport, sync, and MIDI information to the whole network is handled pretty much automatically. However, where you may run into confusion in a large network is in the transmission of audio signals back to a central mix computer.

If you have lots of hardware inputs and outputs on your ASIO cards you don't need to send audio via the chain at all, but can transmit it directly to the master mix computer via one or more of its other hardware Inputs. For example, if you have a Nuendo Digiset interface or 9652 card on Computer 1 you could use ADAT cable 1 for networking, ADAT cable 2 as a direct audio input from Computer 2, and ADAT cable 3 as a direct audio input from Computer 3.

You can also transmit audio via the ring system if you don't have enough hardware I/Os for direct audio transmission. For example, in a four computer scenario you could send audio from Computer 2 into a channel in the mixer in Computer 3, and from there to a channel in the mixer in Computer 4, and from there back to the master mixer in Computer 1. This can certainly be tricky to set up, so generally it is recommended that if you want to set up a complex network, you should make sure to use ASIO cards with at least three separate digital I/Os.

30.4 Application Examples

30.4.1 Using One Computer for VST Instruments

In this example, you are using one computer as your main record and playback machine, and want to use another computer as a virtual synth rack.

1. **Record a MIDI track into Computer 1.**
2. **Once you have finished recording, route the MIDI output of that track to System Link MIDI port 1.**
3. **Now go to Computer 2, open up the VST Instrument rack and assign an instrument to the first slot in the rack.**
4. **Create a new MIDI track in the Project Window of Computer 2, and assign the MIDI output of the track to go to the VST Instrument you selected earlier.**
5. **Assign the MIDI input of the track to be VST System Link port 1.**

   Now, the MIDI track on Computer 1 is routed to the MIDI track on Computer 2, which in turn is routed to the VST Instrument.
6. **Now activate monitoring for the MIDI track on Computer 2, so that it will listen and respond to any MIDI commands coming in.**

   In Cubase SX/SL, you would click the monitor button in the Track list or Inspector.
7. **Press play on Computer 1.**

   It will now send the MIDI information on the track to the VST Instrument loaded on Computer 2.

Even with a slow computer you should be able to stack a whole bunch of extra VST Instruments this way, expanding your sound palette considerably. Don't forget that VST System Link MIDI is also sample accurate, and thus has *much* tighter timing than any hardware MIDI interface ever invented!

30.4.2 Creating a Virtual Effect Rack

The effect sends for an audio channel in Cubase SX/SL can either be routed to an effect (in the VST Send Effects rack) or to any activated Group or Output bus. This allows you to use a separate computer as a "virtual effect rack", by setting things up in the following way:

1. **Go to Computer 2 (the machine you will use as effect rack) and add a new stereo audio track.**
2. **Add the desired effect as an insert effect for the track.**

   Let's say you add a high-quality reverb plug-in.
3. **Open the Mixer and select one of the VST System Link buses as input for the audio track.**

   You want to use a separate System Link bus, which will only be used for this purpose.

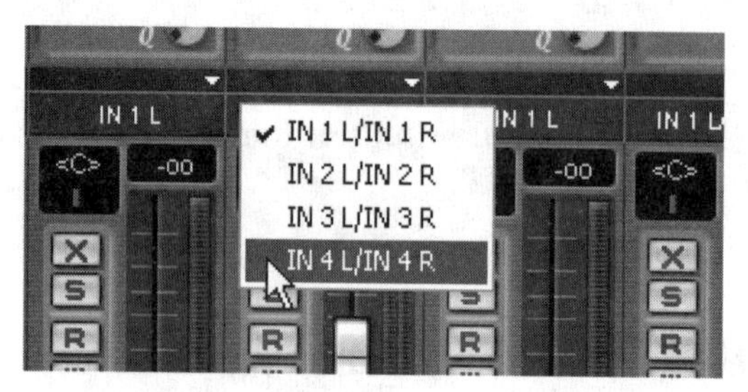

4. **Activate monitoring for the track.**
5. **Now, go back to Computer 1 and select a track to which you want to add some reverb.**
6. **Bring up the effect sends for the track, in the Inspector or the Mixer (Cubase SX only).**
7. **Pull down the send routing pop-up menu for one of the sends, and select the System Link bus assigned to the reverb in step 3.**
8. **Use the send slider/knob to adjust the amount of effect as usual.**

The signal will be sent to the track on Computer 2 and processed through its insert effect, without using any processor power on Computer 1.

You can repeat the steps above to add more effects to the "virtual effect rack". The number of effects available this way is only limited by the number of ports used in the VST System Link connection (and of course by the performance of Computer 2, but given that it won't have to handle any recording or playback, you should be able to use quite a lot of effects).

30.4.3 Getting Extra Audio Tracks

All computers on a VST System Link network are locked with sample accuracy. Therefore, if you find that the hard drive on one computer isn't fast enough to run as many audio tracks as you need, you could record new tracks on one of the other computers instead. This would create a "virtual RAID system", with several disks all operating together. All tracks will remain locked together just as tightly as if they were all running on the same machine. This means that you effectively have an unlimited track count! Need another 100 tracks? Just add another computer.

31 Video

31.1 Background

31.1.1 Video Support in Cubase SX/SL

Cubase SX/SL can play back video films using one of three different playback engines: DirectShow, QuickTime and Video for Windows. This ensures compatibility with as wide a range of video hardware as possible.

Generally there are two ways to play back video:

- Without any special hardware at all, using the computer CPU.
  In this case, the "codec" is in software. While this will be fine in many situations it does put a limit on the size of the video window as well as the quality of the image.
- Using video hardware that for example connects to an external monitor.
  This hardware must then use a suitable codec and have the proper drivers for the platform.

● Continuously updated information about video hardware support and compatibility is available on www.steinberg.net.

31.2 Operations

31.2.1 About the Video Playback Engine

You select a playback engine in the Device Setup dialog, under the "Setup" tab for the Video Player device:

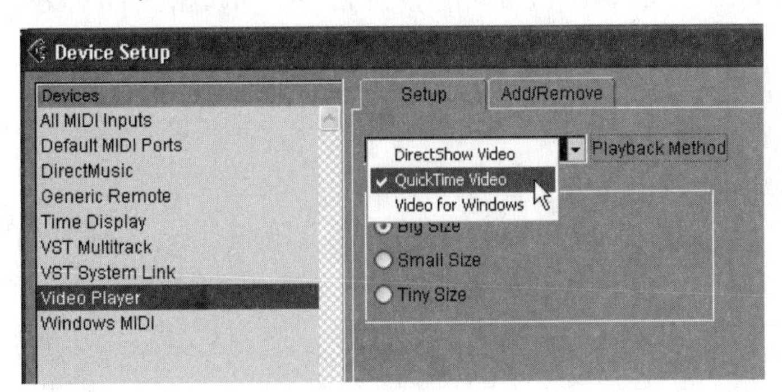

What playback engine to select depends largely on which type of video system you are using, as well as on the file format and codec of the video files you want to work with. Below is a brief guide to which formats you may be able to use with the different playback engines. However, this also depends on the video hardware—please consult the hardware documentation for detailed information.

Playback engine	Video file formats	Codecs
DirectShow	AVI, MPEG	Cinepak, DV, Indeo, M-JPEG, MPEG
QuickTime	QuickTime, AVI, MPEG	Cinepak, DV, Indeo, M-JPEG, MPEG
Video for Windows	AVI	Cinepak, Indeo, M-JPEG (with some video cards)

- Generally, you can expect most Windows hardware to work with DirectShow.
- For the Quicktime playback method to be available, you must have QuickTime installed on your computer.
  A QuickTime installer is included on the Cubase SX/SL CD if required.

31.2.2 Importing a Video File

Video files are imported just as audio files, see page 128.

- **By using the File menu (Import Videofile).**
- **By using drag and drop.**
- **By importing to the Pool first and then dragging to the Project window (see the Pool chapter for details).**

Note:

- To be able to play back the video, you must add a video track (by using the Add Track submenu on the Project menu or Quick menu). You can only have one video track in each project.
- All video files on the track must be of the same size and compression format.
- The audio in the video file is not included.

31.2.3 Playing Back a Video File

Video files are displayed as events/clips on the video track, with thumbnails representing the frames in the film.

A video event on a video track.

- **To view the video on the computer screen (as opposed to on an external monitor), pull down the Devices menu and select Video (or use a key command—by default [F8]).**

  A video window appears. In stop mode, this displays the video frame at the project cursor position.

Playback is done together with all other material, using the Transport panel.

31.2.4 Setting the Window Size

If you are playing back video in a window on your computer screen, you may want to adjust the size: Open Device Setup from the Devices menu, click Video Player in the list and use the Video Window buttons to select a size.

31.2.5 Project Window and Browser Editing Operations

Video clips are played back by events just as audio clips are. You can use all the basic editing operation on video events, just as with audio events (see page 133). The following operations are not possible on the video track:

- **Drawing, Gluing, Muting and Scrubbing.**
- **The video track has no editor and does not make use of parts.**

31.2.6 Pool Operations

For more about operations on video clips in the Pool, see page 402.

31.3 Options

In the Preferences dialog (Event Display—Video page), there are two options for video playback:

- **Show Video Thumbnails.**

  When this is activated, thumbnail frames of the video contents are shown in the track.

- **Video Cache Size.**

  This determines how much memory is available for video thumbnails. If you have long video clips and/or work with a large zoom factor (so that a lot of frames are shown in the thumbnails), you may have to raise this value.

32 ReWire

32.1 Introduction

ReWire and ReWire2 are special protocols for streaming audio between two computer applications. Developed by Propellerhead Software and Steinberg, ReWire provides the following possibilities and features:

- **Real-time streaming of up to 64 separate audio channels (256 with ReWire2), at full bandwidth, from the "synthesizer application" into the "mixer application".**

  In this case, the "mixer application" is of course Cubase SX/SL. An example of a "synthesizer application" is Propellerhead Software's Reason.

- **Automatic, sample accurate synchronization between the audio in the two programs.**
- **The possibility to have the two programs share one sound card and take advantage of multiple outputs on that card.**
- **Linked transport controls that allow you to play, rewind etc, either from Cubase SX/SL or from the synthesizer application (provided it has some kind of transport functionality).**
- **Automatic audio mixing functions of separate channels as required.**

  In the case of Reason for example, this allows you to have separate mixer channels for the different devices.

- **Additionally, ReWire2 offers the possibility to route MIDI tracks in Cubase SX/SL to the other application, for full MIDI control.**

  For each ReWire2 compatible device, a number of extra MIDI outputs will be made available in Cubase SX/SL. In the case of Reason, this allows you to route different MIDI tracks in Cubase SX/SL to different devices in Reason, having Cubase SX/SL serve as main MIDI sequencer.

- **Less total system requirements than when using the programs together in the conventional way.**

32.2 Launching and Quitting

When using ReWire, the order in which you launch and quit the two programs is very important:

32.2.1 Launching for Normal Use with ReWire

1. **First launch Cubase SX/SL.**
2. **Enable one or several ReWire channels in the ReWire Device dialog for the other application.**

   This is described in detail on page 651.
3. **Launch the other application.**

   It may take slightly longer for the application to start when you are using ReWire.

32.2.2 Quitting a ReWire Session

When you are finished, you also need to quit the applications in a special order:

1. **First quit the synthesizer application.**
2. **Then quit Cubase SX/SL.**

32.2.3 Launching Both Programs without Using ReWire

We don't know exactly why you would want to run Cubase SX/SL and the synthesizer application at the same time on the same computer, without using ReWire, but you can:

1. **First launch the synthesizer application.**
2. **Then launch Cubase SX/SL.**

Please also note that the two programs now compete for system resources such as audio cards, just as when running either with other, non-ReWire audio applications.

32.3 Activating ReWire Channels

ReWire supports streaming of up to 64 separate audio channels, while ReWire2 supports 256 channels. The exact number of available ReWire channels depends on the synthesizer application. Using the ReWire Device panels in Cubase SX/SL, you can specify which of the available channels you want to use:

1. **Pull down the Devices menu and select the menu item with the name of the ReWire application. All recognized ReWire compatible applications will be available on the menu.**

   The ReWire panel appears. This consists of a number of rows, one for each available ReWire channel.

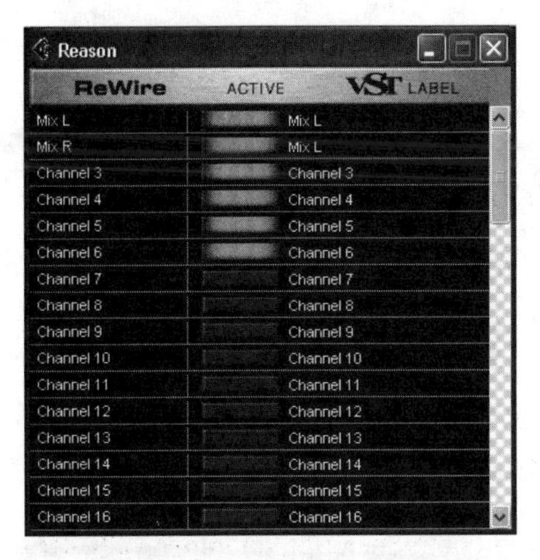

The ReWire panel for Reason.

2. **Click on the green buttons in the "Active" column to activate/deactivate the desired channels.**

   The buttons light up to indicate activated channels. Please note that the more ReWire channels you activate, the more processing power is required.

- **For information about exactly what signal is carried on each channel, see the documentation of the synthesizer application.**

3. **If desired, double click on the labels in the right column, and type in another name.**

   These labels will be used in the Cubase SX/SL Mixer to identify the ReWire channels.

32.4 Using the Transport and Tempo Controls

- This is only relevant if the synthesizer application has some sort of built-in sequencer or similar.

32.4.1 Basic Transport Controls

When you run ReWire, the transports in the two programs are completely linked. It doesn't matter in which program you Play, Stop, Fast Forward or Rewind. However, recording (if applicable) is still completely separate in the two applications.

32.4.2 Loop Settings

If there is a loop or cycle facility in the synthesizer application, that loop will be completely linked to the Cycle in Cubase SX/SL. This means that you can move the start and end point for the loop or turn the loop on or off in either program, and this will be reflected in the other.

32.4.3 Tempo Settings

As far as tempo goes, Cubase SX/SL is always the Master. This means that both programs will run in the tempo set in Cubase SX/SL.

However, if you are not using the Tempo track in Cubase SX/SL, you can adjust the tempo in either program, and this will immediately be reflected in the other.

- If you are using the Tempo track in Cubase SX/SL (if Master is activated on the Transport bar), you should not adjust the tempo in the synthesizer application, since a tempo request from ReWire will automatically deactivate the Master switch in Cubase SX/SL!

32.5 How the ReWire Channels Are Handled in Cubase SX/SL

When you activate ReWire channels in the ReWire Device panels, they will become available as channel strips in the Mixer. The ReWire channel strips have the following properties:

- **ReWire channels appear to the right of the track-based (audio and MIDI) channel strips.**

- **ReWire channels may be any combination of mono and stereo, depending on the synthesizer application.**
- **ReWire channels have the same functionality as regular audio channels.**

  This means you can set volume and pan, add EQ, insert and send effects and route the channel outputs to Groups or Buses. All settings can be automated using the Read/Write functions.
- **All unmuted ReWire channels are included when you mix down to an audio file using the Export Audio Mixdown function (see page 601).**

  This allows you to "convert" your ReWire channels into hard disk tracks. If you want to mix down the ReWire channels only, make sure all audio tracks and VST Instrument channels are muted.

32.6 Routing MIDI via ReWire2

● This feature is only available with ReWire2-compatible applications.

When using Cubase SX/SL with a ReWire2-compatible application, additional MIDI outputs will automatically appear on the MIDI Output pop-up menus for MIDI tracks. This allows you to play the synthesizer application via MIDI from Cubase SX/SL, using it as one or several separate MIDI sound sources.

The MIDI outputs for a Reason song. Here, each output goes directly to a device in the Reason rack.

- **The number and configuration of MIDI Outputs depends on the synthesizer application.**

32.7 Considerations and Limitations

Sample Rates

Synthesizer applications may be limited to audio playback in certain sample rates. If Cubase SX/SL is set to a sample rate other than those, the synthesizer application will play back at the wrong pitch. Consult the documentation of the synthesizer application for details.

ASIO Drivers

ReWire works well with ASIO drivers. By using the Cubase SX/SL bussing system you can route sounds from the synthesizer application to various outputs on an ASIO compatible audio card.

33 File Handling

33.1 File Operations

33.1.1 New Project

The New Project command on the File menu allows you to create a new project, either empty or based on a template:

1. **Select New Project from the File menu.**

   A list of templates is displayed. When you install Cubase SX/SL, a number of templates for various purposes are included, but you can also create your own (see page 658).

2. **Select a template from the list, or select "Empty".**

   A project file dialog appears, allowing you to specify a folder for the new project.

3. **Select an existing project folder or create a new one by typing its name in the dialog.**

   A new, untitled project is created.

33.1.2 Open

The Open command on the File menu is used for opening saved project files. Both Cubase SX/SL project files (extension ".cpr") and project files created in Steinberg's Nuendo (extension ".npr") can be opened (although Nuendo-specific settings will be ignored).

- **Several projects can be open at the same time.**

  The active project is indicated by the red Activate button in the upper left corner of the Project window. To make another project active, click its Activate button.

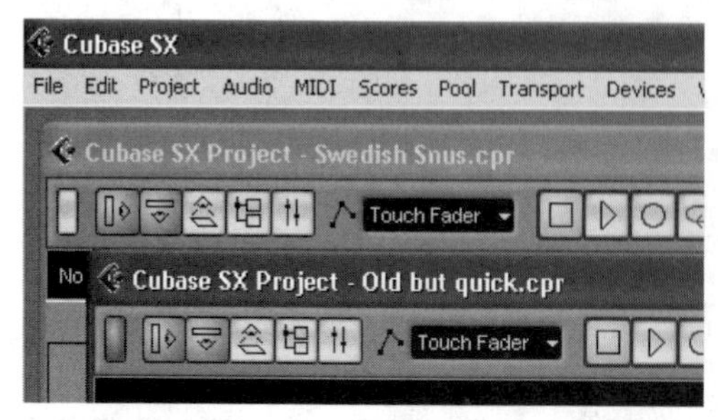

An active project.

- **You can also open project files by selecting a shortcut from the "Recent Projects" submenu on the File menu.**

  This submenu lists the projects you have recently worked with, with the most recent one at the top of the list.

- **Projects can also automatically be opened when you launch Cubase SX/SL.**

  See page 669.

- If you are using Cubase SL, it's fully possible to open a Project file created in Cubase SX. Features not supported by Cubase SL will however not be available. For example, if you open a Cubase SX project that uses more than five insert effects for a channel (or more than 16 VST Instruments) a dialog will appear, informing you that not all effects/instruments can be loaded.

33.1.3 Close

The Close command on the File menu closes the active window. If a Project window is active, selecting Close will close the corresponding project.

- **If the project contains unsaved changes, you will be asked whether you want to save the project before closing it.**

  If you select "Don't Save", and have recorded or created new audio files since saving, you get the choice to delete or keep these.

33.1.4 Save and Save As

The commands Save and Save As allow you to save the active project as a project file (file extension ".cpr"). The Save command stores the project under its current name and location, while Save As allows you to rename and/or relocate the file. If you haven't yet saved the project, or if it hasn't been changed since it was last saved, only Save As will be available.

- Generally, we recommend that you save project files in their project folders, to keep the projects as manageable as possible.

Saving a Default Project

If you always want the same default project to open when you launch Cubase SX/SL, you can save a default project:

1. **Set up a project the way you want it.**
2. **Select "Save As" from the File menu and save the project in the Cubase SX/SL application folder, under the name "default.cpr".**
3. **Open the Preferences dialog and select the User Interface page.**
4. **Open the "On Startup" pop-up menu and select "Open Default Project".**

   The next time you launch Cubase SX/SL, the default project is automatically opened. For details on the other Startup options, see page 669.

33.1.5 Save Project to New Folder

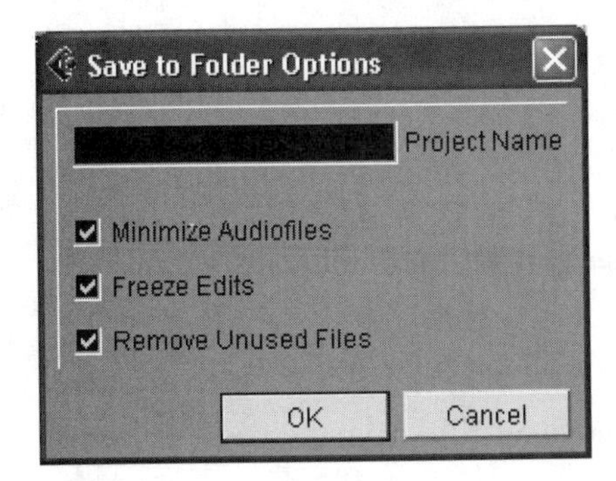

This function is very useful if you want to move or archive your project. If you select this item, you will first be asked where to store the saved project. Then a dialog will appear, with the following options:

Item	Description
Project Name	By default, this will be the current name of the project you're saving, but you can change it if you like.
Minimize Audiofiles	If this is activated, only the audio file portions that are actually used in the project will be included. This can significantly reduce the size of the project folder (if you are using small sections of large files), but it will also mean you cannot make use of the remaining audio file portions if you continue working with the project in its new folder.
Freeze Edits	This will perform a Freeze Edits operation, making all processing and applied effects permanent to each clip in the Pool. See page 351.
Remove Unused Files	When this is activated, only files in the Pool that are actually used in the project will be stored in the new folder.

When you've made your settings, click OK to save the project in the new folder. The original project isn't removed or affected.

33.1.6 Save as Template

This function allows you to save the current project as a template. Templates are always stored in the Templates folder (within the Cubase SX/SL program folder). When you create a new project, the available templates will be listed, allowing you to base the new project on a template.

- **Templates can contain clips and events, just like regular projects.**

  If this is not what you want, make sure to remove all clips from the Pool before you save the project as a template.

33.1.7 Revert

If you select Revert from the File menu, you will be asked whether you really want to revert to the last saved version of the project. If you click "Revert", all changes you have made since the last saving will be discarded.

- **If you have recorded or created new audio files since saving, you will be asked whether you want to delete or keep these.**

33.1.8 The "Cleanup" Function

The Cleanup function on the File menu helps you to save hard disk space by locating, and if you like, deleting unused audio files in the project folders on your disk.

1. **Select "Cleanup..." from the File menu.**

   If there are any open projects, an alert will appear, allowing you to close these. Clicking "Close" closes all open projects and brings up the Cleanup dialog.

2. **If you want to restrict the Cleanup function to a certain folder only, click the "Search Folder" button and select the folder.**

   You should only select a specific folder if you are certain it doesn't contain audio files used in other projects (outside the folder)! See the note below.

   If you want the Cleanup function to be applied to all folders on all hard disks, you don't need to make any special settings, as this is the default mode. After selecting a folder you can reset the function to search all folders by opening the "Search Folder" dialog again and clicking "Cancel".

3. **Click the Start button.**

   Cubase SX/SL will now scan the selected folder (or all hard disks) for Cubase SX/SL project folders and check for audio and image files (in the Audio, Edits, Fades and Images subfolders) that are not used by any project. The found files are listed in the dialog.

4. **When the scan is complete, you can select files by clicking in the list.**

   Use [Ctrl]-click to select several files, and [Shift]-click to select a range of files. You can also click the Select All button to select all files in the list.

● Note: There are situations when the Cleanup function will list files that are not unused!
- If you have moved or renamed files or folders (without updating the project files to use the new paths), there is no way for Cubase SX/SL to know that these files are used in a project.
- If you are performing the Cleanup function on a folder in which there are audio files belonging to other projects (outside the folder), these files will be considered "unused".
- Also, make sure you don't delete any files used in other applications, or files that you generally want to keep!

However, you can safely delete Image files and Fade files (files within the Fades folder of a project) since these can be reconstructed by the program if necessary.

5. **Delete any files you don't want to keep, by selecting them and clicking Delete.**
6. **Close the dialog by clicking its close button.**

33.1.9 Exporting and Importing MIDI Files

Cubase SX/SL can import and export Standard MIDI Files, which makes it possible to transfer MIDI material to and from virtually any MIDI application, on any platform.

Exporting MIDI Files

To export your MIDI tracks as a Standard MIDI File, pull down the File menu and select "MIDI File..." from the Export submenu. A regular file dialog appears, allowing you to specify a location and name for the file. You will then be asked whether the MIDI file should be of Type 0 (all data on a single track, but on different MIDI channels) or Type 1 (data on separate tracks). Which type to choose depends on what you want to do with the MIDI file (in which application or sequencer it should be used, etc.).

Note:

- The MIDI File will contain the Master Tempo, including all changes in the Tempo track.
- Inspector settings for the tracks are not included in the MIDI file!
  To include these, you need to convert the settings to "real" MIDI events and properties by using the Merge MIDI in Loop function for each track, see page 464.

Importing MIDI Files

To import a MIDI file from disk, proceed as follows:

1. **Select "MIDI File..." from the Import submenu on the File menu.**
2. **In the dialog that appears, select whether you want the MIDI file to be imported into the current project, or whether a new project should be created.**
3. **Locate and select the MIDI file in the file dialog that appears, and click Open.**
4. **If you chose that a new project should be created, you are asked to specify a project folder for the new project.**

   Select an existing project folder or create a new one by typing its name in the dialog.

The MIDI file is imported, starting at the beginning of the project. The result depends on the type of MIDI file:

- If the MIDI file is of Type 0 (all data on a single track), only one MIDI track will be created.
  This track will be set to MIDI Channel "Any", allowing all MIDI events to play back on their original channels. You can use the Dissolve Part function on the MIDI menu to distribute the events onto different tracks with different MIDI Channels (see page 481).
- If the MIDI file is of Type 1 (data on several tracks) a number of new MIDI tracks and parts will be created.

In both cases, the Tempo track is adjusted according to the tempo track in the MIDI file.

33.1.10 Importing Older Cubase Files

It is possible to import files created in older versions of Cubase. There are three options for this on the File—Import submenu:

Import Cubase Song

This will open a Song file (extension ".all") created in Cubase 5.0 or later and convert it to a Cubase SX/SL project. When importing a Song, you will be asked to specify a folder for the new project, as usual.

- Cubase Songs can contain more than one Arrangement (containing independent part and event data). If this is the case, you will be asked which one of these Arrangements to import.
  To import all Arrangements in a Cubase Song, simply repeat this for all Arrangements, and save each as a separate project.

The conversion has the following limitations:

Data	Conversion result
MIDI output setting for MIDI tracks	If the output information stored in the original Song doesn't match the current outputs, a "Pending Connections" dialog will appear, allowing you to remap each MIDI output in the Song to a new output.
MIDI track play parameters (Inspector settings)	Only the volume and transpose settings are included; the other parameters (velocity, compression, length and pan) are ignored.
MIDI part play parameters (Inspector settings)	All settings are included, except transpose.

Data	Conversion result
Group tracks	Removed.
Style tracks	Removed.
Chord tracks	Removed.
Drum tracks	Converted to MIDI tracks with drum maps. MIDI output settings for individual drum sounds will be ignored.
Solo/Mute status of tracks	Ignored.
MIDI "effect" devices, such as the arpeggiator and IPS	Removed.
Window layouts	Ignored.
Key command settings	Ignored.
Grooves	Ignored.
MIDI Mixermaps	Removed.
Dynamic events in audio parts (including M-points)	Ignored.
Automation	The VST channel automation is included, but limited to volume, pan and EQ data. Plug-in automation and automation for DSP Factory settings are ignored.
Left/right locator positions and cycle status	Ignored.
Sync settings and status	Ignored.
Master track hitpoints	Removed.
VST Group channels	Removed.
Multiple audio tracks routed to the same audio channel	Will be replaced by separate audio tracks (with separate channels in the Mixer). This is because in Cubase SX/SL there is always one channel per track.
Solo/Mute status of VST channels	Ignored.

- It's also possible to import Songs created in version 3.7x of Cubase.
  However, this will only include the basic audio and MIDI data, ignoring most of the settings.

Import Cubase Arrangement

As mentioned above, a Song in previous versions of Cubase could contain one or several Arrangements. These contained all the part and event data along with file references, but without mixer settings and similar, which were global to all Arrangements in the Song. Arrangements could be saved as separate files, with the extension ".arr".

When you import a Cubase Arrangement into Cubase SX/SL, it will be converted to a project, just as when importing a Song. The same limitations apply.

Import Cubase Part

Just as in Cubase SX/SL, previous Cubase versions used parts as containers for MIDI or audio events. These could be saved as separate files with the extension ".prt". When you import a part file, the following happens:

- A new track is created, with the name of the part.
  That is, the name of the part when it was saved in Cubase, not (necessarily) the file name.
- The part appears as a Cubase SX/SL part, at the left locator position.
- If the imported part was an audio part, the necessary clips and file references are added to the Pool.

● Note that none of these file formats contain any actual audio data. Just as with Cubase SX/SL projects, the files only contain references to audio files. This means that you need access to the referenced audio files as well, to properly import Songs, Arrangements or Parts with audio.

33.1.11 Importing Audio CD Tracks (Cubase SX only)

You can import audio from audio CDs, for use in Cubase SX Projects. This is done by selecting "Import Audio CD" from the Pool menu (or by selecting the "Audio CD..." option from the Import submenu on the File menu).

- **If the project window is active, the imported audio CD track(s) will be inserted on the selected audio track, at the project cursor position.**

  It is also possible to import audio CD tracks into the Pool, which may be the preferred method if you want to import several CD tracks in one go.

Selecting one of the Import Audio CD menu items brings up the following dialog:

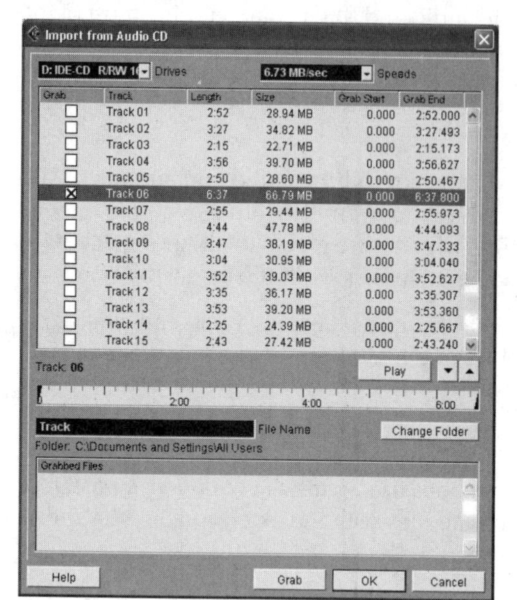

- **If you have more than one CD drive, you use the Drives pop-up menu to select the one holding the audio CD.**
- **The Speeds pop-up menu lists all possible data transfer speeds for the selected CD drive.**

  While you normally want to use the fastest possible speed, you may have to select a slower speed for flawless audio extraction.
- **The main display in the dialog lists all audio tracks on the CD.**

  The columns have the following functionality:

Column	Description
Grab	Activate the checkbox in this column for the track you want to grab (import). To activate more than one checkbox (import more than one track), click and drag over the checkboxes (or press [Ctrl] or [Shift] and click).
Track	When you import an audio CD track, the file will be named according to the name in this column. You can rename a track by clicking in the Track column and typing a new name. You can also apply a name to all audio CD tracks (e.g. the name of the album, see below).
Length	The length of the whole audio CD track, in minutes and seconds.

Column	Description
Size	The file size of the whole audio CD track, in MegaBytes.
Grab Start	You can grab a section of a track if you like. This indicates the start of the section to be grabbed in the track. By default, this is set to the start of the track (0.000) but you can adjust this on the grab selection ruler (see below).
Grab End	Indicates the end of the section to be grabbed in the track. By default, this is set to the end of the track but you can adjust this on the grab selection ruler (see below).

- **You can audition the selected audio CD track by clicking the Play button.**

  The track will be played back from the grab selection start (see below) to the track end (or until you click the button again). During playback, the button is labeled "Stop".

- **The arrow buttons next to the Play button allow you to audition the start and end of the grab selection only.**

  The left button will play a short snippet beginning at the start of the grab selection (see below), while the right button will play a snippet starting just before the end of the grab selection.

- **If you want to import a section of an audio CD track only, you select the track in the list and specify the start and end of the grab selection by dragging the handles in the grab selection ruler.**

  Use the start and end audition buttons to fine tune the selection boundaries.

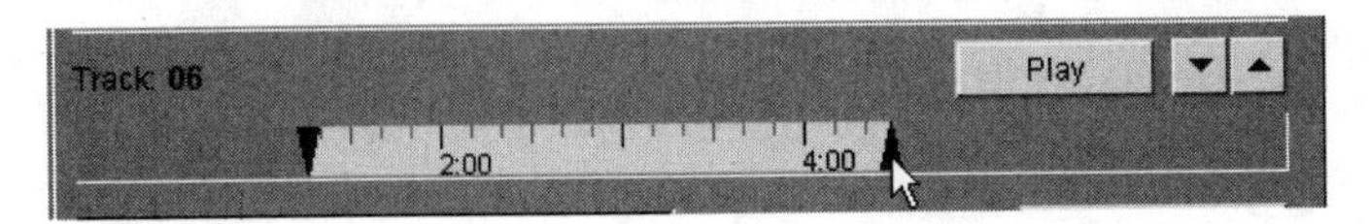

  Note that you can import sections of several audio CD tracks by selecting them in turn and adjusting the grab selection. The grab start and end settings for each track will appear in the list.

- **If you wish, you can change the generic audio file name in the File Name field.**

  By default, the imported audio files will get this name with a track number added (typically Track 01, Track 02, and so on). However, if you have adjusted the track name for a specific audio CD track in the list, the corresponding audio file will use that name instead.

- **By default, imported audio CD tracks will be stored as Wave files in the Audio folder of the current project.**

  You can select another folder by clicking the Change Folder button.

- **Clicking the Grab button will convert the selected audio CD tracks (the tracks for which the Grab checkbox is ticked) to audio files.**

  The grabbed files will be listed at the bottom of the dialog—click OK to actually import the files into the project and close the dialog, or click Cancel to discard the grabbed files.

33.1.12 Importing ReCycle Files

ReCycle, developed by Propellerhead Software, is a program designed especially for working with sampled loops. By "slicing" a loop and making separate samples of each beat, ReCycle makes it possible to match the tempo of a loop and edit the loop as if it was built up of individual sounds. Cubase SX/SL can import two file types created by ReCycle:

- REX files (export file format of the first versions of ReCycle, extension ".rex").
- REX 2 files (file format of ReCycle 2.0 and later, extension ".rx2").

Proceed as follows:

1. **Select an audio track and move the project cursor to where you want the imported file to start.**

   You probably want to import REX files to tempo based audio tracks, since this will allow you to change the tempo later on (having the imported REX file automatically adjust).

2. **Select "Audio File..." from the Import submenu on the File menu.**
3. **Select REX files or REX 2 files with the file type pop-up menu in the file dialog.**
4. **Locate and select the file and click Open.**

   The file is imported, and automatically adjusted to the current Cubase SX/SL tempo.

Unlike a regular audio file, the imported REX file will consist of several events, one for each "slice" in the loop. The events will automatically be placed in an audio part on the selected track, and positioned so that the original internal timing of the loop is preserved.

5. If you now open the part in the Audio Part Editor, you can edit each slice separately by muting, moving and resizing events, adding effects and processing, etc.

You can also adjust the tempo and have the REX file automatically follow (provided that its track is tempo based).

- You can also achieve similar results by using Cubase SX/SL's own loop slicing features.
  See page 385.

33.1.13 Importing Compressed Audio Files

During the last years, various audio compression formats have become very common. The major advantage of using such file formats is that the file size is significantly reduced, with very little degradation of sound quality. This allows for quick download, mass storage and easy transportation.

Cubase SX/SL can import (and export, see page 601) several common audio compression formats. The procedure is the same as when importing any non-compressed audio file, with one important thing to note:

- If you import a compressed audio file, Cubase SX/SL will create a copy of the file and convert this to Wave format before importing it (the original compressed file will not be used in the project). The Wave file will be placed in the designated Project Audio folder. Please be aware that the converted Wave file will be several times larger than the original compressed file!

The following file types are supported:

MPEG Audio Files

MPEG, which stands for Moving Picture Experts Group, is the name of family of standards used for coding audio-visual information (e.g. movies, video, music) in a digital compressed format.

Cubase SX/SL can read three types of audio MPEG files: MPEG Layer 1 (file extension *.mpeg), MPEG Layer 2 (*.mp2) and MPEG Layer 3 (*.mp3). Currently, mp3 is the most common format of these, while the mp2 format is mostly used in broadcast applications.

- Note that the file extension ".mpeg" can also be used by MPEG video files.
  If you select an MPEG video file in the Import Audio dialog you will not be able to import it.

Ogg Vorbis Files

Ogg Vorbis is a relatively new format that is open and patent-free and offers very small audio files maintaining comparatively high audio quality. Ogg Vorbis files have the extension ".ogg".

Windows Media Audio Files

Windows Media Audio is an audio format developed by Microsoft Inc. Due to advanced audio compression algorithms, Windows Media Audio files can be made very small, maintaining good audio quality. The files have the extension ".wma".

33.2 Options and Settings

33.2.1 Auto Save

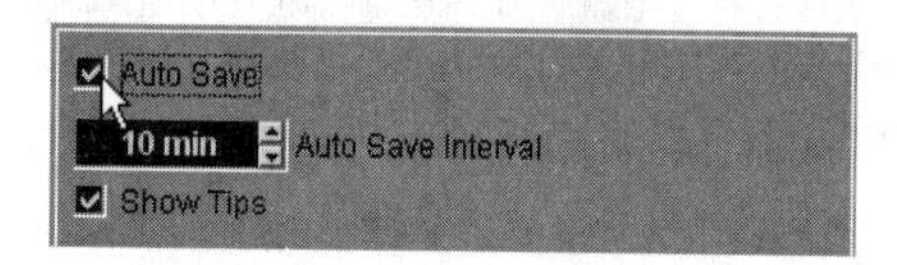

If you activate the Auto Save checkbox in the Preferences dialog (User Interface page), Cubase SX/SL will automatically save backup copies of all open projects with unsaved changes.

- **You specify how often a backup copy should be created with the Auto Save Interval setting.**
- **Backup copies are named "Name.bak", where "Name" is the name of the project. The files are saved in the project folder.**
- **Unsaved projects are also backed up in the same way.**

  Backup copies of unsaved projects will be named "#UntitledX.bak" where "X" is an incremental number, to allow multiple backup copies in the same project folder.

33.2.2 Startup Options

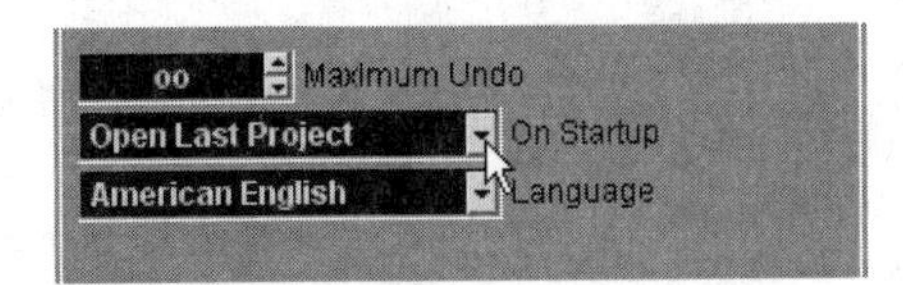

The "On Startup" pop-up menu in the Preferences dialog (User Interface page) allows you to specify what should happen each time you launch Cubase SX/SL. The following options are available:

Option	Description
Do Nothing	Cubase SX/SL launches without opening a project.
Open Last Project	The last saved project is opened on launch.
Open Default Project	The default project is opened (see page 657).
Show Open Dialog	The Open dialog appears on launch, allowing you to manually locate and open the desired project.
Show Template Dialog	The Template dialog appears on launch, allowing you to create a new project from one of the templates.
Show Open Options Dialog	The Open Document Options dialog appears on launch, see below. It allows you to make a different choice each time you launch Cubase SX/SL.

Cubase SX/SL Open Document Options Dialog

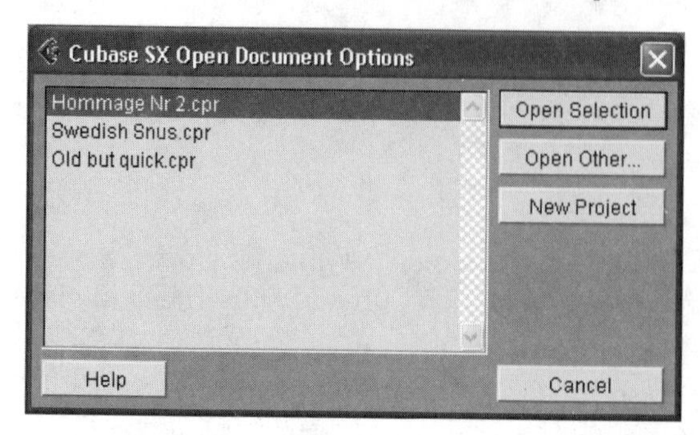

The Cubase SX/SL projects you have used recently are displayed in the list. To open one of them, select it and click the "Open Selection" button. To open another project not listed there, click the "Open Other..." button. A file dialog appears that allows you to look for the desired file on your disk. Click the "New Project" button to create a new project using a template or not.

If you hold down [Ctrl] while launching Cubase SX/SL this dialog will always be displayed, regardless of the startup option selected in the Preferences dialog (User Interface page).

34 Key Commands

34.1 Background

34.1.1 Introduction

Most of the main menus in Cubase SX/SL have key command shortcuts for certain items on the menus. In addition, there are numerous other Cubase SX/SL functions that can be performed via key commands. These are all factory default settings. If you want, you can customize existing key commands to your liking, and also add commands for menu items and functions currently not assigned any.

- You can also assign tool modifier keys, i.e. keys that change the behaviour of various tools when pressed. This is done in the Preferences dialog—see page 678.

How Are Key Command Settings Saved?

Every time you edit or add any key command assignment, this is stored as a global Cubase SX/SL preference—*not* as part of a project. Hence, if you edit or add a key command assignment, any subsequent projects that you create or open will use these modified settings. However, the factory default settings can at any time be restored by selecting "Reset All" in the Key Commands dialog. In addition, you can save (Export) complete key command settings as a "key commands file", which can be stored separately and imported into any project. This way you can quickly and easily recall customized settings, when moving projects between different computers, for example. See later in this chapter for details on how to save complete key command settings.

34.2 The Key Commands Dialog

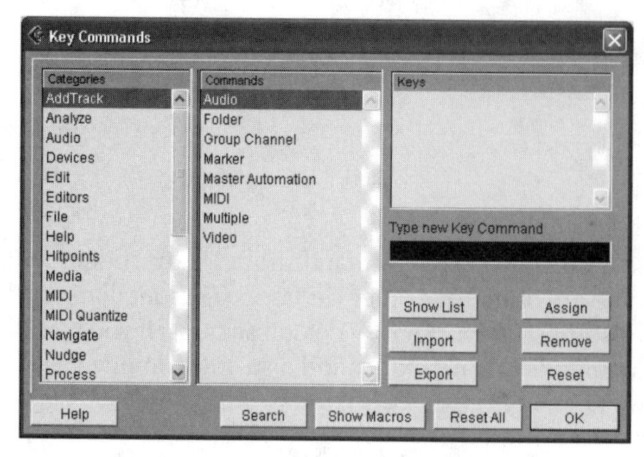

34.2.1 Adding or Modifying a Key Command

In the Key Commands dialog you will find all main menu items and a large number of other functions, all arranged on different "pages" depending on which menu/window they belong to. You can also open a list of the currently assigned key commands by clicking the "Show List" button. To add a key command, proceed as follows:

1. **Pull down the File menu and select "Key Commands...".**

   The Key Commands dialog appears.

2. **Use the list in the Categories column to select the preferred page.**

   You may have to use the vertical scroll bar to display the desired page.

3. **In the Commands list, select the item to which you wish to assign a key command.**

   Already assigned key commands are shown in the Keys section of the dialog.

If a selected item or function has a key command assigned already, it is displayed here.

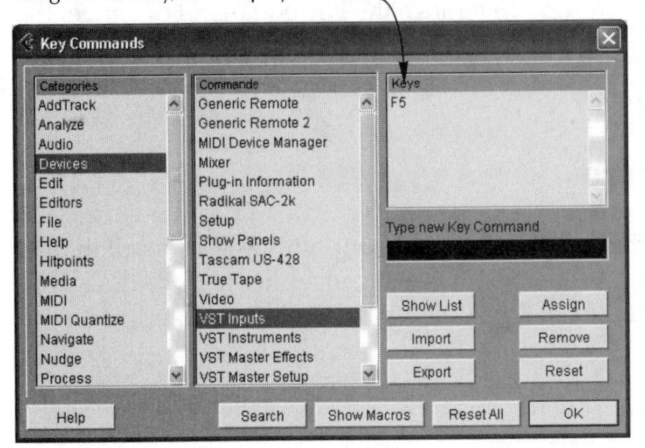

4. **Double-click in the "Type new Key Command" field and enter a new key command.**

   You can choose between any single key or a combination of one or several modifier keys (Ctrl, Alt, Shift) plus any key.

5. **Click the Assign button.**

   The new key command appears in the Keys List.

Please note that this will not replace any key command previously defined for the function. That is, you can have several different key commands for the same function. To remove an assigned key command, see "Removing a key command" below.

- If the key command you enter is already assigned to another function, you will get a prompt asking if you want to replace the currently assigned command or cancel the operation.

6. **Click OK to exit the dialog.**

34.2.2 Removing a Key Command

To remove a key command, proceed as follows:

1. **Pull down the File menu and select "Key Commands...".**
2. **Use the list in the Categories column to select the desired page.**
3. **In the Commands list, select the item you wish to remove.**

   The key command for the item is shown in the Keys list.

4. **Select the key command in the Keys list and click the "Remove" button.**

   You will get a prompt asking if you want to remove the key command or cancel the operation.

5. **Click OK to close the dialog.**

34.2.3 Setting Up Macros

A Macro is a combination of several functions or commands, to be performed in one go. For example, you could select all events on the selected audio track, remove DC offset, normalize the events and duplicate them, all with a single command.

Macros are set up in the Key Commands dialog:

1. **Click the Show Macros button.**

   The Macro settings are shown in the lower part of the dialog. To hide these from view, click the button again.

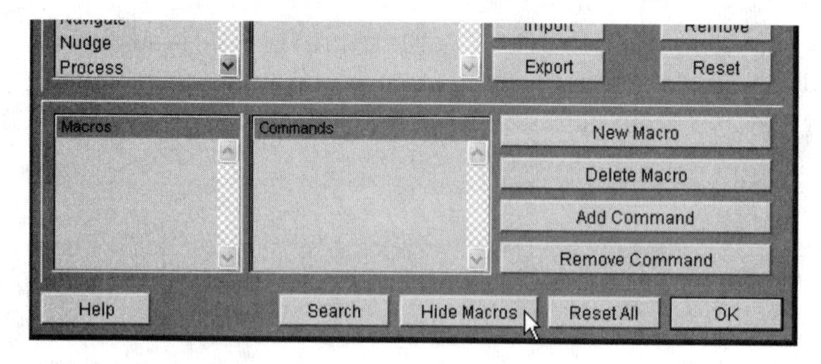

2. **Click New Macro.**

   A new, unnamed Macro appears in the Macros list.

3. **Use the Categories and Commands in the upper half of the dialog to select the first command you want to include in the Macro.**

4. **Click Add Command.**

   The selected command appears in the Commands list in the Macros section.

5. **Repeat this to add more commands to the Macro.**

   Note that commands are added after the currently selected command in the list. This allows you to insert commands "in the middle" of an existing Macro.

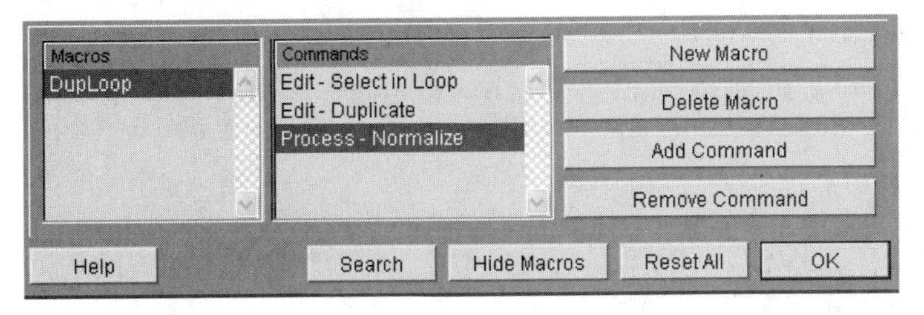

A Macro with three commands.

- **To remove a command from the Macro, select it in the lower Commands list and click Remove Command.**

6. **When you're done, you may want to name the Macro by clicking it in the list to the left and typing a new name.**

After you've closed the Key Commands dialog, all Macros you have created appear at the bottom of the Edit menu, available for instant selection.

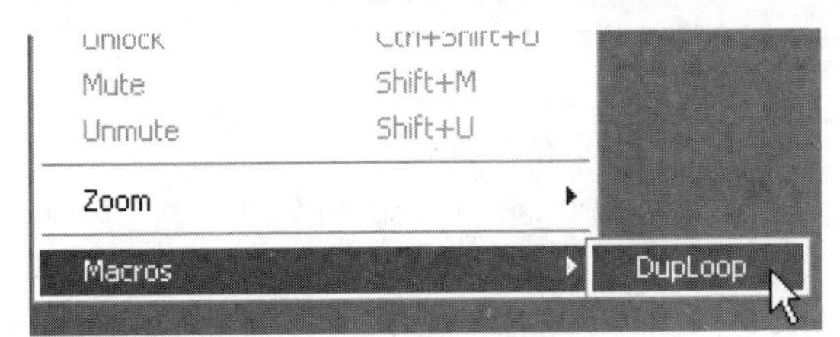

You can also assign key commands to Macros. All Macros you have created appear in the upper section of the Key Commands dialog under the Macros category—just select each Macro and assign a key command as with any function.

- **To remove a Macro, select it in the Macros list in the Key Commands dialog and click Delete Macro.**

34.2.4 Saving Complete Key Command Settings (Export)

As mentioned previously, any changes made to the key commands (and Macros) are automatically stored as a Cubase SX/SL preference. It is also possible to store key commands settings separately. In this way, you can store any number of different complete key command settings for instant recall. Proceed as follows:

1. **Set up the key commands and Macros to your liking.**

   When editing key commands, remember to click "Assign" to keep the changes.

2. **Click "Export".**

   A standard "Save As" dialog appears.

3. **Navigate to the desired folder, and enter a name for the key commands file.**

4. Click "Save".

A separate key commands file is created at the chosen location (the file gets the extension "*.key"). This file is actually a regular text file, and can be edited with any text editor.

34.2.5 Recalling Saved Key Command Settings (Import)

To recall saved key command settings, proceed as follows:

- Note that this operation will replace your existing key commands and Macros! If you want to be able to revert to these settings again, make sure to save them first!

1. Open the Key Commands dialog from the File menu.

2. Click "Import".

3. Select the key commands file you wish to open.

4. Click "Open".

The opened key commands file replaces the current key command settings.

34.2.6 About the "Show List" Function

Clicking this button opens a list of all currently assigned key commands divided into three columns; Keys, Categories and Commands—just like in the main Key Commands dialog. Note that this list only represents an overview and cannot be edited directly.

- If you press a key combination while viewing this list, the list automatically scrolls to the corresponding command (if available) and selects it in the list.
  This allows you to quickly check whether a certain key combination is "taken".

34.2.7 Searching for Key Commands

If you want to know which key command is assigned to a certain function in the program, you can use the Search function in the Key Commands dialog:

1. Click the Search button.

A search dialog appears.

2. **Click in the text field at the top of the dialog and type in the function for which you want to know the key command.**

   This is a standard word search function, so you should type the command as it is spelled in the program. Partial words are OK; to search for e.g. all quantize related commands you could type "Quantize", "Quant", etc.

3. **Press [Return].**

   The found commands are listed below. The left column shows the assigned key commands, if any.

4. **When you're done, click OK to close the dialog.**

34.2.8 About the "Reset" and "Reset All" Functions

These two buttons in the Key Commands dialog will both restore the factory default settings. The following rules apply:

- **"Reset" restores the factory default key command setting for the function selected in the Commands list.**
- **"Reset All" will restore the factory default key commands for all commands.**

● Note that the "Reset All" operation will remove any changes that may have been made to the factory default key commands! If you want to be able to revert to these settings again, make sure to save them first!

34.2.9 The Default Key Commands

As mentioned before there are numerous default key commands. These are listed in the Getting Started book for quick access, but you can also view a list of them in the program:

1. **If you want to keep any unsaved changes that may have been made to the factory default settings, save them first by using the Export function (see page 675).**

2. **Click "Reset All".**

   A prompt appears asking if you want to reset all key commands.

3. **Click "Reset All".**

4. **Now click "Show List".**

   The factory default key commands are shown in the list.

34.3 Setting Up Tool Modifier Keys

A tool modifier key is what you press to get an alternate function when using a tool. For example, clicking and dragging and event with the Arrow tool normally moves it—holding down a modifier key (by default [Alt]) will copy it instead.

The default tool modifier keys are listed in the Getting Started book, but you can customize them if needed. This is done in the Preferences dialog:

1. **Open the Preferences dialog from the File menu and select the Editing—Tool Modifiers page.**

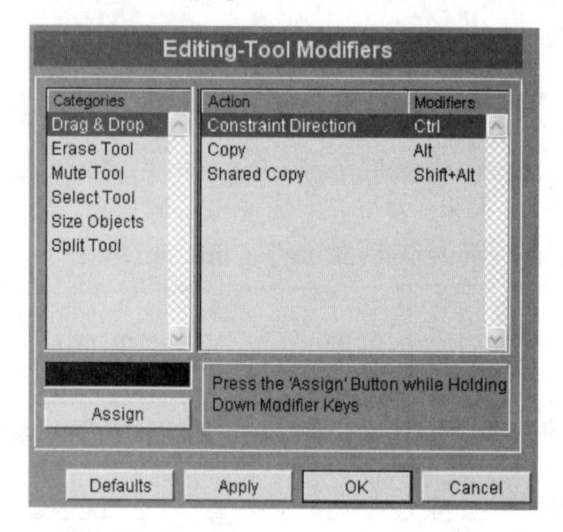

2. **Locate the action for which you want to edit the modifier key, by selecting an option in the Categories list.**

   For example, the "copy" function mentioned above resides in the category "Drag & Drop".

3. **Select the action in the Action list.**
4. **Hold down the desired modifier key(s) and click the Assign button.**

   The current modifier key(s) for the action is replaced. If the modifier key(s) you pressed are already assigned for this tool, you will be asked whether you want to replace them.

5. **When you're done, click OK to close the dialog.**

Appendix

A Menu Reference

A.1 About this Chapter

This chapter lists all main menu items in Cubase SX/SL, for quick reference. However, you won't find deeper explanations, backgrounds or procedures here—for this, please refer to the previous chapters in the manual.

A.2 File Menu

A.2.1 New Project

This item allows you to create a new untitled project. A list appears allowing you to select an empty project or a project template. The factory templates are preconfigured setups to suit various types of projects. A project can be saved as a template, and will then appear on this list.

After making a selection, a project file dialog appears allowing you to specify a folder where all files relating to the new project will be stored. Select an existing folder or click the Create button to create a new folder.

A.2.2 Open...

This item opens a file dialog allowing you to locate and open saved project files. Project files have the extension ".cpr". Several projects can be open at the same time, but only one can be active. The active project is indicated by the red light at the top left corner of the Project window.

A.2.3 Close

This closes the active window. If the Project window is active, the corresponding project will close.

A.2.4 Save

This saves any changes made to the project since you last saved. The Save command stores the project under its current name and location.

A.2.5 Save As...

Save As allows you to specify a new name and a new project folder for the project.

A.2.6 Save Project to New Folder...

This item allows you to save the project into a new empty folder. It has some additional features that can be used for archiving purposes.

When a new empty folder has been selected, a dialog appears where you can change the name of the project and set the following options:

- **You can choose to minimize audio files.**

  This will crop files based on the audio clips referenced in the project. As the clips used in the project may be references to much larger audio files, this can reduce the project size significantly.

- **You can apply Freeze Edits.**

  This will make all processing and applied effects (Cubase SX only) permanent for clips. See page 351.

- **You can choose to remove all unused files.**

When you save a project to a new folder, all files relating to the project based on the options set will be saved in the new project folder. The contents of the original project folder will be left untouched. If you are absolutely certain that you do not have any further need for the original project files you can delete them.

A.2.7 Save as Template...

You can save any project as a template. When you create a new project, the available templates are listed, allowing you to base the new project on the selected template.

Saved templates will contain everything that was in the original project, including clips and events.

A.2.8 Revert

This menu item allows you revert to the last saved version of a project. If any new audio files has been recorded since you last saved, you have the option of keeping or deleting these.

A.2.9 Page Setup...

This item opens the standard Page Setup dialog, used for deciding about paper formats etc., before printing.

A.2.10 Print...

Opens the standard Print dialog, allowing you to select which pages to print, how many copies of each etc.

A.2.11 Import

Audio File...

This command lets you import audio files directly into a project. The imported file will be placed at the current cursor position of the selected audio track.

Audio CD... (Cubase SX only)

This opens the Import from Audio CD dialog where you can import audio from CDs. For details about the dialog, see page 663 or use the Help function in the dialog.

Video File...

This opens a file dialog allowing you to import a video file onto the video track. You do not have to create a video track before importing, it is automatically created. The imported video will be placed at the current cursor position.

Cubase Song/Arrangement/Part...

You can import songs, arrangements and parts created with previous versions of Cubase (3.7 or later). Due to the complete redesign of Cubase SX/SL, there are certain limitations. Exactly what is and isn't imported from the different previous versions is described on page 661.

MIDI File...

You can import Standard MIDI Files of Type "0" (all data on single track) or Type "1" (data on several tracks). When you import, you can choose to import the file into the current project, or to create a new project.

A.2.12 Export

MIDI File...

This allows you to export your MIDI files as a Standard MIDI file. See page 660 for more information.

Audio Mixdown...

This allows you to export all your audio tracks, complete with effects and automation to one or several audio files, in one of several file formats. This is described on page 601.

A.2.13 Preferences...

The Preferences dialog contains various settings and options. The dialog has several pages, that you access by selecting items in the Explorer-like list on the left. To make settings without closing the dialog use the Apply button.

Use the Help button in the dialog for information about the items on the selected page.

A.2.14 Cleanup...

The Cleanup function helps you to save hard disk space by locating unused files which you can delete in the project folders on your disk.

A.2.15 Key Commands...

The Key Commands dialog allows you to create key commands for virtually any Cubase SX/SL function, as well as customizing existing key commands to your liking. Use the Help button in the dialog for information about the items in the dialog.

A.2.16 Recent Projects

This submenu provides shortcuts to the most recent projects you have been working with. The list is chronological with the most recent project at the top of the list.

A.2.17 Quit

This quits the program. If there are any unsaved changes in an open project, you will have the option of keeping these or discarding them before the program quits.

A.3 Edit Menu

A.3.1 Undo/Redo

Cubase SX/SL offers wide-ranging, multiple Undo, allowing you to undo virtually any action you perform.

- **To undo the last performed action, select Undo from the Edit menu, or use the corresponding key command (by default [Ctrl]+[Z]).**

  If you select Undo again, the previously performed action will be undone, and so on.

- **To redo the last undone action, select Redo from the Edit menu or use the corresponding key command (by default [Ctrl]+[Shift]+[Z]).**

  Undone actions will be available for Redo until you perform another action (at which point the "Redo Stack" is cleared—see »History…« below).

● You can specify how many levels of Undo should be available with the "Maximum Undo" setting on the User Interface page in the Preferences dialog on the File menu.

A.3.2 History...

The Edit History window contains a graphic representation of the "Undo Stack" (the performed actions, with the most recent action at the top of the stack) and the "Redo Stack" (the undone actions, with the most recently undone action at the bottom of the stack). The two stacks are separated by a divider line.

The Edit History dialog allows you to undo or redo several actions in one go, by moving the divider between the Undo Stack and the Redo Stack (in essence, moving actions from the Undo Stack to the Redo Stack, or vice versa).

A.3.3 Cut/Copy/Paste

You can cut or copy selected events (or selection ranges) and paste them in again at the current cursor position on the original track(s).

A.3.4 Paste at Origin

This will paste an event to its original position, i.e. where it was originally cut or copied from.

A.3.5 Delete

This will delete all selected events.

A.3.6 Split at Cursor

This splits selected events at the cursor position. If no events are selected, all events on all tracks intersected by the cursor position will be split.

A.3.7 Split Loop

This splits all events at the left and right locator positions.

A.3.8 Range

The items on the Range submenu have the following functions:

Function	Description
Cut Time	Cuts out the selection range and moves it to the clipboard. Events to the right of the removed range are moved to the left to fill out the gap.
Delete Time	The selection range is removed and events to the right are moved to the left to close up the gab.
Paste Time	Pastes the clipboard data at the start position and track of the current selection. Existing events are moved to make room for the pasted data.
Paste Time at Origin	Pastes the clipboard data back at its original position. Existing events are moved to make room for the pasted data.
Split	Splits any events or parts that are intersected by the selection range, at the positions of the selection range edges.

Function	Description
Crop	All events or parts that are partially within the selection range are cropped, that is, sections outside the selection range are removed. Events that are fully inside or outside the selection range are not affected.
Insert Silence	Inserts empty track space at the start of the selection range. The length of the inserted silence equals the length of the selection range. Events to the right of the selection range start are moved to the right to "make room". Events that are intersected by the selection range start are split, and the right section is moved to the right.

A.3.9 Select

The items on this submenu have different functions, depending on whether the regular event selection tool (Arrow tool) or the Range Selection tool is selected:

Event Selection

Option	Description
All	Selects all events in the window.
None	Deselects all events.
In Loop	Selects all events that are partly or wholly between the left and right locator.
From Start to Cursor	Selects all events that begin to the left of the project cursor.
From Cursor to End	Selects all events that end to the right of the project cursor.
All on Selected Tracks	Selects all events on the selected track.

Range Selection

Option	Description
All	In the Project window, this makes a selection that covers all tracks, from the start of the project to the end. In the Sample Editor, this selects the whole clip.
None	Removes the current selection range.
In Loop	Makes a selection between the left and right locator. In the Project window, the selection will span all tracks.
From Start to Cursor	Makes a selection from the start of the project to the project cursor. In the Project window, the selection will span all tracks.
From Cursor to End	Makes a selection from the project cursor to the end of the project. In the Project window, the selection will span all tracks.
Select event	This item (only available in the Sample Editor) selects the audio that is included in the edited event only.
Left Selection Side to Cursor	Moves the left side of the current selection range to the project cursor position.
Right Selection Side to Cursor	Moves the right side of the current selection range to the project cursor position.

A.3.10 Duplicate/Repeat...

- **Duplicate creates a copy of the selected event and places it directly after the original.**

  If several events are selected, all of these are copied "as one unit", maintaining the relative distance between the events.

- **Selecting "Repeat..." from the Edit menu opens a dialog, allowing you to create a number of copies (regular or shared) of the selected event(s).**

  This works just like the Duplicate function, except that you can specify the number of copies.

A.3.11 Fill Loop

This creates a number of copies starting at the left locator and ending at the right locator. The last copy is automatically shortened to end at the right locator position.

A.3.12 Move to

The following functions are available from this submenu:

Function	Description
Move to Cursor	Moves the selected event to the project cursor position. If there are several selected events on the same track, the first event will start at the cursor, and the following will be lined up end-to-start after the first one.
Move to Origin	Moves the selected events to their original positions, i.e. the positions at which they were originally recorded.
Move to Front/ Move to Back	This function doesn't actually change the position of the events, but moves the selected events to the front or back, respectively. This is useful if you have overlapping events, and want to see one that is partially obscured. For audio events, this is an extra important feature, since only the visible sections of events will be played back. Moving an obscured audio event to front (or moving the obscuring event to back) will allow you to hear the whole event on playback. Note that it is also possible to use the "Front" function on the event context menu for this (although this works in a different way—see page 90).

A.3.13 Convert to Real Copy

This creates a new version of a clip (that can be edited independently) and adds this to the Pool.

A.3.14 Lock.../Unlock

If you want to make sure you don't edit or move an event by accident, you can lock the selected event(s). Locking can affect one (or any combination) of the following properties:

Lock Options	Description
Position	If this is locked, the event cannot be moved.
Size	If this is locked, the event cannot be resized.
Other	If this is locked, all other editing of the event is disabled. This includes adjusting the fades and event volume, processing, etc.

To specify which of these properties should be affected by the Lock function, use the "Lock Event Attributes" pop-up menu in the Preferences dialog (Editing page).

Selecting locked events and choosing "Unlock" will unlock the events.

A.3.15 Mute/Unmute

You can mute (silence) events by selecting them and selecting "Mute".

Similarly, you can unmute the selected events by selecting "Unmute".

A.3.16 Zoom

The following options are available on the Zoom submenu on the Edit menu:

Option	Description
Zoom In	Zooms in one step, centering on the position cursor.
Zoom Out	Zooms out one step, centering on the position cursor.
Zoom Full	Zooms out so that the whole project is visible. "The whole project" means the timeline from the project start to the Length set in the Project Setup dialog (see above).
Zoom to Selection	Zooms in horizontally so that the current selection fills the screen.
Zoom to Event	This option is available only in the Sample Editor (see page 364).

Option	Description
Zoom In Vertical	Zooms in one step vertically.
Zoom Out Vertical	Zooms out one step vertically.
Zoom In Tracks	Zooms in selected track(s) one step vertically.
Zoom Out Tracks	Zooms out selected track(s) one step vertically.
Zoom Tracks Exclusive	This zooms in vertically on the selected track(s) and minimizes the height of all other tracks.

A.3.17 Macros

If you have created Macros, these will be available on the Macros submenu. A Macro is a combination of several functions or commands, to be performed in one go. Macros are set up in the Key Commands dialog—see page 674.

A.4 Project Menu

A.4.1 Add Track

This will add a track of the type selected on the Add Track submenu.

Selecting "Multiple" allows you to add a specified number of tracks of a selected type.

A.4.2 Remove Selected Tracks

This will remove all selected tracks and any parts or events on them from the Project window.

A.4.3 Show Used Automation

This will open all used automation subtracks for all tracks.

A.4.4 Hide All Automation

This closes all open automation subtracks.

A.4.5 Pool

This opens the audio Pool, which contains all clips (audio and video) that belong to a project.

A.4.6 Markers

This opens the Marker window. Markers store positions to facilitate quick navigation to important locations in a project.

A.4.7 Tempo Track

This menu item opens the Tempo Track Editor. For tempo based tracks, the tempo can follow the Tempo track (activated with the Master button on the Transport panel), which may contain tempo changes.

A.4.8 Browser

This opens the Project Browser window which provides a list based representation of the project. This allows you to view and edit all events on all tracks by using regular value editing in a list.

A.4.9 Beat Calculator...

This opens the Beat Calculator window. The Beat Calculator is a tool for calculating the tempo of recorded audio or MIDI material.

A.4.10 Notepad

This opens a standard text notepad.

A.4.11 Project Setup...

This dialog contains general settings for a project. See the dialog help for specifics.

A.4.12 Auto Fades Settings...

This opens the Auto Fades dialog, where you can specify various fade options. Use the Help button in the dialog for details.

A.5 Audio Menu

A.5.1 Process

Basically, you apply audio processing by making a selection and selecting a function from the Process submenu. For more details about what is affected see page 330. For details about the functions and parameters in the various processing dialogs, use the Help button in the corresponding dialog.

Envelope

The Envelope function allows you to apply a volume envelope to the selected audio.

Fade In/Out

Allows you to set fade-ins and fade-outs.

Gain

Allows you to change the gain (level) of the selected audio.

Merge Clipboard

This function mixes the audio from the clipboard into the audio selected for processing, starting at the beginning of the selection.

For this function to be available, you need to have cut or copied a range of audio in the Sample Editor first.

Noise Gate

Scans the audio for sections weaker than a specified threshold level, and silences them.

Normalize

The Normalize function allows you to specify the desired maximum level of the audio. It then analyzes the selected audio and finds the current maximum level. Finally it subtracts the current maximum level from the specified level, and raises the gain of the audio by the resulting amount (if the specified maximum level is lower than the current maximum, the gain will be lowered instead). A common use for normalizing is to raise the level of audio that was recorded at too low an input level.

Phase Reverse

Reverses the phase of the selected audio, turning the waveform "upside down".

Pitch Shift

This function allows you to change the pitch of the audio with or without affecting its length. You can also create "harmonies" by specifying several pitches, or apply pitch shift based on a user specified envelope curve.

Remove DC Offset

This function will remove any DC offset in the audio selection. A DC offset is when there is too large a DC (direct current) component in the signal, sometimes visible as the signal not being visually centered around the "zero level axis". DC offsets do not affect what you actually hear, but they affect zero crossing detection and certain processing, and it is recommended that you remove them.

It is recommended that this function is applied to complete audio clips, since the DC offset (if any) is normally present throughout the entire recording.

Reverse

Reverses the audio selection, as when playing a tape backwards.

Silence

Replaces the selection with silence.

Stereo Flip

This function works with stereo audio selections only. It allows you to manipulate the left and right channel in various ways.

Time Stretch

This function allows you to change the length and "tempo" of the selected audio, without affecting the pitch.

A.5.2 Plug-ins (Cubase SX only)

All installed effect plug-ins are available separately on the Audio menu. This allows you to apply effects processing to one or several selected events. See page 347 for more details.

A.5.3 Spectrum Analyzer (Cubase SX only)

This function analyzes the selected audio, computes the average "spectrum" (level distribution over the frequency range) and displays this as a two-dimensional graph, with frequency on the x-axis and level on the y-axis.

A.5.4 Statistics (Cubase SX only)

The Statistics function analyzes the selected audio (events, clips or range selections) and displays a window with various information. Use the Help button in the dialog for details.

A.5.5 Hitpoints

This is a special feature that detects transient attacks in audio material and adds a type of marker, a "hitpoint" at each attack. Once the hitpoints have been correctly set, you can slice up the file which amongst other things enables you to change the tempo without affecting pitch. See page 385 for a full description of this feature.

A.5.6 Detect Silence

The Detect Silence function searches for silent sections in an event, and either splits the event, removing the silent parts from the project, or creates regions corresponding to the non-silent sections.

A.5.7 Event as Region

This function is available when one or several audio events are selected. It creates a region in the corresponding clip, with the start and end position of the region determined by the start and end position of the event within the clip.

A.5.8 Event from Regions

This function is available if you have selected an audio event whose clip contains regions within the boundaries of the event. The function will remove the original event and replace it with event(s) positioned and sized according to the region(s).

A.5.9 Create Region(s)

This allows you to create a region based on the current selection in the Sample Editor.

A.5.10 Events to Part

This allows you to create a part from selected audio events.

A.5.11 Close Gaps

This function is primarily intended for the Hitpoints feature, to close the gaps created when playing back an audio file that has been sliced for tempo changes at a tempo lower than the original.

A.5.12 Dissolve Part

This menu item dissolves a selected audio part and makes any audio events it contains appear as independent objects on the track.

A.5.13 Snap Point to Cursor

This allows you to set the snap point to the current cursor position. See page 366.

A.5.14 Bounce Selection

This allows you to create either a new clip or a new audio file from a selection.

A.5.15 Crossfade

This allows you to create a crossfade between two selected consecutive audio events.

- If the two events overlap, the crossfade will be applied to the overlapping area.
- If they do not overlap (but their respective audio clips do) the events are resized and a crossfade is applied in the overlapping range.

For more information about crossfades, see the chapter "Fades and Crossfades".

A.5.16 Remove Fades

This will remove any fades or crossfades from a selected event.

A.5.17 Open Fade Editor(s)

This opens the Fade dialog for a selected event. Note that this will open two dialogs if the event has both fade-in and fade-out curves.

A.5.18 Find Selected in Pool

This can be used to quickly find the clips in the Pool for events selected in the Project window. When this menu item is selected, the Pool opens with the corresponding clip(s) highlighted.

A.5.19 Adjust Fades to Range

This allows you to adjust a fade area according to a range selection.

A.5.20 Offline Process History

This opens the Offline Process History dialog. In the dialog you can remove some or all processing previously applied to a clip. See the dialog help for details.

A.5.21 Freeze Edits

This allows you to make any processing or applied effects permanent for a clip. See page 351.

A.6 MIDI Menu

A.6.1 Open Key Editor

This opens the Key Editor for a selected MIDI Part. This editor consists of a piano-roll type graphic interface, with the notes shown as boxes in a grid.

A.6.2 Scores Submenu (Cubase SL only)

If you are using Cubase SL, this is where you open the Score Editor and make score settings. Note that the three last items on this submenu are only available when the Score Editor is open and the active window.

Open Score Editor

Opens the Score Editor for the currently selected part(s).

Staff Settings

Brings up a dialog in which you can make settings for the currently active staff (track). In the Score Editor, the active staff is indicated by a black rectangle in the left part of the first visible bar—click in a staff to make it the active staff. For a description of the items in the Staff Settings dialog, please use the Help button in the dialog.

Set Font

Allows you to make font, size and style settings for text you have inserted in the score with the Text tool. If a text block is selected when you make settings in this dialog, the settings will only apply to that text. If you make settings with no text block selected, the settings will be used as default (automatically applied to all text you enter from that point on).

Flip Stems

Flips the direction of the stems of the selected notes.

A.6.3 Open Score Editor (Cubase SX only)

This opens the Score Editor where MIDI data is interpreted as a musical score. See the Score pdf document for details.

A.6.4 Open Drum Editor

This opens the Drum Editor which is designed especially for editing drum and percussion tracks.

A.6.5 Open List Editor

This opens the List Editor. In this editor, MIDI notes, controllers and other events are shown in a list.

A.6.6 Over Quantize

Quantizing is a function that automatically moves recorded notes, positioning them on exact note values. This quantizes the selected MIDI parts or notes, according to the current Quantize pop-up menu setting.

A.6.7 Iterative Quantize

Instead of moving a note to the closest quantize grid position, Iterative Quantize moves it only part of the way. You specify how much the notes should be moved towards the grid with the Iterative Strength setting in the Quantize Setup dialog.

A.6.8 Quantize Setup

In the Quantize Setup dialog you can make various quantize settings. Use the help in the dialog for details.

A.6.9 Advanced Quantize

Quantize Lengths

This will quantize the length of the notes, without changing their start positions. At its most basic level, this function will set the length of the notes to the Length Quantize value on the toolbar of the MIDI editors.

This function is only available from within the MIDI editors.

Quantize Ends

The Quantize Ends function on the Quantize submenu will only affect the end positions of notes. Apart from that, it works just like regular quantizing, taking the Quantize pop-up menu setting into account.

Undo Quantize

You can revert the selected MIDI notes to their original, unquantized state at any time. This is independent from the regular Undo History.

Freeze Quantize

There may be situations when you want to make the quantized positions "permanent". For example, you may want to quantize notes a second time, having the results based on the current quantized positions rather than the original positions. To make this possible, select the notes in question and use this function.

A.6.10 Transpose...

This opens the Transpose dialog, where you can make transpose settings for selected notes.

A.6.11 Merge MIDI in Loop

This combines all MIDI events between the left and right locator on all unmuted tracks and generates a new MIDI part, containing all the events as you would hear them play back. The new part will end up on the selected track, between the locators. You are asked whether to include MIDI insert effects and/or send effects and whether to overwrite (erase) the data on the destination track.

A typical use for this is to "freeze" the settings you have made in the MIDI Track Inspector, applying e.g. MIDI effects to a single part.

A.6.12 Dissolve Part

This item has two uses:

- **To separate events according to MIDI channel when a MIDI Part contains events on different channels (MIDI channel "Any").**
- **To separate MIDI events according to pitch.**

  Drum tracks typically have separate drum sounds for each pitch.

See page 467 for a closer description of these functions.

A.6.13 O-Note Conversion

This function (only available if a drum map has been assigned for the MIDI track) goes through the selected MIDI part(s) and sets the actual pitch of each note according to its O-note setting. This is useful if you want to convert the track to a "regular" MIDI track (with no drum map) and still have the notes play back the correct drum sound.

A.6.14 Functions

Legato

Extends each selected note so that it reaches the next note. You can specify the desired gap or overlap with the "Legato Overlap" setting in the Preferences dialog (MIDI—Function Parameters page).

Fixed Lengths

Resizes all selected notes to the length set with the Length Quantize pop-up menu on the MIDI Editor toolbar.

This function is only available from within the MIDI Editors.

Delete Doubles

Removes double notes, i.e. notes of the same pitch on the exact same position. Double notes can occur when recording in Cycle mode, after Quantizing, etc. This function always affects whole MIDI parts.

Delete Controllers

Removes all non-note Events from the selected MIDI parts. This function always affects whole MIDI parts.

Delete Notes...

Allows you to delete very short or weak notes. This is useful for automatically removing unwanted "ghost notes" after recording. Selecting "Delete Notes..." opens a dialog in which you set up the criteria for the function.

Restrict Polyphony

Selecting this item opens a dialog in which you can specify how many "voices" should be used (for the selected notes or parts). Restricting the polyphony this way is useful when you have an instrument with limited polyphony and want to make sure all notes will be played. The effect is achieved by shortening notes as required, so that they end before the next note starts.

Pedals to Note Length

This function scans for sustain pedal on/off events, lengthens the affected notes to match the sustain pedal off position, and then removes the Sustain Controller on/off events.

Delete Overlaps (mono)

This function allows you to make sure that no two notes of the same pitch overlap (i.e. that one starts before the other ends). Overlapping notes of the same pitch can confuse some MIDI instruments (a new Note On is transmitted before the Note Off is transmitted). This command can then be used to automatically rectify the problem.

Delete Overlaps (poly)

This function shortens notes when required, so that no note begins before another ends. This happens regardless of which pitch the notes have.

Velocity...

Opens a dialog that allows you to manipulate the velocity of notes in various ways.

Fixed Velocity

This function sets the velocity of all selected notes to the Insert Velocity value on the toolbar in the MIDI Editors.

Reverse

This inverts the order of the selected events (or of all events in the selected parts), causing the MIDI music to play backwards. Note though, that the effect is different from reversing an audio recording. With MIDI, the individual notes will still play as usual in the MIDI instrument—it's only the order of playback that is changed.

A.6.15 Logical Editor...

This opens the Logical Editor where you can perform advanced "search and replace" operations on MIDI data. The Logical Editor is described on page 549.

A.6.16 Logical Presets

This submenu contains various presets for use with the Logical Editor.

A.6.17 Drum Map Setup...

This is where you load, create, modify and save drum maps. The list to the left shows the currently loaded drum maps; selecting a drum map in the list displays its sounds and settings to the right.

A.6.18 Reset

This function sends out note-off messages and resets controllers on all MIDI channels. You can use this if you experience hanging notes or stuck controllers etc.

A.7 Scores Menu (Cubase SX only)

The items on the Scores menu are described separately in the pdf document "Score Layout and Printing" (opened from the Windows Start menu or the Help menu in the program).

A.8 Pool Menu

A.8.1 Import Medium...

The Import Medium dialog is used for importing files directly into the Pool. It is only available from the Pool menu when the Pool is open.

A.8.2 Import Audio CD... (Cubase SX only)

This opens a dialog that allows you to import audio from audio CDs.

A.8.3 Import Pool...

Steinberg's Nuendo application can export the Pool as a separate file (file extension ".npl"). Such Pool files can be imported into Cubase SX/SL, by using the Import Pool command on the Pool menu. When you import a Pool file, the file references in it are "added" to the current Pool.

The audio and video files themselves are not saved in the Pool file, only a reference to them. For there to be any point in importing a Pool file, you need access to all reference files (which preferably should have the same file paths as when the Pool was saved).

A.8.4 Export Pool...

This allows you to export the pool as a separate file (see above).

A.8.5 Find Missing Files...

This opens the Resolve Missing Files dialog that can be used to find referenced files that may have been moved or renamed etc.

In the dialog that appears, decide if you want the program to try the find the file for you (Search), if you want to do it yourself (Locate) or if you want to specify in which directory the program should search for the file (Folder).

A.8.6 Remove Missing Files

If the Pool contains audio files that cannot be found or reconstructed, you may want to remove these:

Select this item to remove all missing files from the Pool (and remove their corresponding events from the Project window).

A.8.7 Reconstruct

If a missing file cannot be found (e.g. if you have accidentally deleted it from the hard disk) it will normally be indicated with a question mark in the Status column in the Pool. However, if the missing file is an edit file (a file created when you process audio, stored in the Edits folder within the project folder), it may be possible for the program to reconstruct it by recreating the editing to the original audio file. See page 409.

A.8.8 Convert Files...

This opens the Convert Options dialog which operates on selected files. Use the pop-up menus to specify which audio file attributes you want to keep and which you want to convert.

A.8.9 Conform Files...

This will change all selected files that have different file attributes to what is specified for the project, to conform to this standard.

A.8.10 Create Folder

This allows you to create a new audio subfolder and designate this as your Pool Record folder.

A.8.11 Empty Trash

To delete a file permanently from the hard disk, it must first be moved to the Trash folder. When clips are in the Trash folder they can be removed permanently by using this command.

A.8.12 Remove Unused Media

This function finds all clips in the Pool that are not used in the project, and either moves them to the Pool Trash folder where they can be permanently deleted, or removes them from the Pool.

A.8.13 Prepare Archive...

This command should be used when you want to archive a project. It checks that every clip referenced in the project is located in the same folder.

A.8.14 Set Pool Record Folder

This is used to designate a new Pool Record folder. Select the folder, and choose this command to change the Pool Record folder to the selected folder.

A.8.15 Minimize File

This allows you to change the size of audio files according to the audio clips referenced in a project. The files produced using this option will only contain the audio file portions actually used in the project, which can significantly reduce the size of the project (given that large portions of the audio files are unused).

A.8.16 Update Origin

The original start position where a clip was recorded in the project is shown in the Pool "Origin Time" column. As this value can be used as a basis for the "Insert into Project" Pool menu item (and other functions), you can change it if the Origin Time value is redundant. This can be done by selecting the corresponding clip in the Pool, moving the project cursor to the new desired position and selecting this menu item.

A.8.17 New Version

This allows you to create a new version of a selected clip. The new version appears in the same Pool folder, with the same name but with a "version number" after it, to indicate that the new clip is a duplicate. The first copy made of a clip will logically get the version number "2" and so on.

- Note: Copying a clip does not create a new file on disk, but just a new edit version of the clip (referring to the same original file).

A.8.18 Insert into Project

This allows you to insert clips selected in the Pool to the project. Either the Origin Time value or the current cursor position can decide where the clips are inserted, and is selected on the submenu for this menu item.

A.8.19 Select in Project

If you want to find out which events in the project refer to a particular clip in the Pool you can use this function. Select the clip in the Pool, and use this menu item. The corresponding event(s) will then be selected in the Project window.

A.8.20 Find in Pool...

You can perform a search of the Pool to locate particular clips or regions. You can specify various criteria to match in the dialog that appears.

A.9 Transport Menu

A.9.1 Transport Panel

This opens the Transport panel.

A.9.2 Locators to Selection

This will set the locators to encompass the currently selected range.

A.9.3 Locate Selection

This moves the project cursor to the start of the currently selected range.

A.9.4 Locate Next Marker

This moves the project cursor to the next marker position.

A.9.5 Locate Previous Marker

This moves the project cursor to the previous marker position.

A.9.6 Locate Next Event

This moves the project cursor to the next event start or end on the selected track.

A.9.7 Locate Previous Event

This moves the project cursor to the previous event start or end on the selected track.

A.9.8 Play from Selection Start

This will move the project cursor to the start of the current selection and activate playback.

A.9.9 Play from Selection End

This will move the project cursor to the end of the current selection and activate playback.

A.9.10 Play until Selection Start

This activates playback two seconds before the start of the currently selected range and stops at the selection start.

A.9.11 Play until Selection End

This activates playback two seconds before the end of the selected range and stops at the selection end.

A.9.12 Play until Next Marker

This will activate playback from the current project cursor position to the next marker and stop.

A.9.13 Play Selection Range

This will play back the current selection range and stop at the end.

A.9.14 Loop Selection

This will loop playback of the current selection range.

A.9.15 Use Pre/Post-Roll

If this is ticked, Pre/Postroll is activated. This is described on page 102.

A.9.16 Start Record at Left Locator

If this is ticked, the project cursor will jump to the left locator position and begin recording when you hit the Record button. If this is off (unticked), recording will start directly from the current project cursor position.

A.9.17 Metronome Setup

This opens the Metronome Setup dialog where you can make various metronome settings.

A.9.18 Metronome On

This activates the metronome.

A.9.19 Sync Setup

This opens a dialog where settings relating to synchronization can be made.

A.9.20 Sync Online

This activates synchronization.

A.10 Devices Menu

A.10.1 MIDI Device Manager

The MIDI Device manager allows you to install MIDI devices. You can either select pre-configured MIDI devices from a list, or define a device from scratch. For information about installing MIDI devices, please refer to the chapter "MIDI devices and patches".

A.10.2 Mixer

This opens the Mixer. All audio, MIDI and group tracks in a project have a corresponding channel strip in the Mixer, as do any activated VST Instruments and ReWire channels. The Master bus fader can also be shown in the Mixer.

A.10.3 Plug-in Information

The Plug-in Information window lists all installed VST, DirectX and MIDI plug-ins, and shows various information about them.

A.10.4 True Tape (Cubase SX only)

TrueTape™ is a unique Steinberg technology that emulates the behavior of a professional analog tape recorder. This effect is applied when you record audio—in other words, TrueTape can be viewed as a separate recording mode. Selecting this item opens the TrueTape panel, in which you can activate and set up TrueTape.

A.10.5 VST Inputs

This opens the VST Inputs window, which allows you to activate audio inputs connected to your audio hardware.

A.10.6 VST Instruments

This opens the VST Instruments window, where you can select up to 32 VST Instruments (16 in Cubase SL). When a VST Instrument has been selected for a slot in the window, the corresponding instrument is selectable as a destination on the MIDI output pop-up for MIDI tracks.

A.10.7 VST Master Effects

Up to 8 Master effects can be added to the signal on the Master bus (up to 4 in Cubase SL). The last two effect slots are post Master gain (in Cubase SL there is one—slot 4), which is useful for dithering plug-ins.

A.10.8 VST Master Setup (Cubase SX only)

This opens the VST Master Setup dialog, which is used for selecting various surround configurations.

A.10.9 VST Outputs

The VST Outputs window shows the output buses connected to the physical outputs on your audio hardware.

A.10.10 VST Performance

This window indicates the current CPU load and disk transfer rate.

A.10.11 VST Send Effects

This is used for selecting global send effects. Up to 8 send effects can be selected.

A.10.12 Video

This opens the default video player. The default video player is selected in the Device Setup dialog.

A.10.13 Show Panel

This opens a panel where you can directly select any of the current devices on the Device menu.

A.10.14 Device Setup...

This dialog allows you to add or remove remote control devices and to make various basic settings for audio and MIDI such as selecting ASIO drivers and MIDI ports etc.

A.11 Window Menu

A.11.1 Close

This closes the currently active window. If the active window is a Project window, the project will close.

A.11.2 Close All

This closes all windows including all open projects.

A.11.3 Minimize All

Minimizes all windows.

A.11.4 Restore All

Restores all minimized Cubase SX/SL windows.

A.11.5 Tile Horizontal/Vertical

Arranges the open windows next to each other on screen.

A.11.6 Cascade

Arranges the open windows in a partially overlapping pattern.

A.11.7 Window Layout

A configuration of windows for the active project is called a "Window Layout". By storing different window combinations as Window Layouts, you can quickly switch between different working modes.

A.11.8 Windows…

This opens a dialog where you can manage and make settings for all open windows.

A.11.9 The Open Windows List

Selecting a window from the list at the bottom of the menu brings it to front.

A.12 Help Menu

A.12.1 HTML Help

This opens the browsable HTML help.

A.12.2 Documentation (Acrobat PDF format)

Getting Started

Opens the Getting Started book in Acrobat pdf format. To read this you need to have the Acrobat Reader installed (included with Cubase SX/SL).

Operation Manual

Opens the Operation Manual in Acrobat pdf format. To read this you need to have the Acrobat reader installed (included with Cubase SX/SL).

Score Layout and Printing (Cubase SX only)

Opens the separate pdf document about using Cubase SX Score Editor. To read this you need to have the Acrobat reader installed (included with Cubase SX/SL).

A.12.3 Steinberg on the Web

On the submenu you can select various Steinberg related web pages. Selecting one will open the corresponding page in your default browser. An active internet connection is required.

A.12.4 About Cubase SX/SL

This opens a window with information about the Cubase SX/SL version number etc.

B Parameters of the Included Effect Plug-ins

B.1 DoubleDelay

This effect provides two separate delays that can be either tempo based or use freely specified delay time settings. Cubase SX/SL automatically provides the plug-in with the tempo currently used in the project. The parameters are as follows:

Parameter	Values	Description
Mix	0—100%	Sets the level balance between the dry signal and the effect. If DoubleDelay is used as a send effect, this should be set to maximum (100%) as you can control the dry/effect balance with the send.
Tempo sync on/off		The buttons above the two Delay Time knobs are used to turn tempo sync on or off for the respective delay. If set to off (the buttons are white) the delay time can be set freely with the Delay Time knobs, without sync to tempo.
Delay Time 1	1/1—1/32, 1/1—1/32 Triplet, 1/1—1/32 Dotted or 0—9999ms	This is where you specify the base note value for the delay if tempo sync is on. If tempo sync is off, it sets the delay time in milliseconds.
Delay Time 2	As above	As above.
Feedback	0—100%	This sets the number of repeats for both delays.

Parameter	Values	Description
Tempo Sync 1	×1 to ×10	The note value multiplier for the first delay unit.
Tempo Sync 2	×1 to ×10	As above, but for the second delay unit.
Pan1	-100 to 100%	This sets the stereo position for the first delay.
Pan2	-100 to 100%	This sets the stereo position for the second delay.

You can also change parameters in the graphic display window. This works as follows:

- **If tempo sync is on, you can set the Tempo Sync 1 parameter by dragging the light blue handle left and right.**

  When tempo sync is off, this sets the Delay Time 1 parameter.

- **You can set the Pan 1 parameter by dragging the light blue handle up and down.**
- **The dark blue handle works in the same way but for the corresponding second delay parameters.**

B.2 ModDelay

This is a delay effect that can either be tempo-based or use freely specified delay time settings. The delay repeats can also be modulated. The parameters are as follows:

Parameter	Values	Description
Mix	0—100%	Sets the level balance between the dry signal and the effect. If ModDelay is used as a send effect, this should be set to maximum as you can control the dry/effect balance with the send.
Tempo sync on/off		The button above the Delay Time knob is used to turn tempo sync on or off. If set to off (white button) the delay time can be set freely with the Delay Time knob, without sync to tempo.
Feedback	0—100%	This sets the number of repeats for the delay.
Delay Time	1/1—1/32, 1/1—1/32 Triplet, 1/1—1/32 Dotted or 0—9999ms	This is where you specify the base note value for the delay if tempo sync is on. If tempo sync is off, it sets the delay time in milliseconds.
Tempo Sync knob	x1 to x10	This is the note value multiplier for the delay when tempo sync is used.
DelayMod.	0—100%	This controls the pitch modulation rate for the delay effect.

B.3 DaTube

This effect emulates the characteristic warm, lush sound of a tube amplifier. It is usable both as an insert effect and a send effect:

Parameter	Values	Description
Drive	0—100%	Regulates the pre-gain of the "amplifier". Use high values if you want an overdriven sound just on the verge of distortion.
Balance	0—100%	This controls the balance between the signal processed by the Drive parameter and the dry input signal. For maximum drive effect, set this to its highest value.
Output	-∞—0.000	Adjusts the post-gain, or output level, of the "amplifier".

B.4 Overdrive

Overdrive is a distortion-type effect, emulating the sound of a guitar amplifier. A selection of factory styles is available. Note that these are not stored parameter settings, but different basic overdrive algorithms, with the style names indicating the basic character of each algorithm. The parameters are as follows:

Parameter	Values	Description
Input	-15 to +15dB	Sets the input level.
Output	-15 to +15dB	Sets the output level. As overdrive generates harmonics, it increases the level of the processed signal. You can use the Output fader to compensate for the level increase.
Speaker simulation	On/Off	Simulates the sound of a speaker cabinet.
Factory Styles	Warm, Chordy, Magic OD, Fat Drive, Woody, Bluesy	Select one of six presets, which can be used as they are or as a basis for further "tweaking".
Bass	-15 to +15dB	Tone control for the low frequencies.
Mid	-15 to +15dB	Tone control for the mid frequencies.
Hi	-15 to +15dB	Tone control for the high frequencies.
Drive	0—100%	Governs the amount of overdrive. You can also adjust this by clicking and dragging in the display.

B.5 QuadraFuzz

QuadraFuzz is a high quality distortion effect allowing control over the level divided into four frequency bands both before and after distortion. This high level of control can create a very wide selection of distortion effects, ranging from subtle to extreme. The user interface consists of two windows.

- **The main window features four Filterbank controls, the master Gain and Output controls and an preset selector.**
- **In the editor window (which is opened by clicking the "Edit" button in the lower right corner) the main feature is a frequency band display.**

  This is where you set the width of the frequency bands as well as their level before distortion.

B.5.1 How Does QuadraFuzz Work?

Here's a short description of the three major factors that determine how QuadraFuzz sounds, and where you find the corresponding controls:

- The signal volume control *before* distortion.
  You can use the Gain control on the left side of the QuadraFuzz main window to control the overall input level of the signal that is fed into the distortion stage. The signal is split up into four frequency bands in the editor window, with adjustable width and level controls. These control the input level before distortion.

- The distortion type, based on a selectable distortion characteristic.

- The signal volume control *after* distortion.
  The Output control on the right side of the QuadraFuzz main window controls the overall output level. In addition, the Filterbank controls in the same window allow you to raise or lower the output volume of each separate frequency band that was defined in the editor window.

B.5.2 Editing in the Frequency Band Display

The signal is divided into four frequency bands before being passed to the distortion stage, as explained earlier. You adjust the level and width of these bands in the frequency display.

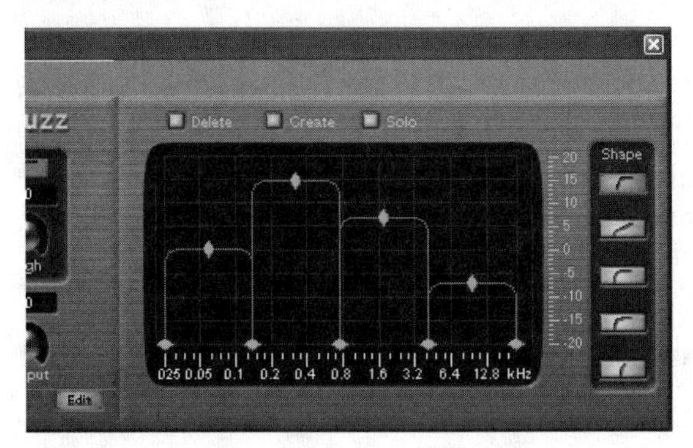

The frequency band display

Two value scales as well as a number of rhomb- and diamond-shaped handles are available.

- The diamond-shaped handles at the bottom are used to define the corner frequencies of the different frequency bands.
- By using the rhomb-shaped handles on top of each frequency band you determine its relative level before distortion.
- The horizontal value scale below the Frequency band display indicates frequency. The maximum value on this scale corresponds to half the sample rate of the audio file used (Nyquist theorem).
- The vertical value scale to the right shows the approximate level of an edited frequency band.
- If you click and hold on one of the handles, its current value is displayed. Depending on the handle type, corner frequency or level is shown.
- The corner frequency handles can be moved by dragging horizontally. The level handles can be moved by dragging them up or down.
- To reset a level handle to 0 dB, hold down the [Shift] key on your computer keyboard and click on the handle.
- If you hold down the [Ctrl] key and move a handle, the values will change in smaller steps.
- The "Solo" button above the frequency band display allows you to monitor individual frequency bands.
  If Solo is activated, one of the four bands is highlighted indicating the selected band. You select other bands by clicking on them.

B.5.3 The Parameters

The following tables list all parameters available in QuadraFuzz.

The parameters in the main window are as follows:

Parameter	Description
Gain dial	This dial can be found in the lower left corner of the QudraFuzz window. You can use it to control the level of the overall input signal before distortion.
Filterbank dials: Low/Low Mid/ High Mid/High	These dials are used to control the output level of the corresponding frequency band *after* distortion. Values between +/- 12 dB can be set for each band.
Presets fader	This is used to select one of the available presets. To select a new preset, click on the fader handle and drag horizontally.
Output dial	This controls the overall output level.

Parameter	Description
Over LED	When lit, this indicates that the total input signal level exceeds 0 dB. This LED does not refer to the output level but solely to the input level before distortion. Levels above 0 dB are subject to strict limiting and cause signal clipping. As this is sometimes what you want, QuadraFuzz also offers this option.
Edit button	By clicking on this button, located in the lower right corner of the main window, you can open or close the editor window.

The parameters in the edit window are as follows:

Parameter	Description
Create	If you click on this, a dialog will open where you can add and name a new preset to the preset set currently in memory. The presets are stored with the project—to make a preset available in other projects you use the File pop-up menu as usual.
Delete	This deletes the selected preset from the preset set currently in memory. If you click on the button, a dialog appears where you can confirm or cancel the action.
Solo	This mutes all frequency bands except the selected band.
Shape buttons	The available distortion characteristics (from bottom to top) create effects from a slight distortion up to a trashy hardcore sound.
Frequency band display	Here you control the level and bandwidth for the four bands, see above.

B.6 SPL DeEsser (Cubase SX only)

A de-esser is used to reduce excessive sibilance, primarily for vocal recordings. Basically, it is a special type of compressor that is tuned to be sensitive to the frequencies produced by the "s" sound, hence the name de-esser. Close proximity microphone placement and equalizing can lead to situations where the overall sound is just right, but there is a problem with sibilants. Conventional compression and/or equalizing will not easily solve this problem, but a de-esser can.

The SPL DeEsser has the following parameters:

Parameter	Values	Description
S-Reduction	0—10	Controls the intensity of the de-essing effect. We recommend that you start with a value between 4 and 7.
Level display		Indicates the dB value by which the level of the sibilant or s-frequency is reduced. The display shows values between 0 dB (no reduction) and minus 20 dB (the s-frequency level is lowered by 20 dB). Each segment in the display represents a level reduction of 2 dB.
Auto Threshold	On/Off	See separate description below.
Male/Female	On/Off	This sets the s-frequency and sibilant recognition to the characteristic frequency ranges of the female or male voice. The center frequency of the bandwidth at which the SPL DeEsser operates is located in the 7 kHz range for the female voice and in the 6 kHz range for the male voice.

B.6.1 About the Auto Threshold Function

Conventional de-essing devices all have a threshold parameter. This is used to set a threshold for the incoming signal level, above which the device starts to process the signal. The SPL DeEsser however has been designed for utmost ease-of-use. With Auto Threshold on (the button is blue) it automatically and constantly readjusts the threshold to achieve an optimum result. If you still wish to determine for yourself at which signal level the SPL DeEsser should start to process the signal, deactivate the Auto Threshold switch. The SPL DeEsser will then use a fixed threshold.

When recording a voice, usually the de-esser's position in the signal chain is located after the microphone pre-amp and before a compressor/limiter. This is useful, as it keeps the compressor/limiter from unnecessarily limiting the overall signal dynamics by reacting to excessive sibilants and s-frequencies.

The Auto Threshold function keeps the processing on a constant level. The input threshold value is automatically and constantly adjusted to the audio input level. Even level differences of say 20 dB do not have a negative impact on the result of the processing. The input levels may vary, but processing remains constant.

B.7 Dynamics

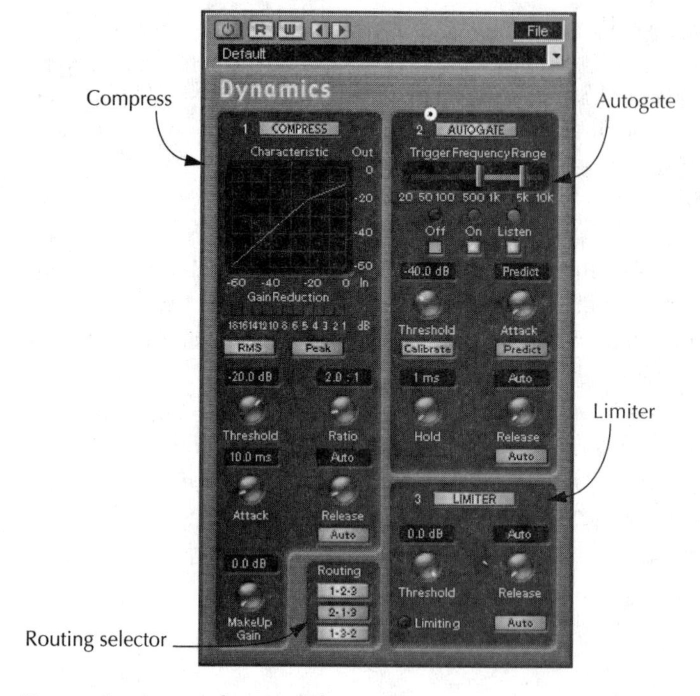

Dynamics is an advanced dynamics processor. It combines three separate processors: Autogate, Compress and Limit, covering a variety of dynamic processing functions. The window is divided into three sections, containing controls and meters for each processor.

B.7.1 Activating the Individual Processors

You activate the individual processors by clicking on their labels. Activated processors have highlighted labels.

B.7.2 Autogate Section

Gating, or noise gating, is a method of dynamic processing that silences audio signals below a certain set threshold level. As soon as the signal level exceeds the set threshold, the gate opens to let the signal through. Autogate offers all the features of a standard noise gate, plus some very useful additional features, such as auto-calibration of the threshold setting, a look-ahead predict function, and frequency selective triggering. Available parameters are as follows:

Parameter	Values	Description
Threshold	-60—0dB	This setting determines the level where Autogate is activated. Signal levels above the set threshold trigger the gate to open, and signal levels below the set threshold will close the gate.
Attack	0,1—100 ms or "Predict mode"	This parameter sets the time it takes for the gate to open after being triggered. If the Predict button is activated, it will ensure that the gate will already be open when a signal above the threshold level is played back. Autogate manages this by "looking ahead" in the audio material, checking for signals loud enough to pass the gate.
Hold	0—1000 ms	This determines how long the gate stays open after the signal drops below the threshold level.
Release	10—1000 ms or "Auto"	This parameter sets the amount of time it takes for the gate to close (after the set hold time). If the "Auto" button is activated, Autogate will find an optimal release setting, depending on the audio program material.

Trigger Frequency Range

Autogate has a feature that allows the gate to be triggered only by signals within a specified frequency range. This is a most useful feature because it lets you filter out parts of the signal that might otherwise trigger the gate in places you don't want it to, thus allowing more control over the gate function. The Trigger Frequency Range function is set using the control in the upper part of the Autogate panel, and the buttons located below it.

The basic operation of the Trigger Frequency Range function is as follows:

1. **While playing back audio, click the "Listen" button.**

   You will now monitor the audio signal, and the gate will be bypassed.

2. **While listening, drag the two handles in the Trigger Frequency Range window to set the frequency range you wish to use to trigger the gate.**

   You will hear the audio being filtered as you move the handles.

- Dragging the left handle to the right will progressively cut frequencies starting from the low end of the frequency spectrum.

- Dragging the right handle to the left will progressively cut frequencies starting from the high end of the frequency spectrum.

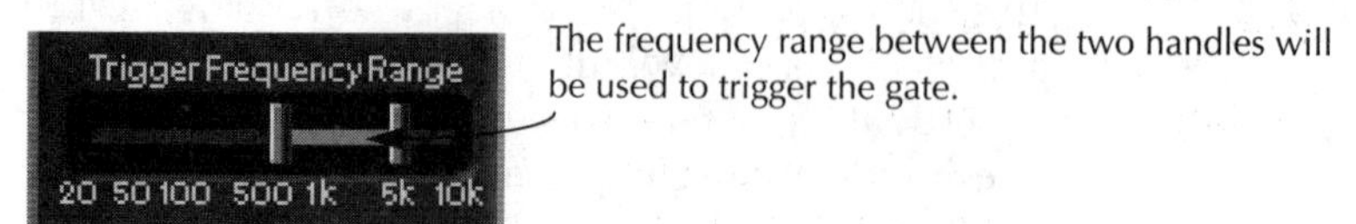

The frequency range between the two handles will be used to trigger the gate.

3. **After setting the frequency range, click the "On" button.**

   Autogate will now use the selected frequency range as the trigger input.

4. **To disable the Trigger Frequency Range function, click the "Off" button.**

   Autogate will now use the unfiltered audio signal as the trigger input.

Calibrate Function

This function, activated by using the Calibrate button located below the Threshold knob, is used to automatically set the threshold level. It is especially useful for material with consistent inherent background noise, like tape hiss. This may most of the time be masked by the audio content, but becomes noticeable during silent passages. Use it as follows:

1. **Find a part of the audio material, preferably not too short, where only the background noise is heard.**

   If you can only find a short background noise section, try looping it.

2. **Play it back, and click on the Calibrate button.**

   The button will blink for a few seconds, and then automatically set the threshold so that the noise will be silenced (gated) during passages where there is no other signal present.

B.7.3 Compress Section

Compress reduces the dynamic range of the audio, making softer sounds louder or louder sounds softer, or both. Compress functions like a standard compressor with separate controls for threshold, ratio, attack, release and make-up gain parameters. Compress features a separate display that graphically illustrates the compressor curve shaped according to the Threshold, Ratio and MakeUp Gain parameter settings. Compress also features a Gain Reduction meter that shows the amount of gain reduction in dB, and a program dependent Auto feature for the Release parameter.

The available parameters have the following functionality:

Parameter	Values	Description
Threshold	-60—0dB	This setting determines the level where Compress "kicks in". Signal levels above the set threshold are affected, but signal levels below are not processed.
Ratio	1:1—8:1	Ratio determines the amount of gain reduction applied to signals over the set threshold. A ratio of 3:1 means that for every 3 dB the input level increases, the output level will increase by only 1 dB.
Attack	0.1—100 ms	This determines how fast Compress will respond to signals above the set threshold. If the attack time is long, more of the early part of the signal (attack) will pass through unprocessed.
Release	10—1000ms or "Auto mode"	Sets the amount of time it takes for the gain to return to its original level when the signal drops below the Threshold level. If the "Auto" button is activated, Compress will automatically find an optimal release setting that varies depending on the audio program material.
MakeUp Gain	0—24dB	This parameter is used to compensate for output gain loss, caused by compression.
Compressor Mode	RMS/Peak	RMS mode operates using the average power of the audio signal as a basis, whereas Peak mode operates more on peak levels. As a general guideline, RMS mode works better on material with few transients such as vocals, and Peak mode better for percussive material, with a lot of transient peaks.

B.7.4 Limiter Section

Limiter is designed to ensure that the output level never exceeds a certain set output level, to avoid clipping in following devices. Conventional limiters usually require very accurate setting up of the attack and release parameters, to totally avoid the possibility of the output level going beyond the set threshold level. Limiter adjusts and optimizes these parameters automatically, according to the audio material. You can also adjust the Release parameter manually. The available parameters are the following:

Parameter	Values	Description
Threshold	-12—0dB	This setting determines the maximum output level. Signal levels above the set threshold are affected, but signal levels below are left unaffected.
Release	10—1000ms or "Auto mode"	This parameter sets the amount of time it takes for the gain to return to its original level when the signal drops below the threshold level. If the "Auto" button is activated, Limiter will automatically find an optimal release setting that varies depending on the audio program material.

B.7.5 Routing Section

In the Routing section you can set the signal flow order for the three processors. Changing the order of the processors can produce different results, and the available options allow you to quickly compare what works best for a given situation. Beside each processor label is a number. These numbers are used to represent the signal flow options shown in the Routing section. There are three routing options:

- 1-2-3 (Compress-Gate-Limit)
- 2-1-3 (Gate-Compress-Limit)
- 1-3-2 (Compress-Limit-Gate)

B.8 VST Dynamics

The VST Dynamics plug-in is similar to the Dynamics plug-in (see page 724), but with the following important differences:

- VST Dynamics has two additional modules: Auto Level and Soft Clip.
- The signal flow is fixed, in the order AutoGate-AutoLevel-Compressor-SoftClip-Limiter.
- VST Dynamics has a higher inherent latency—signals will be delayed when passing through the plug-in.

- While Cubase SX/SL automatically compensates for this latency when the plug-in is used as an insert effect for an audio track, this is not true for Group channels, VST Instrument channels or ReWire channels. Therefore, you should only use the VST Dynamics plug-in as an insert effect for audio track (disk) channels (and possibly as a Master effect, if you're only using a single stereo output bus).

B.8.1 Activating the Individual Processors

You activate the individual processors by clicking on their labels. Activated processors have highlighted labels. You can activate as many processors as you want, but remember that not all processors are designed to work together. For example, "Limit" and "SoftClip" are both designed to ensure that the output never exceeds 0dB, but achieves this in different ways. To have both of them activated would be unnecessary.

- **To turn off all activated VST Dynamics processors, click the lit On button to the right in the panel.**

  Clicking the button again activates the same configuration of processors.

B.8.2 AutoGate Section

This is exactly the same section as the AutoGate in the Dynamics plug-in. See page 724 for details.

B.8.3 AutoLevel Section

AutoLevel reduces signal level differences in audio material. It can be used to process recordings where the level unintentionally varies. It will boost low levels and attenuate high level audio signals. Only levels above the set threshold will be processed, so low level noise or rumble will not be boosted. If the input level is greater than 0dB, AutoLevel will react very fast, because it "looks ahead" in the audio material for strong signal levels and can attenuate levels before they occur, thus reducing the risk of signal clipping. AutoLevel has the following parameters:

Parameter	Values	Explanation
Threshold	-90 to -10dB	Only levels stronger than the set threshold will be processed.
ReactionTime Switch	Slow, Mid, Fast	This parameter sets the amount of time it takes for AutoLevel to adjust the gain. Set this according to whether the program level changes suddenly or over a length of time.

B.8.4 Compressor Section

This is exactly the same section as the Compress section in the Dynamics plug-in. See page 726 for details.

B.8.5 SoftClip Section

SoftClip is designed to ensure that the output level never exceeds 0dB, like a limiter. SoftClip, however, acts differently compared to a conventional limiter. When the signal level exceeds -6dB, SoftClip starts limiting (or clipping) the signal "softly", at the same time generating harmonics which add a warm, tubelike characteristic to the audio material. SoftClip is simplicity itself to use as it has no control parameters. The meter indicates the input signal level, and thus the amount of "softclipping". Levels in the green area (weaker than -6dB) are unaffected, while levels in the yellow-orange-red area indicate the degree of "softclipping". The deep red meter area to the right indicates input levels higher than 0dB.

- Avoid feeding SoftClip with excessively high signal levels as audible distortion may occur, although the output level will never exceed 0dB.

B.8.6 Limiter Section

This is exactly the same section as the Limiter in the Dynamics plug-in. See page 728 for details.

B.9 MIDI Gate

Gating, in its fundamental form, silences audio signals below a certain set threshold level. I.e. when a signal rises above the set level, the Gate opens to let the signal through while signals below the set level are cut off. MIDI Gate however, is a Gate effect that is not triggered by threshold levels, but instead by MIDI notes. Hence it needs both audio and MIDI data to function.

B.9.1 Setting Up

The MIDI Gate requires both an audio signal and a MIDI input to function.

To set it up, proceed as follows:

1. **Select the audio to be affected by the MIDI Gate.**

   This can be audio material from any VST Audio Track, or even a live audio input routed to a VST Audio Track (provided you have a low latency audio card). If a live audio input is used, monitoring must be activated.

2. **Select the MIDI Gate as an Insert effect for the Audio channel.**

3. **Select a MIDI Track to control the MIDI Gate.**

   This can be an empty MIDI Track, or a MIDI Track containing data, it doesn't matter. However, if you wish to play the MIDI Gate in real-time—as opposed to having a recorded Part playing it—the Track has to be selected for the effect to receive the MIDI output.

4. **Select the MIDI Gate from the Output pop-up menu.**

   The MIDI Output from the Track is now routed to the MIDI Gate.

What to do next depends on whether you are using live or recorded audio and whether you are using real-time or recorded MIDI. We will assume for the purposes of this manual that you are using recorded audio, and play the MIDI in real-time.

Make sure the MIDI Track is selected and start playback.

5. **Now play a few notes on your MIDI keyboard.**

   As you can hear, the audio track material is affected by what you play on your MIDI keyboard.

You can now make settings for the MIDI Gate using the following parameters:

Parameter	Values	Description
Attack	0—500	This is used for determining how long it should take for the Gate to open after receiving a signal that triggers it.
Hold	0—3.000	Regulates how long the Gate remains open after a Note On or Note Off message (see Hold Mode below).
Release	0—3.000	This determines how long it takes for the Gate to close (in addition to the value set with the Hold-parameter).

Parameter	Values	Description
Note To Attack	0—127	The value you specify here determines how and to which extent the pitch of the MIDI notes should affect the Attack. If this is set to a positive value, the Attack time will increase with higher note velocities. Negative values will give shorter Attack times with higher velocities. If you do not wish to use this parameter, set it to 0.
Note To Release	0—127	The value you specify here determines how and to which extent the pitch of the MIDI notes should affect the Release. Positive values will increase the Release time and negative values will decrease the Release time. If you do not wish to use this parameter, set it to 0.
Velocity To VCA	0—127	This controls to which extent the velocity values of the MIDI notes determine the output volume. A value of 127 means that the volume is controlled entirely by the velocity values, while a value of 0 means that velocities will have no effect on the volume.
Hold Mode	Note-On/ Note-Off	Use this switch to set the Hold Mode. In Note-On mode, the Gate will only remain open for the time set with the Hold and Release parameters, regardless of the length of the MIDI note that triggered the Gate. In Note-Off mode on the other hand, the Gate will remain open for as long as the MIDI note plays, and then apply the Release parameter. In this case, the Hold parameter has no effect.

B.10 StepFilter

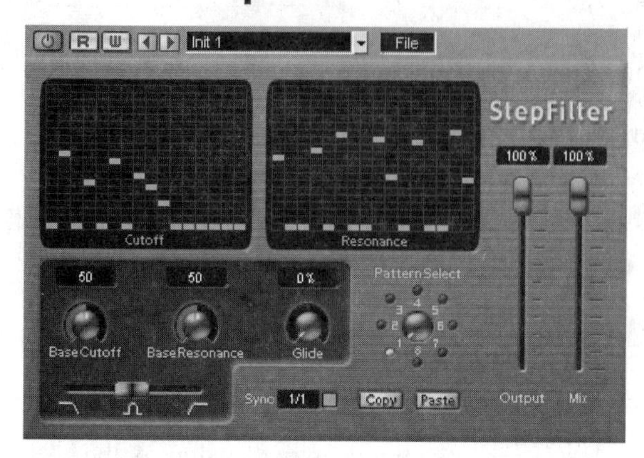

StepFilter is a pattern-controlled multimode filter that can create rhythmic, pulsating filter effects.

B.10.1 General Operation

StepFilter can produce two simultaneous 16-step patterns for the filter cutoff and resonance parameters, synchronized to the sequencer tempo.

B.10.2 Setting Step Values

- **Setting step values is done by clicking in the pattern grid windows.**
- **Individual step entries can be freely dragged up or down the vertical axis, or directly set by clicking in an empty grid box. By click-dragging left or right consecutive step entries will be set to the pointer position.**

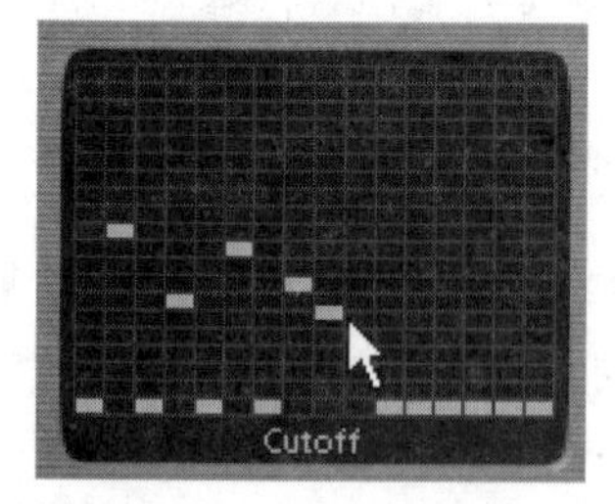

Setting filter cutoff values in the grid window.

- **The horizontal axis shows the pattern steps 1—16 from left to right, and the vertical axis determines the (relative) filter cutoff frequency and resonance setting.**

  The higher up on the vertical axis a step value is entered, the higher the relative filter cutoff frequency or filter resonance setting.

- **By starting playback and editing the patterns for the cutoff and resonance parameters, you can hear how your filter patterns affect the sound source connected to StepFilter directly.**

B.10.3 Selecting New Patterns

- **Created patterns are saved with the song, and up to 8 different cutoff and resonance patterns can be saved internally.**

  Both the cutoff and resonance patterns are saved together in the 8 Pattern memories.

- **To select new patterns you use the pattern selector.**

  New patterns are all set to the same step value by default.

Pattern Selector

B.10.4 Using Pattern Copy and Paste to Create Variations

You can use the Copy and Paste buttons below the pattern selector to copy a pattern to another Pattern memory location, which is useful for creating variations on a pattern.

- **Click the Copy button with the pattern you wish to copy selected, select another pattern memory location, and click Paste.**

  The pattern is copied to the new location, and can now be edited to create variations using the original pattern as a starting point.

B.10.5 StepFilter Parameters:

Parameter/Value	Description
Base Cutoff	This sets the base filter cutoff frequency. Cutoff values set in the Cutoff grid window are values *relative* to the Base Cutoff value.
Base Resonance	This sets the base filter resonance. Resonance values set in the Resonance grid window are values *relative* to the Base Resonance value. Note that very high Base Resonance settings can produce loud ringing effects at certain frequencies.
Glide	This will apply glide between the pattern step values, causing values to change more smoothly.
Filter Mode	This slider selects between lowpass (LP), bandpass (BP) or high-pass (HP) filter modes (from left to right respectively).
Sync 1/1—1/32 (Straight, Triplet or Dotted)	This sets the pattern beat resolution, i.e. what note values the pattern will play in relation to the tempo.
Mix	Adjusts the mix between dry and processed signal.
Gain	Sets the overall volume.

B.11 Chorus

The Chorus plug-in adds short delays to the signal, and pitch modulates the delayed signals to produce a "doubling" effect. The parameters are as follows:

Parameter	Values	Description
Mix	0—100%	Sets the level balance between the dry signal and the effect. If Chorus is used as a send effect, this should be set to maximum as you can control the dry/effect balance with the send.
Shapes	Saw/ Triangle/ Pulse	This sets the modulation waveform. Triangle produces smooth modulation, saw produces ramp shaped modulation and pulse waveform produces stepped modulation.
Frequency	0—5Hz	This sets the modulation rate.
Delay	0—5ms	This controls the depth of the Chorus effect.
Stages	1—3	This adds one or two more delay taps, producing a thicker, multi-layered chorus effect.

- Note that clicking and dragging in the display allows you to adjust the Frequency and Delay parameters at the same time!

B.12 Flanger

Flanger is a classic flanger effect with stereo enhancement. Parameters are as follows:

Parameter	Values	Description
Mix	0—100%	Sets the level balance between the dry signal and the effect. If the Flanger is used as a send effect, this should be set to maximum as you can control the dry/effect balance with the send.
Tempo sync on/off		The button above the Rate knob is used to switch tempo sync on or off. The button is blue when tempo sync is on, and white when it is off.
Rate	1/1—1/32, 1/1—1/32 Triplet, 1/1—1/32 Dotted or 0—5Hz	If tempo sync is on, this is where you specify the base note value for tempo syncing the flanger sweep. If tempo sync is off, the sweep rate can be set freely with the Rate knob, without sync to tempo.
Tempo Sync knob	×1 to ×10	This is the note value multiplier for the flanger sweep when tempo sync is used.
Shape Sync knob	1—16	This changes the shape of the modulating waveform, altering the character of the flanger sweep.
Feedback	0—100%	This determines the character of the flange effect. Higher settings produce a more "metallic" sounding sweep.
Depth	0—100%	This sets the depth of the modulation sweep.

Parameter	Values	Description
Delay	0—100ms	This parameter affects the frequency range of the modulation sweep, by adjusting the initial delay time.
Stereo Basis	0—100%	This sets the stereo width of the effect. 0% is mono, 50% original stereo, and 100% maximum stereo enhancement.

You can also change parameters in the graphic display window. This works as follows:

- **If tempo sync is on, you can set the base note value by clicking the waveform and dragging left and right.**

  When tempo sync is off, this sets the Rate parameter.

- **You can set the Depth parameter by clicking the waveform and dragging up and down.**

  This means you can freely adjust Rate and Depth at the same time by clicking and dragging.

- **By click-dragging the green/blue line in the display left or right you can change the Stereo Basis parameter.**

B.13 Metalizer

The Metalizer feeds the audio signal through a variable frequency filter, with tempo sync or time modulation and feedback control.

Parameter	Values	Description
Output	0—100%	Sets the Output level.
Mix	0—100%	Sets the level balance between the dry signal and the effect. If Metalizer is used as a send effect, this should be set to maximum as you can control the dry/effect balance with the send.
Tempo sync on/off		The button above the Speed knob is used to switch tempo sync on or off. The button is blue when tempo sync is on, and white when it is off.
Speed	1/1—1/32, 1/1—1/32 Triplet, 1/1—1/32 Dotted or 0—10Hz	If tempo sync is on, this is where you specify the base note value for tempo-syncing the effect. Note that there is no note value modifier for this effect. If tempo sync is off, the modulation speed can be set freely with the Speed knob, without sync to tempo.
On button	On/Off	Turns filter modulation on and off. When turned off, the Metalizer will work as a static filter.
Mono button	On/Off	Determines whether the output of the Metalizer will be in stereo or mono.
Sharpness	0—100%	Governs the character of the filter effect. The higher the value, the narrower the affected frequency area, producing sharper sound and a more pronounced effect.
Tone	0—100%	Governs the feedback frequency. The effect of this will be more noticeable with high Feedback settings.
Feedback	0—100%	Sets the amount of feedback. Higher values produces a more "metallic" sound.

- Note that clicking and dragging in the display allows you to adjust the Sharpness and Tone parameters at the same time!

B.14 Phaser

The Phaser plug-in produces the classic "swooshing" sound that characterizes phasing. It works by shifting the phase of the signal and adding it back to the original signal, causing partial cancellation of the frequency spectrum.

Parameter	Values	Description
Mix	0—100%	Sets the level balance between the dry signal and the effect. If the Phaser is used as a send effect, this should be set to maximum as you can control the dry/effect balance with the send.
Tempo sync on/off		The button above the Rate knob is used to switch tempo sync on or off. The button is blue when tempo sync is on, and white when it is off.
Rate	1/1—1/32, 1/1—1/32 Triplet, 1/1—1/32 Dotted or 0—5Hz	If tempo sync is on, this is where you specify the base note value for tempo syncing the Phaser sweep. If tempo sync is off, the sweep rate can be set freely with the Rate knob, without sync to tempo.
Feedback	1—100%	This sets the amount of feedback. A higher value produces a more pronounced effect.
TMP Sync knob	x1 to x10	This is the note value multiplier for the Phaser sweep when tempo sync is used.
Stereo Basis	0—100%	This sets the stereo width of the effect. 0% is mono, 50% original stereo, and 100% maximum stereo enhancement.

You can also change parameters in the graphic display window. This works as follows:

- **If tempo sync is on, you can set the base note value by clicking the waveform and dragging left and right.**

  When tempo sync is off, this sets the Rate parameter.

- **You can set the Feedback parameter by clicking the waveform and dragging up and down.**

  This means you can freely adjust the Rate and Feedback at the same time by clicking and dragging.

- **By click-dragging the blue/green line in the display left or right you can change the Stereo Basis parameter.**

B.15 Ringmodulator

The Ringmodulator can produce complex, bell-like enharmonic sounds. Ring modulators work by multiplying two audio signals. The ring modulated output contains added frequencies generated by the sum of, and the difference between, the frequencies of the two signals.

The Ringmodulator has a built-in oscillator that is multiplied with the input signal to produce the effect.

B.15.1 Parameters

Parameter	Description
Oscillator LFO Amount	LFO Amount controls how much the oscillator frequency is affected by the LFO.
Oscillator Env. Amount	Env. Amount controls how much the oscillator frequency is affected by the Envelope (which is triggered by the input signal). Positive and negative values can be set, with center position representing no modulation. Left of center, a loud input signal will decrease the oscillator pitch, whereas right of center the oscillator pitch will increase when fed a loud input.
Oscillator Wave	Selects the oscillator waveform; square, sine, saw or triangle.
Oscillator Range	Determines the frequency range of the oscillator in Hz.
Oscillator Frequency	Sets the oscillator frequency +/- 2 octaves within the selected range.
Roll-Off	Cuts high frequencies in the oscillator waveform, to soften the overall sound. This is best used when harmonically rich waveforms are selected (e.g. square or saw).
LFO Waveform	Selects the LFO waveform; square, sine, saw or triangle.
LFO Speed	Sets the LFO Speed.
LFO Env. Amount	Controls how much the input signal level—via the envelope generator—affects the LFO speed. Positive and negative values can be set, with center position representing no modulation. Left of center, a loud input signal will slow down the LFO, whereas right of center a loud input signal will speed it up.
Invert Stereo	This inverts the LFO waveform for the right channel of the oscillator, which produces a wider stereo perspective for the modulation.

Parameter	Description
Envelope Generator	The Envelope Generator section controls how the input signal is converted to envelope data, which can then be used to control oscillator pitch and LFO speed. It has two main controls: Attack sets how fast the envelope output level rises in response to a rising input signal. Decay controls how fast the envelope output level falls in response to a falling input signal.
Lock L<R	When this switch is enabled, the L and R input signals are merged, and produce the same Envelope output level for both oscillator channels. When disabled, each channel has its own Envelope, which affect the two channels of the oscillator independently.
Mix	Adjusts the mix between dry and processed signal.
Output	Sets the overall volume.

B.16 Rotary

The Rotary plug-in simulates the classic effect of a rotary speaker. A rotary speaker cabinet features variable speed rotating speakers to produce a swirling chorus effect, commonly used with organs. Rotary features all the parameters associated with the real thing. The included presets provide good starting points for further tweaking of the numerous parameters.

The parameters are as follows:

Parameter	Values	Description
Speed	STOP/SLOW/FAST	This controls the speed of the Rotary.
MIDI Ctrl	Controllers [1] to [16]	Selects the MIDI Continuous Controller for the Speed parameter. See page 746.
Mode	Switched/Variable	Selects whether the SLOW/FAST speed setting is a switch, or a variable control. When switch mode is selected, and Pitch Bend is the controller, the speed will switch with an up or down flick of the bender. Other controllers switch at 64.
Overdrive	0—100%	Applies a soft overdrive or distortion.
Crossover Freq.	200—3000Hz	Sets the crossover frequency between the low and high frequency loudspeakers.
Mic Angle	0—180 degrees	Sets the simulated microphone angle. 0=mono, 180=one mic on each side.
Mic Distance	1—36 Inches	Sets the simulated microphone distance from the speaker.
Low Rotor Amp Mod.	0—100%	Adjusts amplitude modulation depth.
Low Rotor Mix Level	0—200%	Adjusts overall bass level.
Hi Rotor Amp Mod.	0—100%	High rotor amplitude modulation.
Hi Rotor Freq. Mod.	0—100%	High rotor frequency modulation.
Phasing	-100 to 100	Adjusts the amount of phasing in the sound of the high rotor.
Hi Slow	0.0—720 rpm	Fine adjustment of the high rotor SLOW speed.
Hi Rate	0.0—720 rpm/sec	Fine adjustment of the high rotor acceleration time.
Hi Fast	0.0—720 rpm	Fine adjustment of the high rotor FAST speed.
Lo Slow	0.0—720 rpm	Fine adjustment of the low rotor SLOW speed.

Parameter	Values	Description
Lo Rate	0.0—720 rpm/sec	Fine adjustment of the low rotor acceleration time.
Lo Fast	0.0—720 rpm	Fine adjustment of the low rotor FAST speed.
Output		Adjusts the overall output level.
Mix		Adjusts the mix between dry and processed signal.

B.16.1 Directing MIDI to the Rotary

For real-time MIDI control of the Speed parameter, MIDI must be directed to the Rotary.

- **Whenever the Rotary has been selected as a Send or Insert effect, it will be available on the "out:" pop-up menu for MIDI Tracks.**

  If Rotary is selected on the "out:" menu, MIDI will be directed to the plug-in from the selected Track.

B.17 Symphonic

The Symphonic plug-in combines a stereo enhancer, an auto-panner synchronized to tempo and a chorus-type effect. For best results, apply the Symphonic effect to stereo signals.

Parameter	Values	Description
Mix	0—100%	Sets the level balance between the dry signal and the effect. If Symphonic is used as a send effect, this should be set to maximum as you can control the dry/effect balance with the send.
Tempo sync on/off		The button below the Temp sync knob is used to switch tempo sync on or off. The button is blue when tempo sync is on, and white when it is off.
Tempo Sync pop-up	1/1—1/32, 1/1—1/32 Triplet, 1/1—1/32 Dotted	If tempo sync is on, this is where you specify the base note value for tempo syncing the auto-panning.
Tempo Sync knob	x1 to x10	This is the note value multiplier, determining the timing of the auto-panning.
Delay	0—100 ms	This determines the delay time and thus the character of the chorus effect, if activated.
Depth	0—100%	This controls the depth of the chorus effect. If you only want to use Symphonic as an auto-panner or a stereo enhancer, set this to 0%.
Rate	0—100%	This sets the modulation rate for the chorus effect, if activated.
Stereo Basis	0—100%	When the Auto-panner is activated, this sets the stereo width of the panning. When the Auto-panner is deactivated (Tempo sync off), this determines the depth of the stereo enhancer effect. 0% is mono, 50% original stereo, and 100% maximum stereo enhancement.

You can also change parameters in the graphic display window. This works as follows:

- **You can set the Rate parameter by clicking the waveform and dragging left and right.**

- **You can set the Depth parameter by clicking the waveform and dragging up and down.**

  This means you can freely adjust Rate and Depth at the same time by clicking and dragging.

- **By click-dragging the green/blue line in the display left or right you can change the Stereo Basis parameter.**

B.18 Tranceformer

Tranceformer is a ring modulator effect, in which the incoming audio is ring modulated by an internal, variable frequency oscillator, producing new harmonics. A second oscillator can be used to modulate the frequency of the first oscillator, synchronized to the Song tempo if you wish.

Parameter	Values	Description
Output	0—100%	Sets the output level.
Mix	0—100%	Sets the level balance between the dry signal and the effect.
Tone	1—5000Hz	Governs the frequency (pitch) of the modulating oscillator.
Tempo sync on/off		The button above the Speed knob is used to switch tempo sync on or off. The button is blue when tempo sync is on, and white when it is off.

Parameter	Values	Description
Speed	1/1—1/32, 1/1—1/32 Triplet, 1/1—1/32 Dotted or 0—10Hz	If tempo sync is on, this is where you specify the base note value for tempo-syncing the effect. Note that there is no note value modifier for this effect. If tempo sync is off, the modulation speed can be set freely with the Speed knob, without sync to tempo.
On button	On/Off	Turns modulation of the Pitch parameter on or off.
Mono button	On/Off	Governs whether the effect output will be stereo or mono.
Depth	0—100%	Governs the depth of the pitch modulation.
Waveform buttons	Sine, Square, Saw, Reverse Saw, Triangle	Sets the pitch modulation waveform.

- Note that clicking and dragging in the display allows you to adjust the Tone and Depth parameters at the same time!

B.19 Bitcrusher

If you're into lo-fi sound, Bitcrusher is the effect for you. It offers the possibility of decimating and truncating the input audio signal by bit reduction, to get a noisy, distorted sound. You can for example make a 24 bit audio signal sound like an 8 or 4 bit signal, or even render it completely garbled and unrecognizable. Bitcrusher can be used as an insert effect or a send effect. You can of course also use it as a master effect, should you so wish.

Parameter	Values	Description
Mode	I,II,III,IV	Select one of four operating modes for the Bitcrusher. Each mode will produce a different sounding result. Modes I and III are nastier and noisier, while modes II and IV are more subtle.
Depth	0—24	Use this to set the desired bit resolution. A setting of 24 gives the highest audio quality, while a setting of 1 will create mostly noise.
Sample Divider	1—65	This sets the amount by which the audio samples are decimated. At the highest setting (65), nearly all of the information describing the original audio signal will be eliminated, turning the signal into unrecognizable noise.
Mix	N/A	This slider regulates the balance between the output from the Bitcrusher and the original audio signal. Drag the slider upwards for a more dominant effect, and drag it downwards if you want the original signal to be more prominent.
Gain	N/A	Governs the output level from the Bitcrusher. Drag the slider upwards to increase the level.

B.20 Chopper

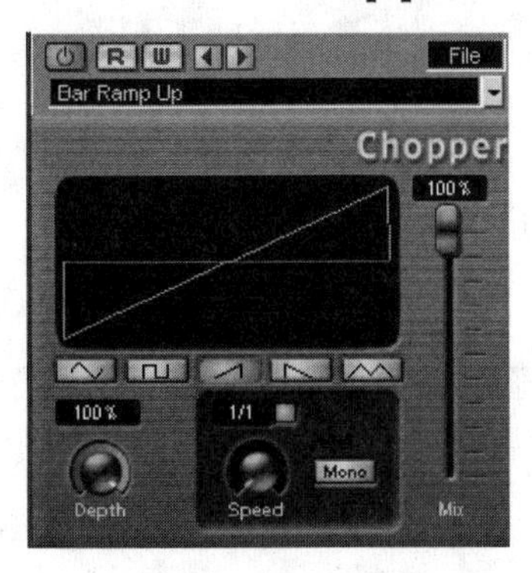

Chopper is a combined tremolo and autopan effect. It can use different waveforms to modulate the level (tremolo) or left-right stereo position (pan), either using tempo sync or manual modulation speed settings.

Parameters are as follows:

Parameter	Values	Description
Mix	0—100%	Sets the level balance between the dry signal and the effect. If Chopper is used as a send effect, this should be set to maximum as you can control the dry/effect balance with the send.
Tempo sync on/off		The button above the Speed knob is used to switch tempo sync on or off. The button is blue when tempo sync is on and white when it is off.
Speed	1/1—1/32, 1/1—1/32 Triplet, 1/1—1/32 Dotted or 0—50Hz	If tempo sync is on, this is where you specify the base note value for tempo-syncing the effect. Note that there is no note value modifier for this effect. If tempo sync is off, the tremolo/auto-pan speed can be set freely with the Speed knob, without sync to tempo.
Stereo/Mono button	Stereo/Mono	Determines whether the Chopper will work as an auto-panner (button set to "Stereo") or a tremolo effect (button set to "Mono").

Parameter	Values	Description
Waveform buttons	Sine, Square, Saw, Reverse Saw, Triangle	Sets the modulation waveform.
Depth	0—100%	Sets the depth of the Chopper effect. This parameter can also be set by clicking in the graphic display.

B.21 Grungelizer

The Grungelizer adds noise and static to your recordings—kind of like listening to a radio with bad reception, or a worn and scratched vinyl record.

Parameter	Values	Description
Crackle	N/A	This adds crackle to create that old vinyl record sound. The farther to the right you turn the dial, the more crackle is added.
RPM switch	33-45-78	When emulating the sound of a vinyl record, this switch lets you set the RPM (revolutions per minute) speed of the record.
Noise	N/A	This dial regulates the amount of static noise added.
Distort	N/A	Use this dial to add distortion.
EQ	N/A	Turn this dial to the right to cut off the low frequencies, and create a more hollow, lo-fi sound.

Parameter	Values	Description
AC	N/A	This emulates a constant, low hum of AC current.
Frequency switch	50—60 Hz	This sets the frequency of the AC current, and thus the pitch of the AC hum.
Timeline	Today—1900	This dial regulates the amount of overall effect. The farther to the right (1900) you turn this dial, the more noticeable the effect.

B.22 Vocoder

The Vocoder can apply sound/voice characteristics taken from one signal source, called the "modulator" and apply this to another source, called the "carrier". A typical application of a vocoder is to use a voice as a modulator and an instrument as a carrier, making the instrument "talk". A vocoder works by dividing the source signal (modulator) into a number of frequency bands. The audio attributes of these frequency bands can then be used to modulate the carrier.

The Vocoder has a built-in carrier (basically a simple polyphonic synthesizer) but you can also use an external carrier, see page 754.

B.22.1 Setting Up—Using MIDI

In this mode, the Vocoder is set up slightly differently than other plug-in effects. This is because this setup requires both an audio signal (as the modulator source) and a MIDI input (to play the carrier) to function. To set up for using an external carrier, see page 754.

To set up for use, proceed as follows:

1. **Select a source for the modulator.**

   The modulator source can be audio material from any audio track, or even a live audio input routed to an audio track (provided you have a low latency audio card).

- **Good modulator source material are talking or singing voices or percussive sounds, e.g. drum loops.**

  Static pads or soft ambient material are generally less appropriate for use as modulators, but there are no absolute rules as to what could be used as a modulator source.

2. **Select the Vocoder as an insert effect for the audio channel with the modulator signal.**

3. **Make sure that the Vocoder Mode switch is set to "MIDI".**

4. **Select a MIDI track.**

   This can be an empty MIDI track, or a MIDI track containing data, it doesn't matter. However, if you wish to play the Vocoder in real-time—as opposed to having a recorded part playing it—the track has to have monitoring activated (or be record enabled) for the Vocoder to receive the MIDI output.

5. **Select "Vocoder" from the MIDI "out:" pop-up menu for the MIDI track.**

   The MIDI Output from the track is now routed to the Vocoder. There is an indicator on the Vocoder panel below the Mode switches that blinks when receiving MIDI.

That concludes setting up—you are now ready to start vocoding!

What you do next depends on whether you are using live or recorded audio as the modulator source and whether you are using real-time or recorded MIDI as the carrier input. We will assume for the purposes of this manual that you are using recorded audio as the modulator, and play the carrier in real-time.

6. **Make sure the MIDI track is record enabled and start playback.**

7. **Now play a few notes on your MIDI keyboard.**

   As you can hear, the audio track material, or rather its formant characteristics, is now applied to the Vocoder's built-in sound source!

B.22.2 Setting Up—Using an External Carrier

There are two modes for using an external carrier:

- "Ext" mode is when the carrier and the modulator can be any two audio sources. The synth section is disabled and grayed out when this mode is selected. MIDI input and the Gap Thru Vocoder parameter are also disabled.

- "Ext+MIDI" mode mixes the audio carrier with the Vocoder's synth sound. This is described on page 755.

To use an external carrier instead of the built-in synth ("Ext mode"), you set up as follows:

1. **Create a Group channel from the Add Track submenu on the Project menu.**
2. **Open an audio file you wish to use as the carrier source and place it on an empty audio track.**
3. **Pan the audio channel full right in the Mixer or in the Inspector.**
4. **Route the output of the audio channel to the group.**
5. **Open an audio file you wish to use as the modulator source and place it on another empty audio track.**

   Events on the two audio tracks (carrier and modulator) have to play back simultaneously for the Vocoder to work.
6. **Pan the modulator audio channel full left in the Mixer or in the Inspector.**
7. **Route the output of the modulator audio channel to the group.**
8. **Select the Vocoder as an insert effect for the group channel.**
9. **Open the Vocoder panel and activate the "Ext." Mode button.**
10. **If you now start playback, the carrier channel will be modulated by the modulator channel!**

    Note that the synth section on the left half of the Vocoder panel and the "Gap Thru" parameter are now disabled.

B.22.3 Setting Up—Using an External Carrier plus MIDI

Setting up is the same as for using an external carrier, except that a MIDI track with its output routed to the Vocoder should also be present. The MIDI track can either play the Vocoder synth in real time or from prerecorded parts. Make sure that monitoring (or record enable) is activated for the track so that the Vocoder synth will receive MIDI played in real time.

- **Set up as described, and activate "MIDI+Ext." mode on the Vocoder panel.**

  Any incoming MIDI now triggers the Vocoder synth, and the synths output is mixed with the audio carrier signal.

B.22.4 Vocoder Parameters

The Vocoder parameters govern the general sound quality of the vocoded sound.

Parameter	Values	Description
Number of Bands	2—24	This governs how many frequency bands the modulator signal is divided into. Fewer bands will provide a thinner more resonant sound, whereas using more bands will make the sound fuller and more intelligible.
Bandwidth	0—100%	This sets the bandwidth for the frequency bands, which affects the overall timbre. Very narrow bandwidth settings will produce a thin, whistle-like sound.
Min./Max. Freq.	40—8000Hz	These parameters set the minimum and maximum frequency limits for the Vocoder, respectively.
log/lin	0—100%	Log/Lin controls how the frequency bands are spaced between the minimum and maximum frequencies. Log = equal spacing in octaves, Lin = equal spacing in Hz. This affects the basic timbre of the Vocoder.
Env.Speed	10—19699ms/ HOLD	This determines the attack and release times of the Vocoder envelope. Fast settings will cause the modulator signal to trigger the Vocoder instantly, longer settings will gradually increase the attack/release times, providing a more subtle Vocoder effect. If set to "HOLD" the modulator is "frozen", and doesn't affect the carrier synth at all.
High Thru	0—100%	This lets through high frequencies around the "S" frequency from the original input signal while notes are played.
Talk Thru	0—100%	Adjusts the level of the original input signal passed to the Vocoder output while notes are played.

Parameter	Values	Description
Gap Thru	0—100%	Gap Thru (only available in MIDI mode) sets the level of the original input signal that is passed to the Vocoder output when no MIDI notes are being played. This lets you apply the Vocoder to a vocal track adding vocoded parts just where you want them.
Output	0—100%	This controls the output level of the Vocoder.
Emphasis	0—100%	This is a highpass filter, gradually cutting lower frequencies while letting high frequencies pass.

B.22.5 Vocoder Synth Parameters

If the built-in synthesizer is the carrier, it is the sound of this instrument that the modulator source is applied to. The synth is polyphonic with up to 8 voices and features 2 oscillators per voice. The synth has the following parameters:

Parameter	Values	Description
Voices	1—8	This sets the number of voices for the synth.
Fine Tune	-100/+100 Cent	Tunes the oscillators in cent (100th of a semitone) steps.
Pitch Bend	1—12 Semitones	Sets the up/down range of the Pitch Bend in semitone steps.
Noise	0—100%	Adds white noise to the sound.
NoiseMod	0—100%	This makes the oscillators modulate the noise level. This gives the noise a rasping sound, turning "sss" into "zzz".
P.Drift	0—100%	Adds random pitch variation to the oscillators.
P.Glide	0—100%	This makes the pitch glide between notes played. The parameter controls the time it takes for the pitch to glide from one note to the next.
P.Bright	0—100%	This is a lowpass filter that can be used to soften the tone of the oscillators. It does not affect the white noise generator.

Parameter	Values	Description
P.Detune	12.00 to 0.00	Allows you to detune one of the oscillators in cent steps.
LFO Rate	1—23Hz	Controls the LFO rate (for vibrato).
Vibrato	0—100%	Adds vibrato to the oscillators. This can also be controlled by using the Mod Wheel.

B.23 SMPTE Generator (Cubase SX only)

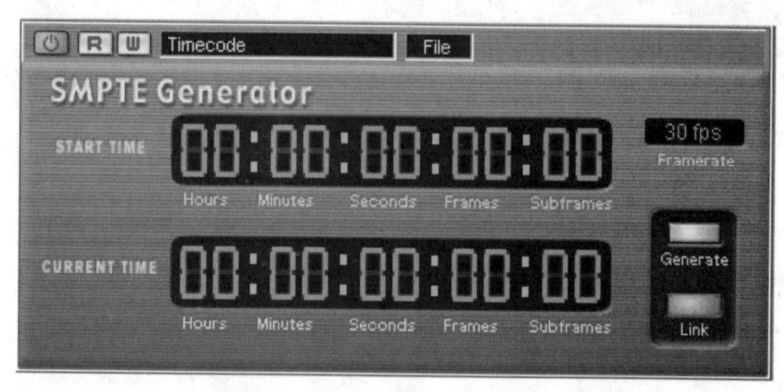

This plug-in is not an effect device. It sends out SMPTE time code to an audio output, allowing you to synchronize other equipment to Cubase SX (provided that the equipment can sync directly to SMPTE time code). This can be very useful if you don't have access to a MIDI to time code converter.

The following items and parameters are available:

- **Generate Button**

  Activate this to make the device generate SMPTE time code.

- **Link Button**

  This synchronizes the time code output to the Transport time positions.
  When Generate and Link are both activated, the time code output will exactly match the play position in Cubase SX.
  Activating the Generate button when Link is off (see below), makes the device send the SMPTE time code in "free run" mode, meaning that it will output continuous time code, independently from the transport status in Cubase SX. If you wish to "stripe" a tape with SMPTE, you should use this mode.

- **Start Time**

  This sets the time at which the SMPTE Generator starts, when activated in "free run" mode (Link button off). To change the Start time, click on a digit and move the mouse up or down.

- **Current Time**

  When Link is on this shows the current position in Cubase SX. If Link is off it shows the current time of the SMPTE Generator in "free run" mode. This cannot be set manually.

- **Framerate**

  This defaults to the frame rate set in the Project Setup. If you wish to generate time code in another frame rate than the Project is currently set to (for example to stripe a tape), you can select another format on the Framerate pop-up (provided that "Link" is off).
  Note, however, that for the other device to synchronize correctly with Cubase the framerate has to be the same in the Project Setup, the SMPTE Generator and in the receiving device.

B.23.1 Example—Synchronizing a Device to Cubase SX

Proceed as follows:

1. **Connect the SMPTE Generator as an insert effect on an audio channel, and route the output of that channel to a separate output.**

   Make sure that no other insert or send effects are used on the time code channel. You should also disable EQ, if this is active.

2. **Connect the corresponding output on the audio hardware to the time code input on the device you wish to synchronize to Cubase.**

   Make all necessary settings in the other device, so that it is set to synchronize to incoming timecode.

3. **Adjust the level of the time code if needed, either in Cubase SX or in the receiving device.**

   Activate the SMPTE Generator in "free run" mode to test the level.

4. **Make sure that the frame rate in the receiving device matches the frame rate set in the SMPTE Generator.**

5. **Activate the Link button.**

6. Activate the Generate Button.

The SMPTE Generator will now output time code that matches the position of the Cubase SX Transport Panel.

- **Press Play on the Cubase SX Transport Panel.**

The other device is now synchronized and will follow any position changes set with the Cubase SX transport controls.

B.24 Reverb A

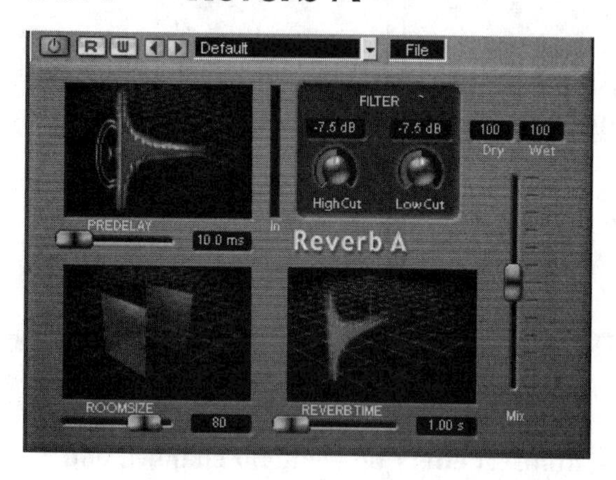

Reverb A is a reverb plug-in which provides smooth, dense reverb effects. Reverb A has the following parameters:

Parameter	Values	Description
Mix	Dry/Wet	Sets the level balance between the dry signal and the effect (wet). If Reverb A is used as a send effect, this should be set to maximum wet, as you can control the dry/wet balance with the send.
Room Size	20—100	This setting determines the "size" of the simulated room environment.
Predelay	0—100ms	This parameter sets a delay between the direct sound and the reverb effect output. A short predelay before the reverb reduces reverb "clutter" which blurs the sound, and makes the reverb effect more natural-sounding.

Parameter	Values	Description
Reverb Time	0,2s—forever	This parameter sets the length of the reverb time.
Filter Hi Cut	-15 to 0dB	This filters out high frequencies for the reverb, which can make the reverb sound softer.
Filter Lo Cut	-15 to 0dB	This filters out the lower frequencies for the reverb. It can be used to reduce low frequency "rumble".

B.25 Reverb B

Reverb is used to add ambience and "space" to recordings. The Reverb B effect features the following parameters:

Parameter	Values	Description
Mix	0—100%	Sets the level balance between the dry signal and the effect. If Reverb B is used as a send effect, this should be set to maximum as you can control the dry/effect balance with the send.
Room Size	0—100%	Governs the "size" of the simulated room environment.
Predelay	0—100%	This parameter sets a delay between the direct sound and the reverb effect output. A short predelay before the reverb reduces reverb "clutter" which blurs the sound, and makes the reverb effect more natural-sounding.

Parameter	Values	Description
Reverb Time	0—100%	This parameter sets the length of the reverb effect.
Damp	0—100%	This parameter "dampens" the higher frequencies, producing a rounder and smoother sounding reverb.

B.26 Mix6To2 (Cubase SX only)

The Mix6To2 Master effect allows you to control the levels of up to six surround channels, and to mix these down to a stereo output. There are ten presets that correspond to the preset (default) surround formats included in the Master Setup. The Mix6To2 allows you to quickly mix down your surround mix format to stereo, and to include parts of the surround channels in the resulting mix.

- **Note that the Mix6To2 does not simulate a surround mix or add any psycho-acoustical artifacts to the resulting output—it is simply a mixer.**

Each of the surround channels has the following parameters:

- Two volume faders that govern the levels of the surround bus to the left and right side of the (master) bus.
- A Link button that links the two volume faders.
- Two Invert buttons allow you to invert the phase of the left and right side of the surround bus.

The Master bus has the following parameters:

- A Link button that links the two Master faders.
- A Normalize button. If activated, the mixed output will be normalized, i.e. the output level will automatically be adjusted so that the loudest signal is as loud as possible without clipping.

C Parameters of Cubase 5 Effect Plug-ins

C.1 Introduction

This chapter contains descriptions for the effects which can be found in the Cubase 5 plug-ins subfolder of your VST plug-ins if you chose to install any of these during the Cubase SX/SL installation. Note that some of these plug-ins are duplicates of the standard Cubase SX/SL plug-ins.

C.2 Autopole

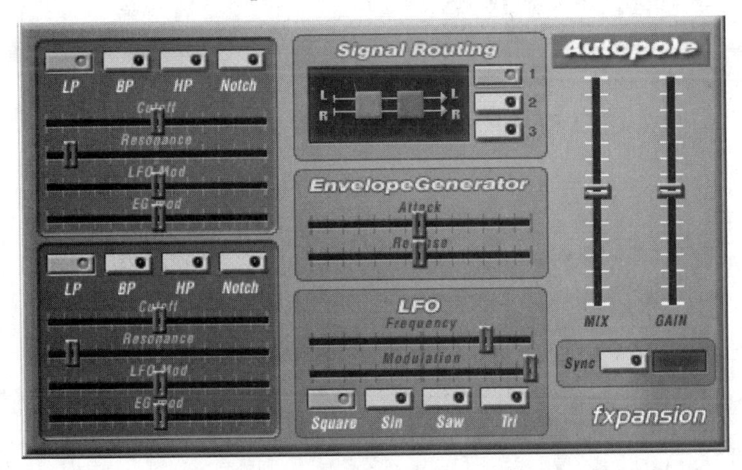

The Autopole is a filter effect containing two separate filters capable of operating in four different modes, an Envelope Generator and an LFO with four different waveforms. It also lets you choose between three different signal routing modes to control how an incoming signal should be sent through the filters.

The Autopole should be used as an insert effect. If you wish to apply it on several channels at once, you can use it as an insert effect on a group channel and then route the desired channels to the group channel.

The parameters for the different "sections" of the Autopole are the following:

C.2.1 The Filters

Parameter	Description
Filter Mode buttons (LP, BP, HP, Notch)	These buttons let you decide in which mode the Filter should operate: LP: This is a Low-Pass Filter that "filters out" the high frequency content of the incoming signal, according to a certain set threshold level. Only signals below the threshold will pass through. BP: This is a Band-Pass filter that only lets signals around the set frequency through, filtering out all other content. HP: This is a High-Pass Filter that "filters out" the low frequency content of the incoming signal, according to a certain set threshold level. Only signals above the threshold will pass through. Notch: This is a filter that cuts off the signals around the set frequency, leaving all other content unaffected.
Cutoff	This is used for setting the Cutoff frequency, i.e. the threshold at which the filter should "kick in". The farther to the right you drag the sliders, the higher the frequency.
Resonance	This affects the resonance of the filter. Increasing the resonance gives a more pronounced, lively filter sound. Be wary of extremely high levels of resonance since they might induce unpleasant distortion.
LFO Mod	These sliders govern how the filter cut-off frequencies are affected by the LFO (see below). The sliders are "zero-centered", meaning that in the middle position (zero), no LFO modulation will be applied. By dragging the sliders to the left or right, you cause an increasing amount of modulation to the cut-off frequency. The difference is that if you drag the sliders to the left, the waveform of the LFO is inverted, creating a different effect.
EG Mod	These sliders work in conjunction with the Envelope Generator settings (see below). They control to which extent the cut-off frequencies of the filters should be affected by the Envelope Generator. Drag the sliders to the right if you want to raise the cut-off frequencies and if you want to lower the frequencies, drag the sliders to the left. Leave the sliders in the middle position if you don't want Envelope data to affect the cut-off frequencies.

C.2.2 Signal Routing

By clicking one of the three buttons, you choose how an input *stereo* signal will pass though the filters. The signal flow chart to the left of the buttons indicates the path:

- **Option # 1 will have the signal from each channel pass through both of the filters in series (one after the other).**
- **With option # 2, the signal from each channel will pass through both of the filters in parallel, and then be mixed at the output.**
- **Finally, option # 3 causes the signals from both channels to each pass through a separate filter. I.e. the left signal only passes through Filter A, and the right signal only passes through Filter B.**

● When using the Autopole with mono material, options 1 and 2 are the best choices (sending the signal through the filters in series or in parallel, respectively).

C.2.3 Envelope Generator

This section controls how the input signal is converted into Envelope data. This, in its turn, affects the EG Mod sliders in the Filter sections and the Modulation slider in the LFO section:

Parameter	Description
Attack	This regulates how fast the Envelope Generator will respond to an input signal as it rises in sound level. The farther to the left you drag the slider, the faster the response will be.
Release	This governs how fast the Envelope Generator will respond to an input signal as it drops in sound level. The farther to the left you drag the slider, the faster the response will be.

C.2.4 LFO

These are the controls for the Low Frequency Oscillator, used for adding continuous filter movement, wah-wah effects, etc:

Parameter	Description
Frequency	This slider controls the speed of the LFO. The farther to the right you drag the slider, the faster the oscillation will be.
Modulation	Use this slider to control how the speed of the LFO should be modulated by the Envelope Generator (and thus by the level of the input signal). If you drag the slider to the left, a loud input signal will cause the LFO to slow down and if you drag to the right, the LFO will speed up. In the middle position, the speed of the LFO is unaffected.
Waveform Buttons	These buttons are used for choosing a waveform for the LFO. You can choose between Square, Sine, Saw and Triangle.

C.2.5 Output Controls

Parameter	Description
Mix	This controls the balance between the output from the Autopole and the input signal. In the middle position, both signals are equally mixed. The higher you drag the slider, the more dominant the effect will be. Conversely, with lower settings the unaffected original signal will be more pronounced.
Gain	This slider regulates the output level from the Autopole. The higher you drag the slider, the higher the level.
Sync	When this is activated, the LFO will restart in intervals according to the current Song tempo, which is useful for tempo sync and special effects. Click the button to activate sync, and then click in the small display to the right to select at which note values the LFO should be restarted: 1/1, 1/2, 1/4, 1/8 or 1/16. For example, setting this to 1/4 will make the LFO restart on each beat (quarter note) according to the current tempo.

C.3 MIDI Comb

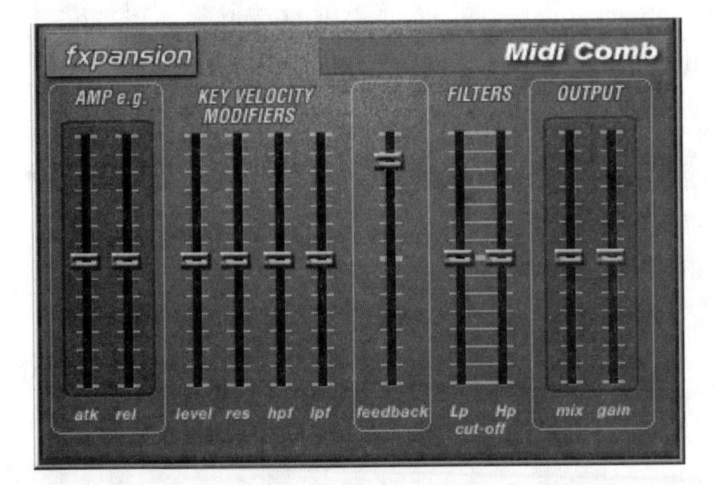

This is a comb filter, which can be described as one or several very short delays with high feedback, causing resonating peaks at certain frequencies. While the MIDI Comb is used as an insert effect on an audio channel, the signals that actually trigger it are the ones sent from a MIDI track.

C.3.1 Setting Up

The MIDI Comb requires both an audio signal and a MIDI input to function.

To set it up, proceed as follows:

1. **Select the audio to be affected by the MIDI Comb.**

   This can be audio material from any audio track, or even a live audio input routed to a audio track (provided you have a low latency audio card). If a live audio input is used, the track has to be record enabled or in Monitor mode.

2. **Select the MIDI Comb as an Insert effect for the audio channel.**

3. **Select a MIDI track.**

   This can be an empty MIDI track, or a MIDI track containing data, it doesn't matter. However, if you wish to play the MIDI Comb in real-time—as opposed to having a recorded part playing it—the track has to be record enabled or in Monitor mode for the effect to receive the MIDI output.

4. **Open the Output pop-up for the MIDI Track.**

   The MIDI Comb is now added to the list.

5. **Select the MIDI Comb from the Output pop-up menu.**

   The MIDI Output from the Track is now routed to the MIDI Comb.

What to do next depends on whether you are using live or recorded audio and whether you are using real-time or recorded MIDI. We will assume for the purposes of this manual that you are using recorded audio, and play the MIDI in real-time.

Make sure the MIDI Track is selected and start playback.

6. **Now play a few notes on your MIDI keyboard.**

   As you can hear, the audio track material is affected by what you play on your MIDI keyboard.

- The MIDI Comb is polyphonic with up to 8 voices, i.e. you can play up to 8 MIDI notes at once and each note will produce a separate resonating tone.

You can now make settings for the MIDI Comb using the following parameters:

C.3.2 Amp e.g.

Parameter	Description
Atk	Use this slider to set the attack time of the resonant tones created by the comb filter—i.e how soon they will start to resonate after being triggered by MIDI notes. The farther down you drag the slider, the shorter the attack.
Rel	This controls the release time of the resonant tones created by the comb filter—i.e. how soon the sound will be cut off. The farther up you drag the slider, the longer the sound will resonate.

C.3.3 Key Velocity Modifiers

Parameter	Description
Level	This determines how the filter responds to MIDI notes with different velocity values. At the middle setting, all tones produced by the filter will sound at an equal level regardless of the velocity values of the MIDI notes that trigger them. If you move the slider upwards, MIDI notes with higher velocity values will produce louder comb filter tones. Conversely, moving the slider downwards causes the level of the filter tones to increase with lower MIDI note velocities.

Parameter	Description
Res	This affects the resonance (feedback) of the produced tones depending on the velocity value of the MIDI notes that trigger them. In the middle position, the resonance is unaffected regardless of velocity. By dragging the slider upwards, tones triggered by MIDI notes with a high velocity value will get increased resonance. By dragging the slider downwards, tones triggered by MIDI notes with a low velocity value will become more resonant.
HPF & LPF	The MIDI Comb features both a High-Pass filter and a Low-Pass filter (see "Filters" below) that can be used for "filtering out" certain frequencies of the resonating tones according to a certain set filter cutoff frequency. These two sliders determine how much the High-Pass and Low-Pass filters should be affected by the MIDI note velocity values. Positive values cause higher velocities to increase the effect of the filters, negative values cause higher velocities to decrease the effect.

C.3.4 Feedback

Parameter	Description
Feedback	This slider governs the amount of effect output from the MIDI Comb that is fed back in again. The more effect feedback, the more complex the sound. Drag the slider upwards to increase feedback.

C.3.5 Filters

Parameter	Description
LP Cut-off	Use this to set the frequency threshold of the Low-Pass Filter. This filter cuts off all of the high frequencies relative to the set threshold. The farther up you drag the slider, the more of the high frequencies will be allowed to pass through.
HP Cut-off	Use this to set the frequency threshold of the High-Pass Filter. This filter cuts off all of the low frequencies relative to the set threshold. The farther down you drag the slider, the more of the low frequencies will be allowed to pass through.

C.3.6 Output

Parameter	Description
Mix	Use this to set the balance between the original, unprocessed signal and the signal affected by the MIDI Comb. In the middle position, they are equally mixed. Drag the slider upwards for a more dominant effect sound and vice versa.
Gain	This controls the output level from the MIDI Comb. Drag the slider upwards to increase the level.

C.4 Mysterizer

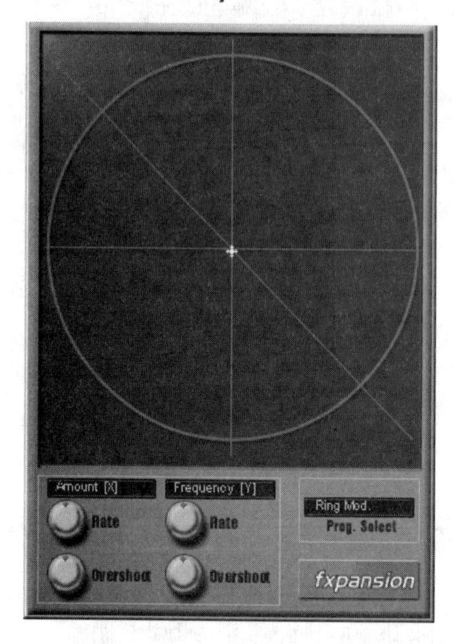

The Mysterizer is a multi-effect plug-in with a unique hands-on user interface. It can be used as an insert effect or a send effect, and allows you to choose between eight different effects. For each effect, you can control two parameters by clicking and dragging in the display, allowing for continuous real-time effect manipulation, subtle sweeping changes or weird, wild mutations.

Here's how to use the Mysterizer:

1. **Play back some audio and route the audio channel through the Mysterizer (either as an insert or a send effect).**
2. **Open the Mysterizer effect control panel and click the Prog Select field to the right to select the desired effect.**

   Each time you click, the next effect is selected. For a list of the effects, see below.
3. **When you have selected an effect you want to use, the two text fields to the left show you which parameters are controlled on the X-axis and Y-axis respectively.**

   In the figure above, the Ring Mod effect is selected, with Amount controlled on the X-axis and Frequency on the Y-axis.
4. **Click in the display and drag the hair cursor to change the parameter settings.**

   The X-axis goes from left to right and the Y-axis goes from top to bottom, which means that the "zero setting" for both axes is in the upper left corner of the display.
5. **Experiment!**

C.4.1 The Rate and Overshoot Knobs

When you move the hair cursor, you will see how the small white dot moves to follow your adjustments. This represents the actual parameter settings. The Rate and Overshoot controls at the bottom of the window control how quickly and accurately the white dot follows your movements—in other words how your mouse movements are "interpreted" by the effect.

- **The Rate knobs determine how fast the Mysterizer will respond when you move the hair cursor to a new position.**

  You can make independent settings for the X- and Y-axis.
- **The Overshoot knobs determine how far from the "target position" the white dot will be allowed to stray along the corresponding axis when moving the hair cursor.**

  Moderate settings can give a more natural feel when a parameter is changed. Maximum Overshoot settings (turning the knob all the way to the right) will cause constant movement back and forth along the corresponding axis relative to the target position, because the white dot will never "reach the target" and come to rest. This can create an undulating, LFO-like special effect, the speed and range of which can be controlled with the corresponding Rate knob.

C.4.2 The Effects

The following effects are available:

Effect	Description	X-axis param.	Y-axis param.
Ring Modulator	An effect with which the incoming audio is ring modulated by an internal, variable frequency oscillator, thereby producing new harmonics.	Amount of effect	Frequency of the built-in oscillator
Comb Delay	A delay with high feedback, causing resonating peaks at certain frequencies.	Feedback amount	Manual delay time (pitch) adjustment
Mono Delay	A monaural delay.	Delay feedback	Delay time
Stereo Delay	A stereo delay with which the repeats are heard in both the left and right channels.	Delay feedback	Delay time
Low-Pass Filter (LP)	A filter that cuts off high frequencies according to a set frequency threshold. Only signals below the cut-off frequency will be heard.	Filter resonance	Filter cutoff frequency
High-Pass Filter (HP)	A filter that cuts off low frequencies according to a set frequency threshold. Only signals above the cut-off frequency will be heard.	Filter resonance	Filter cutoff frequency
Band-Pass Filter (BP)	A filter that cuts off all frequencies except those around the set cut-off frequency.	Filter resonance	Filter cutoff frequency
Distortion	A standard distortion effect.	Drive amount	Tone control

C.5 Phatsync

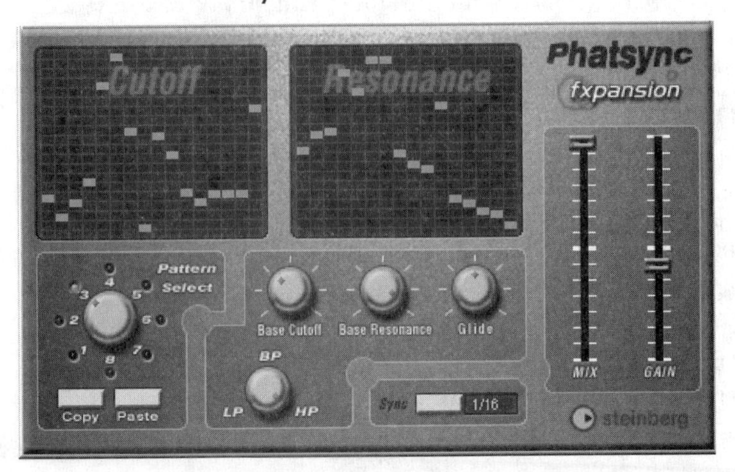

Phatsync is a pattern-controlled multimode filter that can create rhythmic, pulsating filter effects.

C.5.1 General Operation

Phatsync can produce two simultaneous 16-step patterns for the filter cutoff and resonance parameters, synchronized to the sequencer tempo.

C.5.2 Setting Step Values

- **Setting step values is done by clicking in the pattern grid windows.**

  Individual step entries can be freely dragged up or down the vertical axis, or directly set by clicking in an empty grid box. By click-dragging left or right consecutive step entries will be set to the pointer position.

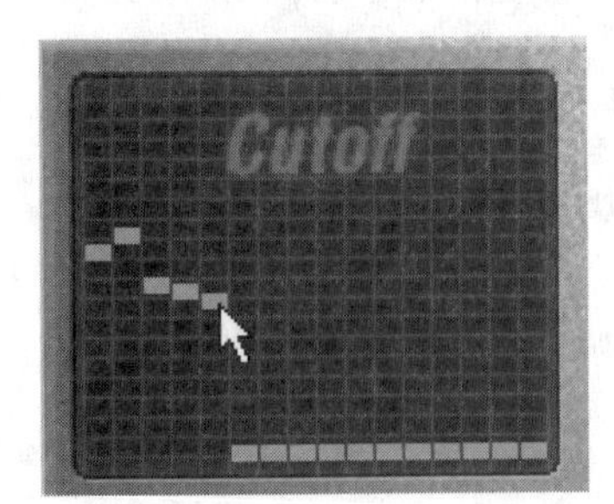

Setting filter cutoff values in the grid window.

- **The horizontal axis shows the pattern steps 1—16 from left to right, and the vertical axis determines the (relative) filter cutoff frequency and resonance setting.**

  The higher up on the vertical axis a step value is entered, the higher the relative filter cutoff frequency or filter resonance setting.

- **By starting playback and editing the patterns for the cutoff and resonance parameters, you can hear how your filter patterns affect the sound source connected to Phatsync directly.**

C.5.3 Selecting New Patterns

- **Created patterns are saved with the song, and up to 8 different Cutoff and Resonance patterns can be saved internally.**

  Both the Cutoff and Resonance patterns are saved together in the 8 Pattern memories.

- **To select new patterns you use the Pattern Selector.**

  New patterns are all set to the same step value by default.

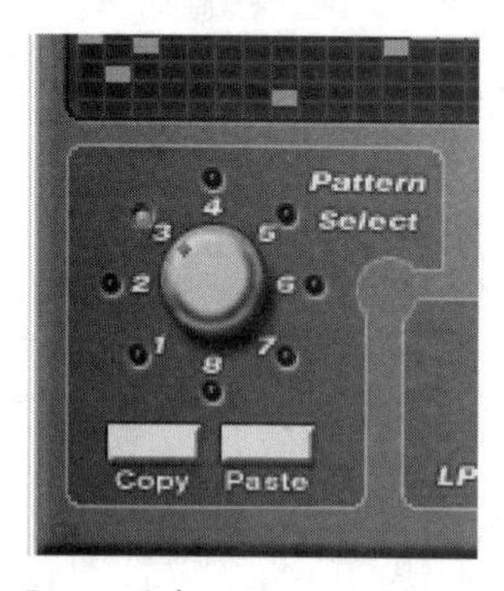

Pattern Selector.

C.5.4 Using Pattern Copy and Paste to Create Variations

You can use the Copy and Paste buttons below the Pattern selector to copy a pattern to another Pattern memory location, which is useful for creating variations on a pattern.

- **Click the Copy button with the pattern you wish to copy selected, then select another Pattern memory location, and click Paste.**

  The pattern is copied to the new location, and can now be edited to create variations using the original pattern as a starting point.

C.5.5 Phatsync Parameters:

Parameter/Value	Description
Base Cutoff	This sets the base filter cutoff frequency. Cutoff values set in the Cutoff Grid windows are values *relative* to the Base Cutoff value.
Base Resonance	This sets the base filter resonance. Resonance values set in the Resonance Grid windows are values *relative* to the Base Resonance value. Note that very high Base Resonance settings can produce loud ringing effects at certain frequencies.
Glide	This will apply glide between the pattern step values, causing values to change more smoothly.
Filter Mode (LP, BP, HP)	This selects between low-pass (LP), bandpass (BP) or high-pass (HP) filter modes.
Sync (1/32, 1/16, 1/8, 1/4)	This sets the pattern beat resolution, i.e. what note values the pattern will play in relation to the tempo.
Mix	Adjusts the mix between dry and processed signal.
Gain	Sets the overall volume.

C.6 Ring Modulator

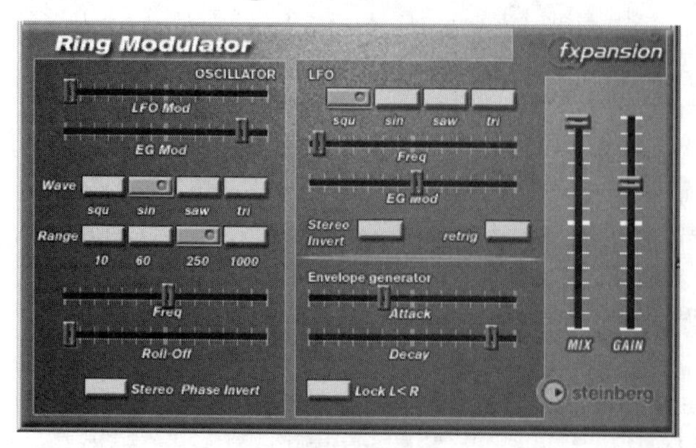

The Ring Modulator can produce complex, bell-like enharmonic sounds. Ring Modulators work by multiplying two audio signals together. The ring modulated output contains added frequencies generated by the sum of, and the difference between, the frequencies of the two signals.

The Ring Modulator has a built-in oscillator that is multiplied with the input signal to produce the effect.

C.6.1 Parameters:

Parameter	Description
Oscillator LFO Mod	LFO Mod controls how much the oscillator frequency is affected by the LFO.
Oscillator EG Mod	EG Mod controls how much the oscillator frequency is affected by the Envelope (which is triggered by the input signal). Positive and negative values can be set, with center position representing no modulation. Left of center, a loud input signal will decrease the oscillator pitch, whereas right of center the oscillator pitch will increase when fed a loud input.
Oscillator Wave	Selects the oscillator waveform; square, sine, saw or triangle.
Oscillator Range	Determines the frequency range of the oscillator in Hz.
Freq	Sets the oscillator frequency +/- 2 octaves within the selected range.

Parameter	Description
Roll-Off	Cuts high frequencies in the oscillator waveform, to soften the overall sound. This is best used when harmonically rich waveforms are selected (e.g. square or saw).
Stereo Phase Invert	Flips the phase of the oscillator waveform on the right channel.
LFO Waveform	Selects the LFO waveform: square, sine, saw or triangle.
LFO Freq	Sets the LFO Speed.
EG Mod	Controls how much the input signal level—via the Envelope Generator—affects the LFO Speed. Positive and negative values can be set, with center position representing no modulation. Left of center, a loud input signal will slow down the LFO, whereas right of center a loud input signal will speed it up.
Stereo Invert	This inverts the LFO waveform for the right channel of the oscillator, which produces a wider stereo perspective for the modulation.
Retrig	Causes the LFO cycle to reset itself at the start of each bar during playback, which can be used for certain LFO effects synchronized to the tempo.
Envelope Generator	The Envelope Generator section controls how the input signal is converted to envelope data, which can then be used to control oscillator pitch and LFO speed. It has two main controls: Attack sets how fast the EG output level rises in response to a rising input signal. Decay controls how fast the EG output level falls in response to a falling input signal.
Lock L<R	When this switch is enabled, the L and R input signals are merged, and produce the same EG output level for both oscillator channels. When disabled, each channel has its own EG, which affect the two channels of the oscillator independently.
Mix	Adjusts the mix between dry and processed signal.
Gain	Sets the overall volume.

C.7 subBASS

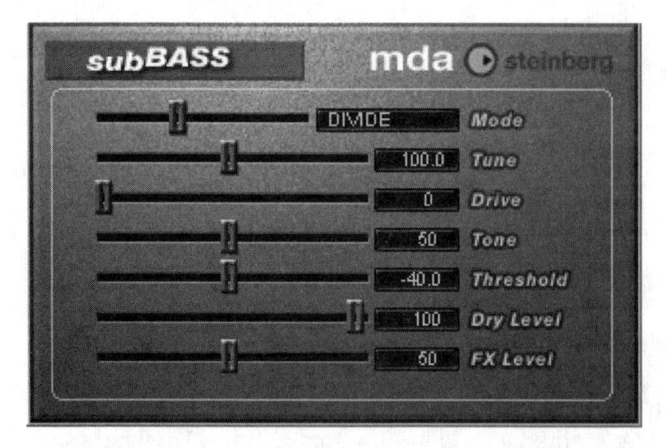

The subBASS is a bass synthesizer, that can generate low frequency content and track the pitch from the audio material for deep, sub-sonic bass effects.

The parameters are as follows:

Parameter	Values	Description
Mode	Boost/Divide/ Trigger	Boost produces a warm bass boost to the signal. Divide generates a pitch tracking signal an octave below the input signal. Trigger adds a decaying "boom" produced by an oscillator, typically triggered by a kick drum.
Tune	20—500Hz	This sets the maximum frequency to be affected. Set as low as possible to avoid unwanted distortion. In "Trigger" mode this sets the oscillator frequency.
Drive	0—100	In Boost mode, raising the Drive parameter adds "crunch" to the effect. In Divide mode, increasing Drive to 50% overdrives the sub-octave signal producing a square wave, and increasing Drive to 100% produces a square wave one octave above (i.e. at the original input frequency). In Trigger mode this changes the tone of the oscillator, with higher settings producing a thinner sound.
Tone	0—100	This is a low-pass filter that can be used to change the brightness of the signal. In "Trigger" mode this sets the decay time of the generated oscillator boom.

Parameter	Values	Description
Threshold	-80dB to 0dB	This sets the threshold for the effect. Increase to "gate" the effect and to cut out unwanted background rumble.
Dry Level	0—100	Sets the level of the original, unprocessed signal.
FX Level	0—100	Sets the level of the processed signal.

C.8 Distortion

The Distortion effect plug-in is capable of producing anything from a soft "crunch" to all-out distortion. There is a selection of factory presets available. Note that these presets are not stored parameter settings, but different basic distortion algorithms. The basic characters of the distortion preset "models" are indicated by their names. The parameters are as follows:

Parameter	Values	Description
Input	-24dB to 0dB	Sets the Input level.
Output	-24dB to 0dB	Sets the Output level. As distortion generates harmonics, it increases the level of the processed signal. You can use the Output fader to compensate for the level increase.
Shapes	Linear, Non-linear 1, Non-linear 2	The Shape parameter determines how much the input signal is affected by the distortion effect. Non-linear 2 will produce the strongest distortion.

Parameter	Values	Description
Contour	0—100%	This is a selective low-pass filter, altering the tonal quality of the distortion.
Drive	0—100%	Governs the amount of distortion.
Factory Presets	Soft, Crunchy, Dirty, Wracky, Evil	Select one of five presets, which can be used as they are, or as a basis for further "tweaking".

C.9 Chopper2

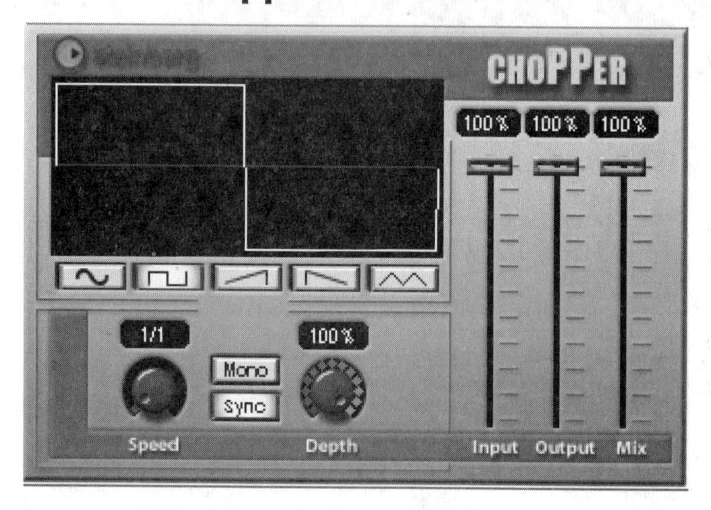

Chopper2 is a combined tremolo and autopan effect. It can use different waveforms to modulate the level (tremolo) or left-right stereo position (pan), either using Tempo Sync or manual modulation speed settings.

The parameters are as follows:

Parameter	Values	Description
Input	0—100%	Sets the Input level.
Output	0—100%	Sets the Output level.

Parameter	Values	Description
Mix	0—100%	Sets the level balance between the dry signal and the effect. If Chopper is used as a send effect, this should be set to maximum as you can instead control the dry/effect balance with the send.
Tempo Sync pop-up	No sync, 1/1 to 1/32, 1/1 to 1/32 Triplet, 1/1 to 1/32 Dotted	When tempo sync is activated (the "Sync" button is lit) clicking the field above the Speed knob opens a pop-up menu, on which you select a note value for tempo-syncing the effect. Note that there is no note value modifier for this effect.
Speed	0—50Hz	When tempo sync is activated (the "Sync" button is lit), this knob selects note values (the same as selecting from the pop-up menu). When tempo sync is deactivated (the "Sync" button is dark), this sets the tremolo/auto-pan speed freely.
Sync button	On/Off	Turns Tempo Sync on or off.
Stereo/Mono button	Stereo/Mono	Determines whether the Chopper will work as an auto-panner (button set to "Stereo") or a tremolo effect (button set to "Mono").
Waveform buttons	Sine, Square, Saw, reverse Saw, Triangle	Sets the modulation waveform.
Depth	0—100%	Sets the depth of the Chopper effect.

C.10 Reverb

Reverb is used to add ambience and "space" to recordings. The reverb effect features the following parameters:

Parameter	Values	Description
Mix	0—100%	Sets the level balance between the dry signal and the effect. If Reverb is used as a send effect, this should be set to maximum as you can instead control the dry/effect balance with the send.
Room Size	0—100%	Governs the "size" of the simulated room environment.
Pre-delay	0—100%	This parameter sets a delay between the direct sound and the reverb effect output. A short predelay before the reverb reduces reverb "clutter" which blurs the sound, and makes the reverb effect more natural-sounding.
Reverb Time	0—100%	This parameter sets the length of the reverb effect.
Damp	0—100%	This parameter "dampens" the higher frequencies, producing a rounder and smoother sounding reverb.

C.11 Reverb 32

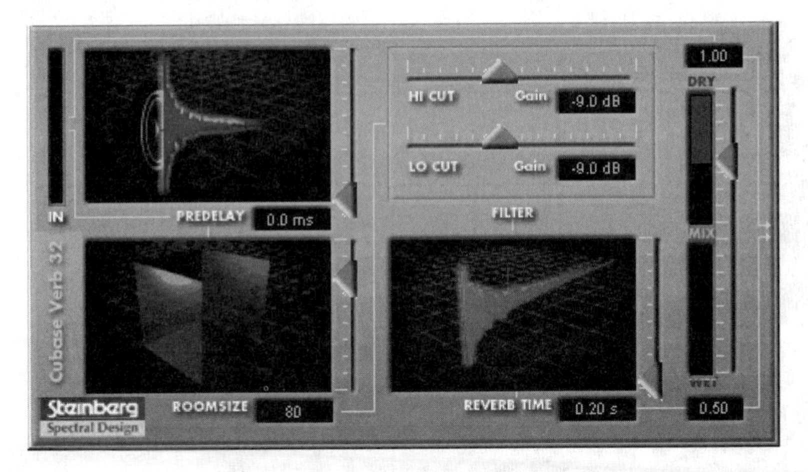

Reverb 32 is a reverb plug-in which provides smooth, dense reverb effects. Reverb 32 has the following parameters:

Parameter	Values	Description
Mix	Dry/Wet	Sets the level balance between the dry signal and the effect (wet). If Reverb 32 is used as a send effect, this should be set to maximum wet, as you can instead control the dry/wet balance with the send.
Room Size	20—100	This setting determines the "size" of the simulated room environment.
Predelay	0—100ms	This parameter sets a delay between the direct sound and the reverb effect output. A short predelay before the reverb reduces reverb "clutter" which blurs the sound, and makes the reverb effect more natural-sounding.
Reverb Time	0,2s—forever	This parameter sets the length of the reverb time.
Filter Hi Cut	-15 to 0dB	This filters out high frequencies for the reverb, which can make the reverb sound softer.
Filter Lo Cut	-15 to 0dB	This filters out the lower frequencies for the reverb. It can be used to reduce low frequency "rumble".

C.12 Metalizer2

The Metalizer feeds the audio signal through a variable frequency filter, with Tempo sync or time modulation and feedback control.

Parameter	Values	Description
Tempo Sync pop-up	No sync, 1/1 to 1/32, 1/1 to 1/32 Triplet, 1/1 to 1/32 Dotted	When tempo sync is activated (the "Sync" button is lit) clicking the field above the Speed knob opens a pop-up menu, on which you select a note value for tempo-syncronizing the effect. There is no note value modifier for this effect.
Speed	0—10Hz	When tempo sync is activated (the "Sync" button is lit), this knob selects note values (the same as selecting from the pop-up menu). When tempo sync is deactivated (the "Sync" button is dark), this sets the modulation speed freely.
On button	On/Off	Turns on and off the filter modulation. When turned off, the Metalizer will work as a static filter.
Sync button	On/Off	Turns tempo sync of the modulation on or off.
Stereo/Mono button	Stereo/Mono	Determines whether the output of the Metalizer will be in stereo or mono.

Parameter	Values	Description
Sharpness	0—100%	Governs the character of the filter effect. The higher the value, the narrower the affected frequency area, producing sharper sound and a more pronounced effect.
Tone	0—100%	Governs the feedback frequency. The effect of this will be more noticeable with high Feedback settings.
Feedback	0—100%	Sets the amount of feedback. Higher values produce a more "metallic" sound.

C.13 Tranceformer2

Tranceformer2 is a ring modulator effect, in which the incoming audio is ring modulated by an internal, variable frequency oscillator, producing new harmonics. A second oscillator can be used to modulate the frequency of the first oscillator, synchronized to the Song tempo if you wish.

Parameter	Values	Description
Input	0—100%	Sets the Input level.
Output	0—100%	Sets the Output level.
Mix	0—100%	Sets the level balance between the dry signal and the effect.

Parameter	Values	Description
Pitch	1—5000Hz	Governs the frequency (pitch) of the modulating oscillator.
Tempo Sync pop-up	No sync, 1/1 to 1/32, 1/1 to 1/32 Triplet, 1/1 to 1/32 Dotted	When tempo sync is activated (the "Sync" button is lit) clicking the field above the Speed knob opens a pop-up menu, on which you select a note value for tempo-syncing the effect. There is no note value modifier for this effect.
Speed	0—10Hz	When tempo sync is activated (the "Sync" button is lit), this knob selects note values (the same as selecting from the pop-up menu). When tempo sync is deactivated (the "Sync" button is dark), this sets the modulation speed freely.
On button	On/Off	Turns modulation of the Pitch parameter on or off.
Stereo/Mono button	Stereo/Mono	Governs whether the effect output will be stereo or mono.
Sync button	On/Off	Turns tempo sync of the modulation on or off.
Depth	0—100%	Governs the depth of the pitch modulation.
Waveform buttons	Sine, Square, Saw, reverse Saw, Triangle	Sets the pitch modulation waveform.

C.14 Karlette

The Karlette is a four-channel delay, that emulates a "tape-loop" echo. The four "tape-heads" can be set to a certain note value, or a certain time, depending on whether Tempo Sync is activated or not. For each of the four "tape-heads", you can set the following parameters:

Parameter	Values	Description
Delay	1/32, 1/16, 1/16*, 1/8, 1/4T, 1/8*, 1/4, 1/2T, 1/4*, 1/2, 3/4, 1/1 Sync Off: 0—2 sec.	With the sync button activated, the delay can be set to a note value synchronized to the Cubase SX/SL tempo. If the sync button is deactivated, the delay can be freely set to a time value.
Volume	Off to OdB	The amplitude of the delay. With the knob turned all the way to the left, the delay is muted.
Damp	0.000 to 1.000	The higher the value, the more the delay is dampened (the high frequencies are attenuated) to produce a more subtle effect.
Pan	L64/< C >/R64	Sets the stereo position for the delay.
Feedback	0.000 to 1.000	Sets the number of delay repeats.

In addition, the following global parameters are available:

Dry/Wet	0—100%	Sets the level balance between the dry signal and the effect. If Karlette is used as a send effect, this should be set to maximum as you can instead control the dry/effect balance with the send.
Sync	On/Off	Turns Tempo Sync on or off.

D Parameters of Earlier VST Effect Plug-ins

D.1 Introduction

This chapter describes the VST Plug-in Effects in the "Earlier VST Plugins" folder if you chose to install these during the Cubase SX/SL installation. These are effects included with previous versions of Cubase, included with Cubase SX/SL for reasons of backwards compatibility.

D.2 Auto Panner

This makes the sound move automatically between the left and right channel.

- This effect would most often be used with "Pre Fader" activated in the channel's send section. Furthermore, in most cases, the channel output should be turned down all the way so that you only hear the output of the effect, not the original signal.

Parameter	Explanation
LFO Freq	This sets the speed of the panning effect.
Width	This sets the depth of the effect, that is, how far out to the left/right speaker the sound should move.
Waveform	This sets the shape of the LFO producing the effect. Sine and Triangle both produce a smooth sweep, but with different characteristics. Sawtooth creates a ramp (sweep from one speaker to the other and then a quick jump back). Pulse makes the signal jump back and forth between the speakers.
Output Level	The stereo output level of the effect.

D.3 Choirus and Choirus 2

- For some computer configurations, the original Choirus effect gave rise to clicks and distorted sound. The Choirus2 effect solves this problem. It is identical to the "Choirus Classic" featurewise, but draws slightly more computer power.

Choirus is a chorus and flanger effect which adds "depth" and "animation" to a sound. It basically works as follows: The original signal is delayed and the amount of delay is continuously varied by an "LFO". This delayed signal is then added back in with the original.

Parameter	Explanation
Time	This is the basic amount of delay applied to the signal. The larger the value, the richer the sound (up to a certain extent). For flanger types of effects, use the lower range of values.
Feedback	This is the amount of output signal re-routed back to the input of the effect. For soft and wide chorus effects, keep this value low. For flanger type effects, raise this value.
Width	Sets the amount of variation in the delay of the signal. The larger the value, the more drastic the effect. This value should be balanced with the Time setting for optimal results.
LFO Freq	This is the speed of the LFO "sweep". The larger the value, the faster sweep.
Glimmer	A low value gives a more "concentrated" sound, while higher values result in a more "animated" sound.
Out Levl	The stereo output level of the effect.

D.4 ESpacial!

This is a reverb effect. It adds "ambience" or "room quality" to the sound. The relationship between the parameters is a little bit intricate, so we suggest you start out by selecting a Program as close to the desired result as possible and then modify the settings as desired. Espacial accepts a mono input only and is used as a Send Effect.

D.4.1 Parameters

Parameter	Explanation
Size	Affects the apparent size of the simulated room.
Width	This parameter also affects the impression of the size and shape of the simulated room. It also affects the "density" and clearness of the reverb.
Time	The decay time of the reverberation.
ER Start	The start time of the Early Reflections—the first "echo" from the walls in a simulated room.
ER Width	Early Reflection "density" and clearness.
ER Gain	The balance between Early Reflections/direct sound in the input to the actual reverb. When this parameter is fully raised, no Early Reflections will be heard at all.
ER Decay	Determines the gradual attenuation of Early Reflections.
ER Outp	The level of Early Reflections in the Effect Output.
Output Level	The stereo output level of the effect.

D.5 Electro Fuzz

This is a simulation of the good old transistor distortion stomp box. It accepts a mono input and can be used as an Insert or Send effect.

The Electro Fuzz has the following parameters:

- **Boost**

  This governs the amount of distortion. If you want to increase the distortion without raising the signal level, you may have to adjust the Volume knob as well.

- **Clipback**

  Raising this parameter will "invert" the part of the signal that is above the clipping level, instead of employing hard clipping. The result is that more 2nd order harmonics are added, changing the character of the distortion.

- **Volume**

  This is a volume control for the output signal from the Electro Fuzz.

D.6 Scopion

The Scopion is an on-board oscilloscope, that analyzes the left or right side of a stereo input signal and displays the waveform contents in real time. It must be used as a Master Effect. The Scopion uses a custom interface. There are three parameters:

Parameter	Description
L/R Switch	Clicking this switch allows you to choose between displaying the left and right side of the stereo input signal.
Time Scale	This knob (directly below the L/R switch) allows you to scale the waveform horizontally.
Gain Scale	This knob (at the bottom of the Scopion window) allows you to scale the waveform vertically.

- **If you click the Scopion label plate below the display, a help screen will be shown, explaining the functionality of the parameters in the window.**

D.7 Stereo Echo

The Stereo Echo is a delay with separate settings for the left and right channel. It can also be used as a single mono delay, in which case the maximum delay time will be doubled.

- The Stereo Echo accepts a mono input only. It is normally used as a Send Effect.

The Stereo Echo has the following parameters:

Parameter	Explanation
Delay1	The delay time for the left channel. The maximum delay time is 500 ms, unless you link both channels for mono operation, in which case the maximum delay time is 1000 ms—see below (1000ms = 1 second).
Feedbck1	The delay feedback for the left channel. Higher values result in a higher number of echo repeats.

Parameter	Explanation
Link 1-2	Activating this switch turns the effect into a mono delay. When Link is on, only the left channel parameters will be available (Delay1, Feedback1, etc).
Delay 2	The delay time for the right channel.
Feedbck2	The delay feedback for the right channel.
Del2 Bal	This parameter determines how much of the left channel output is sent to the right channel input. When set to 0.0 (fully left), then none of the left channel output is added to the right channel input; when it is set to 1.0 (fully right), the right input receives both its normal source and the complete output of the left channel.
Volume L	The output level of the left channel delay.
Volume R	The output level of the right channel delay.

D.8 StereoWizard

The StereoWizard is a stereo width enhancer that takes a stereo input signal and makes it sound "wider". It must be used as a Master Effect or as an Insert effect for a stereo channel pair. StereoWizard will give best result if you use "real" stereo material (as opposed to mono channels panned to different positions in the stereo image), but you could also apply stereo ambience or reverb to a mono signal, and then use Stereo-Wizard to enhance the stereo width of the reverb. The Wizard has the following parameters:

Parameter	Explanation
Amount	Higher values result in a greater stereo width. Normally, you should set this to values between 0.00—0.20; higher values can be used for special effects.
Reverse	Reverses the left and right channel.

D.9 WunderVerb 3

WunderbVerb 3 is a reverb plug-in which provides natural sounding reverb effects, and still uses very little processor power. It accepts a mono input and is used as a Send Effect. Use the Program pop-up to select one of ten Reverb Types:

Reverb Type	Description
Hall	The reverberation of a medium-sized hall.
Large Hall	The reverberation of a larger hall.
Large Room	The reverberation of a large room.
Medium Room	The reverberation of a medium-sized room.
Small Room	The reverberation of a very small room.
Plate	The slightly metallic effect of a plate reverb.
Gated	A special effect, where the reverb is abruptly cut off.
Effect 1	A special "bouncing" effect.
Echoes	An echo (delay) effect.
Effect 2	A special, resonant effect, suitable for "ringing" metal sounds.

WunderVerb 3 uses a custom panel. You can adjust the following parameters:

D.9.1 Size

This is the size of the simulated room. Changing this will affect the density and character of the reverb. If you have selected a Reverb Type where you can hear the individual "bounces" (Effect 1, Echoes, etc), raising the Size will increase the time between each "bounce", like the time control on a delay effect.

D.9.2 Decay

This is the decay time for the reverb. The higher the value, the longer the reverb.

D.9.3 Damp

Raising this value will cause the high frequency contents of the reverb sound to die out quicker. This results in a softer, darker reverb.

E Frequently Asked Questions

This chapter contains answers to some commonly asked questions:

Q: When I import a Cubase 5 Song into Cubase SX/SL why doesn't it sound like it did before?

A: This is dependent on a number of things. For example, Cubase SX/SL doesn't import dynamic events, so if that function was used a lot in the Song there will be a discrepancy. Also, automation is handled differently in Cubase SX/SL. For a complete listing of what is and what is not imported, please refer to page 661 in the File Handling chapter.

Q: When I import a Cubase 5 Song, how do I move around my audio events in the Project window?

A: In Cubase 5, audio events were always placed in a part. In Cubase SX/SL, you can have both audio events and parts containing audio events in the Project window. So if what you want to do is to freely move around the events currently contained in the part—to other tracks for example—the solution is to select the part in the Project window and then select "Dissolve Part" from the Audio menu.

Q: I added my Remote device in the Device Setup but nothing happens.

A: Make sure you selected the right MIDI Input/Output Port for your remote control device. Open the Device Setup dialog, select your device in the Devices list and click the Setup tab.

Q: Where is the Toolbox?

A: Cubase SX/SL has no Toolbox. You select tools via the Quick menu (displayed by right-clicking in a window) or from the toolbar at the top of the current window.

Q: I have problems with audio playback—it stutters intermittently.

A: Check the VST Performance meter (selectable from the Devices menu). If the CPU load is showing high levels, try mixing down some audio tracks and/or VST Instrument channels.

If this doesn't cure the problem, try increasing the Buffer size in the ASIO Control Panel. Open the Device Setup dialog—VST Multitrack page to open the ASIO Control Panel.

Q: Is there any way to edit my audio parts in an external audio editor?

A: Currently there is no direct support for external audio editors. You can always bounce the part you want to edit and open it manually.

Q: I opened an audio file in my external audio editor, but there is no sound when I play it back. What could be the problem?

A: Make sure "Release ASIO Driver in Background" is activated (ticked) in the Device Setup—VST Multitrack dialog on the Devices menu. This allows other audio programs to temporarily "take over" audio playback when Cubase SX/SL is running.

Q: When using a VST Instrument, why is there a delay between playing a note on my MIDI device and the audio output?

A: This is what is referred to as audio system "latency". Latency is the delay between when audio is "sent" from the program and when you actually hear it. The latency value depends on the audio card used and its drivers. Newer audio cards with specific ASIO drivers generally produce very low latency values.

Latency does not occur on MIDI playback to the VST Instrument, only during recording. Hence, if the latency of your audiosystem makes it difficult to play a VST Instrument, a workaround solution is to record using some other MIDI sound source, and switching the track output to the VST Instrument during playback.

Q: I can't seem to activate MIDI Thru to play a connected MIDI device—what's the problem?

A: Make sure the track is record enabled (the Record Enable icon for the track should be red) or is in Monitor mode (the speaker icon is lit).

If the problem persists, make sure MIDI Thru is enabled in the Preferences—MIDI page on the File menu.

If none of this solves the problem, check that you have connected your system properly—read the chapter "Setting up your system" in the Getting Started book.

Index

A

A1 Synthesizer 245
Activate Project button 655
Active ASIO Ports for Data only 639
Active Staff 531
Add Track 126
Adjust Fades to Range 170
Aftertouch
    Deleting 508
    Editing 504
    Recording 98
AIFF files 603
Always use MIDI Clock Start 623
Any (MIDI Channel setting) 96
Apogee UV22 HR 228
APP
    Introduction to 617
    Setting Up 621
Apply Effects 347
AQ button 97, 473
Arpache 5 440
Arpeggiator 440
ASIO 2.0 88
ASIO Direct Monitoring 88
ASIO Positioning Protocol
    Introduction to 617
    Setting up 621
Audio Channels
    Copying Settings 204
    Linking 212
    Making Settings for 200
    Saving Settings 214
Audio Clips
    About 329
    Creating New Versions 402
    Deleting 404
    Locating Events 405
    Managing in Pool 402
    Opening in the Sample Editor 410
Audio Effects
    About 220
    Applying 347
    Automating 306
    Editing 230
    In Surround Configurations 288
    Loading 231
    Naming 230
    Organizing in subfolders 236
    Parameters 234
    Pre/Post fader sends 223
    Saving 231
    Sends 222
    Tempo Sync 219
    Using VST System Link 642
Audio Events
    Blue Handles 169, 170
    Editing in Project Browser 587
    Editing in Sample Editor 359
    Making selections in 367
    Slicing 394
Audio Files
    Converting 416
    Deleting Permanently 405
    Exporting 601
    Format for recording 84
    Formats 411
    Import Options 129
    Importing into Pool 411
    Importing into Project Window 128
    Locating Missing 408
    Reconstructing Missing 409
    Removing Missing 409
Audio Inputs 82
Audio Parts
    About 108
    Creating by gluing events 138
    Creating from Events 131
    Drawing 131
    Editing in Audio Part Editor 377
    Editing in Project Browser 586
    Sliding contents 140
Auditioning
    Audio Part Editor 381
    MIDI Editors 492
    Project window 132
    Sample Editor 364
Auto Fades 179
Auto Monitoring modes 87
Auto Quantize 97, 473

Auto Quantize (Score) 535
Auto Save 668
Auto Scroll 152, 491
Auto Select Events under Cursor 134, 494, 513
Autolatch mode 300
Automation
- About 291
- Channel Automation Track 293
- Editing in Project Browser 591
- Master Automation Track 293
- Modes 300
- Opening subtracks 294
- Plug-in Automation tracks 293
- Reduction Preference 309
- Showing and hiding 294
- Write/Read buttons 299

Automation Events
- About 302
- Editing 303
- Editing in Project Browser 308
- Removing 305
- Selecting 305

Automation Subtracks
- Assigning parameters to 295
- Hiding and Showing 297
- Muting 298
- Opening 294

AutoPan (MIDI effect) 442

B

Backup (.bak) files 668
Bank Select 419
Bars+Beats Linear 489, 573
Beat Calculator 580
Bounce Selection 143, 370, 413
Broadcast Wave files
- Exporting 611
- Recording 85

Browser 583
Buses 207
Bypass
- Effect sends 223
- Insert effects 226

C

Calculate (Hitpoints) 388
Channel (MIDI) 94
Channel Settings
- Audio Tracks 200
- Copying 204
- MIDI Tracks 211

Chase 77
Chn setting 96
Chorder 444
Clean Lengths 537
Cleanup 659
Clef 536
Click 103
Clips, *see "Audio Clips"*
Close 656
Close Gaps 396
CM Motor Mix 315
Color pop-up menu
- MIDI Editors 546
- Project window 127

Compress (MIDI effect) 447
Conform Files 417
Control (MIDI Effect) 448
Controller Display
- About 489
- Adding and Removing Lanes 501
- Editing Events 504
- Editing Velocity 502
- Selecting Event Type 501

Controllers
- Deleting 508
- Editing 504
- Recording 98

Convert Files 416
Convert to Real Copy 136
Cpr files 656
Create Events (Cycle Rec Mode) 90
Create Groove Quantize 395
Create Images During Record 89
Create new controller lane 501
Create Regions (Cycle Rec Mode) 92
Create Slices 394
Crop 148
Crossfades
- Creating 174
- Editing in dialog 177
- Presets 179
- Removing 176

Csh files 415
Cubase 5 Plug-ins 237

Cubase files (previous versions) 661
Cut Time 147
Cycle
- About 82
- Recording Audio 90
- Recording MIDI 98

Cycle Markers
- About 159
- Adding in Marker window 161
- Drawing 164
- Editing 166
- Making selections with 166
- Navigating to 165
- On Marker track 163

Cycle Record modes 98

D

DC Offset 343
Deactivate Punch In on Stop 102
Default Edit Action 486
Default Project 657
Delete
- Audio Files from Disk 405
- Events in Project window 143
- MIDI Controllers 477, 508
- MIDI Drum notes 514
- MIDI Notes 498

Delete Controllers function 477
Delete Doubles function 477
Delete Notes function 478
Delete Overlaps
- Mono 479
- Poly 479

Delete Time 147
Density (MIDI Effect) 449
Detect Silence 352
DirectShow 645
DirectX Plug-ins 237
Disable Hitpoints 390
Disable Inserts 226
Disable Sends 223
Disable Track 76
Display format 116
Display Quantize 534
Display Transpose 536
Dissolve Part
- Audio 131
- MIDI 481

Dither 228
Divide audio events 395
Drag Delay 135
Draw
- Automation Events 303
- Hitpoints 392
- Markers 164
- MIDI Controllers 504
- MIDI Notes 492
- Parts 131

Dropout Time 626
Drum Editor
- Creating and editing notes 512
- Muting drum sounds 514
- Selecting drum maps 519

Drum Machine 257
Drum maps
- About 514
- Making settings 515
- MIDI Channel and Output 518
- O-Note Conversion 521
- Selecting 519
- Setup dialog 519

Drum mode (Timestretch) 346
Drum Name lists 522
Drum Sound Solo 514
Drumstick tool 512
Duplicate 135, 495
Duplicate Track 126

E

Earlier VST Plug-ins 237
Edit as Drums when Drummap is assigned 486
Edit button
- Audio Track Inspector 112
- MIDI Channel Strips 211
- MIDI Track Inspector 431

Editing via MIDI 498
Edits folder 329
Effects
- Bitcrusher 750
- Chopper 751
- Chopper2 780
- Chorus 737
- Datube 716
- Distortion 779
- DoubleDelay 713
- Dynamics 724

Flanger 738
Metalizer 739
Mix8To2 762
ModDelay 714
Overdrive 717
Phaser 741
QuadraFuzz 718
Reverb A 760
Reverb B 761
Ring Modulator 742
Rotary 744
SPL DeEsser 722
StepFilter 734
Symphonic 746
Tranceformer 748
Vocoder 753
VST Dynamics 729
Effects, *see "Audio Effects" or "MIDI Effects"*
Elements (Sample Editor) 360
Enable Record on Selected Track 80
Enable Track 76
Enharmonic Shift 543
Envelope 332
EQ
Bypassing 203
Presets 204
Setting 201
Eraser tool 143
Event as Region 148
Events
Duplicating 135
Locking 141
Moving 134
Muting 143
Overlapping 135, 380
Removing 143
Renaming 137
Renaming all on Track 126
Resizing 138
Resizing with time stretch 139
Selecting 133
Sliding contents 140
Splitting 137
Events (Snap mode) 150
Events from Regions 148
Events to Part 131, 383
Events, *see also"Audio Events"*
Exclusive Solo 196
Export Audio Mixdown 601
Export MIDI Files 660

F

F button 526
Fade handles 169
Fade In/Out functions 171
Faders 194
Fades
Auto Fades 179
Creating 169
Editing in dialog 172
Presets 173
Processing 171
Removing 172
Fill Loop 136
Filter (MIDI) 101
Filter (Project Browser) 590
Filter bar 526
Find Missing Files 408
Find Selected in Pool 406
Fixed Lengths 477
Fixed Velocity 481
Flip Stems 544
Folder parts 156
Folder Tracks
About 153
Moving Tracks into 153
Muting and Soloing 155
Foot button 499
Frame Rates 625
Freeze Edits 351
Freeze Quantize 475

G

Gain 333
Generic Remote Device 324
Glue Tube tool
Project window 138
Score Editor 543
Grid (Snap mode) 150
Groove Quantize 395
Group Channel Tracks
About 107
Routing audio to 206
Using effects with 232
GS Control Panel 458

H

Hitpoint Edit tool 390
Hitpoint Sensitivity 389
Hitpoints
- Auditioning 389
- Background 385
- Calculating 388
- Disabling 390
- Editing manually 392
- Locking 391

Houston 314

I

Ignore Hours 627
Import
- Audio CD Tracks 663
- Audio files 128
- Medium in Pool 411
- MIDI Files 660
- MPEG files 667
- Ogg Vorbis files 668
- Older Cubase Files 661
- REX 666
- Video files 128
- WMA files 668

Import Audio CD 412
Import Cubase Arrangement 663
Import Cubase Part 663
Import Cubase Song 661
Info Line
- Drum Editor 509
- Key Editor 488
- Pool 400
- Project Window 115
- Sample Editor 363
- Score Editor (Cubase SL) 530

I-Note 517
Input (MIDI) 94
Input Transformer 568
Insert Effects (Audio) 225
Insert into Project 406
Insert pop-up menu 524
Insert Silence 148, 369
Insert Velocity 493, 512
Inspector
- Audio tracks 112
- Folder tracks 113
- Handling 111
- MIDI Tracks 429

Interpolate Audio Images 364
Iterative Quantize 473

J

JL Cooper CS-10 316
JL Cooper MCS-3000 317
Jump tempo curve mode 575

K

Key (Scores) 536
Key Commands
- About 671
- Default 677
- Modifying 672
- Recalling Saved (Import) 676
- Removing 673
- Resetting to default 677
- Saving (Export) 675
- Searching for 676
- Show List 676

L

Lanes 379
Latency
- Monitoring 87
- VST System Link 632

Left Locator 159
Legato 477
Length Compression 433
Length Correction 100
Length Quantize 492
Level Faders 194
LFE Slider 286
Line mode
- Automation (Project window) 304
- MIDI Controllers 504
- MIDI Velocity 503

Linear time base 127
List Editor
- Adding events 524
- Editing in the list 525
- Editing in the Value display 528
- Filtering events 526
- Masking events 527

LM-7 Drum Machine 257
LM-9 273

Locate when clicked in empty space 73
Locators 159
Lock 141
Lock Event Attributes 141
Lock Hitpoints 391
Lock Time 627
Logical Editor
- About 549
- Actions 563
- Filter Conditions 552
- Functions 561
- Opening 550
- Presets 551, 567

Loop Icon
- Audio Part Editor 381
- Pool 409
- Sample Editor 365

M

Machine Control
- Introduction to 618
- Setting up 624

Macros 674
Magnetic Cursor (Snap mode) 151
Magnifying Glass tool 119
Markers
- About 159
- Adding in Marker window 161
- Drawing on the Marker Track 164
- Editing in Project Browser 167, 592
- Editing on the Marker Track 163
- ID-numbers 161
- Marker Track 163
- Marker Window 160
- Moving 161
- Removing 161
- Snapping to 150

Mask function 527
Master Automation 307
Master Automation Track 293
Master Effects 227
Master Gain Fader 210
Maximum Undo 685
Merge Clipboard 334
Merge MIDI in Loop 464
Merge Record mode 97
Meter characteristics 205
Metronome
- Activating 103
- Settings 104

Micro Tuner (MIDI Effect) 449
MIDI Channel
- "Any" 96
- In drum maps 518
- Selecting for tracks 95
- Send effects 439

MIDI Clock
- About 615
- Always use "Start" 623
- Transmitting 622

MIDI Connector Button 498
MIDI Device Manager 420
MIDI Devices
- Defining new 424
- Editing patches for 424
- Installing 421
- Selecting patches for 423

MIDI Echo 450
MIDI Effects
- About 436
- Deactivating 462
- Inserts 437
- Presets 439
- Sends 438

MIDI Files 660
MIDI Filter 101
MIDI Input (Editing via) 499
MIDI Input Transformer 568
MIDI Inputs
- Renaming 94
- Selecting for tracks 94

MIDI Notes
- Deleting 498
- Drawing 492
- Editing Velocity 502
- Moving 495, 513
- Muting 497, 514
- Quantizing 468
- Resizing 496
- Selecting 494, 513
- Splitting and Gluing 497
- Transposing 513
- Transposing (function) 476
- Transposing (in editor) 495

MIDI Outputs
- In drum maps 518
- Renaming 94
- Selecting for tracks 95
- Send effects 439

MIDI Parts
- About 108
- Drawing 131
- Editing 486
- Editing in Project Browser 588
- Sliding contents 140

MIDI Reset 99
MIDI Step Sequencer 454
MIDI Thru 93
MIDI Tracks
- Channel Settings window 211
- Selecting patches 423
- Settings 430
- Track Parameters 432

Minimize Files 415
Mix (Cycle Record mode) 98
Mixer
- Activating Buses 207
- Common Panel 191
- Extended channel strips 187
- Group Channels 206
- Link/Unlink Channels 212
- Loading Settings 215
- Master Gain Fader 210
- Pan 197
- Saving Settings 214
- Solo and Mute 196
- View Options 185
- Volume 194

Mixer Selection Follows Project 201
Mixing down to an audio file 601
MMC
- Introduction to 618
- Setting up 624

Modifier Keys 678
Monitor button
- Audio tracks 87
- MIDI tracks 93

Monitoring modes 87
Mono/Stereo button 86
Mono/Stereo Mismatch 130
Move Hitpoints 392
Move to Back 135
Move to Cursor 135
Move to Front 135
Move to Origin 135
MP3 files
- Exporting 607
- Importing 667

MPEG files
- Audio 667
- Video 645

MPEX
- Pitch Shift 339
- Time Stretch 346

Multiple Audio Tracks 126
Musical time base 127
Mute
- Events in Project window 143
- MIDI Notes 497, 514
- Mixer 196
- Tracks 143

Mute Tool 143

N

New Project 117, 655
No Overlap 537
Noise Gate 335
Non Quantize setting 472
Normal Record mode 97
Normal Sizing 138
Normalize 336
Note On Priority 100
Notes to CC 452
Notes, *see "MIDI Notes"*
Npl files 416
Nudge position buttons 75
Numeric Keypad 73, 162

O

Offline Process History 349
Ogg Vorbis files
- Exporting 608
- Importing 668

On Import Audiofile 129
On Processing Shared Clips 330
On Startup setting 669
Online (VST System Link) 637
O-Note 517
O-Note Conversion 521
Open 655

Open Document Options dialog 670
Output (MIDI) 94
Over Quantize 473
Overlapping Events 135, 380
Overview 125
Overwrite (Cycle Record mode) 98

P

Padlock Symbol 141
Pan Law 197
Parable mode
    Automation (Project window) 304
    MIDI Controllers 505
    MIDI Velocity 503
Part Data mode 124
Parts, *see "Audio Parts" or "MIDI Parts"*
Paste at Origin 137
Paste Time 147, 496
Patch Banks 422
Patch Editor (Surround) 288
Pattern Sequencer 454
Peak Hold Time 206
Pedals to Note Length 479
Pencil tool 131
Pending Connections 661
Performance Meter 216
Phase Reverse 337
Pitch Bend
    Deleting 508
    Editing 504
    Recording 98
Pitch Shift 337
Play Icon
    Audio Part Editor 381
    Pool 409
    Sample Editor 365
Plug-in Automation tracks
    About 293
    Creating 294
    Opening 306
Plug-In Information window
    Audio plug-ins 238
    MIDI plug-ins 462
Plug-ins
    Applying 347
    Automating 306
    In Surround Configurations 288
    Organizing 236
    Parameters 234
Poly Pressure events 508
Polyphony (restricting) 479
Pool
    About 397
    Auditioning 409
    Convert Files 416
    Finding Clips in 406
    Handling Audio Clips 402
    Import Medium 411
    Importing Pool Files 416
    Locate Missing Files 408
    Record Folder 413
    Status column icons 401
Postroll 102
Pre/Post Crossfade 331
Precount 104
Preload Waves Plugins on Startup 236
Prepare Archive 414
Preroll 102
Prg field 423
Printing Scores 545
Processing
    About 330
    Plug-ins 347
    Settings and Functions 331
    Undoing 349
Program Change 419
Project
    Activating 655
    Creating 117, 655
    Default 657
    Opening 655
    Saving 656
    Saving Templates 658
Project Browser 583
Project Cursor
    Auto Scroll 152
    Moving 73
    Selecting Events with 134
    Snapping to 151
Project overview line 125
Project Setup dialog 117
Punch In
    Automatic 80
    Manual 80
Punch Out 81

Q

Quantize
- About 468
- Applying 473
- As MIDI effect 453
- Automatic during recording 473
- Creating grooves from audio 395
- Ends 475
- Freezing 475
- Lengths 474
- Setting on Toolbar 469
- Setup dialog 469
- Undoing 475

Quantizer (MIDI Effect) 453
Quick Zoom 120
Quicktime 645

R

R button 299
Radikal Technologies SAC-2K 318
Ramp tempo curve mode 575
Random (Track Parameter) 434
Random Quantize setting 472
Range (Track Parameter) 435
Range Selection tool 144
Read button 299
Real Audio Files 609
Rec Mode 97
Reconstruct 409
Record Catch Range 100
Record Enable 79
Record file type 84
Record Format 84
Recording in MIDI editors 100
ReCycle files 666
Redo 685
Regions
- Creating 371
- Creating from Events 148
- Creating with Detect Silence 354
- Editing 372
- Exporting as Audio Files 413
- Removing 373

Rehearsal tempo 571
Remote Control
- Assigning Remote Key Commands 313
- Devices 314
- Writing Automation 313

Remove DC Offset 343
Remove Fades 172, 176
Remove Missing Files 409
Remove Parameter 305
Repeat 136, 495
Reset 99
Resolution 84
Resolving 616
Restrict Polyphony 479
Return To Start Position on Stop 76
Reverse 343
Reverse (MIDI function) 481
Revert 658
ReWire
- About 649
- Activating 651
- Channels 652
- Routing MIDI 653

REX files 666
Right Locator 159
Roland GS Control Panel 458
Roland MCR-8 318
Ruler 116

S

S button 143
Sample Rate 118
Sample Size 84
Save 656
Save Project to new folder 657
Scissors tool
- Project window 137
- Score Editor 543

Score
- Displaying 532
- Printing 545

Scrubbing
- Project window 132
- Resizing events by 139
- Sample Editor 365

Search Key Commands 676
Select
- Events in Project window 133
- MIDI Notes 494, 513
- Mixer Channels 201, 204

Send Effects (Audio) 221
Sensitivity slider 389

Set Pool Record Folder 413
Shared Copy 136
Shared VST Plug-ins Folder 236
Show Controllers 124
Show Data on Small Track Heights 123
Show Event Names 123
Show Event Volume Curves Always 123, 169
Show Used Automation 301
Show Video Thumbnails 648
Shuffle 537
Shuffle (Snap mode) 150
Silence 343
Sine mode 305, 506
Sizing applies timestretch 139
Sizing Moves Contents 138
Slices
- Auditioning 389
- Creating 394
- Disabling 390
- Locking 391

Snap
- MIDI Editors 546
- Project window 149

Snap Point
- Setting for Clips in Pool 410
- Setting in Project window 149
- Setting in Sample Editor 366

Snap Record Parts to Bars 100
Snap to Zero Crossing 151, 374
Snap Track Heights 120
Solo
- Audio Part Editor 381
- Folder Tracks 155
- MIDI Editors 491
- Mixer 196
- Tracks 143

Solo Group 196, 233
Solo Record in Editors 100
Speaker icon (MIDI Editors) 492
Speaker tool
- Audio Part Editor 381
- Project window 132

Speakers (SurroundPanner) 285
Spectrum Analyzer 355
Split
- Events 137
- Range 148

Split (Piano) Staff 533
Split at Cursor 137, 497
Split Loop 137, 497
Split MIDI Events 138
Square mode 305, 506
Staff Mode 533
Staff Settings 532
Start Record at Left Locator 80
Startup options 669
Static Value Line (Automation) 302
Stationary Cursors 152
Statistics 357
Step Designer 454
Step input 499
Stereo Flip 343
Stereo Pan Law 197
Stereo Split 604
Stop after Automatic Punchout 102
Strip Silence 354
Surround
- About 277
- Applying plug-ins 288
- Positioning sounds 283
- Setting up 281
- Surround Panner 283

Swing 470
Sync Indicator 622
Sync Selection 586
Synchronization
- About 613
- Audio Card settings 620
- Connections for 619
- Formats 614
- Frame Rates 625
- Indicator (Transport bar) 622
- Machine Control 624
- Options 626
- Synchronization Setup dialog 619
- Syncing equipment to Cubase SX/SL 622
- To Timecode 621

Syncopation 537
System Exclusive
- About 595
- Bulk Dumps 595
- Editing 598
- Recording parameter changes 598

T

T button (Scores) 530
Tap Tempo 581
Tascam US-428 321
Templates 658
Tempo
  About 571
  Calculating 580
  Editing 575
  Editing in Project Browser 593
  Setting in Rehearsal mode 578
  Tapping 581
Tempo Based Tracks 127
Time Based Tracks 127
Time format 116
Time Linear 488, 573
Time Signature 579
Time Stretch 344
Timecode
  About 614
  Frame Rates 625
  Synchronizing to 621
Tool Modifier Keys 678
Toolbar
  Audio Part Editor 378
  Drum Editor 509
  Key Editor 487
  List Editor 523
  Pool 399
  Project window 114
  Sample Editor 360
  Score Editor (Cubase SL) 529
Touch Fader mode 300
Track Controls (MIDI Effect) 458
Track FX (MIDI Effect) 461
Track List 110
Track Parameters 432
Track Types 107
Tracks
  Adding 126
  Changing height of 120
  Disabling/Enabling 76
  Locking 142
  Musical/Linear time base 127
  Removing 127
  Renaming 126
  Routing MIDI to VST Instruments 242
  Selecting 126
  Stereo/Mono 130
Transformer (MIDI effect) 550
Transparent Events 123
Transport Menu
  Functions 71
  Playback Options 77
Transport Panel
  Display Format 75
  Hiding and Showing 72
  Key Commands 73
  Overview 71
  Resizing 72
Transpose
  MIDI function 476
  Track Parameter 432
Triangle mode 305, 506
TrueTape 85

U

Undo
  About 685
  Processing 349
  Recording 90
Undo Quantize 475
Unlock 141
Update Origin 401
UV22/UV22 HR 228

V

VB-1 256
Velocity
  Editing 502
  Editing via MIDI 499
  MIDI function 480
Velocity Compression 433
Velocity Shift 433
Video Cache Size 648
Video for Windows 645
Video Playback Engine 645
Video Track
  About 646
  Editing in Project Browser 592
  Showing Thumbnails 648
Volume (Info Line) 194
Volume handle 170
VST Inputs 82

VST Instruments
A1 Synthesizer 245
Activating 242
Automating 245
Channels 243
LM-7 257
LM-9 273
Neon Synthesizer 271
Routing tracks to 242
Selecting patches 244
Using VST System Link 641
VB-1 Bass Synth 256
VST Master Setup 281
VST Outputs 207
VST Performance Window 216
VST Plug-ins 236
VST System Link
About 629
Activating 635
Connections 630
Latency 632
MIDI 638
Putting computers online 637
Requirements 629
Setting up sync 631
Settings 633
VU-Meter Peak's Hold Time 206

W

W button 299
Wave files 606
Wave Image Style 123
Waveform Zooming 119
Waves plug-ins 236
Windows Media Audio files
Exporting 610
Importing 668
Windows MIDI 94
WMA files
Exporting 610
Importing 668
Word Clock
About 615
Selecting for sync 620
Setting up 619
Write button 299

X

X button 143
XG Control Panel 458
X-Over mode 300

Y

Yamaha 01V 323
Yamaha XG Control Panel 458

Z

Zero Crossings 151
Zoom
About 119
Sample Editor 363
Track height 120
Waveforms 119
Zoom N Tracks 120